Contents

- 9 Foreword
- 13 Editor's Introduction
- 21 Editorial Section

Details of Pension Funds
- 161 The Largest UK Pension Funds (listed in order of size)
- 167 The Major UK Pension Funds
- 493 The Major US and Canadian Pension Funds
- 531 The Major European Pension Funds

Advisers

Financial Advisers
- 555 *(a) Banks and Merchant Banks*
- 567 *(b) Stockbrokers*
- 579 *(c) Other Financial Advisers*
- 591 *(d) Pooled Pension Funds*
- 611 Property Advisers
- 659 Forestry and Agricultural Land
- 663 Actuaries
- 667 Pension Fund Consultants
- 689 Insurance Companies
- 709 Miscellaneous
  - *(a) Associations and Professional Bodies*
  - *(b) Public Organisations*
  - *(c) Publications*
  - *(d) Employee Communications*
  - *(e) Computer and Administration Bureaux*
  - *(f) Investment Research*
- 719 Index of Advisers

Clay & Partners
Consulting Actuaries
provide an independent professional approach to all pensions problems. Please write for our Brochure to:

70 Brook Street, London W1Y 2HN. Telephone 01-408 1600

Claybrook Computing Limited

70 Brook Street
London W1Y 2HN
Telephone 01-408 1600
Telex 28604 (Ref. 2406)

A specialist computer company providing a combination of in-depth experience of Pensions together with professional systems and programming expertise.

Directors:
R. E. Barker (Managing)
A. S. Fishman, B.Sc., M.B.C.S., F.P.M.I.
K. G. Whitehead, B.A., F.P.M.I.
A. J. Wilson, B.Sc., A.R.C.S.

Talk pensions with the Pru...

in London,

call Keith Spickett on 01-405 9222

in Bristol,

call Jerry Gunnell on 0272 297661

in Birmingham,

call Roger Rollings on 021-236 9848

in Manchester,

call Malcolm Watson on 061-832 6931

in Leeds,

call Ernest Gardner on 0532 448101

In England, Scotland or Wales, call your nearest office for more details of Prudential's pension plans.

The Prudential Assurance Company Limited, 142 Holborn Bars, London EC1N 2NH

Group with Profit Cash Accumulation Contract...
For groups of 25 or more employees with a complete administration service.

Prudential Company Retirement Scheme...
To augment the state pension with cash benefits on retirement or death.

Additional Voluntary Contribution Contract...
For enabling pension scheme members to augment their payments on retirement in the most tax-efficient way.

Executive Pension Plan...
To reward directors, executives and key employees with attractive retirement benefits in addition to the pensions provided by company or state scheme.

Group Life Assurance and Dependants Income Policies...
To insure for these particular benefits on a non-profit basis or with the alternative of profit-sharing for the large scheme.

Group Investment Linked Plan...
For providing fund management for non-insured funds, entirely or in part, where the first year investment is £100,000 or more. Smaller amounts may be accepted subject to negotiation.

International Group Plan...
Provides world wide pooling of risk for employee death-in-service benefits for multi-national companies.

Prudential Personal Retirement Plan...
To provide pensions and cash payments for the self-employed and others in non-pensionable employment.

Prudential

Talk pension fund investments with PPL...

At the end of October, 1980 Prudential Pensions, through its Group Investment Linked Pension policies, was managing assets exceeding £700 million on behalf of over 200 pension funds.

Trustees of exempt approved pension funds can choose how their contributions are split between our individual funds or leave that decision to us.

We're a wholly-owned subsidiary of the Prudential and we have the benefits of their experience and expertise developed in managing assets exceeding £7,000 million, including a property portfolio valued at over £2,000 million.

A fully descriptive booklet and out latest annual report are available.

call John Clark on 01-405 9222 ext 6048

Prudential Pensions Limited
142 Holborn Bars,
London EC1N 2NH

Pension Funds and their Advisers 1981

AP Financial Registers Ltd

Published 1981 by
A.P. Financial Registers Ltd.
9 Courtleigh Gardens,
London NW11 9JX
Telephone: 01-458 1607

Compiled and edited by
Alan Philipp MBA

First Edition 1978
Second Edition 1979
Third Edition 1980
Fourth Edition 1981

© A.P. Financial Registers Ltd, 1981
Price £21.00

Typeset by Eurotype 73, Computaprint Ltd and Page Bros. (Norwich) Ltd
Printed by Page Bros. (Norwich) Ltd

ISBN 0 906247 05 5 (Cased)
ISBN 0 906247 06 3 (Paper)
ISSN 0140-6647

The publishers wish to record the role played in the conception of this publication by Robin Wills and Barry Drinkwater, without whose idea this book in its present form would not have been published.

No payment is either solicited or accepted for the inclusion of entries in this publication. Every possible precaution has been taken to ensure that the information it contains is accurate at the time of going to press and the publisher cannot accept any liability for errors or omissions however caused. The information contained in this book has in the main been supplied by the organisations listed and for the rest from a variety of sources.

All rights reserved. No part of this publication may be reproduced, stored in a retrieval system or transmitted in any form or by any means, electronic, mechanical, photocopying, recording or otherwise without the prior permission of the publisher.

a new name in property investment

SWEBY COWAN McGLASHAN

Chartered Surveyors

01-408 2131

12 John Princes Street London W1M 9HB and at Covent Garden and Wembley

Providing a complete service for Corporate, Institutional and Private clients in shop, office, warehouse, industrial and residential property to meet individual requirements including acquisition and disposal, portfolio performance and management, funding, development and refurbishment advice.

Independent advice

is available on all aspects of pensions
– in particular self-invested schemes
– from consulting actuaries

DUNCAN C. FRASER & CO.

30 Exchange Street East, Liverpool L2 3QB.   051-236 9771
24-28 Cheapside, London EC2V 6AB.   01-248 6981

LIVERPOOL ✱ LONDON ✱ MANCHESTER ✱ BIRMINGHAM ✱ EDINBURGH ✱ LEEDS
DUBLIN ✱ GUERNSEY ✱ WASHINGTON ✱ TORONTO ✱ SINGAPORE ✱ KUALA LUMPUR

Heywood & Partners for computerised pension administration

- Our computer system PASSMAN provides pension administration for companies of all types and sizes.
- PASSMAN can be run on your company's own computer or ours.
- Provides comprehensive management and personnel data immediately.
- We play a leading role in CLASS – the computerised local authority superannuation system.
- And with these systems we help to administer the pension arrangements of over one million members.
- Heywood & Partners also offer a wide variety of commercial computer services from their Liverpool based computer bureau.
- For details contact Ian Hodgson or Bob Chadwick on 051-236 0881 or at the address below.

Heywood & Partners Limited 30 Exchange St. East, Liverpool L2 3QB.

"1981 will require a far more selective approach to property investment. In these times of high inflation, the first rent review on any property investment is the one by which it is judged"

Extract from Savills Property Outlook 1981
Tim Simon FRICS
Partner - Commercial Investment Department

Anticipating Tomorrow's Property Investment Today

Savills, 20 Grosvenor Hill, Berkeley Square,
London W1X 0HQ.
Tel: 01-499 8644. Telex: 263796.

People and Property

London, Banbury, Beccles, Brechin, Cambridge, Chelmsford, Croydon, Hereford,
Lincoln, Norwich, Salisbury, Wimborne, York, Scotland, Paris, Amsterdam.

Foreword

Michael Pilch
*Director of Noble Lowndes & Partners Limited,
Chairman, National Association of Pension Funds*

The invitation to write this Foreword, which I was delighted to accept, prompts a number of personal reflections about information, communication, competition and private enterprise.

One — that until about three years ago there was no systematic body of published information giving details of individual pension funds. In March 1978, the first edition of *Pension Funds and their Advisers* was brought out. Despite some imperfections, due in part to the reluctance of some pension funds and their advisers to co-operate with the publishers, the new directory undoubtedly revolutionised attitudes towards the disclosure of information.

Two — that in January 1979 the National Association of Pension Funds published its first *Year Book,* giving names and addresses of all members and more detailed information on many of the funds involved. Again, the information was incomplete but represented a substantial advance on previous practice. Would the N.A.P.F. have moved so far and as fast without the stimulus provided by publication of the Alan Philipp's directory? Probably not, although internal pressures and growing recognition on the part of members of the association that the information would be useful to them, as well as to the general public, would almost certainly have resulted in the publication of the Year Book before long in any case.

Three — that subsequent editions, of *Pension Funds and their Advisers* and of the *N.A.P.F. Year Book,* have achieved wider coverage and higher standards. This directory has enlarged its scope to include many overseas pension funds and their advisers, while the N.A.P.F. has concentrated on increasing the proportion of its members making full returns, to the very evident improvement of both publications.

Four — that there have been suggestions, in the press and else-

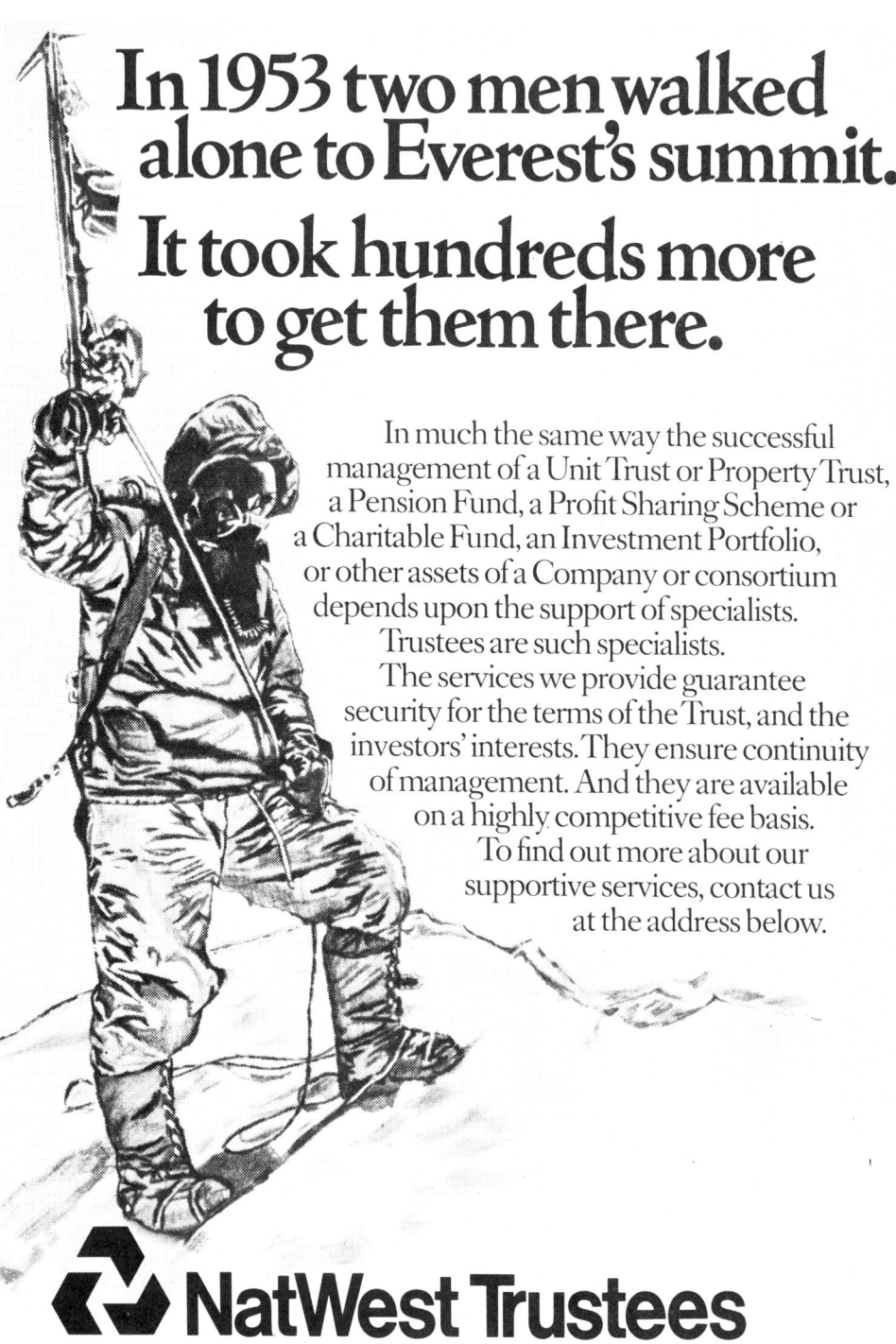

where, that the two publications should merge. Apart from the obvious advantage that pension funds in membership of the N.A.P.F. would have only one form to complete instead of two, it is claimed that a joint publication would provide a more comprehensive and more effective service to its readers and advertisers. Such ideas have been the subject of serious discussion between the N.A.P.F. and the publishers of this directory without, as yet, any positive outcome.

My own belief is that a time will undoubtedly come when it will be right to bring the two together, and that time may not be too far off, but for the present we are still in a development phase. For so long as both publications are financially sound and growing vigorously, the advantages of healthy rivalry and competition outweigh the benefits to be gained by combination.

The best demonstration of N.A.P.F. belief in the merits of private enterprise lies in my acceptance of the invitation to write this Foreword and to wish this new edition of *Pension Funds and their Advisers* well.

Judgement in Property...

St Quintin
CHARTERED SURVEYORS

Vintry House
Queen Street Place
London EC4 1ES
Tel: 01-236 4040   Telex 8812619

1981
1831

WEST END: 39 Dover Street London W1X 3RB Tel: 01-491 8838
LEEDS: 6 Park Place Leeds LS1 2RU Tel: 0532-460235
BRUSSELS: St Quintin S.A. rue Joseph II straat 36-38 1040 Brussels Tel: Brussels 219-32-88 Telex: 61182

Introduction

Alan Philipp, MBA
Editor and Compiler

During the past year there has been a very strong movement by Pension Funds towards a greater disclosure of information. The two most important factors have been, the publication of the Wilson Committee Report on the functioning of the Financial Institutions and the publication by the National Association of Pension Funds of their Code of Conduct.

These major documents stress that Pension Funds should make more information available, particularly to members. The major difference between the two reports is that while the Wilson Committee calls for legislation in the form of a new Pensions Act and the establishment of a Registry, the N.A.P.F. Code encourages more voluntary disclosures. As a result of both these approaches there has been substantially more information available than before. This can clearly be seen by the amount of new information available in this edition of the book as well as through the increased information to be found in the library of the N.A.P.F.

Regrettably there are still a small number of large funds who are unwilling to disclose information, particularly financial, about themselves to outsiders. It would be a great pity if legislation had to be forced on all pension funds because of the failure of a very few to act.

The growth in the amount of information has meant an overall increase in the size of this book. We have now been able to quantify total assets held by Pension Funds exceeding £41,000 million. (There were £34,000 million in 1980.) This indicates that the total assets of all Pension Funds are now in the region of £50,000–£60,000 million. At this level they are as large as, or larger than the Building Societies or Insurance Companies and their faster growth and greater investment flexibility make them even more powerful. We have included in this edition a table listing by size all Pension Funds with assets exceeding £10 million.

THE NAME OF YOUR PENSION FUND MANAGER COULD BE BARCLAYS BANK TRUST COMPANY.

So, what's in a name? Well, let's just say that when it comes to entrusting the care of your company's pension fund to an outside organisation it pays to choose carefully.

As you might expect from its name, Barclays Bank Trust Company is a wholly-owned subsidiary of Barclays Bank.

It is also one of Britain's largest and longest established trust corporations, and it heads a specialist division of the Barclays Group, the one that is devoted almost entirely to the business of professional asset management.

That's one of the reasons why the pension fund portfolios managed by Barclays Bank Trust Company include household names.

But there are other reasons, too. After all, pension fund management is all about performance – maximum growth with minimum risk.

That's why the management team you choose needs to have not just a big name but a lot of wisdom and the information and ability to make the right decisions at the right time.

Barclays Bank Trust Company has the experience, the skill and the resources your employees expect you to look for in pension fund management, whether it be for the complete fund or a substantial part of the portfolio.

And, by the way, we are equally good at pension fund administration.

If you would like a copy of our brochure or would like us to tell you more specifically about the kind of service you can expect from Barclays Bank Trust Company, please write to:

David Moss, Executive Director, Barclays Bank Trust Company Limited, Juxon House, 94 St. Paul's Churchyard, London EC4M 8EH.

BARCLAYTRUST

ANYTHING TO DO WITH MONEY, ASK BARCLAYS FIRST.

This edition includes a series of articles on International Pensions Management and Investment. We have also tried to extend the amount of information available on various European countries. This is not always very easy because in certain countries, such as Switzerland, the Pension Funds are even more secretive than in the UK.

I would like to thank Michael Pilch, the Chairman of the N.A.P.F. for his foreword to this book, as well as thanking all the other Authors for their contributions. Above all, this publication depends on the Pension Funds and their Advisers who supply the relevant information, and our expression of gratitude to them is most pronounced.

Chestertons
Established 1805

Experienced advice on investment and commercial valuation.

Chestertons
Chartered Surveyors

Head Office: 75 Grosvenor Street,
London W1X 0JB. 01-499 0404.
Telex 8812560. And in the City of London,
Kensington, Hyde Park, Little Venice, Chelsea
and Notting Hill Gate.

For all your property needs

Editorial

Articles relating to
international pension
fund management and
investment

ARE YOU IN NEED OF OUR LOCAL KNOWLEDGE?

We have been practising in the Home Counties for over 150 years, and we think we know our area well.

We can advise and assist on:

* purchase or disposal of prime or secondary investments

* opportunities for development funding

* reports on market trends for industrial or office buildings from our own first hand experience

* undertake valuations, rent reviews, or day-to-day management of properties

* provide specialist departments in town planning, rating, and project management

If you think we can be of service to you please contact:

chancellors+co
EST 1827

Commercial Offices
32 Greyfriars Road, Reading, Berks. (0734) 586833
33 Bancroft, Hitchin, Herts. (0462) 4455

Editorial articles in this section

21 **International Retirement Benefits Policy**
    M. D. Riddles, Head of Retirement Benefits, Shell International Petroleum Co. Ltd.

41 **Long Term Benefits — Costs and Disbursements**
    Roger Cobley, International Pensions Manager, Rank Xerox Ltd.

51 **Pension Financing in Europe**
    Stephen R. Baker, Towers, Perrin, Forster & Crosby

65 **International Implications of U.S. Pensions Reporting**
    A. S. Fishman and K. G. Whitehead, Senior Partner, Clay & Partners

77 **International Portfolio Diversification**
    Gordon Popham, Senior Investment Director, J. Henry Schroder Wagg & Co. Ltd.

89 **International Property Investment**
    Quintin Greatrex, Director, City of London & European Property Co.

103 **The Role of the International Benefits Consultant**
    David Callund, Managing Director, Callund & Company Ltd.

119 **Property Investment in a Worldwide Recession**
    Andrew Huntley, Senior Investment Partner, Richard Ellis

135 **Why Invest in Forestry? The Case for Investment Overseas**
    J. A. Fell and G. R. Watt, Economic Forestry Ltd.

139 **Pensions in Europe**
    George Clare and Representatives of William M. Mercer
            France
            Germany
            Belgium
            Netherlands
            Switzerland

155 **Pensions in Ireland**
    Eamon J. Egan, Director, Metropolitan Pension Association (Ireland) Ltd.

Pension fund management: discover how our approach stands up

5 MANAGEMENT CONTINUITY AND INDEPENDENCE

4 HIGHEST STANDARDS OF ADMINISTRATION, COMMUNICATION, REPORTING

3 UNIQUE APPROACH TO U.K. EQUITIES

2 OPTIMUM PORTFOLIO STRUCTURE

1 MODERN TECHNIQUES TO MAXIMISE RETURNS

The Britannia "building block" approach to pension fund management emphasises our five basic principles.

We use the latest techniques; we develop the appropriate portfolio structure; we manage UK equities in a unique way; we maintain the highest standards of administration and communication; and we ensure the continuity and independence of our management.

Our method of managing UK equities involves a three-portfolio approach – a "core" of major market capitalisation stocks (managed with low activity by design), a diversified portfolio of high-yielding shares including smaller companies and an actively managed fund of special situations and "market" opportunities.

Find out more about how we build results. Write or telephone Peter Baker, Britannia Institutional Fund Management Limited, Salisbury House, 31 Finsbury Circus, London EC2M 5QL. Tel: 01-588 2777. Telex: 883781.

BRITANNIA
Institutional Fund Management Limited

International Retirement Benefits Policy

M. D. Riddles
Head of Retirement Benefits, Shell International Petroleum Co Ltd

In determining its retirement benefits policy, an international organisation is concerned with two main areas, namely, arrangements for:
   (a) local company employees,
   (b) expatriate employees worldwide.

Diverse cultural, socio-economic and political backgrounds and legal requirements may well impinge on any consideration of an appropriate retirement benefits policy, as indeed they will affect the values and attitudes of the international organisation.

Retirement benefits policy in relation to expatriate employees is a complex subject worthy of separate consideration. Many papers have already been written on the subject. It is not the intention to cover expatriates in this article, but rather to concentrate on retirement benefits for local company employees.

The degree of control exercised by the parent company in the development of retirement benefits for local company employees at present varies according to the philosophy of the group. Some international companies believe in complete centralised control whilst others follow the policy that the local company should be responsible for retirement benefits for its own employees. However, in the latter case, it would be normal for the parent company to at least monitor local company schemes and provide guidance and assistance for the following reasons:
   (a) many local companies have little or no experience in this field,
   (b) the parent company will wish to satisfy itself as to the appropriateness of any scheme introduced.

This paper considers the design of local schemes and differentiates between the various types. Although it includes a summary of the present pension practices within Europe it nevertheless covers all aspects of international retirement benefit policy worldwide. It also details the considerations which have to be taken into account when setting up a company scheme in a country for the first time, including whether or not a "funded" arrangement is desirable. The final section of the paper is devoted to the company's legal and moral obligations in relation to retirement benefits, particularly as regards adjusting pensions to take some account of inflation.

RETIREMENT BENEFITS FOR LOCAL COMPANY EMPLOYEES

Local company schemes should be designed to fit in with the local pattern and, having regard to local competition, provide a suitable level of benefits. In deciding a suitable level of benefits, company schemes should fully take into account any state pension and leaving indemnity arrangements. In other words, company schemes should include provision for automatic reduction in company retirement benefits where state pensions and indemnities are payable.

In recent years the general trend has been for an increase in pensions provided by the state and a number of countries are providing or planning to provide a state "earnings related" pension on top of the existing state "flat rate" pension. The growth in the level of social security pensions has made it essential for companies who operate high level occupational schemes to integrate their benefits with those provided by the social security system. There are already a number of countries which provide a level of benefits either through the state scheme or industry schemes which at present make topping up company schemes unnecessary. Examples which come to mind are Italy, Brazil and Argentina, which all have state and/or compulsory schemes which provide, for all but the most senior employees, a pension in excess of two-thirds final salary from state pensionable age, assuming of course that the employee has a full contribution record.

TYPES OF RETIREMENT BENEFITS SCHEMES

There are several different types of retirement benefits schemes and the scheme introduced by the local company should be well suited to both the prevailing and the foreseeable conditions. However, it is over optimistic to expect that any scheme will survive unchanged for any lengthy period, and the company must keep its arrangements under review and be prepared to change them as conditions change.

In some countries well established patterns of retirement

Let Wigham Poland Pension Consultants meet your needs with...

Consultancy

Today, tomorrow and into the future, you and your employees need information, technical advice and responsive personal service on pension matters.

Computerised Administration

CEBA, a unique system of Computerised Employee Benefits Administration, has been developed to provide a complete service to the Company and to Scheme Members by offering simplified schedules, annual benefit statements and statutory notices to the D.H.S.S.

Actuarial Services

Our Actuaries provide a full actuarial service for pension funds. They advise on such matters as assessment of funding rates, actuarial valuations and investment strategy, and this advice is made available to our clients.

Trusteeship

Wigham Poland Trustees Ltd. is empowered to act in a fiduciary capacity for pension schemes including the responsibility of administrator under the Social Security Pensions Act 1975 and the Finance Act 1970.

Write or telephone

Wigham Poland Pension Consultants Limited

Bevington House, 24-26 Minories, London EC3N 1BY. Telephone: 01-481 0505.

The bigger the property fund the smaller the risk.

Most pension fund managers are aware of the advantages of investing in property. It is, after all, one of the few investments that has kept pace with inflation since the war.

But, as always, above average potential return can mean above average potential risk.

So it makes eminent sense to minimise your risk by investing in the largest property fund in the country: Legal & General's.

With assets of around £700 million we are able to achieve a sound spread of properties of all types throughout the country and to embark on profitable large scale developments.

Our strong cash flow enables us to buy quickly on favourable terms.

We manage almost all our properties in-house to ensure maximum returns on our investments.

For full information about the Legal & General Property Managed Fund please call me, Keith Hall, on 01-248 2276. Or write to me at the address below.

Legal & General Property Managed Fund

Legal & General Assurance (Pensions Management) Ltd., Temple Court, 11 Queen Victoria Street, London EC4N 4TP.

benefits exist, and where this is so, companies must be guided by national custom and conform to the accepted pattern.

Retirement benefits schemes may be divided into:
1. lump sum schemes
2. pension schemes

In both of these, benefits may be based on the salary/wages earned over the whole of the employee's service (career earnings), or on the salary/wages earned during the final year of service, or on the average salary/wages earned during, say, the last three or five years of service. During recent years, following relatively high periods of inflation, the practice has been to move away from the career earnings type of arrangement towards schemes which provide benefits related to the final year's salary/wage.

PENSION SCHEMES

Within Europe practically all retirement benefits arrangements are provided by way of pension schemes. Pension schemes may be either funded or unfunded. A funded scheme is where assets are set aside each year, usually on an actuarial basis, outside the company to meet the pension liabilities of both pensioners and current employees. An unfunded scheme is where reserves are set aside each year in the company's books and the money is retained within the company until such time as it is needed to meet pensions in payment.

It is common practice within the UK, Holland, Belgium, Denmark and Norway for private sector pension schemes to be funded and the tax provisions in those countries relating to pension schemes make funded arrangements attractive both for the company and the employee. In the UK and Holland most of the larger private sector schemes are self administered, whilst in Belgium and Denmark benefits provided by way of insurance contracts are more usual.

On the other hand, in a number of countries the book reserve scheme is more common, particularly in West Germany where some 80% of pension liabilities are covered by the book reserve system. Book reserve schemes are also common in Austria, Portugal and Spain, although in Spain the new corporate tax law which came into effect on 1st January 1979 requires that pension plans must be funded outside the company in order for employer contributions to be tax deductible. It is unusual for the tax authorities in a country to allow a tax deduction in respect of

Published monthly   **Established 1972**

Pensions World

Covers all the important topics for those professionally concerned: administration — — investment — legislation — union views — pensioner welfare.

Contents guided by an Editorial Board of practising specialists. All articles written by recognised experts.

Regular series on tax, law, trusteeship, insurance, overseas developments — plus news, books, conference reports and PMI activities.

Subscriptions   Standard rate £16.00
NAPF members (additional copies) £11.50
PMI Students £9.35
Bulk purchase for trustees, etc, on application.

Binders available at £4.25 each (inc. VAT and £1.00 postage)

Advertisements   Pensions World is an ideal advertising medium for investment opportunities, administration services, situations, etc.

Subscription and Advertising enquiries to the proprietors:
CARL Communications Ltd, 60 Thames Street,
Sunbury-on-Thames, Middx TW16 6AF. (Tel: Sunbury 82627)

By arrangement the journal carries the Information Bulletin of the NAPF and is distributed to all their members as the official journal of the Association.

Recommended reading for PMI Students.

company book reserve schemes. In West Germany and Austria a tax deduction is, however, allowed provided that the allocation to reserves is carried out in accordance with a basis defined by the tax authorities. No assets are specifically earmarked in the case of a book reserve scheme and the pension scheme members have no priority over other creditors in the event of the company being dissolved. The law in West Germany requires that the reserve must be insured against company insolvency through a special insurance organisation formed for this purpose.

In France retirement benefits over and above those provided by the social security pension arrangements are provided under mandatory membership of multi-employer programmes. Under these programmes employees must be enrolled either into a Cadres or a non-Cadres scheme, depending upon their status. A number of different funding institutions exist, and these are grouped in a central organisation — AGIRC for Cadres and ARRCO for non-Cadres. Additional retirement benefits for employees may be provided by paying further contributions to either the Cadres or non-Cadres scheme as appropriate.

In Finland pension benefits, in addition to the social security flat rate pension, are provided under a compulsory Supplementary Employment Pension Scheme (TEL). The cost of the TEL benefits, which are indexed on the average of a cost of living and wage index, is borne entirely by the employer. A further supplementary plan providing additional benefits to TEL to which the employees may contribute, can be registered by a company provided the plan follows the same general structure as TEL, including the provision of indexed benefits.

Pension benefits for Swedish employees are provided by a National Pension (AFP) and a National Supplementary Pension (ATP) and total costs are borne by the employer. In addition to these national social security pensions, there is a Labour Market Plan (ITP) to which all companies who are members of the Swedish Employers' Federation must belong. The company may either fund the ITP plan through the state Insurance Company or set up a book reserve.

No decisive argument can be adduced in favour of a contributory or non-contributory type of scheme. However, if the scheme is contributory, it will normally be necessary to set up a funded arrangement rather than a book reserve. Obviously for the same cost to the company the contributory scheme will provide a substantially higher range of benefits than the one which is non-contributory. It may also be claimed as a further advantage, perhaps somewhat optimistically, that the need to contribute encourages employees to take a greater interest in their post retirement future and to identify themselves more with the company. On the other hand, it is common experience that the introduction of a contributory scheme leads to wage demands to make up for the contributions payable. Another factor which has to be borne in mind is whether or not the employee is eligible for tax relief on his own contributions.

LUMP SUM SCHEMES
A typical scheme giving lump sum benefits based on career earnings is the provident fund, to which the company and usually the employee pay contributions which are directly related to current earnings. These contributions are invested to earn interest and on retirement the employee receives total contributions plus accumulated interest. Provident funds were very popular in the past, but have largely fallen from favour, particularly within Europe. There are two reasons for this; firstly, a number of revenue authorities are not in favour of the employee receiving a large, tax free lump sum at the end of his service, and have therefore made them unattractive from a tax point of view. The second reason is that where inflation in a country continues at a high rate over a long period, the value of the fund diminishes in real terms where the rate of inflation exceeds the interest earned by the fund.

Retirement gratuity schemes and end of service benefit schemes also provide lump sums, but these are usually calculated as an amount based both on length of service and on final pay. Such schemes are normally introduced where they can be paid free of tax and in those countries where there are large numbers of foreign employees engaged as regionals who return home on retirement, e.g. Indians who work in many Middle East countries and Chinese in many Far East countries.

STUDY REQUIRED BEFORE SETTING UP A RETIREMENT BENEFITS SCHEME
Before setting up any local retirement benefits scheme, a careful study should be made of local conditions, and in particular, it will be necessary to consider the probable duration of the company's operations in the area, i.e., whether these are likely to be short

Chartered Surveyors Development & Town Planning Consultants

We offer you a comprehensive range of specialist services including:

Property Investment

Sale and purchase of Commercial and Industrial Property Investments. Portfolio Management, Funding

Professional Services
Consultancy on Town Planning, Rating, Compulsory Purchase, Property Taxation. Valuation of Properties for Sale, Purchase, Mortgage, Taxation, Insurance or Company Accounting. Plant and Machinery Valuations. Rent Reviews.

Development and Project Management
Site Selection, Feasibility Studies and Financial Appraisals, Planning, Development Finance, Grant Aid, Government Grants, Mortgages.

Industrial and Commercial Agency
Sale, letting and acquisition of Shops, Offices, Factories, Warehouses and Land.

Management and Building Services
Full range of Management and Building Services relating to Commercial and Industrial Property.

EADON LOCKWOOD & RIDDLE

6a Campo Lane, Sheffield S1 2EF.
Tel: 0742-71277, Telex: 547490 ELR.

There is a distinct air of farming in London's West End.

Through our eleven branches, situated in every major farming area in the U.K. channelling up-to-date information into Hill Street, agriculture comes to town! You don't have to go to the countryside to get practical advice on all aspects of selling, purchasing and management of farmland. In this way we can provide the essential link between city and country.

For further information or advice contact – The Agricultural Investment Department G.L. Lyster, MA, DL, FRICS., A.C. Ball, FRICS.

Strutt & Parker

13 Hill Street, London, W1X 8DL. Tel: 01-629 7282
Canterbury, Chelmsford, Cheltenham, Cheshire, Edinburgh
Grantham, Harrogate, Ipswich, Lewes, Norwich, Salisbury

maximise your assets

term or long term, and if the latter, what expansion or contraction of the workforce can be foreseen. In considering the local conditions applying in the country, the following points require particular consideration:
   (1) The state of development of the country and cultural background. A scheme which might be suitable in an industrial urban environment could be quite unsuited in an area still under subsistence agriculture.
   (2) Any retirement benefits scheme operated by other reputable employers, particularly, of course, those of competitors in the same country, and the way in which they may be linked with any state scheme.
   (3) Any state scheme existing or planned and the extent to which company employees may be able to benefit from them. In particular, consideration should be given to the following points:
      — conditions of participation in the scheme.
      — the rates of benefits and from what age they may be payable.
      — how far payments in such schemes are, or will be, adequate to meet the needs of employees etc.
   (4) Any retirement or severance lump sum payments which the company is required to make under the terms of any collective agreement or in accordance with the laws of the country or an already agreed established ex-gratia basis.
   (5) Possible employee representatives demands in the field of retirement benefits. It is important to know whether such representative bodies have any established policy as to the type of benefits which they may seek to obtain (e.g. lump sum or pension).
   (6) The attitude of Government towards company retirement benefit schemes and in particular, any legislation affecting either the taxation or administration of retirement benefits.

LOCAL TAXATION PROVISIONS
Before reaching a decision on any particular type of scheme, it is essential to determine how it will be affected by local tax legislation. The following questions will have to be considered with a view to maximising the benefit to the employee with the minimum cost to the company:
   (1) To what extent are company contributions to a retirement

benefits fund allowable as an expense for tax purposes?
(2) Are company allocations to a reserve for an unfunded scheme for providing pensions or lump sum benefits allowed as an expense?
(3) To what extent are payments for pensions or lump sums made by the company out of a reserve or out of current revenue allowed as an expense?
(4) To what extent are employee contributions to a retirement benefits fund relieved from personal income tax?
(5) To what extent are pensions and lump sum payments receivable by retiring employees taxable?
(6) If a fund is set up is the income it earns from investment taxed and what is the tax position regarding capital profits on sales of investments?

In many countries the effects of taxation can be mitigated if the rules of the scheme are approved by the tax authorities. It is therefore very important to clarify the conditions under which a scheme would receive revenue approval and then to decide whether the company is prepared to meet those conditions. Where approval by the revenue authorities results in more advantageous tax treatment, it will normally be found that the conditions which they impose have a strong influence on the type of scheme which local employers generally introduce. They thus shape a local pattern from which it may in any case be difficult for the company to diverge to any great extent.

FUNDING OF A RETIREMENT BENEFITS SCHEME

A number of factors have to be taken into account when deciding whether or not the retirement benefits scheme should be funded, i.e. assets set aside outside the company to meet the liabilities. These factors include:
(1) Whether funding is allowed by legislation in the country concerned, and if so, what are the restrictions relating to types of investment permitted, etc., and the local taxation laws applicable.
(2) Whether there are suitable investment opportunities, taking into account local legislation.
(3) Whether the long term investment yield can be expected to exceed salary progression, taking into account inflation.
(4) Whether the company is a long term net borrower of funds. If the company is a net borrower, the difference between

Our outstanding position in the property market...

...has been achieved by the accumulation of specialist professional knowledge covering all aspects of the market.

Whatever changes occur in the property investment field, the commercial and management expertise of Barrington Laurance will stand out among the best.

❦ Barrington Laurance
Chartered Surveyors

Property Investment Consultants 71 South Audley Street London W1Y 6HD Tel: 01-492 0141 Telex: 261988

The Property Unit Trusts
Assets exceed £285,000,000

The Pension Fund Property Unit Trust

The Property Unit Trust for Public and General Superannuation Schemes

The Charities Property Unit Trust

The Agricultural Property Unit Trust for Pension Funds and Charities

The Group, established in 1966 and the leader in this specialised market, is always seeking prime property investments.

Please contact R.G. Nightingale F.C.A. for further information.

The Property Unit Trusts
73 Brook Street, London W1Y 1YE
Telephone 01-499 7191

the cost of borrowing and the likely investment return, taking into account the local taxation laws, will need to be examined.
(5) The company marginal rate of return on employed capital compared to market investment return/capital appreciation.

TREATMENT OF DIFFERENT CATEGORIES OF EMPLOYEE
The sharp distinction in the ways of life of different categories of employee, e.g., white collar and blue collar workers, which existed in the past is gradually diminishing as industrial development proceeds, and indeed, in some countries has already disappeared. Just as other differences in the treatment of the various categories of employee are removed where they are no longer relevant or desirable, so should the differences in the retirement benefits offered. However, in some countries the social structure may still call for different types of schemes for different categories of employee. For example, in those areas where white collar staff are predominately urbanised and where operatives still tend after retirement to return to agricultural communities, it may be felt desirable to offer white collar staff a pension scheme, whilst for operatives a lump sum benefit may be more suitable, and be put to better use. In addition, where such operatives return to agricultural communities, administrative difficulties of drawing a regular pension may be considerable. It may also be that skilled and semi-skilled operatives have good opportunities for using a lump sum to set up a small workshop or otherwise establish themselves after leaving the company. However, it should be emphasised that the practicability of setting up a lump sum scheme may be more influenced by local taxation laws.

FACTORS TO BE TAKEN INTO ACCOUNT WHEN DESIGNING A SCHEME
Having chosen a scheme appropriate to local conditions and taking into account the various taxation laws, investment opportunities, etc., a number of other decisions have to be made, such as:
(1) Retirement age — factors which have to be taken into account:
 (a) The age at which the employee, if retired, will be entitled to receive a state old age pension.
 (b) The retirement age adopted by competitors.
 (c) The age at which the company wishes to retire employ-

ees, bearing in mind, if intending to introduce a pension scheme, that the earlier the date of retirement, the costlier the scheme becomes, particularly where the company scheme is integrated with the state old age pension and the company has to meet the cost of the total pension until the state pension becomes payable. It should also be borne in mind that in several countries, e.g. Portugal and Brazil, it is often impossible to compulsorily retire employees before the age of 70. It may therefore be necessary to tailor the package to induce employees to retire earlier than age 70.

(2) Early retirement provisions.

When including any provisions for early retirement on immediate pension, it should be borne in mind that the early retirement reduction factor used in most schemes is 3% per annum, which is approximately only one half of the true actuarial reduction which should be applied.

(3) Formula.
   (a) Pension accrual or lump sum formula.
   (b) Salary on which formula is based.
   (c) Reduction in benefit to take account of other lump sums/pensions receivable by employee, e.g., leaving indemnities, state pensions, etc.

(4) Member Contributions.

Whether or not employees should contribute towards the scheme will normally depend upon:
   (a) Taxation provisions.
   (b) What the competition does.

(5) Dependant's benefits.

Whether or not dependant's benefits should be included in the scheme will largely depend upon the practice within the country. If it is decided to include such benefits, it will be necessary to have a clear definition of dependancy and when the benefits should cease to be paid.

(6) Death in service benefits.

Death in service benefits may be provided by either lump sum payments or pensions to dependants or both. Where a pension is payable to a dependant a decision will be necessary on whether this should be based on service to date or whether it should also include prospective service to normal retirement age.

(7) Commutation.
Where a pension scheme is introduced, the possibility of including an option for the employee to commute part of his pension into a lump sum will often depend upon the taxation provisions in the country concerned.

COMPANY'S LEGAL AND MORAL OBLIGATIONS

Once a scheme has been set up and operating it is normally possible within the regulations of the scheme to amend the provisions in respect of future service. It is not possible to remove rights already acquired in respect of past service. In this connection it would be difficult to change certain expectations of current employees, for instance changing the retirement age without the employee's consent, unless of course it was necessary to amend existing regulations to comply with current legislation.

In deciding the type of benefits to be provided in a particular country the company faces a number of questions which it is often difficult to answer and certainly not all companies approach the problems in the same manner. For instance, it is well known that in countries outside Europe and North America the majority of employees, particularly the younger personnel, prefer lump sum schemes to pension schemes, even though they may be comparatively unattractive from a tax point of view. Indeed, many younger employees even within Europe would prefer an immediate increase in salary in lieu of a retirement benefit arrangement.

Assuming the decision has been taken to set up a retirement benefit scheme, a lump sum arrangement (where this is possible) from the company's point of view, also has many attractions:
(1) It is simple to operate and the formula is readily understood by employees.
(2) Compared with a pension scheme the administration is minimal and ceases when the employee leaves company service.
(3) Employees generally accept that once they have received their lump sum on termination of service, the company has no further obligation towards them — even though they may squander it within a short period of retirement.

On the other hand, the introduction of a pension scheme presents the company with a considerable administrative burden, particularly when account is taken of the enormous ongoing commitment to pay pensions, probably each month, for many years after retirement. However, the administrative burden, although significant, is not the main area of concern these days. It is, of course, inflation. Although there are very few pension schemes outside the public sector which contain a commitment to increase pensions to take account of inflation, it is the practice of many companies to give at least some assistance towards maintaining the value of pensions in payment. Indeed many companies feel that having introduced a pension scheme, they have a moral obligation to give some help in this direction.

Experience has shown that a company which provides small pensions, even where this is combined with a reasonable lump sum, in general receives far more criticism and at times, even abuse, particularly when no attempt is made to adjust pensions to take some account of inflation, than companies who provide only lump sum arrangements or who provide only those retirement benefits required by law.

In view of the above it is interesting to note that many companies are still introducing pension schemes — sometimes in countries with very high inflation rates. Obviously there are a number of reasons:

(1) It may be the normal practice in the country concerned.
(2) Lump sum schemes may be unattractive to both the employer and employee because of local taxation laws.
(3) The paternalistic attitude adopted by many large companies who feel that it is in the interests of both the employee and his family to have the protection of a pension arrangement.

Whatever the reason, it is undoubtedly true that the present prolonged high levels of inflation are placing a severe strain both on social security systems and private pension schemes. Indeed, if rates of inflation are not brought under control and kept within reasonable limits, we shall see in many countries a deterioration in the real levels of retirement benefits provided by the state. Already we have seen this happening in a number of countries as far apart as Brazil and Italy and this process can be expected to continue and possibly spill-over to private pension schemes.

When setting up a pension scheme it is therefore very important to bear in mind the effects of inflation and to ensure as far as possible that the valuation assumptions used are realistic.

CONCLUSION

This article has attempted to outline some of the considerations which have to be taken into account when designing and setting up retirement benefit arrangements for company employees in different countries.

The question is often asked as to whether it would be possible to develop a company scheme which could be adopted by the parent companies' subsidiaries throughout the world.

Unfortunately, although the prospect is very attractive, due to the differing taxation and labour laws in each country and the varying pattern of life styles, this is not a practical proposition. This is true even within Europe, where pension schemes, as opposed to lump sum arrangements, are common. Nevertheless, it should be possible to establish a link between the various schemes to reflect the overall attitude of the organisation, at the same time allowing such schemes to be identified separately within their own environment.

Fund management starts here.

Fund management means: investment analysis, economic research, fixed interest dealing, portfolio management.

dataSTREAM means: UK equities, gilts, international stocks and bonds, economic indicators, market reports, brokers' forecasts, portfolio valuation and accounting.

All directly accessible via a single, cost-effective desk-top terminal. Make it your starting point.

dataSTREAM
INTERNATIONAL INVESTMENT INSIGHT

ATLAS HOUSE · 1 KING STREET
LONDON EC2V 8BX
TEL: 01-600 6411

Long Term Benefits – Costs and Disbursements

Roger Cobley, FIA, ASA, FPMI
International Pensions Manager, Rank Xerox Ltd

The opinions expressed in this article are those of Roger Cobley and not necessarily those of the company which employs him.

INTRODUCTION
International corporations usually operate through subsidiary companies, or branches, established in each of the countries in which the corporation carries on its business. In the majority of cases, the employees of the subsidiary or branch will be local nationals, whose compensation and benefits will be determined largely by good local custom and practice, for it is against the background of local employment conditions generally that the local company will compete for its own personnel. It is usual to find that the local company will establish and administer its own long term benefit plans, the degree of control by the headquarters varying according to individual corporations.

The contributions to these plans, and the accruing reserves and liabilities, represent very significant sums of money, and it is essential that the full implications of each plan be understood. Of course, the plans vary enormously from country to country, but, in very broad terms, they can be classified into two distinct groups.

PLAN DESIGN – THE TWO APPROACHES
The first involves "defined contribution" plans (or money purchase arrangements) where company and employee contract to pay fixed contributions, usually expressed as percentages of salary, to a central fund which is invested for the benefit of the members. Each member has a credit balance in the fund, and his eventual retirement benefit is simply determined by the total contributions paid by him, and on his behalf by the company, plus the interest accumulated on his balance. There is no guarantee of relationship between final salary and benefit, and experience suggests that the member is vulnerable to the incidence of high inflation occurring in the period just before retirement, which tends to devalue his

accumulated balance in real terms; but against this there is the advantage to the company that its liability is entirely limited to the payment of the contributions each year. In accounting terms, the cost of the plan is exactly equal to the contributions set aside each year, and charged against profits for that year, and no further liability can occur.

The second type of scheme is the "defined benefit" plan, of which the so-called final salary arrangement is the most common example. In this scheme, the benefit is defined by three factors — the years of service, the accrual rate per annum (1/60th, 1.3/4% or 2% being commonly found rates) and the salary close to retirement. The benefit is paid for by the member's contribution, the company contribution, and the investment income on the fund. Although in theory it is possible to vary the member's contribution rate, in practice this rarely happens, and certainly never with retrospective effect, and so it is the company contribution which will vary in order to ensure that the necessary funds, including the investment returns, are available to secure the promised benefits whatever they turn out to be. For this reason, the defined benefit plan is sometimes referred to as a "balance-of-cost" scheme.

Although the accrual rate is fixed for the scheme, and the prospective years of service are known for each individual, the third factor in the formula, the final salary, is not known in advance of retirement. So, although estimates may be made of the rate of salary increase for each future year of service, to give a projected final salary, the true cost of the benefit to the company, varying according to both actual final salary and investment return on the fund, cannot be determined during the member's working lifetime.

COST vs. DISBURSEMENT

Bearing in mind the fundamental truth that the true cost cannot be ascertained in advance, it is not surprising that considerable confusion and misunderstanding arises whenever the subject of retirement benefit contributions and costs is discussed. Leaving aside other factors, such as security of members' promised benefits, and legal and fiscal regulations, there is an infinite range of possible methods that a company can use to accrue the necessary funds. At the extreme, the company could decide not to fund at all, and simply use a "pay-as-you-go" system, debiting the actual

Independent Investment Management for Pension Funds

We manage pension funds with assets in excess of £250 million. Each fund receives the personal attention of one of our experienced investment directors. You have your own investment manager without the attendant costs and inflexibility.

We have no conflicting interests, our fees are modest and we make no hidden charges.

For further information, contact Geoffrey Morley,

GMP
Geoffrey Morley & Partners Limited
27 Great James Street, London WC1N 3ES
Telephone 01-405 4151/4

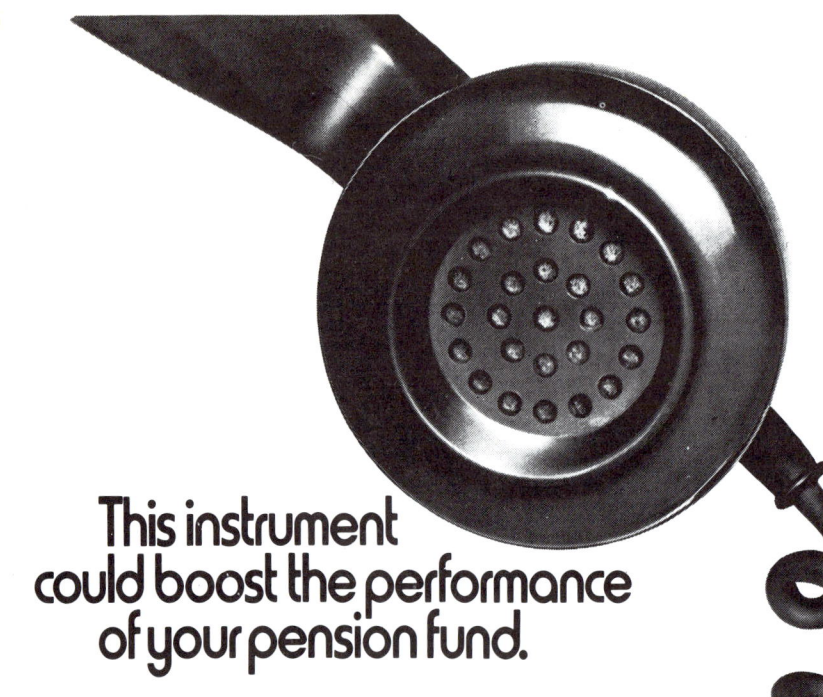

This instrument could boost the performance of your pension fund.

Give it a lift now. Whatever the size of your pension fund the key to higher-than-average performance is good management.

At Electra, our business is to provide this for pension funds. We have the experience, acumen and proven performance success you expect from long-established professional investment managers.

Funds under management total over £400 million.

For a preliminary talk about your own pension fund, or if you would like an explanatory brochure, just lift the telephone, and ask for Mr. Wawn or Mr. Hatt on:—

01-836 7766

Electra
Worldwide Investment Management

Electra Group Services Limited,
Electra House, Temple Place,
Victoria Embankment, London WC2R 3HP.

payments of retirement benefit to the profit of the year in which they fall due. Alternatively, it could settle its account on the actual retirement date of each member by paying a single lump sum, out of that year's profits, exactly sufficient to secure the promised benefit, a form of terminal funding. At the other extreme, it could estimate, at the date of hire, the future salary growth rate of each individual, the expected investment return on the fund for the duration of his future service, and the probability that he will survive in service to retirement date, and calculate the single lump sum required to be charged against profits in the year of hire for that individual's retirement benefit, tacitly acknowledging that some future adjustment, up or down, may be required to accommodate the variations between the actual experience and the estimates originally made.

Whilst these extreme possibilities may exist, most companies fund by spreading the cost of retirement benefits over the working lifetime of each member, either as a result of a conscious choice, or, more likely, because external factors such as fiscal or legal regulations, employee relations, and local custom and practice, dictate that method.

PACE OF FUNDING

In electing to spread the contributions, the company also needs to decide the pace at which the fund will build up each year to meet the benefit promise. In the UK this amounts to a management decision as to the pace at which this cost will be recognised. Unfortunately, a number of countries still exist in which the pace of funding is determined, either by convention, or, even worse, by governmental decree, by a contribution system which is based entirely on current salary with no allowance for future salary increases. In other words, the annual contribution from the company, often implicitly assuming future investment yield, is based on the premise that salary will remain at its present level throughout the member's working lifetime, from which it follows that the company contribution is similarly expected not to vary. The inevitable result of such a system is, for each individual employee, a rapidly increasing contribution rate as he progresses towards retirement date, for each salary rise generates additional retirement benefit related to the whole of his service, but with an ever-decreasing future period over which the fund may be built up to secure each additional slice of benefit.

Where there is a large group of employees with a spread of ages, the effect of this individually increasing funding rate tends to be lost in the averaging process. Under stable conditions, and with a continuous inflow of young new entrants, the aggregate cost may well progress smoothly from year to year. However, this gradual increase should not be allowed to disguise the underlying weakness of the system, for it is a folly to assume that stable conditions can be indefinitely maintained. Retirement benefit plans are not immortal, and it is wrong to rely upon the continued inclusion of future young new entrants to mask the deficiencies of the past.

Eventually, all promised benefits have to be paid for, and if the funding pattern requires only a low contribution rate at the outset, then, obviously, relatively increased contributions will be required later to make up the shortfall. In actuarial terms, and leaving aside external considerations, it can be argued that any one funding pattern is as good as another, provided that its relative strengths and weaknesses are fully analysed and understood.

In management terms there is, however, generally a need for greater discipline as in the corporate financial environment there naturally exists very strong pressure to achieve immediate short term profits, which, among other things, requires management to contain its perceived costs as far as possible. Inevitably, there is a temptation to install a retirement plan with good final salary benefits, for this aids recruitment and retention of the desired standard of personnel, but to opt for a financing pattern which requires only a modest contribution (i.e. a low perceived cost) in the early years.

MANAGEMENT INFORMATION

If such a pattern is chosen, and often there are good reasons for this, both external and internal, it is essential that the full implications, in terms of higher relative costs in later years, are recognised. If the best actuarial estimate of the cost of each year's benefit, with proper allowance for salary increases, investment yields anticipated, discretionary improvements to pensions in payment, and decremental rates, is not known, then clearly the company's prices of products and services will not truly reflect the operational overheads, the profit for the year will be overstated, and the published accounts will not show the true position of the company.

For these reasons, some corporations have now introduced a

WHAT MAKES CLERICAL MEDICAL GROUP PENSION SCHEMES SMOOTH-RUNNING AND PROFITABLE?

Group pension schemes are a worthwhile field of business for any broker to be in. But, to be successful, you need profitable and flexible contracts. Contracts which are smooth-running and backed by good service.

At Clerical Medical we have the answers.

Getting new business off the ground

Every Group Pension Scheme we produce is specifically prepared for the firm concerned. We have a specialist Pensions Development Organisation to help you with the installation of schemes.

Right from the start, we are on call. Not only can we advise on setting up the administrative procedures, but we can help as much or as little as you like in such things as presentation to your client – and his employees – the preparation of handbooks and any other detailed work.

Service to keep the scheme running smoothly

Once the pension scheme has been installed, a Pensions Service team will be on call.

They'll deal quickly and efficiently with every aspect of administration, including pension payments, death claims and the admission of new members.

And you can be sure your team managers will be up-to-date with the latest developments on each of your clients' contracts.

The right formula for every type of client

All our Group Pension Schemes attract interest according to a guaranteed basic formula with additions which reflect the success of Clerical Medical's investment expertise.

And for companies with operations overseas we can offer a comprehensive international service for pensions – and other employee benefits – through our membership of the long-established Aetna/Generali Network.

Why not get in touch with your local Clerical Medical man today? You'll find his address in most telephone directories – and that group pension business can be both smooth-running and profitable.

Offices in: Aberdeen, Ashton-under-Lyne, Belfast, Birmingham, Bradford, Brighton, Bristol, Cambridge, Cardiff, Channel Islands, Chelmsford, Cheltenham, Chester, Colchester, Coventry, Croydon, Dundee, Edinburgh, Exeter, Glasgow, Hull, Inverness, Ipswich, Leeds, Leicester, Lincoln, Liverpool, London (2), Luton, Maidstone, Manchester, Newcastle-upon-Tyne, Norwich, Nottingham, Oxford, Plymouth, Portsmouth, Preston, Reading, Sheffield, Southampton, Watford, Wolverhampton.

CM&G Clerical Medical & General Life Assurance Society
15 St. James's Square, London SW1Y 4LQ. Tel: 01-930 5474
Incorporated in England by Act of Parliament with limited liability No. Z193

T.G. Arthur & Co.

CONSULTING ACTUARIES

*WE PROVIDE INDEPENDENT PROFESSIONAL ADVICE ON
ALL ASPECTS OF OCCUPATIONAL PENSIONS*

17, Highfield Road,
Edgbaston,
Birmingham. B15 3DU.
Telephone: 021-454-6398

Rooms 144/5 Temple Chambers,
Temple Avenue,
London. EC4Y 0DT.
Telephone: 01-353-2476

T.G. Arthur, B.Sc., F.I.A., F.I.S., F.P.M.I. R.J.A. Unwin, B.Sc. (Econ.), F.I.A.
D.G. Hargrave, B.Com., M.Sc., F.I.A.

London Business School

Risk Measurement Service

An essential reference work for investors, professional advisers and financial managers.

The Risk Measurement Service provides risk marketability and performance measures for over 2,000 UK company shares and industry groupings. It includes editorial material, full explanation of all the underlying ideas and in each quarterly issue has highlight tables showing the best and worst performers.

The Risk Measurement Service is available for £145 from Peter Zinkin, London Business School, Financial Services, Sussex Place, Regent's Park, London NW1 4SA. Tel: 01-262 5050, Ext 346.

regular actuarial audit of all retirement plans which enables them to understand better the underlying effects of the many and varied funding patterns which exist. In some cases, the disclosure may lead to pressure from the centre to the subsidiary company for a strengthening of the funding base, but even where this does not happen, or would be contrary to local legislation or practice, internal account will still be taken of the improved estimates of the effects of the existing method.

CONCLUSION
Whether or not the company chooses to change its funding pattern, and contribute at a greater rate to its retirement plan, is much less important than its internal reaction to the improved information available. The published accounts will always show the actual contributions paid, i.e. the disbursement, not the "true" actuarial cost estimate and this figure alone is not sufficient to give a balanced view of events. It is to be hoped that companies will gradually improve the level of information provided. Failure to do so voluntarily may well result in legislated requirements being introduced which will probably be inflexible in their bases, and have a detrimental effect upon the development of this important matter. Provided that companies take the trouble to analyse and understand all the implications of their funding patterns, the necessary financial discipline should follow, with obvious benefit to all concerned.

In the UK where stronger actuarial influence is exerted over the control of the pace of funding, there tends to be less exposure to the risk of potentially damaging future liabilities being disguised in the funding pattern. Elsewhere in Europe, the control is less strong, and it is essential for the multinational corporation to recognise the essential difference between the perceived cost, namely the amount actually contributed to, or reserved for, its pension liabilities, and the underlying actuarially determined best estimate of the true cost attributable to that year's operational expenses. In the next section, detailed consideration is given to the range of financing methods which are commonly available in European countries, and to which the funding patterns are applied.

Towers, Perrin, Forster & Crosby

The advice of TPF&C's actuaries is available to our clients on all aspects of pension design, costing, implementation and administration:

- ☐ actuarial valuations
- ☐ costing of benefit changes
- ☐ long and short term financial forecasting
- ☐ benefit plan design

- ☐ preparation of documentation and liaison with government bodies
- ☐ administrative procedures
- ☐ employee communications including benefit statements

Towers, Perrin, Forster & Crosby
110 Jermyn Street, London SW1Y 6HB
01-839 5666

Offices also in:

Brussels	Caracas	Atlanta	New York
Frankfurt	Sao Paulo	Boston	Philadelphia
Paris		Chicago	Pittsburgh
	Calgary	Cleveland	San Francisco
Hong Kong	Montreal	Dallas	Seattle
	Toronto	Los Angeles	St Louis
	Vancouver	Minneapolis	Tampa
			Washington D.C.

Pension Financing in Europe

Stephen R. Baker, MA, MBA, FIA
Towers, Perrin, Forster & Crosby

INTRODUCTION

The previous article has concentrated on the need for adequate cost recognition procedures and in particular on the need to draw a distinction between the actual cost of providing the promised benefits and the amount which is "disbursed". In many European countries, either as a result of insurance history or as a result of tax or pensions legislation, the financing alternatives often do not result in disbursement charges which adequately reflect the true underlying costs of the pension plans.

Companies which fail to make an adjustment to the "disbursement" item risk seriously understating the true cost of doing business. This in turn will lead to management errors in pricing, financial policy, salary and incentive compensation levels, errors in comparing alternative investment opportunities and, last but not least, errors in evaluating mergers, acquisitions and joint ventures. The result is not just a bookkeeping error but lost, permanently lost, cash.

The purpose of this article is to give a brief outline of the main methods used to finance European pension plans and to highlight where appropriate their key strengths and weaknesses.

Broadly speaking, the financing options can be broken down into four main categories
- unallocated funds
- insurance contracts
- book reserves
- repartition.

This classification is far from perfect, in particular many insurance contracts (e.g. managed funds in the UK) are much closer to unallocated funds than to the traditional deferred annuity or endowment assurance contracts still quite typical on the Continent. Nonetheless the classification, although an over simplification, is helpful in isolating the key issues and will be used throughout this article.

UNALLOCATED FUNDS
(a) Countries Concerned
Unallocated funding through an external financing vehicle is typically the financing method used in the UK. Elsewhere in Europe it is also found in Belgium, Eire and Switzerland, although in these countries insurance still tends to be the more popular arrangement.

Recent changes in the tax legislation may result in an increased use of unallocated funding in Spain and, until a recent favourable US tax amendment, some US companies were considering using an external unallocated funding vehicle in Germany.

(b) Legal and Tax Framework
Unallocated funding is generally associated with a legal framework which permits the accumulation of a fund of assets which is separate from both the employer and the employees.

Although not strictly necessary, unallocated funding in practice is also almost always associated with tax concessions which are designed to encourage employers to part with their cash. A full tax deduction is generally available immediately on any employer and employee contributions invested in the pension plan (some Swiss cantons, however, do not allow a full deduction).

As a further tax concession, the income of a pension fund is usually also tax free. Belgium is an exception in that the ASBL's suffer a 20% withholding tax which is deducted at source.

(c) Actuarial and Investment Aspects
Unallocated funds offer very considerable financial and tax planning opportunities. Correspondingly, they offer considerable potential for damaging errors.

The majority of actuarial financial control techniques, for example, assume that there is some reasonable relationship between investment returns and inflation. Generally, investment returns are assumed to exceed salary inflation by a small margin. In reality, this proves to be a difficult target for investment managers to reach. In the UK, over the last decade, investment performance has fallen well short of this objective.

Final pay pension plans would have come under severe pressure had they not found additional resources from an unexpected quarter. The trick lies in the name. Unallocated funding means just that — the funds are not allocated. No employee has a claim to any of the assets of the fund as no assets have been allocated to him. The only claim he has is to a benefit. The amount which the employer may or may not have contributed to the fund on his behalf is entirely irrelevant. This is most important because it means that where an employee fails for some reason or another to claim his full expected benefit entitlement (e.g. he dies too early) the profit remains in the fund, it does not go to the employee's estate, to an insurance company or to any other outside party.

Now for final pay pension plans, the preserved benefit in respect of employees who leave before reaching normal retirement age is generally calculated in terms of salary as of the date of leaving. As yet, apart from the UK requirement to escalate GMP's, no European country requires such benefits to be increased in line with subsequent inflation, although some employers have taken an independent initiative to do so. This means that employees who leave early will claim a much lower benefit than that originally funded for, and will therefore provide a handsome profit to the pension plan. In the UK this profit has largely been used to offset investment losses, i.e. the losses which have occurred through the failure of actual investment performance to meet actuarial expectations.

Unallocated funding can therefore be seen to share many of the characteristics of a tontine. The lion's share of the fund is applied for the benefit of the survivors.

(d) Comment

Unallocated funds are highly flexible and efficient financing vehicles. Without the need to segregate or otherwise keep track of the "asset shares" of individual employees, the administration expenses are minimised. Further, experience gains (i.e. profits from employees who leave or die before claiming their full expected benefits) are automatically collected by the fund and can be applied to reduce future contributions.

The principal weakness of the unallocated approach is that the "tontine" or "reward for loyalty" element in the method is rather out of date. Most observers these days will regard employee benefits as a form of deferred compensation and not as awards for long service. Two employees doing similar work for a similar period while members of the same employee benefit plan should accrue similar benefits.

ARE YOU GIVING AWAY TOO MUCH PROFIT?

If you are now protecting your pension scheme on original or group life terms it is time to wonder whether you are giving away too much profit which could be utilised to increase the benefits of members of the scheme. You are protecting your scheme because you cannot afford to lose money on the death risk. You only lose money, however, on the risk if the total death claims in a year exceed the total life risk premiums contained in the original premium. What you need is a cover paying the excess above the risk premium. We at NRG have such a scheme

IT IS CALLED STOP LOSS

NRG

Please contact Robin Michaelson or Grahame Pearson for further information and explanation of how this Stop Loss could apply to your Scheme, at

NRG LONDON REINSURANCE COMPANY LIMITED
Fountain House, 130 Fenchurch Street
London EC3P 3BD. Telephone: (01) 626-3851

The fact that the mobile employee forfeits a significant amount of his benefit entitlement is unlikely to prove socially acceptable in the long term.

INSURANCE CONTRACTS

(a) Countries Concerned
Insurance contracts to cover pension obligations are generally available throughout Europe.

(b) Legal and Tax Framework
Virtually all European countries have detailed regulations concerning the setting up, administration and reporting requirements of insurance companies.

In many countries, however, the regulations go far beyond this and control in detail the actuarial methods and the investment policies to be adopted.

The greatest freedom and the greatest variety of insurance contracts is found in the UK. The greatest inflexibility is found in the Netherlands and Germany. In these last two countries, the statutory restrictions are further compounded by restrictive practices adopted by the insurance companies, who have organised themselves into cartels. One or two "maverick" organisations do, however, exist which aim to offer a flexible service to multinational employers.

As far as taxation is concerned, in most European countries contributions to pension insurances are tax deductible. In Germany and Austria, however, any employer contributions are assessed as income to the employee and tax deductions are available only up to a relatively modest level. In Germany, an additional DM 2400 per annum of employer contributions are taxed at a discretionary rate of 10%. In Belgium, a special 4% tax is levied on all insurance premiums.

Where significant tax reliefs are available and where the investment performance of insurance contracts (measured in relation to the positive or negative cash flows to or from the pension plan — as opposed to any claims made in the insurance brochures) compares favourably with either the investment returns which a company can earn from investing in its own business assets or with the savings it could generate through an equivalent reduction in its borrowings, then it makes sense to fund the pension plan through an insurance contract.

(c) Actuarial and Investment Aspects

The law in European countries generally requires pension insurances to be written on the basis of individual level annual premium contracts, or an equivalent series of single premium contracts.

The issue, however, is far from being black and white. In many countries a number of insurance companies are struggling to be more flexible, but for the purposes of this article their efforts, though much appreciated, will be ignored. Insurance will be taken to mean deferred annuity or convertible endowment style contracts funded by level annual premiums or step rate single premiums.

On this basis, the essential difference between insurance funding and unallocated funding is that the legal relationship between the pension plan and the assets is indirect. The pension plan does not own any of the securities in the insurance company's asset portfolio. It merely has a claim to the payment of certain cash flows in accordance with the terms of the insurance policy. The pension plan *vis-à-vis* the insurance company is consequently in much the same position as the individual members of an unallocated fund. That is, the insurance company's assets are unallocated as far as individual pension plans are concerned. Should circumstances evolve in such a way that the actual net cash flows to the policy exceed those which were originally anticipated when setting the premium rates, then the profit falls to the advantage of the insurance company, not the pension plan. Given that the central control authority generally insists on the premiums being calculated on the basis of a low "tariff" rate of interest (typically approximately 4% per annum), this matter is of some importance.

As a rule, a large measure of the profit is returned to the pension plan in the form of a bonus. Human nature being what it is, however, faced with a choice between launching a drive into a new market, or adding an extra fraction to pension fund investment bonuses, it is possible that the claims of the pension funds are not always given the attention they deserve by the managers of insurance companies. This is particularly true of countries with strong insurance cartels. In this respect, the Netherlands deserves special mention as the general practice there is for the insurance company to claim the "excess interest" (that is the interest above the 4% per annum tariff rate) for itself after the first 10 years.

If the appropriateness of the investment practices underlying many European contracts can be questioned, there is little doubt that the actuarial methods are in many cases seriously deficient. The difficulty is that the large part of the insurance laws have been designed without taking inflation into account. The insurance premiums in "tariff" countries are consequently set in terms of frozen benefits.

Social forces in Europe (including actual/proposed legislation in the UK, Netherlands and Switzerland) have, however, resulted in considerable pressure on employers to provide pension benefits based on final salary, i.e. benefits which at least for the period that employees remain in service are linked to inflation.

An employer who estimates his pension costs on the basis of an insurance contract which only provides fixed cash flows, even though the pension plan promises indexed cash flows, is making a serious mistake. A cursory glance at his insurance policy should convince him that it is not the insurance company which will have to make up the cost difference. It is subsequent generations of customers, employees and share holders in his own organisation who will have to pay higher prices, accept lower salaries and lower dividends in order to make up the shortfall.

In a sentence, the actuarial methods are fine for the insurance companies but are seriously off target as far as the management information requirements of the employer are concerned.

(d) Comment

With their wealth of experience in the technical and administrative aspects of pension plans, and with the economies of scale which they can provide with regard both to expenses and to risk exposure, insurance companies have and will always retain a central role in managing European pension plans, especially for small employers.

In many countries however, the lack of competition and an inflexibility on the part of both the insurance companies and the legislators has allowed insurance companies to escape the ruthless drive for productivity which has been forced on so many other industries. In such countries, large and medium sized employers could achieve significant cost savings by switching to an unallocated fund or an internal book reserve arrangement.

INTERNAL BOOK RESERVES

(a) Countries Concerned
Book reserve funding is the celebrated method by which the majority of German pension plans are financed. It is also a popular method for large employers in Austria and is used to a more limited extent in Sweden and the Netherlands.

(b) Legal and Tax Framework
Allocations to book reserves in Germany are only permitted if a legally binding and irrevocable promise to pay the benefit has been made in writing to the employees. As the assets of the pension plan remain within the company (as either plant and machinery, working capital or perhaps as a separate portfolio of securities in the name of the company), there is an obvious problem of benefit security. Members would have little protection if the employer were to go into liquidation. In Germany, this difficulty has been circumvented, in part at least, by the requirement that the vested accrued benefits be reinsured with a central credit insurance agency (PSV) which was especially set up for this purpose.

As regards the tax aspects, allocations to book reserves are tax deductible within tightly controlled limits in both Germany and Austria. Employee contributions are generally not permitted.

(c) Actuarial and Investment Aspects
The easiest way to imagine the financial operation of a book reserve is to consider the reserve as being a loan made to the employer by the pension plan. The two key points which employers have to remember are
- There is a real cost attached to borrowing money from the pension plan; furthermore, this cost is a financing cost not a pension (i.e. labour) cost — if the total allocations to book reserves including interest charges are charged as a pension cost, the management will receive distorted information on relative costs of capital as compared with labour
- Although the benefits have been reserved they have not in fact been paid; the benefits when due will have to be paid in cash, not business assets. An appropriate allowance for this liquidity requirement must therefore be built into the short and medium term cash plans.

With regard to actuarial matters, the basic concept behind the German reserving method (called the "Teilwert" method) is the same as the Entry Age Normal method commonly used in the US. By itself the method would be quite acceptable. The problem is that the tax laws will not permit the inclusion of any general allowance for future salary increases nor any general allowance for future pension increases; this even though pension increases "reasonably" in line with the cost of living are now compulsory.

If a formal promise to pay a specific predetermined amount of increase is made (e.g. 3% per annum) then this can be included in the tax deductible Teilwert reserve. Once promised, however, the fixed amount of increase would have to be paid even if inflation fell to zero. In Germany, where this is a real possibility, employers are obviously reluctant to make any such commitment and cannot in consequence make realistic allocations to their book reserves.

From the standpoint of typical UK actuarial practice, which aims to produce pension costs for final pay plans which remain stable as a percentage of payroll, the German approach leads to significant underfunding.

(d) Comment
Providing adequate tax reliefs are available, internal book reserves are a highly efficient method of financing pension plans. Compared with unallocated funds, the lines of communication between the sources and uses of capital are very much shorter. Investment expenses are consequently reduced.

The principal objection to book reserve financing is that, to be operated without mishap, it requires a degree of financial sophistication which many corporate managements either do not have, or cannot enforce on day to day operating management. Further, without some form of credit insurance, pension plan members (including those actually in receipt of benefit) have little protection should their employer fail.

REPARTITION
(a) Background and Countries Concerned
Repartition is the financing method used almost without exception in France.

If ever the proposed Swiss legislation comes into effect in its original form, repartition will be used there as well to finance post retirement indexation and, temporarily, the initial unfunded liabilities which will be created through the compulsory award of prior service benefits.

Finally, in a less organised and less disciplined form, most European social security institutions are funded on a basis similar to repartition, though in these less formalised arrangements the financing is generally described as "pay-as-you-go".

(b) Legal and Tax Framework

Clearly, in the French situation, employees making contributions to repartition plans need to be very sure that these plans will continue to be in existence when they come to retire. Without a perpetual inflow of new members, the value of contributions will shrink and with it, of course, the value of the pension point. Those employees who remain would therefore risk obtaining benefits far below the levels which they themselves provided for previous generations.

To provide sufficiently convincing guarantees, the French equivalents of the CBI and the TUC (there are several TUCs) have struck a number of formal agreements which now have the force of law.

An employer who elects to join one of the repartition plans must do so with respect to all his employees in the respective classifications (i.e. all works/clerical staff, or all senior staff/ executives). Once contributions start to be paid there can be no going back. This is to secure the entitlements of the current membership through obliging future generations to join the system. In effect repartition works like a kind of closed shop. Future employees who wish to work for existing member firms have to join the club.

Employer and employee contributions are fully tax deductible though there is an overall maximum limit presently of 19%.

(c) Actuarial and Investment Aspects

The investment side of repartition is simple. In the main there are no reserves to be invested.

By contrast the actuarial aspects are highly complex. A detailed description would be beyond the scope of this article. In essence the problem is to ensure that a repartition plan covering a declining industry receives adequate subsidies from plans covering expanding industries, so the same benefits and the same contributions are applied in both instances.

More fundamental perhaps is the problem of maintaining adequate equity between the two competing institutions (i.e.

between AGIRC for "staff" employees and ARRCO for "works" employees) and, above all, in maintaining long term confidence that the system will survive.

An example may help to illustrate the difficulties.

ARRCO collects contributions on Tranche A and B (see the French country profile). AGIRC collect contributions on Tranche B only — separate arrangements with repartition systems outside the two umbrella organisations are used to finance pensions on Tranche C.

The decision as to whether individuals belong to an ARRCO scheme rather than an AGIRC scheme is settled by reference to a national job evaluation system. Jobs which score more than 300 points are automatically AGIRC. Jobs which score less than 200 points are automatically ARRCO. The treatment of jobs which score between 200 and 300 points is left to individual companies to decide.

Over the years with almost all jobs involving an increased use of technology, and thence a need for more formal training and qualifications, the average job grade has increased. There has, so to speak, been inflation in job points as well as in salaries. This has been to the advantage of AGIRC, which has enjoyed a population increase of the order of 4% per year at the expense of ARRCO as jobs which were previously graded too low for AGIRC have been replaced by jobs with a higher grade.

To offset this demographic disadvantage, the parties to the original agreements further agreed a few years ago that all the AGIRC members would also have compulsorily to belong to an ARRCO plan with respect to their Tranche A earnings.

Further, to help ARRCO maintain its benefit standards, a 10% surcharge was imposed. This additional contribution amounts to 10% of the basic contribution and is not applied to purchase additional pension points.

Given that the essence of success in repartition financing is the maximisation of the contribution base, these changes resulted in the pendulum swinging firmly back into ARRCO's favour. Each time the social security ceiling is increased, ARRCO now collects increased contributions from all employees working for companies which are members of the repartition system. AGIRC correspondingly collects less. Worse than that, as the social security ceiling is increasing faster than executive and senior staff salaries, AGIRC's contribution base (called, characteristically perhaps for France, its "assiette") has been shrinking in real terms. Worst of all, however, has been the high rate of unemployment which means that a large section of the population is not contributing at all although, under repartition rules, they continue to acquire pension points at the rate applicable when they were last employed.

All in all AGIRC is now in some difficulty. It was forced to impose a 3% surcharge on contributions and will probably have to impose additional surcharges in the future unless some further fundamental structural changes are introduced to relieve the pressure.

(d) Comment

The repartition plans were originally set up after a disastrous period of inflation which ruined most of the insured pension plans then in existence. The aim was to provide pension benefits which would automatically be indexed in line with inflation.

The objective of providing benefits in "real" rather than "funny" money is a noble one. France in many ways has been ahead of the rest of the industrialised world in that there at least no-one has had the arrogance blithely to assume that inflation can be beaten. Inflation is certainly fought but, in so far as it cannot be eradicated, steps are taken to minimise its adverse social impact and in particular its adverse impact on pension plans. The repartition schemes have been in existence for 30 years now and over this period they have broadly managed to achieve their objective of inflation-proofed pensions. This is a record which few, if any, democracies can match.

The problem is that although the difficulties associated with inflation have successfully been circumvented, this has only been accomplished at the price of substituting the problems associated with demography, i.e. precisely the problems which the actuarial techniques for unallocated funding, insurance and book reserves manage to solve.

For most of France, however, repartition has become almost an article of faith. As long as everyone continues to believe in the system the system will continue to work. Early in 1980, one of France's leading insurance companies ran an advertisement under the caption "Children of 1949, don't count on the babies of 1979 to pay for your pensions". The advertisement caused such an uproar that it had to be withdrawn.

Less overtly, however, a number of French employers are

gradually trying to ease themselves out of repartition, at least as far as Tranche C and Tranche D earnings are concerned.

In this respect the Swiss have demonstrated brilliantly, if for the moment only theoretically, how repartition can be used both selectively and temporarily to achieve a variety of limited objectives. In particular, they demonstrated how repartition once started can, contrary to conventional wisdom in France, gradually be wound down without any undue fuss.

When an understanding of these possibilities becomes more widespread, there is a possible chance that some fundamental changes may be introduced to the French system. For the time being, however, the French are likely to solve their difficulties in their traditional way.

OLIVER'S GUIDES

OLIVER'S GUIDE TO THE CITY OF LONDON – 1980/1981

The seventh edition of Oliver's Guide to the City of London is now available and as previously includes:-

* An up-to-date directory of all major city firms and organisations.
* The only large-scale maps of the City showing every street and office building.
* Street index of 600 city streets.
* A classified section listing firms in the major city business sectors.

Oliver's Guide has now proved itself to be a most useful asset to many companies and organisations, both in the city and further afield. To order your copies please complete the form below and return it to the address shown.

. . . .

To: Oliver's Guides, 9 Courtleigh Gardens, London, NW11 9JX.

Please send   copy/copies of Oliver's Guide to the City of London, 1980/81 edition at £3 each, (plus 40p postage and packing).

I enclose my cheque for £ . . . . payable to A.P. Books

    Name . . . .

    Company . . . .

    Address . . . .

            . . . .

    Telephone No . . . .

International implications of US Pensions reporting.

A. S. Fishman, BSc, FIA, EA, ASA, MAAA, FPMI
and
K. G. Whitehead, BA, FIA, ASA, FPMI
Senior Partners, Clay & Partners

INTRODUCTION
Throughout the world, the last few years have seen intense activity in the pensions industry. In numerous countries, major legislation has recently evolved covering vital issues such as the balance between State and Private pension plans, the disclosure of information to members and the responsibilities of Trustees in the investment of monies.

Such legislation has usually been politically motivated. Social trends, together with the impact of worldwide inflation, have brought into focus the importance of coverage and security of benefits. For similar reasons, pension plan investments have grown to enormous proportions resulting in employers and employees taking a far greater interest than hitherto in the performance of their funds. In such circumstances of dynamic growth and social evolution, Governments have felt unable to simply sit back and watch, even where matters were being handled in a more than satisfactory manner.

The UK is an example where, up to 1978, the pensions industry had evolved in a responsible manner with relatively little Government interference. Of course, there were gaps in the coverage of employees and, on rare occasions, abuses had taken place, but these were minimal.

Nevertheless, after almost a decade of debating complex proposals submitted by successive Government ministers, Crossman, Joseph & Castle, the Social Security Pensions Act 1975 was enacted. Its main provisions were to ensure adequate pensions coverage of employees either under the umbrella of the State or occupational pension schemes. This particular piece of legislation had little or no practical impact on such vital matters as investment, disclosure of information or pension rights on change of employment.

How differently matters have evolved in the US following the enactment on 2nd September 1974 of the Employee Retirement Income Security Act of 1974 (ERISA)! This legislation has directly influenced every facet of the US pensions industry and has provoked other interested parties, such as the American actuarial and accounting professions, into a major re-examination of their roles in the operation of occupational pension plans.

From an international view point, the most controversial aspect of all that has happened in the US over the last six years, has been the impact on the pension plans of US owned overseas companies. Bearing in mind the influence of US companies in the economic structure of virtually all countries in the free world, American pensions legislation and reporting requirements form a major consideration for pensions industries all over the globe.

It is not difficult to understand why this controversy has arisen. For reasons explained later on, there was an overwhelming need for the US pensions industry to have its house put in order by the legislators. Resentment was bound to arise in other countries where few pensions problems had occurred but where it now became necessary for regard to be paid to ERISA and its reporting requirements.

BACKGROUND TO ERISA

The starting point in appreciating the international implications of US pensions reporting is to trace the events leading up to the birth of ERISA.

The origins of ERISA can be found in the endless complaints made by individuals as to their loss of pensions expectations resulting from severe age and service requirements, flagrant financial abuses, and the employment of pension fund monies by a company or union for private purposes.

On the other side of the coin, however, companies were prompted to set up pension plans in the 1940's even though finance was very limited, as contributions to such plans were exempt from wartime wage restrictions. Also contributions were deductible from high wartime corporate tax rates. A further impetus arose in 1945 when the Supreme Court ruled in the Inland Steel case that pension plans were the proper subject of collective bargaining.

Subsequently, the only relevant legislation was the Welfare and Pension Plans Disclosure Act of 1958 which suggested that financial disclosure might ensure financial responsibility.

The turning point came in a "Report to the President on Private Employee Retirement Plans" dated January 1965 by a committee originally appointed by President Kennedy. Basically, this recommended that Federal standards should be imposed on private pension plans in regard to the specific issues of vesting and funding.

There then followed seven years of research, hearings and representations on the implications of Federal standards for private plans. This delay resulted from influences similar, for example, to those experienced in the UK in the years leading up to the enactment of the Social Security Pensions Act 1975, though it must be said that, by comparison with the US, UK legislation was achieved with only a minimum of fuss.

Perhaps the main problem in the US was the sheer number of interested parties and congressional committees who had a say (or felt they should have a say) in determining pensions legislation. Indeed, seven separate congressional committees became involved in strenuous research often employing different firms of pension consultants to assist them. The problems were magnified by the lack of available survey data on private pension plans.

As publicity about the possible new legislation increased, so did the intensity of the "lobby" on the part of the various pressure groups. Of special note, actuaries were represented by several bodies often with conflicting views with the unsatisfactory result, that, in the eyes of Congress, the actuarial profession did not perhaps come over as well as it should have done. On the other hand, the accountants were strongly united in their representations to the authorities. The influence of this was to be felt in subsequent statements produced by US accountants which many actuaries have come to regard as imposing upon their professional responsibilities and which, again, have international reporting implications. This is dealt with below.

Reverting to the sequence of events, the potential legislation up to 1972 had been dealt with as an employee relations issue and had, therefore, come under the aegis of Labor Committees. Because of the favourable tax treatment accorded to pension plans, Finance Committees now insisted that they should become involved and set about preparing their own version of a bill.

The result was that during 1973 and 1974, in both the House of Representatives and the Senate, two versions of a bill were presented and considerable negotiations and compromise were then required in order to achieve one piece of legislation.

Nevertheless, it will come as no surprise to learn that the legislation signed by President Ford on 2nd September 1974 (Labor Day) came over very clearly as having been prepared by different hands. This has given rise to many confusing issues, not least the impact on overseas pension plans.

STRUCTURE OF US OWNED OVERSEAS COMPANIES

The degree of confusion depends on whether the overseas company is set up as a subsidiary operation or as a branch operation. The majority of US owned overseas companies are established as subsidiary operations, though there are a surprising number of branch operations, far more than most people realise.

As far as ERISA and its reporting requirements are concerned, only overseas pension plans of branch operations are affected but even here inconsistencies have arisen. Such plans are exempt from the participation and vesting requirements of that part of ERISA prepared by the Department of Labor. Yet they are not exempt from virtually the same requirements under that section of the Act falling within the jurisdiction of the Department of Treasury, meaning the Internal Revenue Service (IRS).

Furthermore, many US corporations have taken the view that, even though overseas subsidiary plans are outside the jurisdiction of ERISA, they should be regarded as having to conform in the same way as branch plans.

The US parent's desire that overseas subsidiary plans should conform does not necessarily result in pressure for the benefit structure of overseas plan to be changed. It is more a question of the subsidiary plan preparing ERISA-type reports which the US parent is better able to understand having regard to its own domestic experience.

Real pressure from the parent does exist, however, in the area of funding of overseas subsidiary plans, even though this, again, is outside the jurisdiction of ERISA. The point here is that ERISA has provoked accountants into setting standards which apply to both branch and subsidiary plans and this question is discussed more fully later in the article.

REPORTING AND DISCLOSURE REQUIREMENTS OF ERISA

Under ERISA, plan administrators are required to provide a

number of documents. Each member must automatically be provided with a plan description, an annual report, a statement of vested benefits upon termination of employment and details of the joint and survivor annuity option.

On a member's written request, a personal benefits statement, definitive plan documents and annual reports must be provided though a member could be charged with the cost of duplication of voluminous documents. In addition, plan descriptions, documents and annual reports must be made available at the employer's principal office.

Reports must be filed with three different agencies of the Government; the Department of Labor, the IRS and the Pension Benefit Guaranty Corporation (PBGC) which supervises plan termination insurance. These reports cover such matters as full details of a plan, subsequent amendments, changes in status, and an advance statement of the effect on benefits of a proposed merger or termination. The PBGC must be given an annual declaration that premiums have been paid to them and, in the case of a termination and other reportable events, appropriate returns must be made.

The most important return is the annual report Form 5500, which is filed with the IRS and shared with the two other agencies. As a by-product of Form 5500, the IRS furnishes the Social Security Administration with details of deferred vested benefits of members who left employment during the year. This enables the Social Security Administration automatically to provide details of private pension plan benefits when employees apply for social security benefits.

The sheer volume of the reporting requirements, together with overlapping jurisdictions and the resulting bureaucratic tangle, has caused enormous headaches, not only to overseas employers but to the US pensions industry at large. Major employers have somehow coped, but not very well, in conforming with the reporting and disclosure requirements. They have had no alternative but to cope.

Many smaller employers in the US have surrendered to the inevitable. Between the enactment of ERISA and 31st December 1978, 25,000 private plans terminated. These represent 15% of all plans but probably only 2% of all members. This should be contrasted with the UK where the legislation created a climate that enabled existing "small" schemes to thrive and a substantial number of new schemes to be created for the benefit of all concerned.

Reverting to Form 5500, this is by far the most important document to be filed by overseas branch plans. Unless this form is completed annually, tax deductions in the US for pension contributions made to overseas branch plans will not be granted. The main body of Form 5500 is concerned with extremely detailed questions on plan assets. Questions also appear on such matters as membership data, plan amendments and confirmation that Government Departments have been informed of any relevant events occurring in the previous year. Although Form 5500 may prove burdensome, no great points of principle arise as far as overseas branch plans are concerned.

SCHEDULE B AND THE ENROLLED ACTUARY

Attached to the main Form 5500 are a number of schedules providing supplementary information on insurance, the actuarial valuation, and members leaving with vested benefits.

Because of the international implications, special mention must be made of Schedule B, the attachment to Form 5500 dealing with the actuarial valuation.

Schedule B must be signed by an enrolled actuary, a status conferred on individuals able to satisfy the experience and examination requirements of the Joint Board for the Enrollment of Actuaries, a body established under the provisions of ERISA.

Unfortunately, with the exception of a number of actuaries in Canada and a handful elsewhere, fully qualified overseas actuaries have been denied enrollment. This has caused consternation amongst actuaries in many countries such as the UK and Australia, because of the unsatisfactory situation of a local professional being unable to "sign-off" his own actuarial valuation as a consequence of a foreign legislative body refusing to accord him appropriate status. Resentment has thus arisen following the need for a local actuary to find an enrolled actuary, almost inevitably US based, willing to rule upon his valuation and to sign Schedule B. It should be said that, as far as the UK is concerned, strong representations were made to the Joint Board that UK actuaries had been unfairly denied enrollment. Regrettably no progress has been made on this approach.

The question may well be asked as to why Congress decided to set up its own examination and experience arrangements when, to choose an example, the Society of Actuaries in America was well placed to fulfil the required role. The point was that, in the US, there were a number of actuarial bodies, some offering examinations, who were vying to achieve credibility in the public eye. Some bodies were able to exert greater pressure than others on Congress with the intention of ultimately becoming the recognised voice of the profession. Congress had no desire to be in the position of acting as referee between different actuarial bodies, and consequently formed its own licensing procedures.

It would be inappropriate, in this article, to dwell at length on the unfortunate impact that the Governmental arrangements for "licensing" actuaries had on the US professional bodies. Suffice it to say that massive confusion and consternation was caused in regard to such matters as the inter-relationship between the various actuarial organisations. There was also no automatic guarantee that examinations given by professional bodies would suffice for the purposes of exempting candidates from the Joint Board's examinations.

After a considerable degree of statesmanship had been exercised, it was decided that the professional actuarial bodies must work together. The upshot was that the enrolment examinations are now jointly administered by the Joint Board, and several actuarial bodies in the US. Nevertheless, each body remained free to set its own pass mark so that a candidate satisfying the Joint Board might not, for example, obtain the standard set by the Society of Actuaries or vice-versa.

In the light of the above, it is not perhaps surprising that the Joint Board has adopted a tough line in regard to overseas actuaries.

Turning now to the reporting requirements of Schedule B, information must be supplied on the actuarial basis employed and the valuation of assets, accrued liabilities and vested liabilities. The valuation basis must be approved by the IRS and, again, this can cause great problems for overseas plans and their actuaries where local conditions are such that a basis satisfying the IRS would be totally inappropriate. In this connection, it is also worth noting that no definitive glossary of terms exists although a number of drafts have been prepared in the US. Thus, expressions such as accrued liabilities or vested liabilities, which cause difficulties even in America, have resulted in problems of interpretation overseas, where alternative, but just as acceptable, definitions exist.

FINANCIAL ACCOUNTING STANDARDS BOARD

Until recently, the main document produced by the US accounting profession for the guidance of their members on pension fund matters was Opinion No. 8 of the Accounting Principles Board, an offshoot of the American Institute of Certified Public Accountants. In 1973 an independent standard-setting structure known as the Financial Accounting Standards Board (FASB) was formed and this is now regarded in the US as the authority for establishing standards of accounting and reporting.

The momentum produced by ERISA has, amongst other things, prompted the FASB into considering their attitude towards pension plans, and important and far-reaching Statements were published in March and May 1980. The international implications of the documents produced by the American accounting profession are significant. They are held to apply to pension costs incurred outside the United States under plans of overseas operations when included in corporate financial statements intended to conform with generally accepted accounting principles in the United States. Thus, overseas subsidiary plans as well as branch plans are required to conform and the implications are far more comprehensive than ERISA, which applies only to overseas branch plans.

Under Opinion No. 8 which has been in force since November 1966 and which, in fact, is still largely operative, overseas pension plans are required to furnish annual information which has, in the past, proved to be neither particularly onerous, nor indeed of great relevance. Opinion No. 8 sets out those actuarial methods which are acceptable and describes minimum and maximum calculations for pension costs. In this particular respect, it is relevant to note that, as far as unfunded "past service" liabilities are concerned, it was only necessary to pay interest on such commitments and not to make capital repayments.

Incidentally, such pensions costs are taken by the accountants as a charge against profits. They may well differ from the physical payments to the pension plan which results in even further misunderstanding of its financial status and ability to meet its liabilities.

It was due to the growth in unfunded liabilities, with a consequent lack of security of members' benefits, that gave rise to one of the most significant aspects of ERISA, namely the requirement to amortise past service liabilities over a period of years by way of capital as well as interest. Opinion No. 8 also covered the treatment of actuarial gains and losses with the view to smoothing the effects of deviations from the actuarial assumptions as well as ironing out undue fluctuations in the market value of investments.

The main effects on overseas plans were the disclosure requirements of Opinion No. 8, which formed part of the corporate financial statements. Disclosure had to be made on the existence of a pension plan, the employee groups covered, funding policies, provision for pension costs incurred, significant changes that had occurred in the circumstances of the plan and, finally, the misleading statistic of the extent to which the value of vested benefits exceeded the total of the pension fund.

In May 1980 the FASB produced Statement No. 36 which amended the disclosure requirements of Opinion No. 8. Apart from the items mentioned above, Statement No. 36 now requires the disclosure of the actuarial value of vested benefits, the actuarial value of non-vested benefits and the assets available for benefits. From this it will be possible to determine not only the extent of unfunded liabilities but also the extent of overfunded liabilities. The amendment also requires the disclosure of the actuarial interest assumptions used for calculating vested and non-vested liabilities. Perhaps the main impact of this additional information is that it will now be possible to make more meaningful comparisons than hitherto of corporate pension plans.

In view of past abuses, one can understand the concern of the US accounting profession to ensure that statistics showing unfunded liabilities are properly disclosed. To actuaries, however, particularly those overseas, there does appear to be an unwelcome encroachment on their professional duties, which can only result in the "worst" of both worlds, apart from the expense and cost of duplication of information. As already mentioned, the expression "unfunded liabilities" can take on a variety of meanings though these have been narrowed down by the FASB in stating that no allowance for future salary increases should be made. This has resulted in a number of US accountants forming the view that the revision will assist in concealing unfunded liabilities. Indeed, one accountant suggested that the new statement should be titled "Disclosure of Pension Misinformation".

The FASB has made it clear that Statement No. 36 is an interim measure pending completion of a comprehensive investigation on

The Accountants' Guide to Professional Services

Sound financial advice is often based upon a knowledge of the available alternatives. Which service do you need? Which company can supply it?

THE ACCOUNTANTS' GUIDE TO PROFESSIONAL SERVICES has been published to help you make these assessments.

If you are faced with a cash flow problem that can be solved by factoring, or with a client who asks your advice on which computer to install, who to lease it from, or which insurance or pension scheme to buy, you will find the information you need in this book.

Unlike many reference books which simply provide you with a list of names, the company detail within the guide will give you sufficient information to enable you to choose the right option.

We have included sections on Financial Services, Property and Land, Insurance and Pensions, Investment, Computers, Leasing, General Information and a host of other specialist services and products.

THE ACCOUNTANTS' GUIDE TO PROFESSIONAL SERVICES will save you endless hours of research and will provide you with much of the information you may require throughout the year.

Published in February by Sedgerate Ltd, 6 Brook Street, London W1Y 1AA. Tel: 01-629 1703. Complete this form to reserve your copy: please send me _____ copy/copies of the Accountants' Guide to Professional Services, price £10.00 plus £1.50 post and packing. I enclose a cheque for _____

Name _____

Company _____

Address _____

Send to Sedgerate Ltd, 6 Brook Street, London W1Y 1AA

accounting by employers for pension benefits. The US pensions industry awaits the next step with trepidation; overseas industries even more so.

The other document recently produced by the FASB is Statement No. 35 "Accounting and Reporting by Defined Benefit Pension Plans". This supersedes two exposure drafts, the first issued in April 1977, but quickly withdrawn after seven hundred letters of comment were received, and the other issued in July 1979. Statement No. 35 does not involve corporate financial statements but deals with pension plan financial statements produced by plan sponsors. Information is required on such matters as net assets available for benefits; changes in net assets over a plan year; and accumulated plan benefits and how this has changed over the year. This requires a great deal more than any other document of matters normally covered by actuaries and has caused some consternation in the States. Fortunately, it seems unlikely that this Statement applies to overseas pension plans, although there must be a great temptation on the part of corporate managements, for the reasons already mentioned, to apply these standards worldwide.

An important by-product of the heavier demands being made by US accountants, is that annual actuarial valuations are now virtually essential on overseas subsidiary and branch plans. In the UK, where annual valuations are not the norm, this imposes further unnecessary expense on local companies.

CONCLUSION

Those connected with overseas pension plans of a US subsidiary or branch operation, ignore at their peril the far reaching implications of US pensions reporting emanating from ERISA and the FASB. It is, of course, perfectly reasonable for US parent companies to attempt to assess the strengths and weaknesses of all their pension plans throughout the world and it is equally reasonable for them to use as a starting point US domestic legislation and practice. Overseas people should ensure that they fully understand the reasons for the legislation and reporting requirements introduced in the States and then to adapt these, as far as possible, to local conditions. Without such knowledge and the ability to recognise the international implications of US pensions reporting, many overseas pension plans may well end up being organised in a manner totally inappropriate to local needs and practice.

 # Schroders

Pension Fund Investment Management

When experience is essential

Schroders was one of the first to recognise the growing importance of pension funds and the growing need for specialist management services.

Today, over 30 years later, we offer one of the most experienced teams available, backed by full-time research staff in London and overseas; our own investment operations in New York, Zurich, Sydney, Hong Kong and Tokyo; and a property management and investment facility active in the UK and USA.

Schroders' unsurpassed experience is at your disposal.
Just write or telephone:

Schroders
G. H. Popham, Head of Investment Division.
J. Henry Schroder Wagg & Co. Limited, 120 Cheapside,
London EC2V 6DS. Tel: 01-588 4000.

International Portfolio Diversification

Gordon Popham
Senior Investment Director, J. Henry Schroder Wagg & Co Limited

Introduction
At a time when sterling is beginning to be termed a "strong" currency once again, it seems appropriate to focus a discussion of International Portfolio Diversification upon the question "Why should a UK pension fund invest overseas?" If domestic returns are likely to be superior and carry no currency risk, surely there can be no case for foreign investment.

The objective of pension fund asset management is to gain the highest possible rate of return subject to an acceptable level of risk, risk being the possibility that the value of assets, including accrued income, may not rise in line with the value of liabilities. To comply with this objective overseas investment must offer either the prospect of a higher return than is likely to be achieved on domestic assets or an opportunity to reduce overall portfolio risk. Ideally it should offer both.

Returns on overseas assets
Returns on overseas assets may exceed those on domestic assets for a number of reasons. The local economy may experience more rapid growth, Government policy may be more conducive to expansion of corporate profits, underlying productivity growth and technological development may be more rapid, and so on. The relative importance of these trends will, of course, vary from one country to another, and the maximum returns are only likely to be achieved if the process of selection of assets seeks to capitalise upon the most advantageous trends. This is most easily illustrated by looking at examples.

USA
The United States, for instance, has demonstrated in recent years a rate of underlying productivity growth little better than that of the UK, and well below that of Japan or even Germany or France. There are, moreover, questions as to the longer-term political commitment to reduce inflation. That said, the USA has, with

McCARTHY INFORMATION LIMITED

A tailored information service for the Fund Manager

FREE TRIAL OFFER

Monitoring the activities and performance of companies in the UK and overseas can be a troublesome business.

McCarthy Information Ltd can provide part of the solution. Every day we scan the leading business newspapers and magazines around the world. We can supply you with cuttings on virtually any company by sector or country.

Whether your professional intersts are in quoted or unquoted companies as a whole or specifically confined to a sector — banking, property or energy for example, we can help keep you up to date.

For more details of our free trial offer, telephone or write to:

Barbara Bryant, McCarthy Information Ltd.
Manor House, Ash Walk, Warminster, Wilts. BA12 8PY

Tel: 0985 215151

Japan, established a significant technological lead in areas such as data processing and electronics which is likely to be a continuing advantage to US companies in these industries. Moreover, other industrial sectors will benefit directly or indirectly from the shortage of oil and natural gas supplies in North America.

Germany

Germany, on the other hand, though enjoying a stronger rate of productivity growth, is unlikely to experience a rate of economic expansion significantly above the average for OECD countries over the medium term since the labour force is not growing and the Bundesbank has traditionally followed a cautious monetary policy. This very stability and financial conservatism, however, lends attractions to German fixed interest investments, while the German engineering industry, a large proportion of whose business actually lies outside the Federal Republic, is one of the most successful in the world.

France

France has shown one of the highest rates of productivity growth in Europe over the past decade, as the reservoir of under-utilised labour in the agricultural sector has gradually transferred to manufacturing industry. This trend seems likely to continue. Moreover, although price inflation is relatively high, the Plan Barre is resulting in an enormous improvement in corporate profitability and financial strength. Particularly favourably placed are those companies in the technological forefront and which benefit directly from the demographic trends.

Japan

Japan's principal vulnerability is its lack of natural resources, particularly oil. On the other hand, rapid technological development combined with a favourable social attitude to work has produced a dramatic rate of productivity growth which this vulnerability is unlikely to diminish significantly. Once again it is these favourable trends which a UK pension fund investing overseas should seek to capitalise upon in its investment policy.

It is clear from these illustrations that overseas investment policy should be specifically directed to certain assets rather than seeking to gain a general exposure to trends in foreign economies. If this latter approach is followed then the benefits of overseas investment will tend to be diluted and returns in excess of those achievable in domestic markets rendered more difficult to achieve.

Risk

But if the potential for incremental returns exists what about the risks? There are several potential sources of risk in overseas investment. Some shared with domestic investment, some different.

Political Risk

When contemplating overseas investment probably the most important and at the same time least definable risk is that of political change. It is very easy with the benefit of hindsight to look back on a particular political risk as being either very high or very low according to the outcome of subsequent events; and it is in this regard that objective analysis is virtually impossible. The threat of a communist victory in the French election in 1977 or indeed the possibility that the Plan Barre might lead to widescale unrest and rampant inflation may now appear relatively insignificant. The fact that the French market has approximately doubled subsequently suggests that these risks were nonetheless very real at the time. My experience does not go back far enough to know to what extent in 1936 holders of Chinese bonds considered there to be a risk of default on interest payments as a result of an invasion of Manchuria by Japan, but I would doubt that the risk was thought to be high. Political risks of this nature are an aspect of currency mismatching in its broadest sense.

Political risk need not be as extreme as this and a deterioration in the political environment can be gradual and hard to detect at the time. The higher a market is rated the more vulnerable it will be to such a deterioration. In the UK we are perhaps more aware than most of some of the symptoms. Examples one may cite include:

(i) Increasing public expenditure as a percentage of GNP.
(ii) Government subsidies for declining industries followed by nationalisation.
(iii) Price and wage controls.
(iv) Increasing legal protection for unionised labour.

While in the UK there are some grounds for hope that the trend in these respects is about to improve, it may be that in other major economies some recent deterioration has not yet run its course.

Currency Mismatching

Because a UK pension fund's liabilities are denominated in sterling and linked to domestic wage levels it is generally accepted that its assets should also be at least predominantly sterling denominated. To accept a degree of currency mismatching is, however, not very different to a final salary pension scheme adopting a greater exposure to fixed interest investment than required by the purely nominal liabilities on discontinuance. Over the long term currency levels will tend to reflect relative inflation rates, so that an investor in real assets overseas should gain in rising local values what he loses on the exchange rate, and vice versa — other risks being equal.

There are two further observations one might make on this aspect. First to a significant extent the purely currency risk of mismatching can be eliminated by financing overseas investment through a currency loan or swop. This is a separate and complex subject which I do not propose to discuss here.

Secondly, maybe rather too little attention is paid to the very real currency and indeed other overseas risks to which a large number of UK registered companies are exposed. A UK pension fund investing in Shell for example is exposed to many of the mismatching risks that arise when investing in Exxon.

Marketability

Lack of marketability is an important factor adding to the risk of investment. For larger pension funds this effectively excludes from consideration all but the five largest overseas equity markets (USA, Japan, Canada, Germany and France). Although the German and French economies are larger than the British economy, corporate ownership is such that their quoted equity capitalisation is approximately two-thirds and one-third respectively of that of the UK; on top of this in Germany share turnover is considerably less as a result of major equity stakes being held by the big banks.

Lack of Information

Lack of information regarding overseas markets can be considered at two levels; first there is the difficulty for a UK investor obtaining the degree of information that is available to the local investor and obtaining it as quickly. This is probably only adequately overcome by entrusting the investment to an organisation which

ROWE RUDD & CO.

INTERNATIONAL RISK ANALYSIS SERVICE

The development and application of modern investment techniques over the past decade has been an integral part of the continuing drive towards greater efficiency and professionalism in fund management.

Latterly, the growing attraction of international diversification has further increased the need for better information, precision and discipline in the investment process.

The quantitative analysis of portfolio risk and return is now an essential complement to the more traditional skills of the pension fund manager and trustee.

THE SERVICE

The Rowe Rudd International Risk Analysis Service already numbers many leading U.K. and U.S. fund management organisations among its clients.

The Service provides practical and effective tools for monitoring, controlling and measuring portfolio risk and performance.

We offer an independent portfolio risk and return evaluation service for trustees, covering the U.K., U.S. and 12 other European and Far East markets.

For further information contact Paul Thomas or Jason MacQueen on 01-628 8437.

Rowe Rudd & Co.
63 London Wall, London EC2M 5UQ

has its own investment personnel working in the country concerned. At a second level, there is the problem in some countries of company reporting requirements being so inadequate that it is not possible to carry out reliable analysis. While standards are steadily improving internationally, of the major markets considered here, the Japanese market still leaves much to be desired.

Commercial Risk

An analysis of the commercial risk of an equity investment is just the same in a foreign market as in the UK, except insofar as the level of information available may be less. It is perhaps worth observing, however, that the financial gearing of public companies in the UK has long been substantially lower than in other major markets; the overall level of commercial risk in overseas markets may, therefore, be rather higher than in the UK.

Risk Reduction

Much emphasis has been placed in recent years on risk in terms of price volatility judged either in isolation or against whatever principal market an investor chooses as his yardstick; this is, of course, only one aspect of risk and one which is perhaps not of predominant interest to pension funds where long term liabilities and strong cash inflows mean that volatility can be lived with rather more readily than is the case with closed end investment portfolios. Nevertheless the more stable performance that a widely diversified portfolio provides can give greater peace of mind and reduce the risk of a bad decision being taken at the bottom of a cyclical trough.

While by spreading a portfolio across a number of markets in itself reduces volatility, it can be aimed more precisely to provide a balance that will better withstand a variety of economic or political outcomes. This is perhaps best illustrated by an example.

An Example: Inflation and Energy Risks

On the identifiable risks which confront the world economies over the coming five to ten years two of the most important relate to energy and inflation. A well-formed risk spreading strategy can take account of such uncertainties in the following way.

For a UK pension fund, the core of the portfolio can be expected to be domestic bonds and equities. The ideal means of reducing total portfolio risk is to diversify out of the "core" assets into assets which behave inversely with the "core" assets. If a wage explosion depresses the returns on these domestic assets, then an asset which yields high returns precisely because UK inflation is unexpectedly high would be the perfect means of diversification.

In general, perfect inverse relationships are rare. It is more common for markets to be favourably or adversely affected by the same factors, but to a different extent. For example, all economies and stock markets would be harmed by an energy crisis in the 1980's, but both the US and UK are well placed compared with Germany, Japan and France.

A strategy aimed principally at diversification accordingly would emphasise those foreign markets and companies which have strengths precisely where UK markets and companies have weaknesses. That is, the emphasis would be on compensating for the area of vulnerability of UK markets. The inflation "virtues" of Germany relative to the UK would therefore be judged to be more important than its energy "vices", this would be the case whether or not Germany offered the prospect of superior returns.

Overseas Fixed Interest Investment

The abolition of UK exchange controls has, for the first time in forty years, rendered investment in overseas fixed interest securities, or bonds, by a UK pension fund a sufficiently viable proposition to warrant serious consideration. The existence of the investment currency premium provided an even greater barrier to overseas bond investment than to overseas equity investment since it effectively taxed income but not capital gain. Its disappearance on the other hand means that overseas bonds are now available to UK investors on at least the same basis as overseas equities and in some cases on a relatively advantageous basis. For in a number of countries UK investors are subjected to withholding taxes on dividends but not interest.

However, overseas investment of any kind obviously involves the incurrence of currency risk in addition to any risks normally associated with the underlying asset. In equity investment such risk is generally regarded as acceptable insofar as the scope exists to offset it with capital gains on the underlying asset. But in bond investment it is quite clear that such scope is strictly limited. Overseas bond investment has therefore come to be viewed as risky because returns are heavily dependent upon currency movements.

The evidence of the period of floating exchange rates (and indeed of the fixed rate era also) is that over the longer term the movements of an exchange rate between two countries tend to reflect the difference between the inflation rates in those countries. This means that real returns in one currency tend to translate into real returns in another. The implication of this is that, in spite of the currency mis-match, overseas bond investment need be no more risky in real UK terms — i.e. relative to the liabilities of a pension fund which are linked to inflation via wages — than domestic bond investment.

This is entirely borne out by the evidence. The table below shows that in real sterling terms the variability of returns on selected overseas bond markets — a measure of the risk — has actually been significantly lower than the variability of UK gilt returns over the last ten years. Meanwhile the returns themselves have in general been significantly higher on overseas bonds than on UK gilts.

VARIABILITY OF RETURNS ON SELECTED OVERSEAS BOND MARKETS (1970–1979)

IN REAL TERMS (% p.a. in sterling)

	Average Return	Variability*
UK	− 4.9	17.3
US	− 5.3	11.6
Germany	3.8	11.8
France	− 1.1	11.0
Japan	− 1.0	18.8

*As measured by the standard deviation (logarithmic series).

Of course, there is no guarantee that returns on overseas bonds will be positive in real terms in either local currency or sterling. This is dependent upon local inflationary trends and government policy. But selection allows investors to choose those markets where such factors are likely to be most conducive to high real returns. In Germany for instance, monetary policy — and there-

You Can Invest In Small Companies

Our expertise lies in identifying and structuring investment opportunities in smaller private companies internationally.

We evaluate and assess several hundred propositions each year ranging from truly entrepreneurial start-ups to emerging growth companies. We have also backed management to buy out subsidiaries which were no longer compatible with the parent organisation.

Besides equity linked finance we provide substantial management assistance to investee companies, particularly with regard to their overseas market development.

We are increasingly in a position to offer additional investors participation in certain projects which involve capital commitments outside our existing investors criteria but which also require the management input which we can provide.

We would also be pleased to discuss the organisation and management of venture capital funds on behalf of financial institutions.

The Managing Director
CAPITAL PARTNERS INTERNATIONAL LTD
Westland House
17c Curzon Street
London W1Y 7FE
Tel: 01-491 4279
    01-629 9928
Telex: 8953393 CAPPTR G

FINANCE FOR SMALLER COMPANIES

Our experience comes from managing investments of over £900 million.

Our advice is readily available to trustees of pension funds, large and small.

Touche, Remnant & Co.
Winchester House, 77 London Wall, London EC2N 1BN
Telephone: 01-638 1737 Telex: 885703

From June 1981:
Mermaid House, 2 Puddle Dock, London EC4V 3AT
Telephone: 01-236 6565

For further information, please contact Mr. G. W. Hague

fore to some degree inflation – hinges upon the maintenance of attractive rates of return on long-term instruments relative to cash. Consequently real returns on German bonds have been almost consistently positive over long periods of time. Certainly there will be occasions in any country when short term adverse trends cause a significant decline in bond values but if control of inflation is re-established and favourable Government policies are reaffirmed then there is no reason why positive real returns should not re-emerge as the norm.

Moreover, overseas bond investment provides a hedge against untoward trends in the UK gilt market. If, for instance, UK government policies were to encourage consumption at the expense of saving, and monetary control were abandoned, not only would this be likely to result in continuing negative real returns on gilts, it would also tend to depress the exchange rate, thereby boosting returns on assets in countries where inflation seemed likely to be lower than in the UK. In such circumstances overseas bonds would provide a purer hedge than overseas equities since investment in the latter would involve consideration of additional factors — such as trends in corporate profitability.

In summary, the perceived riskiness of overseas bonds would not appear to be borne out by the evidence, and circumstances may well arise under which their inclusion in a UK pension fund asset portfolio would be appropriate.

CONCLUSION

I have attempted to answer the question posed at the beginning of this article by demonstrating that overseas investment can offer both high returns and the opportunity to reduce risk. Moreover I have tried to show that this applies equally to bond and equity investment.

Whether sterling is strong or weak there are arguments in favour of placing a portion of a UK pension fund in overseas assets, and it seems highly likely that this step will be taken by an increasing number of funds over the next few years.

United Kingdom and International Real Estate Investment Services

Investment	Introductions to opportunities satisfying pre-established criteria.
Reports	Impartial assessments and observations on the general structure, opportunities, financial and fiscal considerations of particular national or local markets.
Valuations	Advice on the appraisal, valuation and acquisition of property.
Portfolio Management	A complete property portfolio management service.

Edward Erdman

Surveyors
6 Grosvenor Street, London W1X 0AD
Telephone: 01-629 8191
Telex: 28169

City of London · Glasgow · Chicago · Atlanta · Cincinnatti
Houston · Los Angeles · San Francisco · Washington D.C.
Paris · Bordeaux · Lille · Lyon · Marseille · Nice
Strasbourg · Toulouse · Amsterdam

International Property Investment

Quintin Greatrex
Director, City of London & European Property Company

It is only relatively recently that a truly international property investment market has developed in the Western World. The beginning can probably be traced back some 20 to 25 years when a small number of British developers and institutions started operating in Commonwealth countries and particularly Australia, New Zealand and Canada. Attention turned to the Continent of Europe in the early sixties after the signing of the Treaty of Rome between the Six and particularly a little later at the time Britain applied for Membership of the Community which unfortunately was vetoed by de Gaulle. More recently the United States of America has become a highly sought after area for investment in property notably by the British, the Dutch, and the Germans.

The local markets in which the international property investors operate are of course dominated by local investors but nevertheless the appearance of foreign investors on the scene, at the margin, has often had a considerable upward effect on prices in the short term. However it seems that in terms of yield prices are determined in the local market place and a study of yield patterns in various countries shows that internationally the market is imperfect and by way of example the very wide variation of degree of tenant protection does not appear to be fully reflected in the yield patterns.

This short article will concentrate largely upon property investment in Continental Europe which is by no means a fashionable or favoured area for the British institutional investment at the present time. It is probably still suffering a bad reputation following the disasterous sums of money lost largely by British developers in the mid 1970's. It is interesting, enlightening and a little sobering to study in some depth exactly what went wrong in Europe so that the mistakes made in the early 70's will not be repeated in other parts of the world. Firstly the property market on the Continent of Europe suffered dramatically following the oil crisis but unlike the United Kingdom was not under the direct influence of Anthony Barber's famous 19th December,

PROPERTY INVESTMENT ADVISERS

CONSULTANTS TO PENSION FUNDS ON
ALL ASPECTS OF PROPERTY INVESTMENT
THROUGHOUT THE UNITED KINGDOM
AND OVERSEAS

Hillier Parker
May & Rowden

77 Grosvenor Street, London W1A 2BT
01·629 7666

City of London, Edinburgh, France, Holland, Australia
and Landauer Associates Inc.-U.S.A.

1973 rent freeze and further there was no miners' strike which lead to a three-day week.

The fall in property values occurred somewhat later and for example in central Paris rental values fell during the period 1975/6 and in Brussels the highest rents ever achieved were in 1974/1975.

During the late 60's and very early 70's a handful of British developers carried out a small number of development schemes, mainly offices, in Paris and Brussels which were extremely successful. These success stories quickly filtered back across the Channel and it became almost "de rigeur" for any development company in the UK worth its salt to have a scheme in Europe. This situation coincided with a period during which money was too easily organised, secured upon property and those responsible neglected or forgot that in the short term property values fluctuate. They can go down as well as up. There is a strange phenomenon in the property development market that the amount of new space developed is not as it should be, a function of supply and demand. It is much more likely to be a function of the amount of money available at the time to finance development. This has applied in all major cities right across the Western world. If the money is there there will be people ready to use it to build offices, shops etc regardless of the demand. This strange situation was almost certainly based upon a background of ever increasing property values and rents during the period following the second World War during which most Western economies, even in recession, benefited from some degree of industrial and commercial growth. There was therefore a continuing demand for new space and any imbalance in supply and demand was short lived.

President Pompidou was in power during the early seventies in France with a policy of continuing industrial expansion and developing the Paris Region as a major national and international commercial and administrative centre. The French government was pressing ahead with its ambitious schemes aimed at ensuring that France maintained or improved its position amongst the leading nations of the Western world. In and around Paris metro and road communications were improved, millions of francs were spent to bring the French telephone system into the 20th century. The development of La Defense as a major office centre was being promoted and the new towns of Cergy-Pontoise, Marne la Vallee, Evry and St. Quentin were being developed all with substantial amounts of capital from the private sector.

Are you looking to expand your Property Portfolio?

For nigh on 50 years now Whittinghams have been creating first class industrial and commercial developments throughout the Midlands. Factories and warehouses, shops and offices, around and at the vital heart of England. This long experience has made us respected experts in Midland property affairs.

The essential characteristics of all Whittingham development projects are:

Modern accommodation—designed and built by our own company.

Prime location—Motorway orientated with good communication and access.

First class tenants—the only sort you (or we) would accept.

Attractive initial yields—we''ll show you the figures.

Long term appreciation—we'll show you the facts.

All in all our expertise is your first class investment opportunity.

Over the years many of our complete projects have been absorbed into Pension Funds' property portfolios. And many of our developments have been created on a "Joint Venture" partnership. Our range of schemes is expanding. But, as ever, they're safe and sound . . .

We are *big* enough to undertake most schemes, small medium or large; we're *small* enough to act, re-act, and decide quickly.

Talk to us, whether your interest is in offices or shops or factories or warehouses, whether your concern is for our "Completed Investments Programme" or you would like to discuss a "Joint Venture" proposal.

Telephone us on Wolverhampton (STD code 0902) 53891 and speak to Malcolm Wilcox or Martin Baker. We (and our projects) are so well located that it's easy for us to come and see you, easy for you to view our schemes and our sites . . .

Malcolm Wilcox/Martin Baker,
Whittingham Industrial Developments Limited,
P.O. Box 60 Ettingshall Road,
Wolverhampton. WV2 2JT, England.
Telephone: Wolverhampton (0902) 53891
Whittingham Industrial

We build you into what you want to be

Whittingham Industrial

In Brussels everything seemed to be going in favour of the owner of office property. The European Economic Community was becoming an increasingly important and large organisation with delegations to it from many countries of the world. Brussels became the European centre for many multi-nationals such as Monsanto and ITT and furthermore NATO had been asked to leave Paris by de Gaulle and, having been welcomed to Brussels, had established headquarters close to the Capital. With this great influx of international organisations Brussels flourished. Against this background it is not difficult to understand the thought process of the British. Here virtually on their doorstep were two major cities surging ahead, economically prosperous and requiring modern buildings.

The problems came in 1975 when most of the British buildings were completed and became available for letting. The multinational companies were suffering the world-wide recession and were no longer expanding in Brussels although the Common Market had been expanded and NATO had built and were expanding their own headquarter building. Whilst there were a number of tenants in the market they had a large choice of property and were able to negotiate low rents and rents fell substantially from their 1974/1975 peak. In many cases the developers had suffered serious overrun on their building cost budget largely due to building cost inflation but partly as a result of not taking sufficient care in agreeing the building contract with the contractor to ensure that the building had the finishes and facilities demanded in a market which had evolved very much in favour of the tenant. By far the most serious aspect of the property crash in Europe from the point of view of the British however was the currency risk that had been undertaken. It is an irony or maybe a paradox that the British moved into Europe because they were fearful of the economic situation in their own country and wished to have assets represented in stronger European currencies. All would have been well of course had they achieved profit. In practice losses were incurred which were dramatically increased in sterling terms due to the fall in value of sterling which had taken place.

The most important lesson to be learned from this era and the most simple one is that when investing in property overseas there is always the additional factor of "currency" which must be taken into account. There is no way of avoiding it. Action can be taken

A complete property service to industry & commerce.

Fuller Peiser offer advice on a personal basis. The following give a broad indication of the services offered.

Investment and Finance

Plant and Machinery	Valuation and Disposal
Companies Act Valuations	Property Agency Sales, Purchase and Letting
Compulsory Purchase and Compensation	Landlord and Tenant
Development Appraisal and Planning	Project Management and Building Works
	Overseas
General Valuations	Property Management
Insurance Valuations and Assessing	Rating
	Taxation

For further information regarding any of the above services in the U.K. and abroad, please contact one of the offices listed below.

Fuller Peiser are now on Prestel – Key 2241541 for details of our services.

Head Office,
3-4 Holborn Circus, London EC1N 2HL
Tel. 01-353 6851 Telex 25916

18 Bolton St., Mayfair, London W1Y 7PA
Tel. 01-499 8931 Telex 25916

80 George St., Edinburgh EH2 3BU
Tel. 031-225 9816 Telex 72548

3 Hartshead, Sheffield S1 2EL
Tel. 0742-750161 Telex 547098

to lessen the currency risk but the risk will always exist to a greater or lesser extent. Whilst in the short term it may be possible to assess with a reasonable degree of confidence how parities will move in the future this is impossible in the long term and in the context of this article we are only dealing with property as a long term investment.

Within the European Economic Community the currency risk is probably less. One of the fundamental articles of the Treaty of Rome envisages a common European currency and we are already some little way down that road with the European Monetary System.

A single European currency must however be many years away particularly as the Community is enlarged with Greece becoming a member in 1981 to be followed by Spain and Portugal.

The second lesson to be learned and which must be universal is to be extremely cautious of the band-waggon effect or the sheep mentality. It is not an exaggeration to say that one of the factors that led the British to build offices, particularly in Paris and Brussels, during the early 1970's was simply that it was the thing to do. It was fashionable and the Stock Market liked it.

It is often said that the British property industry is more sophisticated than those in other countries. This however is not proven and if it is the role of property industries in advanced industrial societies to provide accommodation for commerce and industry then other countries perform as well if not better than the United Kingdom. Certainly the UK property industry has little to offer the United States or indeed the Continent of Europe in terms of design and layout of buildings.

Any assessment of design must be subjective to some extent but it is true that overseas there are many examples of extremely fine and imaginative architecture both aesthetically and technically.

The UK has greater flexibility in terms of property tenure which can be used effectively in setting up financing arrangements but it cannot be argued that this makes the UK more sophisticated. The essence of good property investment is surely making the maximum use of the basic elements comprising a property investment (excluding agricultural land) which are the money, the land and the construction within the laws, rules and regulations of the country concerned. There are innumerable examples of high performing investment properties in many

Richard Ellis
World Wide

Investment Property Advisors to Pension Funds and Institutions

Richard Ellis, Chartered Surveyors
64 Cornhill, London EC3V 3PS. Telephone 01-283 3090. Telex 887732

Chicago
Richard Ellis (Midwest) Inc
Standard Oil Building
200 East Randolph Drive
Suite 6545
Chicago, Illinois 60601
Telephone (312) 861 1105
TWX 910 221 5807

Atlanta
Richard Ellis (Southeast) Inc
Suite 1015
3445 Peachtree Road, NE
Atlanta, Georgia 30326
Telephone (404) 231 0400
Telex 810 751 3342

San Francisco
Richard Ellis (Western) Inc
Suite 450
201 California Street
San Francisco
California 94111
Telephone (415) 392 1090

Manchester, Glasgow, Brussels, Paris, Amsterdam, Madrid, Geneva, Sao Paulo, Rio de Janeiro, Hong Kong, Singapore, Johannesburg, Cape Town, Durban, Salisbury, Melbourne, Sydney, Perth, Adelaide, Brisbane.

countries of the world.

The most important fundamental difference in property investment in the United Kingdom and overseas is probably the landlord and tenant relationship which is governed not only by law but to quite an important extent by custom. For centuries in the United Kingdom land has been concentrated, as a generalisation, in the hands of a few important landowners such as the Monarchy, the Church, the family estates or today the insurance companies, the pension funds and the institutions generally. In Europe this has not been the case to the same extent certainly since the influence of Napoleon. Historically in the United Kingdom landlords have been in a better position to impose their terms and hence we have leases where the tenant is responsible not only for normal day to day repair and maintenance but for the structure of the property. Furthermore the tenant commits himself for say 20 to 25 years very frequently in the full knowledge that his business is likely to develop in such a way that he will not wish to stay in the premises for that period and will have to find at some time in the future an assignee which is acceptable to his landlord. In Europe the tenant is in a more favoured position and is able to agree a lease term which fits in more closely with the planning of his business. Commonly lease terms are for nine years with the tenant having the right to quit at the end of the third and sixth year.

It is difficult for a landlord to make a tenant responsible for structural repairs although all day to day maintenance and repair and running costs would normally be charged to the tenant. Rents are generally linked to the cost of living index and reviews to market rents are rare. As leases are generally short the absence of a market rent review is not a serious drawback. However, the indexation of rents can create anomalies when rents payable under leases exceed market rents as they may well do in the short term during a period of high inflation. In such a situation the tenant has a major incentive to serve notice to quit and hope to renegotiate a new lower rent with his landlord. The landlord in such circumstances is clearly negotiating from a position of strength knowing the cost to the tenant of removal and new ingoing works such as partitioning. In most cases however a fair deal is struck between the parties.

It is evident that the management of commercial property overseas is generally far more intensive than in the United Kingdom. It is important for a landlord to ensure that in the market

SAFEPUT
The Singer & Friedlander European Property Trust

SAFEPUT is continuing to seek prime property investments in Europe with particular emphasis on West Germany.

Details to Stephen Chambers BSc, FRICS.

Kalverstraat 152, Amsterdam

ALLSOP & CO

21 Soho Square, London W1V 6AX   Telephone 01-437 6977 Telex 267397

his building enjoys a good reputation in so far as management is concerned. This is becoming increasingly important as service charges rise to very high levels due to high energy costs. A landlord that cares about his buildings and the cost of running them is far more likely to keep his tenants and attract new tenants than the landlord that simply sits back collects the rents and spends the minimum on his property.

Given this background of shorter leases and landlords generally unable to pass the structural repairs to the tenants account it is clearly of vital importance to ensure that any building acquired for long term investment purposes is such that taking all factors into account it will be a building which business, commerce and industry generally will demand for many years to come. It could also be argued that the covenant strength of tenants is less important if leases are short. However properties let to good tenants command appreciably higher investment values.

In the light of the currency problems, the less attractive landlord and tenant relationship and the more intensive management requirement it would be reasonable to question the wisdom of British institutions investing internationally. Leaving aside the generally accepted criteria of having a sensible geographical spread within a large property portfolio it is important if a property investment is to perform for it to be located in an economy which is strong and growing and for business to be thriving and investing for the future. It goes without saying that unless commerce and industry are thriving and growing there will be little demand for accommodation and rental performance is likely to be poor. There are many areas of the Western world which are industrially and commercially far more successful having higher productivity, higher growth rates than the United Kingdom. Even at this difficult recessionary point of the world economic cycle in countries such as Holland, France, Germany and certainly in the United States industrial progress can be felt and certain industries are still thriving and growing and investing. What is seen on the ground can also be seen in the statistics. UK productivity is low, UK investment is low, UK inflation is high and it is clear that compared with our foreign competitors our overall performance as an advanced Western industrial nation is poor. Against this background it would be unrealistic to expect property to continue to perform in real terms as well as in other selected parts of the world.

No article on international property investment would be com-

An Independent Partnership of Property Consultants

Advice on all aspects of Real Estate, Valuation, Acquisition, Sale, Finance on behalf of both occupying and investing clients.

McDaniel & Daw

**BAILEY HOUSE, OLD SEACOAL LANE, LUDGATE HILL
CITY OF LONDON EC4 · TELEPHONE 01-236 4881**

CHARTERED SURVEYORS

Partners: EJC McDaniel, FRICS, FSVA JE Cullis, BSc, FRICS, FSVA MJ Norris, FRICS, FSVA
Associate: BP Cox, AMSST   Consultant: JW aB Daw, FRICS

plete without some comment on the influence of politics in property investment. In the United States environmental considerations have entered the political arena and are becoming increasingly a factor limiting or at least delaying building. In France the French Government is aggressively encouraging major organisations to move outside central Paris into the new towns, La Defense and the provincial cities. In Belgium the Flemish-Waloon political debate drags on with each part of the country demanding its fair share of public expenditure. Unfortunately politics do count in property investment and the wise investor should take the trouble to understand the policies of central and local governments before committing funds.

This is all part of the detailed local knowledge that is required to invest successfully overseas. The best way to obtain this knowledge needs very careful consideration and will depend upon the country concerned. Logically a partnership arrangement with a similar local fund ought to provide the answer but many such arrangements have come to grief in the past. A number of British firms of surveyors have offices overseas often run by first rate people who will understand the funds requirements and understand local conditions. If the right person can be located in one of these firms this is likely to be the best solution coupled with a representative of the investing fund with the ability and knowledge of the market to enable him to accurately assess situations as they arise and ensure appropriate action is taken.

Above all however property investment involves people and in simple terms a property investment is a building where people will work or live and unless it is understood how people spend their lives it is difficult or impossible to provide them with the accommodation which they need.

Make your property investment P.A.Y.

The buying and selling of commercial property investment is a job for the professional.

It demands a wide range of skills and experience to tackle the complexities of valuation techniques, taxation implications and property legislation.

We are ready to advise on every aspect affecting the investment value of a property – from relevant legal documentation, planning and tenancy structure to marketing policy.

Your investments can be handled in the context of direct portfolio planning and management – an informed service tailored to your Fund's specific requirements.

The service, whilst recognising time-honoured procedures, is essentially a creative one. A service designed to keep pace with changing trends... and make your investments PAY.

PEPPER ANGLISS & YARWOOD Chartered Surveyors
5/6 Carlos Place, London, W1Y 6LL. Tel: 01-499 6066.

Property Investment in a Worldwide Recession

Andrew Huntley, FRICS
Senior Investment Partner, Richard Ellis

In the last twelve months the trend towards a more international approach to real estate investment has gathered added momentum. Despite, and probably because of a period of worldwide recession, fund managers and their advisers have increasingly turned to real estate in the search for inflation proof investments. And it is apparent that this move into real estate is becoming ever more international as the traditional sources of property investments begin to dry up.

The purpose of this article is to look in some depth at why the fund managers are looking at international real estate; to investigate why there are such huge sums of investment monies now seeking a safe home, and finally to pinpoint where funds are being invested geographically and why particular areas of the world are of significance in real estate terms.

Investment in bricks and mortar is basically the product of an international industrial economy in relative decline. Ever since the Second World War governments have been wrestling with the twin problems of inflation and industrial stagnation. A battery of political and economic solutions have been tried and it is interesting to note that the severe monetarist policies of Mrs Thatcher in the United Kingdom are perhaps the most positive steps yet taken by any industrialised nation to solve the key problem of inflation. In Britain, America and Europe motor industries are in turmoil, and similar problems can be seen in many other industries such as steel, textiles and electrical goods. Escalating raw material and labour costs in the Western world make profits hard to come by and combined with the ravages of inflation, industry is suffering more seriously than it ever has in the last thirty years.

DIVERSIFICATION OF FUND PORTFOLIOS
The effect of such economic dilemmas on the fund managers has been to force them over the last twenty-five years to look very carefully at their investment policies. The gilt and the equity investment can no longer alone cater for the inflation factor, and

A Property Service for Industry and Commerce

* Acquisition and disposal of industrial, commercial and office property throughout the U.K.
* Valuations for all purposes including fire insurance and plant and machinery.
* Demand research and development appraisal.
* Auctions and tenders.
* Rent Review and Lease Renewal Negotiations.
* Compulsory purchase and compensation.
* Marketing and Reclocation advice.
* Rating and taxation of property.
* Investment and development funding

We are urgently seeking first class commercial investments throughout the property spectrum on behalf of our clients.

All areas of the country will be considered and propositions in the £100,000 to in excess of £2m range would be be of interest. Our Investment Department is located at 1 South Audley Street and Mr L.J. Hibberd will be happy to hear from you.

Chamberlain & Willows
Estate Agents · Surveyors · Valuers

Church House, Ironmonger Lane, London EC2V 8EU 01-606 9611
Hale House, Green Lanes, London N15 TG. 01-882 4633 Telex: 299161
1 South Audley Street, Mayfair, London W1Y 6JS. 01-493 7863

the diversification of fund portfolios has been a significant development of recent years. Well publicised excursions into commodities, art, gold, agricultural land and leisure development have all indicated the underlying need to keep pace with inflation. But by far the most important trend has been the swing into property investment which now accounts for an average 19% of all British pension fund and institutional portfolios. And within this percentage there is a discernible element now being directed into the international arena. Even though the percentages of funds being channelled overseas is miniscule it is evident and clearly destined to grow.

Indeed following the removal of exchange controls it was expected that the volume of international investment would grow, which would in turn have an effect on the volume of funds available for property in the United Kingdom. In reality only a small proportion of fund monies have been spent abroad on property although it seems likely that the percentages will increase. Indeed if the pattern of equity investment is followed it is certain that more monies will be channelled abroad. An interesting statistical fact is that in the first quarter of 1979 institutional investment in company securities was split between £450 million in UK securities and less than £100 million in foreign securities. The first quarter of 1980 saw £300 million going into UK securities and a massive £500 million being directed in foreign securities. It has been suggested that a target of between 10%–15% is being mooted as an acceptable proportion of equity investment overseas for the average institutions, although naturally such predictions are totally dependent on opportunities overseas, the performance of the UK stock market, and naturally the relative attractions of investments such as real estate.

FUNDS LOOK TO INTERNATIONAL ARENA

What is predictable is that the funds will inevitably be forced to look at opportunities on a broader geographical front. To look at the UK alone the awesome volume of institutional monies is already causing severe investment supply problems. The Central Statistical Office's figures for 1979 shows that net investment of pension funds totalled some £4,731 million of which approximately 12% was invested in property either directly or through the medium of Property Unit Trusts. Insurance companies similarly invested a total of £821 million. These huge figures show no signs

Pensions & Charities Property Fund

On behalf of Pensions & Charities Property Fund we are continuing to seek prime shop, office and industrial investments. Finance available for developments and leaseback transactions. Details to J. R. Oxley, B.Sc., FRICS.

ALLSOP & CO

21 Soho Square,
London W1V 6AX

Telephone: 01-437 6977
Telex: 267397

ONE HUNDRED AND EIGHTY YEARS OF EXPERIENCE

Sophisticated, expert appraisal of the property market must be top priority for the Pension Fund Manager.

Confidence in the knowledge and ability of your advisors, building up a strong, sound business relationship is the very crux of building up a sound investment portfolio.

Our many years of experience have given us a unique foundation upon which to establish our investment department, and today Farebrother act for:
- PENSION FUNDS
- INSURANCE COMPANIES
- INVESTMENT TRUSTS
- BANKS ● PRIVATE & PROPERTY COMPANIES

on the valuation, appraisal, purchase, financing, management and sale of commercial investment property in London and throughout the U.K.

FAREBROTHER

Chartered Surveyors. 29 Fleet Street, London EC4Y 1AL. Telephone: 01-353 9344 and 01-583 0303.

of reducing and indeed the increasing level of funds committed to the property sector far outstrips the supply of suitable outlets in property terms. In fact in the UK there has been a small reduction of sums invested in real estate over the past twelve months, but the underlying pressure of substantial monies from both pension contributions and insurance premiums is a constant factor in the investment community. The sheer lack of investment raw materials in the UK is therefore bound to lead to a further interest in opportunities on the international front.

In addition to the volume of UK institutional funds one must not forget the growing sums of monies becoming available from the Middle East, Far East and Japan. The significant re-awakening of the Arab bank system on the back of the expanding OPEC assets is likely to become a potent factor in the international real estate scene. Figures are always difficult to assess in analysing the Arab influence on investment markets. Business Week recently suggested that in 1980 some $80 billion of Arab bank money was being invested in the UK of which 5% could be going into real estate. In the USA the figure suggested was $65 billion with as much as 22% going into property. Similarly the emergence of Japan and Hong Kong as powerful investment centres add to the volumes of monies searching for homes in commercial property on a worldwide basis.

CONTINUING ATTRACTION OF UK
Having briefly reviewed the source of international funds it is relevant to consider where investment monies are being directed geographically. The first move into property by pension funds came in the United Kingdom in the nineteen fifties, although of course the big insurance companies had been property minded for many years. As a result of this tradition of property investment the UK remains a favourite location for institutional monies. Indeed there has been much publicised evidence of Dutch acquisition of UK real estate, and the Arab investors still show a strong penchant for both residential and commercial properties in this country. As a home for property investment the UK, despite its economic problems, still offers many attractions and a feature of recent months has been the stability of investment yields reflecting the presence of continuing institutional demand. The amount of money in the UK emanating from the institutional market seems bound to keep the pressure up on demand for good property in-

vestments.

The types of property attracting the investors will continue to be the prime investments, although there is evidence to suggest that the lack of supply may lead to improvements in the secondary and tertiary markets. Indeed any reduction in interest rates are likely to produce a narrowing of the yield gap between prime and secondary. In highlighting opportunities for the investor in the UK, it is clear that offices will be the principal growth sector in the next twelve months. In many provincial towns the increase in demand has been evidenced by a reduction in the number of empty offices rather than in increased rents, and in such centres one can confidently predict that any further acceleration in demand will be reflected in above average rental growth. It is in areas like this and in the City of London that the most successful investments will be made. Rents in towns west of London have shown particular growth in rentals and in Windsor, as an examples, office rents for prime office accommodation leapt from £8.00 per square foot at the start of 1980 to in excess of £12.00 by the end of the year. In the City of London too rents have continued their rise and a major investment factor is the extremely low level of supply where the current availability is only 1.5 million square feet against a demand level of 2.75 million square feet.

Other investment areas exist in the UK property market both in the retail and industrial/warehouse sectors. The retail trade has suffered badly in recent months but opportunities still exist. On the industrial front short term prospects for rental growth look limited in the light of recession and some oversupply in certain areas.

EUROPEAN OPPORTUNITIES

Looking further afield one must consider Europe where despite considerable variations in the investment market from country to country, Holland and France are both countries with high investment demand being reflected in hardening yields. France's investment market has grown substantially in recent years and it is indicating many parallels with the UK where an influential factor is the severe shortage of first class investments. Paris in particular is suffering from a diminishing supply of office accommodation which in turn is forcing rents up. French and international investors show a keen interest in prime office properties,

The case for comprehensive property services in these difficult times

Gross Fine+Krieger Chalfen

27 Princes Street
Hanover Square
London W1R 8NQ
01-493 3993

CONSULTANT VALUERS & SURVEYORS
OF
INVESTMENT AND COMMERCIAL PROPERTY

HALL PAIN & FOSTER
CHARTERED SURVEYORS

21 LONDON ROAD, SOUTHAMPTON
Tel: (0703) 28915 Telex: 47283

15/19 GUILDHALL WALK, PORTSMOUTH
Tel: (0705) 24421

and there is a discernible awareness of the potential of older buildings with opportunities for renovation and refurbishment. The indexation of rents tends to reduce the interest of investors in standing property investments, but yields continue to remain under pressure simply due to the lack of prime investments.

The Dutch investment market continues to be strong with both local and international funds striving to broaden their portfolios with office, industrial and shop investments in prime locations. Overseas investors are finding opportunities in reversionary shop investments, which tend to be under-valued by local funds. Belgium is currently experiencing a weakening market as a result of currency uncertainties coupled with a continuing oversupply situation. However, the replacement cost of building is currently some 40% above value, a factor which will favourably influence investors once the surplus is absorbed.

Spain offers an interesting potential for the international investor for whereas there is still an oversupply situation in office and industrial space, there is a strong belief that in the event of Spain's successful application to join the European Economic Community there could be a move by multi-national corporations to establish administrative and manufacturing facilities in Spain.

AMERICA – THE GROWTH AREA FOR INVESTMENT

The North American market has been one area of the world that has attracted particular attention from the international property investor. The sheer size of the USA and Canada have inevitably attracted the fund managers who have found difficulties in finding suitable real estate investments with UK and Europe.

There are a number of important factors that make the United States of America a particularly interesting area for the fund manager to consider. Perhaps the most significant of these factors has been the entry of the local US funds into the real estate investment market. In a mirror of the UK pension fund move into real estate in the sixties and seventies the US institutions have begun a significant move into real estate ownership. It has been estimated that pension funds in the US currently control around $700 billion assets and that this figure will grow to $3,000 billion by 1995. Of these total investment holdings currently only about 1.7% is in real estate and over the next fifteen years this percentage will grow to an estimated 10%.

This huge influx of monies will inevitably lead to a major

Use our heads for professional advice on property

Investment
Development
Funding

Consultant Surveyors
London Liverpool and Paris

expansion of the property investment market. Add to the US funds the increasing numbers of international investors appearing on the scene, and it is evident that the USA will become one of the most exciting and potentially rewarding areas for the institutions. Currently the main international investors within the US fall into three main categories — tax exempt funds searching for fully leased commercial buildings in prime locations, taxed funds seeking similar properties but incorporating leverage and private individuals seeking tax shelters through property acquisitions.

A further important factor on the US real estate scene is the increasing strength of the environmental and planning lobbies. As a result of their activities many states have introduced requirements for developers to provide environmental impact statements when seeking building permits. The effect of such controls has been to limit the supply of new developments.

Overall the investment market prospects both in the short and medium term remain good in spite of increases in interest rates. Prime yields have remained stable and even fallen under acute pressure because of strong competition for first class investment properties.

The main professional activity in the real estate investment market in the US has been the acquisition of interests in standing properties and new developments. Interest in investment sales has been especially marked in the retail sector, when fierce competition is forcing traders to re-appraise the financial basis of their asset holdings. Another interesting trend has been the increasing use of the British firms of chartered surveyors in the real estate consulting fields. There is evidence to suggest a big future for the UK surveyors who bring standards of professionalism and independence not seen before in the local market. Already a number of US institutions have appointed UK surveyors with US offices to advise them on real estate investment, and the British professional is becoming an important member of the US investment community.

The Canadian economy is resisting a decline in economic trading levels around the world rather more robustly than the United States. Indeed certain areas of Canada are experiencing boom conditions mainly as a result of the country's exploration of its vast natural resources, the mineral wealth and the oil and gas reserves. Office and industrial development is proceeding apace in places like Edmonton and Calgary and the real estate market is going through a period of some buoyancy. Indeed local pension

THE FLEMING PROPERTY UNIT TRUST

On behalf of over 450 pension funds and charities we are constantly seeking to enlarge and improve our portfolio. We have funds available for prime shop, office, industrial and farmland investments and for leaseback transactions.

Total assets exceed £210m

3/4 Lincoln's Inn Fields, London, WC2
15,850 sq. ft. air-conditioned offices. Tenant: Billiton (U.K.) Limited, a subsidiary of Shell Transport & Trading Company Limited.

THE FLEMING PROPERTY UNIT TRUST
J. Newman, B.Sc. F.R.I.C.S. Robert Fleming & Co. Ltd.
8 Crosby Square, London EC3A 6AN
01-283 2400

funds are increasing their acquisition of prime property investments often from organisations seeking to apply their capital more directly in their businesses.

NEW AREAS UNDER SCRUTINY
In the search for real estate investment the international funds continue to investigate countries outside the traditional areas for investment. Whilst political instability and currency factors often rule our many nations it is evident that some parts of South America and South East Asia do currently have their supporters and a number of real estate transactions have been seen in the last twelve months.

Argentina and Brazil feature as the two nations most regularly looked at by the real estate investor. The economy of Argentina presents a mixed scene of rampant inflation and low levels of manufacturing investment, offset by a strong balance of payment, a hard currency and substantial reserves. Argentina has gained from substantial foreign investment which has gone into improving the country's infra-structure to increase the rate of exploitation of its natural resources. The future potential of the country has attracted the international banks and professional organisations and there has been an influx of multi-national corporations attracted by its potential. This activity has created a healthy demand for rented space, combined with an emerging local development scene seeking havens for cash in the fight against inflation. The risks are substantial but with the right local advice investors can find opportunities in the office and retail sectors.

Brazil also continues to attract investors and financiers for similar reasons — the country's boundless natural resources. Rio de Janeiro and Sao Paulo are developing as fairly sophisticated office centres with local funding, development activity and a steady demand from the financial sector and the multi-nationals. The shortage of land in Rio de Janeiro has created shortage of prime office space and such characteristics are opening up opportunities for developers and investors. Again, however a note of caution must be sounded and investors must be satisfied that short and medium-term returns will warrant the risks.

South East Asia has seen a recent period of explosive growth with the emergence of a number of powerful new trading organisations and the rapid expansion of Hong Kong as one of the financial centres of the world. In Hong Kong the long term prospects are particularly interesting and there are indications that the investment and development sectors of the property market are

We have been advising on the sale and acquisition of property investments for over eighty years.

ESTATE AGENTS, SURVEYORS, VALUERS AND AUCTIONEERS

58 Grosvenor Street, London, W1X 0DD. Tel: 01-629 8151
TELEX: 8955441 — JAYTEE-G
with offices in Manchester, Sheffield and the City of London.

moving closer in their methods of operation to those employed in Western Europe. At present the banks play the major role in property mortgaging and construction financing but as the economy grows this pattern could change providing opportunities for the international investor. Malaysia and Singapore also offer strong investment markets with both countries showing strong property demand factors. In Malaysia there are opportunities for development but very sharp variations between areas mean that extreme caution has to be taken when evaluating the prospects of specific investments. In Singapore the main investment demand comes from owners and occupiers rather than institutions. However with more international corporations locating in Singapore there is strong evidence of more development activity that could provide opportunities for the international investor.

Finally, Australia, with its recent election result providing a boost to the stock market, provides an interesting area for the international investor. A strong demand in the office sector is putting pressures on rents and there is a lively interest in office investments in most of the major cities. Overseas investors have been encouraged by the relaxation of controls on foreign investment and also by the countries economic stability. There is of course a traditional local investment community of pension funds and insurance companies who are active in the market both acting independently but also willing to work in partnership enterprises with overseas developers.

In any overview of this international property scene it is interesting to record that there is a significant development taking place in world property markets. There is no doubt that a gradual transfer of ownership of real estate is taking place as freeholds (or their local equivalents) pass into the hands of pension funds, insurance companies and other investment institutions representing the saver. This transfer provides a huge challenge to the new institutional owners who need to maximise the returns to their trustees and members, but also accept a growing responsibility for maintaining the quality of the environment of greater and greater numbers of workers in industrial, office and retail premises. The effective use of property in industrial society is a fundamental problem and one that takes on a wider significance as the funds become ever more internationally minded. The basic strength, stability and professionalism of the funds and their advisers must surely be an encouraging factor in any forward assessment of our industrial and social environment.

ECONOMIC FORESTRY LTD

Forestry Consultancy and Investment Management for Pension Funds in the United Kingdom and Overseas

A Growing International Service

27, Rutland Square, Edinburgh EH1 2BW. 031-229-5435
26, Old Bailey, London EC4M 7LT.   01-236-8682

Why Invest in Forestry? The Case for Investment Overseas

J. A. Fell, MA, BSc (For), MI (For) and G. R. Watt, BSc (For), B Litt, CDipAF *Economic Forestry Ltd*

What can forestry offer the institutional investor at the present time? It may perhaps be summarised as a medium to long-term investment opportunity in land and timber, which can show a modest but consistent yield of up to 7% in excess of inflation over a period of years through the physical growth of trees, and the performance of the commodity of wood. The attractions of these investment returns were first recognised by certain Funds in 1974 following the aftermath of the property collapse, and in the unusual investment conditions at that time. Since then, there has been increasing interest in forestry, principally by the Managers and Trustees of Pension Funds, who are concerned about maintaining the real value of pensions during a period of high inflation.

Until recently, institutional investment in forestry has been confined to the United Kingdom, since significant financial yields in excess of inflation can be obtained and the investment is denominated in the currency from which eventual pensions will be paid. With the removal of exchange controls and the relative rise in value of Sterling, many Funds have increased the proportion of their investment portfolio overseas. While most of this new investment by Pension Funds has so far been in equities, the opportunities available in forestry overseas merit detailed consideration due to the level of likely financial returns, the possibility of being able to deal in large amounts and the prospect of obtaining a positive cash flow at an early date.

INVESTMENT APPRAISAL

If forestry is to be recognised as an acceptable investment for institutions, it is essential that its financial performance can be compared with other available investment opportunities. Although forestry may appear to be more difficult to analyse than some other investments because the costs and revenues are spread over a long period, appraisal can be undertaken by evaluating the estimated net cash flow over the life of a tree crop or a given investment period. It is suggested for medium and long-term investors in particular, that such an analysis, with subsequent indicated yields, should form the principle basis on which to judge whether forestry is a suitable investment and which individual forestry properties meet investment requirements and are hence appropriate for acquisition.

In any cash flow analysis, various assumptions must be made, and provided these are realistic, the resultant yields may then be comparable with those of other investments. In forestry, it is felt that the analysis of most importance, is that undertaken at constant values since this indicates the real yield of the investment resulting from the physical growth of the tree crop. It may however be appropriate to allow for relative price movements in costs or timber values, or to test the sensitivity of various assumptions. The inclusion of any relative price movements will give an indication of the estimated total real yield from the investment. Allowances for inflation may also be made both to expenditure and income to give yields which may then be compared with other investment opportunities.

The most important items for consideration and inclusion in any cash flow analysis are the costs and receipts relating to the physical growth of the crop, and the performance of the commodity of wood.

PHYSICAL TREE GROWTH

The yield of a forestry investment, disregarding real price increases in the value of timber, comes from the rate of physical growth of the tree crop. While growth is reasonably predictable, it will vary depending on tree species, climate, site type, and the genetical quality and suitability of the trees. Experienced forest managers applying the latest silvicultural techniques on scientific principles, may be able to significantly increase growth rates and hence the performance of any investment.

In general, outside the tropical regions of the world, conifers have physical growth rates higher than those for hardwood species, and hence are more likely to be selected for investment as yields will rely less on increases in the value of the commodity. Conifer yields can vary from very low levels of $1-2m^3$/ha per annum in the northern natural forests of the Northern Hemisphere to about $30-40m^3$/ha per annum in tropical regions. It should however

"Western Forestry"

INTERNATIONAL FORESTRY INVESTMENT and MANAGEMENT SERVICE

HEAD OFFICE:
OLD WELL HOUSE, 130 HOLLAND PARK AVENUE
LONDON W11 4UE
Telephone: 01-229 9629

FORESTRY
A Growing Investment

More and more Pension Funds are realising the benefits of direct investment in forestry. The right properties can provide not only sound security that appreciate as the timber grows inexorably but also an increasing return.

We offer a completely independent professional service and are pleased to advise private and institutional clients on all aspects of forestry including:

Acquisitions of all types of Woodlands throughout the UK and the USA
Sales of Freehold and Leasehold Woodlands
Valuations for all purposes
Portfolio Management

John Clegg & Co.
Agricultural & Forestry Surveyors, Valuers

Bury Estate Office,
Church Street,
Chesham, Bucks.
Tel: (02405) 4711

4, Rutland Square,
Edinburgh,
EH1 2AS.
Tel: 031-229 8800

be noted that the financial yield of a forestry investment is not necessarily directly proportional to the physical growth of the tree crop as land values and other costs and receipts will vary widely between different regions.

TIMBER VALUES

The performance of timber values in relation to other commodities and to inflation is fundamental to the performance of a forestry investment, and therefore requires detailed consideration.

Historical long-term price trends for timber in different countries or regions of the world are often poorly documented or non-existent. An exception is in the USA where they have been maintained over a very long period. While the statistics are for a single country, they most probably have wider application due to the importance of the United States in the international trade in forests products.

Between 1800 and 1976, the Wholesale Price Index of Lumber (sawn timber) in the USA rose almost *20 times relative to the All Commodities Wholesale Price Index which is equivalent to an average annual rate of increase of 1.7%.* There have been periods when the Index has shown little change, but the long-term annual trend of increase has been fairly steady.

Stumpage prices (those paid to the grower) have risen almost twice as rapidly in real terms during this century in the USA in the principle conifer regions on the West Coast and in the South-East. For example, since 1910, the relative price of Douglas Fir stumpage rose on average, 3.5% per annum, while that for Southern Pine increased about 3.2% per annum. There are a number of possible reasons for the differential growth rate between stumpage and product prices, but the result has been that much of the increase in product prices in recent years, has been passed to timber growers, and this trend appears to be continuing.

The future performance of wood as a commodity in the long term in countries where a free market exists, will depend on international supply and demand. The existing situation and likely future developments are reviewed below. However, within the United States there is good evidence to suggest that real price increases of at least 3% p.a. for timber can be anticipated by forest owners in addition to the financial yield resulting from the physical growth of the tree crop.

WOOD — INTERNATIONAL SUPPLY AND DEMAND

The International trade in wood products currently amounts to more than £17,000 million annually, or just over 25% of the value of the world's total annual production. The historical growth in world production cannot be estimated accurately because of the very high fuel component, however, analysis of the world wood removals (Forestry Commission 1978) shows that the average annual rate of increase has been as follows:

1913/1951	1.2%
1951/1961	2.3%
1961/1972	2.2%

The highest rates of increase in harvesting in recent years have occurred in developing countries and in Canada.

WORLD FOREST RESOURCE

About 30% of the world's total land area is classified as forest, but if areas of savannah woodlands and scrub are excluded, this drops to nearly 20%. The map below, Fig. 1 shows how the percentage of forest cover varies between regions of the world.

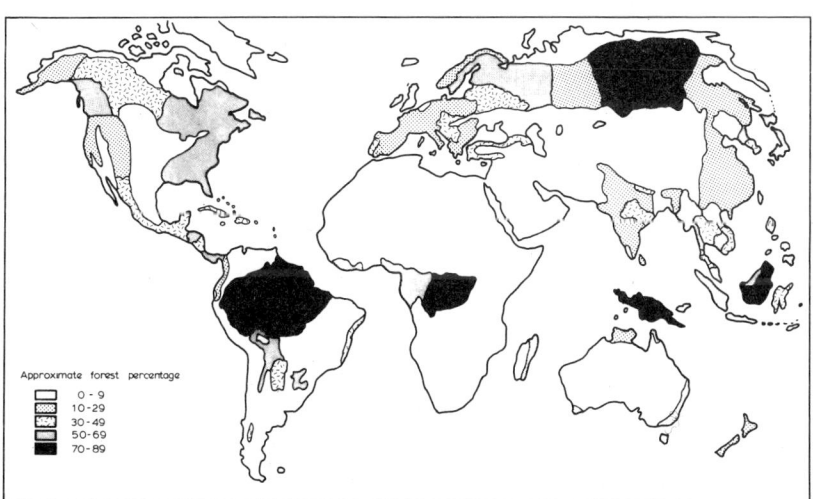

Fig. 1 — Major forest regions of the world (Source: FAO — 1971)

The largest areas of closed forest are in North America, South America and the USSR, which between them, amount to some 73% of the world's total closed forest. It is important to realise that the majority of forests are still of natural origin, and man-made forests are currently only estimated to cover about 100 million hectares, representing about 3% of the total.

The composition of the world's growing stock, which was estimated to amount to 310,000 million cubic metres in 1974, comprises 30–40% conifers and 60–70% hardwoods. Conifers occur principally in North America, Europe and the USSR, while hardwoods dominate in other regions.

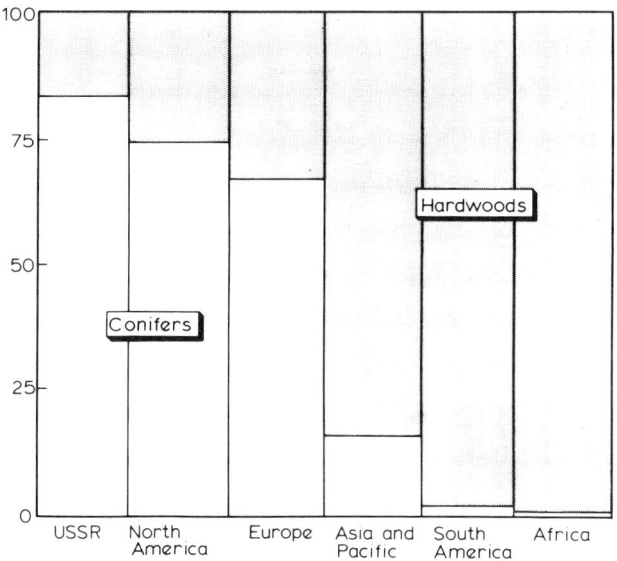

Fig. 2 Percentage composition of the world's forests by tree type (souce: Persson, 1974)

It is however important to appreciate that population pressure can impose limitations on the availability of supplies to the international timber trade, and Fig. 3 shows the volume of timber *per caput* in the different regions of the world.

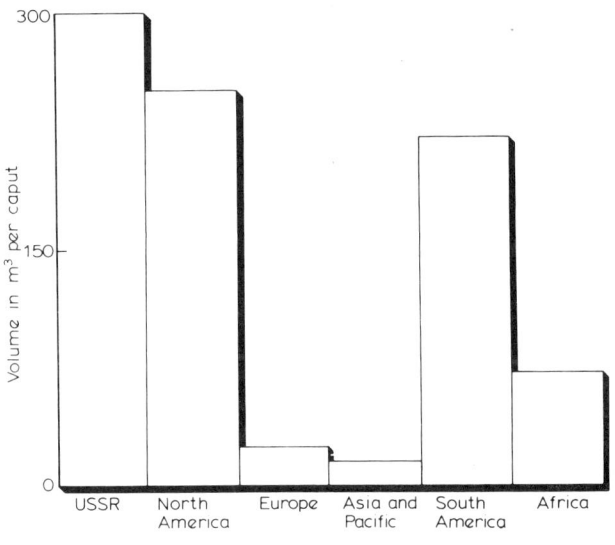

Fig. 3 Volume of timber *per caput* in closed forest (source: Persson, 1974)

WORLD WOOD CONSUMPTION

Approximately 53% of the world's wood production amounting to about 2,500 million cubic metres in 1976, was for industrial use, and of that total, about 60% was in the form of logs for building and manufacturing, 25% for pulpwood with the remainder for other industrial purposes. The remaining 47% of world production was used as fuel wood. Table 1 shows the growth in world consumption in the main primary industrial forest products between 1961 and 1975.

Table 1: World consumption of primary industrial forest products 1961—75.

Category	Consumption (million m^3)				Growth rate 1961—75 percentage per year
	1961	1965	1970	1975	
Sawnwood	335.9	374.2	404.0	385.5	1.0
Wood based panel products	31.6	48.6	69.9	83.0	7.1
Paper and paperboard	77.6	97.3	127.8	132.9	3.9

Source: International Bank for Reconstruction and Development 1978

FUTURE PROSPECTS

It is impossible to make predictions regarding the future supply and demand for wood and wood products with any certainty, but it is possible to provide an indication of the likely pattern of development.

The major sources of future conifer supply will be from North America and the USSR. Canada in particular, is expected to continue to be a major exporter of forest products, both to the USA and Europe, but the cost of wood can be expected to rise as timber will have to come from increasingly inexcessible areas requiring roads and infrastructure. The south-east of the United States is expected to be an area of increasing importance, particularly with respect to wood production from plantations. Although growth rates in that region are below those experienced in the tropics, they are high compared with other temperate regions, and the current total growth of the forests of the south-eastern United States is in excess of that for the whole of Canada. While the USSR has just over half the world's conifer resource, this now lies mainly in Siberia as most of the excessible area to the west of the Urals has been exploited. The Siberian resource which is predominantly larch will require to be developed if current Russian export levels are to be maintained, although due to the isolation of the area, and inhospitable working conditions, this will not be easy. Furthermore, tree sizes are comparatively small, growth rates very slow, and regeneration is likely to prove extremely difficult. In contrast to past performance, little expansion in the supply of wood to world markets is expected to occur from Scandinavia as existing removals there now almost equate to annual growth.

The major future supply of hardwoods which are not so attractive for industrial purposes due to their short fibre length, will be from tropical regions. The two most important areas at present are Indonesia and Malaysia, but once these have been exploited, the only significant new areas of supply are the Amazonian forests of South America, Papua New Guinea, and Zaïre. Neither of the two former areas are considered commercially attractive at present because of the wide diversity of species, and the Zaïrean resource is not currently economically accessible.

Future prospects for wood cannot be assessed by looking at timber resource information in isolation from predicted levels of consumption. A recent study into the balance of world supply and demand (Fig. 4) indicated that demand for wood and wood products is likely to increase, and that by the year 2000, fixed price demand may exceed supply. The alternative to this can only be real price increases for timber, and this has important implications for forestry investors.

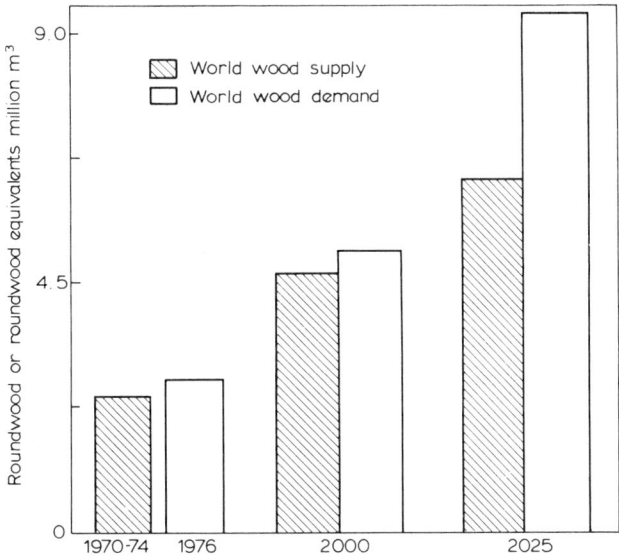

Fig. 4 The world wood supply and demand situation at fixed prices (source: Centre for Agricultural Strategy, 1980)

While past price trends relate to the use of wood as an industrial raw material, it must be recognised that wood is a renewable natural resource of considerable versatility. For instance, wood can already be used for making ethanol, methanol, producer gas, protein and animal feed. Any future increases in the price of oil will make these processes more commercially attractive and hence increase demand for wood.

The prospects for continuing and perhaps accelerating increases in future timber values in the international market therefore look encouraging for the following reasons:
1. Historically timber has performed well as a commodity over a long period based on the available evidence, and this was during a time when there were plentiful supplies of wood and the real cost of energy and oil was falling.

2. Analysis of world wood supply and demand indicates that demand for wood by an increasing population will continue to rise, and that at fixed prices, it will exceed supply by the year 2000. Such a situation will only be overcome if there are real price increases in the value of timber.
3. The past performance of wood as a commodity has been based on traditional uses. Real increases in the cost of oil have introduced the possibility that it may now be economic to use wood in industrial countries as a source of energy or as a chemical feed stock.

INTERNATIONAL FORESTRY INVESTMENT OPPORTUNITIES

Any Pension Fund considering investment in forestry overseas will need to review the potential financial yields available, the political and financial risks involved, and the opportunity of repatriating funds to the United Kingdom. These aspects need to be carefully assessed with the technical aspects of forestry and timber values, before suitable investment opportunities and locations can be identified.

THE UNITED STATES

At the present time, the most attractive area for forestry investment outside the United Kingdom appears to be the United States. The overall financial and political background and conditions for investment in that country are more suitable and better understood by UK investors, than those of most other regions and investment yields for timber growers look attractive.

The location for investment within the United States does however need to be chosen with care in order to achieve investment objectives as the tree species, their growth rates and local markets do vary considerably, and all are fundamental to the financial performance of an investment. Consideration of these factors indicates that the conifer forests in the southern states provide particularly good investment opportunities for those interested in the maximum sustained yield of long-fibred timber, and high financial yields. Further points which merit consideration include:
1. Forests cover approximately 70% of the land area in the South, and almost 90% are owned by private individuals and the forest industry, compared with 40% on the West Coast. In the latter area, private non-industrial ownership is only in the region of 20% of the total timberland compared with 70% in the South,

and hence the pressures of Federal and industrial ownership and the conservationist lobby are likely to be far greater and of more significance on the West Coast than in the South.
2. The current conifer increment in the region is the highest of any in North America, as is shown in Table 2, and is attracting additional industry, particularly from the West Coast. By the year 2000, it is estimated that the southern forests will be producing approximately half the timber requirements of the USA.

TABLE 2

Norther American Wood Fibre Increment
(millions cubic metres/year)

	Softwoods	%	Hardwoods	%	Total
Canada					
British Columbia	92	17	—	—	92
Prairies	19	4	12	5	31
Ontario	25	5	10	4	35
Quebec	41	8	6	2	47
Maritimes	19	4	5	2	24
TOTAL	196	37	33	13	229
United States					
South	166	31	101	38	267
North	37	7	119	45	156
Pacific Coast	88	17	9	3	97
Rocky Mountains	42	8	3	1	45
TOTAL	333	63	232	87	565
TOTAL NORTH AMERICA	529	100	265	100	794

Source: World Wood Fibre Supplies P. H. Jones, 1975

3. The growing conditions for softwoods which account for approximately 75% of timber consumed in the USA are good, growth rates are high by comparison with many other temperate regions, and much of the terrain lends itself to a high degree

of mechanisation and hence relatively low production costs.
4. The southern forests are located close to one of the areas of the United States which has and which is likely to continue to show above average economic growth. The region is also conveniently situated for supplying the European market.
5. The historical price trends for southern pine stumpage have given growers real price increases in excess of 3% per annum this Century.

Detailed analysis of investment returns for conifers in the south eastern United States indicate that yields of between 5/7% per annum in excess of inflation are likely to be achieved on the total investment in crop and land prior to Federal Taxation. Such returns make the South Eastern States a particularly attractive area for investment.

Financial returns in the USA from investment in conifers in the north or in hardwoods are likely to be lower by comparison with those from conifers in the Southern States due to slower tree growth rates. Yields in the former will therefore be more dependant on future timber price increases.

OTHER POSSIBLE COUNTRIES

It is impossible to give more than a brief summary of other areas of the world which may be suitable for long term forestry investment. The following however are locations which have been or are likely to be considered worthy of detailed investigation.

EUROPE

Generally tree growth rates in the UK compare relatively favourably with other areas of Europe. Land in continental Europe is often tightly held and is generally more expensive so that investment on any substantial scale is likely to prove difficult and financial yields may be lower than in the United Kingdom. The environmental pressures are also high in many locations which is a deterrant.

CANADA

While the investment climate is relatively attractive and there is a large well established forest industry, the investment opportunities for timber growing do not look as good as those in the South of the United States. This is because of the significantly lower growth rates in Canada.

AUSTRALIA AND NEW ZEALAND

These two countries provide distinct investment opportunities because of their relative long-term political and financial stability and their expanding forest industries. Growth rates are relatively high and the forest management techniques are some of the best in the world, but the opportunity for acquiring established plantations is limited.

MALAYSIA

Within the Far East region, Malaysia possibly offers one of the most attractive investment opportunities in the long term especially since tree growth rates can be very high. While most forestry activity is currently centred on harvesting existing forests, the trend is towards the development of a plantation programme, particularly in Peninsular Malaysia and Sabah.

BRAZIL

Growth rates in Brazil are particularly attractive and considerable investment in plantations has already taken place there largely financed by Brazilian investors in partnership with overseas forestry companies. However, difficulty in repatriation of funds will pose problems for institutional investors who, in addition, may consider the political and financial risks unacceptable.

OTHERS

If consideration is restricted to their future timber producing potential from plantations, two countries which are likely to be of importance are South Africa and Chile. However, the region with the greatest long term potential is undoubtedly the tropics.

MANAGEMENT OF OVERSEAS FORESTRY INVESTMENTS

For forestry, as for any other overseas investment, it is important to consider the adequacy of local advisers. In the United States for example, where the most attractive overseas forestry investment opportunities are considered to exist at the present time, the forestry management and consultancy organisations in the private non-industrial sector are still relatively small. Their principle work is not with investment forestry and crop yields but with the sale of timber from natural forests as resident owners have to date shown little interest in management or the development of plantations. This is in comparison to the considerable expertise built up

A COMPLETE COMPUTING SERVICE

We are specialists in providing computer services to the pensions industry, and are part of Unilever Computer Services, one of the largest computer bureaux in the UK, which itself is a member company of the Unilever Group.

We have developed and implemented systems for some of the largest pension funds in the country, either for use on their computers or our own.

Our services include:

PENSIONS ADMINISTRATION
- Record Keeping
- Benefit Statements
- Standard Membership Reports
- Special Reports

CONTRACTING OUT
- Statutory Calculations
- DHSS Returns
- Integration with other systems

SPECIALIST SERVICES
- Pension Payments
- Investment
- Valuation

PENSIONS & INSURANCE COMPUTER SERVICES
5 ST. JOHN'S LANE,
LONDON EC1M 4BH

01-250 1500

PENSIONS & INSURANCE COMPUTER SERVICES

in the industrial corporations who for some time have realised the importance of intensive management for sustained yield.

Due to the limited resources of the local advisers in private non-industrial forestry in the United States and their lack of experience in forestry investment management there are sound reasons why funds should retain UK consultants with experience of local conditions where the decision is to proceed with direct timberland investment alone or in conjunction with other funds. The consultant would be able to advise on the most suitable investment policy and programme, on technical aspects of establishment and management of plantations as well as monitoring the financial performance of the investment. If it is decided to proceed in a joint venture with a US Corporation, the services of the consultant would likewise be of greatest importance in ensuring that the agreement was in the investor's long term interest. Only through the employment of competent consultants and managers will the ultimate benefits of a forestry investment be achieved.

CONCLUSIONS

The reason for investing in forestry is that it is likely to show a modest but consistent financial yield in excess of inflation through the physical growth of the tree crop and the performance of the commodity of wood. Some funds have already experienced the benefits from investing in forestry in the United Kingdom but others have been deterred by the small size of the Industry, the limited market in properties of size, and the difficulty of achieving a positive cash flow. With the relaxation of exchange controls and the relatively high value of Sterling, the opportunities available overseas merit consideration.

It is considered that at the present time the most attractive investment opportunities lie in growing conifers in the southern United States where a positive cash flow can be achieved after a short period and where real yields of up to 7% may be obtained prior to taxation. However, due to the small size and relative lack of experience of local managers, investors would be well advised to retain UK consultants with practical experience of the region.

Employee Benefits in Europe

Fourth Edition

A comprehensive review which clearly sets out both the general aspects of social security and occupational benefit plans and their practice in seventeen Western European countries.

This standard work has been revised and expanded. The new edition is produced in a loose-leaf format to accommodate future changes.

Published by:
Callund & Company Ltd
15/17 King Street
St James's
LONDON SW1Y 6QU
Telephone: 01-839 3316

CALLUND

THE SOCIETY OF PENSION CONSULTANTS

Representative of firms engaged in all aspects of pension consultancy.

Further information and membership details from:

The Secretary,
Society of Pension Consultants,
Ludgate House,
Ludgate Circus,
London, EC4A 2AB.

Telephone: 01-353-1688

The Role of the International Benefits Consultant

David Callund,
Managing Director, Callund & Company Ltd

In sophisticated countries, like the UK, the manner in which occupational employee benefit arrangements are structured and financed is complex. The Social Security system has had a long history. Occupational trust funds are also long-established and fiscal legislation has had many years in which to mature. Even with this long experience, an understanding of basic principles relating to the design and financing of employee benefits in the UK is by no means ubiquitous.

As a result, consultants have an important role to play in advising UK corporations on the detail and technicalities concerning the forms of employee welfare which they would like to provide and the way in which the costs of such welfare can best be met and accounted for.

If one were to be naive, one could say that the international consultant undertakes a similar role in connection with employee benefit arrangements outside the UK. In essence, this is his function. In practice, however, his role is generally somewhat different from that of his domestic counterpart.

The very fact that each country adopts its own form of Social Security structure, labour legislation and fiscal regulation, ensures that, in an international context, no two problems can be assumed to be the same. Not only does legislation vary, cultural and historical backgrounds play an important role in the attitude of employers to social welfare provision for their employees. These elements have to be taken into account.

As we have seen in the UK, the well-laid plans of one generation — whether in the field of Social Security provision or in the field of occupational benefits — rarely seem to suit a subsequent generation. All social and economic change cannot be forecast. As a result, existing plans are regularly altered in the light of new circumstances.

If, therefore, one can have no certainty as to the future of employee benefit provision in one's own country, it is evidently more hazardous to speculate on the future development in countries where one is less experienced. The only certainty is that uncertainty will continue.

In the same way that one tries to make a reasonable judgement as to likely developments in one's own country, the international consultant, by virtue of his experience, is able to give an educated opinion as to the likely development elsewhere.

No consultant is able to give truly international advice. The subject is too vast and the variables are too numerous. Nonetheless, because the underlying principles of benefit provision are universal, it is possible for the experienced international consultant to play an invaluable role. His role is to give guidance, to the best of his ability, so that a company will not enter into arrangements which might be unwise, or financially onerous. Even though the detail of employee benefit provision differs from one country to the next, experience of the differences in many countries leads one to a greater understanding of the problems which might arise in any particular territory.

Such experience cannot be gained quickly. It cannot be gained solely by reading about the conditions which apply in any particular country. It can only be gained by applying oneself to the solution of employee benefit problems in the country concerned.

Because of this, the corporate international pensions manager should look for two qualities when he seeks to appoint an international benefits consultant:

i) He should look for broad international experience — both in territorial terms and also in benefit terms;
ii) He should look for pratical experience in those countries where his problems immediately arise.

When referring to territorial and benefit experience, it must be recognised that Social Security systems, for example, may take the form of provident funds or pension arrangements. Social Security pensions may take the form of flat-rate benefits, or earnings-related benefits, or a combination of both. The implications of index-linked pension provision is very different from the implications attaching to an index-linked provident fund. These distinctions need to be fully understood. Similarly, the application of monies towards pension funds in developed countries with their attendant sophisticated tax and Social Security systems may be very different from the application of monies in Third World countries, where tax and Social Security structures themselves might be only in their infancy. In the one, developed capital markets and institutional forms will exist. In the other, the machinery for the investment of monies may be non-existent. Sensitivity to these differences is essential.

Given this broad background as to the qualities which an international consultant must have, the specific functions of a consultant can then be considered. A consultant should assist management to a proper understanding of employee benefit liabilities which they might create; he should assist management to ensure that the right benefits are provided in the most cost-effective way; he should draw to his client's attention the principal aspects of taxation, Social Security and labour legislation as they effect occupational employee benefits; he should be conscious of the economic and demographic factors which would influence the provision and financing of employee welfare in the countries under consideration; he must also be able to distinguish between the various means of financing — pay-as-you-go, or the accumulation of internal or external reserves — to reflect the best interests of his client. The consultant should also be able to assist corporate management in obtaining a better understanding of the labour relations climate in a particular country.

Only then can the more traditional roles of the consultant be employed. Benefit structures can be designed, actuarial valuations can be undertaken, financing media can be chosen and corporate policy can be determined and implemented.

Banks and insurance companies play a significant role in financing abroad — as at home. An understanding of the regulations which govern the contracts which banks and insurance companies may offer is essential. In many countries, government tariffs apply to insurance premiums, and cartels may exist which limit the distribution of surpluses. The implications of such restraints — particularly on the effective yield on contributions, must be understood by your consultant. Similarly, the attractions and pitfalls of multinational insurance contracts must be understood.

In some respects one might say that the international employee benefits consultant must be a Jack of all trades. This does not mean to say that he will be master of none. He must be fully conversant in all the basic skills, and must have the additional quality of a wide experience of the application of those skills in different cultures and national economies.

Benefits International

If your responsibilities
extend beyond the U.K.,
you are bound to find
Benefits International
a useful asset in keeping
you up-to-date with
professional views and
benefits practice worldwide.

Complimentary copies from:

Pension Publications Ltd
30 Queen Anne's Gate
London SW1H 9AW

Telephone: 01-222 8033
Telex: 916283

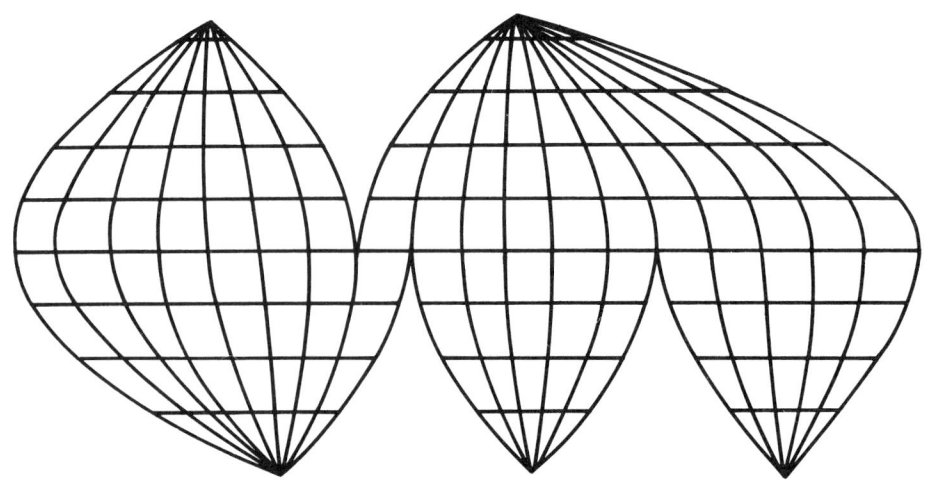

Pensions in Europe

This series of articles have been written by various representatives of William M. Mercer and co-ordinated by George Clare in their London office.

In general, British pension plans are much more highly developed and much more extensive in scope than those operated by companies in continental Europe. There are a number of reasons for this of which the most significant are:
— The ravages of World War II and its effect on personal saving and pre-war pension promises were not felt as much in UK as elsewhere.
— Successive British governments have neither needed nor sought to become as heavily involved as others in the provision of old age security.
— The influence of a strong insurance industry has been notable in stimulating companies to make private pension provision for their employees.
— The ability to "contract out" of part of Social Security is unique to Britain today.

The notes which follow are not intended to be an authoritative guide to continental European pension practice: rather, they seek to identify the more important features of the pensions scene in five countries — Belgium, France, Netherlands, Switzerland and West Germany — where conditions are very different from those in the United Kingdom.

The pension practitioner studying Europe for the first time, will note the marked contrast between the minimum benefit standards as required by law in each country. The selected territories all have widely differing Social Security systems in which the scale of benefits and level of contributions bear little resemblance the one to the other in spite of the "harmonisation" intention behind Articles 117 and 118 of the Treaty of Rome. In some countries, supplementary retirement plans outside Social Security are required: in the five countries under consideration it will be noted that:
— France has a compulsory multi-employer system.

— Industry-wide schemes are mandatory in some industries in the Netherlands.
— The Swiss proposed "compulsory second pillar" incorporates minimum benefit standards applicable to all employers in the country.

In terms of financing pension promises, there are again substantial differences between the European countries. It will be seen that in Europe's most successful industrial country, Germany, book-reserving is the system adopted by most companies. To an extent this practice is derived from favourable tax treatment originating at a time when the retention of capital within industry was crucial to the economy. In France, the concept of pre-funding is virtually unknown and reflects the frequent devaluation of the French Franc in the post World War II period. In Switzerland, the strength of the currency and the impeccable credentials of banking institutions give rise to a pre-funding system which might appear to outsiders to suffer from over-regulation.

The following comments have been prepared by William M. Mercer, the largest firm of international employee benefit consultants. The comments have been prepared by the managers of Mercer offices in each of the five countries, and reflect local feeling. It is the belief of William M. Mercer that effective management of overseas benefit plans calls for a clear understanding of the financial issues involved, coupled with an acceptance of the fact that benefit practices and demands in the labour market are quite different between one country and another. It is hoped that the notes are a constructive aid to this understanding.

BELGIUM

Britain is often accused of class differences, but it is not often realised that Social Security in a number of European countries differentiates between blue and white collar employees. One such country is Belgium where the Social Security system for works' employees is based on all earnings without a ceiling: one result is that Unions have not been active in the benefits area and it is therefore unusual for companies to sponsor private pension plans for works' employees.

As far as staff employees are concerned, Social Security benefits are based on an earnings ceiling which is adjusted annually: in October 1980 this was BF 689,400 (approximately £9,500) i.e. approaching twice national average earnings. While this ceiling appears high it was not always so and in fact the current level is largely due to a radical increase in 1973. The eventual pension objective under the current system is 60% for single persons (75% for married couples) applied to career-average revalued earnings, disregarding earnings in excess of the then ruling ceiling in any year. Since the radical increase in earnings is still very new and the revaluation is not applied to the ceiling applicable to years prior to 1957, it is likely to be some years before anybody will actually retire with a State pension in line with the proposed objectives. Staff employees retiring today with final earnings around the current ceiling, receive a pension of approximately one-third of pay (40% to 50% if married).

The earnings ceiling for contribution purposes, where applicable, may be increased during the year in the event of rises in the cost-of-living exceeding 2%. Both benefit and contribution ceilings are equal each 1st January. The present Social Security contribution rates for salaried employees for retirement, death and disability benefits are 9.8% (employer) and 7.1% (employee) up to the ceiling. For wage earners, there is no earnings ceiling relative to retirement/survivors' benefits or on contributions. The government is currently reviewing the structure of Social Security benefits and any changes recommended are expected to be implemented during 1981.

Company plans for staff employees are common and typically provide a pension of between 60% and 70% of final average earnings, integrated with Social Security. Integration takes many forms of which the most popular are the self-explanatory direct offset method and the step-rate method where the annual accrual rate would be, for example, 0.5% of pay up to the ceiling and 1.5% of pay above the earnings ceiling. Retirement invariably coincides with the State pension ages of 65 for males and 60 for females. Company plans are generally contributory with employees being asked to pay up to 6% of earnings above the Social Security ceiling and a small percentage below.

Most commercial enterprises in Belgium are small and, accordingly, most pension plans tend to be insured. Individual contracts *must* be issued to each member and, if the plan is contributory, a second contract must be issued for pensions purchased with the member's own contributions. The underlying premiums are based on the assumption that 4% interest will be earned on the funds invested. There is currently an annual bonus payable which varies from 1% to 4% of the accumulated reserve depending upon the age of the contract. When a member has participated in an insured plan for five years, his benefits must be fully vested. An unusual feature of insured plans in Belgium is the practice of insurance companies granting house mortgages secured by expected future pensions. The pension is commuted at retirement and the resulting lump sum used to discharge the mortgage. In this respect the adage that "every Belgian is born with a brick in his belly" is supported!

Insurance companies are greatly restricted in their investments and in the sophistication of their products. Consequently, many large companies have elected to fund their pensions through a separate legal entity known as an *ASBL* (*Association sans bût lucratif* — essentially a non-profit corporation). General controlling legislation has applied to *ASBL* since 1975, but since details of the legislation have not been finalised, the real impact has not yet been felt. A draft of the legislation has been under discussion for some time.

Book reserves were sometimes used in the past for financing pension promises, but the new general controlling legislation will terminate this practice — probably from 1981.

Company and employee contributions to both insured and *ASBL* plans are fully tax-deductible. Different tax treatment of lump sum benefits is an inducement to commuting for capital, for pensions and widows' income. Widows' pensions, typically expressed as 60% of the accrued or projected pensions, may be subject to a minimum expressed in lump sum form. This would in any event be the normal form of benefit for those ineligible for a widows' pension.

In marked contrast with the United Kingdom, dividends paid to self-administered pension funds and insurance company managed funds are subject to tax, normally at 20%. In addition, the assets of an *ASBL* are subject to an annual tax of 0.17%.

Labour Law requires that full income must be maintained for 30 days for salaried staff who are disabled. For works' employees, income is maintained at 100% for only seven days with a slightly lower rate being paid for the next 23 days. Thereafter, assuming the employee is at least two-thirds disabled, a Social Security pension is paid equal to 60% of earnings up to a slightly lower ceiling than for retirement benefit purposes. After one year, the benefit is increased to 65% if the disabled employee has dependants or reduced to 43.5% if he does not. Private company practice would normally provide 60% to 80% of pay above the ceiling with a lower percentage below the ceiling where the State is providing a benefit.

FRANCE

For most employees in France, retirement pensions come from two main sources — Social Security and the mandatory multi-employer schemes.

In the Social Security system, benefits and contributions are defined in relation to earnings up to a ceiling, normally designated *Tranche A* earnings. In 1980 these earnings are FF 60,120 (£6,000) per annum which is in the region of national average earnings in industry. Contributions on these earnings amount to 26.25% from the employer and 4.7% from the employee together with 4.5% and 5.5% of *total* pay by employer and employee respectively.

The Old Age Pension payable from age 60 after a full 37½ year contributory career amounts to 25% of revalued *Tranche A* earnings averaged over the best 10 consecutive years. For each quarter by which the pension is deferred, the multiple of 25% is increased by 1¼%, thus giving 50% at age 65 and 75% at age 70 — the latest permissible age for retirement. It is not necessary to cease working in order to obtain the Old Age Pension. In the event of death after retirement, the widow's pension amounts to 50% of the husband's Old Age Pension. On death before retirement, a modest lump sum (three months' *Tranche A* earnings) death benefit is payable and for older widows the State also provides a Widows' pension amounting to 50% of the member's pension payable if he had become disabled. The system includes disability, medical, etc. benefits and family allowances which are particularly generous in France.

The main feature of the French pensions scene is the system of mandatory multi-employer schemes under which, by Collective

Agreement, employees must be enrolled depending upon their status. In this regard, the system provides two main classifications of employee, *Cadre* and *non-Cadre* together with an intermediate category *Cadre Assimilées*. Broadly, a *Cadre* employee has technical/academic qualifications or has supervisory duties and a "job coefficient" of 300 or above. *Non-Cadres* are primarily blue-collar or clerical employees with job coefficients below 200. A further category of senior executives sometimes referred to in French pension terminology are *Cadres Supérieurs*.

Although operating at different levels of contribution, the *Cadre* and *non-Cadre* plans have the following common characteristics:

i) Normal retirement age is 65 for both men and women.
ii) A number of different funding institutions exist, grouped under central organisations (AGIRC for *Cadres*, ARRCO for *non-Cadres*).
iii) Both have a minimum contribution basis, but under AGIRC high contributions may be paid up to a defined maximum. Once granted, higher contributions must not be reduced.
iv) No favourable basic benefits emerge from any particular funding institution — they all act as collecting agencies and AGIRC and ARRCO arrange the internal equalisation of funds. There are some fringe advantages with some institutions which, under the time-lag of the equalisation process, are more often in credit with AGIRC and ARRCO and may have some interest income not enjoyed by institutions in debit.
v) Contributions are used to secure pension points. The system operates on a modified pay-as-you-go basis known in France as *Répartition* under which contributions received are distributed as pensions. The pension point value, and the cost of securing a pension point, are annually adjusted to keep the system in balance. However, contributions were increased by 3% in 1979 without a comparable improvement in benefits.
vi) Widows' pensions are payable in proportion to the deceased member's accrued points.

Contributions to the multi-employer schemes are as follows:
— For *Cadres* there are three bands of earnings: *Tranche A* (as for Social Security): *Tranche B* (earnings between *Tranche A*

ceiling and four times that ceiling): *Tranche C* (earnings between *Tranche B* ceiling and twice that ceiling). Minimum *Cadre* contributions are 2.06% of *Tranche B* from employees and 6.18% from the company. Maximum contributions are 6.18% of *Tranche B* from the employees and 10.3% from the company. The total range is therefore from 8.24% (to be increased to 12.36% in 1981) to 16.48% of *Tranche B*. At present the average is 14.75%, indicating the prevalence of the maximum rate. In addition, following a 1973 agreement, a further 4.4% of *Tranche A* earnings must be paid to a *non-Cadre* institution, affiliated with ARRCO. Of this, only 4% secures pension points, the balance being a surcharge. Finally, the company must pay a minimum of 1½% of *Tranche A* towards death benefits. These do not fall with AGIRC, but are used to secure lump sum death benefits with independent life insurance companies.

— *Non-Cadres* must pay contributions totalling 4.4% of earnings (1.76% from employee and 2.64% from company) up to an earnings ceiling of three times *Tranche A*, i.e. currently FF 180,360 (£17,000) — payable to an ARRCO institution.

— In the case of so-called "Article 36 employees" (*Cadres Assimilées*) the company effectively has the choice between AGIRC and ARRCO and the majority have elected the AGIRC plan.

Funded supplementary pension schemes are not usual in France. The usual method of improving retirement benefits is to pay further contributions to AGIRC and ARRCO to secure extra pension points. For senior management *(Cadres Supérieurs)* contributions ranging from 4% to 17.6% of *Tranche C* earnings may be paid to a separate funding institute where they will earn pension points or alternatively paid to an insurance company to secure a deferred annuity.

Improved death, disability and medical benefits may be secured by paying contributions to an insurance company. Widows' pensions often are improved to a level of 60% of the husband's prospective retirement pension. Disability pensions are not payable under AGIRC before age 65 and so insurance companies may provide a temporary pension payable to age 65 in the event of disability.

Overall, the impact of the multi-employer schemes in France leaves employers with very little choice: as such, the importance of pensions in a British or North American environment is frequently not understood by French management and historically companies in France have not had to develop the special skills associated with pension techniques in countries where pre-funding is customary. Whether or not the *Répartition* system can prevail against a changing demographic background where the ratio of beneficiaries to contributors is constantly increasing, is the question most frequently asked in France.

NETHERLANDS

Social Security provides a flat-rate pension for single persons, with a supplement for married couples, in much the same way as the British system — but at a rather higher level. From the 1st July 1980, the single person's pension is Dfl 12,116 per annum (approximately £2,500) rising to Dfl 17,397 (approximately £3,700) for a married couple. These amounts are updated twice a year in line with the net minimum wage. The net pension for a single person equals 70% of the net retirement pension for couples. Normal State retirement age is 65 for men and women.

Contribution rates to Social Security are high. Up to an earnings ceiling of Dfl 34,584 (approximately £7,400) the employer contributes an average of 27.72% and the employee 24.325%. Above this ceiling, the contribution of both employer and employee is reduced by 4.05% since employees with an income above this ceiling are not covered for compulsory health insurance. Salary ceilings for other contributions are even higher — Dfl 46,400 (approximately £9,900) for retirement and widows' pensions and Dfl 61,570 (approximately £13,100) for sickness, disability and unemployment benefits. The 11.6% contribution for retirement and widows' benefits is borne entirely by the employee. The 9.40% contribution under the General Family Allowance Act, the General Working Incapacity Act and the Exceptional Medical Expenses (Compensation) Act is borne entirely by the employer. Contributions for other benefits are shared equally between employer and employee.

According to a 1975 government report, 15% of the Dutch workforce is self-employed. All but 13% of the 85% employed workforce, are covered for some supplementary benefits and, excluding the public sector scheme, around 60% of private-sector coverage is through the medium of industry funds. Under these industry funds, any employee in a particular industry (i.e. metal trade or hotel business) must be enrolled in the nationally agreed plan for that industry. Not every industry has a mandatory plan and there is considerable variation between benefit levels from one industry to another, and sometimes between different categories of employee within the same industry.

Company sponsored benefits may be provided from one of the following sources: an industry fund, a private company scheme or an insured plan. Although there is still some considerable variation between benefit levels from one industry to another, or from one company to another, benefits are generally gravitating towards a 70% modified final pay pension after 40 years' service, integrated with the flat-rate Social Security benefits. The modification to final pay may entail five-year averaging or the use of pay five or ten years prior to retirement adjusted thereafter only to the extent of national or industry wage movement.

The gravitation to the integrated 70% modified final pay level, is due partly to the influence of practice in major industries, but also to the fact that specific plans have been formulated at national level between federations of unions and companies to ensure that all employed persons enjoy a pension expectation at that level. Agreement was reached in principle many years ago, but there is a continuing debate upon the funding vehicles to be utilised for such mandated benefits.

One of the functions of an industry fund is to ensure that employees can change jobs within an industry without being penalised on the eventual pension upon retirement. This produces two particular characteristics relevant to benefit planning and finance in the Netherlands. First, the industry funds operate a global contribution rate so that the average age of employees in a particular company within the industry is irrelevant; thus, pension costs cannot be held down by recruiting young people (or refusing to hire old people). Second, if the nominated benefit is of a final-pay type, and this is increasingly the case, in industry, funds often operate a so-called *rear balcony system* whereby new employers are responsible for the normal future service benefits plus the past service benefit increases brought about by pay increases within the new employment. This may not be a problem if a global contribution rate applies, but could be of considerable importance if a company has contracted out of the industry fund as explained in the next paragraph.

If a company is already operating a pension plan when the industry fund appropriate to its employees is declared mandatory, then it may use the existing plan (upgraded if necessary) to provide the mandated benefits and to contract out of the industry fund. This enables the company to exercise some control over pension costs by its own recruitment policy, or at least to pay only an equitable contribution for its own employees, regardless of the trend in average age within the industry as a whole. It may also give the company some freedom in selecting appropriate funding vehicles. Clearly this option is not open to a new company in an industry with a mandatory plan.

Where mandatory benefits are insufficient, or where no mandatory industry fund applies, many companies operate self-administered or insured plans (in approximately equal proportions, according to a government report) along the lines outlined earlier. Tax legislation requires that any pension foundation be supervised by a qualified actuary in order to obtain approval from the Chamber of Insurance. Investment in loans to the company, or in shares of the company, are restricted to 5% of the required assets plus surplus reserves, but not more than 10% of the total assets.

Up to a certain level of contribution income, the major insurance companies operate a cartel system on premiums, bonuses, termination penalties and other contract conditions. A particular aspect of the cartel conditions of which a company must beware is the minimum length of time for which the contract must run. This will quite probably be ten years, with automatic renewal for a further five years, or even ten years, unless adequate notice of termination is given. Multi-national network contracts usually over-ride cartel conditions.

Funding systems adopted to satisfy the local requirement for tax approval lack the freedom associated with the British environment. In particular, the actuarial assumptions used are not necessarily to be taken as estimates for the future, but rather as the limit to which the revenue authorities will permit the company to go in anticipating pay increases, etc. It is important to recognise this when a major decision hinges upon cost figures submitted, particularly as the company is obliged by law to fund any promised benefits. In addition to this, a further unusual feature is the availability of full tax deductions for past service liabilities before funding is completed — i.e. in anticipation of future contributions (which will not be deductible when finally paid since advance credit has been taken). In view of this unusual concession there is a tendency for companies to be generous in regard to past service benefits.

Private cover for disability benefits are unnecessary except for the higher paid since Social Security provides up to 80% of pre-disability income (sometimes up to 100% if home care is required) up to a salary of around three times the national minimum wage.

Early resignation plans (*VUT* plans) are becoming very popular in the Netherlands. It is a government-sponsored way of combating unemployment. Under these schemes, employees are able to resign from age 62 or older whilst retaining about 80% of salary to their normal retirement date. The employee remains covered for pension benefits and employer and employee contributions remain due.

SWITZERLAND

An important general characteristic of Switzerland is its stability — both political and economic — which has resulted in very low rates of inflation and particular currency strength in recent years. Nevertheless, in employee benefits terms, Switzerland is a small country with a population of only 6.5 million where the employee benefits scene is influenced by essential differences between some of the *Cantons*.

The Federal Social Security scheme *(AVS-AI)* is based on upgraded revalued earnings up to a ceiling currently at SFr 39,600 per annum (approximately £10,000 — almost 50% greater than national average earnings) as applicable to benefits. In contrast, contributions are charged on total income.

As regards Old Age benefits, these are payable from age 65 for men and 62 for women. Contributions to the system are 5% for retirement, survivors' and long-term disability benefits. The contribution also covers a salary continuation benefit for those on military service. Old Age pensions comprise the sum of a flat-rate pension plus an earnings-related benefit calculated at 20% of career-average revalued earnings. The Old Age Pension is increased by 50% where there is a dependent wife over the age of 62. In the event of death, a widow receives a pension of 80% of the pension in course of payment to her husband or that which would have been payable at normal retirement age provided she is under age 62 with dependent children, or childless having been married at least five years and being at least 45 years of age. In other circumstances, a lump sum death benefit is payable. The system also provides for disability pensions payable where permanent disability is at least 50% after rehabilitation. The full *AI* pension in these circumstances, amounts to the projected old age retirement pension on the assumption that the degree of disability is at least two-thirds. The amount in respect of a 50% disability is a half-rate pension. Supplements are payable for dependants.

Company pension schemes are very common and cover 80% of all employees in Switzerland. Normally such schemes are contributory. There are very few legal requirements applying to company plans although a lengthy law compelling employers to establish benefits of at least a minimum standard (the so-called *Second Pillar*) has been under discussion for some years.

Currently, the most important legal requirement is to use a foundation or a co-operative institution for the purpose of financing. In Swiss Law, a foundation is a non-profit company under which the investment of assets is restricted according to regulations varying by *Canton* and nearly all pension plans use foundations. No sizeable investment in foreign securities is allowed. Company contributions to its foundation cannot be withdrawn: all company contributions are tax-deductable and, in most *Cantons,* not restricted to size. It follows that there is no tax requirement for actuarial valuation of contribution amounts and considerable scope is available for "managing" company deductions.

Some foundations insure benefits and in general insurance is the solution adopted by most of the smaller foundations — with larger ones self-administered. Non-insured plans invest mainly in fixed interest stocks and property and are strictly supervised by the authorities in each *Canton.* Companies are able to borrow money from their foundations provided that a market rate of interest (based on the rate charged on mortgages by *Cantonal* banks) is paid.

Company pensions are generally integrated with *AVS-AI* and would mostly be related to final average pay, providing 60%—70%

after 40 years' service. However, many smaller plans operate on the defined contribution principle. Current trends are towards earlier eligibility and improvement in final-pay formulae. Partial vesting is legally-required after five years' membership with full vesting after 30 years. However, prevailing practice among foreign-based companies is usually more generous than these statutory minima and provides for full vesting after ten or 15 years at the most.

On a federal basis, accident insurance *(SUVA)* covers employees of all industrial companies. In two *Cantons (Geneva* and *Ticino)* coverage is required for all employees. Elsewhere, local authorities may request coverage for employees with earnings below specified limits. Proposed legislation establishing a National Accident Insurance programme covering most of the workforce was accepted by the National Council in 1979 and after some modification is expected to be implemented from 1st January 1983. In the meanwhile, company group accident schemes (occupational and non-occupational) are very common.

One feature of the Swiss financial scene which is well known throughout the world, is its secrecy. An effect of this secrecy is the inability to acquire comprehensive survey information either on company benefit plans or the extent of their financing.

WEST GERMANY

Social Security benefits in West Germany are relatively high but supplementary retirement, death and disability schemes are provided by most companies. The Social Security pension is based on a complex mixture of career earnings, revaluation and final-average pay but as a practical measure it is normally reckoned to fall within the range of 45% and 55% of final earnings below the ceiling — depending upon whether the period of "education" is long or short. For 1980, the ceiling is DM 50,400 (approximately £11,700) — which is almost double national average earnings in Germany. The 1981 ceiling will be DM 52,800 per annum.

Social Security contributions from employees and employers alike are 9% of pay up to a higher ceiling. In 1981, it will be decided if this will become realigned with that for benefits and in any event the contribution rate will rise to 9¼%. Retirement age is flexible and ranges from 60 assuming 35 years of participation in the system. State widows' benefits are 60% of accrued retirement pension unless the employee was under age 55 at death — in which case the widow receives 60% of the pension which would have accrued had the employee survived to age 55. Additions are payable for orphans. The State scheme disability pension is 100% of accrued retirement pension but as in the case of the widows' benefit, this is subject to a minimum accrual to age 55 for claimants under that age. The benefit is reduced by one-third if the disabled employee is unable to follow his normal occupation but could perform other work.

Private pension plans most commonly provide between 10% and 20% of pay up to the Social Security ceiling and 40% to 60% of pay above the ceiling — after a full career. As far as death benefits are concerned, private company schemes follow the same approach as Social Security but it is also common to base the benefit on retirement pensions that would have accrued to age 65 (instead of 55).

Company pension schemes, which are not obligatory, must comply with the *Company Pension Plan Law* of 1974 which includes a minimum vesting requirement (age 35 and 10 years' membership, or 12 years' company service) and a requirement to review pensions in course of payment every three years. This latter rule is very problematic as the law is not specific on the standards to be applied in the triennial review. Labour Court decisions to date have narrowed down the range of possibilities and these are now centred on the requirement to cover 100% of inflation in the prior three years unless it can be proved that such indexation would generate an increase in income exceeding the net increase in income of company employees doing similar work. In such cases, the indexation will be limited so that the retirees' income meets the increase in income given to company employees.

Pension funding methods are probably the most unusual aspect of the German environment. The most popular method, accounting for some 75% of pension liabilities in Germany, is the book reserve system under which a company establishing a pension plan and promising the benefits in writing, may set up a reserve in its books and claim a tax deduction each year for allocation to that reserve. No assets are specifically ear-marked for this reserve and the plan members have no priority ranking over creditors in the event of the company's insolvency. The tax authorities have defined the basis upon which the allocations must be computed, leaving no scope for actuarial judgement on assumptions or methods. To the extent that pensions are vested under the provisions of the 1974 Law (or in course of payment) that law requires that the vested benefits be insured against the company's insolvency through a special insurance organisation *(PSV)* formed for the purpose. The provisional premium rate for the current year for this insurance is 0.08% of the reserve (0.11% was charged in 1979).

Another funding vehicle is the "Support Fund", a separate legal entity which is restricted by limitations placed upon the contributions it may receive by the 1974 Law. Thus, financing restrictions have limited the usefulness of the Support Fund. It may still have advantages in certain circumstances and may be used as a conduit for level insurance premiums which are not subject to the restrictions on contributions formerly applicable to Support Funds. This possibility is, however, rarely used because the establishment of such a fund is based on a non-insurance philosophy. Premiums to the *PSV* are payable for pensions financed through Support Funds based on a fictitious liability established by the 1974 Law.

Under both the Book Reserve and the Support Fund systems, the emerging pensions are taxed as normal income except that 40% is tax-free up to DM 4,800 (approximately £1,100) per year. If a segregated fund is created, the company contributions are considered taxable income and accordingly the emerging benefits are tax-free except for the interest content of any income paid. Segregated funds may either be private funds or insurance contracts. The 1974 Law defined the basis upon which segregated fund contributions from the company could be assessed as taxable income to the employee. In practical terms, the first DM 312 paid by the company is tax-free and the next DM 2,400 will also be tax-free if the company pays a flat tax of 10%. The DM 2,400 may be increased up to DM 3,600 for members of a group of employees if the average for the group is DM 2,400 or less.

Private funds are used by only 200 companies in Germany and that number is declining. One reason is that private funds are regulated as insurance companies, with the same investment restrictions. In this way, their financial viability is limited to groups of employees large enough to function as an independent insurance company.

Pension plans in Germany are normally non-contributory — partly for historical reasons, but also because no employee contributions can be paid to a book reserve system. A contributory plan can be established on the basis of employee contributions being paid to an insurance company with the employer's liability financed through book reserves.

Pensions in Ireland

Eamon J. Egan
Director, Metropolitan Pension Association (Ireland) Ltd

With only a few exceptions all employed persons aged 16 years and over must, regardless of earnings, contribute to Social Security. Most employers then top-up the various flat-rate and wage-related benefits under the State Scheme to a suitable level under company sponsored plans.

As at 1st January 1981, the State Scheme contribution is 4.5% (employee) and 9.8% (employer) on earnings to a ceiling of IR £7,000. Certain classes of employee, notably those in the Civil Service, pay a reduced rate of contribution for a reduced range of benefits — employees in private industry would, however, be invariably covered for all benefits.

The main benefit headings are pensions, survivor benefits, workmen's compensation, maternity, disability, unemployment, sickness and medical care and family allowances. Flat-rate benefits are payable in each case with pay-related supplements in the case of disability, unemployment, maternity and workmen's compensation.

Pensions are paid from age 65 for both men and women provided the employee actually retires from insurable employment. No early retirement provisions exist and while pensions may be deferred, no increases are paid. The full retirement pension amounts to IR £24.50 per week for a single person and IR £40.15 per week for a married couple. This works out at about 23% and 38% respectively of National Average Earnings. The retirement pension is paid to age 66 whereupon the Old Age Pension begins at the same rate. Supplements are paid where the pensioner is over age 80 or the dependent spouse is over age 66. Allowances are also paid for dependent children.

Payment of full benefit is subject to certain contribution conditions and a reduction applies where the average number of contributions is less than 48 p.a. after 1st January 1953 or the date of entry into insurance if later.

The Widow's Pension is IR £22.50 per week with supplements where the claimant is over age 80 or has dependent children. Of the other benefit headings mentioned above, the principal benefit levels are IR £20.45 p.w. (single person) and IR £33.70 p.w. (married couple) for disability and unemployment — together with dependant allowances. All flat-rate benefits are generally reviewed yearly (and occasionally half-yearly).

It is relevant to note that what are known as long-term benefits i.e. Pension and Widow's and Orphans Pensions are taxable whereas all short-term benefits i.e. unemployment, disability etc. are payable tax-free.

Pay-related benefits are geared to earnings between IR £14 p.w. and IR £140 p.w. and subject to a waiting period of two weeks. The benefit payable is:

40% of reckonable earnings for the first 147 days.
30% of reckonable earnings for the next 78 days.
25% of reckonable earnings for the next 78 days.
20% of reckonable earnings for the next 78 days.

For those wholly unemployed, the combined flat-rate and pay-related benefits together with any tax-rebates may not exceed 85% of average net weekly earnings prior to unemployment.

A Government Green Paper published in October 1976 outlined the pros and cons of various systems of providing income related State Pensions. A White Paper has been promised for some time and is now fairly confidently expected in early 1981. The general feeling is that a Dutch style national scheme will be proposed i.e. an up-grading of the present scheme so that an agreed percentage of National Average Earnings would be paid to single and married people. In order to avoid a costly administration process, there would (it is felt) be no contracting-out facility.

As it is, the existing flat-rate State Pension system is currently complemented by a fairly sophisticated private sector pensions movement.

Legislation dealing with employee benefit schemes has mainly followed that in the United Kingdom. The 1972 Finance Act introduced one comprehensive code for the approval of occupational pension schemes and students of the 1970 Finance Act in the UK will note the striking similarity between these two pieces of legislation.

Schemes are set up under irrevocable trusts and can be either insured or self administered. Insurance is probably more common

— mainly because few of the employers are large by European standards. However, managed fund investment is becoming popular and this perhaps reflects the influence of North American based companies not familiar with conventional deferred annuity contracts.

Most plans aim at providing a retirement benefit — usually from age 65 — of two-thirds of final pay after a full career of 40 years. Allowance is made in the formula for state benefits. The benefit package would also typically include widows pension on death in service or in retirement, lump sum death benefits of from one to four times' salary and long term disability benefits to supplement state benefits to an agreed percentage figure. Ad hoc cost of living increases on benefits rather than amounts guaranteed in advance are more the norm — in any event, many schemes have not yet had to meet this problem as the majority are only in being since 1960 or later.

A clear distinction is still usually drawn between white and blue collar workers so that the level of benefit under any of the above headings will depend on the category of employment. Executives are often singled out for above average benefits.

It is relevant to note that under the Anti Discrimination (Pay) Act 1974 men and women on like work are entitled to equal pension rights. There is still some dispute about what constitutes 'equal pension rights' but most *new* schemes tend to provide identical benefits for men and women e.g. spouse's pensions, common entry terms, pension ages etc.

While the majority of schemes are non-contributory, there has been a consistent trend towards contribution arrangements in recent years, a contribution rate of 5% of pensionable earnings being most popular.

Trade Unions have taken an increasing interest in pensions since the early 1970's when a series of National Pay Agreements removed their then prime negotiating area. It can be expected that their continuing influence together with the expected arrival of the Government White Paper on a National Income Related Pension Scheme in early 1981 will serve to maintain the already high level of activity and development in the pensions area.

We can help get you off the ground

If you're thinking of relocating or setting up in business.

We can offer a first class package deal — advance factories from as little as 1,000 sq. ft. up to 27,000 sq. ft. or a fully serviced site on which to build your own. Our team of experts can give help and advice on such things as labour, education, housing, grants and incentives (we're in a special development area...)

So why not visit us and see how the land lies.

Mr. N. R. Batchelor, A.R.I.C.S.,
Commercial Director,
Washington Development Corporation, Usworth Hall, Washington, Tyne & Wear.
Tel: Washington (0632) 463591   Telex: 537210 DC Wash G.

Pension Funds

161 **The Largest UK Pension Funds**
(listed in order of size)

167 **The Major UK Pension Funds**

493 **The Major US and Canadian Pension Funds**

531 **The Major European Pension Funds**

 **Weatherall Green & Smith** CHARTERED SURVEYORS

Property Consultants
Investment Valuers
Portfolio Advisers

throughout the UK, Western Europe & North America

UNITED KINGDOM

London
Weatherall Green & Smith
22 Chancery Lane London WC2A 1LT
01-405 6944 Telex 22446

Weatherall Green & Smith City
24 Austin Friars London EC2N 2EN
01-638 9011 Telex 22446

Leeds
Weatherall Hollis & Gale
29 King Street Leeds LS1 2HP
(0532) 442066 Telex 557544

Also in Wakefield

USA

New York
Weatherall Green & Smith Inc
9 West 57th Street New York NY 10019
(212) 758 3131 Telex 649377

FRANCE

Paris
Weatherall Green & Smith
Weatheralls France S.A.
64 rue La Boetie 75008 Paris
563 05 50 Telex 650788

GERMANY

Frankfurt
Weatherall Green & Smith Gmbh & Co. K.G.
Goethestrasse 23, 6000 Frankfurt am Main
(0611) 29 00 31 Telex 4 13188

Munich
Weatherall Green & Smith Gmbh & Co. K.G.
Promenadeplatz 10 8000 Munich 2
(089) 22 27 17 Telex 5 22616

The Largest U.K. Pension Funds

1. For the six largest pension funds we include estimates of the capital value at end March 1981 as well as the latest value shown on the accounts.
2. Certain figures relate to the total of several funds within a group; such cases have a figure e.g. (2) shown after the name to indicate the number of funds involved.
3. Certain figures are estimates not necessarily supplied by the fund.
4. Full names of each company or fund can be found in the main part of the book.

£ Million	
3,200.0	Post Office (Est.) (latest accounts 2,742.0)
2,650.0	National Coal Board (2) (Est.) (latest accounts 2,367.4)
1,850.0	British Rail (2) (Est.) (latest accounts 1,667.8)
1,550.0	Electricity Supply (2) (Est.) (latest accounts 1,385.1)
1,100.0	British Steel (2) (Est.) (latest accounts 964.0)
1,050.0	I.C.I. (2) (Est.) (latest accounts 951.5)
763.3	Barclays Bank
751.0	Airways
743.1	British Petroleum (2)
716.0	British Gas (2)
641.9	National Westminster Bank
622.9	Universities Superannuation Scheme
615.0	Imperial Group
604.0	Shell
521.0	Unilever
486.2	Lloyds Bank
475.0	Merchant Navy (2)
368.0	Greater London Council
360.0	British Broadcasting Corporation
352.0	Midland Bank
347.8	National Water Council
332.2	Ford Motor Company (2)
320.0	British Leyland (2)
312.1	Prudential
305.0	West Midlands County Council
303.4	Lucas Industries (2)
300.0	G.E.C.
299.4	Greater Manchester Council
294.0	U.K.A.E.A.
270.0	Strathclyde Regional Council
256.1	Allied Breweries
250.0	Reed Group (2)
245.5	Vauxhall
245.2	Rolls-Royce Ltd. (2)
229.9	Philips
218.6	London Transport (2)
213.5	Civil Aviation Authority
210.0	British Aerospace
204.0	Courtaulds
201.2	Bank of England
197.0	West Yorks Metropolitan County Council
186.0	Sun Alliance
183.6	Thorn
182.7	Grand Metropolitan (2)
174.1	Merseyside County Council
170.8	Tube Investments
165.0	Esso Petroleum Co.
164.5	Commercial Union
150.8	Distillers
149.8	Barclays Bank International
149.5	Dunlop
141.4	Royal Insurance
140.0	B.O.C.
138.0	I.B.M.
135.1	Tyne & Wear County Council
134.3	Hampshire County Council
132.9	South of Scotland Electricity Board

INDUCING THE CHAIRMAN TO FACE THE SHAREHOLDERS

Have you ever wished you had taken Independent Professional Advice?

Debenham Tewson & Chinnocks
Chartered Surveyors

Bancroft House Paternoster Square London EC4P 4ET
01-236 1520

44 Brook Street London W1Y 1YB
01-408 1161

3 Castle Street Cardiff CF1 2RJ
0222-398182

Brussels Bahrain Hamburg New York Sydney

Largest UK Pension Funds

£ Million		£ Million	
127.7	South Yorks County Council	67.9	Bass
126.0	Boots	67.9	Rank Xerox
126.0	Lancashire County Council	67.3	Surrey County Council
124.7	Cadbury Schweppes	66.9	Sainsbury
122.7	Metal Box	65.9	Massey Ferguson (3)
121.5	Marks & Spencer	64.1	Northern Engineering Industries
118.0	Plessey Co.	63.4	Babcock International (2)
117.4	National Freight Corporation (2)	63.4	Smiths Industries
115.1	B.I.C.C.	63.2	Glaxo
115.0	National Bus Company	63.0	Rowntree Mackintosh
113.6	Kent County Council	62.2	Devonshire County Council
109.7	P. & O. (2)	62.0	Williams & Glyn's Bank
107.4	Essex County Council	60.0	John Lewis
107.1	Trustee Savings Bank	59.6	Leicestershire County Council
106.0	Guardian Royal Exchange Assurance	58.0	Reckitt & Colman
106.0	Ocean Nestor	56.7	Ciba-Geigy
105.1	Pearl Assurance	55.7	Norfolk County Council
104.9	I.C.L.	54.4	Rio Tinto Zinc
103.3	Lothian Regional Council	53.8	British Airports Authority
102.2	Bank of Scotland	53.4	Woolworth
102.0	Co-operative Wholesale Society	53.2	Northern Ireland Electricity
101.6	Coats Paton	52.7	George Wimpey (3)
101.1	D.R.G. (Dickinson Robinson)	52.3	Carreras
101.0	Avon County Council	52.2	I.M.I. (Imperial Metals)
101.0	Burmah Oil Company	52.0	Berkshire County Council
100.0	General Accident Fire & Life Assurance Corp.	52.0	Halifax Building Society
		51.3	N.C.R.
100.0	Rank Hovis McDougall (2)	50.5	Dorset County Council
92.5	Kodak	50.2	Chloride
92.5	Tate & Lyle	50.0	Associated Engineering
91.2	Royal Bank of Scotland	49.9	Unigate (2)
90.0	Mars	48.2	Port of London Authority
89.4	Whitbread	48.1	Grampian Regional Council
88.8	Pilkington Brothers (4)	48.0	Scottish & Newcastle
86.7	Durham County Council	47.0	British American Tobacco (2)
86.3	Associated British Foods	46.4	Alcan
85.9	Hoover	46.0	John Laing
84.0	Staffordshire County Council	45.3	West Sussex County Council
83.5	Gallagher	44.7	Westland Aircraft (2)
81.8	Port Employers & Dock Workers (2)	44.5	Refuge Assurance Co.
81.0	Fisons	44.5	Trafalgar House
80.3	Cheshire County Council	43.8	Wiggins Teape
80.0	East Sussex County Council	43.3	Gwent County Council
80.0	Northern Ireland Local Government Officers	43.1	Lloyds Bank International
		42.8	United Biscuits
79.8	Standard Telephones & Cables	42.7	North Yorkshire County Council
79.8	Turner & Newall	42.6	North Scotland Hydro-Electric Board
79.3	Co-operative Insurance Society	42.5	Liverpool Victoria Friendly Society (2)
78.5	Humberside County Council	42.2	B.P.B. Industries (2)
77.8	Harmsworth (Associated Newspapers)	42.2	Cambridgeshire County Council
77.0	Michelin (2)	42.2	Spillers
76.7	Blue Circle (Associated Cement) (2)	42.0	Bowater
76.3	Cables & Wireless	41.5	Hereford & Worcester County Council
74.2	Hertfordshire County Council	41.0	Warwickshire County Council
73.7	Wellcome Foundation	40.7	Heinz
73.0	E.M.I.	40.4	Johnson Matthey (3)
72.9	Derbyshire County Council	40.0	Cavenham
72.0	Talbot	40.0	Lincolnshire County Council
70.0	Mid-Glamorgan County Council	40.0	Nestle
70.0	W. H. Smith	39.9	I.T.B.
69.0	Cleveland County Council	38.7	Cumbria County Council
68.0	Norwich Union	38.5	British Printing Corporation (2)

Largest UK Pension Funds

£ Million

38.4	Molins
38.4	Somerset County Council
38.3	Buckinghamshire County Council
38.0	Bedfordshire County Council
38.0	Clydesdale Bank
38.0	Furness Withy (2)
37.2	Powell Duffryn (3)
37.0	Electricity Supply (Eire)
37.0	J. Lyons
36.7	Mobil
35.6	Associated Octel
35.6	Northern Bank (2)
35.2	Thompson Organisation
35.0	West Glamorgan County Council
34.5	South Glamorgan County Council
34.4	Albright & Wilson
34.0	Booker
34.0	Bowring Group
34.0	Social Workers
33.8	Suffolk County Council
33.6	Westminster Press
33.5	Ferranti
32.7	Inco Europe
32.6	C & J Clark
32.5	Associated Biscuit Manufacturers
32.3	Simon Engineering (2)
32.2	University of London (SAUL)
32.0	Thomas Tilling
31.7	Rolls-Royce Motors
31.7	Shropshire County Council
31.4	Proctor & Gamble (2)
31.1	Brooke Bond Liebig
30.9	Royal London Mutual Insurance
30.0	British Council
30.0	Fife Regional Council
30.0	Laporte Industries (Est.)
30.0	Northamptonshire County Council
30.0	United Glass (3)
29.5	Cornwall County Council
29.4	B.B.A.
29.0	Clwyd County Council
29.0	Tarmac
28.8	Hill Samuel
28.0	U.B.M.
28.0	Union International
27.9	Littlewoods
27.9	Northumberland County Council
27.8	Pilots National
27.8	Texaco
27.8	Tootal
27.0	Wiltshire County Council
26.9	Dowty Group
26.9	Honeywell (4)
26.9	Monsanto
26.8	Associated Communications
26.8	Yorkshire Bank (2)
26.6	British Sugar
26.5	Debenham
26.3	British Transport Dock Board (2)
26.2	Grindlays Bank (2)
25.9	London Borough of Newham
25.9	States of Jersey

£ Million

25.1	Central Regional Council
25.0	USMC (2)
24.9	Abbey National Building Society
24.9	Birmid Qualcast
24.9	London Borough of Wandsworth
24.6	NAAFI
24.6	Royal Liver Friendly Society
24.3	Phoenix Assurance
24.2	Gillette U.K.
24.0	Baker Perkins Holdings
24.0	Bovis
23.9	London Borough of Lewisham
23.5	London Borough of Tower Hamlets
23.3	British Home Stores
22.9	Chubb & Son
22.6	Standard Life Assurance Co.
22.5	J. Bibby & Sons (2)
22.4	Burton Group
22.1	Harrods (2)
22.1	London Borough of Barnet
22.1	London & Manchester Group
22.0	British Caledonian
22.0	Stone Platt
21.6	London Borough of Hammersmith & Fulham
21.4	Gestetners
21.4	Scottish Transport
21.1	Johnson & Firth Brown
21.1	London Borough of Haringey
21.0	P.A. Management Consultants
20.9	House of Fraser (3)
20.9	Solicitors Staff
20.9	Wilmot Breedon
20.8	Nationwide Building Society
20.6	Friends' Provident Life Office
20.5	United Dominion Trust
20.4	Norcross
20.4	The 600 Group (2)
20.4	Union Castle Line
20.1	London Borough of Ealing
20.1	London Borough of Islington
19.8	3M United Kingdom
19.6	Haden Carrier (2)
19.1	Tioxide International Ltd.
19.0	Milk Marketing Board
19.0	Sun Life
18.9	Sanaco (Smith & Nephew)
18.8	Petrofina
18.7	Clerical Medical & General Life Assurance Society
18.6	Baring Brothers & Co.
18.3	Lex Service Group
18.0	Thomas Cook
18.0	John Holt
18.0	Transport & General Workers Union
17.8	Portals Group
17.7	Calor Group
17.7	Corporation of Lloyd's
17.5	Northern Foods
17.4	Duport (2)
17.4	Trusthouse Forte
17.3	Reuters

Largest UK Pension Funds

£ Million

17.2	Costain Group
17.1	Sperry Rand
17.0	Hambros Bank
16.9	Charterhouse Group
16.9	Electronic Rentals
16.8	Croda International
16.6	Charter Consolidated
16.5	APV Holdings
16.5	London Borough of Hounslow
16.5	Ransome Hoffmann Pollard
16.2	Doulton & Co.
16.2	London Borough of Bexley
16.0	Kenning Motor Group
15.6	Fitch Lovell
15.4	Equity & Law
15.4	Scottish Amicable Life Assurance Society Ltd.
15.3	Rockware Group
15.3	Provincial Insurance Company
15.2	Rubery Owen
15.2	Scottish Agricultural Industries (2)
15.1	BXL Plastics
15.1	Gulf U.K.
15.0	Berec (U.K.)
15.0	British Enkalon
15.0	Lilly Industries Ltd.
15.0	Sir Robert McAlpine & Sons Ltd.
15.0	Price Waterhouse
15.0	Scottish Widows' Fund & Life Assurance Society
14.8	London Borough of Bromley
14.8	Federated Pension Schemes
14.8	Guardian & Manchester Evening News
14.7	Caterpillar Tractor Co. Ltd.
14.5	Lloyds
14.5	May & Baker Ltd.
14.3	London Borough of Redbridge
14.2	International Harvester Co. of Great Britain
14.0	National Federation of Building Trades Employees
14.0	University of Cambridge
13.9	Pegler-Hattersley (2)
13.4	Coutts & Co.
13.4	Kleinwort Benson
13.0	Manchester Ship Canal
12.8	Sir Alfred McAlpine & Son Ltd.
12.7	Avon Rubber Co. Ltd.
12.6	Royal Arsenal Co-operative Society Ltd.
12.6	Stewart Wrightson
12.5	Dalgety
12.4	Borg-Warner
12.4	Commonwealth Dev. Corporation
12.3	Serck
12.3	Wilkinson Match (3)
12.2	Electrolux (2)

£ Million

12.1	Dupont
12.0	New Towns
11.8	London Borough of Harrow
11.8	J. Henry Schroder Wagg & Co.
11.7	Dumfries & Galloway Regional Council
11.5	Ackroyd & Smithers
11.5	Cummins Engine Company
11.5	International Timber (2)
11.5	Hiram Walker & Sons (Scotland) Ltd.
11.5	Thos. W. Ward
11.4	Isle of Wight County Council
11.3	General & Municipal Workers' Pension Trustee Co. Ltd.
11.3	Royal London Borough of Kingston-upon-Thames
11.3	Sterling-Winthrop Group
11.2	Goodyear Tyre & Rubber Co. (G.B.) Ltd.
11.2	Lindustries
11.1	North Eastern Co-operative Society
11.1	Tozer, Kemsley & Millbourn (Holdings) Ltd.
11.0	London Borough of Sutton
11.0	Peat Marwick Mitchell & Co.
11.0	Zurich Insurance
10.9	Guinness Peat Group
10.9	Samuel Montagu (3)
10.9	Redland (2)
10.8	Extel
10.8	London Borough of Richmond-upon-Thames
10.8	Trident Television Ltd.
10.7	W. S. Atkins & Partners
10.7	Bowmaker
10.6	Birmingham Co-operative Society
10.6	Cornhill Insurance
10.6	Ellerman Lines
10.5	Conoco – Continental Oil Co. Ltd.
10.5	Dunford & Elliot (3)
10.4	Cammell Laird Shipbuilders
10.4	Staveley Industries
10.3	Carlton Industries
10.3	St. Regis
10.2	Mersey Docks & Harbour Company
10.1	Smurfit
10.0	Beecham U.K.
10.0	BPM Holdings
10.0	Carborundum
10.0	Clayton Dewandre (3)
10.0	Cope Allman International
10.0	General Foods
10.0	Hepworth & Son
10.0	Mercury Securities
10.0	Minster Assets Ltd.
10.0	Nuclear Power Group
10.0	Scottish Special Housing Association

An Integrated Management Information System.

WOOD, MACKENZIE & CO. offer a range of computer based services for institutional investors using an ICL 2950 computer. These services cover the needs of a Pension Fund in the areas of Investment Accounting, Management Information and Performance Measurement. The firm does not, as a matter of policy, manage any institutional assets.

☐ **Pension Fund Service**
A specialist service to measure and compare the investment PERFORMANCE of Pension Funds. More than **600 FUNDS** with a total value in excess of **£20,000m.** presently use this service.

☐ **Investment Management Service**
A flexible system which supplies regular VALUATIONS of U.K. and international portfolios and provides sophisticated MANAGEMENT REPORTS. including detailed performance analysis.

☐ **Investment Accounting Service**
A comprehensive service which meets both the basic ACCOUNTING REQUIREMENTS and the MANAGEMENT REPORTING NEEDS of the Pension Fund Accountant.

☐ **Property Management Service**
A system which maintains RECORDS for the professional property investor providing regular desk VALUATIONS and other reports similar in concept to the Investment Management Service.

THE KEY FEATURE OF THE SERVICES IS THE BENEFIT OF TOTAL INTEGRATION. Data supplied by users of the Investment Accounting System provides the necessary input for both the Investment Management Service and the Pension Fund Service.

For further information, including comprehensive explanatory booklets, please contact Dugald Eadie, Ian Hogg or Pat Harkin at the Edinburgh address below.

WOOD, MACKENZIE & CO.
MEMBERS OF THE STOCK EXCHANGE

London: 62-63 Threadneedle Street, London EC2R 8HP. Tel: (01) 600 3600.

Edinburgh: Erskine House, 68-73 Queen Street, Edinburgh EH2 4NS. Tel: (031) 225 8525.

The Major UK Pension Funds

This section of the book contains information on practically all the major UK Pension Funds. It includes details of almost all companies and organisations with over 500 UK employees, as well as some specialist pension schemes not related to purely one employer. Certain smaller schemes are included which are self administered and have assets of over £2 million

The minimum information for all entries consists of the name, address and telephone number of the organisation or company and the name of the company secretary or the person specifically responsable for pension matters. The majority of the major funds have supplied substantially more information and in some cases extra information has been received from other sources.
It should be noted however that many companies with less than 2,000 employees are either insured or have only partly contracted out and therefore the information available is by nature very limited.

AA PENSION FUND TRUSTEES

Fanum House, Basingstoke, Hampshire RG21 2EA
Telephone: 0256-20123

Pensions Manager E.G.Jones

A.A.F.LTD.

Bassington Industrial Estate, Cramlington, Northumberland NE23 8AF
Telephone: 067071-3477

Managing Director W.T.Cosby

Insured with Prudential Assurance Co.Ltd.

Company Employees 550

A.A.H. LTD STAFF PENSION SCHEME

21-24 Bury Street, London SW1Y 6AP
Telephone: 01-839 6131

Secretary W.D.D.Allen, ACIS

Insured with Guardian Royal Exchange Assurance Group

Pension Fund Consultants Godwins Ltd

Auditors Coopers & Lybrand

Company Employees 4,677

Members (at 6.4.80) 935

Pensioners 385

Annual Contributions £1,250,000

AARONSON BROTHERS LTD

Aro House, 18/9 Long Lane, London EC1A 0NT
Telephone: 01-606 8050

Secretary P.J.Wright

Investment Advisers & Stockbrokers Cazenove & Co.

Company Employees 1,131

A.B. ELECTRONIC PRODUCTS GROUP LTD

Abercynon, Mid Glamorgan CF45 4SF
Telephone: 0443-740331

Secretary H.R.Heaven,FCIS

Pension Fund Consultants Noble Lowndes & Partners Ltd

Employees 2,083

Annual Contributions £250,000

ABBEY HOMESTEADS (GROUP) LTD. PENSION & LIFE ASSURANCE SCHEME

Star House, Mutton Lane, Potters Bar, Herts.EN6 2PE
Telephone: 51266

Pension Fund Manager & Secretary R.E.R.Risdon

Directors K.Flynn (Chairman), D.A.Wilson, J.M.Crossman, E.A.Cole

Trustees Abbey Homesteads Pension Fund Ltd

Insured with Norwich Union Life Insurance Society

Pension Fund Consultants John R.Poel & Co.Ltd.

Auditors Ernst & Whinney

Company Employees 700

Members 130

ABBEY LIFE STAFF PENSION SCHEME AND FIELD MANAGEMENT PENSION SCHEME

Abbey Life House, PO Box 33,
80 Holdenhurst Road, Bournemouth BH8 8AL
Telephone: 0202-292373

Secretary to the Trustees A.J.Goodman, FCII, APMI

Trustees Staff Scheme: J.H.Mawhinney, C.J.Baker, Mrs.M.J.Amos
Field Management Scheme: J.H.Mawhinney, C.J.Baker, B.M.Backhouse

Field Management Scheme Insured with Abbey Life Assurance Co.Ltd.

Investment Advisers Abbey Life Investment Services

Actuary N.H.Carpenter, FIA,ASA

Auditors Ernst & Whinney

Company Employees 1,730

	Field	Staff
Active Members	151	1,466
Paid-up Members	31	357
Pensioners	2	7
	£000	£000
Annual Contributions	305	817
Annual Investment Income	-	362
Annual Outflow	58	123
Capital Value	1,260	4,966
Summary of Investments		
Equities	-	1,815
Fixed Interest	-	1,253
Property	-	1,531
Cash & Deposits	-	342
Others	-	25

THE ABBEY NATIONAL AMALGAMATED PENSION FUND

Abbey House, Baker Street, London NW1 6XL
Telephone: 01-486 5555

Secretary C.E.I.Thornton

Investment Manager H.J.Cook

Trustees The Abbey National Pension Fund Trustee Co

Part (12%)Managed by Legal & General (Pensions Management) Ltd

Actuaries R.Watson & Sons

Auditors Dearden, Farrow, Deloitte, Haskins & Sells

Company Employees 7,000

Members 3,485

Pensioners 386

Capital Value £24,850,000

ABBOTT LABORATORIES LTD

Queenborough, Kent ME11 5FL
Telephone: 07956-3371

Secretary L.R.Lee

Employees 642

ABERDEEN CONSTRUCTION GROUP LTD RETIREMENT BENEFITS SCHEME

Angusfield Lane, Aberdeen AB9 1QX
Telephone: 0224-323563

Secretary A.Chapman

Insured with Scottish Widows' Fund and Life Assurance Society

Pension Fund Consultants James M. MacAlaster & Alison Ltd

Auditors Arthur Young McClelland Moores & Co.

Employees 3,437

Members 455

Pensioners 150

Annual Contributions £330,000

Capital Value £2,665,000

ABERGLEN CONSTRUCTION

Balmoral Road, Aberdeen AB9 2LZ
Telephone: 0224-574416

Director J.S.Milne

Employees 720

ABERTHAW & BRISTOL CHANNEL PORTLAND CEMENT CO LTD

Beynon House, Mount Stuart Square, Cardiff, South Glamorgan CF1 6DR
Telephone: 0222-29431

Secretary B.G.Barry,FCA

Employees 857

ACE BELMONT INTERNATIONAL LTD RETIREMENT BENEFIT SCEME

Swinemoor Lane, Beverley, North Humberside
Telephone: 0482-862976

Secretary D.Gladwin

Trustees C.A.Macdonald, F.J.Hibbs, D.Gladwin

Insured with National Provident Institution

Employees 1,000

Members 166

Annual Contributions £75,000

ACROW LTD

8 South Wharf, London W2 1PB
Telephone: 01-262 3456

Secretary N.R.Sullivan

Insured with Scottish Widows' Fund & Life Assurance Society

Employees 6,872

A.D. INTERNATIONAL PENSION FUND

26/40 Broadwick Street, London W1A 2AD
Telephone: 01-734 7801

Secretary R.B.E.Ingham, MA, FCA

Benefits & Pensions Manager R.A.F.White

Stockbrokers & Investment Advisers Phillips & Drew

Actuaries R. Watson & Sons

Pension Fund Consultants Noble Lowndes & Partners Ltd

A.D. INTERNATIONAL PENSION FUND Continued

Auditors Price Waterhouse & Co.
Members 1,244
Pensioners 528

	£000
Annual Contributions	400
Annual Investment Income	411
Gross Annual Outflow	335
Capital Value	7,406
Summary of Investments	
Equities	4,000
Fixed Interest	250
Property	500
Cash & Deposits	250
Others	500

ADAMS & GIBBON LTD.

69-93 Westmorland Road, Newcastle,
Tyne & Wear NE1 4HE
Telephone: 0632-28281

Managing Director P.C.Gibbon

Secretary A.T.Fraser,FCA

Employees 576

ADAMS FOODS LTD. PENSION & ASSURANCE SCHEME

Buxton Road, Leek, Staffs.ST13 6EN
Telephone: 0538-385111

Pension Fund Manager & Secretary D.H.Clarke

Company Secretary J.M.Paterson

Trustees A.Boardman, M.Wood, C.E.Woodward, D.H.Clarke

Insured with Legal & General Assurance Society Ltd

Pension Fund Consultants Professional Assurance Services

Auditors Peat, Marwick, Mitchell & Co.

Employees 2,290

Members 735

Annual Contributions £414,000

Capital Value £1,000,000

ADAMSON BUTTERLEY LTD

Horsehay Works, Telford, Salop TF4 3PU
Telephone: 0952-505881

Managing Director C.F.Griffiths

Employees 1,100

ADCOCK-SHIPLEY DIVISION OF TEXTRON LTD

PO Box 22, Forest Road, Leicester LE5 0FJ
Telephone: 0533-531122

Director A.J.Aldridge

Employees 970

ADDIS LTD & ASSOCIATED COMPANIES 1972 STAFF PENSION & ASSURANCE SCHEME

The Brushworks, Ware Road, Hertford,
Herts SG13 7HL
Telephone: 0992-54221

Secretary D.M.Craik,FCIS

Trustees R.Addis,OBE, R.Addis,Jnr., D.M.Craik

Managed by Eagle Pension Funds Ltd

Auditors Shipley Blackburn

Company Employees 1,800

Members 1,100

Pensioners 200

ADRIA LTD

Strabane, Co Tyrone, Northern Ireland
Telephone: 0504-882568

Secretary T.A.Dunbar

Employees 1,200

ADVANCE CLEANING (LONDON) LTD

11 Frogmore, Wandsworth Park,
London SW18 1HW
Telephone: 01-874 0494

Director L.P.Cummins

Employees 500

ADVANCE LAUNDRIES LTD.

77-83 Upper Richmond Road, Putney,
London SW15 2TD
Telephone: 01-789 8231

Secretary J.A.M.Milner,FCIS

Employees 3,283

ADWEST GROUP PENSION AND ASSURANCE PLAN

The Aerodrome, Reading, Berks RG5 4SN
Telephone: 0734-692351

Pension Fund Manager S.Spencer

Trustees F.V.Waller, S.M.Harley, R.A.Waldron

Part Managed by Friends' Provident Managed Pension Fund

Investment Advisers Warburg Investment Management Ltd.

Stockbrokers Carr-Sebag

Actuaries Clay & Partners

Pension Fund Consultants Metropolitan Pensions Association Ltd

Auditors Peat,Marwick,Mitchell & Co.

Employees 4,000

Members 1,500

Pensioners 580

	£000
Annual Contributions (at 31.10.79)	837
Annual Investment Income	71
Annual Outflow	336
Capital Value	3,135
Summary of Investments	
Equities	670
Fixed Interest	468
Cash & Deposits	619
Managed Fund	1,378

A E G-TELEFUNKEN (UK) LTD
217 Bath Road, Slough, Berkshire SL1 4AW
Telephone: 0735-872101

Secretary F.Simpkin

Employees 525

AER LINGUS
Aer Lingus House, 52 Poland Street,
London W1V 4AA
Telephone: 01-437 8000

Executive C.P.McGrath

Employees 6,000

AERO NEEDLES GROUP LTD
Clive Works, Redditch, Worcs B97 6HB
Telephone: 0527-67771

Secretary H.R.Egerton,FCA

Managed by Legal & General (Pensions Management) Ltd

Employees 786

AERO ZIPP FASTENERS LTD
Unit 3, Waltham Forest Trading Estate,
Black Horse Lane, London E17
Telephone: 01-531 8231

Employees 1,300

AEROQUIP (UK) LTD
Studley Road, Redditch, Worcs.B98 7HQ

Managing Director D.T.McKone

Employees 1,388

AGAHEAT APPLIANCES
PO Box No 4, Grahams Road, Falkirk FK2 7BG
Telephone: 0324-24101

Employees 900

A G B RESEARCH LTD RETIREMENT BENEFITS SCHEME
76 Shoe Lane, London EC4A 3JB
Telephone: 01-353 3172

Secretary D.A.G.Elyan,MA,FCIS

Trustees D.M.Wharrie,FCA, D.A.G.Elyan,MA,FCIS, Noble Lowndes Pensions Ltd.

Investment Advisers Morgan Grenfell & Co.Ltd., Drayton Montagu Portfolio Management Ltd.

Stockbrokers Grenfell & Colegrave

Actuaries Bacon & Woodrow

Pension Fund Consultants Noble Lowndes Pensions Ltd.

Auditors Ernst & Whinney

Company Employees 1,800

Members 995

Pensioners 6

	£000
Annual Contributions	350
Annual Investment Income	150
Capital Value	2,050

Summary of Investments

Equities	1,250
Fixed Interest	500
Property	150
Cash & Deposits	150

AGFA-GEVAERT LTD
27 Great West Road, Brentford, Middlesex
Telephone: 01-560 2131

Secretary J.S.Stabler

Managed by Scottish Amicable Pensions Investments Ltd

Pension Fund Consultants Godwins Ltd

Employees 847

AGRICULTURAL HOLDINGS LTD
Agrihold House, 40 Warton Road, Stratford,
London E15 2JU
Telephone: 01-555 9407

Secretary D.J.Green

Employees 1,097

AIR CALL LTD PENSION SCHEME
Air Call House, 105-111 High Street,
Houghton Regis, Dunstable, Beds.LU5 5EL
Telephone: 0582-64191

Secretary R.F.Pipe

Insured with Norwich Union Insurance Society

Company Employees 1,381

Members 150

Annual Contributions £46,000

AIR HOLDINGS LTD 1958 PENSION SCHEME
Pensions Department, Cayzer House,
2 & 4 St.Mary Axe, London EC3A 8BP
Telephone: 01-283 4343

Pension Fund Manager & Secretary R.L.Hanney, APMI

Assistant Secretary I.G.Cochrane

Trustees K.W.Donald, R.L.Hanney, The Cayzer Trust Co.Ltd.

Insured with The Prudential Assurance Co.Ltd.

Pension Fund Consultants Metropolitan Pensions Association Ltd.

Auditors Deloitte,Haskins & Sells

Company Employees (U.K.) 3,000

Members 1,544

Pensioners 350

Annual Contributions £885,500

AIR PRODUCTS LTD
Coombe House, St George's Square, New Malden, Surrey KT3 4HH
Telephone: 01-942 2424

Secretary D.C.Head

Employees 2,191

AIRFIX RETIREMENT PLAN
17 Old Court Place, London W8 4QF
Telephone: 01-937 3175

Secretary J.H.Morris, FCA

AIRFIX Continued

Trustees Dr.F.D.Norburn, R.R.M.Ehrmann, J.H.Morris

Investment Advisers Warburg Investment Management Ltd

Stockbrokers W. Greenwell & Co

Actuaries Duncan C. Fraser & Co

Employees 2,739

Members 412

Pensioners 47

AIRFLOW STREAMLINES LTD
Main Road, Far Cotton, Northampton NN4 9ES
Telephone: 0604 62261

Secretary R.G.Cartmale

Insured with Commercial Union Assurance Co Ltd

Employees 655

AIRSPRUNG GROUP LTD
Canal Road Industrial Estate, Ladydown, Trowbridge, Wiltshire BA14 8RQ
Telephone: 02214-1411

Secretary B.M.Netley,FCA

Insured with Standard Life Assurance Co

Employees 929

AIRWAYS PENSION SCHEME
Kershaw House, Great West Road, Hounslow, Middlesex TW5 0BX
Telephone: 01-570 7741

Secretary and General Manager Michael J.Kerr, FCA, APMI, MBIM

Financial Controller N.P.Hore,ACMA

Deputy General Manager G.Burwood, ACIS

Investment Manager D.G.Wildsmith,ASIA

Pension Administration Manager Mrs.E.E.Wigley, APMI

Manager, Property Dept H.E.Boone, ARICS

Senior Solicitor D.G.Lindsay,MA,APMI

Trustees (at 1.0.80) R.A.Spencer,FCCA,FBCS,MBIM, FCIT (Chairman), C.R.Moss,BA,FCA (Deputy Chairman), G.S.Bell,MIPM, Captain T.H.Dockerill, FCA, L.J.Fitch,MISM,AMRAes, G.J.Fowler, R.A.Hart, FCA, I.T.Leader,FCA, J.A.McWatt, Captain T.Nisbet, OBE,DFC,MIBS, J.Smith,BSc,FIPM, D.White

Economic Adviser J.P.A.Readman,MA,MBA

Bankers British Linen Bank Ltd.

Stock Exchange Advisers J.B.Alexander, BA, J.A.B.Keeling, DFC, MA, FCA, E.M.P.Welman

Stockbrokers Laing & Cruickshank

Property Advisers Jones Lang Wootton (N.E.H.Taylor,FRICS)

Actuaries R.Watson & Sons

Auditors Ernst & Whinney

Company Employees (British Airways) (at 31.3.80) 50,854

Members 49,218

Pensioners 12,994

Deferred Pensioners 3,326

	£ million
Annual Contributions	80.7
Annual Investment Income	56.4
Annual Outflow	42.6
Capital Value	751.0
Book Value	596.0
Market Value	726.1

Summary of Investments (Market Value)

Equities	334.0
Fixed Interest	110.1
Property	266.1
Cash & Deposits	13.1
Other	2.8

AKROYD & SMITHERS PENSION TRUSTEE LTD.
Austin Friars House, 2-6 Austin Friars, London EC2N 2EE
Telephone: 01-588 4535

Secretary P.J.Wastall,FCIS,AIB,APMI

Trustees Akroyd & Smithers Pension Trustee Ltd.

Investment Advisers Touche,Remnant & Co.

Actuaries Bacon & Woodrow

Auditors Thomson McLintock & Co.

Company Employees Approx.400

Members Approx.400

Pensioners 75

Annual Contributions £470,000

Special Contribution 1980 £2.5 million

Capital Value £11.5 million

AKZO CHEMIE UK LTD PENSION SCHEME
12-14 St.Ann's Crescent, Wandsworth, London SW18 2LS
Telephone: 01-874 7761

Pension Fund Manager & Secretary H.S.C.Fuggle, BSc,MBIM

Trustees Dr.E.M.Hunt, I.E.S.Butler, C.H.Stoor, R.L.C.H. van Embden

Part Insured with Crusader Insurance Co Ltd

Part Managed by Crusader Insurance Co.Ltd; Prudential Pensions Ltd.

Pension Fund Consultants H.Clarkson (Life & Pension Consultants) Ltd.

Auditors Price Waterhouse & Co.

Company Employees 732

Members 605

Pensioners 147

Annual Contributions £480,000

ALADDIN INDUSTRIES LTD RETIREMENT BENEFITS PLAN
Holland House, 6 Church Street, Isleworth, Middlesex TW7 6BG
Telephone: 01-568 6711

Company Secretary M.Speller, FCIS

ALADDIN INDUSTRIES LTD Continued

Pension Fund Consultants H.Clarkson (Life & Pensions Consultants) Ltd
Auditors Arthur Andersen & Co
Company Employees 559
Members 341
Pensioners 141
Annual Contributions £150,000

ALANGATE GROUP OF COMPANIES
6 Great Queen Street, London WC2B 5DG
Telephone: 01-405 7201
Director J.A.Perriam
Employees 500

ALBRIGHT & WILSON LTD. GROUP STAFF SUPERANNUATION FUND & WORKS PENSION FUND
1 Knighsbridge Green, London SW1X 7QD
Telephone: 01-589 6393
Pension Fund Manager W.Screen, APMI
Staff Pension Officer Miss P.Whitehorn
Investment Manager P.W.Clements
Trustees Albright & Wilson Staff Pension Trustees Ltd., Albright & Wilson Works Pension Trustees Ltd.
Property Advisers Gerald Eve & Co
Auditors Peat Marwick Mitchell & Co
Company Employees 6,500
Members 5,888
Pensioners 3,077
Capital Value (1979)£34.4 million

ALCAN ALUMINIUM (UK) LTD. RETIREMENT INCOME & LIFE ASSURANCE PLAN (1972)
Administration Alcan House, South Bar, Banbury, Oxon.OX16 9XJ
Telephone: 0295-4545
Registered Office Alcan House, 30 Berkeley Square, London w1X 6DP
Pensions Manager T.D.Williams, APMI
Company Secretary R.H.A.Forbes
Actuarial Adviser R.B.Provost
Trustees Alcan Pension Trustees Ltd.
Group Pensions Adviser J.W.E.Johnson,CA
Investment Managers County Bank Ltd and N.M.Rothschild Asset Management Ltd
Stockbrokers Phillips & Drew
Pension Fund Consultants Metropolitan Pensions Association Ltd.
Auditors Price Waterhouse & Co
Company Employees 8,300
Members 8,138
Pensioners 2,607

	£000
Annual Contributions	7,844
Annual Investment Income	4,140
Annual Outflow	4,474
Capital Value	46,417
Summary of Investments	
UK Equities	24,177
Fixed Interest	10,870
Property	2,803
Cash & Deposits	3,628
Overseas Equities	4,939

ALCOA OF GREAT BRITAIN LTD PENSION SCHEMES
Alcoa House, PO Box 15, Droitwich, Worcs.WR9 7BG
Telephone: 09057-3411
Pensions Manager Mrs M.B.Steward
Secretary E.A.Jackson
Investment Advisers Robert Fleming Investment Management Ltd
Actuaries R.Watson & Sons
Auditors Coopers & Lybrand
Company Employees 1,800
Members 1,800
Pensioners 350

	£million
Annual Contributions	1.6
Annual Investment Income	0.7
Capital Value	9.2
Summary of Investments	
Equities	5.1
Fixed Interest	2.5
Property Unit Trusts	1.4
Cash & Deposits	0.2

ALENCO INDUSTRIAL COMPONENTS LTD
Belmont Road, Maidenhead, Berkshire SL6 6JP
Telephone: 0628-23423
Director J.I.Bell
Trustees Alenco Pension Trustees Ltd
Employees 1,000

ALEXANDRAS OVERALLS HOLDINGS LTD
Alexandras House, King Square, Bristol, Avon BS2 8ET
Director P.M.Davies
Employees 700

WALTER ALEXANDER LTD
24 St Vincent Place, Glasgow G1 2HQ
Telephone: 041-221 0396,
Secretary J.W.Jarvie & Co
Managed by Scottish Amicable Pensions Investments Ltd
Employees 1,752

ALEXANDERS DISCOUNT (PENSION FUND) LTD

1 St.Swithin's Lane, London EC4N 8DN
Telephone: 01-626 5467

Trustee & Secretary G.K.Piercy

ALEXANDERS HOLDINGS LTD

185 St.Vincent Street, Glasgow G2 5PR
Telephone: 041-248 4523

Chairman J.B.T.Loudon

Insured with Scottish Life Assurance Co.

Employees 532

ALEXANDRA TOWING CO LTD

43 Castle Street, Liverpool L2 9TA
Telephone: 051-227 2151

Secretary G.Gilbert

Employees 1,095

ALFA-LAVAL CO LTD

Great West Road, Brentford, Middlesex TW8 9BT
Telephone: 01-560 1221

Secretary W.D.R.Humphreys

Insured with Legal & General Assurance Society Ltd

Employees 1,068

ALGINATE INDUSTRIES LTD

22 Henrietta Street, London WC2E 8NB
Telephone: 01-240 5161

Secretary G.Latham

Pension Administrator Mrs A.Davidson

Investment Advisers Robert Fleming Investment Management Ltd

Pension Fund Consultants Wyatt Harris Graham Ltd.

Employees 889

ALLAN-BRADLEY INTERNATIONAL LTD

Pauls Way, Bede Industrial Estate, Jarrow, Tyne and Wear NE32 3EN
Telephone: 0632-897771

Director G.J.H.Hutchings

Managed by Legal & General (Pensions Management) Ltd

Employees 1,117

ALLEBONE & SONS LTD

Oakley Road, Rushden, Northants NN10 9XU
Telephone: 09334-4331

Secretary J.J.Tilbrook

Employees 1,495

EDGAR ALLEN, BALFOUR LTD STAFF PENSION & LIFE ASSURANCE SCHEME AND 1978 RETIREMENT & LIFE ASSURANCE SCHEME

Nether Lane, Ecclesfield, Sheffield S30 3TR
Telephone: 0742-467100

Pensions & Insurance Manager D.Walker, FCIS

Insured with Clerical, Medical & General Life Assurance Society

Pension Fund Consultants Metropolitan Pensions Association Ltd.

Auditors Coopers & Lybrand

Company Employees 3,000

	Staff	Retirement
Members	807	1,940
Pensioners	250	150
Annual Contributions	£516,000	£325,000

See also Aurora Holdings Ltd. (Parent Company)

ALLIANCE BUILDING SOCIETY PENSION FUND

Alliance House, Hove Park, Hove, East Sussex BN3 7AZ
Telephone: 0273-775454

Trustee & Secretary R.A.M. Waters FCIS, FCBSI

Auditors Price Waterhouse & Co

Company Employees 1,800

Members 1,400

Pensioners 100

Annual Contributions £1,000,000

Capital Value £9,000,00 (Book Value)

ALLIED BREWERIES PENSION FUNDS

12 Denmark Street, Bristol BS1 5DG
Telephone: 0272-28882

Group Pensions Executive M.H.Oldfield, FPMI

Secretary M.R.Owen,ACIS,APMI

Pension Fund Manager B.S.MacMahon,FPMI

Trustees Allied Breweries Pension Trust Ltd.

Investment Advisers Charterhouse Japhet Ltd., Kleinwort Benson Ltd., Drayton Montagu Portfolio Management Ltd., Morgan Grenfell & Co.Ltd.

Property Advisers Debenham Tewson & Chinnocks; Fletcher King

Actuaries Bacon & Woodrow

Auditors Peat, Marwick, Mitchell and Co

Company Employees 73,000

Members (at 5.4.80) 65,000

Pensioners 14,000

	£000
Annual Contributions	32,170
Annual Investment Income	16,950
Annual Outflow	13,600
Capital Value	256,073
Summary of Investments	
Equities	83,808
Fixed Interest	62,769
Property	96,092
Cash & Deposits	13,404

ALLIED COLLOIDS PENSION FUND

Cleckheaton Road, Low Moor, Bradford BD12 0JZ
Telephone: 0274-671267

Pension Fund Manager & Secretary G.S.Senior

Investment Advisers James Capel & Co

Trustees R.Gill, G.Whitehurst, G.S.Senior

The Major UK Pension Funds **ALL/AME**

ALLIED COLLOIDS Continued

Stockbrokers James Capel & Co.
Actuaries Duncan C.Fraser & Co.
Auditors Dearden Farrow & Co.
Company Employees 884
Members 750
Pensioners 20

ALLIED FARM FOODS LTD
Imperial House, Victoria Street, Grimsby,
S.Humberside DN31 1ET
Telephone: 0472-592222

Secretary D.J.Councell

Employees 7,565

ALLIED INSULATORS LTD (A.I. INDUSTRIAL PRODUCTS LTD.)
PO Box 17, Milton, Stoke-on-Trent ST2 7EE
Telephone: 0782-534321

Secretary D.F.Summerfield, ACIS

Insured with Prudential Assurance Co Ltd

Employees 2,482

ALLIED LEATHER INDUSTRIES LTD GROUP PENSION PLAN
20-24 Tanfield Road, Croydon, Surrey CR0 1AL
Telephone: 01-686 2811

Secretary E.J.Gayler,CA

Employees 2,380

ALLIED PLANT GROUP LTD
79 Beverley Road, Hull HU3 1XR
Telephone: 0482-28052

Secretary R.Harrison, BSc,FCA

Employees 510

ALLIED POLYMER GROUP LTD.
See BTR Ltd.

ALLIED RETAILERS LTD
Allied House, Lombard Street,
West Bromwich B70 8RL
Telephone: 021-553 6771

Secretary G.Tennant

Employees 2,501

ALLIED TEXTILE COMPANIES LTD
High Burton, Huddersfield HD8 0QJ W.Yorks.
Telephone: 0484-4834

Secretary G.Wightman

Insured with Royal Insurance Co Ltd

Employees 2,145

ALLTRANSPORT INTERNATIONAL GROUP PENSION SCHEME
Walton House, Central Trading Estate, Staines,
Middx.TW18 4UX
Telephone: 51341

Director & Secretary R.A.Upsall

Trustees R.J.Wilson (Chairman), T.D.Kearnes,
R.J.McNamara, Miss V.C.McIntosh, J.C.Window

Investment Advisers and Stockbrokers Hoare Govett Ltd.

Actuary P.B.Eastwood,FIA

Auditors Moore, Stephens & Co.

Company Employees 750

Members 130

Pensioners 5

	£000
Annual Contributions	135
Annual Investment Income	120
Annual Outflow	40
Capital Value	1,000
Summary of Investments	
Equities	300
Fixed Interest	650
Cash & Deposits	50

ALPINE HOLDINGS LTD PENSION & LIFE ASSURANCE SCHEME
Alpine House, Honeypot Lane, London NW9 9RU
Telephone: 01-204 3393

Secretary R.J.Whitfield,LLB,ACIS

Assistant to Company Secretary I.Johnson,ACIS

Trustees R.J.Whitfield, D.G.C.Webster,
C.G.O.Onslow Mrs.P.Parr

Insured with Legal & General Assurance Society Ltd

Pension Fund Consultants C.T.Bowring & Layborn Ltd

Auditors Arthur Andersen & Co.

Solicitors Ashurst Morris Crisp & Co.

Employees 883

Members 170

Pensioners 5

Annual Contributions £100,000

ALPINE SOFT DRINKS LTD
Richmond Way, Chelmsley Wood,
Birmingham B37 7TT
Telephone: 021-770 6816

Secretary K.E.Price,FCA

Employees 1,738

ALUMASC LTD
Burton Latimer, Kettering NN15 5JP Northants.
Telephone: 053-672 2121

Director R.L.Whiting

Employees 1,050

ALUMINIUM WIRE & CABLE CO LTD
Registered Office & Wire Division, Port Tennant,
Swansea SA1 8PS
Telephone: 0792-52251

Director R.E.Utiger

Employees 900

ALUSUISSE (U.K.) LTD
97 Penn Road, Wolverhampton WV3 0DN
Chairman Sir Richard Powell
Employees 1,599

A M & S EUROPE LTD.
1 Redcliffe Street, Bristol, Avon BS99 7AE
BS99 7AE
Telephone: 0272-290421
Secretary R.A.J.Mackay
Employees 1,267

A.M.INTERNATIONAL INFORMATION SYSTEMS LTD
P.O.Box 17, Maylands Avenue, Hemel Hempstead, Herts.HP2 7ET
Telephone: 0442-2251
Company Secretary S.E.Kosnowski
Investment Advisers Warburg Investment Management Ltd.
Pension Fund Consultants Noble Lowndes & Partners Ltd.
Company Employees 2,397

AMALGAMATED METAL CORPORATION PENSION SCHEME AND GROUP WORKS PENSION SCHEME
Adelaide House, London Bridge, London EC4R 9DT
Telephone: 01-626 4521
Pensions Manager/Secretary K.E.Cunningham, FCIS, APMI
Company Secretary P.J.Norton,FCIS
Trustees A.M.R.Sylvester,G.G.H.Marriott, P.J.Norton, E.F.B.Nunns, V.H.Sher
Investment Advisers Morgan Grenfell & Co Ltd
Actuaries Hymans, Robertson & Co
Property Advisers Richard Ellis
Auditors Deloitte Haskins & Sells
Solicitors Sacker & Partners
Company Employees 1,339
Members (both schemes) 432
Pensioners 59
Annual Contributions £467,000
Annual Investment Income £480,000
Gross Annual Outflow £125,000
Capital Value £4,698,000

AMALGAMATED POWER ENGINEERING LTD
115 Colmore Row, Birmingham B3 3SA
Telephone: 021-236 7681
Secretary L.A.Leather
Insured with Legal & General Assurance Society Ltd
Employees 4,171

AMALGAMATED UNION OF ENGINEERING WORKERS
110 Peckham Road, London S.E.15
Telephone: 01-703 4231

Capital Value £3.5 million

AMARI STAFF PENSION & LIFE ASSURANCE PLAN
New Bond Street House, 1-5 New Bond Street, London W.1
Telephone: 01-493 9371
Secretary P.R.Bolitho
Insured with Crusader Insurance Co.
Pension Fund Consultants Godwins Ltd.
Auditors Dearden Farrow
Company Employees 821
Members 300

AMBER DAY HOLDINGS LTD
Amber Day House, 113 Redhill Street, London NW1 4BE
Telephone: 01-388 2621
Secretary D.S.Rose,LLB,ACA
Insured with National Provident Institution
Employees 1,895

AMERICAN CAN (UK) LTD (READS PENSION SCHEME)
Orrell Lane, Walton, Liverpool L9 8BW
Telephone: 051-525 3600
Secretary D.G.Sloan,ACIS
Investment Advisers Robert Fleming Investment Management Ltd.
Actuaries Clay & Partners
Auditors Coopers & Lybrand
Solicitors Simmons & Simmons
Company Employees/Members 1,700
Annual Contributions £1,046,000
Annual Investment Income £305,000
Capital Value (at 31.5.80) £3,765,000

AMERICAN EXPRESS PENSION PLAN FOR EMPLOYEES IN THE U.K. & EIRE
171-173, Preston Road, Brighton Sussex, BN1 6BX
Telephone: 0273-693555
Secretary D.T.Hall
Investment Advisers Warburg Investment Management Ltd
Actuarial Advice Obtained through Towers, Perrin, Forster & Crosby Inc.
Auditors Arthur Young McClelland Moore & Co.
Company Employees (Oct.1980) 3,114
Members 1,880
Pensioners 100

	£000
Annual Contributions	1,226
Annual Investment Income	438
Gross Annual Outflow	83
Capital Value (Market Value Sept.1980)	8,530

Summary of Investments

AMERICAN EXPRESS Continued

Equities	5,947
Fixed Interest	1,820
Cash & Deposits	671
Others	92

AMEY ROADSTONE CORPORATION LTD PENSION SCHEME (1978)

15 Stanhope Gate, London W1Y 6AB
Telephone: 01-499 3611

Group Pensions Manager G.F.Dunn,APMI

Pensions Manager D.G.W.Hurst, FCIS, APMI

Pension Fund Consultants Tennant Budd (Life & Pensions Brokers) Ltd

Auditors Turquands Barton Mayhew & Co

Employees 8,000

Members 6,000

Pensioners 450

Annual Contributions £4,500,000

THE AMF (UK) PENSION SCHEME

25-28 Old Burlington Street, London W1X 2BA
Telephone: 01-734 8270

Company Secretary M.G.Vaughan

Trustees 8 managing trustees

Investment Advisers Morgan Grenfell & Co Ltd

Actuaries R.Watson & Sons

Pension Fund Consultants Wyatt Harris Graham Ltd.

Auditors Arthur Young McClelland Moore & Co

Employees 1,240

Members 850

Pensioners 180

	£000
Annual Contributions	282
Annual Investment Income	255
Gross Annual Outflow	121
Capital Value	3,940
Summary of Investments	
Equities	1,627
Fixed Interest	1,016
Property	89
Cash & Deposits	58
Others	787

AMOCO UK LTD.

1 Olympic Way, Wembley, Middx.HA9 0ND
Telephone: 01-902 8820

Secretary S.H.Dunkley

Investment Advisers Robert Fleming Investment Management Ltd.

Employees 2,088

AMP OF GREAT BRITAIN LTD PENSION & ASSOCIATED PENSION PLAN

Terminal House, Merrion Avenue, Stanmore, Middlesex
Telephone: 01-954 2356

H.W. Wheeler,MIPM H.W.Wheeler, MIPM

Secretary D.L. Tozer

Trustees H.W.Wheeler, D.L.Tozer, J.Johnston

Investment Advisers Phillips & Drew

Actuaries Lane,Clark & Peacock

Pension Fund Consultants Wyatt Harris Graham Ltd.

Auditors Arthur Andersen & Co

Company Employees 830

Members 796

Pensioners 92

	£000
Annual Contributions	395
Annual Investment Income	282
Annual Outflow	130
Capital Value	2,660
Summary of Investments	
Equities	1,729
Fixed Interest	820
Cash & Deposits	195

AMPHENOL BORG PENSION PLAN

Thanet Way, Tankerton, Whitstable, Kent CT5 3JF
Telephone: 0227-264411

Pension Fund Manager & Secretary J.R.Turner, FCIS, FCCA

Trustees Amphenol Borg Pension Trustees Ltd.

Investment Advisers Robert Fleming Investment Management Ltd.

Pension Fund Consultants and Actuarial Advice obtained through Towers, Perrin, Forster & Crosby Inc.

Auditors Deloitte, Haskins & Sells

Employees (at 31.7.80) 850

Members (at 1.1.80) 537

Pensioners 41

ARTHUR ANDERSEN & CO

1 Surrey Street, London WC2R 2PS
Telephone: 01-836 1200

Employees 960

ANDERSON STRATHCLYDE LTD

Anderson House, 47 Broad Street, Glasgow G40 2QW
Telephone: 041-554 1800

Secretary R.M.Clive

Managed by Standard Life Pension Funds Ltd

Actuaries R.Watson & Sons

Pension Fund Consultants R.Watson & Sons

Members 4,269

ANDREWS MACLAREN LTD.

Station Works, Long Buckby, Norhampton NN6 7PF
Telephone: 0327-842662

Director J.Myles

Employees 572

ANDREWS PENSION TRUST LTD
139 Oxford Street, London W1
Telephone: 01-437 2996

Secretary R.E.Goodwin, ACIS

Investment Advisers Barclays Bank Trust Co, Phillips & Drew

Actuaries Bacon & Woodrow

Auditors Price Waterhouse & Co

Employees 150

Members 135

Pensioners 35

Annual Contributions £43,000

Capital Value £950,000

ANGLIA BUILDING SOCIETY PENSION PLAN
Moulton Park, Northampton NN3 1NL
Telephone: 0604-495353

Assistant General Manager A.G.Bowers,MA

Investment Advisers Hill Samuel Investment Management Ltd., N.M.Rothschild & Sons Ltd.

Actuarial Advice Obtained through Cubie, Wood & Co.Ltd.

Pension Fund Consultants Noble Lowndes & Partners Ltd.

Auditors Coopers & Lybrand

Employees 2,000

Members 1,470

Pensioners 121

Annual Contributions £1 million

Annual Investment Income £200,000

Capital Value £6,340,000

ANGLIA TELEVISION GROUP LTD.
Anglia House, Norwich NR1 2JG
Telephone: 0603-28366

Secretary G.M.Rae,CA

Insured with Norwich Union Life Insurance society

Employees 643

ANGLO GREAT LAKES CORP LTD
Newburn Haugh, Newcastle on Tyne, Tyne & Wear NE15 8SU
Telephone: 0632-675851

Financial Director & Secretary P.R.Brown

Employees 558

ANGLO-SWISS HOLDINGS LTD
Trout Road, West Drayton, Middlesex UB7 7TP
Telephone: 43644

Secretary J.Shepherd

Employees 604

ANSAFONE LTD.
19 Upper Brook Street, London W1Y 2HS
Telephone: 01-629 9232

Director J.L.Evans

Employees 800

ANTIFERENCE LTD. 1978 RETIREMENT BENEFITS SCHEME
Bicester Road, Aylesbury, Bucks.HP19 3BJ
Telephone: 0296-82511

Director & Secretary K.G.Smith,FCIS,FSCA

Managed by Eagle Pension Funds Ltd.

Auditors Barsham Bradford & Hamilton

Company Employees 800

Members (at 31.3.80) 430

Pensioners 22

Annual Contributions £136,000

Capital Value £905,000

A P PRECISION HYDRAULICS
PO Box 1, Shaw Road, Speke, Liverpool L24 9JY
Telephone: 051-486 2121

Director A.G.Sweetland

Employees 1,100

APPLEYARD GROUP OF COMPANIES LTD
North Street, Leeds LS7 1RD
Telephone: 0532-32731

Pensions Manager W.Russell

Secretary J.E.Clemmitt,FCA

Trustees Appleyard Pensions (Nominees) Ltd

Managed by Legal & General (Pensions Management) Ltd

Actuaries Bacon & Woodrow

Auditors Deloitte Haskins & Sells

Company Employees 2,716

Members (at 5.4.80) 889

Pensioners 127

Annual Contributions £439,000

Capital Value £3,226,000

APPLIED CHEMICALS LTD RETIREMENT BENEFIT SCHEME
Salisbury Road, Uxbridge, Middlesex UB8 2SW
Telephone: 27151

Secretary S.A.Crump, FCIS, ACMA

Pension Fund Consultants Sedgwick Employee Benefit Consultants Ltd.

Employees 523

Members 160

Annual Contributions £55,000

APV HOLDINGS LTD 1974 PENSION SCHEME
Manor Royal, Crawley, West Sussex RH10 2QB
Telephone: 0293-27777

Pensions & Insurance Manager R.K.Arney,APMI

Managed by Prudential Pensions Ltd

Pension Fund Consultants Noble Lowndes & Partners Ltd.

Auditors Peat, Marwick, Mitchell & Co.

Employees 7,492

Members 6,000

Pensioners 950

APV HOLDINGS LTD Continued

Annual Contributions £3.75 million
Capital Value £16.5 million

AQUASCUTUM LIFE ASSURANCE & PENSION PLAN
100 Regent Street, London W1A 2AQ
Telephone: 01-734 6090

Pensions Officer Mrs.C. Durrant

Trustees G.M.Abrahams, Sir Charles Abrahams, KCVO, F.A.Larcombe

Investment Managers Schlesingers Investment Management Services Ltd

Actuaries Bacon & Woodrow

Pension Fund Consultants Bacon & Woodrow

Auditors Maw Temple Gotthard

Solicitors Sacker & Partners

Company Employees 1,841

Members 750

Pensioners 350

	£000
Annual Contributions	276
Annual Investment Income	335
Annual Outflow	179
Capital Value	3,566
Summary of Investments	
Equities	2,215
Fixed Interest	1,238
Cash & Deposits	113

A R A FOOD SERVICES LTD
Eurovending Division, Rex House,
Hampton Road West,
Hanworth, Feltham TW13 6AU
Telephone: 01-898 6001

Director P.L.Thornton

Executive J.Twiselton

Employees 500

ARCOELECTRIC (HOLDINGS) LTD.
Central Avenue, East Molesey, Surrey
Telephone: 01-623 3232

Secretary R.W.Harris

Employees 593

D'ARCY-MACMANUS & MASIUS LTD. 1973 PENSION & DEATH BENEFIT SCHEME
2 St.James's Square, London SW1Y 4JY
Telephone: 01-839 3422

Pension Fund Manager & Secretary R.A.Hickson

Investment Advisers S.G.Warburg & Co.Ltd.

Pension Fund Consultants Metropolitan Pensions Association

Auditors Arthur Andersen & Co.

Company Employees 530

Members 220

Pensioners 45

Annual Contributions £750,000
Capital Value £4,200,000

A. ARENSON (HOLDINGS) LTD RETIREMENT & DEATH BENEFIT SCHEME
Lincoln House, Colney Street, St.Albans,
Herts.AL2 2DX
Telephone: Radlett 7211

Assistant Secretary P.Rozelaar

Trustees Wigham Poland Trustees Ltd.

Managed by Standard Life Pension Funds Ltd.;
Scottish Widows Pensions Management SWF Ltd.;
Scottish Amicable Pensions Investments Ltd.

Actuarial Advice Obtained through Wigham Poland Pension Consultants Ltd.

Pension Fund Consultants Wigham Poland Pension Consultants Ltd.

Auditors Casson Beckman

Company Employees 547

Members 473

Pensioners 5

Annual Contributions £225,000

ARGOS DISTRIBUTORS LTD PENSION SCHEME
112 Station Road, Edgware, Middlesex HA8 7AQ
Telephone: 01-951 1361

Pensions Manager P.R.E.Reynolds,APMI

Stockbrokers Phillips & Drew

Actuaries R.Watson & Sons

Auditors Brebner Allen & Trad, Deloitte Haskins& Sells

Company Employees 3,000

Members 1,005

Pensioners 13

	£000
Annual Contributions	600
Annual Investment Income	140
Gross Annual Outflow	60
Capital Value (At 5.4.80)	2,015
Summary of Investments	
Equities	950
Fixed Interest	710
Cash & Deposits	355

ARGUS PRESS HOLDINGS LTD.
12-18 Paul Street, London EC2A 4JS
Telephone: 01-247 8233

Secretary A.T.Patten,ACIS

Employees 2,181

ARLINGTON MOTOR HOLDINGS LTD
67 High Street, Ponders End,
Enfield, Middx.EN3 4EG
Telephone: 01-804 1266

Secretary L.Scarborough

Insured with Scottish Life Assurance Co

Employees 985

ARMATEX LTD
44 Thomas Road, London E14 7BJ
Telephone: 01-987 8121
Chairman & Managing Director O.Newman
Employees 900

ARMCO LTD PENSION AND ASSURANCE PLAN
Jubilee Road, Letchworth, Herts
Telephone: 046-26 6588
Secretary M.P.Houghton
Other Pension Management Lowndes Associated Pensions Ltd
Trustees 13
Managed by Warburg Investment Management Ltd., Legal & General (Pensions Management) Ltd.
Actuarial Advice Obtained Through Cubie, Wood & Co.Ltd.
Pension Fund Consultants Noble Lowndes & Partners Ltd
Auditors Deloitte & Co.
Members 650
Pensioners 188

	£000
Annual Contributions	550
Annual Investment Income	295
Gross Annual Outflow	298
Capital Value	3,010
Summary of Investments	
Equities	1,796
Fixed Interest	421
Property	675
Cash & Deposits	118

ARMITAGE SHANKS GROUP LTD PENSION SCHEME
Armitage, Rugeley, Staffordshire WS15 4BT
Telephone: 0543-490253
Secretary R.P.B.Udall
Managed by Pensions Management (SWF) Ltd
Employees 3,081
Company Employees (UK) 2,865
Members 2,249
Pensioners 365
Annual Contributions £900,000
Capital Value £3,500,000

ARMOUR FOODS (UK) LTD.
193 St.John Street, London EC1
Telephone: 01-253 8400
Secretary C.Ahwai
Stockbrokers Phillips & Drew
Actuaries Bacon & Woodrow
Company Employees 169
Members 130
Pensioners 248

Annual Contributions £66,000
Capital Value £1,500,000

ARMOUR TRUST LTD.
37 Upper Grosvenor Street, London W1X 9PE
Telephone: 01-629 4382
Secretary R.G.Adamson,FCIS
Insured with Provident Mutual Life Assurance Association
Employees 568

ARMSTRONG CORK CO LTD STAFF & WORKS PENSION & LIFE ASSURANCE SCHEMES 1978
Armstrong House, Chequers Square, Uxbridge, Middx.
Telephone: 89-51122
Company Secretary G.F.Crane
Managed by Legal & General Assurance Society Ltd
Actuaries Clay & Partners
Auditors Peat, Marwick, Mitchell & Co.
Company Employees 1,350
Members 1,150
Pensioners 200
Annual Contributions £389,000
Capital Value £3,683,000

ARMSTRONG GROUP PENSION SCHEME
Gibson Lane, Melton, North Ferriby,
North Humberside HU14 3HY
Telephone: 0482-633311
Secretary K.J.Bateman
Trustees Armstrong Pension Trustees Ltd
Managed by N.M.Rothschild & Sons Ltd & Clerical, Medical & General Life Assurance Society
Stockbrokers James Capel & Co
Property Advisers Charles Charter & Co
Pension Fund Consultants and Actuarial Advice obtained through Hogg Robinson (Benefit Consultants) Ltd
Company Employees 6,576
Members 2,260
Pensioners 370

	£000
Annual Contributions	650
Annual Investment Income	205
Annual Outflow	31
Capital value	2,791
Summary of Investments	
Equities	1,656
Fixed Interest	749
Property	113
Cash & Deposits	238
Others	35

ARMSTRONG PUMPS LTD
Peartree Road, Stanway, Colchester CO3 5JX
Telephone: 0206-79491

The Major UK Pension Funds **ARM/ASS**

ARMSTRONG PUMPS LTD *Continued*

Executive R.C.Jeffrey
Employees 2,000

E.J.ARNOLD & SON LTD 1978 PENSION SCHEME
Butterley Street, Hunslet Lane, Leeds LS10 1AX
Telephone: 0532-442944

Pension Fund Manager and Secretary D.G.Jessop
Other Pension Management Mrs. M.Walker
Trustees E.M.Arnold, J.O.Arnold, D.G.Jessop, R.Brown, R.Edmonson
Investment Advisers Warburg Investment Management Ltd.
Pension Fund Consultants and Actuarial Advice obtained through Bain Dawes & Partners Ltd.
Auditors Spicer & Pegler
Company Employees 830
Members 552
Pensioners 41

	£000
Annual Contributions (to 5.4.80)	408
Annual Investment Income	132
Annual Outflow	101
Capital Value (at 30.9.80)	1,620
Summary of Investments	
Equities	1,119
Fixed Interest	275
Cash & Deposits	227

ARROW HART (EUROPE) LTD RETIREMENT BENEFIT PLAN
Plymbridge Road, Estover Plymouth PL6 7PN
Telephone: 0752-701155

Pension Fund Manager P.J.Russell
Secretary A.R.Lewis
Trustees A.E.Flatman, K.D.Fraser, P.J.Russell
Managed by Prudential Pensions Ltd.
Pension Fund Consultants Godwins (Central Services) Ltd.
Auditors Radford & Sergeant
Company Employees 628
Members 377

	£000
Annual Contributions	145
Annual Investment Income	40
Annual Outflow	7
Capital Value	492
Summary of Investments	
Equities	184
Fixed Interest	169
Property	117
Cash & Deposits	22

OVE ARUP PARTNERSHIP PENSION SCHEME
13 Fitzroy Street, London W1P 6BQ
Telephone: 01-636 1531

Financial Controller S.L.Irons, FCA
Investment Advisers N.M.Rothschild Asset Management Ltd.
Actuaries Clay & Partners
Auditors Clark Pixley
Solicitors Slaughter & May
Company Employees (at 1.5.79) 1,477
Members (at 1.4.80) 1,284
Pensioners 896
Annual Contributions £782,000
Annual Investment Income £316,000
Gross Annual Outflow £101,000
Capital Value £4,868,000

ASBESTOS & RUBBER CO LTD
Waverley Street, Hull, North Humberside
Telephone: 0482-27678

Director T.Martin
Employees 500

A S E A LTD
Villiers House, 41 Strand, London WC2N 5JX
Telephone: 01-930 5411

Director L.T.Cornthwaite
Insured with Scottish Amicable Life Assurance Society
Employees 700

ASH & LACY PENSION FUND
Alma Street, Smethwick, Warley, West Midlands B66 2RP
Telephone: 021-558 2171

Secretary J.W.Lunt
Trustees J.F. Vernon, H.V. Scaldwell, J.W. Lunt
Partly managed by Legal & General Assurance Society Ltd.
Investment Advisers John Carrington & Co Ltd
Actuaries Duncan C.Fraser & Co
Property Advisers Edwards, Bigwood & Bewlay
Auditors Thornton Baker & Co
Company Employees 762
Members 225
Pensioners 65

	£000
Annual Contributions	122
Annual Investment Income	65
Annual Outflow	46
Capital Value	1,173
Summary of Investments	
Equities	436
Property	208
Cash & Deposits	142
Mixed Fund	387

ASHBY & HORNER HOLDINGS LTD.
32/38 Earl Street, London EC2A 2JD
Telephone: 01-377 0266

ASHBY & HORNER HOLDINGS LTD. *Continued*

Secretary L.R.Evans,FCIS
Insured with Sun Life Assurance Society Ltd
Group Employees 949

ASHLEY ACCESSORIES LTD
Morecambe Road, Ulverston LA12 9BN Cumbria
Telephone: 0229-53333

Secretary J.H.Petty,FCA

Employees 1,000

ASHTON BROS & CO.(HOLDINGS) LTD.
P.O.Box 16, Moss Lane, Worsley,
Manchester M28 5NR
Telephone: 061-790 7841

Employees 2,420

ASHTON SHIRTINGS LTD
PO Box 19, Carrfield Mills, Hyde SK14 4NR
Telephone: 061-368 1961

Executive P.Jelley

Employees 500

ASPRO-NICHOLAS PENSION SCHEME
225 Bath Road, Slough, Berkshire SL1 4AU
Telephone: Slough 23971

Pension Fund Manager A.W.Sampson

Secretary R.Blakemore, ACIS

Trustees Aspro-Nicholas (Trustees) Ltd

Investment Advisers Warburg Investment Management Ltd

Actuaries Bacon & Woodrow

Auditors Deloitte Haskins & Sells

Company Employees 1,261

Members (at 1.1.79) 791

Pensioners 333

	£000
Annual Contributions	579
Annual Investment Income	659
Annual Outflow	401
Capital Value	9,000
Summary of Investments	
Equities	3,518
Fixed Interest	3,043
Cash & Deposits	1,739

A.B.M. PENSION SCHEME
c/o **Associated Biscuit Manufacturers Ltd.**
P.O. Box 1, Aintree Biscuit Factory,
Liverpool L9 7BQ
Telephone: 051-525 3661

Pensions Administration Manager and Secretary R.Wink,FCA,APMI

Pensions Director B.R.K.Hunton, FCA, APMI

Trustees ABM Pensions Ltd

Investment Advisers Kleinwort Benson Investment Management Ltd.

Actuaries R.Watson & Sons

Auditors Price Waterhouse & Co
Company Employees 12,031
Members 6,100
Pensioners 2,300

	£000
Annual Contributions	4,000
Annual Investment Income	2,400
Annual Outflow	2,000
Capital Value	32,500
Summary of Investments	
Equities	13,500
Fixed Interest	9,100
Property	4,800
Cash & Deposits	1,600
Others	3,500

ASSOCIATED BOOK PUBLISHERS LTD.
11 New Fetter Lane, London EC4P 4EE
Telephone: 01-583 9855

Secretary D.G.Sampson,ACIS

Employees 558

ASSOCIATED BRITISH FOODS PENSION SCHEME
252-260 Regent Street, London W1P SDA
Telephone: 01-437 7437

Group Pension Manager & Secretary to Trustees A.S.Herbert,FCIS,FPMI

Investment Manager A.D.Schofield

Trustees Associated British Foods Pension Trustees Ltd.

Actuaries Clay and Partners

Pension Fund Consultants Metropolitan Pensions Association Ltd

Auditors Thomson McLintock & Co.

Company Employees 72,000

Members 17,000

Pensioners 6,700

	£000
Annual Contributions	10,544
Annual Investment Income	8,854
Annual Outflow	5,714
Capital Value	86,300
Summary of Investments	
Equities	32,965
Fixed Interest	39,090
Property	8,084
Cash & Deposits	6,120

ASSOCIATED CEMENT WORKS PENSION SCHEME AND STAFF PENSION SCHEME
Portland House, Stag Place, London SW1E 5BJ
Telephone: 01-828 3456

Assistant Secretary and Group Pensions Manager J.P.Moor, MA

Secretary H.W.R.Ham, FCIS

Assistant Secretary T.Keighley, LLB

Trustees Associated Cement Pensions Trustees

ASSOCIATED CEMENT Continued

Trustees Associated Cement Pensions Trustees Ltd., Associated Cement Workmen's Pensions Trustees Ltd.

Investment Advisers County Bank Ltd., Kleinwort Benson Ltd.

Principal Stockbrokers Hoare Govett Ltd.

Property Adviser J.A.C.R.Every-Brown, FRICS

Actuaries R.Watson & Sons

Auditors Pannell Fitzpatrick & Co.

	Works (5.4.80)	Staff (31.12.79)
Members	7,194	4,039
Pensioners	2,875	1,239
	£000	£000
Annual Contributions	5,495	5,641
Annual Investment Income	2,031	3,090
Annual Outflow	1,765	2,236
Capital Value		
Book Value	26,234	41,293
Market Value	28,514	48,156
Summary of Investments (Market Value)		
UK Equities	13,048	18,204
Overseas Equties	2,616	3,612
Fixed Interest	7,828	10,051
Property	2,905	6,564
Property Unit Trusts	1,283	2,386
Cash & Deposits	790	1,216
Others	44	211
Managed Fund		5,912

ASSOCIATED COMMUNICATIONS PENSION SCHEME

17 Gt Cumberland Place, London W1A 1AG
Telephone: 01-262 8040

Pension Fund Manager Miss A.Stephens

Secretary D.S.Williams,LLB,FCIS,APMI

Trustees E.S.Birk, A.R.Lucas, J.Steppings, H.E.Humphreys

Stockbrokers Anderson & Co., W.Greenwell & Co., Cazenove & Co.

Actuaries R.Watson & Sons

Property Advisers Edward Erdman & Co.

Auditors Binder Hamlyn & Co.

Company Employees 5,500

Members 3,106

Pensioners 426

	£000
Annual Contributions	2,700
Annual Investment Income	2,400
Annual Outflow	610
Capital Value	26,750
Summary of Investments	
Equities	13,725
Fixed Interest	10,000

Property	2,400
Cash & Deposits	650

ASSOCIATED CONTAINER TRANSPORTATION SERVICES LTD

Richmond House, Terminus Terrace, Southampton SO9 1GG
Telephone: 0703-34433

Director G.B.Reid

Employees 700

ASSOCIATED DAIRIES STAFF PENSION FUND

Craven House, Kirkstall Road, Leeds LS3 1JE
Telephone: 0532-40141

Pension Fund Manager D.Petch

Secretary to Trustees R.Fawcett

Trustees A.N.Stockdale, E.G.Bousfield, P.R.Baines

Investment Advisers Lazard Securities Ltd

Stockbrokers J. & A. Scrimgeour Ltd

Actuaries Clay & Partners

Pension Fund Consultants Metropolitan Pensions Association Ltd

Auditors Ernst & Whinney

Total Group Employees 22,636

Eligible Company Employees 2,355

Members 1,278

Pensioners 110

	£000
Annual Contributions (1978)	510
Annual Investment Income	144
Gross Annual Outflow	112
Capital Value	2,164
Summary of Investments (1978)	
Equities	401
Fixed Interest	819
Cash & Deposits	348
Others	596

ASSOCIATED ENGINEERING LTD. PENSION FUND

Ince House, 60 Kenilworth Road, Leamington Spa, Warks.CV32 6JZ
Telephone: 0926-21377

Pensions Manager E.L.Rutter, FIA, APMI

Investment Advisers Hill Samuel Ltd and Baring Bros Ltd

Actuaries Lane Clark & Peacock

Pension Fund Consultant Godwins Ltd

Auditors Thomson McLintock & Co.

Company Employees 22,000

Members 14,500

Pensioners 3,000

Annual Contributions £10 million

Capital Value £50 million

ASSOCIATED FISHERIES LTD.

16 Queen Anne's Gate, London SW1H 9AQ
Telephone: 01-222 0404

ASSOCIATED FISHERIES LTD. *Continued*

Secretary J.R.J.Lucas
Insured with Standard Life Assurance Co
Company Employees 3,855

ASSOCIATED HEAT SERVICES LTD. STAFF PENSION SCHEME AND OPERATIONAL PENSION SCHEME
15 Hobart Place, London SW1E 7AE
Telephone: 01-235 9161
Secretary A.E.T.Swayne
Trustees Associated Heat Services Ltd.
Staff Scheme Insured with Legal & General Assurance Society Ltd.
Operational Scheme Insured with Legal & General Assurance Society Ltd.
Pension Fund Consultants Glanvill Enthoven (Life Pensions & Mortgages) Ltd.
Auditors Ernst & Whinney
Company Employees 847

	Staff	Operational
Members	268	464
Pensioners	4	5
Annual Contributions	£225,000	£289,000

ASSOCIATED LEISURE LTD NON-CONTRIBUTORY RETIREMENT BENEFIT SCHEME
Phonographic House, The Vale,
London NW11 8SU
Telephone: 01-450 5251
Company Secretary D.A.G.How,FCIS
Secretary to Trustees Lowndes Associated Pensions Ltd.
Partly Insured with English Insurance Co Ltd
Investment Advisers Hill Samuel Investment Management Ltd
Actuarial Advice Obtained through Cubie, Wood & Co.Ltd.
Pension Fund Consultants Noble Lowndes & Partners Ltd
Auditors Price Waterhouse & Co.
Employees 2,555
Members 888 (incl.78 group life only)
Pensioners 22

	£000
Annual Contributions	131
Annual Investment Income	2
Annual Outflow	37
Capital Value (on self administered part)	230
Summary of Investments	
Equities	103
Fixed Interest	13
Property	13
Cash & Deposits	1

There is also an Executive Pension Plan with 20 members and annual contributions of £141,000. This is insured with English Insurance Co.Ltd.

ASSOCIATED NEWSPAPERS GROUP LTD
Carmelite House, London EC4Y 0JA
Telephone: 01-353 6000

See Harmsworth Pension Funds

THE ASSOCIATED OCTEL CO LTD PENSION PLAN
20 Berkeley Square, London W1X 6DT
Telephone: 01-499 6030
Pensions Secretary J.E.Riley,ACMA
Company Secretary D.M.Vickers
Investment Advisers Barclays Bank Trust Co.Ltd.
Stockbrokers Phillips & Drew
Actuaries R.Watson & Sons
Auditors Price Waterhouse & Co.
Solicitors Linklaters & Paines
Employees 2,831
Members (at 5.4.79) 2,819
Pensioners 833
Annual Contributions £2,459,000
Annual Investment Income £2,291,000
Capital Value £35,630,000

ASSOCIATED PAPER INDUSTRIES LTD PENSION & LIFE ASSURANCE FUND
Silk House, Park Green, Macclesfield,
Cheshire SK11 7NU
Telephone: 0625-610334
Secretary A.Sentance,FCIS
Trustees J.A.Graham, W.Q.C.Mackenzie,FCA, A.Sentance,FCIS
Investment Advisers Morgan Grenfell & Co Ltd
Actuary G.G.Bannerman, AIA, FFA(C.T.Bowring & Layborn Ltd)
Property Advisers Dacre Son & Hartley
Pension Fund Consultants C.T.Bowring & Layborn Ltd
Auditors Ernst & Whinney
Company Employees 1,798
Members 1,286
Pensioners 163

	£000
Annual Contributions (to 29.3.80)	1,100
Annual Investment Income	290
Annual Outflow	228
Capital Value	4,000
Summary of Investments (1979)	
Equities	1,400
Fixed Interest	911
Property	290
Cash & Deposits	207
Others	500

ASSOCIATED WEAVERS LTD.
P.O.Box 11, Weavercraft Mills, Toftshaw Lane, Bradford BD4 6QW
Telephone: 0274-681881

Director T.W.G.Ashdown

Employees 2,200

ASTARON-BIRD LTD
Cyldon Works, Fleets Lane, Poole, Dorset BH15 3BW
Telephone: 060-13 4641

Director B.R.Clark

Employees 750

ATCOST PENSIONS LTD
51 The Pantiles, Tunbridge Wells, Kent
Telephone: 0892-26288

Pension Fund Manager A.Rosier

Secretary D.P.O'Loughnane

Trustees P.Smith, D.Lindsey, D.P.O'Loughnane, P.Down, D.Small

Investment Advisers County Bank Ltd

Actuaries Duncan C. Fraser & Co

Auditors Josolyne Layton-Bennett & Co

Company Employees 700

Members 200

Pensioners 18

	£000
Annual Contributions	120
Annual Investment Income	86
Annual Outflow	92
Capital Value	1,500
Summary of Investments	
Equities	702
Fixed Interest	523
Property	290
Cash & Deposits	65

ATKINS BROTHERS (HOSIERY) LTD
Lower Bond Street, Hinckley, Leics.LE10 1QX
Telephone: 04553-2075

Secretary R.D.Styles

Employees 1,308

W.S.ATKINS & PARTNERS RETIREMENT BENEFITS PLAN
Woodcote Grove, Ashley Road, Epsom, Surrey KT18 5BW
Telephone: 26140

Pension Fund Manager & Secretary R.H.Tomalin

Pensions Officer Mrs. P.Clarke

Trustees K.N.Drobig, J.A.Goldsmith

Investment Advisers Phillips & Drew, Legal & General Assurance Society Ltd.

Stockbrokers Phillips & Drew

Actuaries R.Watson & Sons

Auditors Milne Ross

Company Employees 2,000

Members 1,514

Pensioners 67

	£000
Annual Contributions	1,900
Annual Investment Income	329
Annual Outflow	307
Capital Value	10,700
Summary of Investments	
Equities	8,688
Fixed Interest	1,342
Cash & Deposits	690

ATLAS EXPRESS GROUP LTD PENSION & LIFE ASSURANCE SCHEME
Canon Beck Road, Rotherhithe, London SE16 1DG
Telephone: 01-237 4511

Group Pensions & Insurance Manager Mrs.P.M.Kibble

Insured with Scottish Amicable Life Assurance Society

Pension Fund Consultants Alexander Howden Insurance Brokers Ltd.

Auditors Arthur Young McClelland Moores & Co.

Company Employees 2,181

Members 1,105

Pensioners 100

Annual Contributions £600,000

THE ATLAS STONE CO.LTD.
Artillery House, Artillery Row, London SW1P 1RU
Telephone: 01-222 2091

Secretary P.G.Harvey

Employees 846

AULT & WIBORG GROUP RETIREMENT & DEATH BENEFIT PLAN
71 Standen Road, London SW18 5TJ
Telephone: 01-874 7244

Company Secretary D.J.Smith

Pension Fund Consultant J.H.Minet Life & Pensions Ltd

Company Employees 1,634

Members 1,000

AURORA HOLDINGS LTD PENSION PLAN
Nether Lane, Ecclesfield, Sheffield S30 3TR
Telephone: 0742-467100

Group Executive (Pensions & Insurance) D.Walker

Investment Advisers Keyser Ullmann Pensions Management Ltd

Pension Fund Consultants E.B.S. (Management Services) Ltd.

Auditors Coopers & Lybrand

Company Employees 7,200

Members 288

Pensioners 26

Annual Contributions £264,000

F.AUSTIN (LEYTON) LTD
Argall Avenue, Lea Bridge Estate, London E10 7PZ
Telephone: 01-539 5566

Secretary T.L.Rees

Insured with Norwich Union Life Insurance Society

Employees 589

AUSTIN REED PENSION FUND
PO Box 2, Thirsk, N.Yorks.YO7 1PF
Telephone: 0845-23611

Secretary G.J.Tubb,FCIS

Trustees ARPF (No 1) Ltd and ARPF (No 2) Ltd

Investment Advisers Robert Fleming Investment Management Ltd

Stockbrokers Montagu Loebl Stanley & Co

Property Advisers Hillier Parker May & Rowden

Pension Fund Consultants and Actuarial Advice obtained through Martin Paterson Associates Ltd

Auditors Coopers & Lybrand

Company Employees 1,709

Members (at 31.3.80) 313

Pensioners 268

Annual Contributions £216,000 (1977)

Annual Investment Income £268,000 (1977)

Gross Annual Outflow £160,000 (1977)

Capital Value £3,600,000

AUTOMATED SECURITY (HOLDINGS) LTD.
25-26 Hampstead High Street, London NW3 1QA
Telephone: 01-794 8191

Secretary D.Waller,FCMA

Employees 906

AUTOMOTIVE PRODUCTS LTD PENSION & LIFE ASSURANCE SCHEMES FOR (1)STAFF, (2) HOURLY PAID EMPLOYEES, (3)EXECUTIVE MANAGEMENT
Tachbrook Road, Leamington Spa,
Warwickshire CV31 3ER
Telephone: 0926-27000

Pensions & Salaries Manager J.H.Sellwood

Stockbrokers Phillips & Drew

Actuaries Duncan C.Fraser & Co.

Auditors Deloitte Haskins & Sells

Employees 12,117

Members 6,411

Pensioners 1,551

Annual Contributions £2,176,000

AVANA GROUP LTD.
Avana Buildings, Cardiff CF1 7YH
Telephone: 0222-25521

Secretary T.H.J.Barrett,FCA

Employees 1,624

AVDEL LTD
Mundells, Welwyn Garden City, Herts.AL7 1EZ
Telephone: 07073-28161

Secretary P.H.Brook

Executive F.C.Higgs

Employees 1,100

AVERYS LTD.
Smethwick, Warley, West Midlands B66 2LP
Telephone: 021-558 1112

Company Secretary S.G.Graham

Pensions Officer B.J.Roberts

Investment Advisers J.Henry Schroder Wagg & Co.Ltd.

Company Employees 8,467

AVIS RENT A CAR LTD. UK PENSION PLAN
Avis House, Station Road, Bracknell,
Berks. RG12 1HZ
Telephone: 0344-26644

Pensions & Benefits Manager R.G.Evans,ACII,APMI

Pensions & Benefits Analyst Miss D.M.Chamberlain

Pension Fund Consultants Wyatt Harris Graham Ltd.

Auditors Deloitte,Haskins & Sells

Company Employees (at 31.5.79) 1,694

Members 1,583

Pensioners 32

Annual Contributions £363,000

Annual Investment Income £142,000

Capital Value £1,450,000

AVON COSMETICS PENSION PLAN
Nunn Mills Road, Northampton NN1 5PA
Telephone: 0604-34722

Company Secretary R.P.Smith

Director of Finance J.M.McDonald,ACA

Investment Advisers Robert Fleming Investment Management Ltd.

Pension Fund Consultants Wyatt Harris Graham Ltd.

Company Employees 1,969

Members 1,646

Pensioners 228

Annual Contributions £620,000

Annual Investment Income £587,000

Capital Value £6,458,000

AVON COUNTY COUNCIL SUPERANNUATION FUND
P.O.box 22, Avon House, The Haymarket,
Bristol BS99 7RT
Telephone: 0272-290777

Pension Fund Manager & Secretary D.G.Morgan (County Treasurer)

Trustees Avon County Council

Investment Advisers de Zoete & Bevan, Pember & Boyle,County Bank

Stockbrokers de Zoete & Bevan, Pember & Boyle

Property Agents Hillier Parker May & Rowden

Actuaries Duncan C.Fraser & Co.

AVON COUNTY COUNCIL Continued

Members 20,000
Pensioners 6,600

	£million
Annual Contributions	12.3
Annual Investment Income	7.0
Annual Outflow	6.6
Capital Value	101.0
Summary of Investments	
Equities	38.0
Fixed Interest	38.0
Property	17.0
Cash & Deposits	8.0

AVON RUBBER CO.LTD. RETIREMENT & DEATH BENEFITS PLAN

Bath Road, Melksham, Wilts.SN12 8AA
Telephone: 0225-703101

Chief Pensions Executive Miss G.Fairhurst,ACIS

Pension Fund Manager B.D.J.Hatton,ACII

Investment Managers Morgan Grenfell & Co.Ltd.

Stockbrokers Scrimgeour Kemp Gee Co Ltd.

Actuaries T.G.Arthur & Co.

Property Advisers Standard Life Assurance Co.

Auditors Deloitte Haskins & Sells

Company Employees 6,500

Members 6,000
Pensioners 1,700

	£000
Annual Contributions	4,200
Gross Annual Outflow	1,800
Capital Value	12,729
Summary of Investments	
Equities	6,150
Fixed Interest	2,604
Property	3,000
Cash & Deposits	975

AXMINSTER CARPETS LTD.

Gamberlake, Axminster, Devon
Telephone: 0297-32244

Secretary R.M.Laws,FCA

Employees 600

JOHN AYNSLEY & SONS (LONGTON) LTD.

Portland Works, Sutherland Road, Longton, Staffs.

Chairman J.M.Gillow

Employees 744

AYRSHIRE METAL PRODUCTS LTD.

17 Church Street, Irvine, Ayrshire KA 12 8PH
Telephone: 0284-74171

Secretary Mary D.Stevens

Employees 558

B & Q (RETAIL) LTD.

Third Avenue, Millbrook Trading Estate, Southampton, Hants.SO9 1RE
Telephone: 0703-788313

Secretary J.A.Kennedy

Employees 734

BABCOCK INTERNATIONAL LTD. GROUP STAFF PENSION SCHEME & JOINT WORKS SCHEME

Cleveland House, St.James's Square, London SW1Y 4LN
Telephone: 01-930 9766

Pensions Administration Office 128 Borough High Street, London SE1 1LB
Telephone: 01-407 9471

Company Secretary E.G.W.Lunn,FCIS

Group Assistant Secretary K.T.Williams,APMI

Investment Manager M.J.Tanner

Trustees Babcock Staff Pension Trust Ltd., Babcock Works Pension Trust Ltd.

Part Managed by Eagle Pension Funds Ltd.

Property Advisers Savills, Knight Frank & Rutley

Actuaries R.Watson & Sons

Auditors Coopers & Lybrand

Solicitors Rowe & Maw

Company Employees 21,067

	Staff	Works
Members (at 31.12.79)	8,500	5,888
Pensioners	3,350	1,545
	£000	£000
Annual Contributions	6,633	2,982
Annual Investment Income	3,864	596
Capital Value	55,000	8,428

BADGER LTD PENSION & ASSURANCE SCHEME

Turriff Building, Great West Road, Brentford, Middlesex TW8 9JA
Telephone: 01-560 1200

Director of Finance E.A.Rich, FCA

Pension Fund Consultants Sedgwick Employee Benefit Consultants Ltd.

Auditors Coopers and Lybrand

Company Employees 445

Members 335

Pensioners 35

Annual Contributions £450,000

Capital Value £1,750,000

C.H.BAILEY LTD

Alexandra Docks, Newport, Gwent NP7 2UX
Telephone: 0633-62961

Secretary J.W.Dalgleish,MA

Employees 663

N.G.BAILEY & CO LTD
Heathcote, Ilkley, W.Yorks.LS29 9AS
Telephone: 0943-32121

Secretary G.T.Critchley

Insured with Clerical, Medical & General Life Assurance Society

Company Employees 3,140

BAIRD & TATLOCK (LONDON) LTD
Lane End Road, High Wycombe, Bucks, HP12 4HL

Chairman G.G.Robertson

Employees 758

WILLIAM BAIRD & CO LTD
168 West George Street, Glasgow G2 2NS
Telephone: 041-332 6071

Secretary A.F.Wylie, 153 Moorgate, London EC2M 6XH (01-588 4761)

Insured with Legal & General Assurance Society Ltd

Employees 11,829

BAKER OIL TOOLS (UNITED KINGDOM) LTD
Woodside Road, Bridge of Don, Aberdeen AB2 8BW
Telephone: 0224-702681

Director J.T.Lembcke

Assistant Secretary A.J.Arthur

Employees 525

BAKER PERKINS HOLDINGS LTD GROUP PENSION & LIFE ASSURANCE SCHEME
Westwood Works, Westfield Road, Peterborough PE3 6TA
Telephone: 0733-262000

Pensions Secretary R.South, APMI

Company Secretary J.S.Hardy

Part managed by Equity & Law Managed Funds, Legal & General Managed Funds

Investment Advisers Lloyds Bank Ltd, Morgan Grenfell & Co Ltd

Actuaries Clay & Partners

Pension Fund Consultants Metropolitan Pensions Association Ltd

Auditors Price Waterhouse & Co

Employees 5,247

Members 4,242

Pensioners 1,360

Annual Contributions £3,212,000

Annual Investment Income £774,000

Capital Value £23,996,000

HENRY BALFOUR & CO LTD
Durie Foundry, Leven, Fife KY8 4RW
Telephone: 0333-23020

Managing Director R.R.Gordon

Employees 780

HENRY BALLANTYNE & SON LTD.
March Street Mills, Peebles EH45 8ER
Telephone: 0721-20146

Secretary D.G.Smith

Employees 952

BALLY GROUP (UK) LTD. STAFF RETIREMENT BENEFIT PLANS (2 PLANS)
Hall Road, Norwich, Norfolk NR4 6DP
Telephone: 0603-21414

Secretary D.N.Blott

Insured with Legal & General Assurance Society Ltd.,

Pension Fund Consultants Sedgwick Forbes Benefits Consultants Ltd.

Company Employees 1,100

Members 240

BAMBERS STORES LTD.
Aldersgate House, Crouch Road, New Barnet, Herts.EN5 5HN
Telephone: 01-440 5252

Secretary H.Grant

Employees 2,034

J.C.BAMFORD EXCAVATORS LTD.
Uttoxeter, Rocester, Staffs.ST14 5JP
Telephone: 08893-3121

Director A.P.Bamford

Secretary A.M.Smith

Insured with Prudential Assurance Co.Ltd.

Employees 1,181

BANK OF AMERICA NT & SA UK RETIREMENT & BENEFITS PLAN
25 Cannon Street, London EC4P 4HN
Telephone: 01-236 2010

Assistant Manager D.R.J.Smith

Investment Advisers ana Mangers Investment Advisers and Managers

Pension Fund Consultants & Actuarial Advice Obtained through Towers, Perrin, Forster & Crosby

Auditors Price Waterhouse & Co

Company Employees 1,406

Members 753

Pensioners 20

	£000
Annual Contributions	1,000
Gross Annual Outflow	25
Capital Value	4,500
Summary of Investments	
Equities	50%
Fixed Interests	38%
Cash & Deposits	2%
Others	10%

BANK OF ENGLAND PENSION FUND
Threadneedle Street, London EC2R 8AH
Telephone: 01-601 4444

Secretary A.H.Long, APMI

BANK OF ENGLAND Continued

Investment Manager A.F.Bushell
Actuaries R.Watson & Sons
Capital Value (Market) 201,198
Auditors Deloitte Haskins & Sells
Company Employees 6,500
Members 6,500
Pensioners 5,000

	£000
Annual Contributions (to 29.2.80)	9,948
Annual Investment Income	13,254
Annual Outflow	13,439
Capital value	189,000
Summary of Investments (Market Value)	
Equities	105,179
Fixed Interest	36,359
Property	26,938
Cash & Deposits	11,230
Overseas	20,825
Others	667

BANK OF IRELAND STAFF PENSION FUND

Lower Baggot Street, Dublin 2
Telephone: Dublin 785744

Chief Pensions Officer G.E.Collier
Investment Advisers Investment Bank of Ireland
Property Advisers Lisney & Co
Actuary R.P.Willis, MA, FIA
Auditors Craig Gardner & Co
Company Employees 7,500
Members 737
Pensioners 71

BANK OF NEW SOUTH WALES U.K.STAFF SUPERANNUATION SCHEME

29 Threadneedle Street, London EC2R 8BA
Telephone: 01-588 4020

Assistant Manager F.R.Roufe
Investment Advisers Kleinwort Benson Investment Management Ltd.
Actuaries Bacon & Woodrow
Auditors Ernst & Whinney
UK Employees (at 30.6.80) 421
Members 330
Pensioners 110
Annual Contributions £665,000
Annual Investment Income £180,000
Capital Value £2,800,000

BANK OF SCOTLAND 1976 PENSION FUND

PO Box 5, The Mound, Edinburgh EH1 1YZ
Telephone: 031-225 3291

Clerk to Trustees Hugh D.Robertson (Assistant Staff Manager)
Investment Manager I.A.Watt
Trustees J.A.Lumsden, Lord Balfour of Burleigh, M.F.Strachan, D.Bruce Pattullo, Dr.Joan Smith, W.D.McIntosh, J.H.Watson
Investment Advisers Bank of Scotland Investment Services
Actuaries R.Watson & Sons
Property Advisers Bank of Scotland Property Department
Auditors Arthur Young McClelland Moores & Co.
Company Employees 8,400
Members 5,500
Pensioners and Beneficiaries 2,100

	£000
Annual Contributions	10,200
Annual Investment Income	7,600
Annual Outflow	4,900
Capital Value	102,000
Summary of Investments	
Equities	67,737
Fixed Interest	24,050
Property	6,800
Cash & Deposits	2,159
Others	1,539

BANKERS TRUST CO. UK 1960 PENSION SCHEME

9 Queen Victoria Street, London EC4P 4DB
Telephone: 01-235 5030

Vice President M.J.Dwyer,APMI
Trustees Bankers Trustee & Executor Co Ltd.
Actuaries R.Watson & Sons
Auditors Price Waterhouse & Co.
Company Employees 700
Members 625
Pensioners 55
Capital Value Over £2 million

SIDNEY C.BANKS LTD.

29 St.Neots Road, Sandy, Beds.SG19 1LD
Telephone: 0767-80351

Secretary H.J.Tudball
Employees 703

BANRO CONSOLIDATED INDUSTRIES LTD.

Hospital Street, Walsall WS2 8QQ
Telephone: 0922-21232

Secretary N.Boden
Employees 928

THE BAPTIST UNION OF GREAT BRITAIN AND IRELAND SUPERANNUATION SCHEME

4 Southampton Row, London WC1B 4AB
Telephone: 01-405 9803

Finance Officer D.Lovegrove
Actuaries Bacon & Woodrow
Auditors Wilkins Kennedy & Co
Solicitors Ellis & Fairbairn
Employees 1,3
Members 796

THE BAPTIST UNION OF GREAT BRITAIN AND IRELAND Continued

Pensioners 547
Annual Contributions (to 31.12.79) £245,000
Annual Investment Income £273,000
Capital Value £2,908,000

BARBER & COLMAN LTD
Marsland Road, Sale M33 1UL
Telephone: 061-973 2277
Director J.Norton
Insured with Scottish Life Assurance Co
Employees 600

BARBER-GREENE ENGLAND LTD RETIREMENT BENEFITS PLAN (1972)
Western Way, Bury St Edmunds, Suffolk IP33 3TA
Telephone: 0284-63177
Director of Finance & Administration Company Secretary R.A.Lence, FCIS
Pension Fund Consultants Noble Lowndes & Partners Ltd.
Auditors Spicer & Pegler
Employees 556
Members 362
Pensioners 79
Annual Contributions £289,000

BARCLAYS BANK LTD PENSION FUND
Radbroke Hall, Knutsford, Cheshire WA16 9EU
Telephone: 0565-3888
Pensions Manager M.P.Mawdsley,ACIS,APMI
Investment Manager G.E.Hall
Trustees Barclays Bank Ltd.
Investment Management Barclays Bank Ltd.,54 Lombard Street, London EC3P 3AH
Tel: 01-626 1567
Actuaries R.Watson & Sons
Auditors Price Waterhouse & Co
Company Employees 64,000
Members 57,000
Pensioners 13,000
Annual Contributions £86.4 million
Annual Investment Income £53.4 million
Annual Outflow £42.5 million
Market Value £763.3 million

BARCLAYS BANK INTERNATIONAL LTD U.K. STAFF PENSION FUND (1964)
Barclays House, 1 Wimborne Road, Poole, Dorset BH15 2BB
Telephone: 02013-71212
PensionFund Manager A. Bolton, AIB
Trustees Barclays Bank International Ltd.
Investment Manager N.W. Defreiz, Barclays Bank International Ltd., 54 Lombard Street, London EC3P 3AH

Tel: 01-283 8989
Actuaries R. Watson & Sons
Auditors Deloitte Haskins & Sells
Company Employees 6,300
Members 6,200
Pensioners 1,075
Annual Contributions £9.4 million
Annual Investment Income £11.8 million
Gross Annual Outflow £7.1 million
MarHet Value £149.8 million

BARDON HILL GROUP LTD.
Bardon Hill, Leicester LE6 2TL
Telephone: 0530-36226
Secretary K.J.Cure,ACMA
Employees 580

BARING BROTHERS & CO.LTD. PENSION TRUST FUND
88 Leadenhall Street, London EC3A 3DT
Telephone: 01-588 2830
Company Secretary O.B.Harris,FCA
Actuaries R.Watson & Sons
Auditors Deloitte Haskins & Sells
Solicitors Slaughter & May
Company Employees (at 30.6.80) 416
Members 311
Pensioners 137
Annual Contributions £715,000
Annual Investment Income £1,348,000
Capital Value £18,602,000

CHARLES BARKER ABH INTERNATIONAL LTD.
30 Farringdon Street, London EC4A 4EA
Telephone: 01-236 3011
Secretary J.P.Derriman
Employees 531

BARKER & DOBSON GROUP LTD.
71 Great Peter Street, London SW1P 2BJ
Telephone: 01-937 6312
Pension Manager A.P.Rimmer
Trustees Barker & Dobson Pension Trustees Ltd
Investment Advisers Morgan Grenfell & Co Ltd
Actuaries Duncan C. Fraser & Co
Auditors Pannell Fitzpatrick Co.
Company Employees 2,750
Members 500
Pensioners 750
Annual Contributions £320,000
Annual Investment Income £243,000
Capital Value £2,435,000

THOS. BARLOW (HOLDINGS) LTD. SUPERANNUATION FUND
16 Stratford Place, London W1N 9AF
Telephone: 01-629 6243

Director L.T.Worthing

Stockbrokers Laurence Prust & Co.

Pension Fund Consultants C.T. Bowring & Layborn Ltd.

Auditors Kingsfords

Company Employees 2,294

Members (at 31.3.80) 1,117

Pensioners 43

Annual Contributions £908,000

Annual Investment Income £214,000

Capital Value £2,250,000

BARNARDO STAFF PENSION SCHEME
Tanners Lane, Barkingside, Ilford, Essex IG6 1QG
Telephone: 01-550 8822

Secretary/Finance Director K.L.G.Manley

Other Pension Management Lowndes Associated Pensions Ltd.

Trustees 3 Council Members, 3 Staff Members

Investment Advisers Kleinwort Benson Investment Management Ltd.

Actuaries R.Watson & Sons

Pension Fund Consultants Noble Lowndes & Partners

Auditors Price Waterhouse & Co.

Company Employees 2,700

Members 1,750

Pensioners 850

Deferreed Pensioners 165

	£000
Annual Contributions	1,456
Annual Investment Income	702
Annual Outflow	843
Capital Value	7,121
Summary of Investments	
Equities	2,361
Fixed Interest	2,707
Property	874
Cash & Deposits	750
Others	822

AUGUSTUS BARNETT & SON LTD.
North Woolwich Road, London E16 2BN

Secretary G.J.Clark

Employees 532

BARNSLEY CANISTER CO LTD
Sackville Street, Barnsley, S.Yorks.S70 2DF
Telephone: 0226-89191

Secretary P.J.Kingscott,ACIS

Employees 743

BARON ANDREW LTD
Hawksley Industrial Estate, Manchester Road, Oldham, Lancashire OL8 4PF
Telephone: 061-652 333

Secretary E.R.Archibald

Employees 500

A.G.BARR & CO LTD
1306 Gallowgate, Glasgow G31 4DS
Telephone: 041-554 1899

Secretary G.M.MacLaren

Insured with Prudential Assurance Co.Ltd.

Employees 1,337

BARR & WALLACE ARNOLD TRUST LTD PENSION & LIFE ASSURANCE FUND
21 The Calls, Leeds LS2 7ER
Telephone: 0532-36041

Secretary J.E.Foster

Trustees B. & Wat Pensions Ltd

Investment Advisers Brown, Shipley & Co Ltd

Actuaries Duncan C. Fraser & Co

Auditors Thomson McLintock & Co.

Company Employees 1,824

Members 251

Pensioners 17

	£000
Annual Contributions (to 31.12.79)	188
Annual Investment Income	96
Gross Annual Outflow	42
Capital Value	1,072
summary of Investments	
Equities	475
Fixed Interest	513
Property	1
Cash & Deposits	12
Others	54

BARRATT DEVELOPMENTS LTD.
Wingrove House, Ponteland Road, Newcastle-upon-Tyne NE5 3DP
Telephone: 0632-866811

Company Secretary I.D.McLeod,ACIS,AIB

Secretary R.W.P.James

Assistant Secretary R.D.Farrow

Pension Fund Consultants H.Clarkson (Life & Pension Consultants) Ltd

Company Employees 4,686

Members (Staff Scheme) 700

BARROW HEPBURN GROUP LTD
73 South Audley Street, London W1Y 6JR
Telephone: 01-499 6010

Company Secretary R.D.Farrow

Investment Advisers Electra Group Services Ltd, Robert Fleming Investment Management Ltd

Actuaries Duncan C. Fraser & Co

BARROW HEPBURN GROUP LTD Continued

Pension Fund Consultants H. Clarkson, (Life and Pensions Consultants) Ltd

Employees 769

A.E.BARTHOLOMEW & CO LTD

97/99 Hilliard Road, Northwood, Middlesex
Telephone: 713308

Secretary C.D.Startin

Employees 974

BARTON & SONS LTD

Marriott Road, Netherton, Dudley,
West Midlands DY2 0LA
Telephone: 0384-213661

Secretary A.L.Kendrick

Partly Insured with Prudential Assurance Company Ltd

Investment Advisers Warburg Investment Managers Ltd

Actuaries Duncan C. Fraser & Co

Company Employees 2,308

BARTON TRANSPORT LTD

61 High Road, Chilwell, Nottingham NG9 4AD
Telephone: 0602-254881

Secretary J.W.Morley,FCA

Employees 749

BASF UNITED KINGDOM LTD STAFF SUPERANNUATION SCHEME

PO Box 4, Earl Road, Cheadle Hulme,
Cheadle, Cheshire SK8 6QG
Telephone: 061-485 6222

Company Secretary R.J.Scott

Chairman of the Trustees A.H.Rusling

Part Managed by Scottish Widows' Fund and Life Assurance Society

Investment Advisers Hill Samuel Investment Management Ltd

Actuary S.Wright, FFA (Antony Gibbs Pension Services Ltd.)

Pension Consultants Antony Gibbs Pensions Services Ltd.

Auditors Deloitte Haskins & Sells

Company Employees 672

Members (at 31.12.79) 612

Pensioners 13

	£000
Annual Contributions	385
Annual Investment Income	42
Annual Outflow	76
Capital Value	
Book Value	1,921
Market Value	2,544
Summary of Investments	
SWF	1,664
Hill Samuel	796

BASS LTD EMPLOYEES' SECURITY PLAN

Guardian House, PO Box 49, Cronehills Linkway,
West Bromwich B70 8SE
Telephone: 021-553 6141

Pension Fund Manager J.A.Douthwaite,FCA,APMI

Secretary J.W.Sane, APMI

Trustees J.R.Lloyd (Chairman), R.W.Barnes, R.F.Beer, R.J.Cooper, J.E.Jones, G.R.H.Letts, J.W.Thomas, L.Walls, J.Ward, J.D.B.Williams, P.Williams

Investment Advisers J. Henry Schroder Wagg & Co Ltd

Actuaries R.Watson & Sons, Clay & Partners

Property Advisers Schroder Properties Ltd

Pension Fund Consultants Metropolitan Pensions Association Ltd, Noble Lowndes & Partners Ltd

Auditors Deloitte Haskins & Sells

Solicitors Allen & Overy

Company Employees 61,677

Members 21,212

Pensioners 8,299

	£000
Annual Contributions	16,600
Annual Investment Income	4,300
Gross Annual Outflow	5,300
Capital Value (Book Value)	67,900
Summary of Investments	
U.K. Equities	13,012
Overseas Equities	5,153
Fixed Interest	20,125
Property	9,800
Cash & Deposits	4,000
Managed Funds	15,400
Others	2,252

GEO. BASSETT HOLDINGS LTD

Livesey Street, Owlerton, Sheffield,
S.Yorks.S6 2AP
Telephone: 0742-349391

Company Secretary E.M.Mott

Managed by Legal & General Pensions Management Ltd

Company Employees 4,715

THOMAS BATES & SON LTD

The Old Brickworks, Harold Wood, Romford,
Essex RM3 0JA

Secretary D.Laing

Insured with Commercial Union Assurance Co.Ltd.

Company Employees 695

BATH AND PORTLAND PENSION PLAN

20 Manvers street, Bath BA1 1LX
Telephone: 0225-61266

Pension Fund Manager W.V.Williams

Secretary G.P.P.Hart

Trustees Bath and Portland Pension Trustees Ltd

Investment Advisers Hill Samuel Investment Management Ltd

BATH AND PORTLAND Continued

Actuaries Duncan C.Fraser & Co.
Auditors Peat, Marwick, Mitchell & Co
Company Employees 3,300
Members 1,050
Pensioners 500

	£000
Annual Contributions	800
Annual Investment Income	370
Annual Outflow	140
Capital Value	4,575
Summary of Investments	
Equities	3,415
Fixed Interest	750
Property	310
Cash & Deposits	100

B.A.T INDUSTRIES LTD AND ASSOCIATED COMPANIES

Windsor House, 50 Victoria Street,
London SW1E ONL
Telephone: 01-222 7979

Compensation and Benefits Manager K.Gibbs
Company Secretary B.G.Pearson
Investment Managers F.Cooper, G.M.Duthie, J.S.Sier
Property Manager R.D.Bowls
Total Group Employees 34,911

Certain Subsidiaries of this Group manage their own Pension Funds. The main Subsidiaries are (1) British-American Tobacco, (2) Wiggins Teape and (3) Mardon Packaging. See individual references for each of these.

BATLEYS OF YORKSHIRE LTD.

977 Leeds Road, Huddersfield HD2 1UN
Telephone: 0484-44211

Secretary A.D.Harpin
Employees 509

RICHARD BAXENDALE & SONS LIMITED

Brown Edge Road, Bamber Bridge Preston, Lancs.
Telephone: 0772-36201

Secretary J.Whalley
Employees 832

BAYER UK LTD

Bayer House, Richmond, Surrey TW9 1SJ
Telephone: 01-940 6077

Personnel Manager Elizabeth Hubbick
Company Secretary M.J.M.Mills,FCA
Insured with Legal & General Assurance Society Ltd
Employees 927

Pension Scheme at present being revised

BBA GROUP LTD PENSION FUND

P.O.Box 20, Cleckheaton,
West Yorkshire BD19 6HP
Telephone: 0274-874444

Group Pension Fund Manager J.M.Young, FPMI, FCA
Secretary P.A.Smith,JP,ACIS
Investment Manager J.H.Mear,MA
Trustee BBA Pension Fund Trustees Ltd
Stockbrokers Phillips & Drew
Property Advisers Jones, Lang, Wootton
Actuaries R.Watson & Sons
Auditors Peat Marwick Mitchell & Co.
Company Employees 4,500
Members 4,100
Pensioners 1,000

	£000
Annual Contributions	2,500
Annual Outflow	1,244
Capital Value (at 5.7.80)	29,400
Summary of Investments	
U.K.Equities	9,600
Overseas Equities	1,300
Fixed Interest	4,600
Property	11,000
Cash & Deposits	2,900

BDH 1973 PENSION SCHEME

Broom Road, Poole, Dorset BH12 4NN
Telephone: 0202-745520

Secretary J.R.Vass
Financial Director H.H.Clarke,FCA
Pensions Officer Mrs.C.C.Turner
Trustees BDH Pension Trustees Ltd.
Investment Advisers Phillips & Drew
Actuaries Bacon & Woodrow
Auditors Ernst & Whinney
Company Employees 1,145
Members 1,400
Pensioners 153

	£000
Annual Contributions	732
Annual Investment Income	576
Annual Outflow	150
Capital Value	6,000
Summary of Investments (1979)	
Equities	2,570
Fixed Interest	1,950
Cash & Deposits	220

J.E.BEALE LTD.

11-21 Commercial Road, Bournemouth, Dorset
Telephone: 0202-22322

Secretary M.C.H.Mitchell
Employees 1,086

JOHN BEALES ASSOCIATED COMPANIES LTD
Peveril Works, Peveril Street,
Nottingham NG7 4AQ
Telephone: 0602-72221

Secretary W.P.L.Rogers

Managed by Commercial Union Assurance Co Ltd

Employees 2,011

See also Marathon Knitwear (Nottingham) Ltd.

BEATSON, CLARK & CO LTD
23 Moorgate Road, Rotherham, S.Yorks.S60 2AA
Telephone: 0709-79141

Secretary A.Ferguson

Managed by Legal & General (Pensions Management) Ltd

Employees 1,420

JAMES BEATTIE (WOLVERHAMPTON) PENSION FUND
71-78 Victoria Street, Wolverhampton,
West Midlands WV1 3PQ
Telephone: 0902-22311

Pension Fund Manager/Secretary G.T.Lowndes, FCA

Trustees James Beattie (Wolverhampton) Pensions Ltd

Stockbrokers Sheppards & Chase

Actuarial Advice obtained through Cubie Wood & Co Ltd

Pension Fund Consultants Noble Lowndes & Partners Ltd

Auditors Bertram Kidson & Co

Employees 2,066

Members 632

Pensioners 150

	£000
Annual Contributions	311
Annual Investment Income	261
Annual Outflow	136
Capital Value	2,750
Summary of Investments	
Equities	1,195
Fixed Interest	1,035
Cash & Deposits	174
Others	244

BEAVERBROOK NEWSPAPERS LTD
121-8 Fleet Street, London EC4P 4JT
Telephone: 01-353 8000

Pensions Controller S.Batten

Company Secretary F.L.Tyler

Pension Fund Consultants Godwins Ltd

Employees 7,063

C.H.BEAZER (HOLDINGS) LTD.
2 Midland Bridge Road, Bath BA2 3EY
Telephone: 0225-28401

Secretary A.Chapple

Employees 766

BECHTEL INTERNATIONAL LTD.
Bechtel House, 245 Hammersmith Road,
London W6 8DP
Telephone: 01-741 5245

Pensions Administrator J.S.Walsh, FCIS

BECK & CO (METERS) LTD
Beckmeter Works, Streatham Vale,
London SW16 5HP
Telephone: 01-764 5201

Chairman & Managing Director C.L.Prentice

Employees 500

BECKMAN INSTRUMENTS LTD
Queensway, Glenrothes KY7 5PU
Telephone: 0592-753811

Managing Director D.H.Harcombe

Employees 600

BECTON DICKINSON PENSION SCHEME FOR U.K.EMPLOYEES
Nutritional Research Unit, Cromwell House,
Huntingdon, Cambs.PE18 6ES
Telephone: 0480-890431

Pension Fund Manager C.H.Hill,FCA

Secretary J.West,MIPM

Administrator A.G.Speller

Trustees C.H.Hill, K.F.Rivett, J.D.Lewis, J.H.Cole, Mrs.S.Kynoch, K.A.L.Elsey, J.M.Gross

Investment Advisers J.Henry Schroder Wagg & Co.Ltd.

Actuarial Advice Obtained through Cubie Wood & Co.Ltd.

Pension Fund Consultants Noble Lowndes & Partners Ltd.

Auditors Ernst & Whinney

Company Employees 1,000

Members 975

Pensioners 20

	£000
Annual Contributions	325
Annual Investment Income	80
Annual Outflow	152
Capital Value	1,204
Summary of Investments	
Equities	500
Fixed Interest	380
Property	120
Cash & Deposits	70
Others	90

BEDFORDSHIRE COUNTY COUNCIL SUPERANNUATION FUND
County Hall, Bedford MK42 9AP
Telephone: 0234-63222

Treasurer V.F.Phillips, IPFA, FCA

Superannuation Officer M.G.Vought, APMI

Trustees Bedfordshire County Council

Stockbrokers de Zoete and Bevan, Fielding Newson Smith, Foster and Braithwaite

BEDFORDSHIRE COUNTY COUNCIL Continued

Actuaries R.Watson & Sons
Auditors District Audit
Employees 23,000
Members (at 31.3.80) 8,420
Pensioners 2,195

	£000
Annual Contributions	6,643
Annual Investment Income 3,334	3334
Annual Outflow	4,465
Capital Value	38,017
Summary of Investments	
Equities	21,573
Fixed Interest	12,761
Property Unit Trusts	3,581
Cash & Deposits	102

BEECHAM UK PENSION FUND

Beecham House, Great West Road, Brentford, Middlesex TW8 9BD
Telephone: 01-560 5151

Pensions Manager J.V. Corke

Personnel Director R.E.Newman

Part Insured with Eagle Star Insurance Company Ltd

Investment Advisers Hill Samuel Investment Management Ltd

Actuaries Bacon & Woodrow

Pension Fund Consultants Noble Lowndes & Partners Ltd.

Auditors Price Waterhouse & Co.

Employees(UK) 15,800

Members 11,000

Pensioners 2,000

Annual Contributions £8 million

Capital Value £10 million

BEECHWOOD CONSTRUCTION (HOLDINGS) LTD

Rhosmaen, Llandeilo, Dyfed SA19 7HR
Telephone: 055-82 3781

Secretary K.B.Ferguson

Insured with Scottish Widows' Fund & Life Assurance Society

Employees 559

THE BEJAM GROUP OF COMPANIES PENSION AND ASSURANCE PLAN

1 Garland Road, Honeypot Lane, Stanmore, Middlesex HA7 1LE
Telephone: 01-952 8311

Secretary J.S.Gunn, FCA

Assistant Pensions Manager R. Cohen

Trustees A.W.Perry, J.S.Gunn, R.T.Henderson

Managed by Legal & General Assurance (Pension Management) Ltd.; Scottish Amicable Pensions Investment Ltd.

Pension Fund Consultants & Actuarial Advice Obtained through Wyatt Harris Graham Ltd.
Auditors Stoy Hayward & Co.
Company Employees 3,000
Members 650
Pensioners 16

BELFAST HARBOUR COMMISSIONERS

Harbour Office, Corporation Square, Belfast
Telephone: 0232-34422

Director W.H.Barnett

Executive C.Nimmons

Employees 500

ARTHUR BELL & SONS LTD PENSION FUND

Cherrybank, Perth PH2 0NG
Telephone: 0738-21111

Company Secretary M.C.O.Davies

Secretary J.C.Allison

Trustees R.C.Miquel, D.A.H.Harley, G.T.Cooper

Insured with Scottish Amicable Life Assurance Society

Pension Fund Consultants Metropolitan Pension Association Ltd, Glasgow

Company Employees 1,965

BELL & HOWELL LTD

Lennox Road, Basingstoke, Hampshire RG22 4AW
Telephone: 0256-20244

Secretary B.F.G.Findlay

Insured with Swiss Life Insurance & Pension Co.

Employees 680

BELLING & COMPANY LTD RETIREMENT BENEFITS PLAN

Bridge Works, Southbury Road, Enfield, Middlesex
Telephone: 01-804 1212

Company Secretary L.H.Brittain,FCIS,APMI

Investment Advisers Laing & Cruickshanks

Pension Fund Consultants Noble Lowndes & Partners Ltd

Auditors Hereward Scott Davies & Co.

Company Employees 2,107

Members 1,000

Pensioners 250

Annual Contributions £472,000

Annual Investment Income £289,000

Capital Value £3,368,000

BELLWAY LTD.

Dobson House, Regent Centre, Gosforth, Newcastle-upon-Tyne NE3 3LT
Telephone: 0632-850121

Secretary R.I.Stewart

Insured with Sun Alliance & London Insurance Ltd

Employees 1,121

The Major UK Pension Funds **BED/BEN**

BEMROSE CORPORATION LTD (A) STAFF RETIREMENT BENEFITS PLAN, (B) GROUP WORKS PENSION SCHEME

P.O.Box 52, Wayzgoose Drive, Derby DE2 6XP
Telephone: 0332-31242

Pensions Officer Mrs. B.Lockley,

Company Secretary D.F.Robinson

Secretary Lowndes Associated Pensions Ltd.

Trustees Staff Plan (A) Lowndes Associated Pensions Ltd., D.F.Robinson, C.J.Littlewood, C.A.Brown, N.walker

Trustees Works Plan (B) Lowndes Associated Pensions Ltd., D.F.Robinson, J.Myott, T.Taylor, W.Wawman

Investment Advisers (a) Hill Samuel Investment Management Ltd., (b) Morgan Grenfell & Co.Ltd., S.G.Warburg & Co.Ltd.

Actuarial Advice obtained through Cubie Wood & Co Ltd

Pension Fund Consultants Lowndes Associated Pensions Ltd

Auditors Price Waterhouse & Co.

Company Employees (at 31.7.80) 2,744

	Staff (at 1.1.80)	Works (at 6.4.80)
Members	899	1,748
Pensioners	68	34
	£000	£000
Annual Contributions	581	920
Annual Investment Income	2,486	83
Annual Outflow	157	200
Capital Value	4,067	1,700
Summary of Investments		
Equities	2,486	840
Fixed Interest	472	455
Property	558	81
Cash & Deposits	41	189
Others	509	135

BENDIX PENSION SCHEME

Douglas Road, Kingswood, Near Bristol BS15 2NL
Telephone: 0272-671881

Pension Fund Manager P.M.James

Managed by Legal & General Assurance (Pensions Management) Ltd.; Sun Life Pensions Management Ltd.

Investment Advisers Warburg Investment Management Ltd.

Actuarial Advice Obtained through Cubie, Wood & Co Ltd.

Pension Fund Consultants Lowndes Associated Pensions Ltd.

Auditors Deloitte, Haskins & Sells

Members 1,100(Approx)

Pensioners 95

Annual Contributions £600,000

Capital Value £2.5 million

BENFORD CONCRETE MACHINERY LTD

PO Box 26, The Cape, Warwick CV34 5DR
Telephone: 0926-43466

Secretary C.F.Woffenden

Insured with Scottish Widows' Fund & Life Assurance Society

Employees 789

BENN BROTHERS LTD (SIR ERNEST BENN PENSION FUND)

25 New Street Square, London EC4A 3JA
Telephone: 01-353 3212

Pensions Officer Miss K.H.Smith

Company Secretary J.Secker

Stockbrokers Phillips & Drew

Actuaries Hymans, Robertson & Co.

Auditors Deloitte Haskins & Sells

Company Employees 628

Members 374

Pensioners 207

Capital Value £2,400,000

BENNETT BROS (HOSIERY MFTRS & DYERS) LTD

PO Box 5, Standard Works, Southfield Road, Hinckley Leics
Telephone: 0455-32931

Secretary W.D.Swinfield, FCA, ACMA

Employees 500

BENTALLS SENIOR STAFF PENSION FUND

Wood Street, Kingston upon Thames, Surrey KT1 1TX
Telephone: 01-546 1001

Pension Fund Manager Mrs. C.J.Pumphrey

Secretary A.T.Jones

Trustees L.E.Rowan Bentall, J.Spooner, L.Edward Bentall, T.G.M.Buckley

Investment Advisers County Bank Ltd

Stockbrokers W.Greenwell & Co

Actuaries R.Watson & Sons

Auditors Spicer & Pegler

Company Employees 2,921 (including 1,185 part-time staff)

Members 345

Pensioners 123

	£000
Annual Contributions	257
Annual Investment Income	301
Annual Outflow	146
Capital Value	3,246
Summary of Investments	
Equities	2,079
Fixed Interest	1,040
Cash & Deposits	127

BEREC (U.K.) PENSION FUND

Berec House, 1255 High Road, Whetstone, London N20 0EJ
Telephone: 01-446 1313

Pension Fund Manager & Secretary Alan Thorn, FCIS, FPMI

Trustees Berec (U.K.) Pension Fund Ltd

Stockbrokers Phillips & Drew

Actuaries Bacon & Woodrow

Auditors Josolyne,Layton Bennett & Co.

Company Employees 11,200

Members 7,000

Pensioners 1,400

	£000
Annual Contributions	2,800
Annual Investment Income	1,300
Gross Annual Outflow	1,200
Capital Value	15,000
Summary of Investments	
Equities	9,000
Fixed Interest	5,000
Cash & Deposits	1,000

BERGER, JENSON & NICHOLSON LTD

Berger House, Berkeley Square, London W1X 6NB
Telephone: 01-629 9171

Secretary K.W.Judd

Employees 4,932

S & W BERISFORD GROUP PENSION, LIFE ASSURANCE AND WIDOWS' & CHILDREN'S PENSION SCHEMES

50 Mark Lane, London EC3R 7QJ
Telephone: 01-488 3211

Secretary C.Hackworth, ACIS

Trustees N.G.Hanson, FCA, R.T.Burgess, FCA, C.Hackworth, ACIS

Managed by Pensions Management (SWF) Ltd, Scottish Amicable Pensions Investments Ltd

Stockbrokers W.Greenwell & Co

Actuarial Advice obtained through Cubie, Wood & Co.Ltd.

Property Advisers Kennington

Pension Fund Consultants Noble Lowndes & Partners Ltd

Company Employees 2,936

Members 650

Annual Income £750,000 (1977)

Annual Outflow £300,000 (1977)

Capital Value £3.8 million (1977)

BERISFORDS LTD PENSION FUND AND LIFE INSURANCE SCHEME AND JUNIOR STAFF AND WEEKLY PAID WORKS EMPLOYEES PENSION SCHEME

PO Box 2, Congleton Cheshire CW12 1EF
Telephone: 02602-2864

Pension Fund Manager & Secretary W.N.Thomson, FCA

Trustees S.J.Sebire, E.R.Waller, M.F.Waltho, A.Parker, S.Smith

Insured with Norwich Union Life Insurance Society

Pension Fund Consultants Hogg Robinson (Benefit Consultants) Ltd.

Auditors Touche Ross & Co.

Employees 832

Members (total both schemes) 482

Pensioners 21

Annual Contributions £180,000

BERKSHIRE COUNTY COUNCIL SUPERANNUATION FUND

P.O.Box 12, Shire Hall, Reading, Berks.RG1 3EX
Telephone: 0734-55981

Treasurer M.C.Beasley, BSc(Econ), IPFA, FCA

Investment Adviser K.G.Smith

Property Advisers Jones Lang Wootton

Actuaries Robertson,Hymans & Co.

Employees 26,500

Members 8,700

Pensioners 2,700

Annual Contributions £8 million

Annual Investment Income £4 million

Capital Value £52 million

BERLEI (UK) LTD

Berlei House, Bath Road, Slough, Berks.SL1 4AT
Telephone: 34505

Secretary D.P.R.James

Investment Advisers Hill Samuel Investment Management Ltd

Employees 2,499

BERNARD C.H. & SONS LTD

Anglia House, Main Road, Harwich, Essex
Telephone: 02555-2281

Managing Director T.M.F.Bernard, JP, FCA

Employees 550

BERWICK TIMPO LTD

Wells House, 79 Wells Street, London W1P 3RE
Telephone: 01-637 9421

Pensions Dept. c/o Towry Law Trustees Ltd., High Street,Windsor,Berks.
Telephone: 07535-68244

Secretary T.Goodfellow

Trustees Towry Law Trustee Co.Ltd.

Managed by Sun Life (Pensions Management) Ltd.

Pension Fund Consultants Towry Law (Pension Services) Ltd.

Company Employees 841

Members 60

Pensioners 6

Annual Contributions £50,000

Capital Value £200,000

BESTOBELL PENSION FUND & LIFE ASSURANCE SCHEME

Bestobell House, 16 Bath Road, Slough, Berks.SL1 3SS
Telephone: Slough 33477

Pension Fund Manager & Secretary N.P.Wrighton

Trustee Bestobell Pension Trust Ltd

Managed by Legal & General Assurance Society Ltd

Investment Advisers Godwins Ltd

Pension Fund Consultants and Actuarial Advice obtained through Godwins Ltd

Auditors Fryer, Whitehill & Co.

Solicitors Allen & Overy

Company Employees (at 31.12.79) 3,319

Members (at 1.10.80) 1,935

Pensioners 383

	£000
Annual Contributions (to 30.9.80)	1,352
Annual Investment Income	2
Annual Outflow	367
Capital Value	5,896
Summary of Investments	
Equities/Mixed	4,281
Fixed Interest	4
Property	1,609
Others	12

THE BET GROUP SUPERANNUATION SCHEME

Stratton House, Piccadilly, London W1X 6AS
Telephone: 01-629 8886

Pension Scheme Secretary E.F.Bell, FCIS

Pension Fund Consultants Legal & General Assurance Society Ltd, Noble Lowndes & Partners Ltd

Auditors F.W.Smith Riches & Co

Group Employees 4,231

Members 700

Pensioners 100

Annual Contributions £500,000

BETT BROTHERS LTD. SUPERANNUATION FUND, CASH BENEFIT & LIFE ASSURANCE SCHEME

9 Cox Street, Dundee DD1 9AB
Telephone: 0382-84191

Secretary D.C.Robins

Trustees S.C.Bett, I.C.R.Bett, R.Mitchell, S.Aitken, J.Peterson, D.C.Robins

Insured with Scottish Amicable Life Assurance Society

Pension Fund Consultants Reed Stenhouse Benefit Consultants Ltd.

Company Employees 1,517

Members 200 approx

Pensioners 9

Annual Contributions £152,000

BETTERWEAR PRODUCTS LTD

North Street, Romford RM1 1ET
Telephone: 0708-42233

Director B.C.Willis

Employees 500

BIBBY (1974) PENSION SCHEME AND (1977) PENSION SCHEME

Richmond House, 1 Rumford Place, Liverpool L3 9QQ
Telephone: 051-227 1291

Secretary and Pensions Manager P.D.Goodstein, MA,PhD,APMI

Personnel Director N.G.Price,APMI

Trustees (1974) Pension Scheme

Company Trustees J.Bibby (Chairman), J.R.M.Rocke, N.G.Price, K.A.Allan, L.C.Young

Member Trustees W.B.Bender, B.Clay, A.Griffiths, R.E.Walker

Trustees (1977) Pension Scheme

Company Trustees J.B.Bibby (Chairman) J.R.M.Rocke, N.G.Price, K.A.Allan

Member Trustees E.H.Capstick, R.V.Crawford, J.W.Stoddart

Investment Advisers County Bank Ltd and N.M.Rothschild Asset Management Ltd

Stockbrokers Tilney & Co., Rowe & Pitman

Property Advisers Smiths Gore

Actuaries Duncan C.Fraser & Co.

Auditors Edward Denton & Co.

Company Employees (June 1980) 3,639

	(1974) Scheme	(1977) Scheme
Members (at 5.4.80)	2,687	63
Pensioners	2,457	7
Preserved Pensions	804	9
	£000	£000
Annual Contributions	1,308	287
Annual Investment Income	1,834	187
Gross Annual Outflow	1,634	90
Capital Value (Market Value)	20,021	2,472
Summary of Investments		
U.K.Equities	10,307	1,295
Overseas Securities	1,247	158
Fixed Interest	5,955	488
Agricultural Property	1,272	-
Property Unit Trusts	-	137
Cash & Deposits	736	244
Others	275	55

BICC GROUP PENSION FUND

PO Box 1, Prescot, Merseyside L34 5SZ
Telephone: 051-426 6571

Pension Fund Manager J.B.Dennis, FIA, FPMI

BICC GROUP Continued

Secretary S.R.Muchmore, APMI
Trustees BICC Group Pension Trust Ltd
Investment Managers Morgan Grenfell & Co, Fielding, Newson-Smith & Co
Actuaries R. Watson & Sons
Property Advisers Matthews Goodman & Postlethwaite
Auditors Chalmers Impey & Co
Company Employees 33,047
Members 21,2095
Pensioners 5,889

	£000
Annual Contributions	12,576
Annual Investment Income	9,030
Annual Outflow	6,528
Capital Value	115,085
Summary of Investments	
Equities	61,820
Fixed Interest	29,660
Property	20,104
Cash & Deposits	3,492

BICKLEY J & S LTD

37/45 Faith Rd, Croydon, Surrey

Financial Director & Secretary G.Ellen
Employees 800

BIDDLE HOLDINGS LTD PENSION & LIFE ASSURANCE PLAN

16 Upper Grosvenor Street, London W1X 0BQ
Telephone: 01-493 0532

Secretary F.Papworth
Insured with Scottish Widows' Fund & Life Insurance Society
Actuaries Clay & Partners
Pension Fund Consultants Metropolitan Pensions Association Ltd.
Auditors Touche Ross & Co.
Employees 1,042
Members (at 6.4.80) 336
Pensioners 98
Annual Contributions £160,000

BIFURCATED ENGINEERING LTD RETIREMENT BENEFITS PLAN (1972)

P.O.Box 2, Mandeville Road, Aylesbury, Bucks.HP21 8AB
Telephone: 0296-5911

Pension Fund Manager & Secretary D.Whitehead, FCIS
Trustees J.M.A.Paterson, MA, D.Whitehead, FCIS, G.S.Young, OBE
Investment Advisers Geoffrey Morley & Partners Ltd
Stockbrokers Laurence Prust & Co.

Actuaries & Pension Fund Consultants Clay & Partners
Auditors F.L.Rouse & Co
Company Employees 1,200
Members 920
Pensioners 230

	£000
Annual Contributions	650
Annual Investment Income	120
Gross Annual Outflow	150
Capital Value	2,317
Summary of Investments	
Equities	1,413
Fixed Interest	150
Property Unit Trusts	204
Cash & Deposits	550

BIGGS WALL GROUP PENSION SCHEME

Hampden House, Hitchin Road, Arlesey, Beds.SG15 6RT
Telephone: 0462-751133

Secretary D.W.Brown,FCA
Trustees D.W.Brown, G.V.Brown, Miss S.M.Beard
Insured with Scottish Widows' Fund & Life Assurance Society
Pension Fund Consultants Reed Stenhouse U.K. Ltd.
Auditors Rowland Nevill & Company
Company Employees 504
Members 130
Pensioners 15
Annual Contributions £43,000
Annual Investment Income £38,000
Annual Outflow £24,000

BILLITON (U.K.) LTD

Dominion Buildings, South Place, London EC2M 2RE

Secretary D.E.Church
Employees 1,618

BILTON (1912) LTD.

London Road, Stoke on Trent Staffs.
Telephone: 0782-45584

Secretary A.Shaw
Employees 520

PERCY BILTON LTD STAFF SUPERANNUATION FUND

Bilton House, 54/58 Uxbridge Road, London W5 2TL
Telephone: 01-567 7777

Company Secretary P.G.Myers
Secretary & Personnel Officer I.W.G.Alcock
Actuaries Hymans, Robertson & Co.
Auditors Ball Baker
Company Employees 879
Members 238

PERCY BILTON LTD *Continued*

Pensioners 92
Annual Contributions £190,000
Annual Investment Income £312,000
Capital Value £2,300,000

BINDER HAMLYN RETIREMENT BENEFITS FUND
8 St.Bride Street, London EC4A 4DA
Telephone: 01-681 3521
Secretary E.G.Heaven
Investment Advisers J.Henry Schroder Wagg & Co.Ltd.
Pension Fund Consultants Antony Gibbs Pension Services Ltd.
Members (at 31.3.80) 411
Pensioners 42
Annual Contributions £352,000
Annual Investment Income £188,000
Capital Value £2,585,000

BIRDS (DERSA) LTD
Ascot Drive, Derby
Telephone: 0332-361316
Financial Director & Secretary B.A.Harrison
Employees 635

BIRMID QUALCAST LTD. GROUP STAFF PENSION PLAN AND 1978 WORKS PENSION PLAN
Smethwick, Warley, West Midlands B66 1BW
Telephone: 021-558 1431
Group Secretary A.W.Galbraith,FSCA,APMI
Assistant Group Secretary A.C.Smith,ACIS
Pension Administrator F.W.Woodley
Works Scheme Part Insured, Part Managed by Equity & Law Life Assurance Society Ltd., Legal & General Assurance Society Ltd., Scottish Widows' Fund & Life Assurance Society
Staff Scheme Managed by Legal & General (Pensions Management) Ltd.
Pension Fund Consultants Sedgwick Employee Benefits Consultants Ltd.
Auditors Coopers & Lybrand
Company Employees 14,309

	Staff	Works
Members	2,500	8,000
Pensioners	300	500
	£000	£000
Annual Contributions	2,350	3,700
Capital Value	16,500	8,400

BIRMINGHAM BATTERY & METAL CO.LTD.
P.O.Box 320, Selly Oak, Birmingham B29 6AB
Telephone: 021-472 1151

Secretary H.Annandale,FCA
Employees 625

BIRMINGHAM CO-OPERATIVE SOCIETY LTD EMPLOYEES' SUPERANNUATION FUND
27-38 High Street, Birmingham B4 7SP
Telephone: 021-643 5071
Financial Accountant & Superannuation Officer E.W.Lee, FCIS, CSD
Investment Advisers Drayton Montagu Portfolio Management Ltd
Actuary P.D.Johnson,MA,FIA (Co-operative Insurance Society Ltd.)
Auditors Appleby English & Partners
Employees 5,465
Members 2,765
Pensioners 1,228
Annual Contributions £637,000
Annual Investment Income £880,000
Capital Value £10,598,000

BIRMINGHAM MINT LTD. STAFF PENSION & LIFE ASSURANCE SCHEME
The Mint, Icknield Street, Birmingham B18 6RX
Telephone: 021-236 7742
Financial Director & Secretary Paul A. Tranter, B.Com,FCA
Insured with Guardian Royal Exchange Assurance Group Ltd.
Company Employees 420
Members 80

BIRMINGHAM POST & MAIL STAFF PENSION FUND
See **BPM Holdings Ltd.**

BISHOP'S STORES LTD
Stonefield Way, Ruislip, Middlesex HA4 0JR
Telephone: 01-422 9511
Secretary M.A.Horsfield
Investment Advisers Hill Samuel Investment Management Ltd
Employees 4,208
Members 400

BISON GROUP PENSION FUND
344 Kensington High Street, London W14 8NS
Telephone: 01-602 4744
Secretary D.A.Tunstill, FCIS, APMI
Scheme Administrator C.W.Holliday
Trustees Bison Group Pension Fund Ltd
Investment Advisers Henderson Administration Ltd
Stockbrokers Cazenove & Co
Actuaries Bacon & Woodrow
Auditors Robson Rhodes
Employees 2,900
Members 650
Pensioners 270

BISON GROUP Continued

	£000
Annual Contributions	480
Annual Investment Income	280
Annual Outflow	280
Capital Value	4,746
Summary of Investments	
Equities	2,689
Fixed Interest	1,029
Property	36
Cash & Deposits	510
Others	482

BIWATER GROUP LTD.
Biwater House, Mill Road, Holmwood, Dorking, Surrey RH5 4NU
Telephone: W.O.T. 24101

Secretary D.E.Rackett, FCA, FCIS

Employees 508

CHAS. BIZLEY & CO LTD
Arminghall Cl, Norwich, Norfolk
Telephone: 0603-43441

Director A.S.Lane

Employees 800

BL LTD.
See under British Leyland Ltd.

BLACK & DECKER LTD 1973 PENSION PLAN
Cannon Lane, Maidenhead, Berks.SL6 3PD
Telephone: 062882-2130

Company Secretary F.N.Woolley

Investment Advisers Morgan Grenfell & Co.Ltd.

Pension Fund Consultants Wyatt Harris Graham Ltd.

Auditors Ernst & Whinney

Solicitors McKenna & Co.

Employees 3,443

Members (at 5.4.80) 2,200

Pensioners 340

Annual Contributions £1,647,000

Annual Investment Income £500,000

Capital Value £9,200,000

BLACK & EDGINGTON LTD. GROUP PENSION SCHEME
Port Glasgow, PA14 5XN
Telephone: 0475-42333

Secretary S.B.J.Hodge,CA

Investment Advisers N.M.Rothschild Asset Management Ltd. and Stenhouse Exempt Funds

Actuaries Duncan C.Fraser & Co.

Auditors Welsh Walker & Co.

Company Employees 3,500

Members 850

Pensioners 214

	£000
Annual Contributions	346
Annual Investment Income	186
Annual Outflow	177
Capital Value	2,677
Summary of Investments	
Equities	1,930
Fixed Interest	694
Cash & Deposits	28

PETER BLACK HOLDINGS LTD
Airedale Mill, Keighley, Yorks BD21 3JQ
Telephone: 0535-61177

Secretary H.Rothenberg

Employees 1,697

W.B.BLACK & SONS (HOLDINGS) LTD
1265 Gallowgate, Glasgow G31 4DY
Telephone: 041-556 5151

Director W.B.Black

Employees 500

BLACKDALE-NSE LTD
Howard Way, Temple Field, Harlow, Essex CM20 2AE
Telephone: 02796-26741

Secretary R.B.Baker,FCA

Employees 650

BLACKMAN & CONRAD LTD
St Alphage House, Fore Street, London EC2Y 5DH
Telephone: 01-628 9771

Secretary Mrs.J.Arons

Insured with Clerical, Medical & General Life Assurance

Employees 758

BH BLACKWELL LTD SUPERANNUATION FUND
50 Broad Street, Oxford
Telephone: 0895-9111

Secretary C.A.Palmer, FSCA

Investment Advisers Grieveson Grant & Co

Actuaries & Pension Fund Consultants Lane Clark & Peacock

Auditors Critchley Ward & Pigott

Company Employees 788

Members 435

Pensioners 70

Annual Contributions £326,000

Annual Investment Income £211,000

Capital Value £2,325,000

BLACKWOOD HODGE (1975) PENSION & LIFE ASSURANCE SCHEME
Hunsbury Hill Avenue, Northampton NN4 9QT
Telephone: 0604-61111

Pension Fund Manager D.J.Billingham, ACIS

Company Secretary I.Jenkins,FCIS

BLACKWOOD HODGE Continued

Trustees W.A.Shapland, I.Jenkins, E.L.Coulton, H.M.Hayes

Insured with Guardian Royal Exchange Assurance Ltd (Deferred Annuities & Term Life Assurance

Pension Fund Consultants Reed Stenhouse Benefit Consultants Ltd.

Employees 1,854

Members (at 31.12.79) 916

Pensioners 37

Annual Contributions £575,000

BLACKWOOD, MORTON & SONS (HOLDINGS) LTD BMK ORGANISATION SUPERANNUATION FUND

Burnside Works, Kilmarnock KA1 4HB
Telephone: 0563-21100

Secretary J.F.Gilmour

Employees 2,191

BLAGDEN & NOAKES (HOLDINGS) LTD

16 Hatton Garden, London EC1N 8FJ
Telephone: 01-242 6571

Secretary G.L.Levine

Employees 2,354

GEORGE BLAIR & CO.LTD.

Newcastle Alloy Steelworks, Forth,
Newcastle-on-Tyne NE1 3RB
Telephone: 0632-610711

Managing Director I.L.Blair

Employees 772

THE BLOXWICH LOCK & STAMPING CO LTD

Alexander Works, Bell Lane, Bloxwich,
West Midlands WSO 2JR
Telephone: 0922-76234

Managing Director & Secretary E.L.S.Sanders

Employees 784

BLUE BOAR GROUP (HOLDINGS) LTD.

11 Albert Street, Rugby CV21 2SB
Telephone: 0788-76221

Employees 549

BLUE BELL APPAREL LTD

Park Road East, Calverton, Nottingham NG14 6GD
Telephone: 060744-3088

Managing Director E.A.Morris

Employees 641

BLUE STAR LINE LTD

14 West Smithfield, London EC3A 1AR
Telephone: 01-248 1212

Pension Fund Manager R.W.C.Offwood, FPMI

Employees 2,500

BLUEMEL BROS LTD

The Works, Wolston, Coventry,
West Midlands CV8 3FU
Telephone: 020-335 244

Secretary G.Wolfe, ACMA, FCIS

Employees 511

BLUNDELL-PERMOGLAZE HOLDINGS LTD. (A) SENIOR MANAGEMENT, (B)STAFF SUPERANNUATION FUND & ASSURANCE SCHEME, (C)WORKS PENSION & ASSURANCE SCHEME

York House, 37 Queen Square, London WC1N 3BL
Telephone: 01-242 6877

Secretary J.R.Power

Trustees N.C.Bassett Smith, P.F.M.Coverdale, A.C.Hornsby, R.L.White, also for B & C Schemes J.Wray

Part Managed by Legal & General (Pensions Management) Ltd.

Investment Advisers Electra Group Services Ltd.

Pension Fund Consultants Edward Lumley (Life & Pensions) Ltd.

Auditors Deloitte Haskins & Sells

Company Employees 729

Members (a)25, (b)291, (c)267

Pensioners (a)10, (b)122, (c)57

Annual Contributions (a) £113,000, (b) £243,000, (c)£123,000

Capital Value (a)£795,000, (b)£1,595,000, (c)£501,000

BLYTHE COLOURS LTD

Creswell, Stoke on Trent, Staffs.ST11 9RD
Telephone: 0782-85666

Secretary A.H.Bowyer

Employees 756

BLYTH,GREENE,JOURDAIN & CO.LTD.

Plantation House, Fenchurch Street,
London EC3M 3EE
Telephone: 01-623 2050

Secretary R.A.Schlee

Employees 774

K.O.BOARDMAN INTERNATIONAL LTD

Palmer Mill, Mersey Street, Stockport SK1 2HN
Telephone: 061-480 7611

Secretary F.R.Thorburn,FCA

Employees 1,215

J.BOARDMANS LTD.

60 Leigh Rd, Leigh, Lancs
Telephone: 0942-72271

Secretary T.Wyatt

Employees 500

BOC INTERNATIONAL LTD. NO.1 AND NO.2 PENSION SCHEMES

Hammersmith House, London W6 9DX
Telephone: 01-748 2020

Pension Manager E.A.C.Penfold, FCA, APMI

Secretary P.R.Styles, APMI

Trustees B.O.C. Pensions Ltd. - Corporate and 6 individuals

The Major UK Pension Funds BOC/BOU

BOC INTERNATIONAL LTD. Continued

Principal Stockbrokers Fielding Newson-Smith & Co

Actuaries R.Watson & Sons

Auditors Coopers & Lybrand

Total Employees 18,000

	No.1 Scheme	No.2 Scheme
Members (5.4.80)	7,300	8,250
Pensioners	2,290	3,550
	£ million	£ million
Annual Contributions	5.0	12.0
Annual Investment Income	1.9	8.5
Annual Outflow	1.8	5.6
Capital Value	32.0	108.0
Summary of Investments		
Equities	9.8	36.0
Fixed Interest	17.1	57.1
Property Unit Trusts	2.7	7.6
Cash & Deposits	2.4	7.3

BODDINGTONS' BREWERIES LTD

Strangeways Brewery, Manchester M60 3EL
Telephone: 061-831 7881

Secretary M.D.Fitzgerald

Insured with Legal & General Assurance Society Ltd

Employees 1,433

BODYCOTE INTERNATIONAL LTD

104 Stamford Street, Manchester M16 9LR
Telephone: 061-226 5021

Secretary P.A.Blamires

Employees 1,822

BOLTON GATE CO LTD

Turton St, Bolton, Lancs
Telephone: 0204-32111

Managing Director G.M.Morley

Investment Advisers Illingworth & Henriques

Employees 500

BOND STREET FABRICS LTD.

Wimbledon Works, Wimbledon Street, Leicester LE1 1SN
Telephone: 0533-29596

Joint Managing Directors J.S.Liddell, C.T.Stewart

Stockbrokers Sheppards & Chase

Employees 731

BOOKER PENSION FUND

Glynswood House, 62-68 Oak End Way, Gerrards Cross, Bucks.SL9 8BR
Telephone: 02813-87355

Registered Office Bucklersbury House, 83 Cannon Street, London EC4N 8EJ

Pension Fund Director F.V.C.Millward

Investment Manager D.Taylor

Trustees Bookers Pensions Ltd.

Property Advisers Richard Ellis

Actuaries Duncan C.Fraser & Co.

Auditors Pannell Fitzpatrick & Co.

Company Employees 20,220

Members 7,005

Pensioners 1,672

	£000
Annual Contributions (to 30.6.80)	3,100
Annual Investment Income	3,000
Annual Outflow	2,800
Capital Value	34,600
Summary of Investments	
Equities	16,500
Fixed Interest	11,800
Property	3,800
Cash & Deposits	2,500

BOOSEY & HAWKES LTD SUPERANNUATION FUND

c/o Norfolk House, Wellesley Road, croydon CR9 3EB

Registered Office 295 Regent Street, London W1R 8JH (01-580 2060)

Company Secretary G.W.King

Trustees Lowndes Associated Pensions Ltd.

Investment Advisers National Westminster Bank Ltd., Legal & General Assurance (Pensions Management) Ltd.

Actuarial Advice Obtained through Cubie, Wood & Co. Ltd.

Pension Fund Consultants Noble Lowndes & Partners Ltd.

Auditors Price Waterhouse & Co.

Employees 865

HENRY BOOT & SONS LTD STAFF PENSION & LIFE ASSURANCE SCHEME

Banner Cross Hall, Sheffield S11 9PD
Telephone: 0742-54331

Secretary A.W.Marsh

Company Employees 3,756

Members 1,197

Pensioners 92

ALFRED BOOTH & CO LTD

34 St James's Street, London SW1A 1JA
Telephone: 01-930 8383

Secretary R.J.Teather

Employees 2,210

E.H.BOOTH & CO.LTD

4/6 Fishergate, Preston, Lancs
Telephone: 0772-51701

Chairman J.G.Booth

Insured with Legal & General Assurance Society Ltd

Employees 1,030

BOOTH (INTERNATIONAL HOLDINGS) LTD
Trent Bridge Leather Works, Nottingham NG2 3BT
Telephone: 0602-866382
Managing Director J.S.M.Booth
Secretary P.G.Stribbling
Employees 811

BOOTS PENSION SCHEME
1 Thane Road West, Nottingham NG2 3AA
Telephone: 0602-56111
Pension Fund Manager & Secretary P.H.Taylor, APMI
Trustees Boots Pensions Ltd
Investment Advisers J. Henry Schroder Wagg & Co
Actuaries Bacon & Woodrow
Property Advisers Jones, Lang, Wootton
Auditors Peat, Marwick, Mitchell & Co
Company Employees 68,000
Members 17,900
Pensioners 8,850
Annual Contributions £14.4 million
Annual Investment Income £11.3 million
Annual Outflow £10.3 million
Capital Value £126 million

BORDEN (UK) LTD.
St Christopher Works, North Baddesly, Southampton, Hants SO5 9ZB
Telephone: 0703-732131
Secretary C.T.Starke
Assistant Company Secretary A.J.Phillips
Insured with Clerical, Medical & General Life Assurance
Employees 1,616

BORDERS REGIONAL COUNCIL SUPERANNUATION FUND
Regional Headquarters, Newton St.Boswells, Melrose TD6 0SA
Telephone: 08352-3301
Director of Finance H.Hall, FCA, IPFA, FRVA
Deputy Director of Finance A.G.Lambert
Trustees Borders Regional Council
Stockbrokers Pember & Boyle
Actuaries Robertson, Hymans & Co
Members 1,837
Pensioners 535
Annual Contributions (to 31.3.80) £1,308,000
Annual Investment Income £826,000
Gross Annual Outflow £657,000
Capital Value £8,564,000

BORG-WARNER NO.1 AND NO.2 PENSION PLANS
Corporate Office, PO Box 18, Letchworth, Herts SG6 1NR
Telephone: 04626-2333

Secretary J.Thacker
Administrator D.J.Oversby-Powell
Trustees Borg-Warner Trustees Ltd
Investment Advisers Warburg Investment Management Ltd
Actuaries R.Watson & Sons
Auditors Peat, Marwick, Mitchell & Co.
Company Employees 3,763
Members 3,681
Pensioners 393

	£000
Annual Contributions (at 31.3.80)	1,950
Annual Investment Income	966
Gross Annual Outflow	298
Capital Value	12,402
Summary of Investments	
Equities	6,853
Fixed Interest	3,886
Property	669
Cash & Deposits	485
Others	509

THOMAS BORTHWICK & SONS LTD STAFF SUPERANNUATION SCHEME
Priory House, St John's Lane, London EC1M 4BX
Telephone: 01-253 8661
Pension Fund Manager S.W.Channing
Insured with Prudential Assurance Company Ltd
Employees 4,808

BOS KALIS WESTMINSTER GROUP RETIREMENT BENEFITS SCHEME U.K.
Westminster House, Blacknest, Alton, Hants.GU34 4pu
Telephone: 04204-2424
Group Pensions Manager & Secretary A.P.W.Austin
Trustees B.K.W.Trustee Co. Ltd.
Managed by Pensions Management (SWF) Ltd.
Actuaries R.Watson & Sons
Auditors Temple Gothard
Company Employees 3,800
Members 860
Pensioners 910
Annual Contributions £750,000
Capital Value £5,900,000

BOSTON DEEP SEA FISHERIES
St.Andrew's Dock, Hull, Humberside
Telephone: 0482-27464
Secretary W.Taylor
Employees 671

BOULTON & PAUL GROUP PENSION & LIFE ASSURANCE FUND
Riverside Works, Norwich, Norfolk NR1 1EB
Telephone: 0603-60133
Secretary J.Simmonds
Trustees R.L.Chenhall, R.L.M.Mackie, D.G.Berwick,

BOULTON & PAUL GROUP Continued

Trustees R.L.Chenhall, R.L.M.Mackie, D.G.Berwick, E.D.Johnson, J.C.Young,K.B.Carter, J.F.Chaplin, R.C.Goldsmith, W.A.Poole

Insured with Prudential Assurance Co Ltd

Actuaries Clay & Partners

Pension Fund Consultants Metropolitan Pensions Association Ltd

Auditors Thomson McLintock & Co

Company Employees 4,240

Members 3,000

Pensioners 800

Annual Contributions £850,000

BURT BOULTON HOLDINGS LTD PENSION & LIFE ASSURANCE FUND

Eling House, 100 Eling Lane, Totton,Southampton, Hants SO4 4TP
Telephone: 0703-867011

Secretary J.W.T.Saunders

Employees 1,357

THE WILLIAM BOULTON GROUP LTD.

Navigation Road Burslem, Stoke on Trent ST6 3BQ
Telephone: 0782-85658

Secretary E.R.Oakden

Managed by Legal & General (Pension Management) Ltd

Pension Fund Consultants Sedgwick Employee Benefit Consultants Ltd.

Employees 2,104

BOVIS PENSION FUNDS

Liscartan House, 127 Sloane Street,
London SW1X 9BL
Telephone: 01-730 0811

Secretary D.G.James,APMI

Stockbrokers Fielding Newson-Smith & Co.

Property Advisers Edward Erdman & Co.

Actuaries R.Watson & Sons

Auditors Longcrofts

Company Employees 7,300

Members 2,442

Pensioners 443

Capital Value £24 million

BOWATER EMPLOYEE BENEFIT PLANS

Bowater House, Knightsbridge, London SW1X 7LR
Telephone: 01-584 7070

Pensions Department Hoath Lane, Gillingham, Kent ME 8 ORX
Telephone: 0634-3444

Pension Fund Manager & Secretary P.Nash, FCII, FPMI

Asst Pensions Manager R.R.Barker, ACII

Trustees Bowater Pension Trustees Ltd

Managed by Prudential Pensions Ltd, Legal & General Pensions Management Ltd

Investment Advisers Baring Brothers & Co Ltd, Robert Fleming Investment Management Ltd

Pension Fund Consultants Godwins Ltd

Auditors Ernst & Whinney

Company Employees 21,654

Members 19,300

Pensioners 5,014

Annual Contributions £13,898,000

Annual Investment Income £519,000

Gross Annual Outflow £4,413,000

Capital Value (Market Value) £41,956,000

BOWEY GROUP LTD

William St, South Gosforth, Newcastle on Tyne NE3 1TE
Telephone: 0632-853151

Secretary N.E.Green

Employees 894

BOWMAKER LTD STAFF PENSION SCHEME

Bowmaker House, Christchurch Road,
Bournemouth BH1 3LG
Telephone: 0202-22077

Pension Fund Manager P.W.Poole, AIB

Company Secretary D.A.Wells,FCA

Investment Advisers Lloyds Bank Ltd.

Actuary and Pension Fund Consultant G.G.Bannerman,MA,FFA,FIA (C.T.Bowring & Layborn Ltd.)

Auditors Thornton Baker & Co.

Company Employees 2,294

Members 1,368

Pensioners 175

Annual Contributions £1,341,000

Annual Investment Income £975,000

Capital Value £10,692,000

BOWMAKER (PLANT) LTD.

Watling Street, Cannock,Staffs.WS11 3LL
Telephone: 05435-2551

Managing Director D.Smith

Employees 1,000

THE BOWRING GROUP STAFF PENSION & ASSURANCE PLAN

The Bowring Building, Tower Place,
London EC3P 3BE
Telephone: 01-283 3100

Pension Fund Administrator D.L.Barrett

Secretary I.G.Hawkes

Pension Fund Deputy Administrator C.J.Walton

Trustees C.T.Bowring & Co.(Pension Fund) Ltd.

Investment Advisers Singer & Friedlander Ltd., Electra Group Services Ltd.

Actuaries G.G.Bannerman, B.S.Cairns

Pension Fund Consultants C.T.Bowring & Layborn Ltd.

Auditors Blease Lloyd & Co.

THE BOWRING GROUP Continued

Company Employees 3,700(Approx)
Members 3,151
Pensioners 565

	£000
Annual Contributions	4,797
Annual Investment Income	2,054
Annual Outflow	2,012
Capital Value	34,004
Summary of Investments	
Equities	10,155
Fixed Interest	12,113
Property Unit Trusts	6,154
Cash & Deposits	3,694
Others	1,888

BOWTHORPE HOLDINGS LTD
Gatwick Road, Crawley, West Sussex RH10 2RZ
Telephone: 0293-28888

Secretary E.B.Cox

Insured with Clerical, Medical & General Life Assurance

Employees 1,850

W.BOYES & CO LTD RETIREMENT BENEFITS PLAN
Havers Hill, Eastfield, Scarborough, N Yorkshire
Telephone: 0723-582181

Pension Fund Manager G.Rowbotham

Secretary I.S.Evenden

Trustees G.Rowbotham, Paul Boyes, I.S.Evenden

Managed by Lowndes Associated Pensions Ltd.

Pension Fund Consultants Lowndes Associated Pensions Ltd.

Company Employees 600
Members 170
Pensioners 19
Annual Contributions £150,000

BPB UNITED KINGDOM STAFF PENSION SCHEME & BPB OPERATIVES PENSION SCHEME
Ferguson House, 15-17 Marylebone Road, London NW1 5JE
Telephone: 01-486 4011

Pension Fund Manager L.F.Reynolds, FCIS

Assistant Pension Fund Manager M.P.Lowton

Trustees E.G.F.Johnson (Chairman), A.P.Creedon, B.J.Hogben, L.F.Phillipson, L.F.Reynolds

Investment Advisers & Stockbrokers Scrimgeour, Kemp-Gee & Co.

Property Advisers Hillier Parker May & Rowden

Actuary G.C.Philip FFA

Auditor Arthur Young McClelland Moores & Co.

Solicitors Laces & Co.

Company Employees 8,300

	Operatives	Staff
Members	5,209	2,540
Pensioners	1,419	609
	£000	£000
Annual Contributions	1,191	4,015
Annual Investment Income	689	3,253
Annual Outflow	267	1,434
Capital Value (1980)	7,919	34,227
Summary of Investments (1979)		
Equities	3,449	14,148
Fixed Interest	2,972	14,508
Property	264	2,678
Cash & Deposits	950	3,260

BPM HOLDINGS LTD (BIRMINGHAM POST & MAIL STAFF PENSION SCHEME)
Post & Mail House, 28 Colmore Circus, Birmingham B4 6AX
Telephone: 021-236 3366

Pension Fund Manager & Secretary A.J.Billing, APMI

Trustees 12 Trustees

Stockbrokers & Investment Advisers Phillips & Drew

Actuaries Bacon & Woodrow

Auditors Bloomer Heaven & Co

Company Employees 4,067
Members 1,500
Pensioners 700

	£000
Annual Contributions	568
Annual Investment Income	739
Gross Annual Outflow	300
Capital Value	9,269
Est.Market Value (Nov.1979)	10,000
Summary of Investments	
Equities	6,368
Fixed Interest	339
Property	481
Cash & Deposits	464
Others	1,617

BRABY LESLIE LTD
Cowley Mill Road, Uxbridge, Middx.UB8 2QG
Telephone: 0895-38262

Secretary A.J.Murray, FCIS

Investment Advisers Sheppards & Chase

Employees 1,433

BRADBURY WILKINSON PENSION & LIFE ASSURANCE SCHEME
265 Burlington Road, New Malden, Surrey KT3 4NH
Telephone: 01-947 3271

Secretary J.M.Coward

Investment Advisers Bankers Trust Co., Robert Fleming Investment Management Ltd.

BRADBURY WILKINSON Continued

Pension Fund Consultants Willis Faber Advisory Services Ltd.
Auditors Ernst & Whinney
Company Employees 1,692
Members 1,250
Pensioners 230
Annual Contributions £2,000,000
Annual Investment Income £700,000
Capital Value £8,000,000

BRADFORD & BINGLEY BUILDING SOCIETY STAFF PENSION SCHEME

PO Box 2, Bingley, West Yorkshire BD16 2LW
Telephone: 0274-568111

Secretary F.M.Hallam,FCIS,APMI
Trustees Bradford & Bingley Pensions Ltd
Actuaries Duncan C.Fraser & Co.
Auditors H.W.Simpson,FCA (Smith & Hayward), D.E.Walker,LLB,FCA (Thornton Baker & Co.)
Company Employees 1,600
Members 1,430
Pensioners 87

	£000
Annual Contributions	1,180
Annual Investment Income	1,000
Annual Outflow	168
Capital Value (Book Value)	9,556
Summary of Investments	
Equities	4,670
Fixed Interest	3,634
Property	280
Cash & Deposits	972

ROBT.BRADFORD (HOLDINGS) GROUP PENSION & DEATH BENEFIT SCHEME

Minster House, Arthur Street, London EC4R 9BQ
Telephone: 01-623 3050

Secretary E.W.G.France,FCA
Trustees Godwins (Trustees) Ltd.
Actuaries Lane, Clark & Peacock
Auditors Bullimore
Company Employees 1,849
Members 1,090
Pensioners 271

EDWIN H. BRADLEY & SONS LTD. PENSION PLAN

Okus Rd, Swindon, Wilts SN1 4JJ
Telephone: 0793-28131

Secretary F.Rudler
Trustees L.D.Bradley, R.F.Bradley, E.R.Mainwaring, F.Rudler
Insured with Phoenix Assurance Co.Ltd. Growth Fund Policy
Pension Fund Consultants Stewart Wrightson (Western) Ltd.

Auditors Walter Johnson & Partners
Company Employees 953
Members 773
Pensioners 52
Annual Contributions £209,000
Annual Investment Income £298,000
Annual Outflow £39,500
Capital Value £1,750,000

BRADY INDUSTRIES LTD STAFF RETIREMENT BENEFIT PLAN

Warwickgate House, Warwick Road, Old Trafford, Manchester M16 0QQ
Telephone: 061-872 3266

Secretary S.C.Wright
Pension Fund Manager Lowndes Associated Pensions Ltd.
Trustees A.E.R.Seymour, W.A.Goddard, R.Morgan, W.Nash, A.R.Duff
Stockbrokers Scrimgeour,Kemp-Gee & Co.
Actuarial Advice Obtained through Cubie, Wood & Co.Ltd.
Pension Fund Consultants Lowndes Associated Pensions Ltd.
Auditors Price Waterhouse & Co.
Company Employees 1,346
Members 260
Pensioners 90

	£000
Annual Contributions	217
Annual Investment Income	300
Annual Outflow	164
Capital Value	1,462
Summary of Investments	
Equities	850
Fixed Interest	408
Property	200
Cash & Deposits	5

BRAHAM MILLAR GROUP RETIREMENT BENEFITS SCHEME

Strayfield Works, Clayhill, Enfield, Middx EN2 9JQ
Telephone: 01-363 6622

Secretary A.Sabin, ACMA, FCIS
Insured with Eagle Star Insurance Co Ltd
Company Employees 514
Members 120
Pensioners 6
Annual Contributions £65,000

BRAID GROUP LTD.

82 Derby Road, Liverpool L20 8LR Cheshire
Telephone: 051-933 7575

Secretary S.W.Warren
Employees 1,087

S.A.BRAIN & CO LTD
The Old Brewery, Mary Street, Cardiff
Telephone: 0222-5441

Secretary R.C.May-Hill

Insured with Friends' Provident Life Office

Employees 1,384

BRAITHWAITE & CO ENGINEERS LTD
59 Church Road, Great Bookham, Leatherhead, Surrey KT23 3JJ
Telephone: 58951

Secretary J.J.F.N.McNiven,FCIS

Investment Advisers Lloyds Bank Ltd.

Employees 558

BRAMAH LTD
Holbrook Works, Half Way, Sheffield, S Yorks S19 S92
Telephone: 024683-2251

Secretary T.R.Lister, DFC, FCA

Employees 900

C.D. BRAMALL LTD.
146-148 Tong Street, Bradford, W.Yorks.BD4 9PR
Telephone: 0274-681601

Secretary K.F.Sidall

Employees 524

THE BRAMBER ENGINEERING CO LTD
Springbok Works, Waterloo Road, London NW2 7UJ
Telephone: 01-452 5447

Managing Director D.K.Roberts

Employees 600

H.BRAMMER & CO.LTD. RETIREMENT BENEFIT SCHEMES (4)
Station House, Stamford New Road, Altrincham, Cheshire WA14 1EP
Telephone: 061-928 0838

Pension Fund Manager D.Nicholson

Actuarial Advice Obtained through Cubie, Wood & Co.Ltd.

Pension Fund Consultants Noble Lowndes & Partners Ltd.

Auditors Peat, Marwick, Mitchell & Co.

Company Employees 1,600

Members (total 4 schemes)607

Pensioners 42

Annual Contributions £268,000

Capital Value £636,000

BRANKIN HOLDINGS LTD.
Wanlip Road, Syston, Leicester

Secretary M.Bray

Employees 630

GEO.BRAY & CO. (HOLDINGS) LTD.
Leicester Place, Blackman Lane, Leeds, W Yorks LS2 9BH
Telephone: 0532-35349

Secretary T.Rhodes

Employees 661

BRENGREEN (HOLDINGS) LTD.
61 Cheapside, London EC2V 6AX
Telephone: 01-248 6026

Secretary A.G.Berry,FSCA

Group Employees 10,403

BRENT CHEMICALS INTERNATIONAL LTD
The Ridgeway, Iver, Bucks SL0 9JJ
Telephone: 0753-651812

Secretary J.G.Laurence

Insured with Scottish Widows Fund & Life Assurance Society

Employees 580

BRENT WALKER LTD.
9 Chesterfield Street, London W1X 7HF
Telephone: 01-491 4430

Secretary M.J.Wallis

Employees 918

C.BREWER & SONS LTD STAFF PENSION SCHEME
Albany House, Ashford Road, Eastbourne, East Sussex
Telephone: 0323-36151

Secretary J.R.Grout

Investment Advisers Morgan Grenfell & Co.Ltd.

Actuary T.G.Arthur

Auditors Thomson McLintock & Co.

Company Employees 834

Members 710

Pensioners 160

Annual Contributions £400,000

Annual Investment Income £102,000

Capital Value £2,300,000

BRICKHOUSE DUDLEY LTD
Dudley Road West, Tipton, West Midlands DY4 7XD

Secretary B.Bewley,FCIS

Employees 1,223

BRIDON LTD. (A) 1975 STAFF PENSION SCHEME, (B) STAFF PENSION FUND, AND C WORKS PENSION FUND
Warmsworth Hall, Doncaster, S.Yorks.DN4 9JX
Telephone: 0302-4010

Secretary & Pensions Manager P.C.Ambrose,FCIS

Trustees Bridon Pension Trust Ltd.

Insured with Prudential Assurance Co.Ltd.

Pension Fund Consultants Superannuation Schemes Ltd.

The Major UK Pension Funds **BRH/BRI**

BRIDON LTD. Continued

Employees 7,649
Members (A) 1,011, (B) 500, (C) 3,500
Pensioners (A) 221, (B) 400, (C) 80

BRIDPORT-GUNDRY (HOLDINGS) LTD RETIREMENT BENEFITS PLAN
Bridport, Dorset
Telephone: 0308-56666

Company Secretary E.R.G.Youle
Trustees M.H.Smith, J.C.Gundry, A.C.Sanctuary
Insured with English Insurance Co Ltd
Company Employees 935
Members Works Scheme 197, Staff Scheme 95
Pensioners 121
Annual Contributions £213,000

THE JOHN BRIGHT GROUP LTD. 1974 PENSION & LIFE ASSURANCE FUND
Fieldhouse Mills, Rochdale, Lancs.OL12 0AB
Telephone: 0706-48421

Secretary W.L.Hogan
Finance Director T.R.Crowther
Trustees A.W.Marcroft, J.S.H.Taylor, T.R.Crowther, P.T.Waters, C.W.Reid
Insured with Commercial Union Assurance Company Ltd
Pension Fund Consultants Richards Longstaff Ltd
Company Employees 1,634
Members 220 (approx)
Pensioners 21

BRILLO MANFACTURING CO OF GREAT BRITAIN LTD
Cordwallis Industrial Estate, Maidenhead, Berks
Telephone: 0628-23411

Secretary D.R.Gilronan
Employees 569

BRINTONS LTD STAFF PENSION & LIFE ASSURANCE PLAN AND PENSION FUND
PO Box 16, Exchange Street, Kidderminster, Worcs.DY10 1AG
Telephone: 0562-3444

Pension Fund Manager H.Logie, APMI
Company Secretary K.T.Almond
Part Managed by Eagle Pension Funds Ltd.
Investment Advisers J.Henry Schroder Wagg & Co.Ltd.
Pension Fund Consultants Willis Faber Advisory Services Ltd.
Auditors Peat, Marwick, Mitchell & Co.
Solicitors Linklaters & Paines
Company Employees 2,531

	Staff	Works
Members (at 31.3.80)	591	1,292
Pensioners	160	501
	£000	£000
Annual Contributions	502	-
Annual Investment Income	130	130
Capital Value	2,742	1,221

BRISTOL AEROJET LTD
Banwell, Weston-super-Mare, Avon BS24 8PD
Telephone: 0934-822251

Chairman Dr F.Llewellyn-Smith, CBE
Employees 710

BRISTOL & WEST BUILDING SOCIETY (PENSION TRUSTEES) LTD
Bristol & West Building, Broad Quay, Bristol BS99 7AX
Telephone: 0272-294271

Trustee N.S.Butterfield, OBE, FCIS, FBS
Members 452
Capital Value (29.12.78) £1,735,000

BRISTOL COMPOSITE MATERIALS ENGINEERING LTD
Avonmouth, Bristol BS11 9DU
Telephone: 0272-824821

Director J.I.Edwards
Employees 600

THE BRISTOL-MYERS EMPLOYEE BENEFITS PLAN
Stamford House, Station Road, Langley, Slough, Berks. SL3 6EB
Telephone: 44266

Pension Fund Manager and Secretary D.E.Walker
Trustees Chairman: J.E.Jackson, Trustees: A.J.W.Jackson, C.B.Thompson, S.C.Challoner, A.D.Popham
Insured with Prudential Pensions Ltd
Actuarial Advice Obtained through Wyatt Harris Graham Ltd
Auditors Price Waterhouse & Co
Company Employees 681
Members 414
Pensioners 26

	£000
Annual Contributions	138
Annual Outflow	50
Capital Value	1,297
Summary of Investments	
Equities	470
Fixed Interest	475
Property	335
Cash & Deposits	17

The Major UK Pension Funds **BRH/BRI**

BRISTOL OMNIBUS CO LTD
Berkeley House, Lawrence Hill, Bristol BS5 0DZ
Telephone: 0272-558211
Employees 2,600

BRISTOL STREET GROUP.
See BSG

BRISTOL UNITED PRESS LTD (BUP 1968 PENSION FUND)
Temple Way, Bristol BS99 7HD
Telephone: 0272-20080
Secretary M.J.Gay, FCA
Trustees Bristol United Press (Trustees)Ltd.
Stockbrokers Stock Beech & Co, Hoare Govett Ltd.
Actuaries Bacon & Woodrow
Auditors Deloitte Haskins & Sells
Company Employees 1,400
Members 1,000
Pensioners 120
Annual Contributions £613,000
Annual Investment Income £356,000
Capital Value £3,500,000

BRISTOL WATERWORKS CO
PO Box 218, Bridgwater Rd, Bristol BS99 7AU
Telephone: 0272-665881
Secretary N.H.Bagot
Employees 738

BRITANNIA BUILDING SOCIETY PENSION & LIFE ASSURANCE SCHEME
P.O.Box 20, Newton House, Leek, Staffs
Telephone: 0538-385131
Head of Staff Dept D.W.Bellis
Insured with Royal Insurance Co Ltd
Members 1,080
Pensioners 86

BRITANNIA REFINED METALS LTD
Adelaide House, King William Street, London EC4R 9DX
Telephone: 01-626 7446
Secretary J.F.Bonner
Employees 515

BRITANNIC ASSURANCE CO LTD
Moor Green, Moseley, Birmingham B13 8QF
Telephone: 021-449 4444
Secretary P.Weavers,FCA
Employees 4,360

BRITISH & COMMONWEALTH SHIPPING CO LTD
Cayzer House, 2 & 4 St.Mary Axe, London EC3A 8BP
Telephone: 01-283 4343
Director (Staff Administration) E.R.Duggan
Secretary I.J.Patterson,FCA

Investment Advisers Gartmore Pension Fund Managers Ltd.
Actuaries R.Watson & Son
Company Employees 7,521

BRITISH AEROSPACE PENSION SCHEME
Brooklands Road, Weybridge, Surrey KT13 0SJ
Telephone: 0932-45522
Corporate Pensions Manager D.A.G.Norwood, ACII FPMI
Secretary A.C.Buckley, B.Sc
Trustee British Aerospace Pension Funds Trustees Ltd
Investment Advisers Warburg Investment Management Ltd.
Auditors Peat Marwick Mitchell & Co
Company Employees 70,000
Members 63,000
Pensioners 17,000
Annual Contributions £40 million (est.)
Capital Value (April 1980) £210 million

BRITISH AIRPORTS AUTHORITY SUPERANNUATION SCHEME
2 Buckingham Gate, London SW1E 6JL
Telephone: 01-834 6621
Secretary R.H.Gibbs, APMI
Custodian Trustee Barclays Bank Trust Co Ltd
Managing Trustees P.E.R.Bailey (Chairman), R.J.Bonner, C.J.Burnley, R.Unger, L.S.Dean, R.D.Topley, E.W.Rutherford
Custodian Trustee Barclays Bank Trust Co.
Investment Advisers Hambros Investment Management Services Ltd
Legal Advisers McKenna & Co
Actuaries Bacon & Woodrow
Property Advisers Berkeley Hambro Property Co Ltd
Auditors Touche Ross & Co
Members 7,417
Pensioners 1,023

	£000
Annual Contributions	7,195
Annual Investment Income	3,829
Annual Outflow	2,125
Capital Value (Market)	53,830
Summary of Investments	
Equities	26,698
Foreign Equities	1,304
Fixed Interest	18,753
Property & Property Unit Trusts	4,404
Cash & Deposits	3,975

BRITISH AIRWAYS
See Airways Pension Scheme Kershaw House, Great West Road, Hounslow, Middlesex TW5 0BX
Telephone: 01-570 7741

BRITISH-AMERICAN TOBACCO CO.LTD.& ASSOCIATED COMPANIES STAFF PENSION FUND & PAYROLL PENSION FUND

Westminster House, 7 Millbank, London SW1P 3JE
Telephone: 01-222 1222

Pensions Manager and Secretary (Staff Pension Fund) B.J.Long,APMI

Secretary (Payroll Pension Fund) P.A.Terry

Trustees Westminster Nominees Ltd.

Actuaries Rodney Barnett & Co.

Auditors Deloitte Haskins & Sells

Company Employees 5,000

	Staff	Employees
Members	2,800	1,900
Pensioners	1,200	550
	£000	£000
Annual Contributions	6,300	900
Annual Investment Income	4,800	1,000
Annual Outflow	2,100	500
Capital Value	39,819	7,218
Summary of Investments		
Equities	17,400	3,151
Fixed Interest	11,243	1,459
Property	4,058	1,286
Cash & Deposits	215	517
Others	6,903	805

See also B.A.T Industries Ltd.

BRITISH BATA SHOE CO LTD

East Tilbury, Grays, Essex RM18 8RL
Telephone: 03752-3400

Pensions & Insurance Officer Mrs. J.Grover

Secretary L.T.C.Buffin

Employees 2,520

BRITISH BROADCASTING CORPORATION NEW PENSION SCHEME

Broadcasting House, London W1A 1AA
Telephone: 01-580 4468

Secretary & Pensions Officer P.C.Plummer,FPMI

Head of Pensions Accounts M.A.Notley,FCA

Director of Finance H.P.Hughes

Trustees Four Trustees for the B.B.C., three elected by members

Investment Advisers G.T.Management Ltd., Hill Samuel Investment Management Ltd., Ivory & Sime Ltd., Kleinwort Benson Investment Management Ltd., J.Henry Schroder Wagg & Co.Ltd., Warburg Investment Management Ltd., M & G Investment Management Ltd.

Actuaries R.Watson & Sons

Property Advisers Knight Frank & Rutley

Auditors Deloitte Haskins & Sells

Employees 26,000

Members 20,000

Pensioners 6,500

	£ million
Annual Contributions	42
Annual Investment Income	26
Annual Outflow	16
Capital Value	
Book Value	332
Market Value	360
Summary of Investments (Book Value)	
Equities	194
Fixed Interest	73
Property	31
Cash & Deposits	34

BRITISH CAR AUCTION GROUP LTD.

Expedier House, Union Road, Farnham, Surrey GU9 7PY
Telephone: 0252-726699

Secretary E.L.Plumridge,FCIS

Employees 615

BRITISH CALEDONIAN AIRWAYS LTD GROUP PENSION & LIFE ASSURANCE SCHEME

Gatwick Airport, Horley, Surrey RH6 0LT
Telephone: 0293-27890

Pension Fund Manager S.R.Clifford-Smith, FAAI, APMI

Pensions Officer K.Waller

Trustees Three Company Trustees, Four elected by Members

Chairman of Trustees T.E.Boud,FCA

Managed by Prudential Assurance Company Ltd.

Pension Fund Consultants Sedgwick Employee Benefits Consultants Ltd.

Auditors Ernst & Whinney

Company Employees 6,000

Members 5,500

Pensioners 400

	£000
Annual Contributions	6,500
Annual Outflow	1,500
Capital Value	22,000
Summary of Investments	
Equities	8,000
Fixed Interest	8,000
Property	6,000

BRITISH COUNCIL SUPERANNUATION SCHEME

10 Spring Gardens, London SW1A 2BN
01-930 8466

Pension Fund Manager H.J.Friend,ACIS

Director Service Conditions C.J.M.Thomas

Custodian Trustee Midland Bank Trust Co.Ltd.

Stockbrokers Phillips & Drew, Fielding Newson-Smith & Co.

Property Advisers Ernest Owers & Williams

Actuary Government Actuary

Employees 2,065

Members 2,230

BRITISH COUNCIL Continued

Pensioners 766
Annual Contributions £3.5 million
Annual Investment Income £2.5 million
Capital Value £30.0 million

BRITISH DREDGING GROUP STAFF PENSION FUND

Avondale House, Avondale Road, Cardiff CF1 7XR
Telephone: 0222-388666
Pension Fund Manager D.Derrick
Secretary D.W.Kaye, MA, FCIS
Trustees C.M.Glover, G.D.Kaye M.P.Tonkin
Insured with Crusader Insurance Co Ltd
Company Employees 600
Members 500
Pensioners 130
Annual Contributions £250,000

BRITISH DRIVER-HARRIS CO.LTD. STAFF & WORKS RETIREMENT PLANS

Bird Hall Lane, Cheadle Heath, Stockport, Cheshire SK3 0SB
Telephone: 061-428 6661
Company Secretary C.W.Goudge
Assistant Secretary H.J.Andrews
Pension Fund Consultants Noble Lowndes & Partners Ltd.
Auditors Ernst & Whinney
Employees 476

	Staff	Works
Members (at 30.6.80)	120	340
Pensioners	57	84
	£000	£000
Annual Contributions	92	114
Capital Value	321	278

BRITISH ELECTRIC TRACTION CO.LTD. GROUP SUPERANNUATION SCHEME

Stratton House, Piccadilly, London W1X 6AS
Telephone: 01-629 8886
Company Secretary E.F.Bell,FCIS
Trustees J.E.Hollands (Chairman), J.S.Beazley, E.F.Bell, R.J.Foot, F.D.C.Hopkins, D.Simpson
Insured with Legal & General Assurance Society Ltd.
Pension Fund Consultants Noble Lowndes Pensions Ltd.
Auditors F.W.Smith, Riches & Co.
Group Employees 33,000
Members 700
Annual Premiums £676,000

The major subsidiaries manage their own pension arrangements. See also Rediffusion Ltd.

BRITISH ENGINES LTD PENSION SCHEME

Glasshouse Street, St Peters, Newcastle upon Tyne NE6 1BS
Telephone: 0632-659091
Company Secretary A.Sutherland
Insured with Friends' Provident Life Office
Company Employees 1,000
Members 860

BRITISH ENKALON LTD PENSION SCHEME

25 Randalstown Road, Antrim BT41 4LT
Telephone: 08494 1-3535
Registered Office PO Box 62, Enkalon House, Regent Road, Leicester LE1 9AF (0533-2729)
Pension Fund Investment Director B.J.Eales, FCA, FCT
Secretary I.MacDonald
Trustees R.L.Schierbeek, H.Buckle, B.J.Eales
Stockbrokers Cazenove & Co., Josias Cunningham & Co.
Property Advisers Fletcher King
Actuaries Duncan C.Fraser & Co.
Auditors Thomson McLintock & Co.
Solicitors Lovell King & White
Company Employees/Members 2,500
Pensioners 150
Annual Contributions £1,500,00
Annual Investment Income £1,500,000
Capital Value £15,000,000

BRITISH GAS CORPORATION CENTRAL FUNDS OF THE GAS STAFF AND GAS MANUAL WORKERS PENSION SCHEMES

326 High Holborn, London WC1V 7PT
Telephone: 01-831 6272
Administration Rivermill House, 152 Grosvenor Road, London SW1V 3JL
Telephone: 01-821 1444
Pension Fund Investment Manager A.Phillipson, FCA
Secretary G.J.Pellett
Deputy Investment Manager R.E.W.Minors
Investment Advisers Lazard Securities Ltd. (Staff); Warburg Investment Management Ltd. (Manual); Robert Fleming Investment Management Ltd. (Both)
Property Advisers Weatherall Green & Smith (Staff), Harold Williams, Bennett & Partners (Manual Workers)
Actuaries R.Watson & Sons
Auditors Price Waterhouse & Co.
Employees 104,424

	Staff	Workers
Members	56,405	34,534
Pensioners	20,563	15,465
	£000	£000
Annual Contributions	90,000	23,000

BRITISH GAS CORPORATION Continued

Annual Investment Income	48,000	8,000
Annual Outflow	43,000	10,000
Capital Value	618,000	98,000
Summary of Investments		
Equities	260,000	46,000
Fixed Interest	137,000	24,000
Property	195,000	27,000
Others	26,000	1,000

Each local gas region has autonomous staff and manual employees pension schemes. The central fund runs a unit trust on their behalf with funds as above.

The following is a list of the 12 regions and headquarters with names of the regional administrators, who are also the Schemes secretaries
Headquarters: J.M.Maddox, Pensions Officer, 59 Bryanston Street, London W1A 2AZ
East Midlands Gas: J.S.Barrett,APMI, Superannuation Officer, P.O.Box 145, De Montfort Street, Leicester LE1 9DB
Eastern Gas: K.J.Dearing,ACIS,APMI, Pensions Officer, Star House, Potters Bar, Herts.
North Eastern Gas: J.D.Swallow,IPFA, Superannuation Officer, New York Road, Leeds LS2 7PE
North Thames Gas: R.J.Brown, Pensions Officer, North Thames House, London Road, Staines, Middx.TW18 4AE
North Western Gas: F.Johnson, Superannuation Officer, Welman House, Altrincham, Cheshire
Northern Gas: Mrs.M.S.Rewcastle,FPMI, Pensions Officer, Norgas House, Killingworth, Newcastle-upon-Tyne NE99 1GB
Scottish Region: W.H.Hartley, Payroll & Superannuation Manager, Granton House,West Granton Road, Edinburgh EH5 1YB
South Eastern Region: J.W.Hill, Pensions Officer, 709 Old Kent Road, London SE1
South Western Region: R.M.Miller, Superannuation Officer, Riverside, Temple Street, Keynsham, Bristol
Southern Region: L.K.White, Payroll & Superannuation Officer, P.O.Box 105, Southampton SO9 7GL
Wales Gas: N.Lewis, Payroll Accountant, Snelling House, Bute Terrace, Cardiff CF1 2UF
West Midlands Gas: J.C.Salmon, Administration Accountant, Wharf Lane, Solihull, Warks. B91 2JP

BRITISH HOME STORES 1975 PENSION SCHEME

129-137 Marylebone Road, London NW1 5QD
Telephone: 01-262 3288

Pension Fund Director & Secretary E.J.Thatcher, ACIS

Trustees British Home Stores Employees Trust Ltd

Investment Advisers Kleinwort Benson Ltd

Actuaries Clay & Partners

Property Advisers Browett Taylor & Co, Strutt & Parker

Pension Fund Consultants Metropolitan Pensions Association Ltd

Auditors Peat Marwick Mitchell & Co

Employees (incl part-time) 26,800
Members 14,000
Pensioners 1,600

	£000
Annual Contributions	4,400
Annual Investment Income	1,650
Annual Outflow	1,800
Capital Value	23,433
Summary of Investments	
Equities	8,913
Fixed Interest	4,760
Property	7,000
Cash & Deposits	2,760

BRITISH HOVERCRAFT CORPORATION LTD

East Cowes, Isle of Wight
Telephone: 098-382 4101

Director Sir C.Hartley

Employees 2,000

BRITISH INDUSTRIAL HOLDINGS LTD

North West House, 119/27 Marylebone Road, London NW1 5QB
Telephone: 01-262 6622

Secretary A.J.Urry

Employees 944

BRITISH LAND CO.LTD.

10 Cornwall Terrace, Regent's Park, London NW1 4QP
Telephone: 01-486 4466

Secretary D.Wilson,FCIS

Employees 795

BRITISH LEYLAND LTD BL STAFF PENSION SCHEME AND BL HOURLY PAID EMPLOYEE PENSION SCHEME

35/38 Portman Square, London W1H 0HQ
Telephone: 01-486 6000

Staff Director Pensions B.G.Lane,MA,APMI

Secretary B.Yallop

Manager Pensions Administration G.Carter,ACIS

Trustees (Staff Fund) BL (Staff) Trustees Ltd.

Trustees (Hourly Paid Employees) BL (Hourly Paid) Trustees Ltd.

Investment Advisers Legal & General Assurance Society Ltd., Phillips & Drew, Robert Fleming Investment Management Ltd.

Actuaries Bacon & Woodrow

Pension Fund Consultants C.T.Bowring & Layborn Ltd.

Auditors Coopers & Lybrand

Company Employees 140,000

	Staff Scheme	Employees Scheme
Members (Approx)	38,000	104,000
Pensioners	1,416	3,730

BRITISH LEYLAND LTD Continued

	£ million	£ million
Annual Contributions	28	55
Annual Investment Income	1	10
Capital Value	100	220

BRITISH MANUFACTURE & RESEARCH

Springfield Road, Grantham, Lincs NG31 7JB
Telephone: 0476-5577

Secretary R.A.Smith

Employees 1,164

BRITISH MIDLANDS AIRWAYS

East Midlands Airport, Castle Donnington, nr.Derby DE7 2SB
Telephone: 0332-810741

Secretary S.F.Balmforth

Employees 1,014

BRITISH MOHAIR SPINNERS LTD

PO Box 58, Midland Mills, Valley Road, Bradford BD1 4RL
Telephone: 0274-28456

Secretary S.Yewdall

Employees 1,738

THE BRITISH NATIONAL OIL CORPORATION RETIREMENT BENEFITS PLAN

150 St Vincent Street, Glasgow G2 5LJ
Telephone: 041-204 2525

Secretary R.C.Milligan,FCIS

Pension Fund Administrator R.J.Watt

Trustees BNOC (Pension Trustees) Ltd

Investment Advisers Warburg Investment Management Ltd.

Actuaries R.Watson & Sons

Auditors Thomson McLintock & Co.

Members 1,535

Pensioners 5

Annual Contributions £900,000

Capital Value £3,000,000

BRITISH OLIVETTI LTD RETIREMENT BENEFITS PLANS (1978)

30 Berkeley Square, London W1X 6AH
Telephone: 01-629 8807

Pension Fund Manager W.J.Reece

Secretary J.H.Gainham

Trustees J.H.Gainham, K.Walkerden

Managed by Legal & General (Pensions Management) Ltd

Pension Fund Consultants Godwins Ltd

Auditors Arthur Young, McClelland Moores & Co.

Company Employees 1,600

Members 900

Pensioners 70

Annual Contributions £650,000

Capital Value £5,000,000

THE BP PENSION SCHEME AND THE BP OIL CONTRIBUTORY PENSION FUND (1976)

Britannic House, Moor Lane, London EC2Y 9BU
Telephone: 01-920 8000

Pensions Department General Manager A.Mackenzie, MA, FPMI (01-920 7333)

Assistant General Manager D. Bosdet, CA FPMI (01-920 7332)

Investment Dept General Manager G.J.Titford, FIA (01-920 7388)

Senior Portfolio Manager D.G.Marsh

Property Co-ordinator P.E.Hackwood

Secretary (a) J.E. Wedgbury (The BP Pension Scheme), (b) R.G. Elden (The BP Oil Contributory Pension Fund 1976)

Trustees (a)The British Petroleum Pension Trust Ltd;(b)BP Oil Trustees Ltd

Investment Committee W.P.C.Grassick (Chairman), A.J.Butterworth, J.A.R.Falconer, A.F.Murray, J.Burnett Stuart, C.J. Benson

Actuaries Duncan C. Fraser & Co

Auditors Ernst & Whinney

Property Advisers Debenham Tewson & Chinnocks

Solicitors Linklaters & Paines

Company Employees 35,500

	BP Co Ltd	BP Oil
Members (at 31.12.79)	34,313	219
Pensioners	8,529	686
Deferred Pensioners	3,702	172
	£000	£000
Annual Contributions *	73,008	2,552
Annual Investment Income *	53,988	4,877
Annual Outflow *	38,242	3,732
Capital Value		
Book Value	567,583	26,304
Market Value	715,887	27,217
Summary of Investments		
Fixed Interest	119,199	17,490
Equities	277,287	8,037
Property	289,188	-
Cash,Deposits etc.	30,213	1,690

* 15 month period, 1st January, 1979 to 5th April, 1980 due to change of accounting year.

BRITISH POTTERY MANUFACTURERS FEDERATION

Federation House, Station Road, Stoke on Trent Staffs.

Secretary D.Turner

Insured with Scottish Widows' Fund and Life Assurance Society

BRITISH POTTERY MANUFACTURERS FEDERATION
Continued

Pension Fund Consultants Noble Lowndes & Partners Ltd

BRITISH PRINTING CORPORATION STAFF PENSION & LIFE INSURANCE PLAN AND CONTRACTING OUT PENSION & LIFE ASSURANCE SCHEME

Print House, 44 Great Queen Street,
London WC2B 5AS
Telephone: 01-240 3411

Pension Fund Manager D.P.Duffy, BSc. Econ, ACII

Secretary A.A.J.Harman, LLB, FCIS

Plan Administrator G.Herman

Trustees BPC Pension Trustees Ltd., BPC Pension Trustees (Works Scheme) Ltd.

Managed by Scottish Widows' Fund and Life Assurance Society

Investment Advisers J.Henry Schroder Wagg & Co.Ltd., Robert Fleming Investment Management Ltd., Willis Faber Advisory Services Ltd.

Actuaries R.Watson & Sons

Pension Fund Consultants Godwins Ltd

Auditors Coopers & Lybrand

Company Employees 11,000

	Staff	Contract.Out
Members	2,100	4,400
Pensioners	426	1,348
	£000	£000
Annual Contributions	2,400	4,100
Annual Investment Income	1,630	2,040
Gross Annual Outflow	800	1,300
Capital Value	17,120	21,500
Summary of Investments		
Equities	9,500	10,846
Fixed Interest	5,617	7,465
Property	1,683	2,322
Cash & Deposits	320	873

BRITISH RAILWAYS SUPERANNUATION FUND AND (WAGES GRADES) PENSION FUND

Secretary and Administration Stooperdale Offices, Darlington DL3 6EH
Telephone: 0325-67491

Corporate Offices (HQ) Euston Square, P.O.Box 100, London NW1 2DZ

Telephone: 01-262 3232

Investment Department 22 Finsbury Square, London EC2P 2BQ
Telephone:01-628 3050

General Manager (Investments) John A.Morgan

Controller,Corporate Pensions C.G.Lewin, FIA,FSS, FPMI

Pensions Officer R.J.Goodchild, FIA, APMI

Investment Manager J.J.McLachlan

Assistant Investment Managers N.D.Fitzpatrick, R.D.Attridge

Trustees British Railways Board

Details of Superannuation Fund

General Committee 12 representatives of BR Board, including A.G.Kentridge (Chairman), 12 representatives of members

Secretary W.J.Dunn, APMI

Investment Advisers Hill Samuel Investment Management Ltd., BRB Investment Department

Property Advisers (to both funds) Wright and Partners

Actuaries (to both funds) R.Watson & Sons

Details of (Wages Grades) Pension Fund

Committee Total of 16 members, R.H.Wicox (Chairman)

Secretary C.J.Weston

Investment Advisers Warburg Investment Management Ltd., BRB Investment Dept.

Auditors Peat, Marwick, Mitchell & Co. (also for Superannuation Fund with R.F.Short)

	Super-annuation (at 31.12.79)	Wages Grade (at 5.4.80)
Membership		
Members	71,761	154,078
Pensioners	33,932	40,050
Widows and Children	8,893	5,126
	£ million	£ million
Annual Contributions	40.0	53.0
Annual Investment Income	87.9	37.7
Annual Outflow	39.6	19.4
Capital Value of Fund		
Book Value	1,060.4	408.4
Market Value	1,180.1	487.7
Summary of Investments (Market Value)		
Fixed Interest	97.6	45.0
UK Equities	452.4	204.7
Overseas Investments	24.4	29.6
Property/Property Unit Trusts	158.3	104.8
Direct investments	4.2	2.0
Short-term Loans & Deposits	51.7	30.4
Works of Art	23.6	13.2
Commodities	0.4	0.2
Funding Debt and deposits with BRB	367.6	57.7
Net Current Assets	(0.2)	0.1

It is estimated that by April 1981 the total assets of the Funds will amount to nearly £1,850 million.

BRITISH ROLLMAKERS CORPORATION LTD. (THE)

Weston Road, Crewe, Cheshire CW1 1DB
Telephone: 0270-3412

Secretary A.Lees

Managed by Legal & General Assurance Society Ltd.

BRITISH ROLLMAKERS CORPORATION Continued

Pension Fund Consultants Norman Frizzell (Life & Pensions) Ltd.

Employees 2,283

BRITISH SHIPBUILDERS
136 Sandyford Road,
Newcastle-upon-Tyne NE2 1QE
Telephone: 0632-26772

Pensions Manager A.J.Ashmore,FPMI,ACII

Company Secretary N.G.U.Morris

Investment Advisers Robert Fleming Investment Management Ltd.

Pension Fund Consultants Godwins Ltd.

Auditors Ernst & Whinney

Company Employees 72,700

BRITISH SHOE CORPORATION LTD.
Sunningdale Road, Leicester LE3 1UR
Telephone: 0533-871355

Pensions Officer R.E.Skinner, APMI

Company Secretary D.J.R.Ward

Company Employees 41,000

BRITISH SIDAC GROUP PENSION FUND
Lancots Lane, St.Helens, Merseyside WA9 3ES
Telephone: 0744-24041

Manager Group Staff Administration J.F.Corcoran, BA,FPMI

Company Secretary R.Stewart-Smith

Trustees British Sidac Pension Trust Ltd.

Investment Advisers Hill Samuel Investment Management Ltd., Drayton Montagu Portfolio Management Ltd.

Actuaries Rodney Barnett & Co.

Pension Fund Consultant R.W.Mountjoy

Auditors Chalmers, Impey & Co.

Company Employees 2,319

Members 2,200

Pensioners 474

Annual Contributions £1,555,000

Annual Investment Income £644,000

Capital Value £9,504,000

BRITISH STEAM SPECIALITIES GROUP LTD. PENSION & LIFE ASSURANCE SCHEME
Fleet Street, Lee Circle, Leicester LE1 3QQ
Telephone: 0533-23232

Secretary R.D.Thompson,ACIS

Part Insured with Equity & Law Life Assurance Society Ltd.

Stockbrokers L.Messel & Co.

Actuaries Clay & Partners

Pension Fund Consultants Metropolitan Pensions Association Ltd.

Auditors Price Waterhouse & Co.

Company Employees 1,259

Members 650

Pensioners 40

Contributions £320,000

BRITISH STANDARDS INSTITUTION RETIREMENT BENEFITS PLAN
2 Park Street, London W1A 2BS
Telephone: 01-629 9000

Chief Accountant Mrs.S.R.Harris,FCA

Trustees G.B.R.Feilden, T.W.Howard, Mrs.S.R.Harris, H.A.R.Binney, C.Maidment

Managed by Legal & General (Pensions Management) Ltd.

Investment Advisers Hill Samuel Investment Management Ltd.

Actuarial Advice Obtained through Cubie, Wood & Co.Ltd.

Pension Fund Consultants Noble Lowndes & Partners Ltd.

Auditors Price Waterhouse & Co.

Company Employees 1,100

Members 600

Pensioners 160

	£000
Annual Contributions	700
Annual Investment Income	400
Annual Outflow	400
Capital Value	5,000
Summary of Investments	
Equities	3,300
Fixed Interest	900
Property	800

BRITISH STEEL CORPORATION STAFF AND MANUAL GRADES SUPERANNUATION SCHEMES AND PENSIONS COMMON INVESTMENT FUND
Management 33 Grosvenor Place,
London SW1X 7JG
Telephone: 01-235 1212

Central Pensions Office 31 Oswald Street, Glasgow G1 4PQ

Staff Scheme

Secretary K.Hurst, APMI

Committee Representatives,

Corporation: David Grieves, (Chairman), W.R.Harrison, C.Over, Mrs.A.L.M.Parker, J.Bretherick, G.R.Townsend;

Members: A.C.Cook, D.V.Driscoll, C.W.Gunnee, o.B.Reeves, A.Richmond, D.H.Williams

Manual Grades Scheme O.B.Reeves,

Secretary R.A.McCubbin, APMI

Committee Representatives,

Corporation: David Grieves, (Chairman) G.H.Blakeley, J.Bretherick, M.R.Edwards, H.Ford, L.Raby, V.G.Tyas

Members: W.Sirs, J.Clark, D.A.Elwick, P.Guymer, T.B.Jones, S.B.Roberts, J.Thomas,

Committee of the Investment Fund C.H.Osborne (Chairman), J.Bretherick, A.Crawford,OBE,

BRITISH STEEL CORPORATION Continued

D.V.Driscoll,BEM, C.W.Gunnee, T.B.Jones, J.w.Martin, S.B.Roberts, S.I.Webber

Secretary A.J.Gray

Manager,Pensions Administration J.Bretherick

Manager, Pensions Investments J.W.Martin

Estates Manager R.N.English

Custodian Trustees BSC Pension Fund Nominees Ltd.

Investment Advisers J.A.Mulligan (Throgmorton Management Ltd.),E.M.P.Welman (Baring Bros.& Co.Ltd.)

Actuaries R.Watson & Sons

Auditors Peat, Marwick, Mitchell & Co.

Bankers Williams & Glyn's Bank Ltd.

	Staff	Manual
Members (at 31.3.79	57,398	128,662
Pensioners	21,082	57,074
Deferred Pensions	12,164	37,699
	£000	£000
Annual Contributions	72,208	88,803
Expenditure	38,112	29,967
Total Assets	469,478	500,454

Investment Income is shown below in the Common Investment Fund

These two funds hold units in the BSC Pensions Common Investment Fund whose total income for the year to 31.3.79 was £50,833,000. Assets were as follows:

Summary of Investments
Gilt Edged	216,956
Other Fixed Interest	1,762
Property	252,537
Property Unit Trusts	89,914
U.K.Equities	313,025
Foreign Equities	41,283
Managed funds	6,209
Net Current Assets	42,303
Total Assets	963,989

It is estimated that by April 1980 the total assets of the Funds will amount to nearly £1,100 million

BRITISH SUGAR CORPORATION LTD. STAFF SUPERANNUATION SCHEME & MANUAL WORKERS' PENSION SCHEME

PO Box 26, Oundle Road, Peterborough PE2 9QU
Telephone: 0733-63171

Pension Fund Manager & Secretary P.E.Cooper, FCIS, APMI

Assistant Pension Fund Manager M.D.Bean

Trustees British Sugar Pension Trustees Ltd

Investment Advisers J. Henry Schroder, Wagg & Co Ltd, Robert Fleming Investment Management Ltd

Actuaries R.Watson & Sons
Auditors Deloitte, Haskins & Sells
Company Employees 6,144
Members 4,032
Pensioners 1,530
Annual Contributions £3.2 million
Annual Investment Income £2.6 million
Gross Annual Outflow £1.9 million
Capital Value (Book value) £31 million

BRITISH SYPHON INDUSTRIES LTD PENSION SCHEME

Netherthorpe House, Netherthorpe Road, Sheffield, S.Yorks.S3 7EL
Telephone: 0742-79492

Pension Fund Manager J.S.Hunt

Secretary C.F.Cave,FCA

Pension Fund Consultants Joseph W Burley (Life & Pensions Consultants) Ltd

Company Employees 1,423

Members 910

BRITISH TAR PRODUCTS LTD

123 Pall Mall, London SW1Y 5EA
Telephone: 01-930 5827

Secretary W.M.Connelly

Insured with Legal & General Assurance Society Ltd

Employees 615

BRITISH TIMKEN

Duston, Northampton NN5 6UL
Telephone: 0604-52311

Pension Fund Manager E.W.Fraiel, APMI

Employees 4,100

BRITISH TISSUES PENSION FUND

Brent House, 214 Kenton Road, Harrow, Middlesex HA3 8BS
Telephone: 01-907 4311

Pension Secretaries A.R.Watts, A.Brown

Company Secretary J.B.Andrews

Management Committee Trustees,Advisers and Employees Representatives

Trustees British Tissues (Pensions) Ltd.

Stockbrokers Buckmaster & Moore

Act uary G.Waugh, FFA

Pension Fund Consultants Alexander Howden

Auditors Ernst & Whinney

Company Employees 2,250

Members 1,478

Pensioners 210

Annual Income £490,000

Annual Investment Income £254000

Annual Outflow £148,000

Capital Value £4,800,000

BRITISH TOURIST BOARDS' STAFF PENSION AND LIFE ASSURANCE SCHEME

64 St. James's Street, London SW1A 1NF
Telephone: 01-629 9191

Pensions Administrator Barry Meloy

Secretary W.R.L.Addison

Trustees Chairmen of all the Tourist Boards

Insured with Prudential Assurance Co.Ltd.

Actuarial Advice Obtained through Prudential Assurance Co.Ltd.

Pension Fund Consultants Godwins Ltd.

Auditors Exchequer & Audit Department

Total Employees 870

Members 780

Pensioners 79

Annual Contributions £1,200,000

Annual Outflow £180,000

Capital Value £2,380,000

BRITISH TRANSPORT DOCKS BOARD (SALARIED STAFF) AND (WAGES GRADES) PENSION SCHEMES

Melbury House, Melbury Terrace,
London NW1 6JY
Telephone: 01-486 6621

Pension Fund Manager & Secretary L.J.Taylor, APMI

Investment Advisers Baring Bros. & Co.Ltd.

Actuaries Duncan C.Fraser & Co.

Auditors Price Waterhouse & Co.

Company Employees (at 31.12.79) 11,553

	Staff	Wages Grades
Members	2,027	4,212
Pensioners	610	1,084
	£000	£000
Annual Contributions	1,992	2,033
Annual Investment Income	1,346	720
Capital Value	17,099	9,194

BRITISH TWIN DISC LTD

Knight Road, Strood, Kent
Telephone: 0634-77855

Managing Director P.A.Duke

Employees 550

BRITISH UNITED PROVIDENT ASSOCIATION (BUPA) PENSION & FAMILY SECURITY SCHEME

Provident House, 24-27 Essex Street,
London WC2R 3AX
Telephone: 01-353 9451

Pensions Officer Mrs.L.R.Waller

Insured with Clerical Medical & General Life Assurance Society

Pension Fund Consultants C.E.Heath Urquhart (Life & Pensions) Ltd.

Auditors Thornton Baker

Company Employees 1,575

Members 1,200

Pensioners 97

THE BRITISH UNITED SHOE MACHINERY CO.LTD.

See USMC International Ltd.

BRITISH VENDING INDUSTRIES LTD.

Kestrel House, Garth Road, Morden,
Surrey SM4 4LP
Telephone: 0330-4333

Secretary A.R.Naylor

Employees 586

BRITISH VINEGARS LTD THE B.V.L. PENSION FUND

87 South Lambeth Road, London SW8 1RE
Telephone: 01-735 8100

Pension Fund Manager & Secretary B.A.Killick, ACIS

Trustees British Vinegars Pension Trust Ltd.

Investment Advisers & Stockbrokers Phillips & Drew

Actuaries & Pension Fund Consultants Bacon & Woodrow

Auditors Peat Marwick Mitchell & Co.

Company Employees 500

Members 301

Pensioners 168

Annual Contributions £168,000

Annual Investment Income £107,000

Annual Outflow £88,000

Capital Value £1,232,000

BRITISH VITA GROUP PENSION FUNDS (3 FUNDS)

Soudan Street, Middleton, Manchester M24 2DB
Telephone: 061-643 1133

Pension Fund Administrator N.Harrison

Secretary W.E.Holt

Director Personnel services T.Richardson

Corporate Trustees British Vita Pensions Trust Ltd.

Directors T.Richardson, F.A.Parker, J.Hogden, R.H.Sellers, R.McGee, F.J.Eaton, G.Blunt, L.D.Lawton, D.Critchley, H.Houghton

Investment Advisers N.M.Rothschild Asset Management Ltd.

Actuaries Duncan C.Fraser & Co.

Auditors C.Connelly & Co.

Company Employees 2,842

Members (at 5.4.80) 1,320

Pensioners 123

	£000
Annual Contributions	663
Annual Investment Income	455

BRITISH VITA GROUP Continued

Annual Outflow	173
Capital Value	4,896

Summary of Investments (1979)

UK Equities	1,525
Overseas Equities	358
Fixed Interest	1,168
Property	446
Cash & Deposits	247

BRITISH WATERWAYS BOARD (SALARIED STAFF) PENSION FUND AND (WAGES GRADE) PENSION FUND

Willow Grange, Church Road, Watford WD1 3QA
Telephone: Watford 26422

Pensions Administrator and Secretary Mrs.J.R.Pickett

Trustees British Waterways Board

Investment Advisers J.Henry Schroder Wagg & Co Ltd

Actuaries R.Watson & Sons

Auditors Coopers & Lybrand

Company Employees 3,265

	Staff Fund	Wages Grade
Members	797	1,705
Pensioners	136	268
Annual Contributions (to 31.3.80)	£000 542	£000 885
Annual Investment Income	328	238
Annual Outflow	360	152
Capital Value	4,357	3,367
Summary of Investments		
Equities	2,279	1,631
Fixed Interest	1,134	943
Property	650	405
Cash & Deposits	166	278
Others	128	110

BRITTAINS LTD. STAFF PENSION & LIFE ASSURANCE SCHEME

Cheddleton, Leek, Staffs.ST13 7EF
Telephone: 0538-360372

Secretary J.M.Bloor

Company Secretary A.S.Myatt,FCIS,FCCA

Trustees K.R.Latchford, S.Mallinson, V.Rickless, I.Torevell, A.S.Myatt

Managed by Equity & Law (Mahaged Funds) Ltd

Pension Fund Consultants Metropolitan Pensions Association Ltd

Employees 1,778

Members 312

Pensioners 43

Annual Contributions 14% payroll

G.B.BRITTON & SONS (HOLDINGS) LTD.

Midland Road, Higham Ferrers, Wellingborough, Northants.NN9 8DW
Telephone: 09334-57533

Secretary S.W.Iliffe

Employees 1,991

THOMAS BROADBENT & SONS LTD

Huddersfield HD1 3EA W.Yorks.
Telephone: 0484-22111

Director P.Broadbent

Insured with Legal & General Assurance Society Ltd

Employees 750

JAMES BROADHURST & SONS LTD.

Anchor Pottery, Bridgewood Street, Longton, Stoke-on-Trent,Staffs.

Secretary E.P.Roper

Employees 755

BROADHURST RETIREMENT BENEFITS PLAN

Gadbrook, Northwich, Cheshire
Telephone: 0538-385111

Pension Fund Manager & Secretary D.H.Clarke, ACMA

Trustees L.Royle, J.Batsford, P.Broadhurst, D.H.Clarke

Managed by Provident Mutual Life Assurance Association

Pension Fund Consultants Stewart Wrightson Assurance Consultants Ltd

Members 192

Annual Contributions £71,000

BROCKHOUSE STAFF PENSION SCHEME

Victoria Works, Hill Top, West Bromwich, West Midlands B70 0SN
Telephone: 021-556 1241

Secretary A.Mandley, ACIS

Company Secretary H.W.Bullock,FCIS

Trustees Brockhouse Staff Pensions Ltd.

Managed by Hill Samuel Investment Management Ltd

Investment Advisers Hill Samuel Investment Management Ltd

Actuaries R.Watson & Sons

Pension Fund Consultants Rowe & Maw (Solicitors)

Auditors Percy & Gittins Dudley

Company Employees 3,699

Members 817

Pensioners 371

	£000
Annual Contributions	491
Annual Investment Income	665
Gross Annual Outflow	248
Capital Value	8,500
Summary of Investments	
Equities	3,576
Fixed Interest	614
Property	454
Cash & Deposits	87
Others	330

THE BROCKS GROUP OF COMPANIES LTD

Fleets Lane, Poole, Dorset BH15 3BW
Telephone: 02013-4641

Secretary & Financial Director A.G.Irwin,FCA

Employees 693

BROOK DYEING CO.LTD.

Bottom Mills, Holmfirth, Huddersfield, HD7 1PU

Secretary G.H.Gledhill

Employees 170

BROOK STREET BUREAU OF MAYFAIR LTD

Brook Street House, 47 Davies Street,
London W1Y 2LN
Telephone: 01-629 8866

Managing Director R.Simms

Secretary C.Lowe,FCCA

Insured with Yorkshire General Life Assurance Co Ltd

Employees 909

BBL (BROOKE BOND LIEBIG) PENSION SCHEME

Thames House, Queen Street Place,
London EC4R 1DH
Telephone: 01-248 6422

Executive Director R.D.Crook, FCIS, FPMI

Pensions Manager P.D.Fanning, ACIS, APMI

Secretary & Overseas Pensions Manager T.E.Lythe, BA,LLB,APMI

Trustees Brooke Bond Liebig Pension Trust Ltd, 9 Directors, L.G.Green, FCA (Chairman)

Investment Advisers Robert Fleming Investment Management Ltd, Lloyds Bank Ltd

Actuaries R.Watson & Sons

Auditors Binder Hamlyn

Bankers Lloyds Bank Ltd

Property Advisers Jones Lang & Wootton

Forestry Managers Economic Forestry Ltd., Scottish Woodland Owners Association (Commercial) Ltd.

Solicitors Booker & Partners

Company Employees 9,200

Members (at 31.3.80)	
Contributing Members	5,457
Associate Members	3,331
Pensioners	2,163
Deferred Pensioners	564
	£000
Income (Year to 31.3.80)	
Contributions	4,691
Investment Income	2,023
From Insurance Companies	326
Total Income	7,040
Annual Outflow	2,527
Capital Value	
Book Value	25,251
Market Value*	31,020

Summary of Investments (market value)

Fixed Interest	6,907
U.K.Equities	11,161
Overseas Equities	1,376
Property Unit Trusts	4,000
Property	2,255
Forestry	850
Short-term Deposits	1,397
Advances to Welfare Insurance Co Ltd	400
Net Current Assets	524

* This includes the capital value on Insurance Policies estimated at £2.55 million

BROOKE TOLL ENGINEERING (HOLDINGS) LTD.

Newtown House, Maid Marian Way,
Notts.NG1 6GG
Telephone: 0602-43368

Secretary R.A.Brooke

Employees 617

BROOKS CLEANERS LTD

Ashley Vale, Bristol BS2 9RD
Telephone: 0272-558261

Secretary R.K.Taylor

Employees 690

BROOKTON LTD

271 Winchester Rd, Southampton SO9 3SX
Telephone: 0703-76481

Secretary K.M.Marsh

Employees 670

PETER BROTHERHOOD LTD PENSION SCHEME AND STAFF SUPERANNUATION FUND

Lincoln Road, Walton, Peterborough PE4 6AB
Telephone: 0733-71321

Company Secretary P.L.Hallam

Pension Scheme Managed by Prudential Pensions Ltd.

Staff Fund Managed by Legal & General (Pensions Management) Ltd.

Pension Fund Consultants C.T.Bowring & Layborn Ltd.

Auditors Ernst & Whinney

Company Employees 1,158

	Pension Scheme	Staff Fund
Members	547	383
Pensioners	124	54
	£000	£000
Annual Contributions	251	111
Capital Value	757	2,500

BROWN & JACKSON LTD.

Battle Bridge House, 300 Gray's Inn Road,
London WC1X 8DX
Telephone: 01-278 9635

Secretary K.Peake

Employees 1,266

BROWN & ROOT (UK) LTD. RETIREMENT BENEFITS PLAN
82 Pall Mall, London SW1
Telephone: 01-839 3456
Secretary C.G.Edwards
Employee Benefits Manager A.Beavis
Trustees 5 executive officers
Insured with Swiss Life Insurance & Pension Co
Investment Advisers Swiss Life Insurance & Pension Co
Pension Fund Consultants Jakelis Rolls & Radcliffe Ltd.
Company Employees 2,440
Members 1,900
Pensioners 16
Annual Contributions £773,000
Annual Investment Income £250,000
Annual Outflow £22,000
Capital Value £2,712,000

BROWN & TAWSE LTD
St Leonards Street, London E3 3JQ
Telephone: 01-980 4466
Secretary C.C.W.Milne
Insured with Legal & General Assurance Society Ltd
Employees 1,096

BROWN BOVERI KENT (HOLDINGS) LTD. RETIREMENT & LIFE ASSURANCE BENEFITS SCHEME
Biscot Road, Luton, Beds.LU3 1AL
Telephone: 0582-33722
Group Pensions & Insurance Manager H.E.Shelverton
Insured with Sun Life Assurance Society Ltd
Actuaries Rodney Barnett & Co.
Auditors Arthur Young McClelland Moores & Co.
Employees 4,247
Members (at 1.10.79) 3,535
Pensioners 750
Annual Contributions £2,033,000

BROWN BROTHERS CORPORATION LTD PENSION & LIFE ASSURANCE PLAN
Great Eastern House, Greenbridge Road, Stratton St.Margaret, Swindon,Wilts.SN3 3LB
Telephone: 0793-40151
Pension Fund Manager & Secretary S.C.Waiting
Trustees A.J.Crisp, H.S.Roake, J.G.Holgate, P.Sonley,W.W.Paul, P.J.Horrell, B.R.W.Daughtrey
Investment Advisers Geoffrey Morley & Partners Ltd.
Actuaries Clay & Partners Ltd.
Auditors Price Waterhouse & Co.
Company Employees 3,390
Members 1,800
Pensioners 750
Annual Contributions £1,200,000
Capital Value £4,500,000

DAVID BROWN HOLDINGS LTD.
32 Curzon Street, London W1Y 8BH
Telephone: 01-629 7373
Secretary A.D.Worton
Group Employees 5,349

DAVID BROWN TRACTORS LTD
Meltham Mills, Meltham, Huddersfield HD7 3AR
Telephone: 0484-850361
Secretary F.W.Parker,ACIS
Pension Fund Consultants William M. Mercer Benefits Ltd.
Employees 5,085

JOHN BROWN AND COMPANY LTD
8 The Sanctuary, London SW1P 3JU
Telephone: 01-222 9040
Secretary C.G.Roper
Employees 13,436
There are 6 different pension schemes within the group. All schemes are insured mainly with Scottish Amicable Life Assurance Society. John Brown & Co Ltd is the holding company.

MATTHEW BROWN & CO LTD
Lion Brewery, Blackburn, Lancs BB1 5NH
Telephone: 0254-52471
Secretary J.E.Hare
Managed by Prudential Pensions Ltd, Sun Alliance Fund Management Ltd
Employees 1,273

N.BROWN INVESTMENTS LTD
53 Dale Street, Manchester M60 6ES
Telephone: 061-236 8256
Secretary J.Martin
Stockbrokers Henry Cooke, Lumsden & Co.
Employees 810

BROWN SHIPLEY & CO LTD RETIREMENT & DEATH BENEFITS PLAN
Founders Court, Lothbury, London EC2R 7HE
Telephone: 01-606 9833
Director & Secretary J.A.Higinbottom
Investment Advisers Brown Shipley & Co Ltd
Actuarial Advice obtained through Godwins Ltd
Pension Fund Consultants Holmwoods & Crawfurd (Life & Pension Brokers) Ltd
Auditors Deloitte Haskins & Sells
Company Employees 509
Members (at 31.3.80) 152
Pensioners 65
Annual Contributions £321,000
Annual Investment Income £214,000
Capital Value £2,437,000

BROWNLEE & CO LTD PENSION FUND
City Saw Mills, Port Dundas, Glasgow G4 9TP
Telephone: 041-332 7066

Pension Fund Manager & Secretary D.W.G.Mitchell

Trustees P.A.Barns-Graham, J.F.McLelland, A.M.Nicol

Investment Advisers Scottish United Investors (Management) Ltd.

Stockbrokers Spiers & Jeffrey

Actuaries A.R.H.Collins & Co.

Pension Fund Consultants MacAlaster & Alison

Auditors Arthur Young, McClelland Moores & Co.

Company Employees 610

Members 252

Pensioners 54

	£000
Annual Contributions	141
Annual Investment Income	144
Annual Outflow	102
Capital Value	1,544
Summary of Investments	
Equities	808
Fixed Interest	603
Property	61
Cash & Deposits	75

THE BRUNNING GROUP LTD STAFF PENSION FUND
Brunning House, 100 Whitechapel Road, London E1 1JB
Telephone: 01-247 6525

Financial Director W.F.Morris, FCA

Secretary J.H.Aylett, FCCA

Stockbrokers Paul E.Schweder Miller & Co.

Actuaries Duncan C.Fraser & Co.

Auditors Cook & Co.

Company Employees 803

Members (at 31.3.80) 176

Pensioners 89

Annual Contributions £132,000

Annual Investment Income £244,000

Capital Value £2,544,000

BRUNTONS (MUSSELBURGH) LTD
Wire Mills, Musselburgh EH21 7UG
Telephone: 031-665 2301

Secretary W.S.Watson

Insured with Scottish Amicable Life Assurance Society

Employees 901

BRYANT HOLDINGS STAFF SUPERANNUATION SCHEME
Cranmore House, Cranmore Boulevard, Shirley, West Midlands B90 4SD
Telephone: 021-704 5111

Secretary R.H.D.Hawkins, FCA

Managed by Standard Life Assurance Co

Actuaries Duncan C.Fraser & Co.

Auditors Touche Ross & Co.

Company Employees 1,810

Members 520

Pensioners 85

Annual Contribution £450,000

Capital Value £4,760,000

BRYMILL LTD.
Brymill Steel Works, Tipton, West Midlands DY4 9EF
Telephone: 021-557 3939

Director K.M.Leach

Secretary E.S.Thomas

Employees 510

BSG (1978) PENSION FUND (BRISTOL STREET GROUP)
Burgess House, 1270 Coventry Road, Birmingham B25 8BB
Telephone: 021-707 0490

Pension Fund Manager I.S.O.Williams

Secretary Mrs. B.D.Heyes

Trustees Bristol Street Pensions Trust Limited

Investment Advisers Charterhouse Japhet Ltd

Actuaries and Pension Fund Consultants Duncan C Fraser & Co

Auditors Kidsons

Company Employees 6,476

Members 1,100

Pensioners 51

	£000
Annual Contributions	408
Annual Investment Income	281
Annual Outflow	190
Capital Value	2,405
Summary of Investments	
Equities	1,215
Fixed Interest	794
Property	311
Cash & Deposits	85

BSR LTD
Monarch Works, Powke Lane, Cradley Heath, Warley, West Midlands B64 5QH
Telephone: 0384-65191

Secretary E.T.Evans

Finance Director M.I.A.Fraser

Insured with Provident Mutual Life Assurance Association

Pension Fund Consultants Godwins Ltd.

Employees 16,079

Annual Contributions £80,000

BTR LTD
Silvertown House, Vincent Square, London SW1P 2PL
Telephone: 01-834 3848

BTR LTD Continued

Secretary & Director D.F.P.Sharrock
Pension Manager F.C.Berry
Trustees BTR Pension Fund Ltd
Other Directors Owen Green, J.C.Cahill, N.C.Ireland, W.D.T.Tapley, J.W.McKittrick
Pension Fund Consultants William M. Mercer
Company Employees 15,131
Members 4,000
Pensioners 750

BUCKINGHAMSHIRE COUNTY COUNCIL SUPERANNUATION FUND

County Hall, Aylesbury, Bucks.HP20 1UD
Telephone: 0296-5000
County Treasurer G.B.Ravens,IPFA
Assistant County Treasurer J.C.Minogue,IPFA
Stockbrokers Carr Sebag & Co., Phillips & Drew
Actuaries R.Watson & Sons
Auditors District Auditor
Members 7,650
Pensioners 2,200

	£000
Annual Contributions	5,750
Annual Investment Income	3,620
Annual Outflow	3,260
Capital Value	38,329
Summary of Investments	
Equities	18,086
Fixed Interest	15,315
Cash & Deposits	1,223
Others	3,705

BUCKLEY INVESTMENTS LTD PENSION FUND

Millbuck House, Corporation Street, Rugby CV21 2DW
Telephone: 0788-74911
Secretary T.J.R.Mitson, FCIS
Insured with Norwich Union Life Insurance Society
Pension Fund Consultants Norman Frizzell (Life & Pensions) Ltd.
Auditors Peat, Marwick, Mitchell & Co.
Company Employees 600
Members 190
Pensioners 15
Annual Contributions £80,000

BUCKMAN & HICKMAN LTD

Bank House, 100 Queen Street, Sheffield, S.Yorks.S1 2DW
Telephone: 0742-731111
Director P.J.Ford
Employees 550

BUDENBERG GAUGE CO LTD PENSION & ASSURANCE FUND

PO Box 5, Woodfield Road, Broadheath, Altrincham, Cheshire
Telephone: 061-928 5441
Secretary J.M.Long, FCA
Trustees B.H.C.Budenberg, G.F.Budenberg, J.M.Long
Insured with Legal & General Assurance Society Ltd.
Pension Fund Consultants Estridge & Ropner Ltd.
Auditors Burne Phillips
Company Employees 530
Members 450
Pensioners 70

A.F.BUDGE (CONTRACTORS) LTD.

West Carr Rd, Retford, Notts.DN22 7SW
Telephone: 0777-703781
Chairman & Managing Director A.F.Budge
Insured with Royal Insurance Co.Ltd.
Employees 541

BUILDING DESIGN PARTNERSHIP PENSION FUND & LIFE INSURANCE SCHEME (1973)

Vernon Street, Moor Lane, Preston, Lancs.PR1 3PQ
Telephone: 0772-59383
Pension Fund Manager & Secretary G.Burnstone, MA, APMI
Trustees Building Design Partnership Pension Trustees Ltd.
Directors 4 Partners, 4 Staff (Chairman D.H.Whittle,FRICS, Partner)
Investment Advisers Hambros Investment Management Services Ltd.
Actuarial Advice Obtained through Cubie, Wood & Co.Ltd.
Pension Fund Consultants Noble Lowndes & Partners Ltd.
Auditors Davies Downs & Co.
Partnership Employees 555
Members 485
Pensioners 35

	£000
Annual Contributions	500
Annual Investment Income	345
Annual Outflow	168
Capital Value	
Book Value	4,051
Market Value	4,518
Summary of Investments	
Equities	2,427
Fixed Interest	1,164
Property Unit Trust	456
Cash & Deposits	471

A.F.BULGIN & CO LTD

Bypass Road, Barking, Essex IG11 0AZ
Telephone: 01-594 5588

A.F.BULGIN & CO LTD Continued

Secretary G.A.Stone,FCA
Employees 709

BULLOUGH LTD
85 East Street, Epsom, Surrey KT17 1ED
Telephone: 78-27501
Secretary T.B.Brooks,FCA
Insured with Standard Life Assurance Co.
Employees 2,678

BULMER & LUMB (HOLDINGS) LTD
Buttershaw, Bradford BD6 2NE W.Yorks.
Telephone: 0274-676321
Secretary W.C.Coleman
Trustees Bulmer & Lumb Pension Trustee Co Ltd
Employees 1,444

H.P.BULMER LTD
Plough Lane, Hereford HR4 0LE
Telephone: 0432-6411
Personnel Services Manager Mrs.J.Peck
Secretary P.A.Hall
Insured with Standard Life Assurance Co.
Company Employees 1,914
Members 1,511
Pensioners 230
Annual Contributions £675,000

BUNGE & CO LTD PENSION & LIFE ASSURANCE PLAN
Bunge House, St Mary Axe, London EC3A 8AT
Telephone: 01-283 3429
Secretary E.J.W.Burt,FCIS
Insured with Standard Life Assurance Co.
Employees 985

BUNZL PULP & PAPER LTD
Friendly House, 21-24 Chiswell Street,
London EC1Y 4UD
Telephone: 01-606 9966
Secretary D.C.Latimer
Group Pensions Manager J.H.Weigall, MA, ACIS
Insured with Scottish Amicable Life Assurance Society
Employees 3,099

BURCO DEAN LTD
Accrington Road, Burnley, Lancs.BB11 5DS
Telephone: 0282-25901
Secretary J.Tennant, ACIS
Insured with Prudential Assurance Co Ltd
Employees 1,816

FREDK H.BURGESS LTD
The Green, Wolverhampton Road,
Stafford ST17 4BL
Telephone: 0785-3131

Secretary L.M.Turner
Insured with Guardian Royal Exchange Assurance Ltd.
Employees 1,794

BURGESS PRODUCTS COMPANY (HOLDINGS) LTD GROUP PENSION SCHEMES (3)
Brookfield Road, Hinckley, Leics LE10 2LN
Telephone: 0455-37701
Secretary A.Hopwood
Trustees W.Riddell, F.Fowler, C.B.Cotton, W.Daglish, A.Smith A.Hopwood
Insured with Norwich Union Life Insurance Society
Pension Fund Consultants Adams Heath & Co.Ltd.
Auditors Peat, Marwick, Mitchell & Co.
Company Employees 1,850
Members (Total 3 schemes) 631
Pensioners 145
Annual Contributions £277,000

BURMAH OIL CO.LTD. (5 PENSION FUNDS)
Burmah House, Pipers Way, Swindon, Wilts.SN3 1RE
Telephone: 0793-30151
Secretary D.R.Branch
Benefits Development Manager G.A.Nathan,ACIS, FPMI
Employee Benefits Manager K.W.Ritter, FPMI
Trustees Burmah Group Pension Trust Ltd
Investment Advisers Robert Fleming Investment Management Ltd.
Actuaries Bacon & Woodrow
Pension Fund Consultants Metropolitan Pensions Association Ltd.
Auditors Ernst & Whinney
Solicitors Allen & Overy
Group Employees 17,715
Members (at 30.6.80) 12,000
Pensioners 2,800

	£ million
Annual Contributions	5.5
Annual Investment Income	6.0
Annual Outflow	3.1
Capital Value	101.0
Summary of Investments (1979)	
Equities	42.0
Fixed Interest	17.0
Property	10.0

This information covers the following Pension Funds within the Group:
Burmah Castrol Pension Plan
Burmah Engineering Pension Plan
Burmah Industrial Products Pension Plan
Halfords Pension Plan
Quinton Hazzell Pension Plan

BURNDENE INVESTMENTS LTD
26a York Place, Edinburgh EH1 3EY
Telephone: 031-556 9351

Secretary F.W.Ritchie

Insured with Scottish Provident Institution

Employees 574

BURNETT & HALLAMSHIRE NON-CONTRIBUTORY PENSION TRUST
119 Psalter Lane, Sheffield S11 8YS
Telephone: 0742-57444

Secretary G.H.Dales, FCIS, ATII

Trustees G.H.Dales, D.W.Grosvenor, Lowndes Associated Pensions Ltd.

Stockbrokers Capel Cure Myers

Actuarial Advice obtained through Cubie Wood & Co Ltd

Property Advisers Hallamshire Industrial Estates Ltd

Pension Fund Consultants Lowndes Associated Pensions Ltd

Auditors Thornton Baker

Company Employees 1,450

Members 280

Pensioners 14

	£000
Annual Contributions	70
Annual Investment Income	120
Capital Value	1,616
Summary of Investments	
U.K.Equities	937
Overseas Equities	93
Fixed Interest	412
Cash & Deposits	174

BURNLEY BUILDING SOCIETY RETIREMENT BENEFITS PLAN
Ashworth House, Manchester Road, Burnley, Lancashire
Telephone: 0282-25025

Assistant General Manager A.W.Halstead, ACIS, ABS

Insured with Legal & General Assurance Society Ltd.

Pension Fund Consultants Noble Lowndes & Partners Ltd.

Company Employees 780

Members 620

Pensioners 52

Annual Contributions £320,000

BURNS-ANDERSON LTD.
9 St.John Street, Manchester M3 4DW
Telephone: 061-832 8484

Secretary D.Heap

Employees 678

BURNS INTERNATIONAL SECURITY SERVICES LTD.
100 Warwick Rd, London W5 5PT
Telephone: 01-567 3663

Director D.L.Janis

Executive G.Cameron-Douglas

Employees 600

BURRELL PENSION FUND (1978)
Burrell House, 44 Broadway, Stratford, London E15 1XN
Telephone: 01-555 3155

Personnel Manager Mrs. S.Webb,BA,MSc

Trustees D.Beard, G.M.Greenwood, B.R.Howe, P.H.Joel, B.Pulford

Investment Advisers Hill Samuel Investment Management Ltd

Actuarial Advice Obtained through Cubie, Wood & Co.Ltd.

Pension Fund Consultants Noble Lowndes & Partners Ltd

Auditors Ernst & Whinney

Company Employees 426

Members (at 5.4.80) 279

Pensioners 83

	£000
Annual Contributions	231
Annual Investment Income	85
Annual Outflow	68
Capital Value	1,249
Summary of Investments	
Equities	764
Fixed Interest	134
Property	107
Cash & Deposits	28

JAMES BURROUGH LTD. STAFF RETIREMENT BENEFITS SCHEME
Beefeater House, Montford Place, London SE11 5DF
Telephone: 01-735 8131

Secretary M.H.Brown, FCA, ACMA

Trustees Alan Burrough, N.C.Burrough, R.Moore

Insured with Scottish Widows' Fund & Life Assurance Society

Company Employees 550

Members 350

Annual Contributions £330,000

BURROUGHS MACHINES LTD
Heathrow House, Bath Road, Cranford, Middlesex TW5 9QL
Telephone: 01-759 6522

Secretary N.P.Bulpitt

Employees 5,207

BURTON, DELINGPOLE & CO.LTD.
PO Box 41, Cradley Heath, Warley, W. Midlands B64 6EJ
Telephone: 0384-69181

BURTON, DELINGPOLE & CO.LTD. Continued

Secretary & Director J.C.M.Young

Insured with Legal & General Assurance Society Ltd

Employees 871

THE BURTON GROUP LTD. STAFF SUPERANNUATION FUND

Hudson Road Mills, Leeds, W.Yorks.LS9 7DN
Telephone: 0532-494949

Pensions Secretary K.A.Newboult,ASCA

Pension Scheme Administrator R.Fletcher,ACII

Trustees Montague Burton Pensions Trustees Ltd.

Investment Advisers National Provident Institution, Robert Fleming Investment Management Ltd.

Property Advisers Conway Relf

Actuary G.V.Bayley,FIA (National Provident Institution)

Auditors Price Waterhouse & Co.

Company Employees 11,132

Members 3,011

Pensioners 1,412

	£000
Annual Contributions	2,197
Annual Investment Income	1,961
Annual Outflow	1,683
Capital Value	22,412
Summary of Investments	
Equities	8,314
Fixed Interest	6,831
Property	3,189
Cash & Deposits	2,641
Others	1,437

BURTONWOOD BREWERY CO (FORSHAWS) LTD

Bold Lane, Burtonwood, Warrington, Cheshire WA5 4PJ
Telephone: 09252-22961

Secretary P.J.N.Elsworthy

Employees 623

BUTLER & TANNER LTD. GROUP RETIREMENT BENEFITS PLAN

Selwood Printing Works, Frome, Somerset BA11 1NF
Telephone: 0373-4561

Pension Fund Manager & Secretary J.A.Gale

Other Pensions Management J.R.Tanner, R.Cunningham, A.G.A.Hillman

Trustees Butler & Tanner Group Pension Trustees Ltd.

Investment Advisers Warburg Investment Management Ltd.

Actuarial Advice Obtained through Cubie, Wood & Co.Ltd.

Pension Fund Consultants Noble Lowndes & Partners Ltd.

Auditors Ernst & Whinney

Company Employees 460

Members 360

Pensioners 80

	£000
Annual Contributions	312
Annual Investment Income	51
Annual Outflow	176
Capital Value	849
Summary of Investments	
Equities	600
Fixed Interest	168
Cash & Deposits	55

BUTTERFIELD HARVEY LTD

41-47 Strand, London WC2N 5JJ
Telephone: 01-930 9931

Secretary M.B.White, FCA

Managed by Legal & General (Pensions Management) Ltd, Prudential Pensions Ltd

Employees 3,071

BUTTERLEY BUILDING MATERIALS LTD

Wellington Street, Ripley, Derby
Telephone: 0773-43661

Director P.J.Harper

Executive G.J.Scott

Employees 1,400

BXL PLASTICS LTD. STAFF PENSION FUND AND WORKS PENSION FUND

Buchanan House, 3 St. James's Square, London SW1Y 4JS
Telephone: 01-839 7077

Pension Fund Manager and Secretary for Staff Fund A.C.Morris, AACCA,APMI

Assistant Pensions Manager and Secretary for Works Fund T.A.Brown, FCII, APMI

Trustees Seven for each fund, appointed from Management and Employees

Investment Advisers County Bank Ltd.

Actuaries Duncan C.Fraser & Co.

Auditors Ernst & Whinney

	Staff	Works
Company Employees	936	2,149
Members	891	2,096
Pensioners	712	739
Deferred Pensioners	151	328
	£000	£000
Annual Contributions	1,756	954
Annual Investment Income	1,156	318
Annual Outflow	919	241
Capital Value	11,299	3,773
Summary of Investments		

BXL PLASTICS LTD. Continued

Equities	6,392	2,119
Fixed Interest	3,905	1,037
Property	446	417
Cash & Deposits	555	199

C & A PENSION TRUSTEES LTD (C & A MODES LTD)

North Row, London W1A 2AX
Telephone: 01-629 1244

Pensions Secretary R.J.Holford, FPMI

STUART CABELDU CATERING LTD.

162/164 Arthur Road, Wimbledon Park, London SW19 8AH
Telephone: 01-946 7681

Pension Fund Manager P.G.Bowden

Secretary B.Evans

Insured with Scottish Widows' Fund & Life Assurance Society

Company Employees 800

Members 55

Annual Contributions £22,000

CABLE & WIRELESS SUPERANNUATION FUND

Mercury House, Theobalds Road, London WC1X 8RX
Telephone: 01-242 4433

Pension Fund Secretary J.F.Gray, ACIS

Head of Pensions & Retirements J.A.Weller, ACIS, APMI

Investment Advisers J.Henry Schroder Wagg & Co Ltd, Morgan Grenfell & Co Ltd, R. Watson & Sons

Trustees 11

Capital Value £70,000,000

Actuaries R.Watson & Sons

Auditors Deloitte, Haskins & Sells

Company Employees 11,000

Members 5,900

Pensioners 2,200

	£000
Annual Contributions	8,800
Annual Investment Income	6,900
Gross Annual Outflow	3,000
Capital Value	76,330
Summary of Investments	
Equities	38,760
Fixed Interest	24,450
Property Unit Trusts	5,340
Cash & Deposits	2,300
Others	5,480

CADBURY SCHWEPPES PENSION FUND

Bourneville, Birmingham B30 2LU
Telephone: 021-458 2000

Secretary & Pension Fund Manager O.H.Edwards, APMI, FCA

Trustees Cadbury Schweppes Pension Trust Ltd

Chairman Sir Adrian Cadbury

Chairman of Pensions Executive Committee and Pensions Consultative Committee K.G.Collyer

Accountant J.C.Silburn

Investments Manager A.F.Moody

Property Manager S.J.Smith, FRICS

Investment Advisers Robert Fleming Investment Management Ltd., Kleinwort Benson Investment Management Ltd.

Actuaries R.Watson & Sons

Property Advisers Strutt & Parker

Auditors Price Waterhouse & Co.

Company Employees 29,000

Members (at 5.4.80) 13,347

Pensioners 6,764

Deferred Pensioners 765

	£000
Annual Contributions	12,383
Annual Investment Income	9,852
Gross Annual Outflow	8,192
Capital Value	
Book Value	111,195
Market Value	124,747
Summary of Investments	
U.K.Equities	41,186
Foreign Equities	12,144
Fixed Interest	36,721
Property	26,786
Cash & Deposits	5,450
Net Current Assets	1,318
Other Investments	1,162

CAFFYNS PENSION FUND

4 Meads Road, Eastbourne, East Sussex BN20 7DR
Telephone: 0323-30201

Pension Fund Secretary D.J.M.Caffyn, MA, MSc

Trustees Caffyns Pension Fund Trustees Ltd

Stockbrokers Phillips & Drew

Actuaries R.Watson & Sons

Auditors Thornton Baker & Co

Company Employees 1,782

Members (at 5.4.80) 1,100

Pensioners 290

Annual Contributions £522, 000

Annual Investment Income £630,000

Gross Annual Outflow £130,000

Capital Value £3,560,000

CAKEBREAD ROBEY & CO.LTD.

318-326 Southbury Road, Enfield, Middx.EN1 1TT
Telephone: 01-804 8244

Secretary K.R.Davies

Stockbrokers Strauss, Turnbull & Co.

Employees 547

CALEDONIAN ASSOCIATED CINEMAS LTD. RETIREMENT & DEATH BENEFITS SCHEME

4 Academy Street, Inverness IV1 1LA
Telephone: 0463-37611

Secretary M.J.Paterson,CA

Trustee Caledonian Associated Cinemas Ltd.

Insured with Friends' Provident Life Office

Auditors Peat Marwick Mitchell & Co.

Company Employees 814

Members 155

Pensioners 20

Annual Contributions £41,000

CALEDONIAN HOLDINGS LTD. PENSION SCHEME

Comet Radiovision Services Ltd.
King Charles House, George Street, Hull HU1 3AU
Telephone: 0482-20681

Pension Fund Manager J.D.Cumming

Company Secretary R.W.Towndrow,FCA

Secretary to the Trustees Reed Stenhouse Benefit Consultants Ltd.

Trustees B.A.Nieman, Mr.Conway, J.D.Cumming

Investment Advisers Ivory & Sime Ltd

Actuaries Duncan C. Fraser & Co

Pension Fund Consultants Reed Stenhouse Benefit Consultants Ltd.

Auditors Thomson McLintock & Co.

Members (at 1.4.80) 263

Pensioners 49

	£000
Annual Contributions	355
Annual Investment Income	230
Gross Annual Outflow	85
Capital Value	3,225
Summary of Investments (1979)	
Equities	89%
Fixed Interest	8%
Cash & Deposits	3%

THE CALOR GROUP LTD. RETIREMENT BENEFITS PLAN

Calor House, Windsor Road, Slough, Berks.SL1 2EQ
Telephone: 23824

Pension Fund Manager D.V.Jones, BA, FCIS, APMI

Company Secretary J.S.Shearer

Investment Advisers Morgan Grenfell & Co.Ltd., Hill Samuel Investment Management Ltd.

Actuarial Advice Obtained through Cubie, Wood & Co.Ltd.

Pension Fund Consultants Noble Lowndes & Partners Ltd.

Auditors Price Waterhouse & Co.

Company Employees 4,122

Members (at 5.4.80) 3,857

Pensioners 650

	£000
Annual Contributions (to 5.4.80)	2,861
Annual Investment Income	724
Gross Annual Outflow	614
Capital Value	17,681
Summary of Investments	
Equities	3,994
Fixed Interest	2,460
Property Unit Trusts	1,385
Other Exempt Unit Trusts	9,437
Others	405

CAM GEARS LTD

Wilbury Way, Hitchin, Herts
Telephone: 0462-56751

Secretary K.B.Horton

Managing Director R.A.Pinnington

Employees 2,813

CAMBRIDGE & DISTRICT CO-OPERATIVE SOCIETY LTD EMPLOYEES SUPERANNUATION FUND

P.O.Box 53, Coldhams Lane, Cambridge CB1 3ER
Telephone: 0223-358844

Secretary J.M.Graham,FBIM

Trustees 4 elected from members, 4 elected from directors and chairman of the Board

Investment Advisers Co-operative Bank

Pension Fund Consultants and Actuarial Advice obtained through Co-operative Insurance Society Ltd. and Co-operative Union

Auditors Turquands Barton & Mayhew

Employees 1,131 (Full Time)

Members 707

Pensioners 224

Annual Contributions £128,000

Annual Investment Income £300,000

Annual Outflow £120,000

Capital Value of Fund £2,000,000

CAMBRIDGE COLLEGES FEDERATED PENSION SCHEME

c/o University Financial Board, The Old Schools, Cambridge CB2 1TS
Telephone: 0223-358933

Secretary M.J.Atkin

Trustees Cambridge Colleges Superannuation Trustees Ltd.

Stockbroker Buckmaster & Moore

Pension Fund Consultants and Actuarial Advice obtained through EBS Management Ltd.

Auditors Peters Elworthy & Moore

Members 704

Pensioners 28

	£000
Annual Contributions	378

CAMBRIDGE COLLEGES Continued

Annual Investment Income	93
Annual Outflow	130
Capital Value	1,367
Summary of Investments	
Equities	821
Fixed Interest	314
Property	219
Cash & Deposits	13

CAMBRIDGE UNIVERSITY PRESS CONTRIBUTORY PENSION FUND

University Printing House, Shaftesbury Road, Cambridge CB2 2BS
Telephone: 0223-358331

Pension Fund Officer Mrs J.D.Bulloch

Assistant Secretary P.R.Hodgson,MA,FCA

Trustees The Chancellor, Masters and Scholars of the University, acting through the Cambridge University Press Syndicate

Auditors Binder Hamlyn

Company Employees 715

Members 300

Pensioners 200

CAMBRIDGESHIRE COUNTY COUNCIL

Shire Hall, Castle Hill, Cambridge CB3 0AS
Telephone: 0223-58811

Treasurer J.E.Barton, IPFA

Investment Adviser E.Butler (Investment Manager, Wesleyan & General Assurance Co.)

Stockbrokers de Zoete & Bevan; Scrimgeour,Kemp-Gee & Co.

Actuaries Robertson,Hymans & Co.

Auditors Government-District Audit

Employees (at 31.3.80) 16,609

Members 8,004

Pensioners 2,434

	£000
Annual Contributions	5,600
Annual Investment Income	4,200
Gross Annual Outflow	3,300
Capital Value	42,229
Summary of Investments	
Equities	21,450
Fixed Interest	18,882
Cash & Deposits	1,897

DAVID CAMERON HOLDINGS LTD.

50 Bloomsbury Street, London WC1B 3QT

Secretary D.Cameron

Employees 809

CAMERON IRON WORKS LTD

Houston Road, Livingston, West Lothian
Telephone: 0589-31122

Secretary J.Beattie

Investment Advisers Hill Samuel Investment Management Ltd

Employees 1,760

J. W. CAMERON & CO LTD

Greenbank Offices, Lion Brewery, Hartlepool, Cleveland TS24 7QS
Telephone: 0429-66660

Secretary C.F.Porter

Employees 2,419

CAMFORD ENGINEERING LTD

Argyle Works, Argyle Way, Stevenage, Herts.SG1 2Aa
Telephone: 0438-4400

Secretary J.Gutteridge,ACCA

Employees 1,907

CAMMELL LAIRD SHIPBUILDERS LTD (WORKS) BENEFIT PLAN AND (1956) PENSION SCHEME

New Chester Road, Birkenhead, Merseyside L41 9BP
Telephone: 051-647 9474

Pensions Manager J.E.Bibby, APMI

Investment Advisers Baring Brothers & Co Ltd

Actuaries R.Watson & Sons

Pension Fund Consultants Noble Lownes & Partners Ltd

Auditors Arthur Young McClelland Moores & Co

Solicitors Laces & Co.

Employees 5,400

	Works Plan	1956 Scheme
Members	3,400	850
Pensioners	-	500
	£000	£000
Annual Contributions	50	515
Capital Value	360	10,000

HENRY CAMPBELL & CO LTD

Mossley Mills, Carnmoney Road North, Newtownabbey BT36 8NP, Co Antrim
Telephone: 02313-2333

Director G.G.Campbell

Employees 500

CAMPBELL & ISHERWOOD LTD

Penpoll Works, Hawthorne Road Bootle L20 6LB
Telephone: 051922-4641

Managing Director R.Osborne

Secretary A.Metz

Insured with Scottish Amicable Life Assurance Society

Employees 934

CAMPBELL'S SOUPS LTD

Hardwick Road, King's Lynn, Norfolk PE30 4HS
Telephone: 0553-5051

CAMPBELL'S SOUPS LTD Continued

Chairman J.R.Morris

Insured with Prudential Assurance Co Ltd

Pension Fund Consultants Metropolitan Pensions Association Ltd.

Employees 742

CAMREX (HOLDINGS) LTD EMPLOYEES RETIREMENT BENEFITS SCHEME

Camrex House, 3 Tatham Street, Sunderland, Tyne & Wear
Telephone: 0783-70811

Secretary S.J.Robson

Trustees A.Miller,S.J.Robson

Managed by Scottish Widows Pension Fund Trustees Ltd.

Pension Fund Consultants Furness Houlder (Life & Pensions) Ltd.

Auditors Thornton Baker

Company Employees 1,350

Members 185

pensioners 14

Annual Contributions £191,000

Capital Value £2,000,000

THE CANADA LIFE ASSURANCE CO BRITISH ISLES STAFF & OFFIALS PENSION FUNDS

Canada Life House, High Street, Potters Bar, Herts.EN6 5BA
Telephone: 51122

Administrator,Staff Pension Funds R.A.A.Farrell

Trustees F.L.Strevens, R.J.Jackson, I.C.Gunn, P.L.Grainge, H.Ellis

Auditors Coopers & Lybrand

Company Employees U.K. 500

Members 300

Pensioners 125

	£000
Annual Contributions	495
Annual Investment Income	392
Annual Outflow	170
Capital Value	6,246
Summary of Investments	
Equities	2,587
Fixed Interest	3,247
Property	226
Cash & Deposits	442

CANADIAN PACIFIC COMPANIES (EUROPE) PENSION PLAN

46 Finsbury Square, London EC2A 1DD
Telephone: 01-638 5555

Manager Pension Administration Miss S.Hounsfield

Investment Advisers Bankers Trustee & Executor Co Ltd

Pension Consultants Towers Perrin Forster & Crosby Inc

Auditors Price Waterhouse & Co.

Solicitors Sacker & Company

Company Employees 1,500

Members 975

Pensioners 74

Annual Contributions £720,000

Capital Value of Fund £5,100,000

W.CANNING LTD.

P.O.Box 288, Great Hampton Street, Birmingham B16 6AS
Telephone: 021-236 8621

Group Pension Fund Manager A.W.Smith

Secretary D.H.Harwood

Finance Director D.H.Probert

Insured with Standard Life Assurance Co.

Investment Advisers Hill Samuel & Co.Ltd.

Actuaries Duncan C.Fraser & Co.

Employees 1,984

CANNON ASSURANCE LTD STAFF BENEFITS PLAN

1 Olympic Way, Wembley, Middlesex HA9 0NB
Telephone: 01-902 8876

Company Secretary M.L.Dawbarn, LLB

Auditors Coopers & Lybrand

Employees 264

Members 219

Pensioners 23

Annual Contributions £73,000

Annual Investment Income £292,000

Capital Value £2,798,000

CANNON RUBBER LTD

Ashley Road, Tottenham N17
Telephone: 01-808 6261

Secretary G.Shalet

Employees 560

CANTORS LTD NON-CONTRIBUTORY PENSION TRUST

164/170 Queens Road, Sheffield S2 4DY S.Yorks.
Telephone: 0742-738461

Company Secretary G.C.Hutchinson

Senior Trustee K.J.Kershaw

Actuaries Duncan C.Fraser & Co.

Auditors Thomson McLintock & Co

Solicitors Kershaw Tudor & Co.

Company Employees 717

Members (at 31.12.79) 131

Pensioners 44

Annual Contributions £8,000

Annual Investment Income £80,000

Capital Value £664,000

CANTRELL & COCHRANE (GREAT BRITAIN) LTD. RETIREMENT BENEFITS PLAN

Club House, Hanworth Road, Sunbury on Thames, Middx.TW16 5CA
Telephone: 85555

Assistant Secretary P.F.O'Connor,ACIS

Investment Advisers Henderson Administration Ltd.

Actuarial Advice Obtained through Cubie, Wood & Co.Ltd.

Pension Fund Consultants Noble Lowndes & Partners Ltd.

Auditors Hays Allan

Company Employees 1,150

Members 850

Pensioners 350

Annual Contributions £250,000

Capital Value £1,000,000

CAPE INDUSTRIES LTD STAFF PENSION & LIFE ASSURANCE SCHEME

114 Park Street, London W1Y 4AB
Telephone: 01-499 6022

Pension Fund Manager & Secretary D.R.Stacey, APMI

Part Managed by Legal & General (Pensions Management) Ltd

Investment Advisers N. M. Rothschild Asset Management Ltd

Pension Fund Consultants Metropolitan Pensions Association Ltd.

Auditor Peat Marwick Mitchell & Co.

Company Employees 9,135

Members (at 5.4.80) 2,600

Pensioners 700

Annual Contributions £2,163,000

Annual Investment Income £66,000

Capital Value £8,000,000

CAPPER-NEILL LTD

Bridge Road, Woolston, Warrington, Cheshire WA1 4AU
Telephone: 0925-812525

Secretary R.G.Roberts, FCA

Insured with Scottish Widows' Fund & Life Assurance Society

Pension Fund Consultants Reed Stenhouse Benefit Consultants Ltd

Employees 4,409

CAPSEALS LTD

9 North Street, Rugby CV21 2AB

Secretary S.L.Pennell

Investment Advisers Brown Shipley & Co.Ltd.

Employees 1,066

CARAVANS INTERNATIONAL & ASSOCIATED COMPANIES PENSION & LIFE ASSURANCE PLAN

Emson Close, Saffron Walden, Essex CB10 1HW
Telephone: 0799-27321

Finance Director J.E.Bardwell,FCA

Pension Fund Manager & Secretary M.G.Grimbly

Trustees S.Alper, P.Brown, A.J.Graves, P.Greenwood, J.B.Holland, M.Ridgard, A.J.Smith

Insured with Clerical Medical & General Life Assurance Society

Pension Fund Consultants Richardson,Searles & Co.Ltd., Stewart Wrightson Assurance Consultants Ltd.

Auditors Josolyne Layton-Bennett & Co.

Company Employees (UK) 1,288

Members 300

Pensioners 25

Annual Contributions £180,000

Annual Investment Income £46,000

Annual Outflow £69,000

Capital Value £730,000

THE CARBORUNDUM CO.LTD. EMPLOYEES PENSION SCHEME

Trafford Park Road, Trafford Park, Manchester M17 1HP
Telephone: 061-872 2381

Pension Fund Manager and Secretary B.A.English, ACIS,APMI

Trustees National Westminster Bank Ltd.

Investment Advisers Ivory & Sime Ltd, Kleinwort Benson Investment Management Ltd

Actuaries Lane Clark & Peacock

Pension Fund Consultants and Actuarial Advice Obtained through Wyatt Harris Graham Ltd.

Auditors Coopers & Lybrand

Solicitors Slaughter & May

Company Employees 1,560

Members 1,100

Pensioners 500

	£000
Annual Contributions	950
Annual Investment Income	630
Annual Outflow	500
Capital Value	9,740
Summary of Investments	
Equities	5,270
Fixed Interest	2,900
Property	850
Cash & Deposits	720

CARCLO ENGINEERING GROUP LTD

Hightown Road, Cleckheaton, W.Yorks.BD19 5JU
Telephone: 0274-875700

Secretary A.Cuerden, FCA ACMA

Group Employees 1,479

CARHARTT HAMILTON LTD
East Camperdown Street, Dundee,
Tayside DD1 3LS
Telephone: 0382-44251

Director H.Mee

Employees 900

CARICOR HOLDINGS LTD
197 Knightsbridge, London SW7 1RB
Telephone: 01-589 8111

Secretary R.D.Booker

Insured with Swiss Life Insurance & Pension Co.

Group Employees 1,072

CARLSBERG (GREAT BRITAIN) LTD
29 Bedford Row, London WC1R 4HE
Telephone: 01-965 4011

Chairman A.W.Nielsen

Insured with Legal & General Assurance Society Ltd

Employees 750

CARLTON INDUSTRIES PENSION TRUST
Clifton Heights, Triangle West, Clifton,
Bristol BS8 1EJ
Telephone: 0272-298641

Pension Fund Manager & Secretary D.J.Jordan

Trustees Carlton Industries Pension Trust Ltd

3 Comapny Appointed Directors, 3 Member Directors, 1 Pensioner Director

Stockbrokers Rowe & Pitman

Actuaries R.J.Shrubb & Co.

Auditors Richards & Co

Company Employees 3,466

Members (at 5.4.80) 3,466

Deferred Pensioners 1,892

Pensioners 660

	£000
Annual Contributions	2,501
Annual Investment Income	422
Annual Outflow	656
Capital Value	10,321
Summary of Investments Equities	2,943
Fixed Interest	3,767
Property	2,848

CARNATION FOODS CO LTD
Carnation House, 11 High Road, East Finchley,
London N2 8AW
Telephone: 01-883 6443

Company Secretary K.F.Hall

Investment Advisers Hill Samuel Investment Management Ltd

Employees 713

CARPETS INTERNATIONAL LTD PENSION FUNDS
PO Box 9, New Road, Kidderminster,
Worcestershire DY10 1AL
Telephone: 0562-4071

Secretary N.V.Grimshaw, FCA

Assistant Secretary C.Bridges

Insured with Standard Life Assurance Co

Investment Advisers J. Henry Schroder Wagg & Co Ltd

Pension Fund Consultants Metropolitan Pensions Association Ltd.

Employees 6,280

CARPETS OF WORTH LTD. RETIREMENT BENEFITS SCHEME
Severn Valley Mills, Stourport on Severn,
Worcs.DY13 9HA
Telephone: 02993-4124

Pensions Manager R.C.L.Rowse,APMI

Insured with Sun Life Assurance Society Ltd.

Pension Fund Consultants E.C.Darwin Clayton & Co.Ltd.

Auditors Coopers & Lybrand

Company Employees 1,250

Members (at 16.7.80) 1,033

Pensioners 125

Annual Contributions £512,000

CARR FASTENER CO LTD SALARIED PENSION PLAN AND PENSION PLAN FOR HOURLY PAID EMPLOYEES
Nottingham Road, Stapleford,
Nottingham NG9 8AJ

Director & Secretary H.T.Barnes,FSCA

Insured with Legal & General Assurance Society Ltd

Pension Fund Consultants Towers Perrin Forster & Crosby Inc

Employees 1,100

	Salaried	Hourly Paid
Members	248	529
Pensioners	65	70
	£000	£000
Annual Contributions	249	216
Capital Value	1,237	323

JOHN CARR (DONCASTER) LTD
Watch House Lane, Doncaster DN5 9LR S.Yorks.
Telephone: 0302-21333

Secretary F.Ward

Insured with Norwich Union Life Insurance Society

Employees 1,171

CARRERAS PENSION FUND
Christopher Martin Road, Basildon, Essex
Telephone: 0268-22840

CARRERAS PENSION FUND Continued

Pension Fund Manager & Secretary J.W. Allen, FPMI

Assistant Secretary A.B.Bertolla

Holding Trustees Carreras Superannuation Trustees Ltd, Arcadia Trustees Ltd

Trustees 7 appointed by directors, J. A. Prodger (Chairman) 7 appointed by members

Property Advisers Savills, The James Abbott Partnership

Actuaries Bacon & Woodrow

Auditors Champness Cowper & Co

Company Employees 8,000

Members 7,070

Pensioners 1,308

	£000
Annual Contributions (at 5.4.80)	7,447
Annual Investment Income	4,010
Annual Outflow	1,858
Capital Value	52,285
Summary of Investments	
Equities	28,369
Fixed Interest	14,623
Property	4,122
Cash & Deposits	4,244
Others	927

CARRINGTON VIYELLA GROUP STAFF RETIREMENT BENEFITS PLAN

Pennine House, 39 Well Street, Bradford, West Yorkshire BD1 5NW
Telephone: 0274-33095

Group Pensions Manager S.J.Levine,MA,FPMI

Group Financial Controller H.E.Allison

Trustees CV Pensions Trustee Ltd

Investment Advisers Robert Fleming Investment & Management Ltd, J. Henry Schroder Wagg & Co Ltd

Actuaries Duncan C.Fraser & Co.

Auditors Price Waterhouse & Co.

Company Employees 22,500

CARRON CO.(HOLDINGS) LTD.

Carron, Falkirk, Stirlingshire FK2 8DW
Telephone: 0324-21331

Pensions Officer & Secretary I.M.Bolton,CA

Insured with Sun Life Assurance Society Ltd.

Employees 2,040

CARR'S MILLING INDUSTRIES LTD

Old Croft, Stanwix, Carlisle, Cumbria CA3 9BA
Telephone: 0228-28291

Financial Director & Secretary S.P.Smith

Insured with Sun Life Assurance Society Ltd

Employees 789

CARRS (BIRMINGHAM) LTD.

Westminster Works, West Heath, Birmingam B31 3PG

Director A.N.Carr

Employees 543

CARTER & PARKER LTD.

Gordon Mills, Guiseley, Leeds, West Yorks LS20 9PD
Telephone: 0943-72264/8

Secretary G.L.Bussey

Employees 827

R.G.CARTER (HOLDINGS) LTD & ASSOCIATED COMPANIES PENSION FUND

High Road, Drayton, Norwich, Norfolk NR8 6AH
Telephone: 0603-867355

Secretary G.Furness

Group Pension Fund Administrator J.E.Thaxton, ASCA

Insured with Norwich Union Life Insurance Society

Employees 2,975

Members 276

Pensioners 60

JOSEPH CARTWRIGHT LTD

Cartwright House, 39-43 Monument Hill, Weybridge, Surrey KT13 8SA

Managing Director J.J.Cartwright

Employees 623

R. CARTWRIGHT (HOLDINGS) LTD

Fleet Works, Straight Road, Short Heath, Willenhall, West Midlands WV12 5QY
Telephone: 0922-401606

Managing Director J.C.Northam

Secretary R.L.Teare,FCA

Insured with Guardian Royal Exchange Assurance Group Ltd

Employees 748

CATERPILLAR TRACTOR CO LTD PENSION PLANS

PO Box, Glasgow G2 1JP
Telephone: 0698-812921

Pension Fund Manager & Secretary G.Reardon, FPMI

Benefits Officer S.A.Lauder

Trustees 20, 10 elected by members, 10 elected by company

Investment Managers Baring Bros. & Co.Ltd.

Pension Fund Consultants and Actuarial Advice Obtained through Metropolitan Pensions Association Ltd

Auditors Price Waterhouse & Co

Employees 5,238

Members 4,496

Pensioners 556

CATERPILLAR TRACTOR CO LTD *Continued*

	£000
Annual Contributions	2,300
Annual Investment Income	854
Gross Annual Outflow	526
Capital Value	14,719
Summary of Investments	
Equities	8,761
Fixed Interest	3,617
Property	926
Cash & Deposits	1,353

CATTLE'S (HOLDINGS) LTD STAFF PENSION FUND

142 Beverley Road, Hull HU3 1UZ
Telephone: 0842-659371

Secretary P.H.Prescott

Trustee Cattle's Provident Trust Ltd

Insured with Sun Life Assurance Society Ltd

Stockbrokers Stancliff Todd & Hodgeson

Actuaries R.Watson & Sons

Auditors Thornton Baker

Employees 1,762

Members (at 29.7.80) 836

Pensioners 13

Annual Contributions £250,000

Annual Investment Income £65,000

Capital Value £650,000

SIR JOSEPH CAUSTON & SONS LTD

Tower House, Hopton Street, London SE1 9JL
Telephone: 01-928 2141

Secretary R.H.G.Bondsfield

Insured with Prudential Assurance Co Ltd

Employees 977

CAVAGHAN & GRAY LTD

Harraby Bacon Factory, Carlisle, Cumbria
Telephone: 0228-24451/7

Secretary J.Hogarth, FCA

Employees 783

CAVENHAM GROUP PENSION SCHEME

Cavenham House, By Pass Road, Colnbrook, Berks SL3 0EB
Telephone: 4411

Secretary & Group Pensions Manager Miss C.Y.Edmenson, APMI

Other Pension Management Committee of Management 6 Employer 6 Member

Trustees Cavenham Pension Trustees Ltd

Investment Advisers Banque Occidentale pour l'Industrie et le Commerce

Actuaries Bacon & Woodrow

Auditors Price Waterhouse & Co.

Employees 27,000

Members 8,000

Pensioners 4,500

Capital Value £40 million

CAWDAW INDUSTRIAL HOLDINGS LTD. PENSION & ASSURANCE SCHEME AND 1978 RETIREMENT & DEATH BENEFIT SCHEME

Cawdaw House, Lower Broughton Road, Salford, Manchester M7 9FX
Telephone: 061-792 6811

Director & Secretary B.S.Walton, FCA

Part Insured with Equity & Law Assurance Society Ltd.

Part Managed by Legal & General Assurance (Pensions Management) Ltd.

Pension Fund Consultants and Actuarial Advice Obtained through Godwins Ltd.

Auditors Spicer & Pegler

Company Employees 780

Members 332

Pensioners 252

Capital Value £1,042,000

CAWOODS GROUP STAFF LIFE ASSURANCE & PENSION SCHEME

Southlands, Ripon Road, Harrogate,
N. Yorks HG1 2HY
Telephone: 0423-68068

Secretary & Group Pensions Manager H.S.Clarke

Group Asst. Pensions Manager Mrs C.A.Veasey

Trustees J.C.Cooper, E.Binks, R.I.Lawson

Part Insured with Clerical, Medical & General Life Assurance Society

Part Managed by Baring Bros & Co.Ltd.

Stockbrokers Cazenove & Co

Actuarial Advice obtained through Clerical, Medical & General Life Assurance Society

Pension Fund Consultants E.H.Foster & Co Ltd

Auditors Pannell Fitzpatrick & Co

Company Employees 2,183

Members 460

Pensioners 150

CBS UNITED KINGDOM LTD PENSION PLAN

17-19 Soho Square, London W1V 6HE
Telephone: 01-734 8181

Pension Fund Administrator D.Becker

Secretary G.Shestopal

Treasury Manager R.Gane

Trustees M.Oberstein, J.Field, G.Shestopal, J.Wheeler, R.Kiernan

Investment Advisers N.M. Rothschild Asset Management Ltd

Actuarial Advice Obtained through Towers, Perrin, Forster, Crosby Inc.

Auditors Coopers & Lybrand

Company Employees 1,780

Members 350

Pensioners 17

CBS UNITED KINGDOM LTD Continued

	£000
Annual Contributions	300
Annual Investment Income	60
Annual Outflow	35
Capital Value	1,172
Summary of Investments	
Equities	657
Fixed Interest	334
Property	124
Cash & Deposits	34
Others	23

CEGO (ENGINEERING) LTD.
Western Road, Silver End, Witham,
Essex CM8 3QB
Telephone: 0376-83241

Director Dr.I.C.Perkin

Employees 540

CELCON LTD PENSION FUND
289/293 High Holborn, London WC1V 7HU
Telephone: 01-405 8767

Secretary R.E.White

Pension Fund Consultants Glanvill Enthoven (Life, Pensions & Mortgages) Ltd.

Auditors Safferys

Employees 750

Members 144

Pensioners 4

Annual Contributions £132,000

CELESTION INDUSTRIES LTD
130 Mount Street, London W1Y 5HA
Telephone: 01-499 5641

Secretary D.R.S.Ezekiel

Insured with Standard Life Assurance Co.

Employees 3,421

CEMENT & CONCRETE ASSOCIATION
Wexham Springs, Slough SL3 6PL
Telephone: 02816-2727

Secretary R.W.J.Wilcox

CENTRAL & SHEERWOOD LTD
36 Chesham Place, London SW1X 8HE
01-235 4551
Telephone: 01-235 4551

Secretary A.J.Garrett

Insured with Legal & General Assurance Society Ltd

Employees 4,481

CENTRAL MANUFACTURING & TRADING LTD
303 Halesowen Road, Dudley,
West Midlands DY2 9NR
Telephone: 0384-69434

Secretary M.Hale

Insured with Sun Life Assurance Society Ltd

Pension Fund Consultants Clarkson Head & Harris

Employees 2,428

CENTRAL REGIONAL COUNCIL SUPERANNUATION FUND
Viewforth, Stirling FK8 2ET
Telephone: 0786-3111

Director of Finances J.Broadfoot,B.Comm.,IPFA

Trustees Central Regional Council

Stockbrokers Phillips & Drew, Nivisons

Actuaries Robertson, Hymans & Co.

Employees 11,500

Members 7,500

Pensioners 1,950

	£000
Annual Contributions	3,727
Annual Investment Income	2,400
Annual Outflow	2,000
Capital Value (Market Value)	25,139
Summary of Investments	
Equities	10,328
Fixed Interest	12,354
Property	1,221
Cash & Deposits	742
Others	494

CENTRAL TRUSTEE SAVINGS BANK LTD. PENSION FUND
P.O.Box, St.Mary's Court,
100 Lower Thames Street, London EC3R 6AQ
Telephone: 01-623 5266

Assistant Secretary Mrs. M.A.Wright

Actuaries R.Watson & Sons

Auditors Ernst & Whinney

Company Employees 584

Members 488

Pensioners 4

Annual Contributions £557,000

Annual Investment Income £516,000

Capital Value £2,845,000

CENTRAX TRUSTEES LTD
Shaldon Road, Newton Abbot, Devon
Telephone: 0626-2251

Trustee & Administrator R.Howe

Employees 554

CENTRE HOTELS (CRANSTON) LTD
10 Grosvenor Street, Edinburgh EH12 5EG
Telephone: 031-337 8089

Secretary D.A.Cook

Employees 3,076

CENTREWAY LTD.
1 Waterloo Street, Birmingham B2 5PG
Telephone: 021-643 3941

Secretary E.J.Stott

Employees 1,099

CENTURY OILS GROUP LTD.
Century Works, Century Street,
Hanley,Stoke on Trent ST1 5HU 0782-29521
Telephone: R.Sillitoe

Secretary R.Sillitoe

Insured with Royal Insurance Co.Ltd.

Employees 797

C.H. INDUSTRIALS LTD. LIFE & PENSION SCHEME
28 Lake Street, Leighton Buzzard, Beds.LU7 8RX
Telephone: 0525-377075

Secretary A.G.Biddle

Insured with Royal Insurance Co.Ltd.

Pension Fund Consultants Bain Dawes & Partners Ltd.

Auditors Thornton Baker

Group Employees 1,024

Members 420

Pensioners 13

CHAD VALLEY CO LTD
234 Bradford Street, Birmingham
Telephone: 021427-3241

Secretary C.W.Holden, ACA

Employees 2,500

CHADBURNS HOLDINGS LTD
Park Lane Works, Netherton, Bootle, Merseyside
Telephone: 051525-4155

Employees 587

CHAMBERLAIN GROUP LTD. PENSION SCHEME
130 Buckingham Palace Road, London SW1E 9SF
Telephone: 01-730 0833

Secretary C.A.Wentzel,BA,LLB

Investment Manager S.H.G.Gradidge

Trustees L.F.Chamberlain (Chairman), T.V.Emmerson, S.H.G.Gradidge, A.I.Wilkes, B.F.Overett, G.F.Lewry

Stockbrokers Henderson, Crosthwaite & Co; Kent East Newton & Co

Actuaries Bacon & Woodrow

Employees 1,425

Certain provisions are being changed; no financial information is therefore available at present

CHAMBERLAIN & HILL LTD
Chuckery Foundry, Walsall,
West Midlands WS1 2DU
Telephone: 0922-31411

Secretary F.Grant,FCIS

Employees 765

CHAMBERLAIN PHIPPS LTD STAFF RETIREMENT BENEFIT SCHEME
Wood Street, Higham Ferrers, Wellingborough, Northants.NN9 8HH
Telephone: 09334-53084

Scheme Administrators D.J.Stevenson, R.Throssell

Trustees R.F.Chamberlain, B.H.Chamberlain, D.J.Stevenson

Managed by Pensions Management (S.W.F.) Ltd

Actuaries Bacon & Woodrow

Pension Fund Consultants C.T.Bowring & Layborn Ltd

Company Employees 2,612

Members 360

Pensioners 170

Annual Contributions £175,000 (1977)

Annual Investment Income £11,000 in addition to Managed Fund income

Gross Annual Outflow £30,000 (1977)

Capital Value £1 million (1977)

CHAMPION SPARKING PLUG CO LTD 1974 PENSION & LIFE ASSURANCE SCHEME
Great South West Road, Feltham,
Middx TW14 0PN
Telephone: 01-759 6442

Secretary T.A.Harrison

Insured with Equity & Law Life Assurance Society Ltd

Pension Fund Consultants Metropolitan Pensions Association Ltd.

Auditors Peat, Marwick, Mitchell & Co.

Employees 1,522

Members 983

Pensioners 77

Annual Contributions £623,000

CHANGE WARES LTD
Garth Road, Lower Morden, Surrey SM4 4NA

Secretary M.E.Smith,CA

Employees 669

CHAPMAN GROUP OF COMPANIES NO.1 PENSION SCHEME
Chapman House, Farwig Lane, Bromley,
Kent BR1 3OS
Telephone: 01-464 6566

Secretary Mrs S.M. Carter

Co.Secretary & Secretary to Trustees C.W.Witt

Trustees W.Brooks, B.Coulter, C.R.Ponter, P.M.Whitefield

Part Insured with Sun Life Assurance Society Ltd.

Managed by Commercial Union Pensions Management Ltd., Scottish Amicable Pensions Investments Ltd., Provident Mutual Managed Pension Funds Ltd.

Auditors Arthur Goddard & Co, Josolyne Layton-Bennett & Co

Company Employees 801

Members 226

Pensioners 96

Annual Contributions £274,000

CHARNOS LTD
Corporation Road, Ilkeston, Derbys DE7 4BP
Telephone: 0602-322191

Secretary J.W.Robinson

Employees 1,997

CHARTER CONSOLIDATED PENSION SCHEME
40 Holborn Viaduct, London EC1P 1AJ
Telephone: 01-353 1545

Personnel Department P.O.Box 104, Charter House, Park Street, Ashford, Kent TN24 8EQ

Pension Administrator L.A.Webb

Secretary A.Greig

Investment Manager B.J.Crean

Trustees Charter Consolidated Pension Trustees Ltd

Actuaries Bacon & Woodrow

Property Advisers Herring Son & Daw, Michael Laurie & Partners

Auditors Coopers & Lybrand

Group Employees 11,651

Company Employees 579 (Charter Consolidated Services Ltd.)

Members 507

Pensioners 379

	£000
Annual Contributions	1,081
Annual Investment Income	1,475
Annual Outflow	639
Capital Value	16,619
Summary of Investments	
Equities	6,950
Fixed Interest	6,723
Property	1,640
Cash & Deposits	1,306

THE CHARTERHOUSE GROUP SECURITY BENEFITS SCHEME AND CHARTERHOUSE INDUSTRIES STAFF BENEFITS PLAN
23 St.Swithin's Lane, London EC4N 8AD
Telephone: 01-248 3999

Secretary P.A.G.French

Group Pensions Manager P.B.Godley

Trustees Charterhouse Pensions Ltd

Investment Advisers Charterhouse Japhet Ltd

Actuaries T.G.Arthur & Co.

Pension Fund Consultants Charterhouse Pensions Consultancy (23 St.Swithin's Lane, London EC4)

Auditors Ernst & Whinney

Company Employees 6,145

	Group Scheme	Industries Plan
Members	461	1,126
Pensioners	146	342
	£000	£000
Annual Contributions	1,225	958
Annual Investment Income	1,162	409
Capital Value	10,090	6,827

CHASE MANHATTAN BANK NA
Woolgate House, Coleman Street, London EC2
Telephone: 01-600 6141

Secretary to Pension Trustees Miss S.Toole-Stott

CHELSEA BUILDING SOCIETY RETIREMENT BENEFITS FUND
Thirlestaine Hall, Thirlestaine Road, Cheltenham, Glos.GL53 7AL
Telephone: 0242-21391

Personnel Controller A.H.Davies,ACIS

Managed by Sun Life Pension Ltd.

Pension Fund Consultants Noble Lowndes & Partners Ltd.

Members 225

Annual Contributions £200,000

Capital Value £550,000

CHELTENHAM & GLOUCESTER BUILDING SOCIETY SUPERANNUATION FUND
Cheltenham House, Clarence Street, Cheltenham, Glos.GL50 3JR
Telephone: 0242-36161

Secretary & Financial Director G.G.Vose,FCA,FCBSI

Trustees C.E.Jessop, B.P.Ward, J.J.Cole, T.Overbury, R.C.Stow, G.G.Vose, R.A.Black

Investment Advisers Lloyds Bank Trust Division

Actuaries R.Watson & Sons

Auditors Walter J.Edwards & Co.

Company Employees 721

Members 386

Pensioners 48

	£000
Annual Contributions	457
Annual Investment Income	458
Annual Outflow	59
Capital Value	3,748
Summary of Investments	
Equities	2,271
Fixed Interest	1,152
Property	118
Cash & Deposits	207

CHEMICAL BANK 1974 PENSION PLAN
180 Strand, London WC2R 1ET
Telephone: 01-379 7474

Pensions Manager M.C.Duncombe,AIA

Part Managed by Legal & General (Pensions Management) Ltd., Provident Mutual Life Assurance Association

Pension Fund Consultants Wyatt Harris Graham Ltd.

Employees/Members 600

Pensioners 30

CHEMICAL BANK Continued

Annual Contributions £600,000
Capital Value £3,474,000

C.W.CHENEY & SON LTD.
Factory Road, Hockley, Birmingham B18 5LH
Telephone: 021554-1201

Secretary Miss J.M.Wood

Employees 623

CHERRY VALLEY FARMS LTD
Rothwell House, Rothwell, Lincs LN7 6BG
Telephone: 047289-271

Secretary J.Cross

Insured with London Life Association Ltd.

Employees 500

CHESEBROUGH-POND'S LTD RETIREMENT & LIFE INSURANCE PLAN
Victoria Road, London NW10 6NA
Telephone: 01-965 6575

Company Secretary A.G.Noble, FCIS

Investment Advisers Morgan Grenfell & Co Ltd

Pension Fund Consultants Willis Faber Advisory Services Ltd

Auditors Arthur Young McClelland Moores & Co

Company Employees 517

Members (at 31.3.80) 270

Pensioners 144

Annual Contributions £160,000

Annual Investment Income £166,000

Capital Value £1,800,000

CHESHIRE COUNTY COUNCIL SUPERANNUATION FUND
County Hall, Chester CH1 1SG
Telephone: 0244-602549

County Treasurer C.T.Fletcher,MA,IPFA,APMI

Investment Advisers County Bank Ltd., Fielding Newson-Smith

Actuaries Duncan C. Fraser & Co

Property Advisers Healey & Baker, Cheshire County Valuer

Auditor District Auditor

Employees 40,000

Members 18,300

Pensioners 6,800

	£000
Annual Contributions	12,500
Annual Investment Income	6,900
Annual Outflow	5,900
Capital Value	80,300
Summary of Investments	
Equities	40,300
Fixed Interest	23,200
Property	9,500
Cash & Deposits	5,900
Others	1,400

CHILTERN MOTOR HOLDINGS LTD PENSION & LIFE ASSURANCE SCHEME
The Roundabout, Woodstock Road, Oxford OX2 8LA
Telephone: 0865-511488

Secretary A.A.Edwards

Pension Fund Consultants Godwins Ltd.

Auditors Critchley Ward & Pigott

Employees 586

Members 211

Pensioners 34

Annual Contributions £161,000

Annual Investment Income £68,000

Capital Value £605,000

CHILTONIAN LTD
Manor Lane, Lee, London SE12 0TY
Telephone: 01-852 3333

Secretary P.Cottam

Managing Director C.V.Grindle

Employees 795

W.E.CHIVERS & SONS LTD.
Estcourt Street, Devizes, Wilts.
Telephone: 0380-2121

Secretary P.C.Amor

Employees 533

CHLORIDE U.K. PENSION SCHEME
52 Grosvenor Gardens, London SW1W 0AU
Telephone: 01-730 0866

Group Pensions Manager G.J.Goldring,ACIS

Secretary R.J.Weekley,ACII,APMI

Investment Advisers Lloyds Bank Ltd.

Actuaries Bacon & Woodrow

Auditors Coopers & Lybrand

Company Employees (at 31.3.80) 10,500

Members 6,700

Pensioners 2,471

	£000
Annual Contributions	6,300
Annual Investment Income	4,300
Annual Outflow	3,100
Capital Value (Book Value)	50,200
Summary of Investments	
Equities	29,870
Fixed Interest	14,870
Property	4,860
Cash & Deposits	600

CHRISTIANI & NIELSEN LTD
21-24 Grosvenor Place, London SW1X 7JE
Telephone: 01-636 0921

Secretary O.L.Christensen

CHRISTIANI & NIELSEN LTD Continued

Insured with Norwich Union Life Insurance Society

Employees 602

CHRISTIE-TYLER LTD. RETIREMENT BENEFITS SCHEME

Brynmenyn, Bridgend, Mid-Glamorgan CF32 9LN
Telephone: 0656-721367

Secretary G.E.Jones

Trustees G.M.Williams, R.R.Batchelor, K.C.O'Sullivan, G.E.Jones

Insured with Scottish Provident Institution

Pension Fund Consultants Willis Faber (Wales) Ltd

Auditors Peat, Marwick, Mitchell & Co

Company Employees 3,357

Members 484

Pensioners 12

Annual Contributions £126,000

CHRISTIE, MANSON & WOODS LTD PENSION & LIFE ASSURANCE SCHEME

8 King Street St James's 8 King Street, St.James's,
Telephone: 01-839 9060

Personnel Manager D.R. Dickson

Secretary (to Company and to Trustees) C.W.Witt

Managed by Commercial Union Pensions Management Ltd., Scottish Amicable Pensions Investments Ltd., Provident Mutual Managed Pension Funds Ltd.

Actuaries Cubie, Wood & Co Ltd

Pension Fund Consultants Lowndes Associated Pensions Ltd.

Auditors Peat Marwick Mitchell & Co

Company Employees 550

Members 310

Pensioners 22

Annual Contributions £294,000

Annual Investment Income Automatically reinvested

Gross Annual Outflow £40,000

Capital Value £1,400,000

CHUBB & SON LTD. 1972 PENSION FUND

14-22 Tottenham Street, London W1P 0AA
Telephone: 01-637 2377

Secretary C.E.Kemble

Director and Pension Fund Manager R.G.Howard, FCII, APMI

Trustees Chubb & Son Pensions Ltd

Investment Advisers & Stockbrokers Hoare Govett Ltd

Actuaries R. Watson & Sons

Auditors Deloitte Haskins & Sells

Company Employees 11,900

Members 10,000

Pensioners 1,600

	£ million
Annual Contributions	4.3
Annual Investment Income	2.3
Annual Outflow	1.1
Capital Value	22.9
Summary of Investments	
Equities	6.3
Fixed Interest	11.8
Property	2.3
Cash & Deposits	2.5

CHURCH & CO LTD

St James, Northampton NN5 5JB
Telephone: 0604-51251

Managing Director J.G.Church, FCA

Managed by Pensions Management (SWF) Ltd.

Employees 2,020

CHURCH MISSIONARY SOCIETY

157 Waterloo Road, London SE1 8UU
Telephone: 01-928 8681

Secretary D.P.Barrington

Trustees CMS Pension Trust Ltd.

Pension Consultants & Actuary C I K Forster CBE FIA

Auditors Turquands Barton Mayhew & Co

Employees 112

Members 324

Pensioners 238

Annual Contributions £142,000

Capital Value £3,328,000

CHURCH OF ENGLAND CHILDREN'S SOCIETY PENSION FUND

Old Town Hall, Kennington Road, London SE11 4QD
Telephone: 01-735 2441

Secretary J.B.Trevor Williams,CA,APMI

Trustee Barclays Bank Trust Co Ltd

Investment Managers J. Henry Schroder Wagg & Co Ltd

Actuaries Duncan C. Fraser & Co

Auditors Deloitte Haskins & Sells

Employees 840

Members 360

Pensioners 220 (incl. 20 deferred)

	£000
Annual Contributions	303
Annual Investment Income	289
Capital Value (Market Value at 30.6.80)	3,878
Summary of Investments	
Equities	2,426
Fixed Interest	1,380
Cash & Deposits	72

CHURCH WORKERS' PENSION FUND
53 Tufton Street, Westminster, London SW1P 3QP
Telephone: 01-222 1568

Secretary D.Thackray,FCIS

Actuary M.Short,FIA

Auditors Deloitte Haskins & Sells

Members (at 31.12.79) 2,082

Pensioners 588

Annual Contributions £633,000

Annual Investment Income £578,000

Capital Value £6,200,000

CIBA-GEIGY PENSION SCHEME
Hurdsfield Industrial Estate, P.O.Box 47, Macclesfield, Cheshire SK10 2NT
Telephone: 0625-21933

Chairman of Trustee Board K.M.Townsend,FCA

Secretary and Pensions Manager G.E.West, FPMI, ACII

Trustees C.G.I. Pension Trust Ltd

Investment Managers Touche, Remnant & Co

Stockbrokers Grieveson, Grant & Co

Property Advisers Edward Erdman & Co.

Actuaries Duncan C.Fraser & Co.

Auditors Coopers & Lybrand

Solicitors Addleshaw, Sons & Latham

Company Employees 8,750

Members 7,000

Pensioners 2,000

	£000
Annual Contributions	6,300
Annual Investment Income	4,300
Annual Outflow	2,800
Capital Value	
Book Value	48,200
Market Value	56,700
Summary of Investments (at cost)	
Equities	17,000
Fixed Interest	13,200
Property	8,300
Cash & Deposits	1,400
Others (Overseas)	8,300

CIC INVESTMENT HOLDINGS LTD
Moat House, Welbourn, Herts SG8 6EJ
Telephone: 0763-60611

Secretary A.D.Blackett

Employees 970

CINCINATTI MILACRON LTD
Kingsbury Road, Erdington, Birmingham B24 0QU
Telephone: 021-351 3821

Company Secretary B.I.Burnley

Director Personnel and Administrative Services R.R.Weber

Managed by Legal & General (Pensions Management) Ltd

Pension Fund Consultants Noble Lowndes & Partners Ltd

Employees 2,290

CITY ELECTRICAL FACTORS LTD
Station Road, Kenilworth, Warks.CV8 1JJ
Telephone: 0926-58127

Secretary N.C.Constable

Employees 1,500

CIVIL AVIATION AUTHORITY SUPERANNUATION SCHEME
Aviation House, 129 Kingsway, London WC2B 6NN
Telephone: 01-405 6922

Secretary F.A.Byford

Trustees H.C.Partridge, J.E.Lockwood, J.Banfield, J.H.Penwarne D.J.Rye, E.F.H.Bryant, A.Stark, Miss G.M.E.White

Custodian Trustees National Westminster Bank Ltd

Investment Advisers Hambros Investment Management Services Ltd, Charterhouse Japhet Ltd

Actuaries Bacon & Woodrow

Property Advisers Clive Lewis & Partners

Auditors Arthur Young McClelland Moores & Co

Company Employees 7,500 approx.

Members 7,400

Pensioners 1,203

	£000
Annual Contributions	13,877
Annual Investment Income	17,788
Annual Outflow	5,611
Capital Value	213,504
Summary of Investments	
Equities	102,629
Fixed Interest	70,990
Property	27,858
Cash & Deposits	11,916
Others	111

C. & J.CLARK PENSION FUND
6 Leigh Road, Somerset BA16 0HA
Telephone: 04584-3131

Secretary & Pensions Manager J.F.Bleakley, FCA, FPMI

Pensions Administrator D.Hedley, ACIS, APMI

Trustees 6 Nominated by Company, 4 elected by Members, 1 Pensioner Trustee (coopted)

Investment Advisers J.Henry Schroder Wagg & Co.Ltd.

Actuaries Duncan C. Fraser & Co

Auditors Coopers & Lybrand

Company Employees 13,632

Members (at 5.4.80) 6,566

Pensioners 1,265

Deferred Pensions 1,170

C. & J.CLARK Continued

	£000
Annual Contributions	2,247
Annual Investment Income	2,121
Annual Outflow	1,137
Capital Value	
Book Value	25,598
Market Value	32,573
Summary of Investments	
Equities	19,153
Fixed Interest	6,411
Property	4,727
Cash & Deposits	2,282

JAMES CLARK & EATON LTD.
PO Box 19, Southern Industrial Area, Bracknell, Berks.RG12 4UU
Telephone: 0344 24733

Secretary M.L.Brown

Insured with Commercial Union Assurance Co.Ltd.

Employees 1,494

CLARK, SON & MORLAND LTD
The Farmhouse, Mill Lane, Glastonbury, Somerset BA6 9YH
Telephone: 0458-32222

Secretary J.C.Morland

Employees 1,365

WILLIAM CLARK & SONS LTD
Upperlands, Derry, Londonderry, N. Ireland
Telephone: 064882-214

Employees 700

T.CLARKE & CO.LTD.
Stanhope House, 94-104 Denmark Hill, London SE5 8RX
Telephone: 01-733 5656

Secretary B.Moss

Employees 774

CLEMENT CLARKE LTD.
Clement Clarke House, Springfield Road, Horsham, West Sussex RH12 2DL
Telephone: 0403-68911

Secretary E.E.Bushell

Trustees E.E.Bushell, S.R.A.Bonnett, W.A.Bray, G.M.Pain

Insured with Legal & General Assurance Society Ltd.

Pension Fund Consultant C.A.H.Garstang

Group Employees 919

Members 330

Pensioners 28

T. CLARKE & CO LTD
94-104 Denmark Hill, London SE5 8RX
Telephone: 01 733 5656

Secretary B.Moss

Insured with Prudential Assurance Co Ltd

Employees 879

CLAY CROSS CO LTD
Clay Cross, Chesterfield, Derby S45 9NG
Telephone: 0246-862151

Secretary R.H.Baguley

Employees 1,060

RICHARD CLAY PENSION TRUSTEES LTD
6-16 Huntsworth Mews, London NW1 6DD
Telephone: 01-402 6661

Secretary J.W.L.Nichols

Investment Advisers Fraser Green Ltd

Employees 1,516

CLAYTON DEWANDRE HOLDINGS LTD WORKS, STAFF AND SENIOR STAFF RETIREMENT BENEFIT SCHEMES (1975)
90 Newbold Road, Rugby, Warks.CV21 2NL
Telephone: 0788-74561

Pensions Manager D.J.Brown

Trustees Chemical Bank Trustee Co.Ltd.

Investment Advisers Ivory & Sime Ltd.

Actuaries Bacon & Woodrow

Auditors Arthur Young McClelland Moores & Co.

Solicitors Linklaters & Paines

Employees 3,970

Members (at 5.4.80) 3,800

Pensioners 500

Annual Contributions £2,400,000

Annual Investment Income £75,000

Capital Value £10,000,000

CLAYTON SON & CO (HOLDINGS) LTD
Moor End Works, Hunslet, Leeds, W.Yorks LS10 2BH
Telephone: 0532-705226

Director & Secretary S.Jones, B.Com, FCA

Insured with Eagle Star Insurance Co Ltd

Employees 777

THE CLEANWELL GROUP
Cleanwell House, Hatton Wall, London EC1N 8JL
Telephone: 01-242 5663

Director M.Silver

Employees 1,000

CLERICAL MEDICAL & GENERAL LIFE ASSURANCE SOCIETY STAFF SUPERANNUATION FUND
Narrow Plain, Bristol BS2 0JH
Telephone: 0272-290566

Secretary A.G.Harrison, ACII APMI

Trustees General Reversionary & Investment Co.Ltd.

Investment Advisers Clerical Medical & General Life Assurance Society

Actuary A.G. O'Leary FIA

CLERICAL MEDICAL & GENERAL LIFE ASSURANCE SOCIETY Continued

Auditors Ernst & Whinney
Company Employees 1,050
Members 875
Pensioners 111

	£000
Annual Contributions	1,243
Annual Investment Income	1,351
Annual Outflow	384
Capital Value	18,726
Summary of Investments	
Equities	10,557
Fixed Interest	4,987
Property	688
Cash & Deposits	2,494

CLEVELAND COUNTY COUNCIL SUPERANNUATION FUND

P.O.Box, Municipal Buildings, Middlesborough, Cleveland TS1 2QH
Telephone: 0642-248155

Treasurer B.Stevenson,BA,IPFA
Property Advisers Healey & Baker
Actuaries Robertson, Hymans & Co.
Employees 17,500
Members 14,250
Pensioners 3,150
Annual Contributions £8,150,000
Annual Investment Income £4,500,000
Capital Value £69,000,000

CHARLES CLIFFORD INDUSTRIES LTD

Dog Pool Mills, Stirchley, Birmingham B30 2XJ
Telephone: 021-472 1544

Secretary D.K.D.MacKerrell
Employees 615

CLIFFORD COVERING CO

Spring Road, Hall Green, Birmingham B11 3DN
Telephone: 021-777 5261

Executive R.W.J.Collard
Employees 500

CLIFFORD GROUP PENSION SCHEME FOR SALARIED EMPLOYEES

Woden Road West, Wednesbury, West Midlands WS10 7SY
Telephone: 021-556 1212

Pensions Administrator P.D.Blakemore
Secretary A.A.Carter
Managed by Prudential Pensions Ltd.
Auditors Ernst & Whinney
Employees 2,902
Members 600
Pensioners 190
Annual Contributions £397,000

See also TRW

CLIFFORD'S DAIRIES GROUP PENSION PLAN

Western Road, Bracknell, Berkshire RG12 1QA
Telephone: 0344-25741

Secretary L.N.Eyley,FCIS
Trustees J.Clifford, C.F.Coster, B.A.Lambe, C.G.Burton, P.S.Candy
Managed by Scottish Amicable Pensions Investments Ltd.
Pension Fund Consultants Wyatt Harris Graham
Auditors Jollife Cork & Co.
Employees 1,500
Members 822
Annual Contributions £200,000 approx.

CLUGSTON HOLDINGS LTD PENSION SCHEME

St Vincent House, Normanby Road, Scunthorpe, S. Humberside DN15 8QT
Telephone: 0724-3491

Secretary R.L.Hurst
Insured with Norwich Union Life Insurance Society
Employees 1,170

CLWYD COUNTY COUNCIL SUPERANNUATION FUND

Shire Hall, Mold, Clwyd CH7 6NB
Telephone: 0352-2121

County Treasurer R.C.Greening, IPFA, MBCS
Stockbrokers de Zoete & Bevan
Actuaries R.Watson & Sons
Auditors District Audit
Employees 15,300
Members 7,730
Pensioners 2,524
Annual Contributions £4,350,000
Annual Investment Income £2,833,000
Annual Outflow £2,452,000
Capital Value £29,000,000

CLYDE PORT AUTHORITY PENSION & LIFE ASSURANCE SCHEME

16 Robertson Street, Glasgow G2 8DS
Telephone: 041221-8733

Secretary J.Michael
Trustees J.P.Davidson, J.Mather, J.Michael
Insured with The Scottish Equitable Life Assurance Society Ltd.
Actuarial Advice Obtained through Scottish Equitable Life Assurance Society Ltd.
Pension Fund Consultants Hogg Robinson (Pensions Consultants) Ltd.
Auditors Arthur Young McClelland Moores & Co.
Company Employees 1,150
Members 990
Pensioners 600
Annual Contributions £1,600,000

CLYDE PORT AUTHORITY Continued

Annual Investment £2,200,000
Annual Outflow £1,450,000
Capital Value £9,000,000

CLYDESDALE BANK LTD. PENSION FUND
30 St Vincent Place, Glasgow G1 2HL
Telephone: 041-248 7070

Staff Controller & Scheme Administrator Wm.C.Harvey

Investment Manager J.A.Docherty

Property Advisers D.E. & J.Levy

Actuary D.D.McKinnon,FFA

Auditors Ernst & Whinney

Company Employees 6,000

Members 5,597

Pensioners 1,077

	£000
Annual Contributions	3,750
Annual Investment Income	4,000
Annual Outflow	2,700
Capital Value	38,000

COALITE AND CHEMICALS STAFF & WORKS RETIREMENT BENEFITS PLAN
Buttermilk Lane, Bolsover, Derbyshire S44 6AB
Telephone: 0246-822281

Secretary F.Clifford, FCAA

Trustees C.E.Needham, P.A.Fowler, Lowndes Associated Pensions Ltd

Investment Advisers Baring Brothers & Co Ltd, Morgan Grenfell & Co Ltd

Actuarial Advice obtained through Cubie Wood & Co

Pension Fund Consultants Noble Lowndes & Partners Ltd

Auditors Price Waterhouse & Co

Company Employees 2,500

Members 1,750

	£000
Annual Contributions	900
Annual Investment Income	600
Annual Outflow	400
Capital Value	8,500
Summary of Investments	
Equities	5,300
Fixed Interest	2,200
Property	600
Cash & Deposits	400

COATES BROTHERS & CO.LTD. 1962 STAFF LIFE ASSURANCE & PENSION FUND
1-7 Easton Street, London WC1X 0DP
Telephone: 01-837 2810

Secretary D.W.Wright,FCIS

Trustees Lowndes Associated Pensions Ltd

Insured with English Insurance Company

Pension Fund Consultants Noble Lowndes & Partners Ltd

Employees 1,680

Members 880

Pensioners 50

COATS PATONS SUPERANNUATION FUND (1978)
155 St Vincent Street, Glasgow G2 5PA
Telephone: 041-221 8711

Pension Fund Manager & Secretary J.McNiven, APMI

Investment Manager A.W.Matheson

Assistant Pension Manager P.H.Batty,BSc,FIA,APMI

Trustees Textile Pensions Trust Ltd

Directors W.D.Coats, J.D.F.Miller, R.I.Pugh, C.J.Risk, W.Welsh

Actuaries R.K.Stewart FFA and M.D.Thornton, FFA

Auditor I.Ogle,CA

Company Employees 21,000

Members 10,500

Pensioners 5,500

	£million
Annual Contributions	7.4
Annual Investment Income	6.5
Gross Annual Outflow	6.5
Capital Value	101.6
Summary of Investments	
Equities	75.0
Fixed Interest	0.6
Property	11.0
Cash & Deposits	15.0

D. & H. COHEN LTD.
2 Coustonholm Road, Glasgow G43 1UE
Telephone: 041632-9151

Secretary W.P.Hannah

Insured with Guardian Royal Exchange Assurance Group Ltd

Employees 1,324

COLAS PRODUCTS LTD. THE IBE GROUP PENSION & ASSURANCE SCHEME
Galvin Road Trading Estate, Slough, Berks SL1 4DL
Telephone: 71711

Pension Fund Manager D.Grubb,APMI

Insured with Friends' Provident Life Office

Pension Fund Consultants Wigham Poland Pension Consultants Ltd.

Auditors Price Waterhouse & Co.

Company Employees 800

Members 650

Pensioners 230

Annual Contributions £798,000

COLCHESTER & EAST ESSEX CO-OPERATIVE SOCIETY LTD EMPLOYEES' SUPERANNUATION FUND

Victoria Place, Eld Lane, Colchester, Essex CO1 1LR
Telephone: 0206-77751

Secretary J.E.D.Owen,JP

Trustees Colchester & East Sussex Co-operative Society (Trustees) Ltd.

Investment Advisers & Stockbrokers Phillips & Drew

Property Advisers The James Abbott Partnership

Actuary P.D.Johnson (Co-operative Insurance Society Ltd.)

Auditors Appleby, English & Partners

Company Employees 1,600

Members (at 5.4.80) 852

Pensioners 259

	£000
Annual Contributions	238
Annual Investment Income	320
Annual Outflow	143
Capital Value	2,638
Summary of Investments	
Fixed Interest	1,313
Cash & Deposits	922

R.H.COLE LTD. GROUP PENSION SCHEME

Whitecliff House, 852 Brighton Road, Purley, Surrey CR2 2UY
Telephone: 01-668 4161

Director & Secretary H.Fayers

Trustees Cole Pensions Ltd

Investment Advisers Drayton Montagu Portfolio Management Ltd.

Actuaries Bacon & Woodrow

Auditors Ernst & Whinney

Company Employees 500 (approx)

Members 320

Pensioners 17

	£000
Annual Contributions	300
Annual Investment Income	110
Annual Outflow	21
Capital Value	1,250
Summary of Investments	
Equities	620
FixedInterest	390
Property	180
Cash & Deposits	60

COLGATE-PALMOLIVE PENSION PLAN

76 Oxford Street, London W1A 1EN
Telephone: 01-580 2030

Pension Fund Manager & Secretary P.J.Beazley

Trustees J.M.A.Barker, J.McLean, A.Nimmey P.J.Pilzer

Managed by Legal & General (Pensions Management) Ltd.

Investment Advisers Kleinwort Benson Investment Management Ltd., Legal & General (Pensions Management) Ltd.

Actuarial Advice Obtained through Cubie, Wood & Co.Ltd.

Pension Fund Consultants Noble Lowndes International Ltd.

Auditors Arthur Andersen & Co.

Company Employees 1,400

Members 1,300

Pensioners 360

Annual Contributions £800,000

Capital Value £3,000,000

See also Helena Rubinstein

COLLETT DICKENSON PEARCE INTERNATIONAL LTD RETIREMENT BENEFIT SCHEME

110 Euston Road, London NW1 2DQ
Telephone: 01-388 2424

Executive Benefits Adviser P.G.Nunn,FPMI

Trustees Stewart Wrightson Trustees Ltd.

Insured with Scottish Widows' Fund & Life Assurance Society

Pension Fund Consultants Stewart Wrightson Assurance Consultants

Company Employees/Members 300

Pensioners 13

Annual Contributions £500,000

Annual Outflow £57,000

WM COLLINS & SONS (HOLDING) LTD PENSION & LIFE ASSURANCE SCHEME

Westerhill Road, Bishopbriggs, Glasgow G64 2QT
Telephone: 041772-3200

Pensions Manager J.M.A.Barker

Trustees Scottish Pension Trustees

Secretary A.C.Fyfe, CA

Managed by Hill Samuel Investment Management Ltd

Stockbroker R.C.Greig & Co

Pension Fund Consultants C.T.Bowring & Layborn Ltd.

Auditors Arthur Young McClelland Moores & Co.

Company Employees 2,842

Members 1,800

Pensioners 400

COLONIAL MUTUAL LIFE ASSURANCE SOCIETY LTD. RETIREMENT BENEFIT SCHEME FOR UK EMPLOYEES

24 Ludgate Hill, London EC4P4BD
Telephone: 01-248 9861

Secretary E.J.Haynes, FCIS

Pension Scheme Officer E.N.Finch,ACII,APMI

Trustees The Rt.Hon. The Earl of Ranfurly,KCMG,

The Major UK Pension Funds COL/COM

COLONIAL MUTUAL LIFE ASSURANCE SOCIETY LTD.
Continued

D.Awdry, C.Towers, A.B.McCreadie,LLB, E.J.Haynes,FCIS

Managed by Colonial Mutual Life (Pension Annuities) Ltd

Investment Adviser E.K.V.Redfern, MA, FIA

Actuary R.J.Durden, FIA

Auditors Ernst & Whinney

Company Employees 1,200

Members 1,034

Pensioners 108

Annual Contributions £1,036,000

Annual Outflow £410,000

Capital Value £5,100,000

CHARLES COLSTON GROUP LTD
Colston House, London Road, High Wycombe, Bucks HP11 1BQ

Secretary D.Austen

Employees 1,055

COLT LIFE ASSURANCE AND RETIREMENT SCHEME
c/o Colt International & Associated Companies Ltd.,Havant, Hampshire PO9 2LY
Telephone: 0705-451111

Secretary N.G.J.Boschi, FCA, APMI (Group Treasurer)

Trustees I.J.O'Hea, J.J.O'Hea, A.O'Hea, R.D.Fairchild (Group Financial Director)

Investment Advisers Warburg Investment Management Ltd, Brown Shipley & Co Ltd

Actuaries Lane Clark & Peacock

Pension Fund Consultants Metropolitan Pensions Association Ltd

Auditors Morison Stoneham & Co

Company Employees 1,077

Members 1,046

Pensioners 72

	£000
Annual Contributions	1,268
Annual Investment Income	687
Annual Outflow	100
Capital Value	7,349
Summary of Investments	
Equities	3,282
Fixed Interest	2,150
Property	262
Cash & Deposits	560
Others	1,095

COLTHROP BOARD MILLS
Thatcham, Newbury, Berkshire
Telephone: 0635-62451

Executive G.H.Pike

Employees 850

COLUMBIA RIBBON & CARBON MANUFACTURING CO.LTD. PENSION & LIFE ASSURANCE PLAN
Kangley Bridge Road, Lower Sydenham, London SE26 5AW
Telephone: 01-778 6011

Secretary V.W.Tennant, FCA

Trustees P.C.Jefferies, V.W.Tennant, G.T.Smith, W.C.James, C.R.Bates

Stockbrokers Laurence Prust & Co.

Pension Fund Consultants Antony Gibbs Pension Services Ltd.

Auditors Milne Ross

Company Employees 535

Members 460

Pensioners 97

COMBEN GROUP PENSION TRUST
Clifton Heights, Triangle West, Clifton, Bristol BS8 1EJ
Telephone: 0272-298641

Pension Fund Manager & Secretary D.J. Jordan

Trustees Comben Group Pension Trustees Ltd., 2 Company Appointed Directors, 2 Member Directors

Stockbrokers Rowe & Pitman

Actuaries T.G. Arthur & Co.

Pension Fund Consultants Edis & Co.

Auditors Richards & Co.

Other information is not yet available as the Comben Fund and Membership is in the process of being split off from the Carlton Trust

COMBINED ENGLISH STORES GROUP LTD PENSION FUND
Abney Buildings, 65 Hanover Street, Liverpool L1 3EJ
Telephone: 051-708 7186

Pension Fund Manager Miss A.Worswick,BA

Trustees M.G.Gordon, E.J.A.Haygarth,BCom,FCA, E.C.S.Large,FCA

Investment Advisers Morgan Grenfell & Co Ltd

Actuaries Duncan C.Fraser & Co.

Auditors Ernst & Whinney

Company Employees 4,616

Members 402

Pensioners 55

	£000
Annual Contributions	314
Annual Investment Income	129
Annual Outflow	62
Capital Value	1,509
Summary of Investments	
Equities	595
Fixed Interest	310
Cash & Deposits	68
Others	441

COMET RADIOVISION SERVICES LTD. 1974 PENSION & ASSURANCE SCHEME

King Charles House, 48-50 George Street,
Hull HU1 3AU
Telephone: 0482-20681

Pension Fund Manager & Secretary J.D.Cumming

Trustees M.J.Hollingberry, E.R.Pears,FCA,
J.D.Cumming,MA, G.B.Swinburne,FCA

Managed by Scottish Amicable Pensions Investments Ltd.

Actuarial Advice obtained through C.T.Bowring & Layborn Ltd

Pension Fund Consultants Jowitt & Freeman Ltd.

Auditors Hodgson, Harris & Co

Company Employees 2,800

Members 200

Pensioners 6

	£000
Annual Contributions	300
Gross Annual Outflow	2
Capital Value	1,000
Summary of Investments	
Equities	880
Property Fund	200

COMFORT HOTELS INTERNATIONAL LTD.

167 Queensway, London W2 4XG
Telephone: 01-221 2626

Secretary W.R.Luke,FCA

Employees 1,185

COMMERCIAL CATERING GROUP

56 Abbey Road, Stirling FK8 1LL
Telephone: 0786-63212

Director F.J.Bell

Employees 900

COMMERCIAL UNION ASSURANCE COMPANY LTD CU GROUP STAFF RETIREMENT & DEATH BENEFITS SCHEME

St.Helen's, 1 Undershaft, London EC3P 3DQ
Telephone: 01-283 7500

Pensions Actuary B.W.T.Dawson,FIA

Secretary to Trustees Mrs E.M.Stringer

Trustees G.A.Cameron, B.D.Heney, J.G.T.Carter, A.B.Marshall, C.R.Harris, Sir Francis Sandilands

Actuary J.H.Webb, FIA

Auditors Coopers & Lybrand

Members 8,000

Pensioners 4,750

	£000
Annual Contributions	16,837
Annual Investment Income	12,917
Gross Annual Outflow	12,210
Capital Value	
Book Value	134,153
Market Value	164,521
Summary of Investments	
Equities	60,450
Fixed Interest	45,019
Property	31,319
Cash & Deposits	11,327
Others	1,157

COMMONWEALTH DEVELOPMENT CORPORATION PENSION FUND

33 Hill Street, London W1A 3AR
Telephone: 01-629 8484

Secretary K.J.Knaggs

Trustees J.M.Clay, Sir Peter Meinertzhagen, F.R.Wilson, C.J.Hawkins, R.Williams

Investment Managers Morgan Grenfell & Co.Ltd.

Pension Fund Consultants and Actuarial Advice Obtained through Willis Faber Advisory Services Ltd.

Auditors Peat, Marwick, Mitchell & Co.

Members (at 31.3.80) 362

Pensioners 157

	£000
Annual Contributions	772
Annual Investment Income	1,147
Annual Outflow	416
Capital Value	12,410
Summary of Investments	
Equities	5,022
Fixed Interest	4,064
Property Unit Trusts	3,004
Cash & Deposits	296
Others	24

COMPAIR RETIREMENT BENEFITS PLAN

P.O.Box 73, Hughenden Avenue, High Wycombe,
Bucks.HP13 5BE
Telephone: 0494-21181

Secretary to the Trustees & Group Pension Manager J.A.W.McLeod, APMI

Trustees J.E.Norton, A.R.Taylor, F.R.Goodenough

Investment Advisers Geoffrey Morley & Partners Ltd

Property Advisers Hillier Parker May & Rowden

Actuary P.Sadeque, FIA, APMI

Auditors R.M.Blaikie and Co

Solicitors Slaughter & May

Employees 5,133

Members 4,800

Pensioners 950

Annual Contributions £2,165,000

Capital Value £7,650,000

COMPUTER ANALYSIS & PROGRAMMES (HOLDINGS) LTD

14/15 Gt. James Street, London WC1N 3DY
Telephone: 01-242 0021

Secretary D.R.Taylor

Employees 800

COMMONWEALTH WAR GRAVES COMMISION SUPERANNUATION SCHEME (1952)

2 Marlow Road, Maidenhead, Berks.SL6 7DX
Telephone: 0628-34221

Secretary H.Westland,MIPM

Investment Advisers Williams & Glyn's Bank Ltd,

Actuaries Government Actuary

Auditors Deloitte Haskins & Sells

Members 415

Pensioners 347

Annual Contributions £726,000

Annual Investment Income £551,000

Capital Value £5,517,000

CONCENTRIC LTD & SUBSIDIARY COMPANIES PENSION FUND

Coleshill Road Sutton Coldfield,
West Midlands B75 7AZ
Telephone: 021378-4229

Pension Fund Secretary J.Griffiths

Company Secretary E.A.Morris, FCA

Trustees J.G.Perks, E.A.Morris, J.F.Bell

Managed by Guardian Royal Exchange Assurance Group

Employees 2,356

CONCORD ROTAFLEX LTD.

Concord House, 241 City Road, London EC1V 1JD
Telephone: 01-253 1200

Secretary L.F.Tidd

Employees 828

THE CONCORDIA ELECTRIC WIRE & CABLE CO LTD

Trent Mills, Long Eaton, Notts.NG10 3LP
Telephone: 06076-2231

Secretary B.J.Percival

Employees 600

CONDER INTERNATIONAL LTD

Kingsworthy Court, Kingsworthy, Winchester, Hants.SO23 7SJ
Telephone: 0962-882222

Company Secretary I.S.Turner,FCIS,FCMA

Assistant Secretary P.Williams,FCA

Investment Advisers Hill Samuel Investment Management Ltd., Geoffrey Morley & Partners Ltd.

Actuarial Advice Obtained through Cubie, Wood & Co.Ltd.

Pension Fund Consultants Lowndes Associated Pensions Ltd.

Auditors Morley & Scott

Employees 2,059

Members (at 31.3.80) 1,649

Pensioners 67

Annual Contributions £1,200,000

Annual Investment Income £450,000

Capital Value £5,572,000

CONFEDERATION LIFE INSURANCE COMPANY PENSION PLAN

50 Chancery Lane, London WC2A 1HE
Telephone: 01-242 0282

Actuary G.L.Willman,MA,FIA

Managed by Confederation Life Insurance Co.

Company Employees 510

Members 490

Pensioners 55

Annual Contributions £468,000

Capital Value £3,872,000

CONOCO (CONTINENTAL OIL COMPANY LTD)

Park House, 116 Park Street, London W1Y 4NN
Telephone: 01-493 1235

Pensions Co-ordinator I.S.Parlby

Investment Advisers J.Henry Schroder Wagg & Co Ltd

Pension Fund Consultants Wyatt Harris Graham Ltd.

Auditors Arthur Young, McClelland, Moores & Co.

Members 2,800

Pensioners 100

Capital Value £10,500,000

CONSERVATIVE AND UNIONIST CENTRAL OFFICE AGENTS' SUPERANNUATION FUND

32 Smith Square, London SW1P 3HH
01-222 9000

Investment/Property Advisers Lazard Securities Ltd

Actuaries R.Watson & Sons

Auditors Harvey Preen & Co Ltd

Employees 585

Members 365

Pensioners 211

CONSOLIDATED GOLD FIELDS LTD

49 Moorgate, London EC2R 6BQ
Telephone: 01-606 1020

Pensions Manager A.H.Jackson, MA

Pensions and Insurance Officer P.K.Dann

Total Group Employees 10,366

Other information Head office staff scheme has 250 members and is insured by Eagle Star Insurance Co Ltd and Prudential Assurance Co Ltd

CONSOLIDATED PNEUMATIC TOOL CO LTD

CP House, 97/107 Uxbridge Road,
London W5 5TP
Telephone: 01-567 3411

Secretary D.A.Turner

Insured with Prudential Assurance Co Ltd, Scottish Equitable Life Assurance Society Ltd

Employees 1,825

CONSTANTINE HOLDINGS LTD
York House, Borough Road, Middlesbrough, Cleveland TS1 2HP
Telephone: 0642-432231

Secretary G.W.Bickerton

Insured with Legal & General Assurance Society Ltd

Employees 1,059

CONTAINERBASES PENSION FUND
22-25 Finsbury Square, London EC2A 1RX
Telephone: 01-638 8301

Company Secretary F.J.Page,FCIS

Insured with Commercial Union Assurance Co Ltd

Auditors Coopers & Lybrand

Employees 800

Members 650

Pensioners 15

Annual Contributions £250,000

CONTROL DATA LTD
Aldwych House, 95 Aldwych, London WC2B 4JP
Telephone: 01-580 6484

Secretary W.J.Sykes

Insured with Swiss Life Insurance & Pension Co.

Employees 1,092

THOMAS COOK PENSION FUND
PO Box 36, Thorpe Wood, Peterborough PE3 6SB
Telephone: 0733-63200

Secretary and Group Pensions Manager D.H.Rogers,FPMI

Other Pension Management Committee of 8-4 Employers' and 4 Members' Committee men. Four of whom are Trustees

Investment Advisers Midland Bank Ltd

Actuaries Bacon & Woodrow

Auditors Peat Marwick Mitchell & Co

Employees 4,000

Members 3,500

Pensioners 800

	£000
Annual Contributions	1,600
Annual Investment Income	1,400
Annual Outflow	1,200
Capital Value	18,000
Summary of Investments	
Equities	6,400
Fixed Interest	6,600
Property	1,000
Cash & Deposits	1,200
Others	1,000

COOP AND CO PENSION AND ASSURANCE PLAN 1974
11 Dorning Street, Wigan
Telephone: 0942-41731

Managing Director G.B.Appleby, FCA, ACIS

Pension Fund Consultants Noble Lowndes & Partners Ltd

Auditors Price Waterhouse & Co

Employees 650

Members 31

Pensioners 13

COOPER & ROE LTD.
Station Works, Pasture Lane, Ruddington, Notts NG11 6AJ
Telephone: 0602-216941

Financial Director & Secretary J.R.Dugard, FCA

Employees 603

COOPER INDUSTRIES LTD. GROUP LIFE ASSURANCE & RETIREMENT BENEFITS SCHEME
2 Castle Hill, Dudley, West Midlands DY1 4PS
Telephone: 0384-231281

Secretary M.Grey-Smart

Trustees J.C.Cooper, D.E.Jones, R.W.F.Yates

Insured by Provident Mutual Life Assurance Association

Pension Fund Consultants Alexander Howden Insurance Brokers Ltd

Company Employees 578

COOPER ROLLER BEARINGS CO.LTD. PENSION FUND
Wisbech Road, King's Lynn, Norfolk
Telephone: 0553-63447

Secretary E.S.Link

Trustees R.A.Rogers,LL.B., C.W.Hornigold, E.S.Link

Investment Advisers Stafford Clark & Co.

Stockbrokers Pidgeon de Smitt

Actuaries Bacon & Woodrow

Auditors Ernst Whinney & Co.

Company Employees 650 approx.

Members 470

Pensioners 90

CO-OPERATIVE INSURANCE SOCIETY LTD EMPLOYEES' PENSION & DEATH BENEFIT SCHEME
Miller Street, Manchester M60 0AL
Telephone: 061-832 8686

Secretary A.Duval,FIA

Trustees Chairman of C.I.S.Ltd.plus 3 Representatives each of Employer and Employees

Investment Advisers A.Cochrane, FIA

Pension Consultants P.D.Johnson, FIA

Auditors Thomson McLintock & Co

Company Employees (at 31.12.79) 10,899

Members 10,692

Pensioners 4,979

	£000
Annual Contributions	5,607

CO-OPERATIVE INSURANCE SOCIETY LTD Continued

Annual Investment Income	6,718
Annual Outflow	4,866
Capital Value (Book Value)	79,253
Summary of Investments	
Equities	40,833
Fixed Interest	35,288
Property	79
Cash & Deposits	2,091
Others	962

CO-OPERATIVE RETAIL SERVICES LTD.
29 Dantzic Street, Manchester M4 4BA
Telephone: 061-832 8152

Secretary R.A.Lee,FCIS,FCCA

Employees 14,354

CO-OPERATIVE WHOLESALE SOCIETY EMPLOYEES' PENSION & DEATH BENEFIT SCHEME
PO Box 53, New Century House, Manchester M60 4ES
Telephone: 061-834 1212

Pension Fund Manager R.K.Booth

Secretary G.J.Melmoth

Trustees 6 CWS Ltd. appointees, 5 employee representatives. H.W.Whitehead (Chairman)

Investment Advisers Warburg Investment Management Ltd., Lazard Brothers & Co.Ltd.

Actuary P.D.Johnson, MA, FIA

Auditors Thomson McLintock & Co

Company Employees 30,000

Members 20,000

Pensioners 12,000

	£000
Annual Contributions	8,500
Annual Investment Income	10,900
Annual Outflow	8,000
Capital Value Book value	102,000
Summary of Investments	
Equities	39,000
Fixed Interest	55,100
Cash & Deposits	1,900

COOPERS & LYBRAND ASSOCIATES
Shelley House, 3 Noble Street, London EC2V 7DQ
Telephone: 01-606 4040

Employees 1,951

COPE ALLMAN INTERNATIONAL LTD GROUP PENSION FUND
27 Hill Street, London W1X 8AS
Telephone: 01-493 6737

Secretary A.D.Walford

Investment Advisers Brown, Shipley & Co Ltd

Property Advisers Druce & Co

Pension Fund Consultants and Actuarial Advice obtained through Godwins Ltd

Auditors Josolyne Layton-Bennett & Co.

Employees 7,201

Members 3,300

Capital Value £10 million

COPE SPORTSWEAR LTD.
Skopes House, Seacroft Ring Road, Leeds LS14 1NH
Telephone: 0532-602281

Secretary R.Fearnley

Employees 974

CORAH LTD
PO Box 32, Burleys Way, Leicester LE1 9BB
Telephone: 0533-20811

Secretary J.R.Hardwick, LLB

Insured with Prudential Assurance Co Ltd

Employees 4,191

CORAL LEISURE GROUP LTD
Berkeley Square House, Berkeley Square, London W1X 5PE
Telephone: 01-629 8772

Secretary D.N.Allison

Director of Group Services W.J.Wreford,FCIS

Insured with Scottish Provident Institution

Pension Fund Consultants Stewart Wrightson Assurance Consultants Ltd

Employees 8,918

CORK CO-OPERATIVE MARTS LTD
Cork Farm Centre, Wilton, Cork Eire
Telephone: 021-45733

Chairman J.Mullins

Employees 1,600

CORNHILL INSURANCE CO.LTD. RETIREMENT & DEATH BENEFITS FUND
57 Ladymead, Guildford, Surrey GU1 1DB
Telephone: 68161

Secretary J.Darby, FCIS, APMI

Superintendent Pensions D.A.Griffiths

Trustees Cornhill Insurance Co.Pension Fund Trustees Ltd.

Investment Advisers Morgan Grenfell & Co Ltd

Actuaries Lane,Clark & Peacock

Auditors Ernst & Whinney

Solicitors Slaughter & May

Company Employees 2,821

Members 1,896

Pensioners 250

	£000
Annual Contributions	1,504
Annual Investment Income	808
Annual Outflow	462
Capital Value	10,643
Summary of Investments	

The Major UK Pension Funds COO/COS

CORNHILL INSURANCE CO.LTD. *Continued*

Equities	4,470
Fixed Interest	2,273
Property Unit Trusts	1,571
Cash & Deposits	1,152
Others	1,177

CORNING LTD PENSION PLAN
Wear Glass Works, Sunderland
Tyne & Wear SR4 6EJ
Telephone: 0782-76222

Pensions & Salaries Manager M.Coulson

Investment Advisers Robert Fleming Investment Management Ltd

Pension Fund Consultants Metropolitan Pensions Association Ltd.

Auditors Price Waterhouse & Co.

Company Employees 3,847

Members 2,749

Pensioners 428

Annual Contributions £604,000

Annual Investment Income £571,000

Capital Value £7,189,000

CORNWALL COUNTY COUNCIL SUPERANNUATION FUND
County Hall, Truro TR1 3BD
Telephone: 0872-74282

Pension Fund Manager C.E.J.Cainey (County Treasurer)

Trustees Cornwall County Council

Investment Advisers W.E.Broadfield, M.Arnold

Stockbrokers de Zoete & Bevan, Grieveson Grant

Actuaries Hymans, Robertson & Co.

Employees 10,400

Members (at 31.3.80) 5,970

Pensioners 1,730

	£000
Annual Contributions	4,894
Annual Investment Income	2,633
Annual Outflow	2,776
Capital Value	29,481
Summary of Investments	
Equities	12,800
Fixed Interest	12,600
Cash & Deposits	596
Others	3,485

CORPORATION OF LLOYD'S STAFF PENSION SCHEME
Gun Wharf, Dock Road Chatham, Kent ME4 4TU
Telephone: 0634-407333

Head Office Lime Street, London EC3M 7HA
Telephone: 01-621 0526

Administration Manager J.F.Gentle

Investment Manager S.C.Slingsby

Asst. Manager M.Laurence

Actuaries R. Watson & Sons

Auditors Ernst & Whinney

Solicitors Biddle & Co.

Employees (at 31.12.78) 2,150

Members (at 31.12.79) 1,936

Pensioners 600

Deferred Pensioners 239

Annual Contributions £2,007,000

Annual Investment Income £1,475,000

Capital Value £17,712,000

See also Lloyd's

CORPORATION OF LONDON
PO Box 270, Guildhall, London EC2P 2EJ
Telephone: 01-606 3030

Treasurer T.P.Griggs,MC,IPFA

Superannuation Officer A.F.W.Towell, APMI

JAMES P.CORRY & CO.LTD
Springfield, Belfast 12, N. Ireland
Telephone: 0232-43661

Secretary B.J.Titherington

Employees 500

COSALT LTD
Fish Dock Road, Grimsby,
S. Humberside DN31 3NW
Telephone: 0472-58881

Secretary R.B.Heaton, FCA

Pension Fund Management Lowndes Associated Pensions Ltd.

Trustees J.M.T.Ross, R.B.Heaton, J.C.Goodrich

Managed by Globe Insurance Co.Ltd.

Employees 1,453

COSMOS AIR HOLIDAYS LTD.
Cosmos House, 1 Bromley Common, Bromley, Kent BR2 9LX

Secretary P.S.Albertini

Employees 1,280

A.C.COSSOR LTD SUPERANNUATION FUND AND DATA LOGIC LTD. PENSION & LIFE ASSURANCE SCHEMES
The Pinnacles, Harlow, Essex CM19 5BB
Telephone: 28954

Pension Fund Manager & Secretary A.A.Gurney, ACIS

Trustees Cossor Fund; K.G.Berresford, R.H.Snoad, S.D.Coode-Bate; Data Logic; Data Logic Ltd.

Insured with Cossor; Eagle Star Insurance Co.; Data Logic: Guardian Royal Exchange Assurance

Pension Fund Consultants & Actuarial Advice Obtained through Metropolitan Pensions Association Ltd.

Auditors Coopers & Lybrand

A.C.COSSOR LTD Continued

	Cossor	Data Logic
Company Employees	4,090	600
Members	2,040	165
Pensioners	160	-
	£000	£000
Annual Contributions	1,140	157

COSTAIN GROUP LTD. PENSION SCHEME

1 Kennington Road, London SE1 7QR
Telephone: 01-928 4977

Pensions Manager M.W.Coles,APMI

Secretary G.Langham,FCIS,APMI

Actuarial Advice Obtained through Cubie, Wood & Co.Ltd.

Pension Fund Consultants Noble Lowndes & Partners Ltd.

Auditors Peat, Marwick Mitchell & Co., James Worley & Son

Company Employees 5,500

Members 2,200

Pensioners 332

Annual Contributions £2,237,000

Annual Investment Income £470,000

Capital Value £17,187,000

JOHN COTTON (MIRFIELD) LTD.

Nunbrook Mills, Huddersfield Road, Mirfield, Yorks.WF14 0EH
Telephone: 0924-496571

Secretary P.J.Ackroyd

Employees 591

COUBRO & SCRUTTON (HOLDINGS) LTD. SUPERANNUATION FUND

1 North Court, Great Peter Street,
London SW1P 3LL
Telephone: 01-222 5165

Pension Fund Manager R.L.M.Schlee,MA,ACA

Administrator J.E.Hunt,FCA

Trustees 4 Management Trustees and 4 Member Trustees

Managed by Pensions Management (SWF) Ltd.

Actuaries R.Watson & Sons

Pension Fund Consultants C.T.Bowring & Layborn Ltd.

Auditors Spicer & Pegler

Company Employees 1,500

Members 1,000

Pensioners 50

	£000
Annual Contributions	600
Capital Value	3,000
Summary of Investments	
Equities	1,700
Fixed Interest	1,300

COUNTRY KITCHEN FOODS LTD. PENSION & LIFE ASSURANCE SCHEME

Stock Lane, Langford, Avon BS18 7ES
Telephone: 0934-852751

Accounts Manager K.J.Hoult

Insured with Provident Mutual Life Assurance Association

Company Employees 1,400

Members 78

Pensioners 3

Annual Contributions £80,000

COUNTY NEWSPAPERS LTD.

75 Castle Street, Luton, Beds.
Telephone: 0582-21222

Secretary R.W.S.Gibbs

Employees 801

COURIER PRESS (HOLDINGS) LTD.

Tachbrook Road, Leamington Spa, Warks.

Secretary J.C.Rogers

Employees 739

COURTAULDS LTD. STAFF SUPERANNUATION, SENIOR STAFF SUPERANNUATION AND EMPLOYEES PENSION SCHEMES

18 Hanover Square, London W1A 2BB
Telephone: 01-629 9080

Pension Fund Manager A.Ross Goobey

Secretary B.B.P.Bone

Custodian Trustees Barclays Bank Trust Co.Ltd.

Investments made through Pensions Common Investment Fund (for all schemes)

Property Advisers Hillier Parker May & Rowden

Actuaries R.Watson & Sons

Auditors Price Waterhouse & Co.

Company Employees (UK) 89,020 (full time equivalents)

Members (Staff Superannuation Scheme) 17,215

Pensioners 8,801

	£000
Net Annual Contributions	1,405
Annual Investment Income	20,532
Capital Value (at 31.3.80)	203,976
Summary of Investments	
Equities	111,780
Fixed Interest	43,993
Property	39,528
Cash & Deposits	8,675

COURTNEY, POPE RETIREMENT BENEFITS PLAN AND DIRECTORS PENSION SCHEME

Amhurst Park Works, 341 Seven Sisters Road,
London N15 6RB
Telephone: 01-800 1270

Pension Fund Manager D.A.Bennett

Secretary Mrs.M.C.Walsh

COURTNEY, POPE *Continued*

Other Pension Management Mrs.N.E.Healey
Trustees D.A.Bennett, J.T.Hall, Mrs.M.C.Walsh
Insured with (A) Sun Life Assurance Co. Ltd., (B) Norwich Union Life Insurance Society
Pension Fund Consultants Stewart Wrightson Assurance Consultants Ltd.
Auditors Milne Ross
Company Employees 1,300 approx.
Members 200

COURTS GROUP OF COMPANIES STAFF PENSION SCHEME
Crown House, Morden, Surrey SM4 5ED
Telephone: 01-540 4591

Secretary W.A.Stephens, FCIS
Trustees E.G. Cohen, P.C. Cohen, E.N. Cohen, B.J.R.Cohen
Managed by Equity & Law (Managed Funds) Ltd.
Pension Fund Consultants Reed Stenhouse Benefit Consultants Ltd
Auditors Cooper & Lybrand
Company Employees 2,077
Members 294
Pensioners 123
Annual Contributions £87,000
Capital Value £1,250,000

THE COUTTS STAFF PENSION SCHEME
440 Strand, London WC2R 0QS
Telephone: 01-379 6262

Manager, Staff Relations Dept. B.L.Gale
Trustees 2 Directors, 2 Members
Investment Advisers Coutts & Co.
Stockbrokers James Capel & Co.
Actuaries R.Watson & Sons
Auditors Touche Ross & Co.
Company Employees 1,545
Members 1,525 approx.
Pensioners 242

	£000
Annual Contributions	1,990
Annual Investment Income	1,178
Annual Outflow	998
Capital Value	13,394
Summary of Investments	
Equities	8,970
Fixed Interest	3,668
Cash & Deposits	755

COVENTRY & DISTRICT CO-OP SOC LTD EMPLOYEES SUPERANNUATION FUND
Corporation Street, Coventry, West Midlands
Telephone: 0203-24031

Secretary J.W. Charlton
Trustees Committee of Fund Members and Employer Representatives
Actuary P.D. Johnson
Auditors Appleby English & Partners
Employees 850
Members 608
Pensioners 296

	£000
Annual Contributions	150
Annual Investment Income	230
Annual Outflow	250
Capital Value	2,200
Summary of Investments	
Equities	700
Fixed Interest	900
Cash & Deposits	600

THE COVENTRY EVENING TELEGRAPH STAFF PENSION FUND
Corporation Street, Coventry CV1 1FP
Telephone: 0203-25588

Company Secretary A.J.Hollingsworth
Stockbrokers Kitcat & Aitken
Actuaries Bacon & Woodrow
Auditors Ernst & Whinney
Company Employees 1,070
Members 452
Pensioners 61

COWAN, DE GROOT LTD.
11 John Street, London WC1N 2EG
Telephone: 01-405 0812

Secretary J.Bouchier
Employees 905

T.COWIE LTD.
Millfield House, Hylton Road, Sunderland, Tyne & Wear SR4 7BA
Telephone: 0783-44122

Secretary D.J.Callum
Employees 997

WILLIAM COWLIN (HOLDINGS) LTD.
Stratton Street, Bristol BS2 9BN
Telephone: 0272-22132

Secretary A.D.G.Griffin
Employees 693

COX, MOORE & CO LTD
Milner Road, Long Eaton, Nottingham
Telephone: 06076-5111

Secretary R.G.Steeples
Employees 600

CPC (UNITED KINGDOM) LTD
Claygate House, Esher, Surrey KT10 9PN
Telephone: 62181

Secretary C.K.Cash
Group Personnel Director R.B.Ellis

CPC (UNITED KINGDOM) LTD Continued

Trustees CPC (United Kingdom) Pension Trust Ltd.
Investment Advisers Morgan Grenfell & Co Ltd
Actuaries Bacon & Woodrow
Auditors Thomson McLintock & Co
Company Employees (at 1.9.80) 3,118
Members 2,909
Pensioners 703

A.F. CRAIG & CO LTD
Caledonia Engineering Works, McDowall Street, Paisley, Renfrewshire PA3 2NA
Telephone: 041889-2191

Director R.Gourlay
Employees 600

CRAMPHORN LTD
Cuton Mill, Chelmsford, Essex
Telephone: 0245-46621

Secretary G.W.Evans
Employees 539

CRANE LTD. STAFF & WORKS (1978) PENSION SCHEMES
11-12 Bouverie St., London EC4Y 8AH
Telephone: 01-353 6511

Pension Fund Manager J.Salisbury Jones
Secretary Mrs L.D.Wyatt
Trustees 13
Investment Advisers Kleinwort Benson Investment Management Ltd
Stockbrokers Spencer Thornton & Co.
Actuaries Clay & Partners
Pension Fund Consultants Metropolitan Pensions Association Ltd.
Auditors Russell Limebeer
Company Employees 2,530

	Works	Staff
Members	1,850	660
Pensioners	895	420
	£000	£000
Annual Contributions	612	603
Annual Investment Income	123	292
Annual Outflow	250	250
Capital Value		
Book Value	2,284	8,388
Market Value	2,687	5,751
Summary of Investments		
Equities	665	1,597
Fixed Interest	1,146	1,949
Property Unit Trusts	556	1,185
Foreign Investments	376	868

CRANE FRUEHAUF TRAILERS LTD. STAFF PENSION SCHEME
Hayes Gate House, Uxbridge Road, Hayes, Middlesex
Telephone: 01-848 0225

Secretary W.M.Donald
Managed by Equity Law (Managed Funds) Ltd
Pension Fund Consultants Glanvill Enthoven (Life, Pensions & Mortgages) Ltd.
Employees 2,780

CRANE PACKING LTD.
Crossbow House, Trading Estate, Slough, Berks.SL1 4QX
Telephone: 31122

Secretary J.M.Hutchinson
Employees 981

CRAY ELECTRONICS GROUP RETIREMENT & DEATH BENEFITS PLAN
Power Works, Slade Green Road, Erith, Kent DA8 2HY
Telephone: 38251

Secretary P.J.Davis
Trustees R.Palumbo, T.W.Bore, P.J.Davis, B.L.Mead, D.E.Kimber
Insured with* Standard Life Assurance Co.

* In process of changing from Insured to Managed Fund basis

Actuaries Bacon & Woodrow
Pension Fund Consultants Minet Consultancy Services Ltd.
Auditors Josolyne, Layton-Bennett & Co.
Company Employees 1,126
Members 393
Annual Contributions £340,000

CREDIT DATA LTD
Regency House, 38 Whitworth Street, Manchester M60 1QH
Telephone: 061-236 8511

Secretary G.Lord
Employees 1,010

CRESCENT SHIPPING
Canal Road, Rochester, Kent
Telephone: 0634-79541

Executive D.W.Harris
Employees 560

CRESCENT TOY CO LTD
Cwmbran, Gwent
Telephone: 0495-270441/5

Secretary D.E.Eagles
Employees 600

CREST ENGINEERING (UK) INC
Station House, P.O.Box 75, Harrow Road, Wembley HA9 6EN
Telephone: 01-902 8883

CREST ENGINEERING (UK) INC *Continued*

Director Dr. J.F.Head

Employees 800

CREST NICHOLSON LTD GROUP PENSION & LIFE ASSURANCE SCHEME

Crest House, 91/97 Church Road, Ashford, Middlesex TW15 2NH
Telephone: Ashford 43611

Secretary N.I.Hughes,ACA

Insured with Prudential Assurance Co Ltd

Employees 1,402

CRODA INTERNATIONAL LTD. GROUP STAFF AND WORKS PENSION SCHEMES

Conwick Hall, Snaith, Goole,
North Humberside DN14 9AA
Telephone: 0405-860551

Secretary G.E.Bates,MA

Group Pensions and Salaries Manager B.E.Lakemen

Trustees Croda Trustees Ltd.

Investment Advisers Lloyds Bank Ltd.

Stockbrokers Phillips & Drew

Actuaries R.Watson & Sons

Auditors Kidsons & Co.

Solicitors Slaughter & May

Company Employees 6,727

	Staff	Works
Members	1,501	1,525
Pensioners	331	171
	£000	£000
Annual Contributions	1,500	37
Annual Investment Income	830	90
Capital Value	9,000	820

There is also an International Supplemental Scheme with:

Members 250

Pensioners 15

	£000
Annual Contributions	1,000
Annual Investment Income	500
Capital Value	7,000

JAMES R.CROMPTON & BROS.LTD. RETIREMENT BENEFITS PLAN 1974

Elton Paper Mills, Bury, Lancs.BL8 2AS
Telephone: 061-764 4016

Secretary I.J.Young

Trustees Lowndes Associated Pensions Ltd., P.R.Crompton, M.C.Heyworth, J.Daynes

Investment Advisers Hill Samuel Investment Management Ltd.

Actuarial Advice Obtained through Cubie, Wood & Co.Ltd.

Pension Fund Consultants Noble Lowndes & Partners Ltd.

Auditors Binder Hamlyn

Company Employees 709

Members 443

Pensioners 83

	£000
Annual Contributions	430
Annual Investment Income	50
Annual Outflow	29
Capital Value	1,183
Summary of Investments	
Equities	847
Fixed Interest	207
Property	100
Cash & Deposits	29

CROSBY WOODFIELD LTD.

Wilmere House, Wilmere Lane, Widnes, Cheshire WA8 9UY
Telephone: 051-423 2501

Secretary A.J.Webster,FCA

Employees 567

CROSROL LTD

Pellon Lane Works, Halifax, W.Yorks.HX1 5QB
Telephone: 0422-63521

Secretary J.A.Vachell

Employees 645

CROSS & HERBERT (HOLDINGS) LTD.

41 High Srteet, Egham, Surrey TW20 9DS
Telephone: 01-389 4244

Secretary F.G.Calton,FCA

Employees 723

DEREK CROUCH LTD.

Eye, Peterborough PE6 7UW
Telephone: 0733-222341

Secretary R.Scott,CA,ACMA

Insured with Norwich Union Life Insurance Society

Employees 2,179

CROUDACE LTD

Croudace House, Caterham, Surrey CR3 6XQ
Telephone: 46464

Secretary R.I.Horsell

Employees 600

CROWELL COLLIER & MACMILLAN LTD

Keen House, 61-62 Lincoln's Inn Fields, London WC2A 3XB

Chairman A.L.Baker

Employees 1,030

CROWN AGENTS' SUPERANNUATION SCHEME
4 Millbank, London SW1P 3JD
Telephone: 01-222 7730

Secretary J.F.Salmon

Managers I.W.Angus, F.W.Jourdain, D.V.Butler

CROWN CORK CO LTD
Apexes Works, Scotts Road, Southall, Middx.UB2 5DH
Telephone: 01-574 2468

Secretary V.A.Lowe,FCIS

Insured with Eagle Star Insurance Co Ltd

Employees 1,233

CROWN DECORATIVE PRODUCTS LTD
P.O.Box 37, Crown House, Hollins Road, Darwen BB3 0BG
Telephone: 0254-74951

Director M.Thomas

Executive T.B.Gould

Employees 1,500

CROWN HOUSE STAFF PENSION FUND
2 Lygon Place, London SW1W 0JT
Telephone: 01-730 9287

Pension Fund Manager & Secretary G.J.Dorman

Trustees R.S. Uffindell,G.R. Parker, P.J. King

Investment Advisers Gresham Trust Ltd.

Property Advisers Druce & Company

Actuaries Bacon & Woodrow

Auditors Deloitte Haskins & Sells

Company Employees 5,871

Members 1,200

Pensioners 226

Annual Contributions £1,007,000

Annual Investment Income £505,000

Gross Annual Outflow £292,000

Capital Value £4,841,000

JOHN CROWTHER GROUP LTD
Union Mills, Milnsbridge, Huddersfield, W.Yorks.HD3 4NA
Telephone: 0484-654221

Secretary C.J.Turner

Insured with Friends Provident Life Office

Employees 690

CRUDEN INVESTMENTS LTD
Baberton House, Juniper Green, Edinburgh
Telephone: 031-441 1356

Secretary I.A.Cowan

Employees 2,792

CRUDEN INVESTMENTS LTD. RETIREMENT BENEFITS SCHEME
Baberton House, Juniper Green, Midlothian EH14 5UA
Telephone: 031-442 3862

Secretary I.A.Cowan

Investment Advisers Wood Mackenzie & Co.

Actuaries Duncan C.Fraser & Co.

Pension Fund Consultants H. Clarkson (Scotland) Ltd.

Auditors Whitelaw Wells & Co.

Company Employees 2,792

Members (at 5.4.80) 162

Pensioners 80

Annual Contributions £370,000

Annual Investment Income £49,000

Capital Value £2,040,000

CRUSADER STAFF PENSION & LIFE ASSURANCE SCHEME
Reigate, Surrey RH2 8DL
Telephone: 07372-42424

Secretary R.A.Rayland APMI FCIS

Trustees G.C.Crook, R.V.Craig, D.Ellis, P.B.Grimshaw, K.A.McKenzie

Investment Advisers Crusader Insurance Co Ltd

Actuary W.D.Scattergood,FIA

Auditors Arthur Andersen & Co

Company Employees 1,080

Members 489

Pensioners 197

	£000
Annual Contributions	358
Annual Investment Income	360
Annual Outflow	242
Capital Value	3,800
Summary of Investments (at cost)	
Equities	1,312
Fixed Interest	1,634
Cash & Deposits	705
Others	40

CRYSTALATE (HOLDINGS) LTD
St. Georges House, 14-17 Wells Street, London W1P 3FP
Telephone: 01-323 2727

Secretary J.E.Mackenzie FCA

Employees 1,337

CSE AVIATION LTD STAFF PENSION PLAN
Oxford Airport, Kidlington, Oxford OX5 1RA
Telephone: 08675-4321

Secretary R.W.Littledale,FCA

Trustees Duke of Leinster, I.S.S.Ferris, J.R.Edwards, P.G.Ferrick

Managed by Scottish Amicable Pensions Investments Ltd.

Pension Consultants Willis Faber Advisory Services Ltd

Auditors Peat, Marwick, Mitchell & Co.

Company Employees 600

Members 400

CSE AVIATION LTD Continued

Pensioners 10
Annual Contributions £300,000
Capital Value £1,500,000

CULLEN'S STORES LTD.
Parsonage House, Station Road, Dorking, Surrey RH4 1EA
Telephone: 0306-2291

Secretary W.G.Healey

Employees 730

CULTER GUARD BRIDGE HOLDINGS LTD
Guardbridge, Fife KY16 0UU
Telephone: 033483-551

Secretary J.A.F.Gould

Managed by Legal & General (Pensions Management) Ltd., Pensions Management (SWF) Ltd.

Employees 1,085

CUMBRIA COUNTY COUNCIL
The Courts, Carlisle CA3 8NA
Telephone: 0228-23456

County Treasurer J.R.Ford,IPFA

Investment Advisers B.D.Barton, J.V.Furniss, M.Lander, M.Talbot-Rice

Stockbrokers Grieveson Grant & Co.

Actuaries Duncan C.Fraser & Co.

Auditor The District Auditor

Members (at 31.3.80) 9,000

Pensioners 3,600

	£000
Annual Contributions	6,040
Annual Investment Income	2,862
Annual Outflow	4,435
Capital Value	38,743
Summary of Investments (1979)	
Equities	12,165
Fixed Interest	10,462
Property Unit Trusts	4,125
Cash & Deposits	1,004

CUMMINS ENGINE CO LTD PENSION FUND
46-50 Coombe Road, New Malden, Surrey
Telephone: 01-949 6171

Secretary L.B.Bell

Trustees J.Gray, P.Berryman, F.Osborne, P.Adams, A.Paton, J.Williamson, R.Miller, R.Dale, V.Raine, J.Lowe

Investment Advisers Ivory & Sime Ltd.

Pension Fund Consultants and Actuarial Advice obtained through Willis Faber Advisory Services Ltd

Auditors Arthur Andersen & Co.

Company Employees 4,200

Members 4,000

Pensioners 155

	£000
Annual Contributions	1,500
Annual Investment Income	316
Annual Outflow	200
Capital Value	11,500
Summary of Investments	
Equities	7,900
Fixed Interest	2,800
Cash & Deposits	800

CUNDELL HOLDINGS LTD
Hanbury Road, Chelmsford, Essex CM1 3TA
Telephone: 0245-55271

Secretary J.G.Austin ACA

Employees 1,400

CURRYS LTD GROUP OF COMPANIES (1) PENSION & LIFE ASSURANCE PLAN (1978), (2) STAFF PENSION & LIFE ASSURANCE PLAN
46-50 Uxbridge Road, Ealing, London W5 2SU
Telephone: 01-567 6611

Company Secretary C.J.Hounsell,FCA

Pension Management Committee Michael Curry, M.Creevy, C.J.Hounsell

Trustees National Westminster Bank Ltd

Insured with Clerical, Medical and General Life Assurance Society

Pension Fund Consultants Metropolitan Pensions Association Ltd

Auditors Hogg Bullimore & Co

Company Employees 5,163

Members (1) 2,074, (2) 119

Pensioners 341

Annual Contributions £1,575,000

Annual Outflow £357,000

THE CURWEN PRESS
9/17 North Street, Plaistow, London E13 9HS
Telephone: 01-472 1466

Managing Director B.H.Harley

Employees 2,596

CURZONIA LTD
Curzon Works, Curzon Street, Leicester, Leicestershire
Telephone: 0533-25354

Secretary P.A.Hall

Employees 520

CUTLER HAMMER EUROPA LTD
Igravic Works, Elston Road, Bedford MK42 9LH

Managing Director C.Hansen

Managed by Legal & General (Pensions Management) Ltd., Pensions Management (SWF) Ltd.

Employees 1,112

CYANAMID OF GREAT BRITAIN LTD PENSION SCHEME

154 Fareham Road, Gosport,
Hampshire PO13 0AS
Telephone: 0329-236131

Secretary P.F.Harrison FCA

Trustees Chemical Bank Trustees Co.Ltd.

Investment Advisers Robert Fleming Investment Management Ltd

Actuaries Duncan C.Fraser & Co

Auditors Peat Marwick Mitchell & Co

Solicitors Allen & Overy

Company Employees 1,595

Members 1,910

Pensioners 245

Annual Contributions £1,106,000

Annual Investment Income £292,000

Capital Value £5,800,000

CZARNIKOW GROUP LTD.

66 Mark Lane, London EC3P 3EA
Telephone: 01-480 6677

Secretary G.W.Black

Employees 674

DAILY MAIL & GENERAL TRUST LTD.

New Carmelite House, Carmelite Street,
London EC4Y 0JA
Telephone: 01-353 6000

See Harmsworth Pension Funds

DAILY OFFICE CLEANING CONTRACTORS LTD (THE)

75 Gresham Road, Staines, Middx.
Telephone: 0784-55971

Director B.H.Lloyd

Employees 5,000

THE DAILY TELGRAPH LTD. GROUP PENSION FUND

135 Fleet Street, London EC4P 4BL
Telephone: 01-353 4242

Secretary J.H.Waller

Trustees Lord Hartwell, H.M.Stephen, G.P.Woolley, FCA, J.H.Waller

Investment Advisers 140 Trustee Co.Ltd.

Actuaries Lane Clark & Peacock

Auditors Safferys

Company Employees 3,463

Members 3,343

Pensioners 605

	£000
Annual Contributions	1,600
Annual Investment Income	760
Annual Outflow	392
Capital Value	6,988
Summary of Investments	
Equities	1,095
Fixed Interest	3,780
Property	30
Cash & Deposits	2,083

DAIMLER HIRE LTD.

Radnor House, 1272 London Road,
London SW17 7BA
Telephone: 01-679 1777

Secretary P.G.Appleby

Insured with Prudential Assurance Co.Ltd.

Employees 642

DALE ELECTRIC OF GREAT BRITAIN LTD. 1973 RETIREMENT FUND

Electricity Buildings, Gristhorpe, Filey,
N.Yorks.YO14 9PJ
Telephone: 0723-514141

Secretary and Financial Director C.J.Coole FCA, FCMA

Trustees Dale Electric of Great Britain Ltd.

Insured with Sun Alliance Group

Pension Fund Consultants Michael Jubb & Co.

Employees 1,072

DALGETY LTD. PENSION FUND

19 Hanover Square, London W1R 9DA
Telephone: 01-499 7712

Pensions Manager & Secretary B.E.Gandy, ACIS

Trustees Dalgety Pension Trust

Investment Advisers Lazard Securities Ltd., Robert Fleming Investment Management Ltd.

Actuaries R.Watson & Sons

Pension Fund Consultants Metropolitan Pensions Association Ltd.

Auditors Spicer & Pegler

Company Employees 17,345

Members 2,000

Pensioners 450

	£000
Annual Contribution	1,750
Annual Investment Income	850
Gross Annual Outflow	500
Capital Value	12,500
Summary of Investments	
Equities	2,100
Fixed Interest	2,400
Others	3,100

DALKEITH KNITWEAR LTD.

Nottingham Road, Alfreton, Derbyshire DE5 7FN
Telephone: 077383-2663

Secretary W.H.R.Pike

Employees 594

DAMART THERMAWEAR (BRADFORD) LTD.

Bowling Green Mills, Park Road, Bingley, W.Yorks.
Telephone: 09766-7071

Director K.Holden

Employees 500

DAMES & MOORE
123 Mortlake High Street London SW14 8SN
Telephone: 01-876 0495
Partner C.V.Logie
Employees 1,500

DANEPAK LTD.
Caxton Way, Thetford, Norfolk
Telephone: 0842-4521
Secretary T.M.Carmichael
Insured with Norwich Union Life Insurance Society
Employees 1,497

DANIEL CONSTRUCTION CO. INTERNATIONAL
6 Lithgow Place, College Milton North,
East Kilbride G74 1PR
Telephone: 03552-44411
Director J.Walker Murray
Employees 1,200

DANISH BACON COMPANY PENSION FUND
Howardsgate, Welwyn Garden City, Herts.AL8 6NN
Telephone: 23421
Pension Fund Manager & Secretary W.A.Riley, APMI
Trustees 6
Stockbrokers Scrimgeour, Kemp-Gee & Co.
Actuaries R.Watson & Sons
Auditors Ernst & Whinney
Company Employees 3,000
Members 716
Pensioners 348 (incl. 103 widows)

	£000
Annual Contribution	422
Annual Investment Income	740
Gross Annual Outflow	479
Capital Value	8,235
Summary of Investments	
Equities	4,186
Fixed Interest	3,667
Others	382

DANKS GOWERTON LTD.
257 Halesowen Road, Netherton, Dudley,
West Midlands DY2 9PG
Telephone: 0384-66417
Secretary E.Evans
Employees 658

W.DARLINGTON & SONS LTD.
Station Road, Rustington, Littlehampton,
Sussex BN16 3RF
Telephone: 09062-3232
Director J.A.Connell
Employees 860

DARLINGTON & SIMPSON ROLLING MILLS LTD.
Rise Carr Rolling Mills, Darlington, Co.Durham
Telephone: 0325-65326

Secretary J.Whittaker
Employees 1,000

DART INDUSTRIES LTD.
43 Upper Grosvenor Street, London W1V 0BE
Telephone: 01-629 7861
Secretary E.Bibby
Insured with Swiss Life Insurance & Pension Co.
Employees 1,024

DARTMOUTH INVESTMENTS LTD.
Oxford Street, Bilston, West Midlands WV14 7EG
Telephone: 0902-49281
Secretary B.E.Priory,FCIS
Employees 676

DART SPRING CO.LTD.
Overend Street, West Bromwich,
West Midlands B70 6EX
Telephone: 021-553 1861
General Manager F.Bownes
Employees 900

DATA CARD (UK) LTD.
New Lane, Havant, Hants.PO9 2NR
Telephone: 0705-486444
Secretary D.J.Cowen
Employees 613

DATA RECORDING INSTRUMENT CO.LTD. SUPERANNUATION FUND
Hawthorne Road, Staines, Middx.TW18 3BJ
Telephone: 51388
Fund Secretary M.A.Haining
Trustees DRI Pensions Trust Ltd.
Directors H.McK.Simpson (Chairman), M.F.Dudson, R.G.Gilbert, Mrs.D.C.J.Kerr, S.Orpwood, E.O.Wilson
Investment Managers Hill Samuel Investment Management Ltd.
Actuaries Duncan C.Fraser & Co.
Pension Fund Consultants Wigham Poland
Solicitors Wigham Poland Pension Consultants Ltd.
Auditors Deloitte, Haskins & Sells
Company Employees 1,700
Members 600
Pensioners 530

	£000
Annual Contributions	238
Annual Investment Income	150
Annual Outflow	140
Capital Value	2,110
Summary of Investments	
Equities	1,427
Fixed Interest	324
Property	173
Cash & Deposits	48
Others	139

DATASKIL LTD.
Reading Bridge House, Reading, Berks.RG1 8PN
Telephone: 0734-581258

Director P.V.Ellis

Employees 900

DATSUN UK LTD.
109 Gloucester Place, London W1H 3PH

Secretary F.Shannon,FCA

Employees 627

DAVENPORT'S BREWERY (HOLDINGS) LTD.
The Brewery, Bath Row, Birmingham B15 1NB
Telephone: 021-643 5021

Company Secretary R.A.Wright

Pensions Officer I.Russell

Investment Advisers Lazard Securities Ltd.

Employees 2,053

DAVIDSON & CO.LTD.
Sirocco Engineering Works, Belfast BT5 4AG
Telephone: 0232-57251

Director W.R.A.Stafford

Employees 900

DAVIES & NEWMAN HOLDINGS LTD.
36-38 New Broad Street, London EC2M 1NH
Telephone: 01-638 4080

Secretary D.P.Herbert

Insured with Norwich Union Life Insurance Society

Pension Fund Consultants C.T.Bowring & Layborn Ltd.

Employees 3,477

J.T.DAVIES & SONS LTD.
7 Aberdeen Road, Croydon, Surrey CR0 1EQ
Telephone: 01-681 3222

Secretary G.S.F.Gill

Employees 709

WILLIAM DAVIES & CO. (LEICESTER) LTD.
Forest Road, Loughborough, Leics.
Telephone: 0509-63404

Chairman W.Davies

Employees 500

GODFREY DAVIS LTD.
Davis House, Wilton Road, Victoria, London SW1V 1LA
Telephone: 01-834 8484

Secretary G.G.M.Nokes,FCA

Insured with Provident Mutual Life Assurance Association

Employees 2,271

DAVY STAFF PENSION SCHEME & WORKS PENSION SCHEME
15 Portland Place, London W1A 4DD
Telephone: 01-637 2821

Pensions Secretary J.Claxton

Trustees Davy Pension Trustees Ltd.

Insured with The Prudential Assurance Co. Ltd. (Staff and Works),Equity & Law Life Assurance Society Ltd. (Works)

Investment Advisers Lazard Securities Ltd.

Actuaries Clay & Partners

Pension Fund Consultants Metropolitan Pensions Association Ltd.

Company Employees (UK) 10,502

Members Staff 3,000, Works 1,500

Annual Contributions Staff £2,000,000,Works £500,000

DAWNAY DAY GROUP LTD. 1971 SUPERANNUATION FUND
Garrard House, 31 Gresham Street, London EC2V 7DT
Telephone: 01-600 7533

Secretary Mrs.A.V.Langfield

Trustees Lord Alport, B.Medhurst, J.W.P.Johnston (Company Secretary)

Insured with Clerical,Medical & General Life Assurance Society

Pension Fund Consultants Metropolitan Pensions Association Ltd.

Employees 1,762

DAWSON INTERNATIONAL LTD
Kinross KY13 7DH
Telephone: 0577-63521

Secretary R.A.B.Miller

Insured with Scottish Widows' Fund and Life Assurance Society

Pension Fund Consultants Reed Stenhouse Benefit Consultants Ltd.

Employees 5,983

DCL & ASSOCIATED COMPANIES PENSION SCHEME
c/o The Distillers Company Ltd.
12 Torpichen Street, Edinburgh EH3 8YT
Telephone: 031-229 2468

Pension Scheme Manager A.N.T.Robertson, FPMI, ACIS

Company Secretary W.H.Elgood,CA

Investment Advisers Internal

Actuary G.C.Philip,FFA

Auditors Arthur Young McClelland Moores & Co.

Company Employees 20,240

Members 13,817

Pensioners 7,497

Deferred Pensioners 4,418

	£000
Annual Contributions	8,906
Annual Investment Income	11,399
Annual Outflow	7,402
Capital Value	147,216

Summary of Investments

DCL & ASSOCIATED COMPANIES *Continued*

Equities	98,677
Fixed Interest	25,899
Property	18,950
Cash & Deposits	3,099
Others	591

THE DE LA RUE CO.LTD. (1) STAFF, CONTRIBUTORY PENSION FUND, (2) WORKS, HOURLY & WEEKLY PAID STAFF PENSION SCHEME, (3) CROSFIELD ELECTRONICS LTD, COMBINED STAFF & WORKS PENSION FUND

De La Rue House, 3-5 Burlington Gardens, London W1A 1DL
Telephone: 01-734 8020

Pensions Manager R.E.E.Conisbee,APMI,ACCA

Trustees (1) P.F.Orchard, D.A.Moore, B.J.Isted, D.S.Paravicini; (2) Numerous: (3) R.G.A.Dunkley, D.H.Bent, W.A.Hayward, P.R.E.Conisbee

(1) Insured with Sun Life Assurance Society Ltd.

(2) Managed by Sun Life Pensions Management Ltd.

Actuaries (for Crosfield) Lane Clark & Peacock

Pension Fund Consultants Glanvill Enthoven (Life Pensions & Mortgages) Ltd.

Auditors Price Waterhouse & Co.

Company Employees 6,300

Members (1) 1,200, (2) 3,000, (3) 600

Pensioners (1) 350, (3) 40

Annual Contributions (1) £1,150,000, (2) £1,000,000

Annual Outflow (1) £200,000

Capital Value (2) £4,500,000

	Crosfield £000
Annual Contribution	550
Annual Investment Income	230
Annual Ouflow	20
Capital Value	2,800
Summary of Investments	
Equities	1,400
Fixed Interest	800
Property Unit Trusts	100
Cash & Deposits	500

DEAN, SMITH & GRACE LTD.

Worth Valley Works, Keighley, W.Yorks. BD21 4TG
Telephone: 05352-5261

Secretary R.W.Hole

Employees 678

DEARDEN FARROW RETIREMENT BENEFITS SCHEME

1 Serjeants' Inn, Fleet Street, London EC4Y 1JD
Telephone: 01-353 2000

Partners Responsible for Pension Fund G.Bunney

Secretary R.R.Nuttall

Trustees G.P.Townend, G.Bunney, T.J.Bisseker, N.Riley

Insured with Crusader Insurance Co.Ltd.

Employees 600
Members 152
Pensioners 69
Annual Contributions £110,000

DE VERE HOTELS AND RESTAURANTS LTD.

7 Queen Street, Mayfair, London W1X 8EP
Telephone: 01-499 3828

Secretary G.F.Tribe

Employees 2,859

DEBENHAMS PENSION PLAN

1 Welbeck Street, London W1A 1DF
Telephone: 01-408 4444

Secretary and Pension Fund Executive D.Blair FCIS FPMI

Pensions Administration Manager P.W.Baverstock, APMI

Pensions Accountant Miss I.Russell

Trustees Debenhams Pension Trust Ltd

Investment Advisers Geoffrey Morley & Partners Ltd

Property Advisers Fletcher King

Actuarial Advice Obtained through Cubie, Wood & Co.Ltd.

Auditors Josolyne Layton-Bennett & Co

Company Employees 27,872 (21,758 Full-time equivalent)

Members (at 5.4.80) 10,137

Pensioners 4,896

	£000
Annual Contributions (to 5.4.80)	4,978
Annual Investment Income	2,046
Annual Outflow	3,370
Capital Value Market Value	26,537
Summary of Investments	
UK Equities	15,367
Foreign Securities	4,302
Fixed Interest	1,755
Property	2,545
Cash & Deposits	2,155
Others	321
Building Societies	92

DEBORAH SERVICES LTD

10 South Parade, Wakefield, W.Yorks.WF1 5PH
Telephone: 0924-78222

Secretary A.D.Broadhead ACA

Employees 1,352

THE DECCA STAFF PENSION & LIFE ASSURANCE SCHEME

9 Albert Embankment, London SE1 7SW
Telephone: 01-735 8111

Pensions Administrator L.A.Oughton

Trustees Decca Pension Trustee Ltd

Managed by Friends Provident Life Office

Investment Advisers & Stockbrokers E.R.Lewis & Co.

The Major UK Pension Funds DEC/DEX

THE DECCA *Continued*

Pension Fund Consultants and Actuarial Advice obtained through Metropolitan Pensions Association Ltd

Auditors Cooper Basden & Adamson

Company Employees 9,770

Members 4,227

Pensioners 477

	£000
Annual Contributions	3,104
Annual Investment Income	213
Capital Value	2,068
Summary of Investments (1979)	
Equities	670
Fixed Interest	995
Property	25
Cash & Deposits	100
Others	25

DEELEY CONSTRUCTION GROUP LTD.

William House, Torrington Avenue, Coventry, West Midlands CV4 9GY
Telephone: 0203-462521

Director G.W.Deeley

Employees 600

DEL MONTE FOODS LTD

Astronaut House, Hounslow Road, Feltham, Middlesex

Managing Director P.E.Solari

Employees 560

DELOITTE HASKINS & SELLS RETIREMENT & DEATH BENEFITS PLAN

P.O.Box 207, 128 Queen Victoria Street, London EC4P 4JX
Telephone: 01-248 3913

Pensions Manager P.J.Jackson ACII ACIB APMI

Trustees Deloitte Pension Trustee Co.Ltd.

Investment Advisers Scott Goff Hancock & Co., Fraser Green Ltd., Martin Currie Investment Management Ltd.

Actuaries Duncan C.Fraser & Co.

Auditors Bagshaw & Co.

Company Employees/Members 3,000

Pensioners 350

DELSON & CO LTD

Latimer Road, Alvechurch, Birmingham B48 7NR
Telephone: 021-445 2711

Secretary Mrs.M.M.Moulton

Insured with Clerical, Medical & General Life Assurance

Employees 547

THE DELTA METAL CO.LTD. (1970) GROUP STAFF PENSION & LIFE ASSURANCE PLAN AND GROUP (1978) PENSION PLAN

1 Kingsway, London WC2B 6XF
Telephone: 01-836 3535

Pension Fund Manager G.F.Banks, FCA, APMI

Secretary W.Davidson, FCIS

Assistant Group Pensions Manager M.J.Redston

Trustees Delta Metal First Nominees Ltd., Delta Metal Second Nominees Ltd.

Staff Plan Insured with Prudential Assurance Co.Ltd., Legal & General Assurance Society Ltd.

Group Pension Plan Insured with Norwich Union Life Insurance Society

Actuaries R.Watson & sons

Pension Fund Consultants Hogg Robinson (Benefit Consultants) Ltd.

Auditors Deloitte, Haskins & Sells

Company Employees 19,908

	Staff Plan	1978 Plan
Members	6,215	12,797
Pensioners	2,500	2,400
Annual Contributions	£6,087,000	£5,420,000

DENBYWARE LTD

Denby Pottery, Denby DE5 2NX
Telephone: 0773-3641

Secretary N.A.W.Wheatley

Managed by Prudential Pensions Ltd.

Employees 999

DENE SHIPPING CO LTD

43 Fetter Lane, London EC4A 1BA
Telephone: 01-353 0262

Director R.G.Crawford

Employees 600

E.M.DENNY (HOLDINGS) LTD.

Battlebridge House, Tooley Street, London SE1 2RJ
Telephone: 01-407 3171

Secretary T.L.Baldwin,FCA

Insured with Standard Life Assurance Co

Employees 624

DERBYSHIRE COUNTY COUNCIL SUPERANNUATION FUND

County Offices, Matlock, Derbyshire DB4 3AH
Telephone: 0629-3411

Treasurer Eric Cobb IPFA

Investment Adviser Norman Pilkington

Property Adviser Strutt & Parker

Actuaries R.Watson & Sons

Auditors District Audit

Employees 55,000

Members 17,000

Pensioners 5,425

	£000
Annual Contributions	11,500
Annual Investment Income	4,853
Capital Value	72,893

DERBYSHIRE COUNTY COUNCIL Continued

Summary of Investments
Equities 51,604
Fixed Interest 12,132
Property 2,622
Cash & Deposits 402

THE DERITEND STAMPING CO.LTD. PENSION FUND
St.Richard's House, Victoria Square, Droitwich, Worcs.WR9 8DS
Telephone: 09057-71601

Secretary D.C.Reeves

Trustees D.J.Mead, D.C.Reeves, J.R.Welch

Managed by Provident Mutual Life Assurance Association

Pension Fund Consultants Stewart Wrightson (Midlands) Ltd.

Auditors Peat, Marwick, Mitchell & Co.

Company Employees 2,200

Members 1,517

Annual Contributions £700,000

DESOUTTER BROS (HOLDINGS) LTD
319 Edgware Road, The Hyde, London NW9 6ND
Telephone: 01-205 7050

Secretary R.Fogg

Investment Advisers Warburg Investment Management Ltd

Pension Fund Consultants Noble Lowndes & Partners Ltd

Employees 1,189

J.A.DEVENISH & CO LTD RETIREMENT BENEFITS SCHEME
Trinity House, 15 Trinity Street, Weymouth, Dorset DT4 8TP
Telephone: 03057-74511

Secretary J.A.Luthwaite

Insured with Scottish Widows' Fund & Life Assurance Society

Pension Fund Consultants Minet Consultancy Services Ltd.

Auditors Ernst & Whinney

Employees 722

Members 310

Pensioners 47

Annual Contributions £243,000

DEVILBISS CO.LTD.
Ringwood Road, Bournemouth, Dorset BH11 9LH
Telephone: 02016-71111

Secretary D.J.Smith

Employees 516

DEVON COUNTY COUNCIL SUPERANNUATION FUND
County Hall, Topsham Road, Exeter EX2 4QJ
Telephone: 0392-77977

Treasurer B.J.Weston

Investment Advisers L.C.T.Cottrell

Stockbrokers de Zoete & Bevan

Property Advisers A.Faulkner

Property Agents Chestertons

Actuaries R.Watson & Sons

Auditor District Auditor

Employees 34,000

Members 16,600

Pensioners 6,400

	£000
Annual Contributions	12,000
Annual Investment Income	6,000
Annual Outflow	8,000
Capital Value (at 31.3.80)	62,200
Summary of Investments	
Equities	27,894
Fixed Interest	25,837
Property & Property Unit Trusts	2,780
Cash & Deposits	4,143
Others	1,546

DEVRO LTD
Moodiesburn, Chryston, Glasgow G69 0JE
Telephone: 0236-872261

Secretary A.G.Dow

Insured with Legal & General Assurance Society Ltd

Investment Advisers Ivory & Sime, N.M.Rothschild Asset Management Ltd

Employees 739

I.J.DEWHIRST HOLDINGS LTD.
Duwear House, Westgate, Driffield, N.Humberside YO25 7TH
Telephone: 0377-42561

Secretary D.C.McQueen

Insured with Commercial Union Assurance Co.Ltd.

Employees 2,012

DEWHURST DENT LTD
Union Mills, Arrow Street, off Vernon Street, Bolton BL1 2PT
Telephone: 0204-384488

Secretary J.Andrew

Employees 1,205

DEWRANCE & CO.LTD.
Trevithick Works, East Gillibrands Estate, Skelmersdale, Lancs.

Chairman R.F.Schnoes

Employees 501

DEXION GROUP PENSION & ASSURANCE SCHEME
Hunton Park, Hunton Bridge, King's Langley, Herts. WD4 8PN
Telephone: 09277-66161

Secretary D.G.Reynolds BA FCIS

Trustees N.P.Bailey, M.Batt, J.Botfield, P.Crockett, D.G.Reynolds, G.H.Thompson

DEXION GROUP Continued

Investment Advisers Kleinwort Benson Investment Management Ltd.

Pension Fund Consultants and Actuarial Advice Obtained through Metropolitan Pensions Association Ltd.

Auditors Price Waterhouse & Co.

Company Employees 1,450

Members 900

Pensioners 70

	£000
Annual Contributions	900
Capital Value	5,000
Summary of Investments	
Equities	2,200
Fixed Interest	1,400
Property	1,300
Cash & Deposits	100

DIAMOND H CONTROLS LTD
Vulcan Road North, Norwich, Norfolk NR6 6AM
Telephone: 0603-45291

Financial Director J.McCulloch,BA,FCIS

Secretary E.M.Wilkinson

Insured with Commercial Union Assurance Co Ltd

Employees 1,013

DIAMOND SHAMROCK EUROPE LTD.
See Lankro Mahler Pension Fund

THE DICKINSON ROBINSON GROUP LTD
See DRG Pension Fund

DICTAPHONE CO LTD
Alperton House, Bridge Water Road, Wembley, Middx.HA1 1BH
Telephone: 01-903 1477

Secretary R.A.Falise

Employees 800

DIE CASTING MACHINE TOOLS LTD.
152 Green Lanes, London N13 5UL
Telephone: 01-886 2271

Director E.A.Burke

Employees 650

DIGITAL EQUIPMENT CO LTD (UK) STAFF PENSION PLAN
Digital House, 252-256 Kings Road, Reading, Berkshire
Telephone: 0734-583555

Compensation & Benefits Specialist J.Cartland

Investment Advisers J.Henry Schroder Wagg & Co.Ltd.

Actuaries Clay & Partners

Auditors Coopers & Lybrand

Company Employees 1,650

Members 2,000

Capital Value £4,170,000

DIPLOMA LTD
20 Bunhill Row, London EC1Y 8LP
Telephone: 01-638 0934

Secretary A.M.R.Parkinson

Employees 1,928

THE DISTILLERS COMPANY LTD
See DCL Pension Schemes

DIVERSEY RETIREMENT BENEFITS PLAN (1969)
Weston Favell Centre, Northampton NN3 4PD
Telephone: 0604-405311

Pension Fund Secretary Mrs R.L.Snow

Trustees Diversey Ltd.

Actuarial Advice Obtained through Cubie, Wood & Co.Ltd.

Pension Fund Consultants Noble Lowndes & Partners Ltd.

Auditors Coopers & Lybrand

Company Employees 880

Members 665

Pensioners 53

	£000
Annual Contributions	535
Capital Value	2,999
Summary of Investments	
Equities	2,274
Property	725

DAVID DIXON & SON HOLDINGS LTD. PENSION SCHEME
York Mount Suite, Dudley House,
Upper Albion Street, Leeds LS2 8PN
Telephone: 0532-446925

Secretary R.C.Calvert

Insured with Phoenix Assurance Co. Ltd., Crown Life Pensions Ltd.

Pension Fund Consultants Bartlett & Co. (Life & Pensions)Ltd.

Auditors Coopers & Lybrand, Fuller Ball & Co.

Company Employees 972

Members 465

Pensioners 10

Annual Contributions £75,000

Capital Value £380,000

DIXONS PHOTOGRAPHIC LTD. RETIREMENT & EMPLOYEE SECURITY SCHEME
18-24 High Street, Edgware, Middlesex HA8 7EG
Telephone: 01-952 7011

Secretary & Pension Fund Administrator G.D.Budd, BA,FCIS

Trustees S.Kalms, E.Shenton, G.D.Budd

Investment Advisers Drayton Montagu Portfolio Management Ltd

Pension Fund Consultants and Actuarial Advice Obtained through Stewart Wrightson Assurance Consultants Ltd.

DIXONS PHOTOGRAPHIC LTD. *Continued*

Auditors Hereward, Scott, Davies & Co
Company Employees 4,416
Members 1,451
Pensioners 80

	£000
Annual Contributions	820
Annual Investment Income	240
Annual Outflow	50
Capital Value	4,300
Summary of Investments	
Equities	34.4%
Fixed Interest	20.7%
Property Unit Trust	10.5%
Cash & Deposits	5.7%
Managed Fund (Scottish Widows)	28.7%

DOBSON PARK INDUSTRIES LTD. STAFF PENSION & ASSURANCE SCHEME

Dobson Park House, Colwick Industrial Estate, Nottingham NG16 2SW
Telephone: 0602-249231

Pensions Manager G.A.Stuart,ACIS

Trustees C.F.Ward, G.J.Chibbett, E.I.Walker-Arnott

Part Managed by Legal & General (Pensions Management) Ltd, Prudential Pensions Ltd

Investment Advisers Robert Fleming Investment Management Ltd

Pension Fund Consultants Godwins Ltd

Employees 6,011

DOGGARTS LTD

Auckland House, Market Place, Bishop Auckland, Co.Durham DL14 7NL
Telephone: 0388-2101

Secretary C.Robbins

Employees 776

DOLAN PACKAGING LTD.

Dolan House, Manor Lane, Holmes Chapel, Crewe, Cheshire CW4 8AD
Telephone: 0477-37351

Secretary E.L.Foster,FCA

Employees 978

DOM HOLDINGS LTD

Roysia House, Royston, Herts
Telephone: 0763-44111

Chairman D.O.McIntyre

Secretary S.E.Cooper,FCA

Employees 705

DOMTAR PAPER MILLS LTD

Grangetown, Sunderland, Co Durham
Telephone: 0783-73292

Managing Director J.H.Kila

Employees 544

DON BROTHERS, BUIST & CO LTD

St.James Road, Forfar, Angus DD8 2AL
Telephone: 0307-2171

Secretary E.S.Gourlay

Employees 1,429

DORADA HOLDINGS LTD STAFF & WORKS PENSION SCHEME

Dorada House, Dorking, Surrey RH4 1RB
Telephone: 0306-5941

Secretary J.D.Newman,FCCA

Trustees Stewart Wrightson Trustees Ltd

Insured with Provident Mutual Life Assurance Association (Deferred Annuity Policy)

Pension Fund Consultants Stewart Wrightson Assurance Consultants Ltd.

Company Employees 2,100

Members 832

Pensioners 28

Annual Contributions £459,000

THE DORMAN SMITH PENSION FUND

Atherton Works, Blackpool Road, Preston, Lancs PR2 2DQ
Telephone: 0772-728271

Secretary K.F.Blackshaw FCA

Trustees Pension Trustees Ltd

Stockbrokers Grieveson, Grant & Co

Actuaries Duncan C.Fraser & Co

Auditors Hallidays

Company Employees 1,216

Members 300

Pensioners 22

	£000
Annual Contributions	159
Annual Investment Income	101
Annual Outflow	31
Capital Value	986
Summary of Investments	
Equities	40%
Fixed Interest	60%

DORNAY FOODS

P.O.Box 15, Hansa Road, King's Lynn PE30 4JE
Telephone: 0553-61200

Employees 600

DORSET COUNTY COUNCIL

County Hall, Dorchester, Dorset DT1 1XJ
Telephone: 0305-3131

Treasurer D.M.Gasson,BA,IPFA

Superannuation Officer F.J.Crichard APMI

Investment Advisers Lloyds Bank Ltd.

Stockbrokers Scrimgeour Kemp-Gee & Co., de Zoete & Bevan

Auditors District Auditor

Members 13,000

DORSET COUNTY COUNCIL *Continued*

Pensioners 4,500
Annual Contributions £7.0 million
Capital Value £50.5 million

ROBERT M.DOUGLAS HOLDINGS LTD

395 George Road, Erdington,
Birmingham B23 7RZ
Telephone: 021-356 4888

Director & Secretary S.J.Pedlar
Investment Advisers Hichens, Harrison & Co
Employees 3,495

DOULTON & CO.LTD.

46 Pall Mall, London SW1Y 5LW
Telephone: 01-839 7391

Secretary P.W.Borneman
Company Employees 17,000
Members Staff 2,300, Works 4,000

Capital Value (1977) Staff £7.4 million, Works £1.4 million

DOW CHEMICAL PENSION PLAN

Meadowbank, Bath Road, Hounslow,
Middx.TW5 9QY
Telephone: 01-759 2600

Pension Fund Manager E.Huggins
Secretary S.Taylor
Trustees Dowchemco Pension Trust Ltd.
Directors E.H.Huggins, C.A.Bell, T.E.Knapp, P.J.Scarborough
Investment Advisers Robert Fleming Investment Management Ltd.
Pension Fund Consultants and Actuarial Advice Obtained through Wyatt Harris Graham Ltd.
Auditors Deloitte Haskins & Sells
Employees 520
Members 510
Pensioners 106

	£000
Annual Contributions	532
Annual Investment Income	439
Annual Outflow	50
Capital Value	6,471
Summary of Investments	
Equities	3,216
Fixed Interest	1,304
Property	863
Cash & Deposits	152
Others	836

DOWDING & MILLS LTD

193 Camp Hill, Bordesley, Birmingham B12 0JJ
Telephone: 021-773 8431

Secretary J.C.Greves,FCA

Insured with Legal & General Assurance Society Ltd.
Employees 1,236

G.H.DOWNING & CO.LTD.

Brampton Hill, Newcastle-under-Lyme ST5 0QU
Telephone: 0782-615381

Secretary A.J.Tooth
Insured with Royal Insurance Co Ltd
Employees 668

DOWNS SURGICAL LTD. (1978) PENSION AND LIFE ASSURANCE SCHEME

Church Path, Mitcham, Surrey CR4 3UE
Telephone: 01-648 6291

Pension Fund Manager D.S.McMillan
Trustees N.G.Shove, P.B.Latham, D.S.McMillan, D.Cordock, W.E.McConnell
Managed by The London Life Association Ltd.
Investment Advisers Scottish Amicable Pensions Investments Ltd.
Actuarial Advice Obtained through The London Life Association Ltd.
Pension Fund Consultants Martin Paterson Associates Ltd.
Auditors Ernst & Whinney
Company Employees 730
Members 594
Pensioners 78
Annual Contributions £400,000
Capital Value £1,000,000 approx.

DOWTY GROUP PENSION SCHEME

Arle Court, Cheltenham, Glos.GL51 0TP
Telephone: 0242-21411

Pension Scheme Director and Secretary to the Trustees K.R.Forrest,BA,FPMI
Company Secretary J.R.Skae,FCA
Investment Advisers Hoare Govett Ltd, Cazenoves, Legal & General Assurance (Pensions Management) Ltd
Actuarial Advice Obtained through Cubie, Wood & Co.Ltd.
Pension Fund Consultants Noble Lowndes & Partners Ltd
Auditors Tansley Witt & Co
Company Employees 14,829
Members 13,731
Pensioners 2,869

	£000
Annual Contributions	7,768
Annual Investment Income	1,114
Annual Outflow	4,077
Capital Value	26,913
Summary of Investments	
Equities	14,865
Fixed Interest	6,162
Property	5,284
Cash & Deposits	602

DRAKE & SCULL LTD.

32-33 Lowndes Street, London SW1 9AX
Telephone: 01-637 4661

Pensions Manager M.J.Wilson

Secretary R.J.Simpson

Pension Fund Consultants Noble Lowndes & Partners Ltd.

Employees 2,918

DREAMLAND ELECTRICAL APPLIANCES LTD.

Hythe, Southampton, Hants.SO4 6YE
Telephone: 0703-845565

Secretary J.F.Ware

Insured with Sun Life Assurance Society Ltd.

Employees 900

LOUIS DREYFUS & CO LTD PENSION FUND

City Gate House, Finsbury Square,
London EC2A 1QA
Telephone: 01-628 9600

Pensions Secretary G.M.Ruddle ACIS APMI

Stockbrokers Cazenove & Co.

Actuaries Bacon & Woodrow

Auditors Price Waterhouse & Co

Solicitors Richard Butler & Co.

Employees 251

Members (at 1.4.80) 198

Pensioners 97

Annual Contributions £379,000

Annual Investment Income £310,000

Capital Value £3,440,000

DRG PENSION FUND

The Dickinson Robinson Group Ltd.
Bristol BS99 7QY
Telephone: 0272-294294

Secretary and Group Pension Fund Manager B.G.Laycock,ACIS,APMI,ACII

Administration Manager M.F.Greensides

Superintendent Members & Financial Services A.L.Hughes

Investment Manager R.C.Brown,BA,ASIA

Personnel Director I.N.Turner

Trustees 7 (For Company) J.S.Camm, G.Bar, J.A.Crabb, I.N.Turner, (For Members) T.H.Ford, A.M.Kennedy

Investment Advisers Hill Samuel Investment Management Ltd

Actuaries Lane, Clark & Peacock

Property Advisers Richard Ellis

Pension Fund Consultants Noble Lowndes & Partners Ltd

Auditors Price Waterhouse & Co

Company Employees 27,000 Worldwide; 19,500 U.K.

Members 14,600

Pensioners 6,300

	£000
Annual Contributions	8,600
Annual Investment Income	7,100
Annual Outflow	6,800
Capital Value	101,100
Summary of Investments	
Equities	49,100
Fixed Interest	14,500
Property	36,100
Cash & Deposits	1,400

DU PONT (UK) LTD PENSIONS FUND

Du Pont House, 18 Bream's Buildings, Fetter Lane, London EC4A 1HT
Telephone: 01-242 9044

Secretary T.G.Wright

Trustees P.R.Brock, J.L.Foght, R.E.Delong, H.M.Burgess, T.G.Wright, A.C.Holyer

Investment Advisers Robert Fleming Investment Management Ltd

Actuaries Bacon & Woodrow

Auditors Price Waterhouse & Co

Company Employees (at 31.12.79) 3,524

Members 2,842

Pensioners 104

	£000
Annual Contributions	2,045
Annual Investment Income	945
Annual Outflow	258
Capital Value	12,116
Summary of Investments (Market Value)	
Equities	2,366
Fixed Interest	1,707
Property	960
Cash & Deposits	343
Others	387
Deposit Administration	6,353

DUBILIER LTD

Chaucer Trading Estate, Launton Road, Bicester, Oxon OX6 0TU
Telephone: 08692-42035

Secretary F.Hayhurst

Insured with Legal & General Assurance Society Ltd

Employees 1,335

DUCTILE STEELS LTD WORKS RETIREMENT PLAN 1978 AND STAFF RETIREMENT BENEFITS PLAN 1973

Planetary Road, Willenhall,
West Midlands WV13 3SW
Telephone: 0902-732244

Secretary J.E.Roberts

Pensions Officer W.R.Reynolds APMI

Trustees Lowndes Associated Pensions Ltd.

Actuarial Advice Obtained through Cubie Wood &Co. Ltd.

Pension Fund Consultants Noble Lowndes & Partners Ltd

DUCTILE STEELS LTD Continued

Auditors Price Waterhouse & Co.
Company Employees 2,000
Members 1,188
Pensioners 30

	£000
Annual Contributions	500
Annual Investment Income	70
Annual Outflow	150
Capital Value	1,010
Summary of Investments	
Equities	460
Fixed Interest	280
Property	220
Cash & Deposits	50

DUFAY BITUMASTIC LTD

Darlington Road, Shildon, Co Durham DL4 2QP
Telephone: 038884-2541

Secretary B.Henley,FCA

Managed by Legal & General (Pensions Management) Ltd.

Employees 610

DUMFRIES & GALLOWAY REGIONAL COUNCIL SUPERANNUATION FUND

Kirkbank, Council Offices, Dumfries DG1 2DD
Telephone: 0387-62323

Pension Fund Manager David Y.Booth,IPFA (Director of Finance)

Superannuation Office A.G.M.Brown

Trustees Finance Committee

Stockbrokers Pember & Boyle

Actuaries Robertson, Hymans & Co

Members 2,520

Pensioners 993

	£000
Annual Contributions	1,500
Annual Investment Income	1,105
Annual Outflow	600
Capital Value (at 31.10.79)	11,712
Summary of Investments	
Equities	6,263
Fixed Interest	4,814
Property	135
Cash & Deposits	500

DUN & BRADSTREET LTD

26-32 Clifton Street, London EC2P 2LY
Telephone: 01-247 4377

Managing Director M.A.Bardsley

Investment Advisers John Carrington & Co.Ltd.

Employees 833

DUNFORD & ELLIOTT LTD GROUP RETIREMENT BENEFITS PLANS FOR (A) STAFF EMPLOYEES, (B) WORKS EMPLOYEES AND (C) EXECUTIVES

East Hecla Works, Sheffield, S.Yorks.S9 1TZ
Telephone: 0742-440353

Pensions Manager B.D.J.H.Hatton,ACII

Secretary M.R.Lindsay,FCIS,APMI

Investment Advisers Hill Samuel & Co Ltd, Legal & General Managed Fund, Sun Alliance Fund Management

Pension Fund Consultants Grindlays Brandts Life & Pension Consultants Ltd.

Company Employees 4,415

	Staff	Works
Members	784	1,907
Pensioners	314	1,293

Annual Contributions (1974) £500,000

Capital Value £2,500,000

The Executive Plan has 36 members, Annual Contributions of £22,000 and a Capital Value of £1,200,000

ALFRED DUNHILL LTD.

30 Duke Street, London SW1Y 6DL
Telephone: 01-493 9161

Secretary J.Wood,FCIS

Employees 955

DUNLOP LTD MALE & FEMALE PENSION SCHEME

Dunlop House, Ryder Street, London SW1Y 6PX
Telephone: 01-930 6700

Pension Department 148/158 Westgate Road, Newcastle Upon Tyne NE99 1TG
Telephone: 0632-22656

Pension Fund Manager N.R.Preston,MA

Remuneration & Pensions Adviser R.W.Willsmore, FIA

Trustees Dunlop Pensions Trust Ltd.

Investment Advisers Baring Brothers & Co Ltd, Lazard Securities Ltd, Phillips & Drew

Actuaries Duncan C.Fraser & Co.

Auditors Ernst & Whinney

Company Employees 36,000

Members 34,000

Pensioners 7,800

	£000
Annual Contributions	18,870
Annual Investment Income	13,412
Annual Outflow	7,861
Capital Value (Market Value)	149,500
Summary of Investments	
Equities	71,000
Fixed Interest	50,100
Property	16,200
Cash & Deposits	12,200

A.L.DUNN & CO LTD
Caldwell Road, Nuneaton CV11 4NE
Telephone: 0682-61211

Director M.J.Compton

Employees 950

G.A.DUNN & CO PENSION SCHEME
335/345 Royal College Street, Camden Town, London NW1
Telephone: 01-886 7196

Joint Managing Director R.E.Hale

Actuaries R.Watson & Sons

Auditors Price Waterhouse & Co.

Members 439

Pensioners 261

Annual Contributions £305,000

DUNN & WILSON GROUP LTD.
Meadow Street, Falkirk FK1 1RT
Telephone: 0324-21594

Secretary D.Liddle

Employees 1,097

RICHARD DUNSTON (HESSLE) LTD
Haven Shipyard, Hessle, Hull, North Humberside
Telephone: 0482-649261

Secretary C.S.Thane

Employees 500

DUPLE INTERNATIONAL LTD
Vicarage Lane, Blackpool, Lancashire FY4 4EN
Telephone: 0253-62251

Financial Director R.J.Richards FCA

Investment Advisers Industrial & Commercial Finance Corporation Ltd

Employees 1,474

DUPORT GROUP STAFF PENSION & LIFE ASSURANCE PLAN
Duport House, Hagley Road, Birmingham B16 8JU
Telephone: 021-454 6100

Pension Fund Manager & Secretary S.W.J.Parker, LLB,FCA

Other Pension Management G.N. Brown

Trustees E.C. Sayers, J.H. Russell, J.N. Bridson, C.R. Gray, P.F. Scurlock

Investment Advisers Morgan Grenfell & Co. Ltd. - Guardian Royal Exchange Assurance Ltd.

Actuaries Clay & Partners

Pension Fund Consultants Metropolitan Pensions Association Ltd.

Auditors Clement Keys & Co.

Company Employees 8,000

	Staff Plan	Works Plan
Members	1,574	4,096
Pensioners	741	1,564
Deferred Pensioners	1,129	2,022

	£000	£000
Annual Contributions	1,500	2,900
Annual Investment Income	500	1,100
Gross Annual Outflow	1,500	2,600
Capital Value		
Book Value	4,900	9,000
Market Value	7,600	9,800

DURACELL U.K. PENSION PLAN
Mallory House, Gatwick Road, Crawley, Sussex
Telephone: 0293-26041

Pension Fund Manager J.A.Trott

Secretary S.G. Bentley

Trustees Duracell UK Pension Plan Trustees Ltd.

Investment Advisers County Bank Ltd.

Actuaries Bacon & Woodrow

Auditors Price Waterhouse & Co

Employees 946

Members 490

Pensioners 62

	£000
Annual Contributions	345
Annual Investment Income	143
Gross Annual Outflow	79
Capital Value	1,642
Summary of Investments	
Equities	1,043
Fixed Interest	547
Cash & Deposits	52

DURAPIPE INTERNATIONAL LTD.
Norton Canes, Cannock, Staffs.WS11 3NS
Telephone: 0543-79909

Secretary R.R.Catmur

Employees 526

DURHAM CHEMICAL GROUP LTD.
Crown Chemical Works, Birtley, Chester-le-Street, Co.Durham DH3 1QX
Telephone: 0632-402361

Secretary S.J.Langman

Employees 912

DURHAM COUNTY COUNCIL SUPERANNUATION FUND
County Hall, Durham DH1 5UE
Telephone: 0385-64411

County Treasurer J.M.Wright,IPFA

Chief Executive & Clerk P.Dawson

Trustees Durham County Council

Merchant Bankers Hill Samuel & Co.Ltd.

Stockbrokers de Zoete & Bevan, and Fielding Newson-Smith & Co

Actuaries R.Watson & Sons

Auditors District Auditor

The Major UK Pension Funds DUR/ECC

DURHAM COUNTY COUNCIL Continued

Members 16,000
Pensioners 6,200

	£000
Annual Contributions	10,400
Annual Investment Income	6,400
Annual Outflow	5,800
Capital Value	
Book Value	65,400
Market Value	86,737
Summary of Investments Market Value	
Equities	49,584
Fixed Interest	24,234
Property	750
Cash & Deposits	5,217
Property Unit Trusts	6,952

DUTTON FORSHAW GROUP PENSION PLAN

c/o Towry Law House, High Street, Windsor, Berks.
Telephone: 07535-68244

Head Office Moor Lane, Preston, Lancs. Telephone: 0772-22901

Secretary T.Goodfellow

Trustees Towry Law Trustee Co.Ltd.

Managed by Sun Life (Pensions Management) Ltd., Norwich Union (Pensions Management Ltd.

Pension Fund Consultants Towry Law (Pension Services) Ltd.

Company Employees 3,950

Members 1,650

Pensioners 52

Annual Contributions £600,000

Capital Value £2,400,000

DYFED COUNTY COUNCIL

County Hall, Carmarthen, Dyfed SA31 7JP
Telephone: 0267-4251

Treasurer B.H.R.Evans

J.DYKES (HOLDINGS) LTD

175 West George Street, Glasgow G2 2LD
Telephone: 041-221 6242

Chairman H.Dykes

Insured with Phoenix Assurance Co Ltd

Employees 538

J. & J. DYSON LTD

Griffs Works, Stannington, nr.Sheffield, S.Yorks.S6 6BW
Telephone: 0742-348663

Secretary T.M.O'Brien

Managed by Eagle Pension Funds Ltd

Investment Advisers Drayton Montagu Portfolio Management Ltd.

Employees 1,965

EAGLE STAR INSURANCE COMPANY LTD

1 Threadneedle Street, London EC2R 8BE
Telephone: 01-588 1212

Pensions Manager R.F.Hubbard,BA,FIA,APMI

Employees 7,637 (plus 6,456 employees in Grovewood Securities)

EAST KENT PACKERS LTD.

Whitstable Road, Faversham, Kent ME13 8BQ
Telephone: 079582-2227

Secretary R.D.Marks

Employees 594

EAST LANCASHIRE PAPER GROUP LTD

Church Street East, Radcliffe,
Manchester M26 9PR
Telephone: 061-724 6521

Secretary K.Wood

Insured with Sun Life Assurance Society Ltd

Employees 1,521

EAST MIDLAND ALLIED PRESS LTD GROUP SUPERANNUATION FUND

Apex House, Oundle Road, Peterborough PE1 1RY
Telephone: 0733-68900

Pensions Secretary B.J.Allpress

Assistant Managing Director G.Russell,CA

Insured with Eagle Star Insurance Co Ltd

Pension Fund Consultants Godwins Ltd

Company Employees 1,864

Annual Contributions (Year to 31.12.76) £11,000

Investment Income £60,000

Capital Value (Book value) £601,000

EAST SUSSEX COUNTY COUNCIL SUPERANNUATION FUND

County Hall, Lewes, Sussex BN7 1SF
Telephone: 07916-5400

Treasurer and Licence Officer J.Unsworth IPFA MBCS

Superannuation Officer J.H.Smith APMI

Trustees East Sussex County Council

Investment Adviser A.W. Passmore

Stockbrokers de Zoete & Bevan, Fielding Newson-Smith & Co.

Actuaries Robertson, Hyman & Co.

Auditors District Auditor

Employees (excluding Teachers) 14,000

Members (including other Employing Authorities) 12,000

Pensioners 5,100

	£000
Annual Contributions	11,700
Annual Investment Income	5,400
Annual Outflow	8,700
Capital Value (September 1980)	80,000

Summary of Investments

EAST SUSSEX COUNTY COUNCIL *Continued*

Equities	46,400
Fixed Interest	23,300
Property	3,700
Cash & Deposits	600
Others	6,000

EASTERBROOK, ALLCARD & CO LTD

Albert Works, Penistone Road, Sheffield,
S.Yorks.S6 2FN
Telephone: 0742-349361

Secretary R.J.Armitage

Director H.E.McGee

Employees 757

EASTERN COUNTIES FARMERS LTD PENSION SCHEME

86 Princes Street, Ipswich, Suffolk IP1 1RU
Telephone: 0473-217070

Group Insurance Officer J.Perrett

Company Secretary P.Holder

Investment Advisers Charterhouse Japhet Ltd, Lloyds Bank Ltd

Actuaries Duncan C.Fraser & Co

Auditors Ensors Scrutton Goodchild & Sanderson

Company Employees 715

Members (at 5.4.80) 695

Pensioners 75

Annual Contributions £446,000

Capital Value £2,186,000

EASTERN COUNTIES NEWSPAPERS 1949 PENSION FUND

Prospect House, Rouen Road, Norwich,
Norfolk NR1 1RE
Telephone: 0603-28311

Secretary A.N.Wright

Insured with Equity & Law Life Assurance Society Ltd

Pension Fund Consultants Metropolitan Pensions Association Ltd.

Auditors Ernst & Whinney

Employees 1,311

Members 900

Pensioners 180

Annual Contributions £800,000

EASTERN GAS

Star House, Mutton Lane, Potters Bar,
Herts.EN6 2PD
Telephone: 75-51151

Regional Pension Fund Manager & Secretary K.J.Dearing,ACIS,APMI

Trustees R.E.Stead, D.W.Hill, S.J.Kilbourn, K.J.Dearing

Eastern Gas administered several Funds which have been closed to new members since 1.5.49. In addition it maintains responsibilities for the Gas Industry's Open Schemes.

Stockbrokers Hoare Govett Ltd.

Actuaries and Pension Fund Consultants R.Watson & Sons

Auditors Pannel Fitzpatrick & Co.

Members (Closed Schemes) 12

Pensioners 399

	£000
Annual Investment Income	244
Annual Outflow	530
Capital Value (March 1980)	2,127
Summary of Investments	
Equities	358
Fixed Interest	1,535
Property	50
Cash & Deposits	105
Others	79

J.B.EASTWOOD LTD

Burns Lane, Warsop, Notts.NG20 0QG
Telephone: 062-384 2581

Secretary D.J.Councell

Employees 5,753

EATON LTD.

Eaton House, Staines Road, Hounslow,
Middx.TW4 5DX
Telephone: 01-572 7313

Secretary E.A.Knowles

Employees 2,558

EATON AXLES LTD.

Durham Way, Aycliffe Industrial Estate,
nr.Darlington, Co Durham DL5 6BY
Telephone: 032571-2551

Secretary M.W.Barrett

Employees 1,350

EATOUGHS LTD

Hinckley Road, Earl Shilton, Leicester
Telephone: 0455-44461

Secretary R.A.Jackson

Employees 810

ECCLESIASTICAL INSURANCE OFFICE LTD STAFF RETIREMENT BENEFIT FUND

Beaufort House, Brunswick Road,
Gloucester GL1 1JZ
Telephone: 0452-28533

Secretary A.J.Sanford, FCIS

Trustees E.I.O.Trustees Ltd

Investment Advisers Investment Committee of Ecclesiastical Insurance Office Ltd

Stockbrokers Grievson Grant & Co., Gilbert Elliott & Co.

Property Advisers Cluttons

Actuary P.C.Sparkhall,FIA

Pension Fund Consultants Ecclesiastical Insurance Office Ltd

Auditors Dearden Farrow

Company Employees 306

ECCLESIASTICAL INSURANCE OFFICE LTD Continued

Members 239
Pensioners 34

	£000
Annual Contributions	263
Annual Investment Income	127
Annual Outflow	110
Capital Value	2,362
Summary of Investments	
Equities	1,245
Fixed Interest	692
Property	425

ECONOMIC FORESTRY GROUP RETIREMENT & DEATH BENEFITS PLAN

Forestry House, Great Haseley, Oxford OX9 7PG
Telephone: 08446-571

Secretary J.G.Roberts,FCA

Insured with Standard Life Assurance Co.Ltd.

Pension Fund Consultants Fenchurch Life & Pensions Ltd.

Auditors Touche Ross & Co.

Company Employees Approx.660

Members (at 1.4.80) 120

Pensioners 8

Annual Contributions £100,000

Capital Value £500,000

ECONOMIC GROUP LTD

Cowley Hill Road, Uxbridge, Middlesex UB8 2QG
Telephone: 0895-38262

Chairman J.S.Hinde

Employees 3,781

ECONOMIST NEWSPAPER LTD.

25 St.James's Street, London SW1A 1HG
Telephone: 01-930 5155

Secretary R.A.Forty

Employees 512

EDBRO (HOLDINGS) LTD

Lever Street, Bolton, Lancashire BL3 6DJ
Telephone: 0204-28888

Secretary W.Taylor,FCA

Insured with Commercial Union Assurance Co Ltd

Employees 1,556

EDEN CONSTRUCTION LTD

Durranhill, Carlisle, Cumbria CA1 3NR
Telephone: 0228-28251

Director J.M.Long

Employees 900

EDGE SHOES LTD.

Forward Works, Wellington Road, Bilston, West Midlands WN14 6BE
Telephone: 0902-43611

Chairman R.H.Rooker

Employees 550

EDRINGTON HOLDINGS LTD.

106 West Nile Street, Glasgow G1 2QX

Director Miss J.F.Robertson

Employees 831

EDWARDS HIGH VACUUM

Manor Royal, Crawley, Sussex RH10 2LW
Telephone: 0293-28844

Director R.H.Robinson

Employees 1,150

EDWARDS MORGAN LTD.

Sunborne House, Featherbed Lane, Shrewsbury, Salop SY1 1NS
Telephone: 0743-4674

Chairman M.A.Grant

Employees 660

ELBAR INDUSTRIAL LTD.

6 John Street, London WC1N 2ES
Telephone: 01-242 9921

Secretary J.M.Ralph

Employees 1,225

ELBEO LTD GROUP SCHEME

Lenton Lane, Nottingham NG7 2NS
Telephone: 0602-861327

Secretary P.Stellmacher

Trustees O.W.Kingdon, P.Stables, P.Stellmacher

Insured with Guardian Royal Exchange Assurance Ltd.

Company Employees 626

Members 90

Pensioners 3

Annual Contributions £23,000

Annual Outflow £50,000

ELDRIDGE POPE & CO LTD NON STAFF PENSION FUND AND STAFF PENSION FUND

Dorchester Brewery, Dorchester, Dorset DT1 1QT
Telephone: 0305-4801

Pensions Administrator G.L.Ayers,FCCA

Investment Advisers Warburg Investment Management Ltd.

Stockbrokers W.Greenwell & Co.

Actuaries Bacon & Woodrow

Auditors Whinney Murray & Co

Solicitors Slaughter & May

Company Employees 1,087

	Non-Staff Fund	Staff Fund
Members (at 5.4.80)	144	193
Pensioners	12	57

ELDRIDGE POPE & CO LTD Continued

	£000	£000
Annual Contributions	92	157
Annual Investment Income	9	190
Capital Value	158	1,482

ELECO HOLDINGS LTD

Sphere Works, Campfield Road, St.Albans, Herts AL1 5HU
Telephone: 54525

Secretary M.J.Webster

Insured with Legal & General Assurance Society Ltd

Employees 904

ELECTRICAL & INDUSTRIAL SECURITIES LTD

6 Sloane Square, London SW1W 8EE
Telephone: 01-730 9187

Secretary J.J.Hobbs

Insured with Prudential Assurance Co Ltd, Royal Insurance Co Ltd

Employees 1,875

ELECTRICAL ELECTRONIC TELECOMMUNICATION & PLUMBING UNION (EETPU) STAFF PENSION SCHEME

Hayes Court, West Common Road, Bromley, Kent BR2 7AU
Telephone: 01-462 7755

Pension Office A.Pickering

Stockbrokers Foster & Braithwaite

Actuaries Duncan C.Fraser & Co

Auditors Stoy Hayward & Co

Company Employees 400

Members 350

Pensioners 120

Capital Value £2,400,000

ELECTRICITY SUPPLY BOARD (EIRE) GENERAL EMPLOYEES' SUPERANNUATION SCHEME AND MANUAL WORKERS' SUPERANNUATION SCHEME

Lower Fitzwilliam Street, Dublin 2, Republic of Ireland
Telephone: 01/765831

Head of Superannuation Brendan J.Clear

Stockbrokers Butler & Briscoe

Actuaries Duncan C.Fraser & Co

Auditors Stokes Kennedy Crowley

Total Employees (Ireland) 10,800

Members (Ireland) 9,400

Pensioners (Ireland) 1,300

Annual Contribution £5,000,000

Capital Value of Fund £37,000,000

ELECTRICITY SUPPLY (STAFF) SUPERANNUATION SCHEME AND (INDUSTRIAL STAFF) SUPERANNUATION SCHEME

30 Millbank, London SW1P 4RD
Telephone: 01-834 2333

Secretary F.P.Toomer,ACIS,FPMI

Secretary K.E.Glover,APMI

Committee (Both Staff & Industrial Schemes) 10 Board Representatives, 10 Member Representatives

Committee Chairman A.W.Bunch,CBE

Standing Sub-Committees 8 members
Chairman: M.B.Cannan

Investments Sub-Committees 7 members;
A.W.Bunch (Chairman)

District Sub-Committees There are 13 districts, including headquarters

Nominee Company Electricity Supply Nominees Ltd.

Investment Advisers Lazard Securities Ltd. (D.A.Robinson)

Actuaries Bacon & Woodrow

Property Advisers Richard Ellis (A.J.M.Huntley)

Agricultural & Forestry Advisers Bidwells (Sir Francis Pemberton)

Auditors Peat, Marwick Mitchell & Co.

	Staff Scheme	Industrial Scheme
Members (at 31.3.80)	71,082	66,227
Pensioners	22,078	23,888
	£000	£000
Annual Contributions	110,514	64,871
Annual Investment Income	62,715	25,438
Annual Outflow	71,687	40,724
Capital Value		
Book Value	836,635	337,961
Market Value	993,228	391,947
Summary of Investments Market Value		
Equities	430,810	168,190
Fixed Interest	177,867	81,978
Property	317,142	120,295
Agriculture & Forestry	20,835	7,903
Cash & Deposits	40,284	11,173
Others	6,290	2,408

It is estimated that by April 1981 the total assets of the Funds will amount to about £1,550 million

ELECTROCOMPONENTS LTD

Maple House, 37-45 City Road, London EC1P 1HX
Telephone: 01-253 1222

Group Secretary R.J.Glennie,ACIS

Chairman & Trustee R.A.Marler,ACIS,ACMA

Trustees Electrocomponents Pension Trustees Ltd.

Investment Advisers Ivory & Sime Ltd.

Actuaries Duncan C.Fraser & Co.

ELECTROCOMPONENTS LTD Continued

Auditors Wilkins Kennedy & Co.
Company Employees 1,345
Members 662
Pensioners 33
Annual Contributions £491,000
Annual Investment Income £154,000
Capital Value £2,085,000

ELECTROLUX WORKS PENSION SCHEME AND GROUP STAFF PENSION FUND

Electrolux Works, Oakley Road, Luton, Beds,LU4 9QQ
Telephone: 0582-53255

Company Secretary & Director F.Hearne MA FCIS
Managed by Legal & General (Pensions Management) Ltd.
Investment Advisers Baring Bros.& Co.Ltd.
Stockbrokers Phillips & Drew
Actuaries Bacon & Woodrow
Pension Fund Consultants Hogg Robinson (Benefit Consultants) Ltd.
Auditors Price Waterhouse & Co.
Company Employees 5,280

	Staff	Works
Members (at 31.3.80)	1,412	1,512
Pensioners	238	76
	£000	£000
Annual Contributions	1,166	764
Annual Investment Income	878	69
Capital Value	11,011	1,177

ELECTRONIC RENTALS GROUP PENSION SCHEME

Electronic House, Churchfield Road, Weybridge, Surrey KT13 8DB
Telephone: 53377

Pension Fund Manager & Secretary E.F.Guyver, ACMA,FCIS
Asst.Group Pensions Administrator J.E.Moult
Trustees E.R.G. Trust Corporation Ltd.
Investment Advisers Baring Brothers & Co.Ltd.
Actuaries Duncan C.Fraser & Co
Auditors Josolyne Layton-Bennett & Co
Solicitors Norton,Rose,Botterell & Roche
Company Employees 9,300
Members 4,901
Pensioners 245

	£000
Annual Contributions	3,800
Annual Investment Income	1,055
Annual Outflow	504
Capital Value	16,900
Summary of Investments	
UK Equities	6,944
Foreign Equities	1,464
Fixed Interest	4,165
Property	3,040
Cash & Deposits	277

ELF (GB) GROUP PENSION PLAN

Elf House, P.O.Box 80, Woodlands Road, Altrincham,Cheshire WA14 1HD
Telephone: 061-928 6477

Personnel & Training Manager M.S.Marsh
Company Secretary S.C.Clairmonte
Insured with Swiss Life Pension & Insurance Co.
Auditors Ernst & Whinney
Company Employees 650
Members 398
Pensioners 40
Annual Investment Income £76,000
Annual Outflow £10,000
Capital Value (at 1.1.79) £800,000

ELLERMAN LINES LTD

12-20 Camomile Street, London EC3A 7EX
Telephone: 01-283 4311

Secretary P.C.Pratt
Group Pension Fund Manager J.M.Riddle
Actuaries R.Watson & Sons
Auditors Touche Ross & Co.
Solicitors Hill Dickinson & Co.
Employees 4,783
Members (at 5.4.80) 1,076
Pensioners 467
Annual Contributions £727,000
Capital Value £10,561,000

B.ELLIOTT & CO LTD (1978) STAFF PENSION & ASSURANCE SCHEME AND WORKS PENSION SCHEME

167 Imperial Drive, Harrow, Middx.HA2 7JP
Telephone: 01-868 1244

Pensions Director T.J.Smith,FCII,FPMI
Manager R.A.Penn
Managed by Legal & General (Pensions Management) Ltd, Prudential Pensions Ltd
Works Scheme Insured with The Prudential Assurance Co.Ltd.
Stockbrokers de Zoete & Bevan
Pension Fund Consultants C.T.Bowring & Layborn Ltd.
Auditors Melman Pryke & Co.
Employees 3,015
Members (Staff) 1,200, (Works) 770
Pensioners (Staff) 53, (Works) 140

B.ELLIOTT & CO LTD Continued

Annual Investment Income (Staff) £1,200,000
Capital Value (Staff) £5,027,000

THE ELLIOTT GROUP OF PETERBOROUGH LTD
Glebe Works, Glebe Court, Peterborough PE2 8EE
Telephone: 0733-52151

Secretary P.H.Brindley

Insured with Legal & General Assurance Society Ltd

Employees 961

ELLIOTT TURBOMACHINERY LTD EMPLOYEES BENEFIT PLAN
40 Medina Road, Cowes, Isle of Wight PO31 7DA
Telephone: 0983-294111

Secretary W.G.Wright

Trustees D.E.Lewis, W.G.Wright, R.Bishop, R.Toole

Insured with Swiss Life Insurance & Pension Co.

Pension Fund Consultants Willis Faber Advisory Services Ltd.

Company Employees 800

Members 309

Pensioners 83

Annual Contributions £202,000

Annual Investment Income £34,000

Annual Outflow £21,000

Capital Value £484,000

ELLIS & EVERARD LTD. COMPANY PENSION SCHEME 1978
140 New Walk, Leicester LE1 7JL
Telephone: 0533-542498

Secretary R.J.Geary

Company Secretary D.R.Wells,FCA

Managed by Charterhouse Japhet Ltd and Friends Provident Managed Pension Funds Ltd

Pension Fund Consultants Noble Lowndes & Partners Ltd.

Employees 566

ELLIS & GOLDSTEIN (HOLDINGS) LTD GROUP PENSION SCHEME
P.O.Box 5, Rowdell Road, Northolt, Middx UB5 5QT
Telephone: 01-845 7777

Secretary P.Wiard FCA

Actuaries Duncan C.Fraser & Co

Employees 4,296

Members 1,187

Pensioners 200

Annual Contributions £225,000

Annual Investment Income £200,000

Gross Annual Outflow £75,000

Capital Value £1.5 million

ELLIS MECHANICAL SERVICES LTD
118-120 Garratt Lane, London SW18 4FX
Telephone: 01-874 0911

Secretary R.W.Newman

Employees 750

GEORGE ELLISON LTD STAFF/WORKS PENSION SCHEMES
P.O.Box 280, Wellhead Lane, Perry Barr, Birmingham B42 2TD
Telephone: 021-356 4562

Company Secretary & Pension Fund Manager D.I.Watts

Trustees P.F.Swain, D.I.Watts, A.Cooksey, W.Bayliss, J.Sidwell

Insured with Standard Life Assurance Co.

Pension Fund Consultants Daly, Harvey, Yetman

Company Employees 450

Members 430

Pensioners 50

Annual Contributions £288,000

ELSON & ROBBINS LTD
Portland Mills, Bennett Street, Long Eaton, Nottingham NG10 4HL
Telephone: 060-762225

Secretary D.E.Fisher

Insured by Guardian Royal Exchange Assurance Group Ltd

Employees 1,379

ELSWICK-HOPPER LTD
St. Mary's Works, Barton-on-Humber, South Humberside DN18 5HE
Telephone: 0625-32167

Secretary M.Goodall,FCA

Insured with Legal & General Assurance Society Ltd

Employees 736

EMI GROUP PENSION SCHEME
91A High Street, Crawley, Sussex RH10 1BA
Telephone: 0293-24208

Secretary & Manager Group Pensions & Insurance Dept. B.G.Woolford FPMI FCII

Trustees EMI Pension Trust Ltd

Investment Advisers County Bank Ltd.

Actuaries Bacon & Woodrow

Auditors Coopers & Lybrand

Employees 33,000

Members 20,779

Pensioners 4,281

	£000
Annual Contributions	15,000
Annual Investment Income	4,500
Annual Outflow	5,200
Capital Value	73,000

Summary of Investments

EMI GROUP Continued

Equities	36,000
Fixed Interest	22,000
Property	9,000
Cash & Deposits	3,000
Others	3,000

EMPIRE STORES (BRADFORD) LTD GENERAL STAFF RETIREMENT BENEFITS SCHEME

18 Canal Road, Bradford,
West Yorkshire BD99 4XB
Telephone: 0274-29544

Secretary A.R.Clare FCA

Trustees R.Scott, D.Hale, H.Farrar

Insured with The Scottish Life Assurance Company

Auditors Arthur Young McClelland Moores & Co.

Company Employees 3,700

Members 1,300

Pensioners 200

ENDOLITHIC CO.LTD.

239 Shaftesbury Avenue, London WC2
Telephone: 01-836 4705

Secretary D.A.W.Clift

Employees 536

ENERGY SERVICES & ELECTRONICS LTD

Panton House, 25 Haymarket, London SW1Y 4EN
Telephone: 01-930 7751

Secretary G.S.Halls

Managed by Pensions Management (SWF) Ltd.

Employees 549

ENFIELD HIGHWAY CO-OPERATIVE SOCIETY LTD. EMPLOYEES SUPERANNUATION FUND

112 Ordnance Road, Enfield, Middx.EN3 6BT
Telephone: 9-719600

Secretary K. Ward

Assistant Secretary G.A.Cooper

Trustees 6 Employer Representatives, 5 Employee Representatives

Actuarial Advice Obtained through Co-operative Insurance Society Ltd.

Pension Fund Consultants Co-operative Union Ltd.

Auditors Appleby English & Partners

Company Employees 1,100

Members 611

Pensioners 186

	£000
Annual Contributions	143
Annual Investment Income	197
Gross Annual Outflow	131
Capital Value	1,799
Summary of Investments	
Equities	513
Fixed Interest	1,286

ENGELHARD INDUSTRIES LTD PENSION SCHEME

St Nicholas House, St Nicholas Road, Sutton, Surrey SM1 1EH
Telephone: 01-643 8080

Secretary S.F.Norton,FCIS

Part Managed by Legal & General (Pensions Management) Ltd

Investment Advisers de Zoete & Bevan, Warburg Investment Management Ltd

Actuaries Bacon & Woodrow

Auditors Arthur Andersen & Co.

Employees 1,987

Members (at 1.1.80) 1,542

Pensioners 232

Annual Contributions £840,000

Annual Investment Income £340,000

Capital Value £6,679,000

ENGLISH CARD CLOTHING CO LTD

Acre Street, Huddersfield HD3 3EB
Telephone: 0484-654145

Secretary A.J.N.Tilley,CA

Insured with Commercial Union Assurance Co Ltd

Employees 855

ENGLISH CHINA CLAYS LTD

John Keay House, St Austell, Cornwall PL25 4DJ
Telephone: 0726-4482

Pensions Manager T.H.Stone

Company Secretary D.A.Langford,ACIS

Investment Advisers J.Henry Schroder Wagg & Co.Ltd.

Employees 11,940

ENGLISH FUSTIAN MANUFACTURING CO LTD

12 Market Street, Hebden Bridge,
West Yorkshire HX7 6AA
Telephone: 042284-2431

Secretary N.Smith,FCA

Employees 708

EPICURE HOLDINGS LTD.

110 Jermyn Street, London SW1Y 6HB
Telephone: 01-839 5200

Secretary V.M.Ormerod,FCIS

Employees 520

EQUITABLE LIFE ASSURANCE SOCIETY PENSION FUND & LIFE ASSURANCE SCHEME

Walton Street, Aylesbury,
Buckinghamshire HP21 7QW
Telephone: 0296-89771

Head Office 4 Coleman Street, London EC2R 5AP
Telephone: 01-606 6611

Pensions Secretary R.J.Malpass

Insured with Equitable Life Assurance Society

Company Employees 700

Members 650

EQUITABLE LIFE ASSURANCE SOCIETY Continued

Pensioners 65
Annual Contributions £394,000

EQUITY & LAW STAFF PENSION SCHEME (1975)
Amersham Road, High Wycombe,
Bucks. HP13 5AL
Telephone: 0494-33377
Secretary W.M.Brown,MA,FIA
Managed by Equity & Law Managed Funds Ltd.
Auditors Price Waterhouse & Co.
Company Employees (at 30.6.80) 1,500
Members 1,250
Pensioners 159

	£000
Annual Contributions	1,400
Annual Outflow	770
Capital Value	15,400
Summary of Investments	
Equities	6,000
Fixed Interest	4,900
Property	3,900
Cash & Deposits	100

ERF (HOLDINGS) LTD. (A) 1978 WORKS PENSION SCHEME AND (B) PENSION & LIFE ASSURANCE PLAN FOR STAFF
Sun Works, Sandbach, Cheshire CW11 9DN
Telephone: 09367-3223
Financial Director & Secretary J.W.Hobbs,FCA
Pensions Scheme Administrator K.Lowe,FSCA
Trustees (a) E.P.Foden, C.Acton, J.W.Hobbs, (b) Gilroy, Broome & Scrini (Trustees) Ltd.
Insured with (b) Clerical, Medical & General Life Assurance Society
Investment Advisers (Works) Warburg Investment Management Ltd.
Actuaries Duncan C.Fraser & Co.
Company Employees 1,599

	Staff	Works
Members	411	1,020
Pensioners	22	3
	£000	£000
Annual Contributions	280	637
Capital Value	950	-

ERITH & CO LTD
530 High Road, London E11 3EQ
Telephone: 01-556 8888
Secretary M.A.Wright,FCA
Insured with Friends' Provident Life Office
Employees 590

ERNST & WHINNEY STAFF PENSION & LIFE ASSURANCE SCHEME
57 Chiswell Street, London EC1Y 4SY
Telephone: 01-628 6088
Partner H.G.Powys Greenwood,FCA
Investemt Advisers Investment Trust Services Ltd.
Actuaries Duncan C. Fraser & Co.
Company Employees 2,683
Members 350
Pensioners 80
Annual Contributions £240,000
Capital Value £6.0 million

ESB INDUSTRIALS LTD
Station Approach, St. Mary Cray, Orpington, Kent BR5 2PQ
Managing Director J.L.Woollett
Employees 944

ESPERANZA LTD.
18 Rood Lane, London EC3M 8AP
Telephone: 01-623 6155
Secretary G.W.Tregaskes,FCA
Employees 1,152

ESPLEY-TYAS PROPERTY GROUP PLC.
Park Hall, Salford Priors, Evesham, Worcs.WR11 5SQ
Secretary T.C.Stevenson,CA
Finance Director P.F.B.Cooper,CA
Employees 820

ESSEX COUNTY COUNCIL SUPERANNUATION FUND
County Hall, Chelmsford, Essex CM1 1JZ
Telephone: 0245-67222
County Treasurer E.A.Twelvetrees,IPFA
Trustees Essex County Council
Investment Advisers D.A.Pease,FCA, C.M.Hughes
Stockbrokers Cazenove & Co., de Zoete & Bevan
Actuaries R.Watson & Sons
Property Advisers Weatherall Green & Smith
Auditor District Auditor
Employees 55,000
Members 21,700
Pensioners 8,200

	£ million
Annual Contributions	15.3
Annual Investment Income	8.4
Gross Annual Outflow	11.1
Capital Value	107.4
Summary of Investmen	
Equities	69.3
Fixed Interest	27.0
Property	7.0
Cash & Deposits	2.5

ESSEX WATER CO
342 South Street, Romford, Essex RM1 2AL
Telephone: 70-46076

Secretary A.A.Stewart

Employees 1,057

ESSO RETIREMENT & DEATH BENEFIT PLAN
76-118 Victoria Street, London SW1E 5JW
Telephone: 01-834 6677

Head of Pensions & Benefits P.G.Kelly

Secretary N.A.Halton

Investment Manager R.H.Crowther

Asst.Investment Manager M.S.Hays

Trustees Esso Pension Trust Ltd

Property Advisers Jones Lang Wootton

Company Employees 8,864

Members (at 31.12.79) 10,485

Capital Value £165 million

ESTATES PROPERTY INVESTMENT CO LTD (EPIC PENSION FUND)
81 East Street, Epsom, Surrey KT17 1EB
Telephone: Epsom 24942

Director D.V.Udall FCA

Trustees D.V.Udall, S.J.S.Eley

Actuaries Bacon & Woodrow

Auditors Brebner Allen & Trapp

ESTEE LAUDER COSMETICS LTD.
71-72 Grosvenor Street, London W1X 0BH
Telephone: 01-493 9271

Secretary S.H.Magram

Employees 1,127

ETAM LTD
187 Oxford Street, London W1
Telephone: 01-437 5655

Secretary C.A.Scholes

Insured with National Mutual Life Assurance Society Ltd

Employees 1,547

EUROPEAN FERRIES LTD
P.O.Box 12, 1 Camden Crescent, Dover, Kent CT16 1LD
Telephone: 0304-204040

Secretary B.K.Clifford

Insured with Standard Life Assurance Company

Employees 5,879

EUROTHERM INTERNATIONAL LTD.
Albany House, Station Road, West Drayton, Middlesex

Secretary D.W.Downham

Investment Advisers Robert Fleming Investment Management Ltd

Actuaries Robertson, Hymans & Co.

Employees 735

EVA INDUSTRIES LTD
Crabtree Lane, Clayton, Manchester M11 4GX
Telephone: 061-370 9521

Secretary W.R.Graham

Insured with Legal & General Assurance Society Ltd

Employees 1,567

J.L.EVE CONSTRUCTION COMPANY PENSION FUND
17 Hillside, Ridgway, Wimbledon, London SW19 4NJ
Telephone: 01-946 3085

Secretary A.M.Dand

Trustees R.G.Woodwark, G.M.Hough

Part Managed by Norwich Union Life Insurance Society

Investment Advisers County Bank Ltd.

Actuaries Clay & Partners

Pension Fund Consultants Metropolitan Pensions Association Ltd

Auditors Buzzacott & Co

Company Employees 450

Members 160

Pensioners 60

	£000
Annual Contributions	135
Annual Investment Income	68
Annual Outflow	134
Capital Value	1,790
Summary of Investments	
Equities	493
Fixed Interest	291
Property	7
Cash & Deposits	86
Managed Funds	913

F.T.EVERARD & SONS LTD. (A) GROUP PENSION FUND AND (B) 1970 PENSION & LIFE ASSURANCE PLAN
The Wharf, Greenhithe, Kent DA9 9NW
Telephone: 0322-842345

Director Miss E.A.Everard

Insured with (a) Commercial Union Assurance Co.Ltd. (b) Legal & General Assurance Society Ltd.

EVERARDS BREWERY LTD STAFF PENSION SCHEMES
39 Castle Street, Leicester LE1 5WL
Telephone: 0533-56951

Pension Fund Manager J.G.Robertson

Finance Director P.Stephens

Employees 1,055

EVERED AND COMPANY HOLDINGS LTD STAFF & WORKS PENSION SCHEMES
P.O.Box 21, Lewisham Road, Smethwick, Warley, West Midlands B66 2BW
Telephone: 021-558 3191

Secretary A.W.Sandland CA ACMA

EVERED AND COMPANY HOLDINGS LTD Continued

Assistant Company Secretary P.J.Dunn

Trustees Sir Timothy Harford Bt., R.J.C.James, M.Morris, A.W.Sandland

Insured with Prudential Assurance Co Ltd

Pension Fund Consultants and Actuarial Advice Obtained through Metropolitan Pensions Association Ltd

Auditors Whinney Murray & Co

Company Employees 776

Members 465

Pensioners 350

Annual Contributions £278,000

J.EVERSHED & SON LTD.

Dolphin House, Dolphin Road, Shoreham-by-Sea, Sussex
Telephone: 07917-5555

Secretary R.G.Woodman

Employees 536

EVODE STAFF PENSION FUND AND SUPERANNUATION FUND FOR WORKS EMPLOYEES

Common Road, Stafford ST16 3EH
Telephone: 0785-57755

Secretary J.E.Linnell,FCA,ACMA

Trustees Evode Pension Trust Ltd.

Investment Advisers J.Henry Schroder Wagg & Co.Ltd.

Property Advisers Louis Taylor & Sons

Actuaries Duncan C.Fraser & Co.

Auditors John W.Hinks & Co.

Solicitors Allen & Overy

Company Employees 1,054

	Staff	Works
Members (at 5.4.80)	489	199
Pensioners	68	25
	£000	£000
Annual Contributions	586	131
Annual Investment Income	193	31
Capital Value	2,834	492

GEORGE EWER & CO LTD

53-55 Stamford Hill, London N16 5TD
Telephone: 01-800 8010

Managing Director H.G.Ewer

Insured with Provident Mutual Life Assurance Association

Employees 712

THE EXCHANGE TELEGRAPH COMPANY (HOLDINGS) LTD; EXTEL GROUP PENSION FUND

Extel House, East Harding Street, London EC4P 4HB
Telephone: 01-353 1080

Secretary T.B.King, APMI

Trustees A.B.Brooker, R.R.St.J.Barkshire, R.J.Pyper

Stockbrokers Mullens & Co.

Property Advisers Fawdry & Evans

Actuaries R.Watson & Sons

Auditors Deloitte Haskins & Sells

Solicitors Field, Fisher & Martineau

Company Employees 2,500

Members (at 31.12.79) 1,328

Pensioners 324

Deferred Pensioners 182

	£000
Annual Contributions	1,135
Annual Investment Income	942
Annual Outflow	648
Capital Value	
Book Value	10,797
Market Value	10,664
Summary of Investments	%
Equities	43
Fixed Interest	24
Property	22
Cash & Deposits	11

EXCHEM HOLDINGS LTD

Commonwealth House, 1-19 New Oxford Street, London WC1A 1NV
Telephone: 01-405 6065

Chairman P.M.L.J.Chatel de Brancion

Employees 884

EXETER BUILDING & CONSTRUCTION GROUP LTD.

Marwood House, 60 St.Davids Hill, Exeter, Devon
Telephone: 0392-52272

Secretary C.Turner

Employees 891

THE EXPANDED METAL CO LTD STAFF SUPERANNUATION FUND

1 Butler Place, London SW1N 0PS
Telephone: 01-222 7766

Pension Fund Manager & Secretary J.D.K.Hewitt

Trustees Expamet Pension Trustees Ltd

Investment Advisers Robert Fleming Investment Management Ltd.

Actuaries Bacon & Woodrow

Auditors Price Waterhouse & Co.

Employees 1,074

Members 647

Pensioners 171

THE EXPANDED METAL CO LTD Continued

	£000
Annual Contributions	434
Annual Investment Income	190
Annual Outflow	183
Capital Value Book Value	2,584
Market Value	3,201
Summary of Investments	
Equities	1,772
Fixed Interest	809
Property Unit Trusts	588
Cash & Deposits	12
Others	21

EXPORT PACKING SERVICE GROUP PENSION AND LIFE ASSURANCE FUND

152 Staplehurst Road, Sittingbourne,
Kent ME10 1XS
Telephone: 0795-24422

Pension Fund Manager and Secretary A.Pearson

Trustees EPS Pension Trustees Ltd.

Managed by Legal and General Assurance Society Ltd.

Company Employees 1,800

Members 1,450

Pensioners 150

Annual Contributions £700,000

Capital Value £4,000,000

EXPRESS & STAR GROUP PENSION SCHEME

51-53 Queen Street, Wolverhampton,
West Midlands
Telephone: 0902-22351

Secretary H.S.Powell,FCIS

Trustees M.G.D.Graham, L.J.Stallard, J.D.Allatt, P.Wynn, B.Blakeley

Stockbrokers Hoare Govett Ltd.

Actuaries R.Watson & Sons

Auditors Deloitte, Haskins & Sells

Company Employees 1,618

Members 1,083

Pensioners 33

	£000
Annual Contributions	754
Annual Investment Income	294
Annual Outflow	94
Capital Value	3,237
Summary of Investments	
Equities	1,264
Fixed Interest	1,088
Property	136
Cash & Deposits	749

EXTEL GROUP PENSION FUND

See Exchange Telegraph Co.

EYRE & SPOTTISWOODE LTD

2 Serjeants' Inn, London EC4Y 1LU
Telephone: 01-353 9751

Director A.F.J.Crosthwaite-Eyre

Employees 600

FABERGE INC PENSION SCHEME

The Ridgeway, Iver, Bucks.SL0 9JG
Telephone: 0753-654666

Senior Pension Representative A.P.Davidson

Trustees Chemical Bank Trustee Co.

Actuaries Clay & Partners

Pension Fund Consultants Frank B.Hall & Co.Inc

Company Employees 400

Members 185

Pensioners 10

Annual Contributions £150,000

Annual Investment Income £50,000

Annual Outflow £40,000

Capital Value £500,000

FAIRBAIRN LAWSON LTD

P.O.Box 32, Wellington Street, Leeds,
W.Yorks.LS1 1JL
Telephone: 0532-32041

Secretary A.C.Rattenbury FSCA

Insured with Scottish Life Assurance Co., Scottish Widows' Fund & Life Assurance Society

Employees 1,502

FAIRCLOUGH GROUP LIFE & PENSION SCHEME (1974)

Sandiway House, Northwich, Cheshire CW8 2YA
Telephone: 0606-883885

Group Pensions Manager and Secretary D.C.Morgan

Pensions Administrator Ms I.A.S.Tipler

Pension Fund Consultants and Actuarial Advice obtained through Sedgwick Employee Benefits Consultants Ltd.

Auditors Armitage & Norton

Company Employees 8,447

FAIREY HOLDINGS LTD STAFF PENSION & LIFE ASSURANCE PLAN AND PENSION & LIFE ASSURANCE PLAN FOR HOURLY PAID EMPLOYEES

Cranford Lane, Heston, Hounslow,
Middx.TW5 9NQ
Telephone: 01-759 0692

Group Pensions Manager P.J.Horsfield

Trustees G.L.Williamson, D.Pow, J.Uttley, A.Simmons

Staff Fund Insured with Clerical Medical & General Life Assurance Society

Hourly Paid Fund Insured with Prudential Assurance Company Ltd.

Pension Fund Consultants Godwins (Central) Ltd.

Auditors Peat Marwick Mitchell & Co

FAIREY HOLDINGS LTD Continued

Company Employees 2,796

Members 2,237

Pensioners 624

FAIRHOLT INDUSTRIAL HOLDINGS LTD. STAFF PENSION & LIFE ASSURANCE SCHEME (A) AND GROUP VOLUNTARY MEMBERSHIP SCHEME (B)

129 Groveley Road, Sunbury-on-Thames, Middx.TW16 7JZ
Telephone: 01-751 0046

Secretary R.F.Cantwell

Insured with (a) Provident Life Assurance Co.Ltd., (b) Prudential Assurance Co.Ltd.

Pension Fund Consultants Reed Stenhouse Benefit Consultants Ltd.

Employees 1,026

Members 150 in each scheme

FALCON CATERING EQUIPMENT

P.O.Box 4, Grahams Road, Falkirk FK2 7BG
Telephone: 0324-24101

Employees 600

FALLS FLAX SPINNING COMPANY LTD

5-7 Conway Street, Belfast BT13 2DG
Telephone: 0232-23463

Director J.M.Kelly

Executive R.Scott

Employees 500

FALMER JEANS LTD

Northway House, Whetstone, London N20 9LP
Telephone: 01-446 2121

Director A.A.Landau

Employees 700

FAMOUS ARMY STORES LTD

Sunbeam House, Woolton Road, Garston, Liverpool L19 5PH
Telephone: 051-427 5151

Managing Director A.M.Wilson

Employees 600

S.W.FARMER & SON LTD STAFF PENSION SCHEME

Courthill Road, London SE13 6HD
Telephone: 01-852 4334

Secretary C.R.C.Rhodes

Trustees A.E.A.Farmer,B.D.Farmer,H.A.Tucker

Insured with Norwich Union Insurance Society Ltd.

Pension Fund Consultants Stewart Wrightson Assurance Consultants Ltd.

Company Employees 662

Members 200

Annual Contributions £130,000

THE FARNELL GROUP OF COMPANIES 1978 RETIREMENT & DEATH BENEFIT SCHEME

81 Kirkstall Road, Leeds, W.Yorks.LS3 1HR
Telephone: 0532-38421

Secretary H.C.Elstone,FCA

Managed by Equity & Law (Managed Funds) Ltd.

Auditors Alexander Sagar & Co.

Company Employees 842

FARRANS (CONSTRUCTION) LTD

Kingsway, Dunmurry, Belfast BT17 9NU
Telephone: 0232-611122

Secretary J.A.McCullough

Employees 1,000

FEDERATED INSURANCE CO LTD STAFF PENSION SCHEME

Marsland House, Marsland Road, Sale, Cheshire M33 3AQ
Telephone: 061-969 7311

Secretary P.G.Turner FCIS

Actuaries Duncan C.Fraser & Co

Auditors Touche Ross & Co

Solicitors Linklaters & Paines

Company Employees 477

Members (at 5.4.80) 347

Pensioners 103

Annual Contributions £206,000

Annual Investment Income £385,000

Capital Value £3,582,000

FEDERATED PENSION SCHEMES

Rosehill, Park Road, Banstead, Surrey SM7 3BX
Telephone: 25-57272

Secretary and General Manager G.W.Darroch

Deputy General Manager A.H.Wilcock,APMI

Central Council 41 Members

Executive 11 Members, Chairman H.V.G.Upton,FCA

Policy Scheme

Panel of Life Offices 9 assurance companies

Participating Institutions (at 31.12.79) 399

Membership 11,501 (including 7,125 nurses and midwives)

Benefits Granted £3,087,000

Funded Schemes

Employers 375 and 45 individual schemes (at 31.3.80)

Members 4,931

Net Assets £11 million

FEDERATED SUPERANNUATION SYSTEM FOR UNIVERSITIES

25A Station Road, South Norwood, London SE25 5AH
Telephone: 01-653 0840

Secretary J.Fleming,FCIS,ACA

Actuaries Duncan C.Fraser & Co.

FEDERATED SUPERANNUATION SYSTEM FOR UNIVERSITIES Continued

Auditors Peters Elworthy & Moore

Members (at 31.12.79) 6,900

Annual Contributions £6,725,000

FELIXSTOWE DOCK & RAILWAY CO

Felixstowe Dock, Felixstowe, Suffolk IP11 8SY
Telephone: 039-424433

Secretary T.L.Savage

Employees 1,309

FENCHURCH GROUP PENSION SCHEME

136 Minories, London EC3N 1QN
Telephone: 01-505 3333

Secretary F.W.Bowden

Management Fenchurch Trustees Ltd.

Investment Advisers Fraser Green Ltd. Legal & General (Pension Management) Ltd.

Actuarial Advice Obtained through Fenchurch Trustees Ltd.

Auditors Pannell Kerr Forster

Company Employees 550

Members 380

Pensioners 90

	£000
Annual Contributions	400
Annual Investment Income	260
Annual Outflow	200
Capital Value	3,018
Summary of Investments	
Equities	1,031
Fixed Interest	1,297
Property	560
Cash & Deposits	130

See also Guinness Mahon

J.H.FENNER & CO. (HOLDINGS) LTD. PENSION SCHEME

Marfleet, Hull HU9 5RA
Telephone: 0482-781234

Director W.L.Black

Secretary R.L.Galloway

Pensions Officer I.E.White

Insured with The Prudential Assurance Co.Ltd.

Pension Fund Consultants Reed Stenhouse Benefit Consultants Ltd.

Auditors Hodgson Harris & Co.

Employees 5,201

Members 2,618

Pensioners 213

FENWICK LTD SUPERANNUATION FUND

39 Northumberland Street,
Newcastle-upon-Tyne NE99 1AR
Telephone: 0632-25100

Secretary I.J.Dixon FCA APMI

Managed by Legal & General (Pensions Management) Ltd

Pension Fund Consultants Godwins Ltd.

Employees 1,891

FERGUSON INDUSTRIAL HOLDINGS LTD RETIREMENT BENEFITS SCHEME

Appleby House, Appleby-in-Westmoreland, Cumbria CA16 6XH
Telephone: 0930-51402

Secretary M.B.Saint

Trustees D.S.Vernon, A.Smith, F.N.Wilson, M.B.Saint

Part Insured with Scottish Widow's Fund & Life Assurance Society

Pension Fund Consultants Bain Dawes & Partners Ltd.

Auditors Price Waterhouse & Co.

Employees 2,705

Members 350

Pensioners 20

Annual Contributions £324,000

FERRANTI PENSION SCHEME

Bridge House, Park Road, Gatley, Cheadle, Cheshire SK8 4HZ
Telephone: 061-428 3644

Pensions Administrator Mrs.S.Gleig

Company Secretary T.W.Grime FCIS APMI

Assistant Company Secretary D.Mackinnon,ACCA

Trustees T.W.Grime, J.R.Pickin, T.J.Lunt, O.P.Simpson, A.C.Wesley

Managed by Prudential Pensions Ltd

Pension Fund Consultants and Actuarial Advice obtained through Godwins Ltd

Auditors Thornton Baker & Co

Company Employees 17,270

Members 14,300

Pensioners 3,000

	£000
Annual Contributions	16,300
Gross Annual Outflow	2,150
Capital Value	33,500
Summary of Investments	
Equities	13,000
Fixed Interest	10,500
Property	10,000

DENIS FERRANTI METERS LTD.

Gorddinog, Llanfairechan, Gwynedd LL33 0HS
Telephone: 0248-53232

Secretary F.Davidson

Employees 629

FIAT-ALLIS UNITED KINGDOM LTD

Essendine, Stamford, Lincs PE9 4LE
Telephone: 0730-2471

Secretary T.W.Hepper

Employees 644

FIAT MOTOR CO.(UK) LTD. SUPERANNUATION FUND

Great West Road, Brentford TW8 9DG Middx.
Telephone: 01-568 8822

Administrator D.A.Norris

Group Pensions Manager J.L.King

Company Secretary I.W.Davies

Insured with Crown Life Insurance Company

Pension Fund Consultant EB Consultants Ltd.

Employees 655

Members 650

FIDELITY RADIO LTD

Victoria Road, London NW10 6ND
Telephone: 01-965 8771

Secretary M.Spink

Investment Advisers Hambros Investment Management Services Ltd

Pension Fund Consultants Towry Law (Pension Services) Ltd.

Employees 783

FIFE REGIONAL COUNCIL SUPERANNUATION FUND

Fife House, North Street, Glenrothes, Fife KY7 5LT
Telephone: 0592-754411

Secretary & Director of Finance R.Venters

Investment Advisers R.Nivison & Co, Pember & Boyle

Actuaries Robertson, Hymans & Co

Auditors Controller of Audit

Employees 15,061

Members 9,268

Pensioners 1,1681

	£000
Annual Contributions	4,221
Annual Investment Income	2,949
Annual Outflow	1,989
Capital Value	20,950
Summary of Investments	
Equities	13,233
Fixed Interest	13,107
Property	1,659
Cash & Deposits	1,950

FINANCE FOR INDUSTRY LTD.

91 Waterloo Road, London SE1 8XP
Telephone: 01-928 7822

Secretary B.L.Mann

Pension Fund Investment Manager J.L.Evans

Employees 867 (plus 1,433 in industrial subsidiaries)

See also Industrial & Commercial Finance Corp.Ltd.

FINANCIAL TIMES LTD

Bracken House, 10 Cannon Street,
London EC4P 4BY
Telephone: 01-248 8000

Pensions Administrator & Assistant Secretary L.D.Courtier

Employees 1,690

ALEXANDER FINDLAY & CO LTD

P.O.Box 2, Parknauk Works, Motherwell ML1 1BZ
Telephone: 0698-62301

Director D.Watson

Executive F.Carroll

Employees 1,000

FINDUS PENSION FUND

Pelham Road, Cleethorpes,
South Humberside DN35 7JU
Telephone: 0472-59141

Pensions Secretary A.S.Dutton

Trustees Findus Pension Trust Ltd.

Chairman G.S.Phillips

Investment Advisers & Stockbrokers Phillips & Drew

Property Advisers Felixstowe Investment Co.Ltd.

Actuaries Lane Clark & Peacock

Pension Fund Consultants Metropolitan Pensions Association Ltd.

Auditors Peat, Marwick, Mitchell & Co.

Company Employees 6,002

Members 3,017

Pensioners 158

	£000
Annual Contributions	2,491
Annual Investment Income	514
Annual Outflow	373
Capital Value	7,330
Summary of Investments	
Equities	3,665
Fixed Interest	1,812
Property	1,158
Cash & Deposits	578
Others	117

FINE ARTS DEVELOPMENTS GROUP PENSION FUND

Fine Art House, Queen Street, Burton upon Trent, Staffs DE14 3LP
Telephone: 0283-66311

Secretary P.G.Berryman CA

Pension Fund Manager Mrs M.Gleeson

Trustees Fine Art Developments (Pensions) Ltd

Investment Advisers County Bank Ltd, Ivory & Sime Ltd

Actuaries Duncan C.Fraser & Co

Pension Fund Consultants Reed Stenhouse Benefit Consultants Ltd.

Auditors Binder Hamlyn

Company Employees 3,230

FINE ARTS DEVELOPMENTS GROUP *Continued*

Members 1,340
Pensioners 165

	£000
Annual Contributions	548
Annual Investment Income	165
Annual Outflow	240
Capital Value	2,588
Summary of Investments	
Equities	2,196
Fixed Interest	338
Cash & Deposits	54

JAMES FINLAY & CO LTD STAFF SUPERANNUATION FUND

Finlay House, 10-14 West Nile Street, Glasgow G1 2PP
Telephone: 041-204 1321

Group Accountant R.Fraser,ACIS,FCCA

Accountant W.Walker,CA

Trustees Sir Colin Campbell, S.R.Stephens, W.Lamond, R.J.K.Muir, G.W.Gilmour, R.Fraser, R.McCraken

Investment Advisers James Finlay Investment Management Ltd.

Actuaries D.D. McKinnon, FFA

Pension Fund Consultants Metropolitan Pensions Association Ltd.

Auditors Arthur Young McClelland Moores

Group Employees (at 1.1.80) 1,810

Members 91

Pensioners 100

	£000
Annual Contributions	174
Annual Investment Income	117
Annual Outflow	219
Capital Value	2,046
Summary of Investments	
Equities	1,741
Fixed Interest	305
Cash & Deposits	87

FIRESTONE TYRE & RUBBER CO.LTD.

Great West Road, Brentford, Middlesex
Telephone: 01-560 4141

Secretary J.J.Hines

Managed by Legal & General (Pensions Management) Ltd

Employees 3,943

FIRST NATIONAL FINANCE CORPORATION LTD PENSION & LIFE ASSURANCE FUND

St Alphage House, Fore Street, London EC2P 2HJ
Telephone: 01-638 2855

Secretary S.J.Clayman,LLB

Associate Director P.W.Stone,FCIS

Investment Advisers Hambros Investment Management Services Ltd.

Actuarial Advice Obtained through Cubie, Wood & Co.Ltd.

Pension Fund Consultants Noble Lowndes Pensions Ltd.

Auditors Touche Ross & Co.

Solicitors Titmuss Sainer & Webb

Employees 817

Members (at 31.3.80) 536

Pensioners 28

Annual Contributions £320,000

Annual Investment Income £195,000

Capital Value £2,075,000

FIRTH FURNISHINGS LTD

Clifton Mills, Brighouse, W.Yorks.
Telephone: 0484-3371

Secretary J.Littlewood

Employees 1,289

GEORGE FISCHER (GREAT BRITAIN) LTD

Britannia Works, Kempston Road, Bedford MK42 9DH
Telephone: 0234-55291

Secretary P.E.Hart

Employees 1,354

FISHBURN PRINTING INK CO LTD

Cassiobury Mills, 94 St Albans Road, Watford, Herts.WD2 4BU
Telephone: Watford 28282

Chairman G.V.R.Watson

Secretary A.C.Jackson

Managed by Legal & General (Pensions Management) Ltd.

Employees 608

JAMES FISHER & SONS LTD

Fisher House, Barrow in Furness, Cumbria LA14 1HR
Telephone: 0229-22323

Secretary D.E.Pippard

Insured with Friends' Provident Life Office, Guardian Royal Exchange Assurance Group Ltd

Employees 666

FISONS PENSION FUND

Fison House, Princes Street, Ipswich, Suffolk IP1 1QH
Telephone: 0473-56721

Pension Fund Manager P.G.Markwell

Secretary E.Cameron, ACIS

Managing Trustee C.M.Rope

Investment Manager J.C.S.Bird

Trustee Fisons Pension Trust Ltd

Actuaries Lane, Clark & Peacock

Property Advisers Oxborrows

Auditors Price Waterhouse & Co

Solicitors Biddle & Co.

FISONS Continued

Company Employees 10,800
Members 9,100
Pensioners 3,000
Annual Contributions £9.7 million
Annual Investment Income £5.5 million
Gross Annual Outflow £2.1 million
Capital Value £80 million

FITCH LOVELL PENSION SCHEME
1 West Smithfield, London EC1A 9LA
Telephone: 01-248 6431

Pension Fund Manager P.Sutton,APMI
Secretary S.Guthrie-Brown
Trustees Fitch Lovell Pension Scheme Trustees Ltd.
Investment Advisers Warburg Investment Management Ltd
Stockbrokers Cazenove & Co
Actuaries R.Watson & Sons
Property Advisers Collier & Madge
Auditors Kidsons
Company Employees 18,061 including 6,558 part-time
Members 4,000
Pensioners 1,000

	£000
Annual Contributions	2,056
Annual Investment Income	1,199
Annual Outflow	951
Capital Value	15,645
Summary of Investments	
Equities	9,954
Fixed Interest	3,798
Property	1,004
Cash & Deposits	889

FLEMING & BRITISH AMERICAN OPTICAL INDUSTRIES LTD
Radlett Road, Watford, Herts.WD2 4LJ
Telephone: Watford 33522

Secretary Miss M.Wright
Employees 951

FLEXELLO CASTORS PENSION FUND
Bath Road, Slough, Berkshire SL1 4ED
Telephone: Slough 23841

Secretary J.A.Punter
Trustees 6 Employees
Insured with Clerical, Medical & General Life Assurance Society
Auditors Ernst & Whinney
Company Employees 535
Members 250
Pensioners 35
Annual Contributions £195,500

FLIGHT REFUELLING (HOLDINGS) LTD
Brook Road, Leigh Park, Wimbourne, Dorset BH21 2BJ
Telephone: 0202-882121

Secretary T.J.C.Waterson
Insured with Sun Life Assurance Society Ltd
Company Employees 1,192

F.M.C.LTD
19-23 Knightsbridge, London SW1X 7NF
Telephone: 01-235 5081

Pension Fund Manager R.A.Parsons
Investment Advisers Hill Samuel Investment Management Ltd
Actuaries Bacon & Woodrow
Employees 6,400
Members 3,000
Capital Value £2 million (est)

FODENS LTD.
Elworth Works, Sandbach, Cheshire CW11 9HZ
Telephone: 09367-3244

Secretary A.M.George
Insured with Legal & General Assurance Society Ltd.
Pension Fund Consultants Estridge & Ropner Ltd.
Employees 2,957

E.FOGARTY & CO.LTD.
Havenside, Boston, Lincs.PE21 0AH
Telephone: 0205-61122

Secretary A.H.Holmes,FCA
Employees 1,623

JOHN FOLKES HEFO LTD
Hefo House, 18 Hagley Road, Stourbridge, West Midlands DY8 1PZ
Telephone: 03843-6622

Secretary D.J.Newey,FCCA
Employees 2,967

FOOTWEAR INDUSTRY INVESTMENTS LTD
Richmond House, 199/205 Richmond Road, London E8 3NP
Telephone: 01-985 9381

Secretary I.R.Kidgell,ACIS
Insured with Scottish Widows' Fund & Life Assurance Society
Employees 728

FORD & WESTON HOLDINGS LTD
Sun Alliance & London House, Curzon Street, Derby
Telephone: 0332-364064

Secretary B.I.R.White
Employees 716

MARTIN FORD LTD
Eden House, 451-453 Holloway Road, London N7 6LP
Telephone: 01-272 7871

The Major UK Pension Funds FOR/FRA

MARTIN FORD LTD *Continued*

Secretary M.D.Ford

Employees 623

FORD MOTOR COMPANY LTD. SALARIED CONTRIBUTORY PENSION FUND AND HOURLY PAID CONTRIBUTORY PENSION FUND

Room 1/552, Eagle Way, Brentwood, Essex CM13 3BW
Telephone: 0277-253000

Secretary to Management Committee D.A.S.Hatt

Pension Fund Manager A.T.L.Pitt, MA, FPMI

Director Industrial Relations R.J.Ramsey

Director Finance S.Thomson

Management Committee (Salaried Contributory Fund) R.A.Shepherd (Chairman), D.J.Dymond, D.A.Elliott, A.T.L.Pitt, R.J.Shillitoe, S.Cree, M.P.Harris

Management Committee (Hourly Paid Fund) R.A.Shepherd (Chairman), M.P.Harris, J.Macrae, A.T.L.Pitt, D.L.Lanning, W.T.McGuire, A.Penny, B.Phillips, P.J.Riley, M.G.Torrance

Director, Industrial Relations R.J.Ramsey

Director, Finance S.Thomson

Trustees National Westminster Bank Ltd

Actuaries Bacon & Woodrow

Auditors Coopers & Lybrand

Investment Managers Baring Brothers & Co.Ltd., J.Henry Schroder Wagg & Co.Ltd., N.M.Rothschild & Sons Ltd., Ltd., Morgan Grenfell & Co.Ltd., (Salaried Fund); Hill Samuel Investment Management Ltd., Robert Fleming Investment Management Ltd. (Hourly Paid); Kleinwort Benson Ltd., Warburg Investment Management Ltd. (Both Funds)

Company Employees 80,000

	Salaried	Hourly Paid
Members (at 31.3.80)	15,536	50,204
Pensioners 3,419	3,264	9,120
	£000	£000
Annual contributions	23,858	24,007
Annual Investment Income	13,881	10,622
Annual Outflow	9,502	9,515
Capital Value		
Book Value	164,856	133,889
Market Value	180,000	152,000
Summary of Investments (Book Value)		
Equities	95,423	86,409
Fixed Interest	48,962	36,050
Property & Property Unit Trusts	7,442	2,222
Cash & Deposits	10,072	8,792
Net Current Assets	2,957	416

FORMAN HARDY HOLDINGS LTD

PO Box 99, Forman Street, Nottingham, Notts NG1 4AB
Telephone: 0602-45521

Secretary B.C.Bailey

Employees 755

B.FORSTER & CO.LTD.

Central Mill, Leigh, Lancs.WN7 1TF

Chairman D.Forster

Employees 720

FORTH PORTS AUTHORITY PENSION SCHEME

Tower Place, Leith, Edinburgh EH6 7DB
Telephone: 031-554 4343

Personnel Manager W.R.Miller

Investment Advisers Fraser Green Ltd.

Actuaries Duncan C.Fraser & Co.

Auditors Deloitte Haskins & Sells

Company Employees 761

Members 690

Pensioners 373

Annual Contributions £873,000

Capital Value £4,141,000

FORWARD TECHNOLOGY INDUSTRIES LTD GROUP PENSION SCHEME

2 Pont Street, London SW1X 9EL
Telephone: 01-235 9196

Secretary M.M.Bolger

Trustees K.Cobley, J.E.V.Green, C.L.Corman, A.T.Jamieson

Part Managed by Legal & General (Pension Management) Ltd.

Stockbrokers Panmure Gordon & Co.

Property Advisers D.E.& J.Levy

Actuaries R.Watson & Sons

Auditors Deloitte, Haskins & Sells

Company Employees 2,200

Members 1,600

Pensioners 90

	£000
Annual Contributions	600
Annual Investment Income	60
Annual Outflow	240
Capital Value	1,830
Summary of Investments	
Equities	624
Fixed Interest	815
Property	340
Cash & Deposits	50

FOSECO MINSEP GROUP UK RETIREMENT BENEFITS PLAN 1975, EXECUTIVE RETIREMENT BENEFITS PLAN 1978 AND FOSECO WORKS RETIREMENT BENEFITS PLAN 1978

36 Queen Anne's Gate, London SW1H 9AR
Telephone: 01-222 7030

Secretary D.H.J.Lester

Trustees Stewart Wrightson Trustees Ltd.

FOSECO MINSEP GROUP *Continued*

Insured with Clerical, Medical & General Life Assurance Society

Pension Fund Consultants Stewart Wrightson Assurance Consultants Ltd

Auditors Ernst & Whinney

Company Employees 3,153

Total Members 1,536

Pensioners 150

Annual Contributions £1 million

FOSTER BROTHERS PENSION & LIFE ASSURANCE PLAN

Marshall Lake Road, Shirley, Solihull, West Midlands
Telephone: 021-744 8555

Secretary F.B.Taylor

Part Insured with Phoenix Assurance Co Ltd (Growth Fund Policy)

Stockbrokers Laurence Prust & Co

Pension Fund Consultants Noble Lowndes & Partners Ltd

Employees 4,655

Members 2,000

Pensioners 250

JOHN FOSTER & SON LTD

Black Dyke Mills, Queensbury, Bradford, W Yorkshire BD13 1QA
Telephone: 0274-882271

Secretary G.D.Breton

Employees 1,036

FOSTER WHEELER LTD

Foster Wheeler House, Station Road, Reading, Berkshire RG1 1LX
Telephone: 0734-585211

Pensions Officer T.A.Evans

Managed by Sun Life Pensions Management Ltd

Investment Advisers Morgan Grenfell & Co Ltd

Pension Fund Consultants Hogg Robinson (Employee Benefits) Ltd

Employees 3,527

FOSTER WHEELER POWER PRODUCTS LTD. STAFF PENSION & LIFE ASSURANCE PLAN

Greater London House, Hampstead Road, London NW1 7QN
Telephone: 01-388 1212

Pensions Manager R.K.Ede,APMI

Investment Advisers Warburg Investment Management Ltd.

Actuarial Advice Obtained through Cubie, Wood & Co.Ltd.

Pension Fund Consultants Noble Lowndes International Ltd.

Auditors Coopers & Lybrand

Company Employees 1,725

Members (at 31.3.80) 1,062

Pensioners 176

Annual Contributions £660,000

Capital Value £3,308,000

FOTHERGILL & HARVEY LTD. PENSION SCHEME FOR (A) STAFF EMPLOYEES AND (B) WORKS EMPLOYEES

Summit, Littleborough, Lancashire OL15 9QP
Telephone: 0706-78831

Secretary J.Pinney,ACIS

Trustees W.R. Parker, L. Stevens, J. Pinney

Insured with Legal & General Assurance Society Ltd

Pension Fund Consultants Reed Stenhouse Benefit Consultants Ltd.

Company Employees 1,088

Members (a) 228,(b)372

Pensioners (a) 53, (b) 4

Annual Contributions (a)£282,000,(b)£157,000

Capital Value (a)£917,000,(b)£172,000

FOX BROTHERS & CO LTD

PO Box 2, Wellington, Somerset TA21 0AW
Telephone: 082-347 2271

Director M.P.Fox

Employees 600

FOXBORO-YOXALL LTD

Redhill, Surrey RH1 2HL
Telephone: 0737-65000

Secretary D.A.Pritchard

Employees 1,185

FOX'S BISCUITS LTD

PO Box 10, Batley, Yorkshire WF17 5JG
Telephone: 0924-474333

Secretary G.R.Buttery

Employees 1,583

FPA CONSTRUCTION GROUP PENSION & LIFE ASSURANCE FUND

Barkers Pool House, Burgess Street, Sheffield S1 2HF
Telephone: 0742-27162

Company Secretary R.Savage

Trustees B.J.Ward, R,Savage, T.Hill

Insured with Yorkshire General Life Assurance Co Ltd

Pension Fund Consultants Alexander Howden Insurance Brokers Ltd

Company Employees 1,027

Members 160

Annual Income £63,000

FRAM EUROPE LTD

Llantylisant, Pontyclun, South Glamorgan
Telephone: 0443-223000

Managing Director P.F.Harte

FRAM EUROPE LTD Continued

Investment Advisers Hill Samuel Investment Management Ltd
Employees 797

FRAMES TOURS LTD.
92 Southampton Row, London W.C.1
Director J.D.Frame
Employees 654

FRANCIS INDUSTRIES GROUP RETIREMENT BENEFITS SCHEME
Magson House, Luddendenfoot, Halifax, W.Yorks.HX2 6DD
Telephone: 0422-882568
Pension Fund Manager & Secretary L.Green, FCIS
Trustees D.Dudley Morgan, R.H.Shorer, L.Green
Insured with Prudential Assurance Co Ltd
Pension Fund Consultants Clarkson Tiley & Hargeaves Ltd.
Company Employees 2,156
Members 864

FRANCIS PARKER PENSION PLAN
Francis House, Shopwyke Road, Chichester, West Sussex PO20 6AD
Telephone: 0243-780011
Pension Fund Manager and Secretary M.T. Hearn FCA
Trustees A.Flower, L.W.Stevens, J.MacDonald, M.J. Smith FCA, M.T. Hearn FCA, A. Liddle
Investment Advisers Industrial & Commercial Finance Corp.Ltd.
Pension Fund Consultants and Actuarial Advice Obtained through Wyatt Harris Graham Ltd.
Auditors Binder Hamlyn
Company Employees 982
Members 156
Pensioners 62

	£000
Annual Contributions	72
Annual Investment Income	103
Gross Annual Outflow	46
Capital Value	1,363
Summary of Investments	
Equities	837
Fixed Interest	434
Property	92

FRANDEE LTD.
Springfield Way, Anlaby, Hull HU10 6RW
Telephone: 0482-54234
Secretary M.A.Brown
Employees 850

FRANKIPILE LTD
Davis House, High Street, Croydon, Surrey CR9 1PB
Telephone: 01-686 7171

Secretary P.E.B.de Buriatte,FCA
Insured with Norwich Union Life Insurance Society
Employees 575

FREEMANS RETIREMENT & LIFE ASSURANCE PLAN
139 Clapham Road, London SW9 0HR
Telephone: 01-735 7644
Director & Secretary E.F.T.Cribb
Pension Fund Manager Mrs.S.M.Nuthall
Trustees A.Rampton, R.H.C.Aldred, T.A.Donnelly, J.W.Gale, E.F.T.Cribb
Investment Advisers Morgan Grenfell & Co.Ltd.
Actuaries Bacon & Woodrow
Auditors Touche Ross & Co.
Solicitors Slaughter & May
Company Employees 5,150
Members 3,000
Pensioners 425

	£000
Annual Contributions	1,396
Annual Investment Income	439
Annual Outflow	415
Capital Value	5,957
Summary of Investments	
Equities	2,128
Fixed Interest	1,814
Property Unit Trusts	678
Cash & Deposits	77
Others	510

FRENCH KIER GROUP PENSION AND ASSURANCE SCHEME
Tempsford Hall, Sandy, Bedfordshire SG19 2BD
Telephone: 0767-40111
Secretary R.J.Jeeves
Trustees W.E.Bradshaw, W.Fox, A.M.Gammage, P.G.Lord, E.J.Mantle, H.C.Cottrell, D.A.George
Managed by Scottish Widows' Managed Fund, Legal & General (Pensions Management) Ltd., Scottish Amicable Pensions Investment Ltd.
Actuarial Advice Obtained through Godwins (Central Service) Ltd.
Pension Fund Consultants Godwins (Central) Ltd.
Auditors Peat, Marwick, Mitchell & Co.
Company Employees 5,458
Members 1,216
Pensioners 241

THOMAS FRENCH & SONS LTD
Sharston Road, Wythenshaw, Manchester M22 4TH
Telephone: 061-998 1811
Secretary S.Morgan
Employees 728

FRIENDS' PROVIDENT LIFE OFFICE RETIREMENT & DEATH BENEFITS SCHEME (1974)

Pixham End, Dorking, Surrey RH4 1QA
Telephone: 0306-5055

Manager Pensions Department P.Silvester,FIA, APMI

Secretary R.I.Shuker,BA,LLB,ACII

Company Employees 1,206

Members 1,018

Pensioners 448

Capital Value £20,530,000

FRIGOSCANDIA LTD

Scania House, Hoddesdon, Herts.EN11 8TT
Telephone: 099-24 45511

Director S.V.Westerberg

Employees 830

FRIZZELL GROUP LTD PENSION FUND

Frizzell House, 14-22 Elder Street, London E1 6DF
Telephone: 01-247 6595

Pension Fund Manager D.A.Smith

Trustees N.R.Frizzell, A.J.Horton, R.N.Godden

Insured with Standard Life Assurance Co

Auditors Price Waterhouse & Co.

Company Employees 1,306

Members 800

Pensioners 150

Annual Contributions £933,000

FULGO METALS LTD

Northway House, High Road, Whetstone, London N20
Telephone: 01-466 4381

Director G.P.Cornes

Executive M.E.Graley

Employees 5,000

FULLER, SMITH & TURNER LTD. PENSION PLAN

Griffin Brewery, Chiswick, London W4 2QB
Telephone: 01 994 3691

Pension Fund Manager R.I.Turner,FCA

Secretary R.G. Bryan

Insured with Norwich Union Life Insurance Society

Company Employees 1,000

Members 288

Pensioners 40

FURNESS PENSION SCHEME/RETIREMENT PLAN

105 Fenchurch Street, London EC3M 5HH
Telephone: 01-481 2525

Pension Fund Manager & Secretary M.N.Potter, ACIS,APMI

Assistant Pensions Manager B.A.Salsbury

Trustees Furness Withy Pension/Retirement Trustees Ltd.

Investment Advisers Hambros Investment Management Service Ltd., Kleinwort Benson Ltd.

Actuaries R.Watson & Sons

Auditors Gane, Jackson & Walton

Company Employees 5,624

Members 4,000

Pensioners 1,650

	£000
Annual Contributions	4,000
Annual Investment Income	3,350
Annual Outflow	2,300
Capital Value	38,000
Summary of Investments (1979)	
Fixed Interest	11,000
Fixed Interest	2,975
Property	2,500
Cash & Deposits	3,000

FURNITURE INDUSTRIES LTD

Ercol Buildings, London Road, High Wycombe, Bucks.HP13 7AE
Telephone: 0494-21261

Secretary G.W.Ray

Employees 581

W.J.FURSE & CO LTD

Traffic Street, Nottingham
Telephone: 0602-868213

Secretary D.W.Lock

Employees 550

FFYFES GROUP LTD. 1968 PENSION & LIFE ASSURANCE PLAN

15 Stratton Street, Piccadilly, London W1A 2LL
Telephone: 01-499 3411

Manager Employee Benefits R.Norton-Amor,MA

Group Chief Accountant J.A.Benns

Company Secretary W.E.Grisley

Managed by Pensions Management (SWF) Ltd.

Actuaries Bacon & Woodrow

Pension Fund Consultants Metropolitan Pensions Association Ltd.

Auditors Arthur Young McClelland Moores & Co.

Solicitors Slaughter & May

Company Employees 1,958

Members 695

Pensioners 278

Annual Contributions £530,000

Annual Investment Income £514,000

Capital Value £5,520,000

GAF (GREAT BRITAIN) LTD

PO Box 70, Blackthorne Road, Colnbrook, Slough,Bucks.SL3 0AR
Telephone: 964-4567

Secretary I.S.Jones

Employees 1,242

GALLAHER PENSION SCHEMES

Gallaher Limited, 65 Kingsway,
London WC2B 6TG
Telephone: 01-242 1290

Group Pensions Adviser & Secretary L.H.Edwards, MA

Pensions Manager (Group Planning) W.Hitchings, APMI

Pensions Manager (Tobacco) M.P.Newberry, APMI

Pensions Manager (Non-Tobacco) Miss L.Parker,BA

Trustees Gallaher Pensions Ltd. (trustee of 9 schemes)

Investment Advisers Lazard Securities Ltd., Legal & General Assurance Society Ltd

Property Advisers Chestertons

Forestry Advisers Economic Forestry Group, Fountain Forestry, Tilhill Forestry

Farming Partners Velcourt Ltd.

Actuaries Duncan C.Fraser & Co.

Auditors Hill Vellacott

Group Employees 26,530

Members 18,950

Pensioners 3,700

	£000
Annual Contributions	11,493
Annual Investment Income	4,479
Annual Outflow	4,623
Capital Value	83,500

Summary of Investments	%
Equities	18
Fixed Interest	18
Property	46
Cash & Deposits	8
Others	10

GALLIFORD BRINDLEY LTD

Leicester Road, Wolvey, Hinckley,
Leicestershire LE10 3HL
Telephone: 0455-220533

Secretary E.Pugh

Trustees Barclays Bank Trust Co.Ltd.

Investment Managers Barclays Bank Trust Co.Ltd.

Actuaries Clay & Partners

Auditors Thomas May & Co.

Company Employees 2,300

J.W.GALLOWAY LTD

139/45 Copland Road, Glasgow G51 2ST
Telephone: 041-427 5231

Secretary W.O.Munro

Employees 712

GARDNER-DENVER HOLDINGS (UK) LTD PENSION FUND

Callywhite Lane, Dronfield, Sheffield S18 6XT
Telephone: 0246-413301

Pensions Officer E.J.Crawley

Investment Advisers Fraser Green Ltd.

Actuaries Duncan C.Fraser & Co.

Auditors Price Waterhouse & Co.

Employees 849

Members 622

Pensioners 107

Annual Contributions £498,000

Annual Investment Income £164,000

Capital Value £1,927,000

J.GARDNER & CO LTD

Gardener Industrial Est, Kent House Lane,
Beckenham, Kent
Telephone: 01-778 6080

Secretary E.E.Newbald, MC, FCA

Employees 600

GARNER SCOTBLAIR LTD

The Garage, Bermondsey, London SE1 3AQ
Telephone: 01-237 1181

Secretary J.A.Fooks,MA,FCA

Insured with Commercial Union Assurance Co Ltd

Employees 900

GARROD & LOFTHOUSE LTD.

Hyde House, Langley Street, London WC2H 9JG
Telephone: 01-240 3320

Secretary H.J.Court

Employees 698

GARTON ENGINEERING LTD

Bridge Works, Bilport Lane, Wednesbury,
W Midlands WS10 0NU
Telephone: 021-556 1921

Secretary J.C.Hayward

Part managed by Standard Life Pension Funds Ltd

Insured with Norwich Union Life Insurance Society

Employees 971

GARTSIDE SPINNERS PENSION SCHEME

c/o Shiloh Spinners Ltd., Royton, Oldham,Lancs.
Telephone: 061-624 8161

Secretary R.Coop

Trustees E.T.Gartside, B.Clegg, L.Holland, A.Bradbury

Insured with Friends' Provident Life Office

Pension Fund Consultants Noble Lowndes & Partners Ltd.

Company Employees 750

Members 154

Pensioners 61

GATEWAY BUILDING SOCIETY PENSION FUND

Administrative Centre, PO Box 18, Worthing,
West Sussex BN13 2QD
Telephone: 0903-64441

Secretary D.N. Burford,FCCA

Company Employees 700

Members 583

GATEWAY BUILDING SOCIETY Continued

Pensioners 47

	£000
Annual Contributions	521
Annual Investment Income	309
Annual Outflow	78
Capital Value	3,252
Summary of Investments	
Equities	1,683
Fixed Interest	1,100
Property	164
Cash & Deposits	305

THE GEEST (1972) PENSION SCHEME

White House Chambers, Spalding, Lincs PE11 2AL
Telephone: 0775-61111

Pension Fund & Insurance Manager R.J.R.Fox, APMI

Trustees The Geest Organisation (Trustees) Ltd

Investment Advisers Morgan Grenfell & Co. Ltd., Kleinwort Benson Investment Management Ltd.

Pension Fund Consultants and Actuarial Advice Obtained through Godwins Ltd.

Auditors R.J.Weston & Co.

Company Employees 5,500

Members 1,800 Pension and Life, 3,000 Life Assurance Only

Pensioners 350

	£000
Annual Contributions	1,300
Annual Investment Income	495
Annual Outflow	1,100
Capital Value	8,200
Summary of Investments	%
Equities	45
Fixed Interest	30
Property	10
Cash & Deposits	5
Others (Mainly U.S. equities)	10

GEI INTERNATIONAL

West Street, Dunstable,Beds.LU6 1TA
Telephone: 0582-601201

Secretary D.J.Mant,ACCA,ACIS

Insured with Prudential Assurance Co.Ltd.

Employees 3,155

A.& J. GELFER LTD

30 Dora St, Glasgow G40 4EU
Telephone: 041-554 8711

Secretary J.Roberts

Employees 645

GENERAL ACCIDENT FIRE & LIFE ASSURANCE CORPORATION LTD UK PENSION SCHEME (1980)

General Buildings, Perth, Tayside PH1 5TP
Telephone: 0738-21202

Deputy Secretary L.W.Mansfield, FCIS

Deputy General Manager & Actuary C.G.Myers, MA, LLB, FIA, FFA

Company Employees 9,516

Members 7,000

Pensioners 2,000

Capital Value £100 million

GENERAL & MUNICIPAL WORKERS' PENSION TRUSTEE COMPANY LTD

Thorne House, Ruxley Ridge, Claygate, Esher, Surrey KT10 OTL
Telephone: 78-62081

Secretary M.J.White

Deputy Secretary & Pension Administrator G.T.Pearson, BA

Trustees GMW Pension Trustee Co. Ltd

Directors D. Basnett (chairman), B. Bonsey, V.G. Duncombe, R. Lovelock, J.P.W. Milne, A. Platt, L.F. Jarvest, K. Smith

Investment Advisers Phillips & Drew

Actuaries Bacon & Woodrow

Members 727

Pensioners 192

	£000
Annual Contributions	1,065
Capital Value (Market Value at 31.12.79)	11,338
Summary of Investments	
Equities	5,390
Fixed Interest	5,540
Cash & Deposits	312
Others	96

GENERAL COUNCIL OF BRITISH SHIPPING RETIREMENT BENEFITS PLAN

30/32 St.Mary Axe, London EC3A 8ET
Telephone: 01-283 2922

Director of Administration M.R.Hindle,FCA

Investment Advisers & Stockbrokers Cazenove & Co.

Actuarial Advice Obtained through Cubie, Wood & Co.Ltd.

Auditors Morison Stoneham & Co.

Company Employees 370

Members (at 31.12.79) 354

Pensioners 188

Annual Contributions £508,000

Annual Investment Income £320,000

Capital Value £3,715,000

GENERAL ELECTRIC COMPANY LTD THE GEC PLAN AND SELECTED BENEFITS SCHEME

132 Long Acre, London WC2E 9AH
Telephone: 01-836 3444

Pension Fund Manager M.C.W.Patterson, FPMI

Pension Office PO Box 20, Lichfield Road, Stafford ST17 4LN (0785-54543)

Deputy Pensions Manager A.F.Mallett, APMI

Investment Manager P.Olney

GENERAL ELECTRIC COMPANY LTD Continued

Trustees Stanhope Pension Trust Ltd.
Chairman E.S.Jamieson
Secretary to Trustees Yvonne de la Praudiere
Company Employees 155,000
Actuaries Bacon & Woodrow
Auditors Touche Ross & Co.
Solicitors Sacker & Partners
Members (GEC Plan) (at 5.4.80) 48,427
Pensioners 22,205

	£000
Annual Contributions	28,833
Annual Investment Income	22,209
Gross Annual Outflow	20,879
Capital Value	261,282
Summary of Investments	
Equities	89,252
Fixed Interest	83,516
Property	69,836
Cash & Deposits	16,251
Others	2,427

THE GENERAL ENGINEERING CO. (RADCLIFFE) LTD.
Station Works, Bury Road, Manchester M26 9UR
Telephone: 061-723 3271

Secretary A.Swan
Employees 832

GENERAL FOODS LTD (GB) PENSION SCHEME
Maxwell House, Banbury, Oxfordshire OX16 7QU
Telephone: 0295-4433

Assistant Secretary D.A.Preece
Secretary G.R.Claybourn
Investment Advisers Robert Fleming Investment Management Ltd, N.M.Rothschild Asset Management Ltd
Pension Fund Consultants Towers Perrin Forster & Crosby Inc
Auditors Price Waterhouse & Co
Company Employees 2,089
Members 1,804
Pensioners 274
Capital Value £6,422,000

GENERAL INSTRUMENT U.K. LTD
Beeton's Way, Bury St Edmunds, Suffolk
Telephone: 01-439 1891

Managing Director M.Shapiro
Employees 1,112

GENERAL MILLS UK LTD
1 Bedford Row, London WC1R 4BZ
Telephone: 01-878 4891

Secretary J.C.Anderson
Employees 1,749

GENERAL MOTORS LTD
High Street North, Dunstable, Beds LU6 1BO
Telephone: 0582-64264

See Vauxhall & Associated Companies Pension Fund for further details

GENERAL SUPERINTENDENCE CO (UK) LTD
Orchard Lea, Winkfield, nr Windsor, Berks
Telephone: 03447-4111

Secretary J.H.Dawson
Employees 500

S.R.GENTOLO LTD
Dodworth Road, Barnsley, S Yorks
Telephone: 0226-41434

Director P.Wolff
Employees 3,300

GERRARD INDUSTRIES LTD. GROUP PENSION SCHEME
Wharf Road, Kilnhurst, Rotherham, S.Yorks.S62 5SX
Telephone: 0709-587123

Personnel Manager M.Baker
Management Services Manager J.F.Holden
Insured with The Prudential Assurance Co.Ltd.
Pension Fund Consultants Godwins (Central) Ltd.
Auditors Price Waterhouse & Co.
Company Employees 540
Members 500
Pensioners 50

G.M.GERRARDS LTD.
West End House, 156-159 The Broadway, Southall, Middx.
Telephone: 01-574 2400

Secretary J.S.Russell,ACIS
Employees 1,034

GESTETNER PENSION SCHEME
PO Box 466, 41 Fawley Road, Tottenham, London N17 9LT
Telephone: 01-808 1050

Secretary & Pension Fund Manager D.Posner, APMI
Trustees Gestetner Pensions Ltd
Investment Manager M.B.David
Actuaries Bacon & Woodrow
Auditors Deloitte Haskins & Sells
Company Employees 4,028
Members 3,854
Pensioners 1,201

	£000
Annual Contributions	2,894
Annual Investment Income	2,014
Annual Outflow	1,595
Capital Value	21,359

GESTETNER PENSION SCHEME Continued

Summary of Investments
- Equities 9,073
- Fixed Interest 7,276
- Property 3,883
- Cash & Deposits 1,127

GIBBON DUDLEY PENSION FUND (1977), STAFF PENSION FUND AND WORKS PENSION FUND

P.O.Box 19, Dibdale Road, Dudley,
West Midlands DY3 2AQ
Telephone: 0384-57481

Secretary R.W.Evers,ACMA,APMI

Pensions Officer M.C.Hope,ACIS,APMI

Trustees Gibbons Dudley Pensions Ltd.

Investment Advisers J.Henry Schroder Wagg & Co.Ltd.

Actuaries Bacon & Woodrow

Auditors Cooper Adamson & Co.

Solicitors Linklaters & Paines

Company Employees 2,237

Members Staff 666, Works 963

Pensioners Staff 124

	£000
Annual Contributions (Est.)	300
Annual Investment Income	200
Annual Outflow	100
Capital Value Market Value at 5.4.78	2,622
Summary of Investments	
Equities	1,500
Fixed Interest	649
Cash & Deposits	78

ANTONY GIBBS HOLDINGS LTD PENSION AND LIFE ASSURANCE PLAN

3 Frederick's Place, Old Jewry, London EC2R 8HD
Telephone: 01 588 4111

Secretary C.Fiddian-Green

Trustees Sir Philip de Zulueta (Chairman), G.Fitton, C.Gill, J.W.L.Howard

Investment Advisers Antony Gibbs Investment Management Ltd.

Actuaries Lane,Clark & Peacock

Pension Fund Consultants Antony Gibbs Pensions Services Ltd.

Auditors Spicer & Pegler

Company Employees 603

Members 486

Annual Contributions £616,000

Annual Investment Income £557,000

Annual Outflow £146,000

Capital Value £4,218,000

GIDDINGS & LEWIS-FRASER LTD. STAFF & WORKS PENSION SCHEMES

Wellgate Works, Arbroath, Tayside DD11 3AU
Telephone: 0241-73811

Secretary & Financial Director G.M.Ross

Insured with Scottish Widows' Fund & Life Assurance Society

Pension Fund Consultants Reed Stenhouse Benefit Consultants Ltd.

Company Employees 627

Members Staff 206, Works 370

Pensioners Staff 29, Works 62

GILBARCO LTD

Crampton Close, Basildon, Essex
Telephone: 0268-3090

Manging Director F.J.Drakeman

Employees 610

GILL & DUFFUS GROUP LTD.

201 Borough High Street, London SE1 1HW
Telephone: 01-407 7050

Secretary J.E.H.Brown

Employees 600

GILLETTE UK LTD

Great West Road, Iseleworth, Middlesex TW7 5NP
Telephone: 01-560 1234

Retirement Benefits Manager & Secretary M.J.B.Watson,FCA,ATII

Investment Advisers Morgan Grenfell & Co Ltd, Warburg Investment Management Ltd

Actuaries R.Watson & Sons

Auditors Peat, Marwick, Mitchell & Co.

Solicitors Slaughter & May

Company Employees 2,691

Members (at 31.3.80) 1,993

Pensioners 1,090

Annual Contributions £2.4 million

Annual Investment Income £2.2 million

Capital Value £24.2 million

GILTSPUR LTD

56 Thames Street, Windsor, Berks SL4 1QW
Telephone: 07535-3431

Secretary A.L.Mercer,ACIS

Investment Advisers Ansbacher Investment Management Ltd

Employees 3,224

GLACIER FOODS LTD

Glacier House, Brook Green, London W6 7BT
Telephone: 01-603 2040

Secretary D.S.Mitchell

Employees 2,591

GLAXO GROUP PENSION SCHEME

Clarges House, 6-12 Clarges Street,
London W1Y 8DH
Telephone: 01-493 4060

Pension Fund Manager & Secretary N.A.Lilley

Investment Manager K.M.N.Fergusson

Group Pensions Manager S.Galpert

Trustees Glaxo Trustees Ltd (to The Glaxo Group Pension Scheme and The Glaxo Executive Pension Scheme)

Investment Advisers Robert Fleming Investment Management Ltd., Baring Bros. & Co.Ltd.

Actuaries Bacon & Woodrow

Property Advisers Debenham Tewson & Chinnocks

Auditors Clark Pixley

Company Employees 15,602

Members 12,272

Pensioners 4,886

	£000
Annual Contributions (year to 31.3.78)	6,484
Annual Investment Income	6,470
Annual Outflow	3,543
Capital Value	
Book Value	55,255
Market Value	63,222
Summary of Investments	
Equities (book value)	13,088
Fixed Interest	37,475
Property	7,546
Cash & Deposits	1,108
Others	200
Less Loans	(4,162)

GLAZIN & BERRY LTD.

Victoria Works, Pilmuir Street, Dunfermline
Telephone: 0380-31551

Director R.M.Harris

Employees 700

GLC SUPERANNUATION FUND

County Hall, London SE1 7PB
Telephone: 01-633 3288

Pension Fund Manager,Actuary and other matters E.A.Drake, FIA, FPMI

Pension Fund Manager, Investments C.A.McArdell

Property Advisers Hillier Parker May & Rowden

Actuaries Bacon & Woodrow

Auditors District Auditor

Members 39,000

Pensioners 21,000

	£million
Annual Contributions	43
Annual Investment Income	32
Gross Annual Outflow	22
Capital Value	368
Summary of Investments	
Equities	155
Fixed Interest	94
Property	80
Cash & Deposits	39

M.J.GLEESON (CONTRACTORS) LTD

Haredon House, London Road, North Cheam, Sutton,Surrey SM3 9BS
Telephone: 01-337 6688

Secretary A.E.Lewsey

Employees 2,634

ROBERT GLEW & CO LTD RETIREMENT BENEFITS PLAN

Robin Mills, Leeds Road, Bradford,
W.Yorks.BD10 9TE
Telephone: 0274-612561

Chairman R.W.Glew

Pension Management Lowndes Associated Pensions Ltd.

Trustees R.W.Glew, R.E.Chadwick, N.G.Weatherill, Lowndes Associated Pensions Ltd.

Investment Advisers Hill Samuel Investment Management Ltd.

Actuarial Advice Obtained through Cubie Wood & Co.Ltd.

Auditors Peat Marwick Mitchell & Co.

Company Employees 793

Members 225

Pensioners 33

	£000
Annual Contributions	120
Annual Investment Income	65
Annual Outflow	18
Capital Value	885
Summary of Investments	
Equities	632
Fixed Interest	195
Property	54
Cash & Deposits	4

W & J GLOSSOP LTD

Amisfield House, Hipperholme, Halifax,
W.Yorks.HX3 8NF
Telephone: 0422-202266

Chairman G.G.Briggs,FCIS

Employees 737

GLOUCESTERSHIRE COUNTY COUNCIL

Quayside Wing, Shire Hall, Gloucester GL1 2TJ
Telephone: 0452-21444

Treasurer T.N.Hobson, IPFA

Superannuation Officer A.C.Searle, APMI

GLOVER & MAIN LTD

Chamber of Commerce House, 75 Harborne Road, Edgbaston, Birmingham B15 3DB
Telephone: 021-454 5289

Secretary J.A.Sibley

Employees 7,448

GLYNWED LTD
Headland House, New Coventry Road, Sheldon, Birmingham B26 3AZ
Telephone: 021-742 2366

Pensions Administrator A.D.Lloyd

Group Employee Benefits Manager K.E.O'Neill, FCIS, FCMA

Managed by Legal & General (Pensions Management) Ltd.

Employees 13,615

A.GOLDBERG & SONS LTD
21 Candleriggs, Glasgow G1 1LD
Telephone: 041-552 4959

Secretary Miss Y.A.Stevenson

Employees 1,615

GOLDEN LTD
Berkeley Square House, Berkeley Square, London W1A 1BX
Telephone: 01-629 8240

Secretary J.Gilmartin

Employees 954

GOMME STAFF PENSION FUND
Spring Gardens, High Wycombe, Bucks HP13 7AD
Telephone: 0494-26250

Pension Fund Manager D.F.Gomme

Secretary S.White

Trustees G.F.Gomme, F.C.B.Covell, G.E.Rolfe, R.M.Clay, R.M.Hewitt, C.R.Green

Investment Advisers & Stockbrokers de Zoete & Bevan

Actuaries Bacon & Woodrow

Property Advisers Guthrie, Hills & Marchant

Auditors Peat Marwick Mitchell & Co

Employees 2,050

Members (at 31.7.80) 287

Pensioners 59

	£000
Annual Contributions	253
Annual Investment Income	296
Annual Outflow	126
Capital Value (at 16.6.80)	3,284
Summary of Investments	
Equities	376
Fixed Interest	1,565
Property	1,193
Cash & Deposits	131
Others	19

GOODHEW MATTHEWS LTD
Highview House, Tattenham Crescent, Epsom Downs, Epsom, Surrey KT18 5BL
Telephone: 25-53377

Director G.E.Goodhew

Employees 800

THE GOODYEAR TYRE & RUBBER COMPANY (GREAT BRITAIN)LTD STAFF PENSION AND LIFE ASSURANCE PLAN
Bushbury, Wolverhampton, West Midlands WV10 6DH
Telephone: 0902-22321

Pension Fund Manager R.K.Morris, FSCA, MBIM

Other Pension Management A.Lloyd, Mrs A.Woolvin

Trustees W.A.Parker, O.G.Shaffer, K.R.Wilson

Partly Managed by Legal & General Assurance (Pensions Management) Ltd

Investment Advisers Baring Brothers & Co Ltd

Pension Fund Consultants & Actuarial Advice obtained through Willis Faber Advisory Services Ltd.

Auditors Price Waterhouse & Co

Company Employees 9,337

Members 2,620

Pensioners 184

	£000
Annual Contributions	1,500
Annual Outflow	500
Capital Value	9,030
Summary of Investments	
Equities	4,050
Fixed Interest	2,310
Property	2,510
Cash & Deposits	162

There is also a Life Assurance and Voluntary Contribution Plan for Factory Operatives

Members 6,617

Pensioners 795

Capital Value £2,200,000

GORDON & GOTCH RETIREMENT BENEFITS PLAN (1972) (A) AND SUPERANNUATION FUND (B)
30 St Bride Street, London EC4A 4DJ
Telephone: 01-353 5211

Group Secretary G.H.H.Salter

Pensions Secretary A.L.Lasham

Trustees (b) Gordon & Gotch Superannuation Fund Ltd.

(a) Insured with Provident Mutual Life Assurance Association

Investment Advisers & Stockbrokers Fielding Newson-Smith & Co.

Actuary R.Sharp

Pension Fund Consultants Stewart Wrightson Assurance Consultants Ltd.

Auditors Everett Pinto & Co.

Company Employees 478

Members 343

Pensioners 27

Annual Contributions £233,000

Capital Value £883,000

GOSFORTH INDUSTRIAL HOLDINGS LIMITED
Sunley House, Regent Centre,
Regent Farm Road, Gosforth,
Newcastle upon Tyne NE3 3QA
Telephone: 0632-842311

Director F.Brown

Company Secretary P.R.Little

Trustees T.McIver, J.M.Jardine, R.H.Dickinson, F.Brown

Insured with Scottish Provident Institution

Pension Fund Consultants Willis Faber Advisory Services Ltd.

Auditors Price Waterhouse & Co.

Employees 1,996

GOUGH BROTHERS LTD. PENSION & LIFE ASSURANCE SCHEME
Durham House, 12 Upper Green Wharf, Mitcham, Surrey CR4 3YE
Telephone: 01-640 5131

Secretary D.V.Element,FCA

Insured with Guardian Royal Exchange Assurance

Employees 547

Members (August 1980) 80

Pensioners 15

GOUGH COOPER & CO LTD
Wilmington House, Wilminton, Dartford, Kent DA2 7EF
Telephone: 23400

Secretary G.J.Trussler

Insured with Guardian Royal Exchange Assurance Group Ltd

Employees 683

GOULD ADVANCE LTD
Raynham Road, Bishops Stortford CM23 5PF
Telephone: 0279-55155

Director G.C.Pope

Executive P.Gajewski

Employees 726

GOWRINGS LTD.
160 Basingstoke Road, Reading, Berks.
Telephone: 0734-85333

Secretary M.J.Oldland

Employees 596

G P G INTERNATIONAL LTD
Cranford, Blackdown, Leamington Spa CV32 6RQ
Telephone: 0926-27933

Director S.E.Darmon

Employees 1,850

GRA PROPERTY TRUST LTD.
White City Stadium, Wood Lane, London W12 7RU
Telephone: 01-743 0152

Secretary T.S.Kerry,CA

Employees 917

G.R.(HOLDINGS) LTD
68 Upper Thames Street, London EC2V 3RR
Telephone: 01-248 2990

Secretary R.A.G.Nagle,FCIS

Employees 832

W.R.GRACE LTD. PENSION PLAN
Northdale House, North Circular Road, London NW10 7UH
Telephone: 01-965 0611

Pension Fund Manager E.R.C. Smyth

Trustees P.R.Johnston, D.J.Bradley, A.Mott, R.G. Jeffrey

Managed by Bankers Trustee & Executor Co.Ltd.

Actuaries Lane, Clark & Peacock

Auditors Price Waterhouse & Co

Company Employees/Members 1,400

Pensioners 138

	£000
Annual Contributions	1,356
Annual Investment Income	634
Annual Outflow	367
Capital Value	8,588
Summary of Investments	
Equities	5,546
Fixed Interest	2,364

JOHN GRAHAM (DROMORE) LTD
Lagan Mills, Dromore, N. Ireland
Telephone: 0846-692291

Director Sir John Graham

Executive Mrs J.P.Graham

Employees 700

GRAHAM-REEVES LTD
Manor House, Totnes, Hants TQ9 5DQ
Telephone: 0803-863900

Director W.T.Pearson

Employees 1,750

GRAMPIAN HOLDINGS LTD STAFF RETIREMENT BENEFITS PLAN (1974)
Stag House, Castlebank Street, Glasgow G11 6DY
Telephone: 041-357 2000

Company Secretary W.G.B.Roy, CA

Secretary Scottish Pension Trustees Ltd

Trustees D.C.Greig, W.Y.Hughes, A.A.Hughes, W.G.B.Roy, Scottish Pension Trustees Ltd

Managed by Scottish Widows' Managed Fund

Investment Advisers Scottish Widows' Fund and Life Assurance Society

Property Advisers Jones Lang Wootton

Actuaries Hymans, Robertson & Co.

Pension Fund Consultants Scottish Pension Trustees Ltd

Auditors Arthur Young, McClelland Moores & Co

Company Employees 3,102

GRAMPIAN HOLDINGS LTD Continued

Members 691
Pensioners 14
Annual Contributions £594,000
Annual Investment Income £240,000
Annual Outflow £449,000
Capital Value £3,893,000

GRAMPIAN REGIONAL COUNCIL SUPERANNUATION FUND

Woodhill House, Ashgrove Road West, Aberdeen AB9 2LU
Telephone: 0224-682222

Pension Fund Manager T.Carter (Director of Finance)

Secretary Regional Director of Law and Administration

Other Pension Management Finance Committee operating through a small sub-committee

Trustees Regional Council

Investment Advisers and Stockbrokers Pember & Boyle, Scrimgeour, Kemp-Gee & Co.

Actuaries Robertson, Hymans & Co

Auditors Deloitte Sells & Co.

Employees 21,000 (including part-time)

Members 10,359
Pensioners 3,696

	£000
Annual Contributions (to 31.3.80)	8,697
Annual Investment Income	4,468
Annual Outflow	5,426
Capital Value (Market)	48,052
Summary of Investments	
Equities	24,876
Fixed Interest	24,160
Property	309
Cash & Deposits	3,214
Others	3,251

GRANADA GROUP LTD

36 Golden Square, London W1R 4AH
Telephone: 01-734 8080

Company Secretary D.James, FCIS

Pensions Officer G.D.Asplin

Insured with Clerical, Medical & General Life Assurance, Legal & General Assurance Society, Scottish Mutual Assurance Society

Pension Fund Consultants Minet Consultancy Services Ltd.

Company Employees 11,427

No Other Information Available

GRAND METROPOLITAN GROUP PENSION SCHEME AND SENIOR EXECUTIVES PENSION SCHEME

2 Caxton Street, London SW1H 0QE
Telephone: 01-222 9050

Group Pensions Manager A.G.Shepherd, LLB, FCIS, FPMI

Secretary M.A.Coombe, FCIS, FCII, FPMI

Trustees Grand Metropolitan Pension Trust Ltd

Chairman D.J.Dickinson, FCA

Investment Advisers Ansbacher Investment Management Ltd., Barclays Bank Trust Co.Ltd., Warburg Investment Management Ltd., Hill Samuel Investment Management Ltd.

Actuaries Bacon & Woodrow

Pension Fund Consultants Noble Lowndes & Partners Ltd

Auditors Thomson McLintock & Co

Solicitors Herbert Smith & Co.

Company Employees 100,000

	Group Scheme	Executive Scheme
Members (at 30.9.80)	34,100	415
Pensioners	8,262	75
Deferred Pensions	16,148	111
	£ million	£ million
Annual Contributions	19.6	1.8
Annual Investment Income	13.0	1.7
Annual Outflow	7.8	0.5
Capital Value		
Book Value	133.3	15.9
Market Value	163.7	19.0
Summary of Investments		
Equities	76.1	11.4
Fixed Interest	29.5	4.2
Property	43.4	1.9
Cash & Deposits	10.7	0.8
Managed Funds	4.3	0.3
Others	(0.5)	0.5

GRANT BROS LTD

14-32 High Street, Croydon, Surrey CR9 9AR
Telephone: 01-688 4400

Secretary E.R.Pooley

Employees 662

JAMES GRANT & CO (EAST) LTD

34-56 North Bridge, Edinburgh EH1 1YU
Telephone: 031-225 2822

Pension Fund Manager R.D.Garland

Secretary J.G.Henderson

Trustees J.Kearney, R.D.Garland, T.Gambles, J.G.Henderson

Insured with Prudential Assurance Co.Ltd.

Pension Fund Consultants Reed Stenhouse Benefit Consultants Ltd.

Company Employees 800
Members 200
Pensioners 50
Annual Contributions £240,000

WILLIAM GRANT & SONS LTD. WORKS, STAFF & SENIOR EXECUTIVES PENSION FUNDS

208 West George Street, Glasgow G2 2PE
Telephone: 041-248 3101

Secretary J.Allan Denholm,CA

Trustees A.G.Gordon, J.A.Denholm, G.W.Jenkins

Insured with Clerical, Medical & General Life Assurance Society

Pension Fund Consultants Holmwoods & Crawfurd (Life & Pension Brokers) Ltd.

Auditors Arthur Young McClelland Moores & Co

Employees 876

Members (at 4.7.80) 810

Pensioners 101

Annual Contributions £560,000

A GRANTHAM LTD

PO Box 120, 179 Preston Road, Brighton, E. Sussex BN1 4HG
Telephone: 0273-550155

Secretary M.R.Hutchinson

Employees 549

GRATISPOOL INTERNATIONAL HOLDINGS LTD UK RETIREMENT BENEFITS SCHEME

Unitair Centre, Great South West Road, Feltham, Middx.TW14 8NJ
Telephone: 01-751 3351

Secretary R.E.Sims,ACIS

Pension Fund Consultants Minet Consultancy Services Ltd.

Auditors Ernst & Whinney

Company Employees 1,200

Members 150

Annual Contributions £7,000

Market Value £300,000

GRATTAN WAREHOUSES LTD STAFF PENSION SCHEME

Anchor House, Ingleby Road, Bradford, W.Yorks.BD99 2XG
Telephone: 0274-575511

Company Secretary K.M.Gray, FCA

Pension Scheme Secretary R.Hornsby,APMI

Insured with Scottish Mutual Assurance Society

Pension Fund Consultants Reed Stenhouse Benefit Consultants Ltd.

Auditors Arthur Young McClelland Moores & Co.

Company Employees 5,591

Members 3,925

Pensioners 620

CHARLES GRAY (HOLDINGS) LTD

Francis Street, Dundee DD3 8HJ
Telephone: 0382-88312

Secretary S.C.Beaton

Insured with Life Association of Scotland Ltd.

Employees 1,409

GRAYLAW HOLDINGS LTD

394-424 High Road, Leyton, London E10 6QE
Telephone: 01-556 9611

Secretary R.Rowan

Employees 810

GREAT UNIVERSAL STORES LTD

PO Box 99, 3 Dale Street, Manchester M60 1XA

Head Office Universal House, Tottenham Court Road, London W1A 1BZ
Telephone: 01-636 4080

Pensions Officer G.J.Walker

Company Secretaries T.G.Brassington, N.Stocks

Trustees G.U.S. Trustees Ltd.

Investment Advisers County Bank Ltd.

Employees 34,649

GREATER LONDON COUNCIL

See GLC Superannuation Fund

GREATER MANCHESTER COUNCIL SUPERANNUATION FUND

County Treasury, County Hall, Piccadilly Gardens, Manchester M60 3HR
Telephone: 061-247 3421

County Treasurer J.M.Marriott, IPFA, MBCS

Superannuation Officer A.Edwards

Management Investment Advisory Panel

Trustees Greater Manchester County Council

Managed by 3 Managers (1) Stockbroker, (2) Insurance House, (3) County Valuer

Investment Advisers Advisory Panel in consultation with managers

Actuaries Duncan C. Fraser & Co

Property Advisers County Valuer and Estates Surveyor

Auditors District Auditor

Members 71,442

Pensioners 23,473

	£000
Annual Contributions	41,898
Annual Investment Income	24,442
Annual Outflow	20,505
Capital Value (Market Value)	299,420
Summary of Investments	
Equities	175,068
Fixed Interest	65,429
Property	48,607
Cash & Deposits	10,316

GREATER NOTTINGHAM CO-OPERATIVE SOCIETY LTD EMPLOYEES' SUPERANNUATION FUND

243 Derby Road, Lenton, Nottingham NG7 1QP
Telephone: 0602-44021

Financial Controller W.O.Watts

Secretary F.E.Doherty

Investment Advisers Singer & Friedlander Ltd.

GREATER NOTTINGHAM CO-OPERATIVE SOCIETY LTD
Continued

Actuary P.D.Johnson,FIA (Co-operative Insurance Society Ltd.)
Pension Fund Consultants Co-operative Union Ltd.
Auditors Appleby English & Partners
Company Employees 5,000
Members 1,360
Pensioners 885

	£000
Annual Contributions	426
Annual Investment Income	828
Annual Outflow	487
Capital Value	7,614
Summary of Investments	
Equities	1,089
Fixed Interest	6,317
Cash & Deposits	208

H.J.GREEN & CO LTD
311 Portland Road, Hove, East Sussex BN3 5ST
Telephone: 0273-417275

Chairman J.Jensen
Employees 627

R & H GREEN AND SILLEY WEIR LTD
Interknit House, Royal Albert Dock,
London E16 2QX
Telephone: 01-476 2121

Secretary R.H.Pelham
Employees 1,580

GREENALL WHITLEY & CO LTD
Wilderspool Brewery, Warrington,
Cheshire WA4 6RH
Telephone: 0925-51234

Joint Secretaries A.Anderson, A.W.A.Spiegelberg
Employees 11,841

GREENBANK INDUSTRIAL HOLDINGS LTD.
Orient Works, Gate Street, Blackburn,
Lancs.BB1 3AJ
Telephone: 0254-50401

Secretary L.Whittle
Employees 557

GREENBROOK SECURITIES LTD.
119-127 Marylebone Road, London NW1 5QR
Telephone: 01-262 6622

Secretary D.R.Green
Employees 870

GREENE, KING & SONS LTD. STAFF PENSION SCHEME & EMPLOYEES PENSION FUND
Westgate Brewery, Bury St Edmunds, Suffolk
Telephone: 0284-63222

Company Secretary H.G.Lines, FCIS
Stockbrokers James Capel & Co.
Actuaries R.Watson & Sons
Auditors Josiah Beddow & Son
Solicitors Linklaters & Paines
Company Employees 1,702

	Staff Scheme	Employees Fund
Members	400	700
Pensioners	73	280
Annual Contributions	£200,000	£200,000
Capital Value	£1,250,000	£1,000,000

GREENFIELDS LEISURE LTD.
Armadale Road, Feltham, Middx.TW14 0LT
Telephone: 01-890 8181

Secretary P.W.Monaghan
Employees 748

GREEN'S ECONOMISER GROUP
Calder Vale Road, Wakefield, W.Yorks.WF1 5PF
Telephone: 0924-78211

Secretary D.H.Butters
Employees 1,115

GREENWOODS (MENSWEAR) LTD
White Cross, Guiseley, Leeds, W.Yorks.LS20 8ND
Telephone: 0943-72282

Secretary R.C.Blomfield
Employees 1,267

GREGGS BAKERIES LTD
1 Lambton Road, Newcastle upon Tyne,
Tyne & Wear NE2 4RX

Director I.D.Gregg
Employees 1,320

GRESHAM LIFE ASSURANCE SOCIETY LTD. STAFF PENSION AND ASSURANCE FUND
P.O.Box 1, 2-6 Prince of Wales Road,
Bournemouth, Dorset BH4 9HD
Telephone: 0202-767655

Secretary and Administrator P.A. Brown FCIS FCII
Actuary D.J.Hoskin,FIA
Fund Accountant N.E.J. Harris,FCII
Trustees L.Ginsburg,MA,FFA (Chairman),
J.S.Leighton,BA,FIA, W.R.Hill, J.C.Costello,ACII,
Mrs.F.M.Owen, P.R.Sussex,TD, S.C.Evans,BSc,FIA
Investment Advisers N.M.Rothschild Asset Management Ltd.
Auditors Peat, Marwick, Mitchell & Co.
Company Employees 312
Members 286
Pensioners 156

	£000
Annual Contributions (at 31.12.79)	415
Annual Investment Income	326
Annual Outflow	220
Capital Value	4,345
Summary of Investments	

GRESHAM LIFE ASSURANCE SOCIETY LTD. Continued

Equities	3,168
Fixed Interest	1,064
Cash & Deposits	31

GRESHAM LION LTD RETIREMENT BENEFITS PLAN 1973
Gresham House, Twickenhan Road, Feltham, Middx.TW13 6HA
Telephone: 01-894 5511

Pension Fund Manager & Secretary Mrs.P.L.Trinick

Company Secretary D.Kelly

Other Pension Management Lowndes Associated Pensions Ltd.

Managed by Friends' Provident Managed Pension Funds Ltd.

Actuarial Advice obtained through Cubie, Wood & Co.Ltd.

Pension Fund Consultants Noble Lowndes & Partners Ltd.

Auditors Price Waterhouse & Co.

Company Employees 881

Members 367

Pensioners 17

Annual Contributions £300,000

Capital Value £1,000,000

GRIEVESON, GRANT & CO STAFF PENSION FUND
PO Box 191, 59 Gresham St, London EC2P 2DS
Telephone: 01-606 4433

Pension Fund Manager K.Barclay-Brown

Secretary N.G.N. Ashford FCA

Trustees Grievson, Grant Pension Trustees Ltd.

Stockbrokers Grieveson,Grant & Co.

Actuaries Duncan C.Fraser & Co.

Auditors Spicer & Pegler

Company Employees 528

Members 338

Pensioners 46

	£000
Annual Contributions	300
Annual Investment Income	149
Annual Outflow	62
Capital Value	2,376
Summary of Investments	
Equities	1,620
Fixed Interest	756

R.GRIGGS & CO.LTD.
Cobbs Lane, Wollaston, Wellingborough, Northants.NN9 7SW
Telephone: 0933-665391

Director W.H.Griggs

Executive J.Stubbs

Employees 520

GRIMSHAW HOLDINGS LTD.
Western House, Uxbridge Road, Hillingdon, Middx. UB10 0LY
Telephone: 01-573 1002

Secretary H.F.Wylie

Employees 605

GRINDLAYS BANK U.K. GROUP PENSION SCHEMES
36 Fenchurch St., London EC3P 3AS
Telephone: 01-626 6599

Pension Fund Manager L.A.J.Peagam, FPMI, FCII

Secretary R.Collinge, FCII

Investment Managers Lloyds Bank Ltd

Actuaries R.Watson & Sons

Property Advisers Debenham Tewson & Chinnocks

Pension Fund Consultants Metropolitan Pensions Association Ltd.

Auditors Coopers & Lybrand

Company Employees UK - 1500

Members 1,216

Pensioners 838

	£000
Annual Contributions	2,050
Annual Investment Income	1,590
Annual Outflow	1,410
Capital Value	26,216
Summary of Investments	
Equities	13,474
Fixed Interest	7,673
Managed Fund	1,834
Cash & Deposits	3,325

GRINDLEY OF STOKE (CERAMICS) LTD
Lambert Street, Tunstall, Stoke on Trent Staffs.
Telephone: 0782-312105

Secretary G.Hammersley,ACMA

Employees 1,503

GRIPPERODS HOLDINGS LTD.
36-40 Jermyn Street London SW1Y 6DN

Secretary J.F.Young

Employees 502

T.GROCOCK & CO.(ROTHWELL) LTD.
Gordon Shoe Works, Gordon Street, Rothwell, Northants
Telephone: 0536-710444

Secretary A.E.Burditt

Employees 532

GROSVENOR ESTATES PENSION SCHEME
53 Davies Street, London W1Y 1FH
Telephone: 01-408 0988

Secretary & Pension Fund Manager D.Paterson

Trustees I.M.P.Staines, S.R.Coggan, R.M.C.Jones, P.H.D.Crichton, M.D.T.Loup

Investment Advisers Geoffrey Morley & Partners

GROSVENOR ESTATES Continued

Ltd. (UK Portfolio), J.Henry Schroder Wagg & Co.Ltd. (US Portfolio)
Actuaries Clay & Partners
Auditors Champness, Cowper & Co.

GROUP 4 TOTAL SECURITY LTD
Farncombe House, Broadway, Worcs WR12 7LJ
Telephone: 038681-2621
Secretary D.E.W.Taylor
Employees 3,762

GROUP LOTUS CAR COMPANIES LTD
Hethal Airport, Norwich, Norfolk NR14 8EZ
Telephone: 0953-603411
Secretary F.R.Bushell
Employees 682

GROVE CRANES LTD
Cowley, Oxford OX4 3LP
Telephone: 0865-776271
Director J.M.Benchoff
Employees 500

GROVEBELL LTD.
Rawlplug House, 147 London Road, Kingston-on-Thames, Surrey KT2 6NR
Telephone: 01-549 6484
Secretary R.Smith
Employees 600

GRUNDIG INTERNATIONAL LTD
40-42 Newlands Park, London SE26
Telephone: 06-659 2468
Secretary W.Noakes
Employees 1,160

GRUNDY (TEDDINGTON) LTD
Somerset Road, Teddington, Middx
Telephone: 01-977 1171
Secretary C.S.Wooldridge
Employees 1,065

THE GUARDIAN AND MANCHESTER EVENING NEWS LTD CONTRIBUTORY PENSION SCHEME
164 Deansgate, Manchester M60 2RR
Telephone: 061-832 7200
Group Personnel Manager M.G.Bolton, APMI
Investment Advisers N.M.Rothschild Asset Management Ltd.
Actuaries Duncan C.Fraser & Co.
Auditors Coopers & Lybrand
Solicitors Lovell White & King
Company Employees 3,382
Members (at 31.3.80) 2,182
Pensioners 613
Annual Contributions £1,627,000
Annual Investment Income £1,263,000
Capital Value 14,751,000

GUARDIAN ROYAL EXCHANGE PENSION FUND
68 King William Street, London EC4N 7BU
Telephone: 01-283 7101
Pension Fund Manager Guardian Royal Exchange Assurance Ltd.
Pensions Actuary G.T.C.Barnes,MA,FIA
Company Employees 8,400
Members 7,834
Pensioners 2,917
Deferred Pensioners 616
Annual Contributions £10 million
Annual Investment Income £8 million
Capital Value £106 million

GUEST & CHRIMES LTD
PO Box 9, Don Street, Rotherham, S.Yorks.S60 1DQ
Telephone: 0709-2035
Secretary D.Chapman
Employees 625

GUEST, KEEN & NETTLEFOLDS LTD
PO Box 55, Smethwick, Warley, West Midlands B66 2RZ
Telephone: 021-558 3131
Joint Group Pension Fund Managers D.J.Stewart, APMI, ACII, R.H.Beardshaw, FIA, APMI
Corporate Staff Director Pensions and Salary Administration G.Simpson
Insured with Prudential Assurance Co.
Company Employees 72,542
Members 60,000
Pensioners 11,000

ARTHUR GUINNESS SON & CO.LTD. PENSION FUND
Park Royal Brewery, London NW10 7RR
Telephone: 01-965 7700
Pension Fund Manager J.A.C.Moriarty, FPMI
Secretary A.J.Scrine, FCIS, APMI
Assistant Pensions Manager R.A.Evans,ACII
Trustees 12
Investment Advisers Baring Brothers & Co.Ltd
Stockbrokers James Capel & Co
Actuaries R.Watson & Sons
Property Advisers Weatherall Green & Smith
Pension Fund Consultants C.E.Heath, Urquhart (Life & Pensions) Ltd., C.T.Bowring & Layborn Ltd., Noble Lowndes & Partners Ltd.
Auditors Ernst & Whinney
Company Employees 12,650
Members 3,149
Pensioners 1,167
Deferred Pensions 446

The Major UK Pension Funds **GUI/HAL**

ARTHUR GUINNESS SON & CO.LTD. *Continued*

	£000
Annual Contributions	3,108
Annual Investment Income	2,116
Annual Outflow	2,530
Capital Value (Market 31.12.78)	28,919
Summary of Investments	
Equities	14,000
Fixed Interest	6,819
Property	7,092
Cash & Deposits	329
Others	679

GUINESS PEAT GROUP PENSION PLAN

32 St Mary at Hill, London EC3P 3AJ
Telephone: 01-623 9333

Secretary F.W.Bowden

Management and Trustees Fenchurch Trustees Ltd

Investment Advisers Guinness Mahon & Co Ltd

Actuarial Advice obtained through Fenchurch Trustees Ltd.

Auditors Pannell Kerr Forster

Company Employees 2,400

Members 700

Pensioners 150

	£000
Annual Contributions	1,000
Annual Investment Income	700
Annual Outflow	500
Capital Value	7,879
Summary of Investments	
Equities	4,723
Fixed Interest	1,511
Property	657
Cash & Deposits	988

See also Fenchurch Group

GULF U.K. PENSION SCHEME

2 Portman Street, London W.1H 0AN
Telephone: 01-493 8040

Secretary Mrs.M.P.Pearce

Management A Committee of 5, appointed by the Company

Trustees Bankers Trustee & Executor Co

Investment Advisers Bankers Trustee & Executor Co.

Actuaries Bacon & Woodrow

Auditors Coopers & Lybrand

Company Employees 1,489

Members 1,454

Pensioners 260

	£000
Annual Contributions	2,016
Annual Investment Income	1,557
Annual Outflow	347
Capital Value	15,112
Summary of Investments	
Equities	7,879
Fixed Interest	5,352
Property	637
Cash & Deposits	1,244

A.GUNN (HOLDINGS) LTD.

Atlantic Street, Broadheath,
Altrincham, Cheshire WA14 5DN
Telephone: 061-941 2631

Secretary A.W.Deakin

Employees 792

GUTHRIE GROUP PENSION & LIFE ASSURANCE PLAN FOR STAFF EMPLOYEES

The Guthrie Corporation Ltd,
120 Fenchurch Street, London EC3M 5AA
Telephone: 01-626 5052

Secretary C.F.Openshaw

Trustees A.W.Easter, A.R.Langan, C.F.Openshaw, S.White

Insured with Provident Mutual Life Assurance Association

Pension Fund Consultants Holmwoods & Crawfurd (Life & Pension Brokers) Ltd.

Auditors Deloitte Haskins & Sells

Company Employees 3,553

Members 860

Pensioners 200

Annual Contributions £768,000

Annual Investment Income £225,000

Annual Outflow £180,000

Capital Value £2,450,000

GWENT COUNTY COUNCIL SUPERANNUATION FUND

County Hall, Cwmbran, Gwent NP4 2XH
Telephone: 06333-67711

Treasurer T.J.Evans, IPFA

Actuaries R.Watson & Sons

Employees (excluding Police, Firemen & Teachers) 11,500

Members 10,022

Pensioners 3,850

Capital Value £43,283,000

GWYNEDD COUNTY COUNCIL

Gwynedd County Council, County Offices
Caernarvon LL55 1SH
Telephone: 0286-4121

Treasurer W.E.Evans, BA, FCA, IPFA

HABITAT DESIGN HOLDINGS LTD

Hithercroft Road, Wallingford, Oxon OX10 9EU
Telephone: 0491-35000

Pension Fund Manager & Asst.Company Secretary Shaun Doran

Secretary T.A.S.Butler

HABITAT DESIGN HOLDINGS LTD Continued

Trustees T.O.Conran, M.E.Tyson, M.I.Peacock

Insured with Provident Mutual Life Assurance Association

Pension Fund Consultants Sedgwick Employee Benefits Consultants Ltd.

Company Employees 1,300

Members 400

HADEN CARRIER STAFF PENSION SCHEME AND OPERATIVES PENSION SCHEME

PO Box 14, 7-12 Tavistock Square,
London WC1H 9LZ
Telephone: 01-387 1288

Secretary D.J.Nash, APMI

Management 3 management trustees for each scheme with 3 member trustees for Staff Scheme, 2 member trustees for Operatives Scheme

Trustees Hadens Pension Trust Ltd. for Operatives Scheme, Second Haden Pension Trust Ltd. for Staff Scheme

Investment Advisers Baring Brothers & Co Ltd

Actuaries R.Watson & Sons

Solicitors Rowe & Maw

Auditors Arthur Andersen & Co.

Company Employees 5,059

	Staff	Operatives
Members	1,992	555
Pensioners	372	174
	£000	£000
Annual Contributions	2,003	148
Investment Income	1,050	50
Annual Outflow	700	90
Capital Value	18,013	1,618
Summary of Investments		
Equities	7,239	-
Fixed Interest	4,115	-
Property	562	-
Others	373	-

HALIFAX BUILDING SOCIETY STAFF RETIREMENT FUND 1974

PO Box 60, Trinity Road, Halifax,
W.Yorks.HX1 2RG
Telephone: 0442-65777

Investment Advisers Sun Alliance & London Insurance Group

Auditors Armitage & Norton, Peat, Marwick, Mitchell & Co.

Company Employees 8,500

Members 5,500

Pensioners 400

	£000
Annual Contributions	4,000
Annual Investment Income	4,800
Annual Outflow	1,000
Capital Value	52,000
Summary of Investments	
Equities	26,000
Fixed Interest	23,000
Cash & Deposits	3,000

HALL & WOODHOUSE LTD.

The Brewery, Blandford St.Mary, Dorset
Telephone: 02582-2141

Secretary F.K.Pike

Employees 887

DAVID A.HALL LTD. RETIREMENT BENEFITS PLAN (1972)

East Main Street, Broxburn,
West Lothian EH52 5AW
Telephone: 0506-853300

Secretary L.Murray

Pension Management Scottish Pension Trustees Ltd.

Managed by Pensions Management (SWF) Ltd.

Actuarial Advice Obtained through Cubie, Wood & Co.Ltd.

Auditors Price Waterhouse & Co.

Company Employees 660

Members 408

Pensioners 5

Annual Contributions £185,000

Capital Value £913,000

HALL ENGINEERING (HOLDINGS) LTD. 1971 PENSION SCHEME AND WORKS RETIREMENT BENEFIT SCHEME 1974

Harlescott Lane, Shrewsbury SY1 3AS
Telephone: 0743-59541

Secretary M.A.Youens

Trustees R.N.C.Hall, C.H.Griffin, D.R.Tudor

Managed by Ivory & Sime as part of Stenhouse Exempt Fund

Investment Advisers Ivory & Sime

Actuaries Duncan C. Fraser & Co

Pension Fund Consultants Hogg Robinson (Benefit Consultants) Ltd

Auditors Touche Ross & Co.

Company Employees 2,700

Members 1,670

Pensioners 410

Annual Contributions 1971 Scheme - £740,000, 1974 Scheme - £1,104,000

MATTHEW HALL & CO.LTD. STAFF PENSION SCHEME

101-108 Tottenham Court Road,
London W1A 1BT
Telephone: 01-636 3676

Secretary P.L.L.Smith, ACIS

Trustee D.G.Hewett

Part Insured with Legal & General Assurance Society Ltd.

MATTHEW HALL & CO.LTD. Continued

Investment Advisers J.Henry Schroder Wagg & Co.Ltd.

Pension Fund Consultants Metropolitan Pensions Association Ltd.

Auditors Deloitte, Haskins & Sells

Company Employees 7,208

Members 1,300

Pensioners 140

Annual Contributions £1,500,000

HALLAM GROUP OF NOTTINGHAM LTD
Langley Mill, Nottingham NG16 4AN
Telephone: 07737-66141

Secretary A.L.Oakey

Company Employees 635

HALLE MODELS LTD
Park Lane, Macclesfield, Cheshire SK11 6TP
Telephone: 0625-23685

Director B.W.Halle

Employees 800

WILLIAM HALLEY & SONS LTD. 1968 AND 1978 GROUP RETIREMENT BENEFITS SCHEMES
Wallace Craigie Works, Dundee DD4 6BB
Telephone: 0382-40304

Secretary I.R.Hunter,CA

Insured with Scottish Life Assurance Co.

Employees 584

Members 305

Pensioners 13

Annual Contributions £145,000

HALLIBURTON MANUFACTURING & SERVICES LTD
17 Hanover Square, London W1R 0ER
Telephone: 01-629 7611

Managing Director L.F.Mermis

Insured with Swiss Life Insurance & Pension Co

Employees 1,000

HALLITE HOLDINGS LTD
130 Oldfield Road, Hampton, Middx TW12 2HT
Telephone: 01-941 2244

Managing Director J.Gordon

Secretary P.J.Garner

Employees 701

HALMA GROUP PENSION PLAN
Halma House, Kingsbury Road, London NW9 8UU
Telephone: 01-205 0038

Secretary M.J.Arthur

Trustees Noble Lowndes & Partners Ltd.

Managed by Commercial Union Managed Fund Unit

Actuarial Advice Obtained through Cubie Wood & Co.Ltd.

Pension Fund Consultants Noble Lowndes & Partners Ltd.

Auditors Price Waterhouse & Co.

Company Employees 881

JAMES HALSTEAD (HOLDINGS) LTD (A)STAFF SUPERANNUATION SCHEME, (B)HOURLY PAID EMPLOYEES PENSION & LIFE ASSURANCE SCHEME, (C)BELSTAFF INTERNATIONAL LTD SCHEME
PO Box 3, Radcliffe New Road, Whitfield, Manchester M25 7NR
Telephone: 061-796 9050

Secretary P.S.P.Knight

Trustees A.B.Morrall, G.Halstead, J.Hilton

Managed by Scottish Amicable Pension Investments Ltd.

Actuary Stephen Wright, FFA

Pension Fund Consultants Antony Gibbs Pension Services Ltd.

Auditors J.Wild & Co.

Eligible Employees 840

Members (a) 210, (b) 230, (c) 52

Pensioners (a) 39, (b) 8

Annual Contributions (a)£170,000, (b)£8,500, (c) £12,000

Annual Outflow (a) £44,353, (b) £30,157, (c) £353

Capital Value (a) £901,860, (b) £153,698, (c) £21,956

HAMBROS LIFE ASSURANCE LTD. STAFF PENSION PLAN AND BRANCH MANAGERS PENSION PLAN
Hambro Life House, Station Road, Swindon, Wilts.SN1 1EL
Telephone: 0793-28291

Pension Plans Co-ordinator C.T.Briggs,BA

Actuaries Bacon & Woodrow

Auditors Peat, Marwick, Mitchell & Co.

Company Employees 1,400

	Staff	Managers
Members	1,224	119
Pensioners	8	7
Annual Contributions	£865,000	£460,000
Capital Value	£5,592,000	£2,422,000

HAMBROS LTD STAFF PENSION SCHEME
41 Bishopsgate, London EC2P 2AA
Telephone: 01-588 2851

Secretary A.M.Tibbles

Investment Director J.S.Cumming,BA,CA

Trustees Three Directors, Two Officials and One Staff Member

Investment Advisers Hambros Investment Management Services Ltd.

Actuaries Duncan C. Fraser & Co.

HAMBROS LTD *Continued*

Auditors Peat, Marwick, Mitchell & Co.
Solicitors Norton, Rose, Botterell & Roche
Company Employees 970
Members 830
Pensioners 260
Annual Contributions £614,000
Annual Investment Income £994,000
Capital Value £17,000,000

HAMILTON CARHARTT LTD
East Camperdown Street, Carolina Port,
Dundee DD1 3LS
Telephone: 0382-44251
Director F.Mee
Employees 800

E.R.HAMMERSLEY & CO LTD
PO Box 23, Hillcrest Avenue, Cradley, Halesowen,
West Midlands B63 2QH
Telephone: 0384-69178
Secretary B.G.Evans
Employees 700

HAMMOND & CHAMPNESS LTD
159 St John Street, London EC1V 4JQ
Telephone: 01-253 9081
Secretary C.M.Barnard
Insured with Standard Life Assurance Co
Employees 1,036

HAMPSHIRE COUNTY COUNCIL SUPERANNUATION FUND
The Castle, Winchester, Hampshire SO23 8UB
Telephone: 0962-4411
County Treasurer Geoffrey Price, IPFA, MBIM
Investment Advisers Baring Bros & Co Ltd
Trustees Hampshire County Council
Property Advisers Richard Ellis
Actuaries R.Watson & Sons
Council Employees (at 31.3.80) 50,000 (includes 25,000 teachers, police and firemen covered by national superannuation schemes)
Members 21,500
Pensioners 8,250

	£000
Annual Contributions	20,200
Annual Investment Income	9,800
Annual Outflow	13,500
Capital Value (at 30.9.80)	134,263
Summary of Investments	
Equities	82,837
Fixed Interest	30,823
Property	15,853
Cash & Deposits	4,750

HAMPSON INDUSTRIES LTD
Brandon Way, West Bromwich,
West Midlands B70 9PG
Telephone: 021-553 2071
Secretary M.Holdsworth
Insured with Standard Life Assurance Co
Employees 2,521

HANDSWORTH DAIRIES LTD
Island Road, Handsworth, Birmingham,
W Midlands B21 8LD
Telephone: 021-523 9211
Secretary J.H.Cox
Employees 578

HANGER INVESTMENTS LTD
Dilworth House, 190 Broad street,
Birmingham B15 1EA
Telephone: 021-643 7131
Secretary M.F.Cook
Employees 908

HANSON TRUST LTD.
180 Brompton Road, London SW3 1HP
Telephone: 01-589 7070
Secretary P.J.Turner
Employees 4,087

HARBOUR & GENERAL WORKS (STEVIN) LTD.
Stevin House, Springwell Road, Gateshead,
Tyne & Wear NE9 7SP
Telephone: 0632-462011
Managing Director C.W.R.R.Coard
Employees 550

HARDYS & HANSONS LTD
Kimberley Brewery, Nottingham NG16 2NS
Telephone: 0602-383611
Secretary J.D.Harrison
Employees 864

HARGREAVES GROUP LTD PENSION FUNDS
Bowcliffe Hall, Bramham, Wetherby,
West Yorkshire LS23 6LP
Telephone: 0937-843535
Secretary to the Trustees W.Plumb, APMI
Investment Advisers Kleinwort Benson Investment Management Ltd.
Actuaries Bacon & Woodrow
Auditors Thomson McLintock & Co.
Solicitors Slaughter & May
Company Employees 2,714
Members (at 31.3.80) 1,750
Pensioners 225
Annual Contributions £1,221,000
Annual Investment Income £581,000
Capital Value £8,930,000

M HARLAND & SON LTD 1973 PENSION SCHEME

Land of Green Ginger House, Springfield Way, Anlaby, Hull HU10 6RN
Telephone: 0482-561166

Director & Secretary D.G.Pattison, FCA, MBCS

Actuarial Advice Obtained through Cubie, Wood & Co.Ltd.

Pension Fund Consultants Noble Lowndes & Partners Ltd.

Auditors Thornton Baker

Company Employees 548

Members 445

Pensioners 34

Annual Contributions £246,000

Capital Value £627,000

HARLAND AND WOLF STAFF PENSION SCHEME

Queen's Island, Belfast BT3 9DU
Telephone: 0232-58456

Secretary T.J.Weir

Trustees Five

Insured with Eagle Star Insurance Co. Ltd.

Investment Advisers and Stockbrokers Mullens & Co.

Pension Fund Consultants C.T.Bowring & Layborn Ltd.

Auditors Price Waterhouse and Co.

Company Employees 7,260

Members 1,618

Pensioners 1.021

Annual Contributions £1,902 (Year to 30.7.80)

F.W.HARMER & CO LTD

Havers Road, Norwich, Norfolk NR3 2DS
Telephone: 0603-47222

Secretary G.S.Westwell

Employees 797

HARMO INDUSTRIES LTD

Wharfdale Road, Tyseley, Birmingham B11 2DF
Telephone: 021-706 5811

Secretary J.A.George

Pension Fund Consultants Godwins Ltd.

Employees 1,011

THE HARMSWORTH PENSION FUNDS

Carmelite House, Carmelite Street, London EC4Y 0JA
Telephone: 01-353 6000

Pension Fund Manager & Secretary C.J. Cornwall, FIA,FCIS,FPMI

Investment Manager R.L.Marten

Trustees 11

Actuaries R.Watson & Sons

Property Advisers Gerald Eve & Co

Auditors Deloitte, Haskins & Sells

Company Employees 12,828

Members 8,613

Pensioners 3,300

	£000
Annual Contributions	7,428
Annual Investment Income	7,041
Annual Outflow	3,703
Capital Value	77,831
Summary of Investments	
Equities	33,059
Fixed Interest	25,281
Property	15,362
Cash & Deposits	3,880

HARRIS & SHELDON GROUP LTD

North Court, Packington Park, Meriden, Warwickshire CV7 7BR
Telephone: 0676-22990

Secretary J.S.Roylance

Trustees Harris & Sheldon Group Pension Trustees Ltd

Investment Advisers Warburg Investment Management Ltd

Employees 3,801

L.G.HARRIS & CO.LTD. PENSION TRUST

Stoke Prior, Bromsgrove, Worcs.B60 4AE
Telephone: 0527-31441

Secretary B.Middleton

Managed by Pensions Management (SwF) Ltd.

Pension Fund Consultants Hogg Robinson (Benefit Consultants) Ltd.

Auditors Deloitte Haskins & Sells

Company Employees 485

Members 333

Pensioners 139

Annual Contributions £171,000

Annual Investment Income £14,000

Annual Outflow £134,000

Capital Value £1,765,000

M.P.HARRIS (HOLDINGS) LTD

28 Wilton Road, Bexhill on Sea, E Sussex
Telephone: 0424-216301

Secretary A.J.Bourner

Employees 679

PHILLIP HARRIS (HOLDINGS) LTD

Lynn Lane, Shenstone, Staffs WS14 0EE
Telephone: 0543-480077

Secretary S.R.Shirley,FCIS

Insured with Legal & General Assurance Society Ltd.

Employees 508

HARRIS QUEENSWAY GROUP LTD

Harris House, 76 High Street, Orpington, Kent BR6 0LX
Telephone: 0689-36977

HARRIS QUEENSWAY GROUP LTD *Continued*

Secretary H.W.H.Ellis,FCA
Insured with Provident Mutual Life Assurance Association
Employees 2,833

HARRISON GROUP PENSION SCHEME

Coates Lane, High Wycombe, Bucks.HP13 5EZ
Telephone: 0494-33321
Pensions Secretary E.J.Jones
Investment Advisers London & Associated Investment Trust Ltd
Actuaries Bacon & Woodrow
Auditors Tansley Witt & Co
Company Employees 1,768
Members 1,100
Pensioners 500
Annual Contributions £400,000
Capital Value £4,000,000

T.C.HARRISON LTD

53-67 London Road, Sheffield, S.Yorks.S2 4LD
Telephone: 0742-29091
Secretary A.G.Moody,FCA
Employees 1,400

HARRISONS & CROSFIELD LTD

1-4 Great Tower Street, London EC3R 5AB
Telephone: 01-626 4333
Secretary L.Gladwish, FCA
Part insured with Clerical, Medical & General Life Assurance
Group Employees 5,342

The main subsidiaries run separate pension funds.

HARRODS LTD. & ASSOCIATED COMPANIES STAFF FUND AND MANAGERS AND BUYERS FUND

87-135 Brompton Road, London SW1X 7XL
Telephone: 01 730 1234
Secretary L.F.Drewitt,CA
Assistant to Company Secretary D.J.R.Snelling
Trustees Harrodian Trustees Ltd.
Investment Advisers Finance For Industry Ltd.
Actuaries Bacon & Woodrow
Auditors Hays Allan
Solicitors McKenna & Co.
Employees 6,600

	Staff	Managers
Members	5,000	900
Pensioners	2,000	250
	£000	£000
Annual Contributions	1,622	859

Annual Investment Income	727	570
Capital Value	12,648	9,494

HARTWELLS PENSION PLAN (1971)

Seacourt Tower, West Way, Oxford OX2 0JP
Telephone: 0865-48003
Secretary P.C.Barrett, BSc, FCA
Trustees F.S.Huggins, H.Barrett,FCA, P.F.Huggins
Investment Advisers Barclays Bank Trust Company Ltd
Actuarial Advice obtained through Cubie Wood & Co Ltd
Pension Fund Consultants Noble Lowndes & Partners Ltd
Auditors Thornton Baker & Co
Company Employees 2,101
Employees 1,872
Members 1,009
Pensioners 117
Annual Contributions (to 31.8.79) £393,000
Annual Investment Income £314,000
Annual Outflow £253,000
Capital Value £3,919,000

J & J HASLETT LTD

Derriaghy, Dunmurry, Belfast
Telephone: 0232-618311
Secretary J.Millar
Employees 650

H.A.T. GROUP PENSION SCHEME (1976)

Barley Wood, Wrington, Avon BS18 7SA
Telephone: 0934-862604
Pension Fund Manager and Secretary K.R.Middleton
Trustees A.C.V.Telling, D.M.Telling, K.Melling, G.Ross Goobey, K.R.Middleton
Managed by Legal & General (Pensions Management) Ltd.
Auditors 1,000
Company Employees 1,000
Members 850
Pensioners 55
Annual Contributions £450,000
Capital Value £1,800,000

HAWKER SIDDELEY GROUP LTD

18 St James's Square, London SW1Y 4LJ
Telephone: 01-930 6177
Company Secretary G.B.White
Assistant Secretary and Pension Fund Manager G.V.Scott, FPMI
Trustees Hawker Siddeley Pensions Trustees Ltd
Employees 43,000

HAWKINS STEEPLE GROUP LTD.
Osprey House, Queen Victoria Street, Blackburn, Lancs
Secretary C.F.Steeden
Employees 1,306

HAWKINS & TIPSON LTD. GROUP PENSION SCHEME
Head Office Marlow House, Hailey Road, Thamesmead, Erith,Kent DA18 4AL
Telephone: 01-310 0211
Administrative Office Summerheath Road, Hailsham, East Sussex BN27 3DT
Telephone:0323-840771
Investment Co-ordinator J.E.Hawkins
Administrative Officer Miss Clare Hawke
Secretary T.P.Taylor
Trustees E.Franks, N.J.Hawkins, R.G.Coates, T.P.Taylor
Pension Fund Consultants Godwins Ltd.
Auditors Kingsford
Company Employees 1,170
Members 711
Pensioners 166
Annual Contributions £267,000
Capital Value £1,100,000

HAWTHORN LESLIE (ENGINEERS) LTD PENSION FUND
PO Box 4, St Peter's Works, Newcastle upon Tyne NE6 1BY
Telephone: 0632-656043
Assistant Company Secretary R.H.Soones, ASCA
Chief Cashier D.J.Barclay
Managed by Pensions Management (SWF) Ltd.
Pension Fund Consultants Martin Paterson Associates Ltd.
Company Employees 700
Members 472
Annual Contributions £92,000
Capital Value £750,000

HAYMARKET PUBLISHING LTD
54-62 Regent Street, London W1N 8AP
Telephone: 01-439 4244
Secretary D.B.Fraser
Employees 550

HAYMILLS (CONTRACTS) LTD
Empire House, Hanger Green, London W5 3BD
Telephone: 01-997 5602
Secretary W.U.B.Reid,FCIS
Employees 867

HEAL & SON HOLDINGS LTD PENSION FUND
196 Tottenham Court Road, London W1A 1BJ
Telephone: 01-636 1666
Pension Fund Manager & Secretary J.H. Wood
Trustees Heal's Pension Trustees Ltd.

Director D.A.W.Hamilton (Chairman), O.S.Heal, P.R.Lane, M.Wells
Insured with London Life Association Ltd.
Stockbrokers Phillips & Drew
Actuaries Duncan C. Fraser
Auditors Brewer & Co.
Company Employees 527
Members 182
Pensioners 75

	£000
Annual Investment Income	52
Annual Outflow	49
Summary of Investments	
Equities	199
Fixed Interest	298

A.HEALD LTD
Elm Grove, Didsbury, Lancs M20 0RR
Telephone: 061-445 8841
Secretary R.W.Nichol
Employees 588

C.E.HEATH & CO LTD
Cuthbert Heath House, 151/54 Minories, London EC3N 1NR
Telephone: 01-488 2488
Secretary B.Thompson
Insured with Standard Life Assurance Co.
Employees 1,172

W.HEFFER & SON LTD.
20 Trinity Street, Cambridge CB2 3NG
Telephone: 0223-358351
Secretary N.Heffer,FCA
Insured Scheme
Pension Fund Consultants Alexander Howden Insurance Brokers Ltd.
Employees 558

H.J.HEINZ COMPANY LTD. 1975 PENSION PLAN
Hayes Park, Hayes,Middx.UB4 8AL
Telephone: 01-573 7757
Company Secretary J.A.Ross
Manager, Pensions & Insurance Services C.J.Squires,DMS
Investment Advisers J.Henry Schroder Wagg & Co.Ltd.
Actuaries Bacon & Woodrow
Auditors Shipley Blackburn
Employees 10,099
Members (at 31.3.80) 7,900
Pensioners 2,300
Capital Value £40.7 million

J & W HENDERSON LTD
82 Market Street, Aberdeen, Scotland AB9 2HW
Telephone: 0224-29313

J & W HENDERSON LTD *Continued*

Secretary A.M.Paton,CA
Insured with Legal & General Assurance Society Ltd
Pension Fund Consultants Godwins Ltd
Employees 501

P.C.HENDERSON LTD STAFF PENSION SCHEME

Tangent Works, Harold Hill, Romford, Essex RM3 8UL
Telephone: 04023-45555

Secretary C.Winter
Trustees Henderson Pension Trustees Ltd
Investment Advisers Charterhouse Japhet Investment Management Ltd.
Actuaries Duncan C. Fraser & Co
Auditors Knox Cropper
Company Employees 890
Members 731
Pensioners 80
Annual Contributions £444,000
Annual Investment Income £153,000
Annual Outflow £145,000
Capital Value £2,100,000

HENDERSON-KENTON LTD. RETIREMENT BENEFITS PLAN

Blue Star House, Highgate Hill, London N19 5PF
Telephone: 01-272 0288

Pension Fund Manager & Secretary C.N.Brown, FCIS,MBIM
Trustees I.A.Horwood, H.W.H.Ellis, C.N.Brown
Managed by Noble Lowndes Pensions Ltd.
Investment Advisers Phillips & Drew
Stockbrokers Phillips & Drew
Property Advisers Harvey Spack, Field & Co.
Actuaries Hymans, Robertson & Co.
Pension Fund Consultants Noble Lowndes & Partners Ltd
Auditors Clark Pixley
Company Employees 1,700
Members 250
Pensioners 35
Annual Contributions £168,000

HENLEY FORKLIFT GROUP LTD.

Newbridge Road Industrial Estate, Pontllanfraith, Gwent NP2 2XF
Telephone: 0495-225555

Secretary J.H.K.Forster,FCA
Employees 512

HENLYS LTD

385-387 Euston Road, London NW1 3AX
Telephone: 01-387 4444

Secretary A.T.Till
Insured with Legal & General Assurance Society Ltd
Employees 4,000

HEPWORTHS PENSION FUND

J.Hepworth & Son Ltd., Claypit Lane, Leeds, W.Yorks.LS2 8AP
Telephone: 0532-440265

Secretary P.Bailey
Assistant Comapny Secretary P.N.Baxendale,ACIS
Trustees Hepworth Trustee Co Ltd
Investment Advisers Electra Group Services Ltd
Stockbrokers Cazenove & Co
Property Advisers J.Hepworth & Son Ltd
Annual Investment Income £380,000
Actuaries Duncan C.Fraser & Co.
Auditors Thornton Baker
Solicitors Alsop Stevens Batesons & Co.
Company Employees (at 31.3.80) 3,835
Members 1,613
Pensioners 319
Annual Contributions £1,159,000
Annual Investment Income £876,000
Capital Value £10,021,000

HEPWORTH CERAMIC GROUP STAFF PENSION & LIFE ASSURANCE SCHEME (WORKS)

Genefax House, Tapton Park Road, Sheffield S10 3FJ
Telephone: 0742-306577

Pension Fund Manager C.Ball,APMI
Secretary to Trustees G.Stork
Insured with Scottish Amicable Life Assurance Society
Pension Fund Consultants Sedgwick Employee Benefits Consultants Ltd.
Auditors Peat, Marwick, Mitchell & Co., Price Waterhouse & Co.
Company Employees 10,000
Members Staff 3,000, Works 5,000
Pensioners Staff 300, Works 500
Annual Contributions Staff £ 2,536,000, Works £1,111,000

ALFRED HERBERT LTD

PO Box 50, Matlock Road, Coventry CV1 4JU
Telephone: 0203-88866

Secretary J.D.Ellson
Group Pensions Manager D.Shaw, APMI
Pension Fund Consultants Jowitt & Freeman
Auditors Peat Marwick Mitchell & Co
Members 4,500
Pensioners 1,400

HERCULES LTD. PENSION & LIFE ASSURANCE SCHEME

20 Red Lion Street, London WC1R 4PB
Telephone: 01-404 4000

Pension Fund Manager R.J.Samworth

Trustees English Pension Trustees Ltd.

Insured with Guardian Royal Exchange Assurance Group

Company Employees 439

Members 396

Pensioners 25

Annual Contributions £282,000

HERDMANS LIMITED

Sion Mills, Strabane, N Ireland
Telephone: 066-265 421

Director J.P.Herdman

Secretary I.W.Browne

Employees 700

HEREFORD & WORCESTER COUNTY COUNCIL SUPERANNUATION FUND

County Hall Spetchley Road, Worcester WR5 2NP
Telephone: 0905-353366

County Treasurer A.B.Turner,IPFA,FCA

Members (at 31.3.80)
Hereford & Worcester C.C. 5,602
11 Other Authorities 3,861

Total Contributors 9,463

Pensioners 3,431

	£000
Income	
Contributions	8,017
Investment Income	3,784
Transfers	645
Total	12,446
Expenditure	5,675
Capital Value	
Book value	37,097
Market value	41,548
Summary of Investments (at market value)	
UK Equities	21,250
Overseas Equities	1,328
Fixed Interest	14,429
Property Unit Trusts	3,922
Cash & Deposits	1,487
Net Current Assets	1,918

HERMAN SMITH PENSIONS LTD.

Cinderbank Works, Dudley,
West Midlands DY2 9AH
Telephone: 0384-52791

Pension Fund Managaer Andrew G.Mott

Secretary R.D.Oerton

Trustees Herman G.Smith, M.Herman-Smith, R.Herman-Smith, K.Tennant, R.D.Oerton

Investment Advisers Legal & General Assurance Society Ltd.

Actuaries & Pension Fund Consultants Duncan C.Fraser & Co.

Auditors Frank H.Hyam

Company Employees 600

Members 350

Pensioners 30

HERON CORPORATION LTD

Heron House, 19 Marylebone Road
London NW1 5JL
Telephone: 01-486 4477

Secretary to Pension Fund Miss P.Beresford

Finance Director A.G.E.Spears

Company Secretary H.Dobin

Part Insured with Scottish Provident Institution

Company Employees 4,959

Members 1,500

HERRBURGER BROOKS LTD

Shenstone Works, Meadow Lane, Long Eaton
Nottingham NG10 2FG
Telephone: 060-76 5218

Secretary J.M.Smith

Insured with Standard Life Assurance Co

Employees 550

HERTFORDSHIRE COUNTY COUNCIL SUPERANNUATION FUND

County Hall, Hertford SG13 8DQ
Telephone: 54242

Treasurer C.C.Jasper,IPFA,DPA,MBIM

Investment Advisers N.M.Rothschild & Sons Ltd.

Stockbrokers Rowe & Pitman

Actuaries R.Watson & Sons

Auditors District Auditor

Employees 29,700 (equivalent whole time)

Members 15,000

Pensioners 4,700

	£000
Annual Contributions	7,500
Annual Investment Income	5,500
Annual Outflow	4,700
Capital Value	74,200
Summary of Investments	
Equities	47,000
Fixed Interest	17,500
Property	7,000
Cash & Deposits	2,700

HESTAIR LTD

10 Castle Hill, Windsor, Berks.SL4 1PD
Telephone: 95-54945

Secretary J.S.Sainsbury,FCA

Managed by Legal & General (Pensions Management) Ltd

Pension Fund Consultants Godwins Ltd

Employees 2,645

HEWDEN-STUART PLANT LTD

135 Buchanan Street, Glasgow G1 2JA
Telephone: 041-221 7331

HEWDEN-STUART PLANT LTD *Continued*

Secretary A.W.Deakin

Insured with Scottish Widows' Fund & Life Assurance Society

Employees 3,700

HEWLETT-PACKARD LTD. EMPLOYEE BENEFIT PLAN

King Street Lane, Winnersh, Berks.RG11 5AR
Telephone: 0734-784774

Secretary J.B.Penrose, FCA

Personnel Manager P.A.Ward

Investment Advisers Robert Fleming Investment Management Ltd

Pension Fund Consultants Noble Lowndes & Partners Ltd

Company Employees 1,424

Members 1,150

Pensioners 15

Annual Contributions £500,000

Capital Value £2,250,000

HEYGATES LTD. GROUP PENSION & LIFE ASSURANCE SCHEME

Bugbrooke Mills, Northampton NN7 3QH
Telephone: 0604-83081

Company Secretary E.Myers,ACCA

Part Insured with Royal Insurance Co.Ltd.

Stockbrokers Henry Cooke Lumsden & Co.

Pension Fund Consultants R.J.Lett (Insurance Brokers) Ltd.

Auditors Clifford Towers Woodroffe & Co.

Company Employees 700

Members 415

Pensioners 47

Annual Contributions £197,000

Annual Investment Income £18,000

Capital Value £154,000

HEYWOOD WILLIAMS GROUP LTD PENSION AND LIFE ASSURANCE PLAN

Bayhall Works, Huddersfield, W.Yorks.HD1 5EJ
Telephone: 0484-20581

Secretary H.R. Harrison

Managed by Prudential Pensions Ltd., Warburg Investment Management Ltd.

Actuaries Clay & Partners

Pension Fund Consultants Metropolitan Pensions Association Ltd.

Auditors Ernst & Whinney

Company Employees 860

Members 505

Pensioners 375

	£000
Annual Contributions	250
Annual Investment Income	200
Annual Outflow	130
Capital Value	1,700
Summary of Investments	
Equities	550
Fixed Interest	400
Property	750

HICK, HARGREAVES & CO LTD

Soho Works, Bolton, Greater Manchester BL3 6DB
Telephone: 0204-23373

Director R.F.D.Reed

Employees 675

HICKING PENTECOST & CO.LTD. STAFF & EMPLOYEES PENSION SCHEME

Queens Road, Nottingham NG2 3AT
Telephone: 0602-868275

Secretary G.J.St.John-Grewcock,FCIS

Investment Advisers Antony Gibbs Investment Management Ltd

Pension Fund Consultants Antony Gibbs Pension Services Ltd.

Auditors Price Waterhouse & Co.

Company Employees 1,433

Members 400

Pensioners 75

Capital Value £1,250,000

HICKSON & WELCH (HOLDINGS) LTD. GROUP PENSION SCHEME (1978)

Castleford, West Yorkshire WF10 2JT
Telephone: 0977-556565

Pension Fund Manager E.R.Barker,MA,FCA,APMI

Company Secretary C.Livsey

Investment Advisers and Stockbrokers Sheppards & Chase

Actuarial Advice obtained through Cubie Wood & Co Ltd

Pension Fund Consultants Noble Lowndes & Partners Ltd

Auditors Price Waterhouse & Co.

Company Employees 2,300

Members 1,664

Pensioners 156

Annual Contributions £1,900,000

Annual Investment Income £750,000

Annual Outflow £600,000

Capital Value £7,500,000

HIELD BROTHERS LTD

Briggella Mills, Bradford, W.Yorks.BD5 0QA
Telephone: 0274-71181

Secretary J.T.Barraclough

Insured with Legal & General Assurance Society Ltd.

Employees 760

HIGGS & HILL LTD. SUPERANNUATION FUND AND LIFE ASSURANCE SCHEME

Crown House, Kingston Road, New Malden, Surrey KT3 3ST
Telephone: 01-942 8921

Trustees' Secretary Mrs.E.B.Clark

Trustees 4 members of Parent Board and 2 members of Staff

Investment Managers Coutts & Co.

Actuaries Bacon & Woodrow

Pension Fund Consultants Hogg Robinson (Benefit Consultants) Ltd.

Auditors Longcrofts

Company Employees 1,800

Members 800

Pensioners 220

Annual Contributions £600,000

Capital Value (at 5.4.80) £4,239,229

HIGHAMS LTD STAFF RETIREMENT BENEFITS PLAN

Wood Nook Mills, Accrington, Lancashire BB5 0PP
Telephone: 0254-34641

Assistant Secretary A.W. Huddleston FCIS

Other Pension Management E.R.Dann,ACMA

Trustees W.M. Higham, M.A. Higham, E.R. Dann

Investment Advisers Hill Samuel Investment Management Ltd.

Stockbrokers Sheppards and Chase

Actuarial Advice Obtained through Cubie Wood & Co.Ltd.

Pension Fund Consultants Noble Lowndes & Partners Ltd.

Auditors Price Waterhouse & Co.

Company Employees 1,800

Members 107

Pensioners 114

	£000
Annual Contributions	181
Annual Investment Income	90
Annual Outflow	95
Capital Value	1,251
Summary of Investments	
Equities	636
Fixed Interest	270
Property	119
Cash & Deposits	15
Others	121

HIGHLAND ELECTRONICS GROUP LTD

Highland House, 8 Old Steine, Brighton, E Sussex BN1 1EJ
Telephone: 0273-693688

Secretary R.G.Oxlade,FCA

Employees 725

HIGHLAND FABRICATORS STAFF PENSION FUND

P.O.Box 4, Nigg Tain, Ross-shire
Telephone: 086285-666

Administration Manager T.Clement,CA

Investment Advisers Fraser Green Ltd.

Actuaries Duncan C.Fraser & Co.

Auditors Arthur Andersen & Co.

Company Employees 1,958

Members 263

Pensioners 1

Annual Contributions £119,000

Capital Value £296,000

HIGHLAND REGIONAL COUNCIL

Regional Buildings, Glenurquhart Road, Inverness IV3 5NX
Telephone: 0463-34121

Director of Finance J.W.Bremner

HIGSONS BREWERY LTD. STAFF PENSION FUND

127 Dale Street, Liverpool L2 2JJ
Telephone: 051-236 1255

Secretary H.E.Thomas

Trustees E.Lance, H.E.Thomas, G.L.Garrett, L.Bull, J.B.H.Mellon

Insured with Royal Insurance Co Ltd

Company Employees 2,050

Members 300

Pensioners 30

Annual Contributions £110,000

Annual Outflow £20,000

THE CHARLES HILL OF BRISTOL STAFF PENSION FUND AND RETIREMENT BENEFIT SCHEME

Albion Dockyard, Bristol BS1 6UY
Telephone: 0272-24101

Pension Fund Manager & Secretary H.J.Phillips

Financial Director J.G.Luckwell,FCA,ACMA

Trustees C.H.B.Pension Trust Corporation

Stockbrokers Stock Beech & Co.

Actuaries Bacon & Woodrow

Auditors Price Waterhouse & Co

Company Employees 673

Members (Total 2 Funds) 410

Pensioners 209

Annual Contributions £126,000

Annual Investment Income £240,000

Gross Annual Outflow £126,000

Capital Value £3,000,000

HILL SAMUEL GROUP PENSION SCHEME

100 Wood Street, London EC2P 2AJ
Telephone: 01-628 8011

Secretary to the Trustees R.C.G.Gardner

HILL SAMUEL GROUP Continued

Trustees The Hon. P.M.Samuel, P.E.Beaven, J.Chellone, A.E.Conway, S.C.Gee, M.A.Thorman, Sir Peter Thornton

Investment Advisers Hill Samuel Investment Management Ltd.

Actuarial Advice Obtained through Cubie, Wood & Co.Ltd.

Trustees Agents and Pension Fund Consultants Cubie Wood & Co. Ltd.

Auditors Price Waterhouse & Co.

Company Employees 3,756

Members (at 31.3.80) 3,517

Pensioners 689

	£000
Annual Contributions (to 31.3.80)	5,473
Annual Investment Income	1,336
Annual Outflow	3,961
Capital Value (Market Value)	28,785
Summary of Investments	
Equities	19,780
Overseas Equities	2,687
Fixed Interest	3,913
Property	2,378
Net Cash & Deposits	26

Subsidiaries include Hill Samuel & Co.Ltd., Noble Lowndes & Partners Ltd., and Cubie, Wood & Co.Ltd.

HILL STANLEY & SON LTD

The Cleveland Bakery, Marsh Street, Cannon Park, Middlesbrough, Cleveland TS1 5JN
Telephone: 0642-247898

Director H.R.Hill

Employees 600

HILLALDAM COBURN LTD

Red Lion Rd, Tolworth, Surbiton, Surrey KT6 7RE
Telephone: 01-397 5151

Director C.E.Aldam

Executive J.Langley

Employees 500

HILLARDS LTD

Spen Lane, Gomersal, Cleckheaton,
West Yorkshire BD19 4PW

Secretary K.Broadhead

Insured with Scottish Widows' Fund & Life Assurance Society

Employees 3,209

HILTON INTERNATIONAL HOTELS (UK) LTD

London Hilton Hotel, 22 Park Lane, W1A 2HH
Telephone: 01-493 8000

Secretary R.J.C.Warburton

Other Pension Management Rolando G.R. Ciaravaglia

Trustees R.M.Henderson, J-P.Piquet, R.J.C.Warburton, R.G.R.Ciaravaglia

Insured with Swiss Life Insurance and Pension Co. Ltd.

Actuaries Clay & Partners

Auditors Deloitte, Haskins & Sells

Company Employees 1,467

Members 177

Pensioners 10

Annual Contributions £10,000

Annual Investment Income £36,800

Annual Outflow £19,600

HILTONS FOOTWEAR LTD

98 Scudamore Road, Braunstone,
Leicester LE3 1UP
Telephone: 0533-872173

Secretary J.S.Parr

Managed by Pensions Management (SWF) Ltd.

Employees 1,118

HINCKLEYS LTD

Sandiron House, Beauchief, Sheffield,
S.Yorks.S7 2RA
Telephone: 0742-369011

Director Mrs. D.K.Hinckley

Employees 600

HINKINS & FREWIN (GROUP) LTD.

53 West Way, Botley, Oxford OX2 0QB
Telephone: 0865-723221

Secretary L.A.Lane

Employees 801

AMOS HINTON & SONS LTD. PENSION & ASSURANCE SCHEME

P.O.Box 24, Master Road, Thornaby,
Stockton on Tees TS17 0BD
Telephone: 0642-69123

Secretary A.P.Orr, CA

Trustees W.K.Hinton, W.P.C.Hinton, R.F.Hinton, A.P.Orr

Insured with Legal & General Assurance Society Ltd

Actuarial Advice obtained through Metropolitan Statistical Services Ltd

Pension Fund Consultants Metropolitan Pensions Associates Ltd

Employees 2,189

HIRST & MALLINSON GROUP PENSIONS LTD.

Perseverance House, Firth Street, Huddersfield,
W.Yorks.HD1 3BZ
Telephone: 0484-42054

Pension Fund Manager & Secretary M.C.Elstub

Directors A.J.Glock, K.Thornton, M.D.Crompton, M.C.Elstub

Stockbrokers Fielding, Newson-Smith & Co

Property Advisers King & Co.

Auditors Armitage & Norton

Company Employees 820

C & J HIRST & SONS LTD
P.O.Box A5 Sunnybank Mills, Longwood, Huddersfield HD3 4TJ
Telephone: 0484-653035

Director E.M.Dodson

Employees 500

J.H.HIRST LTD
Whitewell Works, Waterfoot, Rossendale, Lancs.BB4 9HT
Telephone: 07062-4988

Director W.Hirst

Executive P.Bibby

Employees 550

HOARE GOVETT LTD STAFF & SPECIAL EXECUTIVES PENSION FUNDS
Heron House, 319/325 High Holborn, London WC1V 7PB
Telephone: 01-606 9800

Pension Fund Manager A.D. Izzard

Secretaries M.J.Mercer, Mrs.D.Kenworthy

Trustees 8 members, 1 pensioner

Investment Advisers Hoare Govett Ltd

Actuaries Lane Clark & Peacock

Auditors Touche Ross & Co

Employees 386

Members 341

Pensioners 77

Annual Contributions £418,000

Annual Investment Income £660,000

Annual Outflow £88,000

Capital Value £7,000,000

THE HOBART MANUFACTURING CO LTD NO. 2 PENSION SCHEME
Hobart Corner, New Southgate, London N11 1QW
Telephone: 01-368 1211

Secretary J.L.Abel Smith, MA

Company Employees 1,005

Members 488

HOBBS (QUARRIES) HOLDINGS LTD.
Backwell House, Backwell, Bristol BS19 3QD
Telephone: 027-583 2031

Secretary E.G.D.James,FCA

Insured with Legal & General Assurance Society Ltd

Employees 1,068

HODGE COMPANIES PENSION FUND
18 London Street, London EC3R 7LA
Telephone: 01-481 8511

Secretary & Administrator D.A. Morris,ACIS,APMI

Secretary/Financial Director K.J.Ashley

Trustees Hodge Trustees Ltd.

Investment Advisers Robert Fleming Investment Management Ltd.

Actuaries Bacon & Woodrow

Pension Fund Consultants C.T.Bowring & Layborn Ltd.

Auditors Gane, Jackson & Walton

Company Employees 330

Members 180

Pensioners 55

	£000
Annual Contributions	187
Annual Investment Income	151
Annual Outflow	83
Capital Value (Market Value at 30.6.80)	2,218
Summary of Investments	
Equities	1,378
Fixed Interest	507
Cash & Deposits	249
Others	84

HOECHST UK LTD. PENSION & LIFE ASSURANCE SCHEME
Hoechst House, Salisbury Road, Hounslow, Middlesex TW4 6JH
Telephone: 01-570 7712

Benefits and Administration Manager I.Peacock

Investment Advisers J.Henry Schroder Wagg & Co Ltd

Pension Fund Consultants and Actuarial Advice Obtained through Willis Faber Advisory Services Ltd

Auditors Coopers & Lybrand

Group Employees 1,700

Company Employees 1,730

Members 1,500

Pensioners 80

	£000
Annual Contributions	1,800
Annual Investment Income	286
Annual Outflow	306
Capital Value	
Book Value	6,941
Market Value	7,778
Summary of Investments	
UK Equities	2,935
Foreign Equities	1,020
Fixed Interest	2,288
Property	669
Cash & Deposits	29

S.HOFFNUNG & CO LTD
1/2 Finsbury Square, London EC2A 1AP
Telephone: 01-628 0561

Secretary Mrs.E.M.Dodwell

Employees 2,486

HOGG ROBINSON GROUP LTD
Lloyd's Chambers, 9/13 Crutched Friars, London EC3N 2JS
Telephone: 01-709 0575

Secretary A.Dawe,FCIS

HOGG ROBINSON GROUP LTD *Continued*

Insured with Standard Life Assurance Co

Employees 2,400

THE HOLLAS GROUP LTD. PENSION & ASSURANCE SCHEME

Century House, Ashley Road, Hale, Altrincham, Cheshire WA15 9TD
Telephone: 061-928 6622

Secretary Keith Harrison

Trustees K.Harrison, B.C.Taylor, J.A.Brides

Insured with Legal & General Assurance Society Ltd.

Pension Fund Consultants Bowring Schofield Ltd. (K.Hughes)

Company Employees 587

Members 83

Pensioners 3

Annual Contributions £55,000

L.B.HOLLIDAY & CO LTD

PO Box 822, Huddersfield, W.Yorks.HD2 1UH
Telephone: 0484-21841

Secretary A.M.Pearson,JP,FCA

Employees 731

HOLLIS BROS & E.S.A. LTD

Craven Hall, Hull HU9 1NT
Telephone: 0482-20791

Secretary J.F.Dowzall

Insured with Legal & General Assurance Society Ltd, Scottish Widows' Fund & Life Assurance Society

Pension Fund Consultants Sedgwick Employee Benefits Consultants Ltd.

Employees 2,247

HOLSET PENSION & LIFE ASSURANCE SCHEME

Turnbridge, Huddersfield, West Yorkshire HD1 6RD
Telephone: 0484-22244

Secretary K.Haigh,FCCA,ACIS

Trustees P.J.F.Croset, F.Cotton, K.Davies, K.Haigh, C.Hannah, R.B.Hesselden, E.Palfreeman

Investment Advisers Ivory & Sime Ltd.

Pension Fund Consultants Willis Faber Advisory Services Ltd.

Auditors Arthur Andersen & co.

Company Employees 1,700

Members 1,651

Pensioners 62

	£000
Annual Contributions (to 31.3.80)	429
Annual Investment Income	166
Annual Outflow	186
Capital Value (Market Value)	2,626

Summary of Investments	%
UK Equities	48.7
US Equities	24.0
Fixed Interest	21.5
Cash & Deposits	5.8

Associated Company Cummins Engine Co.Ltd.

JOHN HOLT PENSION SCHEME

India Buildings, Water Street, Liverpool L2 0QF
Telephone: 051-236 8881

Pension Fund Manager T.Cook, BSc., APMI

Other Pension Management N.Miller, S.Edwards

Trustees Lazard Brothers & Co Ltd

Investment Advisers Lazard Securities Ltd

Actuaries Duncan C.Fraser & Co

Auditors Deloitte, Haskins & Sells

Solicitors Alsop, Stevens, Batesons & Co.

Company Employees 4,036

Members 1,159

Pensioners 378

	£000
Annual Contributions	1,180
Annual Investment Income	1,420
Annual Outflow	1,350
Capital Value (Market Value)	17,970

Summary of Investments	
Fixed Interest	6,380
UK Equities	6,442
Property	2,348
Overseas Equities	1,991
Cash & Deposits	656
Others	153

HOLT LLOYD INTERNATIONAL LTD

Lloyds House, Alderley Road, Wilmslow, Cheshire SK9 1QT
Telephone: 09964-26838

Secretary P.Hannam,FCA

Managed by Legal & General (Pensions Management) Ltd

Investment Advisers Morgan Grenfell & Co Ltd

Employees 724

HOME BREWERY CO LTD PENSION SCHEME

The Brewery, Daybrook, Nottingham NG5 6BU
Telephone: 0602-269741

Director & Pension Fund Manager A.Orgill, APMI

Insured with Scottish Amicable Life Assurance Society

Actuaries Clay & Partners

Pension Fund Consultants Metropolitan Pensions Association Ltd.

Auditors Hubbart Durose & Pain

Company Employees 1,651

Members 458

Pensioners 121

HOME CHARM LTD

Cline Road, New Southgate, London N11 2NA
Telephone: 01-368 0141

Secretary R.Rimington

Employees 1,458

HOME COUNTIES NEWSPAPERS

75 Castle Street, Luton, Beds LU1 3AH
Telephone: 0582-2022

Secretary P.D.Mackay

Insured with Yorkshire & General Life Assurance Co Ltd

Employees 803

THE HOMFRAY & CO.LTD. GENERAL PENSION FUND AND MANAGEMENT PENSION FUND

Greenhill Mills, Crange Road, Batley, W.Yorks.WF17 6LL
Telephone: 0924-473131

Secretary M.Hartley, FCIS

Investment Manager G.S.Haigh

Management Committee for General Fund only

Trustees D.G.Armitage, D.E.Gillam, G.S.Haigh, Homfray General Pensions Trust Ltd. (General Fund), and Homfray Management Pensions Trust Ltd. (Management Fund)

Partly Managed by Legal & General Assurance (Pensions Management) Ltd

Investment Advisers M & G Investment Management Ltd.

Stockbrokers Hoare Govett Ltd

Actuaries Duncan C.Fraser & Co

Auditors Armitage & Norton

Company Employees 1,575

	Management fund	General fund
Members (at July 1980)	112	590
Pensioners	67	416
	£000	£000
Annual Contributions	168	335
Annual Investment Income	45	88
Annual Outflow	44	50
Capital Value	1,553	2,573

HONEYWELL LTD. MANAGEMENT, RETIREMENT AND PENSION PLANS

Charles Square, Bracknell, Berkshire RG12 1EB
Telephone: 0344-24555

Pension Fund Manager & Secretary J. Chilton

Trustees Bankers Trustee & Executor Co.Ltd.

Managed by Bankers Trustee & Executor Co.Ltd.

Actuaries R.Watson & Sons

Auditors Deloitte Haskins & Sells

Solicitors Rowe & Maw

Company Employees 5,400

Members 420(MP), 3,300(RP), 1,600(PP)
Pensioners 3(MP), 243(RP), 126(PP)

	£000
Annual Contributions	3,318
Annual Investment Income	1,399
Annual Outflow	708
Capital Value	26,863
Summary of Investments	
Equities	16,915
Fixed Interest	8,633
Cash & Deposits	1,315

HONGKONG BANK GROUP LONDON STAFF PENSION FUND

PO Box 199, 99 Bishopsgate, London EC2P 2LA
Telephone: 01-638 2300

Secretary R.P.Thomas

Trustee Hongkong & Shanghai Bank (Trustee) Ltd.

Actuaries Bacon & Woodrow

Auditors Peat, Marwick, Mitchell & Co.

Solicitors Stephenson Harwood

Company Employees (UK) 1,500

Members 900

Pensioners 300

Annual Contributions £1.5 million

Capital Value £18 million

HOOVER STAFF PENSION SCHEME

Perivale, Greenford, Middx.UB6 8DX
Telephone: 01-997 3311

Pension Fund Manager & Secretary B.Saunders, FPMI

Admininstrative Manager Miss M.M. Tudor

Trustees Hoover Trust Fund Ltd

Investment Advisers County Bank Ltd.,Highclere Investments Ltd.

Actuaries Hymans Robertson & Co

Property Advisers Jones Lang Wootton

Auditors Brewer & Co

Company Employees 11,000

Members 10,800

Pensioners 3,360

	£000
Annual Contributions	8,675
Annual Investment Income	6,350
Annual Outflow	4,125
Capital Value	85,890
Summary of Investments	
Equities	51,338
Fixed Interest	1,180
Property	22,025
Cash & Deposits	11,347

HOPKINSONS HOLDINGS LTD PENSION & LIFE ASSURANCE SCHEME

Britannia Works, Huddersfield, W.Yorks.HD2 2UR
Telephone: 0484-22171

HOPKINSONS HOLDINGS LTD Continued

Finance & Administration Director H.Mellor, FCMA
Company Secretary P.K.Thomas
Chief Financial Accountant B.C.du Feu, ACA
Insured with Prudential Assurance Co.Ltd.
Actuaries Clay & Partners Ltd.
Pension Fund Consultants Metropolitan Pensions Association Ltd.
Auditors Price Waterhouse & Co.
Company Employees 3,750
Members 1,700

HORNE BROS.LTD. STAFF PENSION SCHEME
Durigo House, King Edwards Road,
London E9 7SG
Telephone: 01-986 3166

Secretary R.H.L.Buckey, FCIS
Stockbrokers Cazenove & Co.
Property Advisers Hillier Parker May & Rowden
Actuaries R.Watson & Sons
Auditors Binder Hamlyn
Employees 1,106
Members 496
Pensioners 283
Annual Contributions £276,000
Annual Investment Income £275,000
Capital Value £2,819,000

HORNSEA POTTERY CO LTD
Hornsea, Humberside HU18 1UD
Telephone: 040-12 2161

Director D.Rawson
Executive H.Franks
Employees 800

HORSTMANN GEAR GROUP LTD
Newbridge Works and Albion Works,
Bath BA1 3EF
Telephone: 0225-21141

Director B.G.Horstmann
Employees 1,500

THE HOSIERY MANUFACTURING CO LTD
Ballot Road, Irvine, Ayrshire KA12 OHP
Telephone: 029-47 78277

Secretary & Financial Director C.Gillis, CA
Employees 500

HOUSE OF FRASER GROUP PENSION & DEATH BENEFIT PLANS FOR (A)STAFF, (B) MANAGEMENT, (C)EXECUTIVES
69 Buchanan Street, Glasgow G1 3LE
Telephone: 041-221 6401

Secretary D.K.Milligan, CA
Trustees Sir Hugh Fraser Bt., W.G.Crossan, F.B.Marley,FCIS, G.Willoughby

Managed by Legal & General Assurance Society Ltd.
Pension Fund Consultants Godwins (Central) Ltd.
Auditors Touche Ross and Co.
Company Employees 24,500
Members 9,796
Pensioners 1,636
Annual Contributions £4,549,000
Annual Investment Income £3,320
Capital Value £20,850,000

THE HOUSE OF LEROSE LTD.
50-55 Henrietta Street, Birmingham B19 3PR
Telephone: 021-236 9061

Secretaary C.Mullen
Employees 727

HOVERINGHAM GROUP RETIREMENT BENEFIT SCHEME (1974)
Hoveringham, Nottingham NG14 7JY
Telephone: 060745-3671

Pension Fund Manager & Secretary A.D.Callaghan, FCIS
Trustees R.Whiteside, A.D.Callaghan, G.F.Williamson
Managed by M & G Investment Management Ltd.
Actuaries R.Watson & Sons
Auditors Hodgson, Harris & Co.
Company Employees 2,167
Members 1,991
Pensioners 276

	£000
Annual Contributions	1,415
Annual Investment Income	850
Annual Outflow	250
Capital Value	6,500
Summary of Investments	
Equities	5,000
Fixed Interest	1,500

HOVERLLOYD LTD.
49 Charles Street, London W1
Telephone: 01-493 5525

Secretary A.Ramsey
Employees 575

HOW GROUP LTD
Intersection House, Birmingham Road,
West Bromwich, West Midlands B70 6RX
Telephone: 021-553 6101

Secretary Mrs B.E.Crow
Insured with Scottish Life Assurance Co
Employees 1,662

C.A.E.C.HOWARD LTD
St Johns Works, Bedford MK42 ODR
Telephone: 0234-63171

C.A.E.C.HOWARD LTD Continued

Director C.A.E.C.Howard
Employees 700

H.R.HOWARD & SONS LTD
Oxford Mills, Oxford Street,
Ashton under Lyne OL7 0LT
Telephone: 061-330 5671

Director R.E.W.Newman
Executive J.B.Barlow
Employees 750

HOWARD HUMPHREYS & PARTNERS PENSION PLAN
Thorncroft Manor, Dorking Road, Leatherhead,
Surrey KT22 8JB
Telephone: 037-23 76190

Secretary to Trustees T.L.Stiles
Pension Fund Manager P.J.Slater (Lloyds Bank)
Trustees C.E.Dupenois, T.L.Stiles, R.L.Klein, E.C.Watts
Managed by Lloyds Bank Trust Division
Investment Advisers Lloyds Bank Investment Dept.
Actuaries Clay & Partners
Auditors Arthur Andersen & Co.
Company Employees 522
Members 273
Pensioners 15

	£000
Annual Contributions	225
Annual Investment Income	132
Annual Outflow	54
Capital Value	1,500
Summary of Investments	
Equities	715
Fixed Interest	460
Property	260
Cash & Deposits	65

JOHN HOWARD & CO.LTD.
Victory House, Meeting House Lane, Chatham,
Kent ME4 4PP
Telephone: 0634-402040

Secretary R.A.Howard
Insured with Commercial Union Assurance Co. Ltd.
Employees 952

HOWARD MACHINERY LTD
Saxham, Bury St.Edmunds Suffolk IP28 6QZ
Telephone: 0284-63266

Secretary N.D.Dunnett
Investment Advisers Hill Samuel Investment Management Ltd.
Employees 1,732

HOWDEN GROUP LTD
195 Scotland Street, Glasgow G5 8PJ
Telephone: 041-429 2131

Secretary T.Dibble
Insured with Legal & General Assurance Society Ltd
Employees 2,989

ALEXANDER HOWDEN GROUP LTD
22 Billiter Street, London EC3M 2SA
Telephone: 01-488 0808

Company Secretary M.S.Reynolds
Employees 2,789

HOWMET TURBINE COMPONENTS CORPORATION
Kestrel Way, Exeter, Devon EX2 7LG
Telephone: 0392-70731

Executive R.L.Ward
Employees 600

HTV GROUP LTD. (HARLECH TELEVISION)
The Television Centre, Cardiff CF1 9XL
Telephone: 0222-21021

Secretary G.S.Tovey,FCIS,ACA
Insured with Norwich Union Life Insurance Society
Employees 1,246

HUDDERSFIELD & BRADFORD BUILDING SOCIETY PENSION SCHEME
Permanent House, Westgate, Bradford,
West Yorkshire BD1 2AU
Telephone: 0274-34822

Staff Manager (Administration) A.Calvert, FBS
Company Employees 740
Members 712
Pensioners 77

HUMBERSIDE COUNTY COUNCIL SUPERANNUATION FUND
PO Box 13, County Hall, Beverley,
North Humberside HU17 9BA
Telephone: 0482 867131

Director of Finance J.A.Parkes, MA, IPFA
Trustees Investment Group consists of members of County Council and District Councils with Adviser, Broker and Director of Finance
Investment Adviser J.Morgan
Stockbroker de Zoete and Bevan
Actuaries R.Watson & Sons
Auditors Government Audit
Members (at 31.3.80) 15,200
Pensioners 6,500

	£000
Annual Contributions	11,800
Annual Investment Income	5,900
Annual Outflow	8,300
Capital Value (at 30.9.80)	78,500
Summary of Investments	
Equities	44,228
Overseas Equities	4,138
Fixed Interest	20,079

HUMBERSIDE COUNTY COUNCIL *Continued*

Property 6,423
Cash & Deposits 3,542

HUMPHREYS & GLASGOW LTD
22 Carlisle Place, London SW1P 1JA
Telephone: 01-828 1234

Secretary R.C.Carsley

Insured with Standard Life Assurance Co

Employees 1,560

HUNSLET (HOLDINGS) LTD
Hunslet Engine Works, Leeds, W.Yorks.LS10 1BT
Telephone: 0532-32261

Secretary D.R.Macfarlane

Employees 898

HUNT & MOSCROP (MIDDLETON) LTD
Apex Works, Middleton, Manchester M24 1QS
Telephone: 061-653 6116

Secretary J.Hall

Employees 855

HUNTING ASSOCIATED INDUSTRIES LTD AND HUNTING GIBSON LTD
Woolwich House, 43 George Street, Croydon, Surrey CR9 1AY
Telephone: 01-680 9062

and at Avenfield House, 118-127 Park Lane, London W1Y 4HN
Telephone: 01-493 9781

Pension Fund Manager J.F.Stevens, FCA, APMI

Secretary R.Woodcock, FCCA

Pension Consultant E.H.Baker, APMI

Part Insured with London Life Association Ltd.

Investment Advisers Gartmore Pension Fund Managers Ltd.

Actuaries Lane Clark & Peacock

Auditors Price Waterhouse & Co.

Employees 4,736

Members 5,416

Pensioners 12

Annual Contributions £806,000

Annual Investment Income £23,000

Capital Value £566,000

HUNTINGDON RESEARCH CENTRE

See Becton Dickinson

THE HUNTLEIGH GROUP LTD
Glover Street, Redditch, Worcs.B98 7BQ
Telephone: 0527-63621

Secretary D.C.Mitten

Employees 698

CHARLES HURST LTD
10 Adelaide St, Belfast BT2 8GB
Telephone: 0232-30566

Secretary B.A.Thompson

Employees 848

N.HYER LTD
Princess House, Eastcastle Street, London W1
Telephone: 01-580 5888

Secretary F.Hyer

Employees 600

I & J.HYMAN LTD.
Hollyville, Holmfirth Road, Greenfield, Oldham, Lancs.OL3 7DR
Telephone: 04577-4727

Secretary J.R.Clough,FCA,ACMA

Employees 1,353

HYSTER LTD PENSION FUND & LIFE ASSURANCE SCHEME
Portland Road, Irvine, Ayrshire KA12 8JG
Telephone: 0294-74141

Benefits Administrator K.P.Donald

Company Secretary H.Cowan

Managed by Scottish Amicable Pensions Investments Ltd.(SCAMPI)

Auditors Peat, Marwick, Mitchell & Co.

Employees 905

Pensioners 40

Annual Contributions £527,000

Capital Value £2,900,000

IBA STAFF PENSION PLAN
Crawley Court, Crawley, Winchester, Hants SO21 2QA
Telephone: 0962-823434

Secretary F.B.Symons

Head Personnel Administration G.Whitaker

Trustees 7

Insured with Clerical, Medical & General Life Assurance Society

Pension Fund Consultants and Actuarial Advice obtained through Bain Dawes & Partners Ltd

Company Employees 1,362

Members approx.1,300

Pensioners 108

IBIS-KENDAL HOLDINGS LTD.
Ibis Works, Kendal,Cumbria
Telephone: 0539-22621

Secretary J.P.Parkinson

Employees 554

IBM UNITED KINGDOM PENSION & LIFE ASSURANCE PLAN
PO Box 41, North Harbour, Portsmouth, Hampshire PO6 3AU
Telephone: 0705-321212

Secretary A.F.Green

Benefits Policy Manager C.D.Yates

Pensions Specialist S.D.B.Ellis

IBM UNITED KINGDOM Continued

Investment Adviser D.N.MacKendrick

Pension Fund Accountant J.T.Moss

Trustees E.R.Nixon (Chairman), J.R.Bache, J.W.Fairclough, J.W.H.Miller, J.B.Morgans, L.H. Peach, D.R.H.Taylor

Investment Managers J.Henry Schroder Wagg & Co.Ltd., N.M.Rothschild & Sons Ltd., Ivory & Sime, Phillips & Drew, Robert Fleming Investment Management Ltd., Scottish Widows' Fund and Life Assurance Society

Investment Performance Measurement Consultant Wood Mackenzie & Co.

Actuaries Clay & Partners

Pension Fund Consultants Metropolitan Pensions Association Ltd.

Auditors Price Waterhouse & Co.

Company Employees 15,635

Members 15,635

Pensioners 363

	£000
Annual Contributions	18,500
Annual Investment Income	9,300
Annual Outflow	1,400
Capital Value	138,000

Summary of Investments	%
UK Equities	45
Overseas Equities	10
Fixed Interest	26
Property	15
Cash & Deposits	3
Others	1

IBSTOCK JOHNSEN LTD

Ibstock, Leicestershire LE6 1HS
Telephone: 0530-60531

Secretary R.C.List

Group Employment Services Manager F.Oldroyd

Insured with Royal Insurance Co Ltd

Brokers Brabstock,Blunt & Thompson

Property Advisers Conrad Ritblat & Co.

Employees 1,317

ICL PENSION FUND

85-91 Upper Richmond Road, Putney,
London SW15 2TE
Telephone: 01-788 7272

Pension Fund Manager J.T.Latham, FPMI

Secretary P.J. Gates

Accountant J.A.Holmes

Trustees ICL Pension Trust Ltd

Investment Advisers Hambros Investment Management Services(Equities), Morgan Grenfell & Co. (Equities), Mullens & Co. (Gilts)

Actuaries Duncan C.Fraser & Co.

Property Advisers Jones Lang Wootton

Auditors Deloitte Haskins & Sells

Solicitors Sacker & Partners

Company Employees 25,000

Members (at 5.4.80) 18,000

Pensioners 2,400

	£000
Annual Contributions	11,034
Annual Investment Income	9,326
Annual Outflow	3,397
Capital Value (at 5.4.80)	104,920

Summary of Investments	
Equities	55,217
Fixed Interest	30,305
Property	13,165
Cash & Deposits	6,233

THE IDC GROUP LTD RETIREMENT BENEFIT SCHEME

Stratford upon Avon, Warwickshire CV37 9NJ
Telephone: 0789-4288

Secretary E.A.Shaw,FCA

Managed by Pensions Management (SWF) Ltd.

Pension Fund Consultants Hogg Robinson (Benefit Consultants) Ltd.

Company Employees 1,029

Members 368

Pensioners 11

Annual Contributions £300,000

Capital Value £1,500,000

IDEAL STANDARD LTD. WORKS RETIREMENT BENEFITS PLAN (1971) AND STAFF RETIREMENT BENEFITS PLAN (1967)

Ideal Works, PO Box 60, National Avenue,
Hull HU5 4JE
Telephone: 0482-46461

Pension Fund Manager/Company Secretary H. Mellor, FCMA

Pensions Administration Manager E.Waddington, ACIS

Trustees N.F. Bennett, H. Mellor, I.F. Fielding

Investment Advisers Ivory & Sime Ltd.

Actuaries Bacon & Woodrow

Auditors Arthur Young McClelland Moores & Co.

Company Employees 1,225

Members Staff 358, Works 836

Pensioners Staff 168, Works 95

IGIS LTD.

116-126 Grafton Road, London NW5 4BG
Telephone: 01-485 7171

Secretary N.J.Poyton

Employees 914

ILLINGWORTH, MORRIS & CO LTD PENSION SCHEME

Victoria Road, Saltaire, Shipley,
W.Yorks.BD18 3LD
Telephone: 0274-582222

ILLINGWORTH, MORRIS & CO LTD Continued

Joint Pension Fund Managers Miss D.E.Carver, V.Escolme, FCA

Investment Advisers Robert Fleming Investment Management Ltd

Actuaries Bacon & Woodrow

Auditors Peat, Marwick, Mitchell & Co.

Company Employees 7,554

Members 1,510

Pensioners 250

Annual Contributions £862,000

Annual Investment Income £362,000

Capital Value £4,763,000

IMI PENSION FUND

PO Box 216, Kynoch Works, Witton,
Birmingham B6 7BA
Telephone: 021-356 4848

Pension Fund Manager P.Longhurst

Assistant Pension Fund Manager & Secretary J.R.Atkinson

Manager Investment Dept. R.O.Bogle

Trustees IMI Pension Trust Ltd

Actuaries R.Watson & Sons

Property Advisers Edwards Bigwood & Bewlay

Auditors Peat Marwick Mitchell & Co

Employees 25,553

Members (at 31.3.80) 17,411

Pensioners 709

	£000
Annual Contributions	12,404
Annual Investment Income	4,639
Gross Annual Outflow	1,798
Capital Value	
Book Value	52,379
Market Value	55,156
Summary of Investments	
Equities	20,630
Fixed Interest	18,705
Property	54462
Cash & Deposits	4,200
Others	3,382

IMPERIAL CANCER RESEARCH FUND PENSION SCHEME

44 Lincoln's Inn Fields, London WC2A 3PX
Telephone: 01-242 0200

Secretary A.B.L.Clarke O.B.E.

Pensions Manager T.W.Attwood, APMI

Treasurer A.P.Thomas, CA

Investment Advisers Mullens & Co

Actuaries Bacon & Woodrow

Auditors Tansley Witt & Co.

Employees 780

Members 503

Pensioners 48

	£000
Annual Contributions	581
Annual Investment Income	433
Gross Annual Outflow	165
Capital Value	4,980
Summary of Investment	
Equities	2,644
Fixed Interest	1,899
Cash & Deposits	419

IMPERIAL CHEMICALS STAFF PENSION FUND AND IMPERIAL CHEMICALS WORKERS' PENSION FUND

Imperial Chemical House, Millbank,
London SW1P 3JF
Telephone: 01-834 4444

Head of Pensions Department W.G.Ashley, FCA, FPMI

General Manager (Investments) A.Conlong, BSc (Econ), FSS, APMI

Secretaries S.W.French, APMI (Staff Fund),
A.Erskine, APMI (Workers' Fund)

Actuaries Thomson McLintock & Co

Trustees 20, for each fund, split equally between members and management

Bankers Bank of Scotland (Staff Fund), Lloyds Bank Ltd. (Workers' Fund)

Actuaries R.Watson & Sons

Auditors Thomson McLintock & Co.

Company Employees 90,000 Approx.

	Staff	Workers
Members (at 31.3.80)	31,982	47,318
Pensioners	23,152	31,920
Deferred Pensioners	5,432	4,263
	£000	£000
Annual Contributions	61,140	44,179
Annual Investment Income	42,924	20,820
Annual Outflow	53,313	34,316
Capital Value (Book Value)	473,452	239,212
(Market Value)	634,200	317,400
Summary of Investments (Book Value)		
UK Equities	197,986	104,682
Overseas Equities	44,277	22,813
Fixed Interest	101,214	52,138
Property	128,722	63,378
Cash & Deposits	85,615	41,761
Others	1,475	914
Borrowings	(85,837)	(46,474)

It is estimated that by April 1981 the total assets of the Funds will amount to about £1,050 million

IMPERIAL CONTINENTAL GAS ASSOCIATION NON-CONTRIBUTORY PENSION FUND

14 Moorfields Highwalk London EC2Y 9BS
Telephone: 01-628 3272

IMPERIAL CONTINENTAL GAS ASSOCIATION
Continued

Pension Fund Manager & Secretary M.Drinkwater, FCIS, APMI
Stockbrokers Grieveson Grant & Co.
Actuaries R.Watson & Sons
Auditors Touche Ross & Co.
Solicitors Slaughter & May
Company Employees 4,192
Members 45
Pensioners 15

	£000
Annual Contributions	82
Annual Investment Income	130
Annual Outflow	68
Capital Value	1,300
Summary of Investments	
Equities	776
Fixed Interest	462
Cash & Deposits	118

IMPERIAL GROUP LTD. PENSION FUNDS
Bedminster, Bristol BS99 7JR
Telephone: 0272-666961

Pension Fund Manager R.Neale,MA,FIA,ASA,FPMI
Investment Adviser J.R.Haigh, MA, FIA, FSS
Investment Manager N.W.H.Ferguson, BSc, FIA
Trustees The ITC Pension Trust Ltd, The ITC Pension Investment Ltd
Pension Fund Titles Imperial Tobacco Pension Fund, St. Anne's Board Mill Company Pension Fund, Imperial Distributors Pension Fund, Robert Fletcher Pension Fund, Player & Wills (Ireland) Pension Fund, Grosvenor Pension Fund, Imperial Foods Pension Scheme, Evans Adlard Pension Fund, Courage Staff Pension Fund, Courage Employees Pension Fund, Courage Retail Managers Pension Fund
Property Advisers Richard Ellis
Actuaries R.Watson & Sons, Lane, Clark & Peacock (Courage Funds)
Auditors Deloitte, Haskins & Sells
Company Employees 90,400
Members 51,000
Pensioners 24,000

	£ million
Annual Contributions	31.4
Annual Investment Income	34.4
Annual Outflow	26.5
Capital Value	615.0
Summary of Investments	
Equities	250.0
Fixed Interest	66.0
Property	311.0
Cash & Deposits	(19.0)
Others	7.0

IMPERIAL LIFE RETIREMENT & DEATH BENEFIT FUND (GB)
London Road, Guildford, Surrey
Telephone: 0483-71255

Secretary to the Trustees W.A.Foote
Pension Fund Administrator D.M.Milton
Pension Fund Assistant P.J.Spry
Trustees J.A.Kempton, R.H.Wain, W.N.Anderton, Miss E.Hogg, E.R.Paton, D.A.R.Richards, J.E.Barlow
Investment Advisers Internal Investment Department
Actuary W.Law, FIA
Auditors Coopers & Lybrand
Company Employees 790
Members 700
Pensioners 46

	£000
Annual Contributions	908
Annual Investment Income	393
Annual Outflow	106
Capital Value (Market Value)	4,172
Summary of Investments	
Equities	1,213
Fixed Interest	1,687
Cash & Deposits	1,272

IMPERIAL LONDON HOTELS LTD.
Imperial Hotel, Russell Square, London WC1B 5BB
Telephone: 01-837 3655

Secretary H.R.Walduck
Employees 951

INBUCON LTD RETIREMENT BENEFITS SCHEME
Knightsbridge House, 197 Knightsbridge, London SW7 1RN
Telephone: 01-584 6171

Pension Fund Manager Miss D. Newnham
Secretary R.F.Harrison
Assistant Secretary A.S.Tointon
Trustees Royal Trust Company of Canada
Investment Advisers Royal Trust Company of Canada
Actuaries Hymans, Robertson & Co.
Auditors Touche Ross & Co.
Company Employees 313 (excludes subsidiaries with own pension schemes)
Members 147
Pensioners 79

	£000
Annual Contributions	210
Annual Investment Income	150
Annual Outflow	175
Capital Value	1,370
Summary of Investments	

INBUCON LTD *Continued*

Equities	559
Fixed Interest	496
Property	141
Cash & Deposits	72
Others	102

INCHCAPE & CO LTD

40 Mary Axe, London EC3A 8EU
Telephone: 01-283 4680

Pension Fund Manager K.W.Rose, APMI

Pensions Manager Mrs. C.E.Wadey

A variety of schemes are operated covering directors and staff in the United Kingdom and Overseas. These schemes are both self-administered and insured, and a number of different advisers are employed depending on location. In the United Kingdom and certain overseas locations the consulting actuaries are Hymans Robertson & Co.
In certain other overseas locations, advisers are Wyatt Harris Graham Ltd Hong Kong, Duncan C. Fraser & Co Kuala Lumpur, Malaysia

Employees (UK) 7,604

Most of the Group's business is overseas, and this figure does not include the substantial number of employees of the overseas subsidiaries and associated companies.

Major U.K. subsidiaries include Mann Egerton & Co.Ltd and Bain Dawes Ltd.

Head Office Staff are members of the Inchcape Group (U.K.) Pension Scheme, covering some 460 staff. It is self-administered and has assets of about £6,018,000

INCO EUROPE LTD. PENSION & LIFE COVER PLAN

Thames House, Millbank, London SW1P 4QF
Telephone: 01-834 3888

Employee Benefits Officer E.C.Cook,APMI

Trustees International Nickel Trustees Ltd

Directors G.Ursell-Smith, D.J.Boyd, E.C.Cook, M.Eley, C.E.Moore

Investment Advisers Morgan Grenfell & Co Ltd and Bankers Trust Ltd

Actuarial Advice obtained through Metropolitan Pensions Association Ltd

Property Advisers Strutt & Parker

Auditors Price Waterhouse & Co

Company Employees/Members 4,000

Pensioners 1,350

	£000
Annual Contributions	2,100
Annual Investment Income	2,400
Annual Outflow	1,750
Capital Value	32,700
Summary of Investments	
Equities	21,800
Fixed Interest	7,500
Property	2,000
Cash & Deposits	1,400

INDEPENDENT BROADCASTING AUTHORITY

(See IBA)

INDEPENDENT ORDER OF ODD FELLOWS - MANCHESTER UNITY FRIENDLY SOCIETY EMPLOYEES' SUPERANNUATION FUND

'Odd Fellows House', 40 Fountain Street, Manchester M2 2AB
Telephone: 061-832 9361

Secretary R.Henry, FBAA

Trustees M.U. Pension Trustees Ltd.

Investment Advisers Pember & Boyle

Actuaries/Pension Fund Consultants R.Watson & Sons

Auditors Wilson Martin Clarke & Co

Employees 1,700

Members 111

Pensioners 54

Annual Contributions £39,000

Annual Investment Income £98,000

Capital Value £832,000

INDUSTRIAL AND COMMERCIAL FINANCE CORPORATION LTD. STAFF PENSION PLAN

91 Waterloo Road, London SE1 8XP
Telephone: 01-928 7822

Company Secretary W.T.Siddle,LLB,FCIS,APMI

Actuaries Lane Clark & Peacock

Auditors Ernst & Whinney

Employees 430

Members 400

Pensioners 85

Annual Contributions £600,000

Capital Value £7,000,000

INGERSOLL-RAND LTD

Bowater House, Knightsbridge, London SW1X 7LU
Telephone: 01-584 5070

Secretary H.V.Houllon

Pension Fund Consultants Noble Lowndes & Partners Ltd.

Employees 2,880

INITIAL SERVICES GROUP RETIREMENT PLAN

300 Goswell Road, London EC1V 7LU
Telephone: 01-837 2828

Secretary N.J.R.Mullan,LLB,ACA

Other Pension Management A.R.Appleby

Trustees Initial Nominees Ltd.

Insured with Legal & General Assurance Society Ltd.

Pension Consultants Noble Lowndes & Partners Ltd

Auditors Peat Marwick Mitchell & Co

The Major UK Pension Funds INI/IRA

INITIAL SERVICES GROUP *Continued*

Company Employees (UK) 19,500
Members 3,000
Pensioners 550
Annual Contributions £1,300,000
Capital Value £3,000,000

INLAND REVENUE STAFF FEDERATION
7 St Georges Square, London SW1V 2HY
Telephone: 01-834 8254
General Secretary A.M.G.Christopher

THE INSTITUTE OF CHARTERED ACCOUNTANTS IN ENGLAND & WALES STAFF PENSION FUND
PO Box 433, Chartered Accountants' Hall Moorgate Place, London EC2P 2BJ
Telephone: 01-628 7060
Office Manager M.Luke
Senior Personnel Officer R.Collier
Deputy Secretary A.Dunlop
Stockbrokers & Investment Advisers Phillips & Drew
Actuaries Bacon & Woodrow
Auditors Myers Davies & Co, Robson Rhodes
Employees 294
Members 187
Pensioners 27
Capital Value £2,325,000

INTERDOM HOLDINGS LTD
Brigg Road, Scunthorpe, South Humberside
Secretary J.R.Baker
Employees 1,264

INTERNATIONAL AERADIO LTD.
Aeradio House, Hayes Road, Southall, Middx.UB2 5NJ
Telephone: 01-574 2411
Personnel Director A.J.Underwood
Secretary R.A.Payne,FCIS
Insured with Equitable Life Assurance Society
Annual Contributions Est.£1 million

INTERNATIONAL CHEMICAL CO LTD
11 Chenies Street, London WC1E 7EY
Telephone: 01-636 8080
Secretary C.M.Cooke
Employees 535

INTERNATIONAL COMPUTERS LTD
See ICL Pension Funds

INTERNATIONAL HARVESTER GREAT BRITAIN MANAGERIAL PENSION SCHEME AND NON-MANAGERIAL PENSION SCHEME
259 City Road, London EC1P 1AD
Telephone: 01-253 8422

Pension Fund Manager & Secretary R.D.Austin, APMI
Investment Managers Robert Fleming Investment Management Ltd, Scottish Amicable Pension Investments Ltd
Actuaries Bacon & Woodrow
Auditors Deloitte Haskins & Sells
Company Employees 6,000

	Managerial	Non-Managerial
Members	600	4,300
Pensioners	80	1,300
	£000	£000
Annual Contributions	800	1,900
Annual Investment Income	142	420
Annual Outflow	203	650
Capital Value (Market Value)	3,725	10,500
Summary of Investments (at Cost)		
Equities	580	1,640
Fixed Interest	556	1,600
Property	181	513
Cash & Deposits	121	350
Others	1,500	3,740

INTERNATIONAL NICKEL TRUSTEES LTD
See Inco Europe

INTERNATIONAL PAPER COMPANY LTD UK PENSION FUND
4/5 Grosvenor Place, London SW1X 7HD
Telephone: 01-245 9411
Company Secretary and Personnel Administrator J.S.A.Laidman
Pension Fund Title The International Paper UK Pension Fund
Investment Advisers N.M.Rothschild Asset Management Ltd
Pension Consultants Kwasha Lipton Inc, William M Mercer Benefits Ltd
Auditors Arthur Andersen & Co
Solicitors Allen & Overy
Company Employees 637
Members 347
Pensioners 33
Annual Contributions £107,000
Annual Investment Income £55,000
Capital Value £914,000

INTERNATIONAL SYNTHETIC RUBBER CO LTD
Brunswick House, Brunswick Place, Southampton, Hampshire SO9 3AT
Telephone: 0703-3423
Secretary B.R.Tizzard
Employees 892

INTERNATIONAL TIMBER GROUP PENSION PLAN AND STAFF PENSION PLAN

PO Box 118, Carpenters Road, London E15 2DY
Telephone: 01-985 3300

Secretary L.Hedden, FCIS

Pensions Administrator G.F.Oldham, APMI

Trustees R.E.Groves, C.C.Lorenzen, D.K.N.Hillas, R.W.Jewson (both schemes), W.N.Clayton, A.A.Simpson (Staff), D.F.Brown, J.Senior (Group)

Bankers National Westminster Bank Ltd

Investment Advisers N.M.Rothschild Asset Management Ltd, Morgan Grenfell & Co Ltd

Pension Fund Consultants and Actuarial Advice obtained through Willis Faber Advisory services Ltd

Auditors Pannell Fitzpatrick & Co

Employees 3,726

	Staff	Group
Members (at 5.4.80)	1,571	1,460
Pensioners	392	350
Deferred Pensioners	323	325
	£000	£000
Annual Contributions	1,226	723
Annual Investment Income	597	274
Annual Outflow	386	225
Capital Value		
Book Value	7,483	3,068
Market Value	8,144	3,361
Summary of Investments (Book Value)		
UK Equities	3,553	1,526
Overseas Equities	485	209
Fixed Interest	1,888	812
Property	588	255
Cash & Deposits	281	130
Others	527	76

INTERNATIONAL WOOL SECRETARIAT RETIREMENT BENEFITS PLAN

Wool House, 6-7 Carlton Gardens,
London SW1Y 5AE
Telephone: 01-930 7300

Pension Fund Manager & Secretary A.E. Meeson FCCA, ACIS, APMI

Trustees Five

Partly Insured with Yorkshire General Life Assurance Co.Ltd., Clerical, Medical & General Life Assurance Society

Investment Advisers & Stockbrokers Cazenove & Co.

Actuaries Bacon & Woodrow

Auditors Josolyne Layton-Bennett & Co.

Company Employees (UK) 500

Members 300

Pensioners 35

	£000
Annual Contributions	310
Annual Investment Income	260
Annual Outflow	98
Capital Value	3,264
Summary of Investments	
Equities	812
Fixed Interest	809
Cash & Deposits	1,580
Others	63

INVER HOUSE DISTILLERS LTD

Moffat Distilleries, Towers Road, Airdrie
Strathclyde
Telephone: 02364-69377

Secretary C.W.Rae

Managed by Legal & General (Pension Management) Ltd

Employees 704

THE INVERESK GROUP STAFF PENSION PLAN AND EMPLOYEES PENSION SCHEME

Clan House, 19 Tudor Street, London EC4Y 0BA
Telephone: 01-353 2323

Pension Fund Manager & Secretary K.A.Fuller, FCIS, APMI

Company Secretary D.Jackson

Trustees Inveresk Trustees Ltd

Investment Advisers S.G.Warburg & Co Ltd

Actuaries Bacon & Woodrow

Auditors Josolyne Layton-Bennett & Co

Company Employees 2,450

Members (Staff plan) 650

Pensioners 50

Annual Contributions £633,000

Capital Value of Fund £5,069,000

INVICTA MOTORS LTD.

23 Lower Bridge Street, Canterbury, Kent
Telephone: 0227-51777

Secretary J.M.Davis

Employees 530

IRANIAN OIL SERVICES LTD (THE 3 FINSBURY SQUARE CONTRIBUTORY PENSION SCHEME)

3 Finsbury Square, London EC2A 1AR
Telephone: 01-606 9811

Pension Secretary V.E.Stuchbery, FCCA, APMI

Chief Accountant M.E.Harley, FCA

Investment Advisers John Govett & Co. Ltd.

Actuaries Bacon & Woodrow

Auditors Peat Marwick Mitchell & Co

Employees 600

Members 327

Pensioners 152

Annual Contributions £865,000

Annual Investment Income £640,000

Capital Value £7,285,000

IRAQ PETROLEUM PENSIONS LTD.
33 Cavendish Square, London W1M 0AA
Telephone: 01-629 9405

Pension Fund Manager K.E.Parry,FCIS,FPMI

Assistant Manager R.S.Camp

THE IRON TRADES EMPLOYERS INSURANCE ASSOCIATION LTD STAFF TRUST
Iron Trades House, 21-24 Grosvenor Place, London SW1X 7JA
Telephone: 01-235 6033

Secretary S.E.Speer, FCA

Investment Advisers Gartmore Investment Ltd

Actuaries R.Watson & Sons Ltd.

Auditors Gane Jackson & Walton

Employees 716

Members 166

Pensioners 166

ISLE OF MAN GOVERNMENT
Civil Service Department, Government Offices, Bucks Road, Douglas, Isle of Man
Telephone: 0624-26262

Secretary Civil Service Commission G.Carter, FCIS

Employees 2,000

ISLE OF MAN STEAM PACKET CO.LTD.
Imperial Buildings, Douglas, Isle of Man
Telephone: 0624-3824

Secretary R.A.Kissack

Employees 535

ISLE OF WIGHT COUNTY COUNCIL SUPERANNUATION FUND
County Hall, Newport, Isle of Wight PO30 1UD
Telephone: 0983-524031

Pension Fund Manager D.A.Tuck,IPFA,FRVA (County Treasurer)

Trustees The County Council

Stockbrokers de Zoete & Bevan

Actuaries Hymans, Robertson & Co.

Auditors District Auditor

Employees 4,500

Members 1,860

Pensioners 586

	£000
Annual Contributions	1,400
Annual Investment Income	750
Annual Outflow	800
Capital Value	11,350
Summary of Investments	
Equities	6,300
Fixed Interest	4,000
Cash & Deposits	600
Others	450

THE ITB PENSION FUNDS
Star House, 69/71 Clarendon Road, Watford, Herts.WD1 1QL
Telephone: 26264

Pension Fund Manager M.J.Foskett,ACII

Pensions Director A.F.Johnson, APMI

Accountant D.Davidson,ACIS

Trustees 7 Employers, 7 Members

Investment Advisers Touche, Remnant & Co

Principal Stockbrokers Wood, MacKenzie & Co

Actuary The Government Actuary

Property Advisers St. Quintin

Auditors Touche Ross & Co.

Employees (at 31.3.80) 5,035

Members 4,331

Pensioners 398

Deferred Pensioners 528

	£000
Annual Contributions	5,740
Annual Investment Income	3,484
Annual Outflow	1,232
Capital Value (Market value)	39,942
Summary of Investments	
Equities	20,594
Fixed Interest	9,872
Property	4,019
Cash & Deposits	4,701
Others	756

ITT
See Standard Telephone & Cables

JACKSON GROUP LTD.
Dobbs Lane, Kesgrave, Ipswich, Suffolk
Telephone: 047362-2701

Secretary E.A.Worsley,FCIS

Employees 600

J. & H.B.JACKSON LTD
Websters Sidings, Stoney Stanton Road, Coventry, West Midlands CV6 5DL
Telephone: 0203-89051

Secretary R.F.Hayes

Insured with Provident Mutual Life Assurance Association

Employees 1,346

WILLIAM JACKSON & SONS LTD SUPERANNUATION & LIFE ASSURANCE SCHEME
40 Derringham Street, Hull HU3 1EW
Telephone: 0482-224131

Secretary G.S.Nurse

Assistant to Company Secretary D.Collinson

Insured with Legal & General Assurance Society Ltd.

Employees 5,140

JACOBS MANUFACTURING CO LTD
Archer Road, Sheffield, .S.Yorks.S8 0JS
Telephone: 0742-50018

Secretary A.D.H.West

Insured with Scottish Widows' Fund & Life Assurance Society

Employees 613

JOHN JAMES GROUP OF COMPANIES LTD
42 Baldwin Street, Bristol BS1 1PP
Telephone: 0272-24281

Secretary W.T.Powell

Employees 1,495

JARROLD & SONS LTD
5 London Street, Norwich, Norfolk NR2 1JF
Telephone: 0603-60661

Pension Fund Manager J.Henderson,FCIS

Secretary G.Bloxsom, ACIS

Chairman of Trustees A.C.Jarrold

Pension Fund Consultants Wyatt Harris Graham Ltd

Auditors Price, Waterhouse & Co

Company Employees 1,466

J. JARVIS & SONS (PENSIONS) LTD
239 Vauxhall Bridge Road, London SW1V 1HH
Telephone: 01-834 8411

Secretary J.R.Sheppard, FCIS, MBIM

Pensions Officer P.W.Edmonds

Stockbrokers Pidgeon de Smitt

Actuaries Clay & Partners

Auditors J.Foster (Bromhead Foster & Co.)

Employees 951

Members 163

Pensioners 54

Annual Contributions £150,000

Annual Investment Income £100,000

Capital Value £1,100,000

JAYCEE FURNITURE LTD
Bexhill Road, Brighton, East Sussex BN2 6QQ
Telephone: 0273-34081

Secretary J.R.A.Wallis,FCA

Insured with Clerical, Medical & General Life Assurance

Employees 704

J.B. HOLDINGS LTD
Johnston House, Hatchlands Road, Redhill, Surrey RH1 1BG
Telephone: Redhill 42466

Secretary A.L.Fidler

Insured with Guardian Royal Exchange Assurance Group Ltd

Employees 1,143

JELSON LTD
370 Loughborough Road, Leicester LE4 5PA
Telephone: 0533-61541

Secretary G.W.James

Insured with Commercial Union Assurance Co.Ltd.

Employees 1,211

ROBERT JENKINS (HOLDINGS) LTD STAFF PENSION FUND
Wortley Road, Rotherham, S.Yorks.S61 1LT
Telephone: 0709-556464

Secretary R.M.H.Malthouse BA(Hons),ACIS

Trustees Lowndes Associated Pensions Ltd.

Investment Advisers Baring Brothers & Co. Ltd.

Actuarial Advice Obtained through Cubie Wood & Co. Ltd.

Pension Fund Consultants Lowndes Associated Pensions Ltd.

Auditors Price Waterhouse & Co.

Company Employees 780

JENKS & GATTELL LTD
Phoenix Works, Wednesfield, Wolverhampton WV11 3PU
Telephone: 0902-731271

Secretary T.D.Leece

Employees 717

JENNERS PRINCES STREET EDINBURGH LTD
47-52 Princes Street, Edinburgh EH2 2YJ
Telephone: 031-225 2442

Secretary G.S.Morgan

Employees 600

JENTIQUE (HOLDINGS) LTD
South Green, Dereham, Norfolk NR19 1PR
Telephone: 0362-2121

Secretary R.M.Morritt,FCA

Employees 1,010

S.JEROME & SONS (HOLDINGS) LTD.
Victoria Works, Shipley, W.Yorks.BD17 7EF
Telephone: 0274-57251

Secretary G.H.Newton,FCA

Employees 512

JESSUPS GROUP OF COMPANIES PENSION AND LIFE ASSURANCE PLAN (1973)
London Road, Romford, Essex RM7 9QS
Telephone: 70-22311

Secretary J.R.Ganney,FCIS

Trustees J.R.Ganney,A.Jessup, G.R.Lucas

Insured with Clerical, Medical and General Life Assurance Society

Pension Fund Consultants Bain Dawes & Partners Ltd.

Auditors Frazer Whiting & Co.

Company Employees 494

Members 247

JESSUPS GROUP OF COMPANIES *Continued*

Pensioners 20

Annual Contributions 10.8% of pensionable salaries

Annual Investment Income (to 5.4.80) £60,000

Capital Value (at 5.4.80) £695,000

JEWISH MEMORIAL COUNCIL PENSIONS FUND

Woburn House, Upper Woburn Place
London WC1H OEP
Telephone: 01-387 3081

Secretary J.Zaltzman

Chairman A.Rosenzweig

Investment Advisers N.M.Rothschild & Sons Ltd.

Stockbrokers Carr-Sebag

Actuaries Hymans Robertson & Co

Auditors Shooter Greene & Co.

Members (at 1.6.80) 77

Pensioners 89

Annual Contributions £70,000

Annual Investment Income £352,000

Capital Value £2,850,000

H. A. JOB LTD PENSION FUND

Raleigh Way, Hanworth, Feltham, Middx.TW13 7NN
Telephone: 01-890 2261

Secretary A.R.Whitton, ACMA

Trustees S.Roberts, R.Culver, A.R.Whitton, D.H.Roberts, N.Pile, T.N.N.Grose

Stockbrokers and Investment Advisers Grieveson, Grant & Co

Actuaries and Pension Fund Consultants Bacon & Woodrow

Auditors Brooking Knowles & Lawrence

Company Employees 900

Members 874

Pensioners 138

	£000
Annual Contributions	170
Annual Investment Income	21α
Annual Outflow	126
Capital Value	2,012
Summary of Investments	
Equities	1,333
Fixed Interest	799
Property	13
Cash & Deposits	722
Others	117

JOHNSON & FIRTH BROWN GROUP STAFF AND WORKS PENSION SCHEMES

PO Box 61, Weedon Street, Sheffield S9 2GA
Telephone: 0742-449955

Pensions Manager C.W.Pearce, APMI

Deputy Group Pensions Manager S.J.Pegg,ACIS, APMI

Trustees Johnson & Firth Brown (Trustees) Ltd

Investment Advisers Barclays Bank Trust Company Ltd

Actuaries Duncan C. Fraser & Co

Company Employees 13,879

Members 2,600 (1977)

Pensioners 450 (1977)

	Staff £000	Works £000
Annual Contributions (to 5.4.80)	1,971	762
Annual Investment Income	1,288	92
Gross Annual Outflow	1,836	694
Capital Value (Market Value)	20,865	2,156

JOHNSON & JOHNSON LTD UK GROUP RETIREMENT PLAN

260 Bath Road, Slough, Berkshire
Telephone: 31234

Assistant Company Secretary B.M.Scoones

Secretary L.Hope

Investment Advisers Ivory & Sime, N.M.Rothschild Asset Management Ltd

Pension Fund Consultants Noble Lowndes & Partners Ltd

Auditors Coopers & Lybrand

Solicitors Linklaters & Paines

Company Employees 2,191

Members 1,670

Pensioners 460

Annual Contributions £684,000

Capital Value £6,900,000

JOHNSON GROUP CLEANERS STAFF PENSION SCHEME AND NON-CONTRIBUTORY PENSION SCHEME

Mildmay Road, Bootle, Merseyside L20 5EW
Telephone: 051-933 6161

Pensions Fund Manager & Secretary Miss A.F.Smith

Investment Advisers Barclays Bank Trust Co.Ltd.

Actuaries Duncan C. Fraser & Co

Auditors Deloitte Haskins & Sells

Employees 5,286

	Staff	Non-Contrib.
Members (at 5.4.80)	459	2,123
Pensioners	427	946
	£000	£000
Annual Contributions	309	8
Annual Investment Income	448	148

JOHNSON GROUP CLEANERS Continued

Capital Value (Book Value) 4,550 1,478

JOHNSON MATTHEY STAFF PENSION SCHEME AND WORKS PENSION SCHEME
100 High Street, Southgate, London N14 6ET
Telephone: 01-882 6111

Pension Fund Manager & Secretary P.F.Brock, ACIS, APMI

Trustees Johnson Matthey (Nominees) Ltd

Investment Advisers Standard Chartered Bank Ltd

Actuaries R.Watson & Sons

Auditors Arthur Young McLelland Moores & Co

Company Employees 5,800

	Staff	Works
Members	1,686	2,560
Pensioners	432	1,019
	£000	£000
Annual Contributions	1,508	1,499
Annual Investment Income	2,500	1,235
Annual Outflow	1,004	716
Capital Value	26,075	13,037
Summary of Investments		
Equities	11,996	5,678
Fixed Interest	13,415	6,804
Cash & Deposits	468	645
Others	196	(89)

There is also a Superannuation Fund with 30 members and 96 pensioners. Its Capital Value is £1,288,000

JOHNSON WAX LTD RETIREMENT & LIFE ASSURANCE PLAN
Frimley Green, Camberley GU16 5AJ Surrey
Telephone: 0276-63456

Pension Fund Manager F.K.Ross

Trustees Mrs.G.O.Hubbold, M.S Spark, J.W.Valentine

Insured with Standard Life Assurance Company

Pension Fund Consultants Reed Stenhouse Benefit Consultants Ltd.

Employees/Members 790

Pensioners 88

Annual Contributions £746,000

H. & R. JOHNSON-RICHARDS TILES LTD
Highgate Tile Works, Tunstall, Stoke-on-Trent, Staffordshire ST6 4JX
Telephone: 0782-85611

Secretary T.Meredith

Insured with Royal Insurance Co Ltd

Employees 4,368

JOHNSTON ALLEN & CO LTD
Victoria Street, Lurgan, Armagh
Telephone: 07622-2366

Secretary J.F.Johnston

Employees 1,330

A.A.JONES & SHIPMAN LTD RETIREMENT BENEFITS PLAN
Narborough Road South, Leicester LE3 2LF
Telephone: 0533-896 222

Secretary W.Kemplin

Pension Fund Manager E.Watts

Trustees F.W.Brooks, R.H.Male, R.P.Bull, E.Watts

Managed by Legal & General (Pensions Management) Ltd

Investment Advisers Kleinwort Benson Investment Management Ltd

Actuarial Advice Obtained through Cubie, Wood & Co.Ltd.

Pension Fund Consultants Noble Lowndes & Partners Ltd

Auditors Peat, Marwick, Mitchell & Co.

Company Employees 1,500

Members 1,300

Pensioners 140

JONES, STROUD (HOLDINGS) LTD RETIREMENT BENEFITS PLAN (1972)
Vida Mills, New Street, Long Eaton, Nottingham NG10 1HF
Telephone: 06076-4421

Secretary Mrs J.Butler

Company Secretary P.R.Rimmer,FCIS

Trustees P.L.Jones, D.L.Jones, P.W.Jones

Actuarial Advice obtained through Cubie Wood & Co Ltd

Pension Fund Consultants Noble Lowndes & Partners Ltd

Auditors Daffern & Co.

Company Employees 1,895

Members 230

Annual Contributions £130,000

Annual Investment Income £71,000

Annual Outflow £115,000

Capital Value (Market Value) £1,314,000

JOPLINGS LTD.
John Street, Sunderland, Tyne & Wear SR1 1OP
Telephone: 0783-57601

Secretary J.Askew

Employees 614

JOSOLYNE LAYTON-BENNETT
Metropolis House, 39 Tottenham Court Road, London W1
Telephone: 01-636 7777

Employees 790

J.T.GROUP LTD.
Bush House, 72 Prince Street, Bristol BS1 4HU
Telephone: 0272-290651

Secretary D.A.Bignold

Employees 503

K SHOES STAFF AND SENIOR MANAGEMENT PENSION SCHEMES
Netherfield, Kendal, Cumbria LA9 7BT
Telephone: 0539-24343

Pensions Secretary B.Haigh

Company Secretary J.R.Peat

Trustees J.R.Peat, J.A.Stretch, M.E.Wells, J.A.Ormerod

Stockbrokers Grieveson, Grant & Co.

Actuaries Duncan C.Fraser & Co.

Auditors Peat, Marwick, Mitchell & Co.

Employees 5,723

Members 850

Pensioners 150

	£000
Annual Contributions	880
Annual Investment Income	537
Annual Outflow	405
Capital Value	5,554
Summary of Investments	
Equities	3,013
Fixed Interest	2,130
Cash & Deposits	411

KAGAN TEXTILES LIMITED
Gannex Mills, Elland, West Yorkshire
Telephone: 042-27 3371

Director W.J.Attack

Employees 750

KALAMAZOO LTD
Kalamazoo Works, Northfield,
Birmingham B31 2RW
Telephone: 021-475 2191

Secretary G.D.Braithwaite

Insured with Prudential Assurance Co Ltd

Employees 2,211

KANGOL LTD
Norfolk Street, Carlisle, Cumbria CA2 5HX
Telephone: 0228-31711

Managing Director T.A.O'Donnell

Director O.M.Vangstad

Insured with Commercial Union Assurance Co Ltd

Employees 1,488

KAY-METZELER LTD.
Waterhouse Mill, Bollington, Macclesfield, Cheshire
Telephone: 0625-73366

Secretary D.D.Slater

Employees 1,146

E. & E. KAYE LTD STAFF PENSION & ASSURANCE SCHEME AND KAYE WORKS PENSION FUND
Queensway, Ponders End, Enfield, Middx.EN3 4SS
Telephone: 01-804 1601

Pension Fund Manager & Secretary R.H.Johnston, FCA

Trustees G.Davies, P.L.Denis, C.W.Scott

Investment Advisers Drayton Montagu Portfolio Management Ltd.

Actuaries Duncan C.Fraser & Co.

Auditors Peat, Marwick, Mitchell & Co.

Solicitors Rowe & Maw

Company Employees 800

Members (at 31.3.79) Works Fund 154, Staff Scheme 185

Pensioners Works Fund 19, Staff Scheme 3

	£000
Annual Contribution (Total) (to 31.3.79)	156
Annual Investment Income	63
Capital Value	888
Summary of Investments	
Equities	382
Fixed Interest	372
Property Unit Trust	111
Cash & Deposits	23

THE KAYE ORGANIZATION LTD
Kingsclere Road, Basingstoke, Hampshire
Telephone: 0256-3131

Secretary J.H.K.Forster

Employees 5,887

See also Lansing Bagnall Ltd.

KEARNEY & TRECKER MARWIN LTD
Crowhurst Road, Hollingbury, Brighton,
East Sussex BN1 8AU
Telephone: 0273-507255

Secretary Dr.F.T.Hamblin

Employees 1,104

G.J.KEDDIE & SONS LTD
Southend on Sea, Essex SS1 1LA
Telephone: 0702-62426

Secretary D.P.Cooper

Employees 600

KELLOGG COMPANY OF GT BRITAIN LTD
Park Road, Stretford, Manchester M32 8PA
Telephone: 061-865 4411

Secretary J.K.Johnson

Managed by Prudential Pensions Ltd

Investment Advisers Drayton Montagu Portfolio Management Ltd

Employees 3,579

KELSEY INDUSTRIES LTD

Kelsey House, Wood Lane End, Hemel Hempstead, Herts HP2 4RQ
Telephone: 0442-61291

Secretary D.R.Graham

Insured with Standard Life Assurance Co

Employees 678

KELVINATOR LTD

New Chester Road, Bromborough Wirral, Cheshire L62 3PE
Telephone: 051-334 2781

Secretary L.H.Young

Employees 510

T.W.KEMPTON LTD

Burley Mills, Burleys Way, Leicester LE1 3TR
Telephone: 0533-536521

Secretary J.B.Shepherd

Insured with Scottish Widows' Fund & Life Assurance Society

Employees 1,561

KENDALL & SONS LTD STAFF PENSION AND LIFE ASSURANCE SCHEME

St James Street, Leicester LE1 3SR
Telephone: 0533-22595

Company Secretary S.H.Rowland

Pension Fund Managers Godwins (Central Services) Ltd.

Trustees M.F.Bailey, S.H.Rowland, B.D.Youngman

Insured with Norwich Union Life Insurance Society

KENNEDY & DONKIN PENSION & LIFE ASSURANCE PLAN

Premier House, Woking, Surrey GU21 1DG
Telephone: 04862-5900

Partnership Secretary S.J.Marchment, APMI, AMBIM

Trustees C.M.Mitchell, R.B.Croft

Insured with Clerical, Medical & General Life Assurance Society

Pension Fund Consultants Griffiths & Armour

Auditors Coopers & Lybrand

Employees 761

Members 540

Pensioners 80

Annual Contributions £372,000

KENNEDY R. S. & CO LTD

Bushey Mill Lane, Watford, Herts
Telephone: Watford 26655

Employees 600

KENNING MOTOR GROUP STAFF PENSION SCHEME

Manor Offices, Old Road, Chesterfield S40 3QT
Telephone: 0246-77241

Pension Fund Manager T.J.German, FCCA

Investment Advisers Hill Samuel Investment Management Ltd.

Actuaries Duncan C.Fraser & Co.

Auditors Carlines

Solicitors Alsop Stevens Bateson & Co.

Company Employees 6,972

Members (at 31.3.80) 2,010

Pensioners 524

Annual Contributions £1,177,000

Annual Investment Income £1,594,000

Capital Value £16,017,000

KENRICK & JEFFERSON LTD (A) 1G59 FACTORY PENSION SCHEME AND (B) 1972 STAFF PENSION PLAN

High Street, West Bromwich, West Midlands B70 8NB
Telephone: 021-553 1001

Pension Fund Manager and Secretary W.H.Thomas

Trustees K.H.Jefferson, R.G.Dickinson, W.H.Thomas, D.G.Smith

Insured with Norwich Union Life Insurance Society, Prudential Assurance Co.Ltd.

Actuaries Clay & Partners

Pension Fund Consultants Metropolitan Pensions Association Ltd.

Auditors Price Waterhouse & Co.

Company Employees 805

Members (A) 282, (B) 166

Pensioners (A) 112, (B) 56

Annual Contributions (A) £135,000, (B) £144,000

KENT CO-OPERATIVE SOCIETY LTD SUPERANNUATION FUND

Maidstone Road, Chatham, Kent
Telephone: 0634-44955

Chief Executive Officer F.A.Creese

Trustees Kent Co-operative Society Ltd.

Investment Advisers & Stockbrokers Sheppards & Chase, Vivian Gray & Co.

Property Advisers G.L.Hearn & Partners

Actuary P.D.Johnson

Pension Fund Consultants Co-operative Insurance Society -P.D.Johnson

Auditors Appleby English and Partners

Company Employees 593

Members 214

Pensioners 71

	£000
Annual Contributions	63
Annual Investment Income	69
Annual Outflow	43
Capital Value	662
Summary of Investments	
Equities	36
Fixed Interest	218

KENT CO-OPERATIVE SOCIETY LTD Continued

Cash & Deposits	50
Others	358

KENT COUNTY COUNCIL SUPERANNUATION FUND

County Hall, Maidstone, Kent ME14 1XQ
Telephone: 0622-671411

County Treasurer W.B.Taylor MA IPFA

Assistant Treasurer(Management) S.A.Mercer BSc IPFA

Investment Officer N.W.Dowsett,ACCA

Managed by Baring Brothers & Co. Ltd, Pember & Boyle, LAMIT

Stockbrokers Pember & Boyle

Property Advisers Richard Ellis

Actuaries R.Watson & Sons

Auditors District Auditor

Members 24,600

Pensioners 10,690

	£000
Annual Contributions	18,880
Annual Investment Income	9,660
Annual Outflow	13,060
Capital Value	113,560
Summary of Investments	
Equities	57,260
Fixed Interest	28,500
Property	16,660
Cash & Deposits	7,670
Others	3,470

GEORGE KENT LTD

134 Biscot Road, Luton, Bedfordshire LU3 1AL
Telephone: 0582-21151

Secretary W.C.Oldham,FCA

Employees 4,354

KENT MESSENGER GROUP OF COMPANIES PENSION FUND AND LIFE INSURANCE SCHEME

Messenger House, New Hythe Lane, Larkfield, Maidstone, Kent ME20 6SG
Telephone: 0622-77880

Chairman H.R.P.Boorman

Trustees Kent Messenger Ltd.

Insured with Norwich Union Life Insurance Society

Company Employees 713

Members 411

Annual Contributions £317,554

KENYONS (BAKERS & CATERERS) LTD

Crossfield Street Bakery, Blackburn, Lancs
Telephone: 0254-55495

Secretary T.Stanley

Employees 600

KEYSER ULLMANN LTD GROUP PENSION FUND

25 Milk Street, London EC2V 8JE
Telephone: 01-606 7070

Company Secretary T.K.Day, FCIS

Pensions Expert Dr.P.Campbell

Investment Advisers Keyser Ullmann Pensions Management Ltd

Actuaries Bacon & Woodrow

Auditors Spicer and Pegler

Solicitors Paisner & Co.

Group Employees 676

Company Employees 227

Members 180

Pensioners 52

Annual Contributions £344,000

Capital Value £2,800,000

WALTER KIDDE CO LTD

Lux Works, Belvere Road, Northolt, Greenford UB5 5QW
Telephone: 01-845 7711

Director N.Lindsay

Insured with Norwich Union Life Insurance Society

Employees 714

KILLICK, MARTIN & CO.LTD.

Eastgate, 73 Leman Street, London E1 8ET

Managing Director D.W.Gravell

Employees 525

KIMBERLY-CLARK LTD PENSION SCHEME

Larkfield, Maidstone, Kent ME20 7PS
Telephone: 0622-77700

Company Secretary A.F.Stenning, APMI,ACII

Pensions Officer E.Valdus, ACII

Trustees Kimberly-Clark Pension Trust Ltd.

Investment Advisers J.C.Woodward, Reed International Ltd. and Ivory & Sime

Actuaries R.Watson & Sons

Property Advisers Richard Ellis

Auditors Deloitte Haskins & Sells

Company Employees/Members 2,803

Pensioners 254

	£000
Annual Contributions	1,581
Annual Investment Income	794
Annual Outflow	421
Capital Value	8,897
Summary of Investments	
Equities	3,975
Fixed Interest	3,020
Property	736
Cash & Deposits	605
Others	561

KIRK & KIRK LTD
Atlas House, 15-25 Ewell Road, Cheam,
Sutton, Surrey SM3 8DD
Telephone: 01-643 8969

Secretary D.K.Jones

Employees 576

KITCAT & AITKEN NEW STAFF PENSION FUND
The Stock Exchange, London EC2N 1HP
Telephone: 01-588 6280

Pension Fund Manager N.O.Taube

Secretary R.B.Collin

Trustees N.O.Taube, P.S.Nuttall, P.M.Evans Lombe, P.A.Mason

Stockbrokers Kitcat & Aitken

Actuaries Hymans, Robertson & Co.

Auditors Spicer & Pegler

Company Employees 158

Members 109

Pensioners 19

Annual Contributions £71,000

Annual Investment Income £80,000

Capital Value £1,287,000

ROBERT KITCHEN TAYLOR & CO LTD
Lynton House, 7 Tavistock Square,
London WC1H 9LS
Telephone: 01-387 0966

Secretary K.J.Powling

Insured with Guardian Royal Exchange Assurance Group Ltd

Employees 1,057

KLA INTERNATIONAL LTD
Berkeley Square House, Berkeley Square,
London W1X 6BY
Telephone: 01-491 3958

Secretary P.J.Miall

Employees 750

KLEEN-E-ZEE HOLDINGS LTD
Ansteys Road, Hanham, Bristol BS15 3DY
Telephone: 0272-670861

Secretary I.M.Prachar

Investment Advisers N.M.Rothschild Asset Management Ltd

Employees 622

KLEINWORT, BENSON STAFF PENSION FUND
20 Fenchurch Street, London EC3P 3DB
Telephone: 01-623 8000

Assistant Director Personnel P.F.G.Barnes, MIPM, FCIS

Trustees Kleinwort, Benson (Trustees) Ltd.

Investment Advisers Kleinwort, Benson Investment Management Ltd.

Property Advisers Kleinwort, Benson Unit Managers Ltd.

Actuaries Bacon & Woodrow

Auditors Spicer & Pegler

Company Employees/Members 1,050

Pensioners 150

	£000
Annual Contributions	1,500
Annual Investment Income	770
Annual Outflow	366
Capital Value	13,417
Summary of Investments	
Equities	7,460
Fixed Interest	3,936
Property	1,521
Cash & Deposits	500

RICHARD KLINGER LTD
Klingerit Works, Sidcup, Kent DA14 5AG
Telephone: 01-300 7777

Secretary R.J.Telling

Insured with Norwich Union Life Insurance Society

Pension Fund Consultants Noble Lowndes & Partners Ltd.

Company Employees 933

Members 403

Pensioners 96

Annual Contributions £285,000

KLYNTON DAVIS LTD.
Forest Road, Leicester
Telephone: 0533-22203

Secretary C.J.D.Morgan

Employees 1,201

KNEELS OF EXETER
Cowley Bridge Road, Exeter, Devon EX4 5AA
Telephone: 0392-71291

Director T.L.Crockatt

Employees 500

KODAK LTD. PENSION PLAN 1970
PO Box 66, Kodak House, Station Road,
Hemel Hempstead, Herts.HP1 1JU
Telephone: 0442-61122

Manager Employee Benefits V.W.Thomson, DFM, FCIS, FPMI

Part Managed by Legal & General (Pensions Management) Ltd.

Investment Advisers Robert Fleming Investment Management Ltd., Ivory & Sime

Actuaries Clay & Partners

Pension Fund Consultants Metropolitan Pensions Association Ltd

Auditors Price Waterhouse & Co

Company Employees 10,500

Members 10,255

Pensioners 4,636

KODAK LTD. *Continued*

	£000
Annual contributions	8,559
Annual Investment Income	5,802
Annual Outflow	3,400
Capital Value	
book Value (5.4.80)	81,881
Market Value	92,514
Summary of Investments (Market Value)	
Equities	40,048
Fixed Interest	26,837
Property Units	21,594
Cash & Deposits	4,035

KODE INTERNATIONAL LTD. PENSION FUND

43 Bath Road, Swindon, Wilts.SN1 4AS
Telephone: 0793-33671

Pension Fund Manager K.L.Walker

Secretary J.D.Averies

Trustees K.L.Walker, M.L.Caherty, Mrs.M.M.Hall

Managed by Legal & General Assurance Society Ltd.

Stockbrokers Buckmaster & Moore

Pension Fund Consultants and Actuarial Advice Obtained through Hogg Robinson (Pensions Consultants) Ltd.

Auditors Peat, Marwick, Mitchell & Co.

Company Employees 600

Members 250

Pensioners 5

Annual Contributions £105,000

KONE MARRYAT SCOTT PENSION PLAN AND EXECUTIVE PENSION PLAN

Wellington Road South, Hounslow, Middlesex TW4 5JN
Telephone: 01-570 7799

Secretary N.Hillier

Trustees Kone Marryat Scott Pension Trustees Ltd.

Managed by Metropolitan Pensions Association Ltd.

Auditors Peat, Marwick, Mitchell & Co.

Company Employees 1,250

Members 550

KRAFT FOODS LTD RETIREMENT BENEFITS PLAN

St.George's House, Bayshill Road, Cheltenham, Glos GL50 3AE
Telephone: 0242-36101

Secretary J.M.Richardson

Trustees Kraft Pension Trustees Ltd.

Investment Advisers Kleinwort Benson Investment Management Ltd.

Pension Fund Consultants Noble Lowndes & Partners Ltd.

Company Employees 3,669

Members 2,800

Pensioners 200

KWIK SAVE DISCOUNT GROUP LTD

87 Lord Street, Liverpool L2 6PH
Telephone: 051-236 7551

Head Office Warren Drive, Prestatyn, Clwyd LL19 7HV, Telephone:07456-2351

Secretary N.H.Fairclough

Pension Fund Consultants Cook & Co

Employees 3,810

KYLE STEWART (CONTRACTORS) LTD. RETIREMENT BENEFITS PLAN

Ardshiel House, Empire Way, Wembley, Middx.HA9 0NA
Telephone: 01-902 5321

Manager Legal & Insurance Department D.W.Ford, ACIS

Managed by Sun Life Pensions Management Ltd.

Pension Fund Consultants Stewart Wrightson Assurance Consultants Ltd.

Auditors Silver Altman & Co.

Company Employees 1,130

Members 303

Pensioners 17

Annual Contributions £431,000

Capital Value £2,036,000

KYLE STORES LTD.

Kyle House, College Street, Petersfield, Hants.GU31 4AX

Managing Director F.R.Northcott

Employees 806

L & M HOLDINGS LTD

Norman Road, Broadheath, Altrincham, Cheshire WA14 4ES
Telephone: 061-928 6131

Secretary A.Taylor

Managed by Clerical, Medical & General Life Assurance Society

Employees 1,979

LADBROKE GROUP LTD. 1973 PENSION SCHEME

Chancel House, Neasden Lane, London NW10 2XE
Telephone: 01-459 8031

Pension Fund Manager & Secretary J.P.Summers, FCCA, AMBIM

Trustees Five Trustees

Stockbrokers Phillips & Drew

Actuarial Advice obtained through Metropolitan Pensions Association Ltd

Pension Fund Consultants Metropolitan Pensions Association Ltd

Company Employees 19,011

Members 1,059

Pensioners 48

The Major UK Pension Funds KOD/LAN

LADBROKE GROUP LTD. *Continued*

Annual Contributions £580,000 (1977)
Annual Investment Income £139,000 (1977)
Annual Outflow £82,000 (1977)
Capital Value £1,749 million (1977)

LADIES PRIDE OUTERWEAR LTD
346 St Saviours Rd, Leicester LE5 4HT
Telephone: 0533-730071
Secretary K.J.Norman,FCIS
Insured with Phoenix Assurance Co Ltd
Employees 900

JOHN LAING PENSION FUND
Page Street, London NW7 2ER
Telephone: 01-959 3636
Pension Fund Manager D.O.Best
Secretary Miss M.G.Jones
Investment Manager R.I.Cockerton
Director of Group Personnel Services R.Cocker
Trustees The John Laing Pension Trust Ltd.
Stockbrokers Capel-Cure Myers Ltd., James Capel & Co., Scrimgeour, Kemp-Gee & Co., Quilter Hilton Goodison & Co.
Property Consultant J.A.S.Hepburn, FRICS
Actuarial Advice Obtained through Towers, Perrin, Forster & Crosby Inc.
Pension Fund Consultants Noble Lowndes & Partners Ltd
Auditors Thomson McLintock & Co
Company Employees 18,600
Members 5,150
Pensioners 1,039

	£000
Annual Contributions	4,416
Annual Investment Income	3,469
Annual Outflow	2,011
Capital Value	42,968
Summary of Investments	
UK Equities	15,422
Overseas Equities	1,696
Fixed Interest	8,642
Property	13,790
Cash & Deposits	2,034
Others	1,384

There is also a Pension & Life Assurance Scheme for Laing Properties Ltd.

1,800 John Laing also have an Executive Pension Scheme with the following details:
Members 1,800
Pensioners 120

Annual Contributions £200,000
Capital Value £3,000,000

LAIRD GROUP LTD (THE)
10 St James's Street, London SW1A 1EF
Telephone: 01-839 6441
Secretary W.I.K.Hunter
Pension Fund Consultants and Actuarial Advice obtained through Godwins Ltd.
Employees 8,162

LAKE & ELLIOT LTD
Chapel Hill, Braintree, Essex CM7 6QY
Telephone: 0376-20202
Secretary R.H.Biddle,ACCA,ACIS
Insured with Legal & General Assurance Society Ltd
Employees 1,560

LAKELAND LAUNDRIES HOLDINGS LTD
Abbey Road, Barrow in Furness, Cumbria
Telephone: 0229-20800
Director A.G.Milligan
Employees 887

LAKER AIRWAYS (INTERNATIONAL) LTD.
Gatwick Airport, Crawley, Sussex
Secretary R.W.Robinson,FCA
Employees 1,656

WILLIAM LAMB & CO (FOOTWEAR) LTD
Bottomport Road, Stanley Wakefield, W Yorkshire
Telephone: 0924-823541
Chairman Mrs.R.E.Lamb
Employees 600

LAMBERT HOWARTH GROUP LTD
Rossendale Works, Waterfoot, Rossendale, Lancs BB4 9LJ
Telephone: 07062-3587
Secretary J.S.Whiteley
Employees 1,527

LAMPACK LTD
Broomhills Industrial Estate, Rayne Road, Braintree Essex
Telephone: 0376-23708
Director M.P.Moseley
Employees 1,100

LANCASHIRE COUNTY COUNCIL SUPERANNUATION FUND
County Hall, Preston, Lancs.PR1 8XJ
Telephone: 0772-54868
Treasurer W.O.Joliffe, IPFA, FCA
Actuaries Duncan C.Fraser & Co.
Auditors District Auditor
Employees 29,500
Members 27,600
Pensioners 14,500

LANCASHIRE COUNTY COUNCIL Continued

Annual Contributions £19.6 million
Annual Investment Income £19.4 million
Capital Value £126.0 million

THE LANCASHIRE FOOTWEAR MANUFACTURERS ASSOC

Farholme Lane, Stacksteads, Bacup, Lancashire
Telephone: 070-683 4151

Executive A.E.Lewis

Employees 10,000

LANCASHIRE UNITED TRANSPORT LTD

Howe Bridge, Athelton, Manchester
Telephone: 05234-3501

Secretary D.A.Overbury

Employees 1,300

LANCER BOSS GROUP LTD.

Grovebury Road, Leighton Buzzard, Beds.LU7 8SR
Telephone: 0525-372031

Secretary L.H.Browne,FCA

Employees 985

THE LAND SECURITIES INVESTMENT TRUST LTD.

Landsec House, 21 New Fetter Lane,
London EC4P 4PY
Telephone: 01-353 4222

Secretary L.A.Jones

Employees 524

LANDIS & GYR LTD.

Victoria Road, North Acton, London W3 6XS
Telephone: 01-922 5311

Secretary A.J.Spring

Investment Advisers Warburg Investment Management Ltd.

Employees 889

LANKRO MAHLER & LANKRO AUGMENTATION PENSION FUND

Emerson House, Albert Street, Eccles,
Manchester M30 0BH
Telephone: 061-707 3244

Pensions Manager Mrs.B.J.Whitten

Trustees 4 elected by subscribers, 4 Board appointed

Stockbrokers Panmure Gordon, J & A Scrimgeour, L.Messel, H.Cooke Lumsdens

Actuaries R.Watson & Sons

Property Advisers Hampton & Sons, Druce & Co, Bernard Thorpe & Partners

Auditors Burne Phillips

Employees 1,750

Members 1,048

Pensioners 111

Deferred Pensioners 300

	£000
Annual Contributions	1,028
Annual Investment Income	689
Annual Outflow	126
Capital Value (at 5.4.80)	9,800
Summary of Investments (at 5.4.78)	
Equities	2,543
Fixed Interest	2,847
Property	1,055
Cash & Deposits	780

LANSING BAGNALL LTD

Kingsclere Road, Basingstoke,
Hampshire RG21 2XJ
Telephone: 0256-3131

Pensions & Insurance Consultants B.Parkinson,OBE

Employees 4,000

LAPORTE INDUSTRIES (HOLDINGS) LTD PENSION FUND

Hanover House, 14 Hanover Square
London W1R 0BE
Telephone: 01-629 6603

Pensions Director R.I.Hanson,MA,APMI

Pension Fund Secretary J.D.Riley,MA,ACIS

Trustees Laporte Pension Fund Trustees Ltd.

Investment Advisers Warburg Investment Management Ltd.

Actuaries R.Watson & Sons

Auditors Peat, Marwick, Mitchell & Co.

Company Employees 4,358

Members 4,200

Pensioners 2,000

Annual Contributions £3.3 million

Capital Value £30 million

JAMES LATHAM LTD.

Leeside Wharf, Clapton, London E5 9NG
Telephone: 01-806 3333

Secretary T.G.Kemp

Employees 542

LAUGHTON & SONS LTD

Warstock Road, Birmingham B14 4RT
Telephone: 021-474 5201

Secretary B.N.Higgs,FCA

Employees 933

LAURENCE, SCOTT & ELECTROMOTORS LTD. (1) MANUAL WORKERS PENSION SCHEME, (2) RETIREMENT BENEFITS PLAN 1972, (3) GOTHIC WORKS PENSION FUND

Gothic Works, Norwich, Norfolk NR1 1JD
Telephone: 0603-28333

Secretary B.D.Jordan,FCCA,FCIS

Other Pension Management G.B.Tubby

Trustees Gothic Works Pension Fund, B.D.Jordan, W.McCraith, P.M.Tapscott

(1) and (2) Insured with Norwich Union Life Insurance Society

LAURENCE, SCOTT & ELECTROMOTORS LTD.
Continued

(3) Gothic Works Pension Fund Self Administered, information below relates primarily to this scheme

Investment Advisers & Stockbrokers Montagu, Loebl, Stanley & Co., Laurence, Prust & Co.

Pension Fund Consultants Stewart Wrightson Assurance Consultants Ltd.

Auditors Peat, Marwick, Mitchell & Co.

Company Employees 3,865

Members (All funds) 3,500

Pensioners 1,119

	£000
Annual Contributions	2,400
Annual Investment Income	64
Annual Outflow	63
Capital Value	700
Summary of Investments	
Equities	553
Fixed Interest	125
Cash & Deposits	22

THE LAW SOCIETY PENSION & ASSURANCE SXHEMES
113 Chancery Lane, London WC2A 1PL
Telephone: 01-242 1222

Secretary Finance & Administration A.J.Merrett, FCA,FBIM

Insured with Legal & General Assurance Society Ltd.

Actuarial Advice Obtained through Cubie, Wood & Co.Ltd.

Pension Fund Consultants Noble Lowndes & Partners Ltd.

Members (total 3 schemes) 955

Pensioners 237

JOHN LAWRENCE (GLASGOW) LTD
137 West Regent Street, Glasgow G2 2JH
Telephone: 041-248 40131

Secretary J.O.C.Hunter

Insured with Sun Life Assurance Society Ltd

Employees 1,140

WALTER LAWRENCE LTD RETIREMENT BENEFITS SCHEME
Lawrence House, Sun Street, Sawbridgeworth, Herts CM21 9LX
Telephone: 0279-725001

Pension Fund Manager T.R.Davis

Financial Director T.J.C.Mawby

Employees 1,977

Trustees T.J.C.Mawby, H.J.Search, B.J.Prichard, A.Styles

Insured with Legal & General Assurance Society Ltd.

Investment Advisers Henderson Administration Ltd.

Actuaries Clay & Partners

Pension Fund Consultants Sedgwick Employee Benefits Consultants Ltd

Auditors Peat, Marwick, Mitchell & Co.

Company Employees 2,321

Members 420

Pensioners 90

Annual Contributions £658,300

LAW'S STORES
Saltmeadows Road, Gateshead,
Tyne & Wear NE8 3BQ
Telephone: 0632-70266

Secretary R.Evans

Insured with Scottish Equitable Life Assurance Society

Employees 1,432

LAWTEX LTD
Lawtex House, Holt Lane, Failsworth,
Manchester M35 9NH
Telephone: 061-682 7555

Secretary K.L.Brazier

Employees 859

LAZARD BROTHERS & CO.LTD. STAFF PENSION FUND
21 Moorfields, London EC2P 2HT
Telephone: 01-588 2721

Director D.A.Roberts

Staff Manager G.M.Craig-McFeely,ACIS

Investment Advisers Lazard Securities Ltd.

Actuaries Clay & Partners

Pension Fund Consultants Metropolitan Pensions Association Ltd.

Auditors Deloitte Haskins & Sells

Solicitors Linklaters & Paines

Company Employees 430

Members 334

Pensioners 154

Annual Contributions £822,000

Annual Investment Income £260,000

Capital Value £4,800,000

LEOPOLD LAZARUS SUPERANNUATION SCHEME
Gotch House, 20-34 St.Bride Street,
London EC4A 4DL
Telephone: 01-583 8060

Pensions Administrator R.S.de Saram, LLB,FCA

Part Insured, Part Managed by Provident Mutual Life Assurance Society

Pension Fund Consultants Stewart Wrightson Pension Consultants Ltd.

Auditors Griffith Miles Sully & Co.

Company Employees 500

Members 103

Pensioners 10

Capital Value £150,000

L.C.P. HOLDINGS LTD STAFF & WORKS PENSION & ASSURANCE SCHEMES

Pensnett Trading Estate, Pensnett, Brierley Hill, West Midlands DY6 7LZ
Telephone: 0384-46123

Pensions Director L.J.Stevens,ACIS,APMI

Investment Advisers J.Henry Schroder Wagg & Co.Ltd.

Actuaries Duncan C.Fraser & Co.

Auditors Thomson McLintock & Co.

Company Employees 3,289

	Staff	Works
Members (at 31.3.80)	630	702
Pensioners	105	15
	£000	£000
Annual Contributions	473	309
Annual Investment Income	201	25
Capital Value	2,364	562

EDWARD LE BAS LTD PENSION & ASSURANCE SCHEME

Claydon, Ipswich, Suffolk IP6 OJD
Telephone: 0473-830431

Trust Secretary H.T.Chaplin

Insured with Legal & General Assurance Society Ltd.

Pension Fund Consultants C.E.Heath Urquhart (Life & Pensions) Ltd.

Auditors Westcott Wilson

Company Employees 705

Members 533

Pensioners 135

Annual Contributions £381,000

LEAD INDUSTRIES GROUP LTD

Clements House, 14 Gresham Street, London EC2V 7AT
Telephone: 01-606 4400

Secretary T.W.Waller

Group Pensions Officer Miss K.M.Hertherington

Part Insured with Prudential Assurance Co Ltd

Part Managed by Prudential Pensions Ltd.

Actuaries Clay & Partners

Pension Fund Consultants Metropolitan Pensions Association Ltd.

Auditors Thomson McLintock & Co.

Company Employees 5,345

Members 4,000

Pensioners 700

Annual Contributions £2,583,000

Annual Investment Income £2,160,000

HARRIS LEBUS LTD

PO Box 7, Woodley Aerodrome, Reading, Berks RG5 4SD
Telephone: 0734-692731

Secretary R.G.Willmott,FCA

Insured with Legal & General Assurance Society Ltd

Employees 927

LEC REFRIGERATION LTD

Shripney Works, Bognor Regis, West Sussex PO22 9NQ
Telephone: 0243-33161

Secretary D.E.Durrant

Insured with Scottish Widows' Fund & Life Assurance Society

Employees 1,598

ARTHUR LEE AND SONS LTD

PO Box 54, Trubrite Steel Works, Meadow Hall, Sheffield S9 1HG
Telephone: 0742-387272

Secretary W.Ingram, CA

Insured with Eagle Star Insurance Co Ltd

Employees 2,415

DAVID LEE & CO.(LINCOLN) LTD.

Welbeck Estate, Welbeck, Worksop, Northants.

Secretary H.Ledger

Employees 653

WILLIAM LEECH (BUILDERS) LTD STAFF PENSION & LIFE ASSURANCE SCHEME

City House, 1-3 City Road, Newcastle upon Tyne NE99 1PG
Telephone: 0632-29954

Secretary J.Livingston

Trustees William Leech Ltd.

Insured with Equitable Life Assurance Society

Company Employees 2,223

Members 310

Pensioners 37

LEEDS PERMANENT PENSION SCHEME TRUSTEES LTD

Permanent House, The Headrow, Leeds LS1 1NS
Telephone: 0532-38181

Secretary P.Hemingway

S.LEFFMAN LTD PENSION & ASSURANCE SCHEME

Provident Place, Bridgewater, Somerset TA6 7EA
Telephone: 0278-424044

Secretary S.E.P.Eydmann,ACIS,ACMA

Insured with Legal & General Assurance Society Ltd.

Pension Fund Consultants Noble Lowndes & Partners Ltd.

Company Employees 750

Members 86

S.LEFFMAN LTD Continued

Pensioners 41

Annual Contributions £87,000

LEGAL & GENERAL ASSURANCE SOCIETY LTD.

Temple Court, 11 Queen Victoria Street,
London EC4N 4TP
Telephone: 01-248 9678

Company Secretary J.E.Neill

Pensions Manager W.A.Sibly

Employees 5,383

LEICESTER BUILDING SOCIETY PENSION AND ASSURANCE SCHEME

Oadby, Leicester LE2 4PF
Telephone: 0533-717272

Pension Fund Administrator M.J.S.Ward,BA

Secretary J.B.Gibbins,FCA

Trustees G.L.Aspell, J.D.Barnes, K.W.Bowder, B.N.Eckhard, K.Moorby, G.N.Corah

Insured with Legal & General Assurance Society Ltd.

Pension Fund Consultants Metropolitan Pensions Association Ltd.

Auditors Thompson McLintock & Co.

Company Employees (at 1.9.80) 1,516(F/T), 328(P/T)

Members (at 1.4.80) 1,200

Pensioners (at 1.9.80) 82

Annual Contributions £1,261,000

Capital Value (at 1.1.80) £4,600,000

LEICESTER MERCURY (F.HEWITT & SON 1927) LTD

St.George Street, Leicester LE1 9FQ
Telephone: 0533-20831

Director J.S.Wallwork

Employees 550

LEICESTERSHIRE CO-OPERATIVE SOCIETY

4 Union Street, Leicester LE1 4HA

Secretary G.L.Fyfe

Actuary P.D.Johnson,FIA (Co-operative Insurance Co.)

Auditors Appleby, English & Partners

Members (at 26.1.80) 1,740

Pensioners 483

	£000
Annual Contributions	271
Annual Investment Income	315
Capital Value	4,553
Summary of Investments	
Equities	1,832
Fixed Interest	1,478
Property	334
Cash & Loans	886
Others	21

LEICESTERSHIRE COUNTY COUNCIL SUPERANNUATION FUND

County Hall, Glenfield, Leicester LE3 8RB
Telephone: 0533-871313

County Treasurer R.Hale, IPFA

Trustees Leicestershire County Council

Investment Adviser A.C.B.Urwin

Stockbrokers Phillips and Drew

Actuaries R.Watson and Sons

Property Adviser G.D.Brigham,FRICS, County Estates Surveyor

Auditors District Audit

Employees 27,500

Members (at 31.3.80) 12,788

Membership Covers: Leicestershire County Council, all District Councils and 10 other organisations

Pensioners (at 31.3.80) 3,932

	£000
Annual Contributions (at 31.3.79)	9,206
Annual Investment Income	4,341
Annual Outflow	6,607
Capital Value	
Book Value	46,914
Market Value	59,629
Summary of Investments (market value at 31.3.80)	
Equities	35,385
Fixed Interest	10,734
Property	12,029
Cash & Deposits	1,481

LEIGH INTERESTS LTD.

Lindon Road, Brownhills, Walsall WS8 7BB
Telephone: 05433-5151

Secretary D.W.Phillips

Employees 567

P.LEINER & SONS LTD. PENSION FUND

c/o Cook and Co, 87 Lord Street,
Liverpool L2 6PH
Telephone: 051-236 7551

Secretary Cook & Co

Trustees P.Leiner & Sons Pension Ltd

Stockbrokers Tilney & Co

Actuaries Duncan C.Fraser & Co

Pension Fund Consultants & Auditors Cook & Co

Company Employees 740

Members 125

Pensioners 81

	£000
Annual Contributions	149
Annual Investment Income	73
Annual Outflow	83
Capital Value	996
Summary of Investments	
Equities	416
Fixed Interest	289

P.LEINER & SONS LTD. *Continued*

Cash & Deposits	83
Others	187

THOMAS WILLIAM LENCH HOLDINGS LTD
Excelsior Works, Rowley Regis, Warley,
W Midlands B65 8BT
Telephone: 021-559 1530

Secretary A.E.Totney

Employees 909

LENNONS GROUP LTD
Corporation Street, St Helens,
Merseyside WA9 1LD
Telephone: 0744-23216

Secretary I.Smart,FCIS

Insured with Norwich Union Life Insurance Society

Employees 1,918

LEP GROUP LTD (THE)
Sunlight Wharf, Upper Thames Street,
London EC4P 4AD
Telephone: 01-236 5050

Secretary P.W.S.Percival

Managed by Clerical, Medical & General Life Assurance

Employees 2,402

LESLIE AND GODWIN (HOLDINGS) LTD.
Dunster House, Mark Lane, London EC3P 3AD
Telephone: 01-623 4631

Company Secretary D.C.Dengate

Employees 1,202

Subsidies include Godwins Ltd. (Pension Fund Consultants)

LESNEY PRODUCTS & CO LTD
93 Burleigh Gardens, Southgate, London N14 5AQ
Telephone: 01-882 3811

Secretary D.J.Stormont, FCIS

Trustees L.C.Smith, R.S.Evans

Insured with Friend's Provident Life Office

Pension Fund Consultants Alexander Howden Insurance Brokers

Company Employees 7,977

Members 1,750

Pensioners 22

Annual Contributions £600,000

J.E.LESSER & SONS (HOLDINGS) LTD PENSION & LIFE ASSURANCE SCHEME
The Lesser Building, 141/9 Staines Road,
Hounslow, Middx TW3 3JB
Telephone: 01-570 7755

Company Secretary P.A.Willers,MA

Assistant Group Secretary B.J.Thomas

Managed by Sun Alliance Fund Management Ltd.

Pension Fund Consultants Alexander Howden Insurance Brokers Ltd.Life & Pensions Division

Auditors Bennett Nash Woolf & Co.

Company Employees 942

Members 350

Pensioners 10

Annual Contributions £250,000

Capital Value £1,600,000

LETRASET INTERNATIONAL LTD
7 Apple Tree Yard, London SW1Y 6LD
Telephone: 01-930 8161

Secretary C.M.Bate

Insured with Prudential Assurance Co Ltd

Employees 1,377

CHARLES LETTS (HOLDINGS) LTD STAFF AND WORKS PENSION & LIFE ASSURANCE SCHEMES
Diary House, 77 Borough Road, London SE1 1DW
Telephone: 01-407 8891

Secretary D.F.Denby,FCIS

Trustees D.F.Denby, F.Willis, A.Neill (Staff),
D.F.Denby, P.Oakes, A.Neill (Works)

Insured with Standard Life Assurance Co

Company Employees 650

Members Staff 177, Works 273

Pensioners Staff 36, Works 29

Annual Contributions Staff £196,000, Works £165,000

LEVI STRAUSS (UK) LTD
Moulton Park Industrial Estate, Northampton

Managing Director W.J.Gerrish

Employees 935

JOHN LEWIS PARTNERSHIP PENSION SCHEME
10 Clipstone Street, London W1A 3DF
Telephone: 01-637 3434

Pension Fund Manager R.A.Dennis, BA, FIA, APMI

Assistant Pension Fund Manager G.C.Worth

Pension Fund Secretary A.Chatfield

Accountant J.J.Cox

Trustees John Lewis Partnership Pension Trust Ltd

Investment Advisers Geoffrey Morley & Partners Ltd, Phillips & Drew

Actuaries R.Watson & Sons

Auditors Price Waterhouse & Co

Company Employees 26,000

Members 13,000

Pensioners 5,000

Annual Contributions £5.5 million

Annual Investment Income £2 million

Annual Outflow £1 million

Capital Value £60 million

LEWIS WOOLF GRIPTIGHT LTD
144 Oakfield Road, Selly Oak,
Birmingham B29 7EE
Telephone: 021-472 4211

Director E.Hurst

Executive R.E.Bowen

Employees 500

LEX SERVICE GROUP LTD. PENSION SCHEME
17 Great Cumberland Place, London W1H 8AD
Telephone: 01-723 1212

Pension Fund Manager A.J.Bennet, APMI

Trustees Lex Pension Trustees Ltd

Investment Advisers Warburg Investment Management Ltd

Actuaries Duncan C.Fraser & Co

Company Employees 9,300

Members 9,100

Pensioners 900

	£000
Annual Contributions	3,900
Capital Value	18,300

Summary of Investments (1979)	
Equities	7,300
Fixed Interest	2,600
Property	1,600
Cash & Deposits	900

LEYLAND PAINT AND WALLPAPER LTD. PENSION & LIFE ASSURANCE SCHEME
Northgate, Leyland, Preston, Lancs PR5 2LT
Telephone: 07744-21481

Secretary P.G.Gardiner, FCA, ATII

Trustees P.W.A.Simmonds, P.Pettman, B.Jones, E.G.Cottrell, F.Cumpstey

Part insured with Eagle Star Insurance Company Ltd

Part managed by National Westminster Bank Ltd (Trustee Dept)

Investment Advisers National Westminster Bank Ltd

Stockbrokers Williams De Broe, Hill Chaplin & Co

Actuaries Clay & Partners

Pension Fund Consultants Metropolitan Pensions Association Ltd

Auditors Peat Marwick Mitchell & Co

Company Employees 1,784

Members 1,000

Pensioners 150

Annual Contributions £420,000

Annual Investment Income £30,000

Capital Value £500,000

LEY'S FOUNDRIES AND ENGINEERING LTD
Colombo Street, Derby DE3 8LY
Telephone: 0332-45671

Secretary J.S.Binmore

Insured with Standard Life Assurance Co

Employees 3,551

LIBERTY & CO LTD
25 Great Marlborough Street, London W1R 6AH
Telephone: 01-734 1234

Secretary S.F.Saunders, FCA

Insured with Scottish Mutual Assurance Society

Employees 755

THE LIFE ASSOCIATION OF SCOTLAND LTD STAFF RETIREMENT BENEFITS SCHEME
10 George Street, Edinburgh EH2 2YH
Telephone: 031-225 8494

Pension Fund Manager and Secretary J.Innes, ACII

Trustees Sir Robert Erskine-Hill, Bt., G.W.Burnet, WS, J.M.Souness, FFA, K.McLean, ACII, W.Cranston, ACII

Managed by LAS Pensions Management Ltd.

Actuary J.Paterson, BSc., FFA

Auditors Thornton Baker & Co.

Company Employees/Members 355

Pensioners 56

	£000
Annual Contributions	401
Annual Investment Income	118
Annual Outflow	207
Capital Value	2,660

Summary of Investments	
Equities	403
Fixed Interest	449
Managed Fund	1,808

F.J.C.LILLEY LTD RETIREMENT BENEFITS PLAN (1975)
331 Charles Street, Glasgow G21 2QX
Telephone: 041-552 6565

Secretary S.G.Robson

Trustee J.Aitken, T.M.Bisset, D.S.Steen

Insured with Norwich Union Life Insurance Society

Pension Fund Consultants Norman Frizzell Life & Pensions Ltd

Company Employees 4,500

Members 456

Annual Contributions £325,000

LILLY INDUSTRIES LIMITED PENSION PLAN
Lilly House, Hanover Square, London W1R 0PA
Telephone: 01-629 7433

Secretary and Adviser Benefits Administration W.N.Jones

Trustees Eli Lilly Group

Managed by Legal & General (Pensions Management) Ltd.

Investment Advisers N.M.Rothschild Asset Management Ltd.

Pension Fund Consultants Towers, Perrin, Forster & Crosby Inc.

Auditors Ernst & Whinney

LILLY INDUSTRIES LIMITED Continued

Company Employees 2,300
Members 2,100
Pensioners 420

	£000
Annual Contributions	2,000
Annual Outflow	500
Capital Value	15,000

Summary of Investments	%
Equities	52
Fixed Interest	28
Property	12
Cash & Deposits	7

LINCOLNSHIRE COUNTY COUNCIL SUPERANNUATION FUND

County Offices, Lincoln LN1 1YL
Telephone: 0522-29931

County Treasurer D.G.Barrett,BA,IPFA

Senior Superannuation Officer R.E.Davidson,APMI

Investment Advisers Equity & Law Life Assurance Company

Stockbrokers de Zoete & Bevan

Actuaries R.Watson & Sons

Employees 21,000
Members 10,000
Pensioners 3,500

	£000
Annual Contributions	5,000
Annual Investment Income	2,000
Gross Annual Outflow	2,000
Capital Value (1979)	40,000

Summary of Investments (1978)	
UK Equities	12,128
Overseas Equities	933
Fixed Interest	7,144
Cash & Deposits	570
Others	1,625

LINCROFT KILGOUR GROUP LTD PENSION AND LIFE ASSURANCE PLAN

7/8 Warwick Street, London W1A 3AQ
Telephone: 01-437 0404

Secretary D.G.Griffiths

Other Pension Management D.H.R.Holland

Trustees D.G.Griffiths, B.V.Hartwell, A.D.R.Holland, R.G.R.S.Sinclair, P.F.Spratt, D.H.R.Holland

Insured with Standard Life Assurance Company

Pension Fund Consultants Bain Dawes Partners Ltd

Auditors Peat, Marwick, Mitchell & Co.

Company Employees 1,000
Members 110
Annual Contributions £140,000

PETER LIND & CO.LTD.

44 Wallington Square,
Wallington,Surrey SM6 8RU
Telephone: 01-669 4400

Secretary C.L.Penn,MA,FCCA

Employees 523

LINDUSTRIES LTD STAFF PENSION PLAN

Millbuck House, 37 Clarendon Road, Watford, Herts.WD1 1AJ
Telephone: 49722

Secretary H.A.Cameron

Investment Advisers J. Henry Schroder Wagg & Co Ltd & Baring Bros & Co Ltd

Actuarial Advice obtained through Cubie Wood & Co Ltd

Pension Fund Consultants Noble Lowndes & Partners Ltd.

Auditors Ernst & Whinney

Company Employees 6,325
Members (at 30.6.80) 1,000
Pensioners 400

	£000
Annual Contributions (at 1.7.78)	986
Annual Investment Income	749
Gross Annual Outflow	584
Capital Value	11,175

Summary of Investments (at 31.12.77)	
Equities	3,008
Fixed Interest	1,926
Property	283
Cash & Deposits	80
Others	464

A.G.LINFIELD (HOLDINGS) LTD

Chesswood Nurseries, Thakeham, Pulborough, West Sussex RH2 3EL
Telephone: 07983-2345

Secretary G.P.Bird

Employees 750

LINFOOD HOLDINGS LTD PENSION SCHEME

Linfood Pension Trustees Ltd. Brettenham House, 14 Lancaster Place, London WC2E 7EJ
Telephone: 01-379 6050

Secretary P.J.F.Moore

Trustees Linfood Pension Trustees Ltd.

Managed by Fenchurch Trustees Ltd.

Investment Advisers Fraser Green Ltd

Property Advisers Bacchus Gathercole & Partners

Pension Fund Consultants Fenchurch Group

Auditors Thornton Baker

Solicitors Herbert Smith & Co.

Company Employees 15,000
Members 4,000

	£000
Annual Contributions	3,000
Annual Investment Income	750

LINFOOD HOLDINGS LTD Continued

Capital Value	9,000

Summary of Investments
Equities	2,500
Fixed Interest	2,500
Cash & Deposits	500
Others	4,500

LINK HOUSE HOLDINGS LTD GROUP PENSION SCHEME

Robert Rogers House, New Orchard, Poole, Dorset BH15 1LU
Telephone: 02013-71171

Secretary A.H.Coy,FCIS

Insured with Norwich Union Life Insurance Society

Pension Fund Consultants Glanvill Enthoven (Life Pensions & Mortgages) Ltd.

Auditors Dixon Wilson & Co.

Company Employees 589

Members 393

Pensioners 36

Annual Contributions £269,000

LIN-PAC CONTAINERS LTD STAFF PENSION FUND

1 Charles Street, Louth, Lincolnshire LN11 0LA
Telephone: 0507-601101

Secretary A.T.Smith

Trustees Linpac Pension Trustees Ltd.

Managed by M & G Investment Management Ltd.

Actuaries Duncan C. Fraser & Co.

Auditors Streets & Co.

Company Employees 3,200

Members 366

Pensioners 10

	£000
Annual Contributions	233
Annual Investment Income	114
Annual Outflow	4
Capital Value	1,375

Summary of Investments
Equities	694
Fixed Interest	212
Property	150
Cash & Deposits	203
Others	116

LINREAD GROUP PENSION SCHEME

PO Box 21, Sterling Works, Cox Street, Birmingham B3 1RP
Telephone: 021-233 2525

Secretary R.D.Jefferies

Trustees D.G.Lyall, R.F.Hiatt, K.J.Morris

Investment Advisers Hambros Investment Management Ltd

Property Advisers Druce & Co.

Actuaries Duncan C.Fraser & Co.

Auditors Thomson McLintock & Co.

Company Employees 1,042

Members 778

Pensioners 93

	£000
Annual Contributions	300
Annual Investment Income	100
Annual Outflow	50
Capital Value	2,045

Summary of Investments
Equities	986
Fixed Interest	627
Property	156
Cash & Deposits	276

LINTON AND HIRST LTD

Parsonage Road, Stratton St Margaret, Swindon, Wilts SN3 4RN
Telephone: 79382-2471

Financial Director M.G.Casling

Managed by Commercial Union Pensions Management Ltd.

Pension Fund Consultants Bain Dawes & Partners Ltd.

Company Employees 600

Members 420

Annual Contributions £300,000

Capital Value £1,000,000

LISTER AND CO LTD

Manningham Mills, Bradford, Yorkshire BD9 4SH
Telephone: 0274-42222

Secretary G.M.Woodhead

Employees 3,171

THE LITTLEWOODS STAFF PENSION SCHEME

J.M.Centre, Old Hall street, Liverpool X L70 1AB
Telephone: 051-236 8022

Secretary & Group Pensions Manager J.Reynolds, FCII, APMI

Management Committee Management consists of Company Nominees and elected members representatives

Trustee The Littlewood Pensions Trust Ltd

Stockbrokers Gronfoll & Colegrave

Property Advisers Healey & Baker

Actuaries Duncan C.Fraser & Co.

Auditors Deloitte Haskins & Sells

Solicitors Nabarro Nathanson

Company Employees 45,080

Members 6,308

Pensioners 1,154

	£000
Annual Contributions	3,822
Annual Investment Income	2,612
Annual Outflow	1,869
Capital Value	27,906

Summary of Investments

The Major UK Pension Funds LIT/LOG

THE LITTLEWOODS Continued

Equities	13,387
Fixed Interest	10,873
Property	1,224
Cash & Deposits	2,209
Others	213

THE LIVERPOOL DAILY POST & ECHO STAFF PENSION FUND

P.O.Box 48, Old Hall Street, Liverpool L69 3EB
Telephone: 051-227 2000

Pension Fund Manager and Secretary H.D.Clarke

Stockbrokers Tilney & Co.

Actuaries Duncan C. Fraser & Co.

Auditors Touche Ross & Co.

Company Employees 1,150

Members 988

Pensioners 293

LIVERPOOL VICTORIA FRIENDLY SOCIETY STAFF PENSION FUND AND STAFF WIDOWS SCHEME

Victoria House, Southampton Row,
London WC1B 4DB
Telephone: 01-405 4377

Actuary J.F.Lambeth,FIA

Assistant Actuary J.G.Wibberley, MA, FIA

Secretary L.L.Munns,FIA

Trustees S.B.Wyatt, W.P.Broomfield,
G.R.G.Johnson, C.P.Mayhew

Auditors Rowley Pemberton Roberts & Co

Company Employees 4,000 Approx.

	Staff Fund	Widows Scheme
Members	3,285	1,198
Pensioners	3,270	457
	£000	£000
Annual Contributions	2,171	60
Annual Investment Income	3,631	584
Annual Outflow	2,510	215
Capital Value	36,731	5,766
Summary of Investments		
Equities	7,768	1,310
Fixed Interest	22,345	3,760
Property	5,630	545
Cash & Deposits	19	7
Others	969	144

WALTER LLEWELLYN & SONS LTD 1971 STAFF PENSION SCHEME

16-20 South Street, Eastbourne,
East Sussex BN21 4XE
Telephone: 0323-21300

Pensions Administrator P.R.Ellis

Insured with Sun Alliance & London Insurance

Company Employees 925

Members 228

Pensioners 6

F.H.LLOYD GROUP 1978 PENSION SCHEME

James Bridge Steel Works, Wednesbury,
West Midlands WS10 9SD
Telephone: 021-526 3121

Director & Secretary R.R.Harris, ACIS

Insured with Standard Life Assurance Co.

Pension Fund Consultants Hogg Robinson (Benefit Consultants) Ltd

Auditors Deloitte, Haskins & Sells

Company Employees 4,579

Members 4,000

Pensioners 1,000

LLOYD MAUNDER LTD

Willand, Cullompton, Devon
Telephone: 0884-820410

Secretary G.G.Heycock

Employees 644

LLOYD'S SUPERANNUATION FUND

Lloyd's, Lime Street, London EC3M 7HA
Telephone: 01-621 0526

Pension Fund Manager A.B.Richards,APMI

Actuaries R.Watson & Sons

Auditors Ernst & Whinney

Solicitors Biddle & Co.

Members 1,215

Pensioners 352

Deferred Pensions 365

Annual Contributions £1.8 million

Annual Investment Income £1.2 million

Capital Value £14.5 million

LLOYDS AND SCOTTISH LTD GROUP PENSION & EMPLOYEE BENEFIT SCHEME

Finance House, Orchard Brae, Edinburgh EH4 1PF
Telephone: 031-332 2451

Secretary W.S.Cockburn

Company Secretary E.G.C.Turnbull

Deputy Chairman W.W.Renilson

Group Personnel Manager H.D.Hopkins

Investment Advisers Royal Bank of Scotland Investment Dept

Actuaries A.R.H.Collins & Co.

Auditors Peat, Marwick, Mitchell & Co.

Company Employees 7,335

Members 1,620

Pensioners 121

Capital Value £2.7 million (est)(1977)

LLOYDS BANK LTD RETIREMENT BENEFITS SCHEMES

71 Lombard Street, London EC3P 3BS
Telephone: 01-626 1500

LLOYDS BANK LTD Continued

Manager (Pensions Administration) W.M.Hull

Assistant Manager (Pensions Administration) Miss H.M.Worsfold

Secretary D.H.Davies, APMI

Investment Managers J.A.Langford,AIB, B.C.Clark, FCA

Trustees Sir Jeremy Morse, KCMG, Sir Michael Clapham, KBE, A.J.Davis, F.W.Crawley, J.A.M.Kirkby, E.Robson

Investment Advisers Lloyds Bank Ltd Investment Department

Actuaries R.Watson & Sons

Auditors Price Waterhouse & Co.

Solicitors Linklaters & Paine

Company Employees 43,000

Members 41,200

Pensioners 8,100

	£million
Annual Contributions	50.5
Annual Investment Income	38.6
Annual Outflow	27.2
Capital Value	486.2
Summary of Investments	
Equities	220.2
Fixed Interest	144.6
Property	85.0
Cash & Deposits	9.8
Others	26.6

LLOYDS BANK INTERNATIONAL LTD PENSION SCHEME
40-66 Queen Victoria Street, London EC4P 4EL
Telephone: 01-248 9822

Pension Fund Manager & Secretary L.P.Simpson

Investment Advisers Lloyds Bank Ltd

Property Advisers E.A.Shaw & Partners, Bidwells

Actuaries Bacon & Woodrow

Auditors Ernst & Whinney

U.K.Employees/Members 1,500

Pensioners 450

	£000
Annual Contributions	3,805
Annual Investment Income	2,854
Annual Outflow	1,712
Capital Value	43,108
Summary of Investments	
Equities	25,858
Fixed Interest	9,814
Property	6,667
Cash & Deposits	829

LLOYD'S, CORPORATION OF
See Corporation of Lloyds

LOAKE BROTHERS LTD
Wood Street, Kettering, Northants
Telephone: 0536-2801

Secretary R.Tyldesley

Employees 510

THOMAS LOCKER (HOLDINGS) LTD
Church Street, Warrington, Cheshire WA1 2SU
Telephone: 0925-51212

Secretary H.H.Collinson

Insured with Standard Life Assurance Co.

Employees 881

LOCKWOODS FOODS LTD PENSION FUND
Bridge Road, Long Sutton, Spalding, Lincs PE12 9EQ
Telephone: 0406-362101

Secretary D.A.C.Sprague

Trustees K.H.Blacklock, N.G.Horton-Mastim, W.J.Long

Insured with Eagle Star Insurance Co.Ltd.

Pension Fund Consultants Minet Consultancy Services Ltd.

Auditors Whiting & Partners

Company Employees 2,307

Members 216

Pensioners 29

F. AND A.E.LODGE LTD.
Tandem House, Tandem Industrial Estate, Waterloo, Huddersfield
Telephone: 0484-22671

Secretary J.K.Lodge

Employees 650

LOEW'S (GREAT BRITAIN) LTD.
11 Mansfield Street, London W1M 0AH

Managing Director L.A.Tisch

Employees 580

LOGABAX LTD
1-7 Wesley Avenue, London NW10 7BZ
Telephone: 01-965 0061

Director J.Chevalier

Employees 1,000

LOGICA LTD PENSION FUND & LIFE ASSURANCE SCHEME
64 Newman Street, London W1A 4SE
Telephone: 01-637 9111

Company Secretary S.W.Piercy, FAAI

Trustees P.C.Harbridge, P.J.Coen, W.F.Key, J.F.Polhill, S.Sarmiento

Insured with Confederation Life Insurance Co.

Pension Fund Consultants Martin Paterson Associates Ltd.

Company Employees 700

Members 200

Annual Contributions £240,000

LOMBARD NORTH CENTRAL LTD
Lombard House, Curzon Street, London W1A 1EU
Telephone: 01-499 4111

Secretary J.S.Thomas,FCA

Employees 3,093

LONDON & EUROPEAN GROUP LTD.
28 Lichfield Street, London WC2H 9NJ
Telephone: 01-379 6687

Secretary J.E.Paterson,CA

Employees 836

LONDON AND MANCHESTER GROUP PENSION SCHEME
Winslade Park, Exeter, Devon EX5 1DS
Telephone: 0392-52155

Pension Fund Manager and Secretary
P.R.Anderson, MA, Barrister

Trustees Lonmanpen Ltd.

Auditors Spain Brothers & Co.

Solicitors Sacker & Partners

Company Employees 2,045

Members 1,562

Pensioners 746

	£000
Annual Contributions	1,480
Annual Investment Income	2,300
Annual Outflow	927
Capital Value	22,140
Summary of Investments	
Equities	9,807
Fixed Interest	5,896
Property	1,715
Cash & Deposits	1,781
Others	2,942

LONDON & MIDLAND INDUSTRIES LTD.
45 Nottingham Place, London W1M 4BL
Telephone: 01-486 6341

Secretary J.R.P.Davies,FCIS

Insured with Standard Life Assurance Co

Employees 1,500

LONDON & MIDLAND STEEL SCAFFOLDING LTD.
27 Eccleston Street, London SW1W 9NR

Secretary E.R.Hammond

Employees 568

LONDON & NORTHERN GROUP LTD
Essex Hall, Essex Street, London WC2R 3JD
Telephone: 01-836 9261

Secretary C.C.Mullett

Employees 5,345

LONDON & PROVINCIAL POSTER GROUP LTD.
76-86 Brigstock Road, Thornton Heath, Surrey CR4 7JA
Telephone: 01-689 2131

Secretary G.B.Smethurst,MA,ACIS

Employees 607

LONDON & SCANDINAVIAN METALLURGICAL CO LTD
45 Wimbledon Hill Road, London SW19 7LZ
Telephone: 01-947 1221

Secretary M.A.Finn

Insured with Norwich Union Life Insurance Society

Employees 601

LONDON BOROUGH OF BARKING
Civic Centre, Dagenham, Essex RM10 7BY
Telephone: 01-592 4500

Treasurer J.Willmott,IPFA,ACIS

LONDON BOROUGH OF BARNET SUPERANNUATION FUND
Town Hall, Hendon, London NW4 4BG
Telephone: 01-202 8282

Director of Financial Services G.W.Hopkins,IPFA, FCA,FRVA

Superannuation Officer G.Young, APMI

Trustees Barnet LBC

Investment Advisers Mr. P. Oldham, Commercial Union Assurance Co.

Stockbrokers Scrimgeour Kemp-Gee & Co., Fielding Newson Smith & Co.

Actuaries R.Watson & Sons

Auditors District Auditor

Employees 6,900

Members 5,100

Pensioners 1,320

	£000
Annual Contributions	3,900
Annual Investment Income	2,200
Annual Outflow	2,700
Capital Value	22,100
Summary of Investments	
Equities	11,890
Fixed Interest	7,770
Property	640
Cash & Deposits	1,800

LONDON BOROUGH OF BEXLEY SUPERANNUATION FUND
Town Hall, Erith, Kent DA8 1TL
Telephone: 01-303 7777

Treasurer G.J.Folwell, IPFA, FRVA

Trustees Lord Mayor & Burghesses

Investment Advisers Henderson Administration, A.Ashford

Stockbrokers Phillips & Drew

Actuaries Duncan C.Fraser & Co.

Auditors District Audit

Employees 6,808

Members (at 31.3.80) 2,739

Pensioners 1,152

LONDON BOROUGH OF BEXLEY Continued

	£000
Annual Contributions	2,963
Annual Investment Income	897
Annual Outflow	2,275
Capital Value	16,212

Summary of Investments
Equities	8,191
Fixed Interest	5,084
Property Unit Trusts	570
Cash & Deposits	1,627
Others	740

LONDON BOROUGH OF BRENT

Brent Town Hall, Forty Lane, Wembley, Middlesex HA9 9HR
Telephone: 01-903 1400

Pension Fund Manager A.N.Boulter,IPFA,FRVA (Director of Finance)

Actuaries R.Watson & Sons

Auditors District Auditor

LONDON BOROUGH OF BROMLEY SUPERANNUATION FUND

Sherman House, Sherman Road, Bromley, Kent BR1 3TE
Telephone: 01-464 3333

Borough Treasurer N.Newton,BA,IPFA

Secretary R.Roweth, IPFA (Deputy Borough Treasurer)

Management Committee 4 Councillors, Ivory & Sime Ltd., Borough Treasurer and NALGO

Investment Advisers Ivory & Sime Ltd.

Actuaries R.Watson & Sons

Auditors District Auditor

Employees 8,000

Members 3,950

Pensioners 1,500

	£000
Annual Contributions	3,284
Annual Investment Income	1,772
Annual Outflow	2,557
Capital Value	18,612

Summary of Investments
Equities	8,168
Fixed Interest	6,680
Cash & Deposits	2,685

LONDON BOROUGH OF CAMDEN

Town Hall, Euston Road, London NW1 2RX
Telephone: 01-278 4444

Treasurer F.B.Budd, IPFA

Superannuation Officer R.S.Coles, APMI

LONDON BOROUGH OF THE CITY OF WESTMINSTER

Westminster City Hall, Victoria Street, London SW1E 6QW
Telephone: 01-828 8070

Director of Finance D.J.Hopkins,BSc,IPFA,FRVA

LONDON BOROUGH OF CROYDON

Taberner House, Park Lane, Croydon, Surrey CR9 3JS
Telephone: 01-686 4433

Treasurer N.P.Hepworth,IPFA

Superannuation Officer C.Grimshaw, APMI

LONDON BOROUGH OF EALING SUPERANNUATION FUND

Town Hall, New Broadway, Ealing, London W5 2BY
Telephone: 01-579 2424

Director of Finance R.J.Chalkley,IPFA

Trustees London Borough of Ealing

Managed by Barclays Bank Investment Trust Co.Ltd.

Actuaries R.Watson & Sons

Company Employees 13,000

Members 6,000

Pensioners 1,200

	£000
Annual Contributions	2,740
Annual Investment Income	1,790
Annual Outflow	1,570
Capital Value	20,090

Summary of Investments
Equities	7,035
Fixed Interest	5,036
Property Unit Trusts	1,749
Cash & Deposits	1,166
Others	5,107

LONDON BOROUGH OF ENFIELD

Civic Centre, Silver Street, Enfield, Middx.EN1 3XF
Telephone: 01-366 6565

Treasurer J.Cherry,IPFA

LONDON BOROUGH OF GREENWICH

Municipal Offices, 45-53 Wellington Street, London SE18 6RA
Telephone: 01-854 8888

Treasurer S.J.Tunbridge, IPFA, FCA, ACIS

Superannuation Officers G.F.Packer, APMI, G.L.Wye, APMI

LONDON BOROUGH OF HACKNEY SUPERANNUATION FUND

Municipal Offices, Stoke Newington Church Street, Stoke Newington N16 0JR
Telephone: 01-800 1282

Director of Finance J.Beha,BA,IPFA

Principal Superannuation Assistant B.S.Harris, APMI

Investment Advisers County Bank Ltd.

Actuaries R.Watson & Sons

Property Advisers County Bank, Vigers Ltd

Auditors District Auditor

Employees 6,550

345

LONDON BOROUGH OF HACKNEY Continued

Members (at 31.3.80) 5,044
Pensioners 1,378
Annual Contributions (at 31.3.78) £2,868,000
Capital Value (at 31.7.78) £12,765,000

LONDON BOROUGH OF HAMMERSMITH AND FULHAM SUPERANNUATION FUND

Town Hall, King Street, Hammersmith,
London W6 9JU
Telephone: 01-748 3020

Director of Finance C.Howe,IPFA

Superannuation Officer C.G.Cannons, APMI

Stockbrokers Pember & Boyle, Phillips & Drew, Fielding Newson-Smith & Co.

Employees 5,240

Members 4,095

Pensioners 1,104

Annual Contributions £2,800,000

Annual Investment Income £1,741,000

Capital Value £21,617,000

LONDON BOROUGH OF HARINGEY SUPERANNUATION FUND

Civic Centre, PO Box 264, High Road,
Wood Green, London N22 4LE
Telephone: 01-888 1282

Comptroller & Treasurer D.Eacott,IPFA,FRVA

Superannuation Officer I.Benson

Trustees Haringey London Borough Council

Investment Advisers & Stockbrokers Phillips & Drew, Fielding Newson-Smith & Co.

Actuaries R.Watson & Sons

Auditors District Auditor

Employees 7,285 (Excludes teachers)

Members 5,100

Pensioners 1,286

	£000
Annual Contributions	3,861
Annual Investment Income	1,780
Annual Outflow	2,102
Capital Value	
Book Value	18,792
Market Value	21,086
Summary of Investments	
Equities	13,466
Fixed Interest	4,936
Property	1,534
Cash & Deposits	1,150

LONDON BOROUGH OF HARROW

Civic Centre, Harrow, Middx.HA1 2UJ
Telephone: 01-863 5611

Secretary Director of Finance (D.A.Adams)

Stockbrokers (Investment Advisers) Mullens & Co., Grieveson, Grant & Co.

Actuaries Hymans, Robertson & Co

Company Employees 8,513
Members 2,894
Pensioners 665

	£000
Annual Contributions	1,817
Annual Investment Income	969
Annual Outflow	1,237
Capital Value (Book value)	11,760
Summary of Investments	
Equities	4,773
Fixed Interest	3,960
Property	2,060
Cash & Deposits	967

LONDON BOROUGH OF HAVERING

Town Hall, Romford, Essex RM1 1UW
Telephone: 46040

Director of Finance P.Hudd,IPFA

LONDON BOROUGH OF HILLINGDON

Civic Centre, Uxbridge, Middx UB8 1UW
Telephone: 50111

Treasurer E.C.Spence, IPFA, ARVA

Superannuation Officer J.Standing, APMI

LONDON BOROUGH OF HOUNSLOW SUPERANNUATION FUND

The Civic Centre, Lampton Row, Hounslow,
Middx.TW3 4DN
Telephone: 01-570 7728

Secretary The Borough Treasurer (R.T.Treadway, IPFA)

Investment Advisers & Stockbrokers Pember & Boyle

Actuaries R.Watson & Sons

Auditors District Auditor

Company Employees 9,900

Employees 3,700

Pensioners 1,050

	£000
Annual Contributions	2,586
Annual Investment Income	1,481
Annual Outflow	2,139
Capital Value (Market Value)	16,450
Summary of Investments	
Equities	8,798
Fixed Interest	5,183
Property Unit Trusts	1,478
Cash & Deposits	991

LONDON BOROUGH OF ISLINGTON SUPERANNUATION FUND

Town Hall, Upper Street, Islington,
London N1 2UD
Telephone: 01-226 1234

Treasurer E.W.Dear, IPFA

Investment Managers Henderson Administration Ltd., Hill Samuel Investment Management Ltd.

Property Advisers Hill Samuels Property

Actuaries R.Watson & Sons

LONDON BOROUGH OF ISLINGTON *Continued*

Auditors District Audit
Employees 6,000
Members 5,200
Pensioners 1,080

	£000
Annual Contributions	3,000
Annual Investment Income	1,500
Annual Outflow	2,034
Capital Value	20,063
Summary of Investments	
Equities	6,922
Fixed Interest	6,172
Property	2,962
Cash & Deposits	4,007

LONDON BOROUGH OF LAMBETH

Lambeth Town Hall, Brixton Hill,
London SW2 1RW
Telephone: 01-274 7722

Treasurer J.E.Halligan, IPFA
Superannuation Officer Miss E.Heumann

LONDON BOROUGH OF LEWISHAM SUPERANNUATION FUND

Town Hall, Catford, London SE6 4RX
Telephone: 01-690 4343

Treasurer E.H.A.Akers,IPFA,FRVA,ASCA
Trustees The Mayor and Burgesses
Stockbrokers Phillips & Drew
Actuaries Hymans Robertson & Co
Property Advisers Property Unit Trusts
Company Employees 7,876
Members 5,572
Pensioners 1,410

	£000
Annual Contributions	4,326
Annual Investment Income	1,988
Annual Outflow	2,217
Capital Value	23,901
Summary of Investments	
Equities	13,864
Fixed Interest	6,794
Property	1,698
Cash & Deposits	1,545

LONDON BOROUGH OF MERTON

PO Box 364, Town Hall, Broadway,
Wimbledon, London SW19 7NR
Telephone: 01-946 8070

Treasurer J.Hutchinson, IPFA

LONDON BOROUGH OF NEWHAM SUPERANNUATION FUND

New Municipal Offices, 91 The Grove, Stratford,
London E15 1EW
Telephone: 01-534 4545

Secretary Direct of Finance (John Samuel,BA,IPFA)

Trustees The Mayor and Burgesses
Investment Managers County Bank Ltd.
Property Advisers E.W.Wallaker & Co.
Actuaries R.Watson & Sons
Auditors District Auditor
Employees (at 31.3.80) 14,089
Members 5,580
Pensioners 2,791

	£000
Annual Contributions	3,291
Annual Investment Income	2,418
Annual Outflow	1,928
Capital Value	
Cost	21,995
Market Value	25,867
Summary of Investments	
Equities	9,193
Foreign Securities	2,295
Fixed Interest	5,509
Property	6,471
Cash & Deposits	2,400

LONDON BOROUGH OF REDBRIDGE SUPERANNUATION FUND

22-26 Clements Road, Ilford, Essex IG1 1BD
Telephone: 01-478 3020

Borough Treasurer S.A.Fuller
Investment Advisers and Stockbrokers Pember & Boyle, Fielding, Newson-Smith & Co
Actuaries R.Watson & Sons
Auditors District Audit
Employees 4,000 (Excluding Teachers and part-time employees)
Members 3,000
Pensioners 1,165

	£000
Annual Contributions	1,979
Annual Investment Income	1,286
Annual Outflow	1,042
Capital Value (Cost Value at 31.3.80)	14,257
Summary of Investments	
Equities	6,844
Fixed Interest	6,569
Cash & Deposits	66
Others	778

LONDON BOROUGH OF RICHMOND UPON THAMES SUPERANNUATION FUND

York House (Municipal Offices),
Twickenham TW1 3AA
Telephone: 01-892 4466

Internal Management Director of Finance (B.Davies, IPFA, FCA, FRVA)
Superannuation Officer L.C.Bryan,APMI
Stockbrokers Laing & Cruickshank
Actuaries R.Watson & Sons
Members 2,374
Pensioners 874

LONDON BOROUGH OF RICHMOND UPON THAMES
Continued

	£000
Annual Contributions	2,200
Annual Investment Income	1,000
Annual Outflow	1,500
Capital Value (Book Value)	10,750
Summary of Investments	
Equities (unit trusts)	1,415
Fixed interest	7,986
Property (unit trusts)	1,315
Cash & Deposits	34

LONDON BOROUGH OF SOUTHWARK
Municipal Offices, Spa Road, London SE16 3QN
Telephone: 01-237 6677

Treasurer G.Corless

Superannuation Officer R.A.C.Whittington, APMI

LONDON BOROUGH OF SUTTON
Civic Offices, St. Nicholas Way, Sutton,
Surrey SM1 1EA
Telephone: 01-661-5000

Director of Finance W.T.Shay,IPFA

Superannuation Officer A.C.Baxter,APMI

Investment Advisers Hoare Govett Ltd. and L.A.M.I.T.

Stockbrokers Hoare Govett Ltd.

Actuaries R.Watson & Sons

Company Employees 7,300

Members 2,084

Pensioners 730

	£000
Annual Contributions	1,576
Annual Investment Income	970
Annual Outflow	1,606
Capital Value	
Cost Value	9,385
Market Value (at 31.3.80)	11,018
Summary of Investments	
Equities	5,817
Fixed Interest	4,154
Property	759
Cash & Deposits	288

LONDON BOROUGH OF TOWER HAMLETS SUPERANNUATION FUND
Town Hall, Patriot Square, London E2 9LN
Telephone: 01-980 4831

Pension Fund Manager B.Dixon

Director of Finance D.J.Regan,BSc,IPFA

Investment Managers Guinness Mahon & Co.Ltd.

Stockbrokers Capel-Cure Myers & Co.

Property Advisers Debenham Tewson & Chinnocks (with Guinness Mahon)

Actuaries R.Watson & Sons

Auditors District Auditor

Employees 6,000

Members 4,300

Pensioners 1,500

	£million
Annual Contributions	2.8
Annual Investment Income	1.8
Annual Outflow	2.0
Capital Value	23.5
Summary of Investments	
Equities	13.0
Fixed Interest	7.5
Cash & Deposits	3.0

LONDON BOROUGH OF WALTHAM FOREST
Town Hall, Walthamstow, London E17 4JA
Telephone: 01-527 5544

Director of Finance D.E.Lewis,IPFA

LONDON BOROUGH OF WANDSWORTH SUPERANNUATION FUND
Town Hall, Wandsworth High Street,
London SW18 2PU
Telephone: 01-874 1545

Director Of Finance A.J.Newman, IPFA, ACIS

Investment Panel Two Members from Majority Party, one Member from Minority Party, Director of Finance, Actuary, Partner from each of two firms of Stockbrokers

Stockbrokers Fielding,Newson-Smith & Co., Pember & Boyle

Actuaries Hymans, Robertson & Co.

Auditors District Auditor

Members 5,400

Pensioners 1,106

	£000
Annual Contributions (to 31.3.80)	4,610
Annual Investment Income	2,353
Annual Outflow	2,124
Capital Value (Market Value)	25,293
Summary of Investments	
UK Equities	11,644
Fixed Interest	8,300
Property Unit Trusts	2,447
Cash & Deposits	307
Overseas Investments	2,504
Others	91

LONDON BRICK COMPANY LTD
12 York Gate, Regents Park, London NW1 4QL
Telephone: 01-487 4321

Secretary H.D.Howe

Insured with Eagle Star Insurance Company Ltd

Pension Fund Consultants C.E.Heath Urquhart (Life & Pensions) Ltd.

Employees 9,488

LONDON CO-OPERATIVE SOCIETY LTD
54 Maryland Street, Stratford, London E15 1JE

THE LONDON LIFE ASSOCIATION LTD STAFF SUPERANNUATION SCHEME (1974)

81 King William Street, London EC4N 7BD
Telephone: 01-626 0511

Pensions Manager W.B.McBride,MA,FFA,FPMI

Managed by London Life Managed Funds Ltd.

Company Employees 553

Members 629

Pensioners 74

Annual Contributions £730,000

Capital Value £4,763,000

LONDON ROYAL BOROUGH OF KENSINGTON & CHELSEA SUPERANNUATION FUND

Town Hall, Hornton Street, London W8 7NX
Telephone: 01-937 5464

Director of Finance R.S.Webber, IPFA, FCCA

Superannuation Officer M.R.Farnell, APMI

Managed by Investment Panel and Advisers

Stockbrokers Henderson Crosthwaite & Co, L. Messel & Co

Property Advisers Healey & Baker

Members 2,850

Pensioners 660

Annual Contributions £1.6 million (1977)

Annual Investment Income £500,000 (1977)

Gross Annual Outflow £2.8 million (1977)

Capital Value £6.4 million (1977)

LONDON ROYAL BOROUGH OF KINGSTON ON THAMES SUPERANNUATION FUND

Guildhall, Kingston on Thames, Surrey KT1 1FU
Telephone: 01-546 2121

Director of Finance and Administration G.N.Hollis, IPFA

Managed by Barclays Bank Trust Company Ltd.

Actuaries R.Watson & Sons

Members 2,625

Pensioners 773

	£000
Annual Contributions	1,600
Annual Investment Income	927
Annual Outflow	1,100
Capital Value	11,300
Summary of Investments	
Equities	4,952
Fixed Interest	3,525
Property	676
Cash & Deposits	737
Others	1,410

LONDON SCOTTISH FINANCE CO LTD DUPONT BROTHERS PENSION FUND

Speakers House, 39 Deansgate, Manchester M3 2BE
Telephone: 061-834 2861

Company Secretary M.G.West,FCA

Trustee E.W.J.Taylor,FCIS

Stockbrokers Bendon Langner & Co.

Property Advisers David A.Hawkins & Co.

Actuarial Advice Obtained through Cubie, Wood & Co.Ltd.

Pension Fund Consultants Noble Lowndes & Partners Ltd.

Auditors Leech Peirson Evans & Co

Company Employees 445

Members 203

Pensioners 126

Annual Contributions £33,000

Capital Value £3,400,000

LONDON TRANSPORT & LONDON TRANSPORT 1970 SUPERANNUATION FUND

Pension Management, 31-35 Tothill Street, London SW1H 9LX
Telephone: 01-222 5600

Investment Management 55 Broadway, London SW1H 0BD

Secretary F.D.Wilmshurst,APMI

Pension Fund Officer C.N.Coles,FIA,APMI

Management Committees Superannuation Fund: H.Whitaker (Chairman) and 11 other Members
Pension Fund:John C.F.Cameron (chairman) and 15 other members

Trustees Superannuation Fund: London Transport Trustee Co.Ltd. R.M.Robbins (Chairman) and 6 other directors
Pension Fund: The London Transport Pension Fund Trustees Ltd. J.G.Glendinning (Chairman) and 15 other directors

Investment Advisers Superannuation Fund: Baring Brothers & Co.Ltd.,
Pension Fund: Morgan Grenfell & Co.Ltd., N.M.Rothschild & Sons Ltd.

Consulting Actuaries R.Watson & Sons

Auditors Deloitte Haskins & Sells

Company Employees 60,000

	Super-annuation Fund	Pension Fund
Members (at 31.12.79)	12,920	35,550
Pensioners	3,860	10,990
	£000	£000
Annual Contributions	13,574	22,130
Annual Investment Income	7,807	8,051
Annual Outflow	7,190	8,333
Capital Value		
Book Value	96,016	100,990
Market Value	105,409	113,185
Summary of Investments		
Equities	44,478	44,973
Fixed Interest	20,852	25,023
Property	33,030	33,593
Cash & Deposits	7,049	9,596

LONDON WEEKEND TELEVISION SUPERANNUATION SCHEME

South Bank Television Centre, Upper Ground, London SE1 9LT
Telephone: 01-261 3434

Secretary C.J.Orr,FCA

Trustees LWT Pension Fund Trustees Ltd.

Directors G.H.Ross Goobey, P.McNally, I.Scaife, C.L.Orr

Investment Advisers Fraser Green Ltd.

Pension Fund Consultants and Actuarial Advice obtained through Godwins Ltd

Auditors Peat, Marwick, Mitchell & Co

Company Employees 2,386

Members (at 31.12.79) 1,131

Pensioners 74

	£000
Annual Contributions	1,602
Annual Investment Income 630	391
Annual Outflow	221
Capital Value	7,241
Summary of Investments	
Equities	2,336
Fixed Interests	2,020
Property	456
Cash & Deposits	700

LONE STAR PRODUCTS LTD

Holloways Lane, Welham Green, Herts.
Telephone: 07072-67471/5

Director E.A.Burks

Employees 650

LONG & HAMBLY LTD. PENSION FUND

Slater Street, High Wycombe, Bucks.HP13 6ET
Telephone: 0494-26141

Secretary & Administrator J.W.Franklin

Trustees J.W.Franklin, J.L.Woodman, R.M.Payne, R.A.E.Andrews

Insured with Sun Life Assurance Society Ltd.

Pension Fund Consultants Rea Brothers (Life Loans & Pensions) Ltd.

Auditors Robson Rhodes & Co.

Company Employees 1,238

Members 246

Pensioners 35

Annual Contributions £180,000

JAMES LONGLEY (HOLDINGS) LTD. STAFF PENSION FUND

East Park, Crawley, West Sussex RH10 6AP
Telephone: 0293-21221

Secretary D.G.Henley

Managed by The National Federation of Building Trades Employers Pension Trustee Ltd.

Employees 1,004

LONGMAN HOLDINGS LTD

5 Bentinck Street, London W1
Telephone: 01-935 0121

Secretary J.D.Williamson

Employees 915

LONGTON INDUSTRIAL HOLDINGS LTD

473 King Street, Longton, Stoke on Trent, Staffs.ST3 1EU
Telephone: 0782-314433

Secretary E.J.Sherratt

Managed by Pensions Management (SWF) Ltd

Employees 1,046

LONRHO LTD SUPERANNUATION SCHEME

Cheapside House, 138 Cheapside, London EC2V 6BL
Telephone: 01-606 9898

Company Secretary M.J.Pearce

Pensions Manager D.A.Gilpin

Pension Fund Consultants Willis Faber Advisory Services Ltd

Investment Managers Keyser Ullmann Pensions Management Ltd.

Total Group U.K. Employees (Sept.1979) 60,000

Scheme covers employees of Lonrho Ltd. and two subsidiaries with about 150 employees. There are several other schemes in the Lonhro Group each individually managed.

LONSDALE UNIVERSAL LTD RETIREMENT BENEFIT SCHEME

York House, York Parade, Great West Road, Brentford, Middx.TW8 9AB
Telephone: 01-560 7331

Pension Fund Manager & Secretary G.E.Clarke, FCA

Insured with Sun Life Assurance Society

Company Employees 2,410

Members 700

Pensioners 220

Annual Contributions £420,000

LOOKERS LTD

776 Chester Road, Stretford, Manchester M32 0QH
Telephone: 061-865 4433

Secretary R.W.Atkinson

Company Subcribes to Motor Agents Association Pension Plan

Company Employees 1,125

Members 770

LOPEX LTD

St.Martin's House, 110 St.Martin's Lane, London WC2N 4BH
Telephone: 01-836 0281

Secretary J.A.Eales

Stockbrokers Panmure Gordon & Co.

LOPEX LTD Continued

Property Advisers Richard Ellis

Employees 801

LOTHIAN ELECTRIC MACHINES LTD STAFF PENSION & BENEFIT SCHEME
Hospital Road, Haddington, East Lothian EH41 3PD
Telephone: 062-082 3611

Secretary R.Higgin

Pension Management Reed Stenhouse Benefit Consultants Ltd

Trustees I.McCallum, R.Higgin, J.Porter

Investment Advisers Ivory & Sime (Invested in Stenhouse Exempt Fund)

Actuaries Duncan C.Fraser & Co.

Pension Fund Consultants Reed Stenhouse Benefit Consultants Ltd.

Auditors Thomson McLintock & Co.

Company Employees 550

Members 129

Pensioners 15

Annual Contributions £105,000

Annual Investment Income £10,500

Annual Outflow £5,000

Capital Value £316,000

LOTHIAN REGIONAL COUNCIL SUPERANNUATION FUND
George IV Bridge, Edinburgh EH1 1UQ
Telephone: 031-229 9292

Secretary & Director of Finance R.A.Adam,CA

Trustees The Finance Committee of Lothian Regional Council

Stockbrokers & Investment Advisers Pember & Boyle, R.Nivison & Co.

Property Advisers Donaldson & Sons

Actuaries Robertson, Hymans & Co.

Auditors Controller for Local Authority Accounts in Scotland

Employees 36,000

Members 20,000

Pensioners 5,600

	£000
Annual Contributions	13,600
Annual Investment Income	8,100
Annual Outflow	6,000
Capital Value	103,300
Summary of Investments	
U.K.Equities	49,085
Overseas Equities	6,064
Fixed Interest	35,103
Property	8,953
Cash & Deposits	4,100

THE LOVABLE CO LTD
Faringdon Avenue, Harold Hill, Romford, Essex RM3 8TD
Telephone: 040-23 49511

Director A.Pelican

Employees 800

LOVELL'S GROUP PENSION SCHEME
1 Broad Walk, Bristol BS4 2QX
Telephone: 0272-770711

Director/Secretary F.A.Perkins, FCIS, APMI

Trustees Lovells Pension Trustees Limited

Chairman D.D.Lovell

Stockbrokers Stock Beech & Co.

Actuaries Bacon & Woodrow

Property Advisers J.P.Sturge & Sons

Pension Fund Consultants Bacon & Woodrow

Auditors Thomson, McLintock & Co

Company Employees 517

Members 257

Pensioners 84

	£000
Annual Contributions	301
Annual Investment Income	159
Annual Outflow	139
Capital Value	2,020
Summary of Investments	
Equities	929
Fixed Interest	752
Property	219
Cash & Deposits	19
Others	25

Y J LOVELL (HOLDINGS) LTD PENSION & LIFE ASSURANCE FUND
Marsham House, Station Road, Gerrards Cross, Bucks.SL9 8ER
Telephone: 87333

Group Pensions Manager S.L.Clay

Insured with Scottish Amicable Life Assurance Society

Pension Consultants Stewart Wrightson Assurance Consultants Ltd

Company Employees 2,226

Members 1,300

Pensioners 180

Annual Contributions £1.6 million

Capital Value £4.0 million

THE LOW & BONAR GROUP LTD.
Faraday Street, Dundee DD1 9JA
Telephone: 0382-817141

Group Pensions Manager W.F.R.Kydd

Actuaries Duncan C.Fraser & Co

Auditors Thomson McLintock Co.

Company Employees 4,800

(a) The Low & Bonar Group Retirement Benefit Schemes

THE LOW & BONAR GROUP LTD. Continued

Trustees Low & Bonar Pension Trustees Ltd

Secretary W.F.R.Kydd

Managed by Reed Stenhouse Benefit Consultants Ltd.

(b) Bibby & Barron Group Staff Benefit Scheme 1972

Trustees Bibby & Baron Pension Trustees Ltd

Secretary R.Thompstone

Managed by Reed Stenhouse Benefit Consultants Ltd.

There are various other small insured schemes (Approx. 550 members)

	(a)	(b)
Members	900	200
Pensioners	325	100
	£000	£000
Annual Income	900	200
Annual Outflow	275	100
Capital Value	4,500	1,750

WM. LOW & CO LTD RETIREMENT PENSION SCHEME

PO Box 73, Baird Avenue,
Dryburgh Industial Estate, Dundee DD1 9NF
Telephone: 0382-814022

Secretary J.L.Millar, CA

Trustees J.P.Rettie, I.W.Stewart, J.L.Millar

Insured with Scottish Widows Fund & Life Assurance Society

Employees 3,478

LOWE & FLETCHER LTD

Church Street, Willenhall, West Midlands
Telephone: 0902-66531

Director G.J.Robinson

Employees 600

ROBERT H. LOWE & CO LTD

The Roldane Mills, Congleton, Cheshire CW12 1JQ
Telephone: 026-02 77911

Secretary J.M.Kinder,FCA

Employees 783

LOWMAN MANUFACTURING CO.LTD.

The Island, Lowman Green, Tiverton, Devon

Secretary I.Heathcoat Amery

Employees 587

LOWTON CONSTRUCTION GROUP LTD.

Pocket Nook Lane, Lowton St.Marys, Warrington, Cheshire WA3 1AD
Telephone: 05235-673121

Executive D.Neylon

Employees 750

LRC INTERNATIONAL PENSION SCHEME

North Circular Road, London E4 8QA
Telephone: 01-527 2377

Pensions Manager J.F.Galloway, APMI

Trustees LRCI Pensions Trust Ltd

Investment Advisers and Stockbrokers Charles Stanley & Co

Actuaries Duncan C.Fraser & Co

Auditors Ernst & Whinney

Company Employees 6,288

Members 5,500

Pensioners 767

Annual Contributions £1,523,000

Annual Investment Income £523,000

Gross Annual Outflow £275,000

Capital Value £8,823,000

LUCAS STAFF PENSION FUND AND WORKS PENSION FUND

Lucas Industries Ltd, Great King Street, Birmingham B19 2XF
Telephone: 021-554 5252

Secretary H.D.Spottiswoode, MA, FCA

Assistant Company Secretary D.H.Hallam

Investment Dept 44-46 Park Street, London W1Y 4DJ (01-493 6793)

Investment Manager J.G.Kettlewell

Assistant Manager K.Florence

Trustees Lucas Staff Pension Trust Ltd. and Lucas Works Pension Trust Ltd.

Investment Advisers Hill Samuel & Co.Ltd.

Actuaries R.Watson & Sons

Pension Fund Consultants Metropolitan Pensions Association Ltd

Auditors Ernst & Whinney

Solicitors Evershed & Tomkinson

Company Employees 69,631

	Staff Fund	Works Fund
Members	21,141	40,737
Pensioners	5,320	8,646
	£ million	£ million
Annual Contributions	15.3	19.0
Annual Investment Income	10.1	4.3
Gross Annual Outflow	7.0	7.4
Capital Value (Book Value)	138.9	64.6
(Market Value)	207.4	96.0
Summary of Investments		
Equities	172.7	83.6
Fixed Interest	22.8	6.9
Property	9.2	4.7
Cash & Deposits	0.2	0.2
Others	2.6	0.6

W. LUCY & CO LTD
Eagle Works, Walton Well Road, Oxford OX2 6EE
Telephone: 0865-57411
Director G.I.B.Dick
Employees 500

THE LUMMUS CO LTD RETIREMENT BENEFITS PLAN
100 Fetter Lane, PO Box 64, London EC4P 4BA
Telephone: 01-831 7300
Pensions Administrator Mrs.I.E.Karnoutsos
Company Secretary M.F.West
Investment Advisers Baring Brothers & Co Ltd
Pension Consultants Lowndes Associated Pensions Ltd
Auditors Price Waterhouse & Co
Company Employees 1,335
Members 975
UK Pensioners 77
Annual Contributions £951,000
Annual Investment Income £917,000
Capital Value £3,453,000

LWT (HOLDINGS) LTD
See London Weekend Television

LYE SPENCER STEEL SERVICES
Stourbridge Road, Lye, Stourbridge,
West Midlands
Telephone: 038-482 4161
Executive G.P.Fuller
Employees 651

S.LYLES LTD
Jilling Ing Mills, Earls Heaton, Dewsbury,
W.Yorks.WF12 8LX
Telephone: 0924-463161
Secretary R.Ellis
Insured with Sun Life Assurance Society
Employees 502

M & G GROUP HOLDINGS LTD. PENSION SCHEME
Three Quays, Tower Hill, London EC3R 6BQ
Telephone: 01-626 4588
Secretary D.Phillips
Investment Advisers M & G Investment Management Ltd
Company Employees 275
Members 131
Pensioners 18
Annual Contributions £255,000
Capital Value £3,040,000

MABEY & JOHNSON LTD
Floral Mile, Twyford, Reading, Berks.RG10 9SQ
Telephone: 0735-22 3921
Secretary M.J.Van Brugen

Managed by Standard Life Pension Funds Ltd
Employees 736

MACARTHY GROUP PENSION SCHEME
Frankland Moore House, 185-7 High Road,
Chadwell Heath Romford Essex RM6 6NR
Telephone: 01-597 0911
Pensions Manager Mrs.W.M.England,BSc,ACII, APMI
Trustees Macarthys Group Pensions Ltd.
Investment Advisers Warburg Investment Management Ltd
Pension Fund Consultants & Actuarial Advice Obtained through Metropolitan Pensions Association Ltd.
Auditors Bird Lucklin & Sheldrake
Company Employees 2,833
Members 941
Pensioners 177

	£000
Annual Contributions	684
Annual Investment Income	255
Annual Outflow	227
Capital Value (at 31.3.80)	3,412
Summary of Investments (1979)	
Equities	2,392
Fixed Interest	669
Cash & Deposits	133

MACFARLANE GROUP (CLANSMAN) LTD.
Clansman House, Sutcliffe Road,
Glasgow G13 1AH
Telephone: 041-959 4444
Secretary A.Reekie,CA
Insured with Scottish Amicable Life Assurance Society
Employees 1,031

HUGH MACKAY & CO LTD
PO Box 1, Freeman's Place, Durham DH1 1SH
Telephone: 0385-64444
Secretary M.R.Pullen,FCCA,ACMA
Investment Advisers Hill Samuel Investment Mangement Ltd, Ivory & Sime
Employees 580

J.MACKAY (DRAPERS) (HOLDINGS) LTD.
Caledonian House, Caledonian Street,
Paisley PA3 2JG
Telephone: 041-887 9151
Secretary R.J.Jamieson
Employees 1,419

MURDOCH MACKENZIE LTD
12-14 Draffen Street, Motherwell,
Strathclyde ML1 1NL
Telephone: 0698-65171
Secretary W.N.Niven
Employees 532

JAMES MACKIE HOLDINGS LTD.

Albert Foundry, Springfield Road,
Belfast BT12 7ED
Telephone: 0232-27771

Employees 4,500

MACKINNON OF SCOTLAND LTD.

Kirshaws Road, Coatbridge, Strathclyde ML5 4SL
Telephone: 0236-23231

Secretary B.W.S.Boucher-Myers

Insured with Standard Life Assurance Co

Employees 826

MACMILLAN LTD STAFF PENSION SCHEME

4 Little Essex Street, London WC2R 3LF
Telephone: 01-836 6633

Company Secretary R.A.C.Phillips

Pension Fund Management Lowndes Associated Pensions Ltd.

Trustees A.D.A.Macmillan, F.H.Whitehead, Mrs. S.D.Browne, B.J.J.Mckenzie, Mrs. I.M.Harman, M.J.Allen, Lowndes Associated Pensions Ltd.

Insured with Clerical, Medical & General Life Assurance Society

Pension Fund Consultants Noble Lowndes & Partners Ltd.

Auditors Touche Ross & Co.

Company Employees 800

Members 550

Pensioners 50

Annual Contributions £550,000

Annual Investment Income £200,000

Annual Outflow £180,000

Capital Value £2,500,000

MACMILLAN BLOEDEL CONTAINERS LTD PENSION PLAN (1976)

24/30 King Street, Watford, Herts WD1 8BP
Telephone: 92-42306

Secretary P.S.Butterick, FCA

Trustees Royal Trust Company of Canada

Managed by Royal Trust Company of Canada and Standard Life Pension Funds Ltd

Pension Fund Consultants and Actuarial Advice obtained through Hogg Robinson (Benefit Consultants) Ltd

Auditors Robertson & Maxtone Graham

Company Employees 1,517

Members 1,100

Pensioners 139

	£000
Annual Contributions	960
Annual Investment Income	295
Gross Annual Outflow	150
Capital Value	4,560

Summary of Investments

Equities	1,912
Fixed Interest	1,099
Cash & Deposits	125
Others	1,001

DONALD MACPHERSON GROUP LTD RETIREMENT BENEFITS PLAN

Three Quays, Tower Hill, London EC3R 6EL
Telephone: 01-623 1795

Pension Fund Administrator Lowndes Associated Pensions Ltd.

Secretary R.H.Coles (L.A.P.)

Trustees H.K.Cushing, M.R.Blow, A.F.R.Close, F.Roberts, Lowndes Associated Pensions Ltd.

Managed by English Insurance (Pensions Management) Ltd.

Investement Advisers M & G Investment Management Ltd.

Actuarial Advice Obtained through Cubie, Wood & Co.Ltd.

Pension Fund Consultants Lowndes Associated Pensions Ltd.

Auditors Dearden Farrow

Company Employees 2,250

Members 1,112

Pensioners 157

Annual Contributions £1,170,000

Annual Outflow £210,000

Capital Value £5,600,000

MACTAGGART, SCOTT & CO LTD

PO Box No 1, Hunter Avenue, Loanhead EH20 9SP
Telephone: 031-440 0311

Director R.L.Scott

Employees 600

MADDOCK LTD.

Newcastle Street, Burslem, Stoke-on-Trent, Staffs.ST6 3QD

Secretary S.Cooke

Employees 579

JOHN MADDOCK & CO LTD

Oakengates, Telford, Salop TF2 6DQ
Telephone: 0952-612121

Director T.P.Jones

Executive W.V.wallace

Employees 550

MAGNATEX (HOLDINGS) LTD

Bath Road, Heathrow, Hounslow, Middlesex
Telephone: 01-759 9111

Secretary J.J.Davey

Executive R.L.Longdon

Employees 581

THE MANGAVOX STAFF PENSIONS & LIFE ASSURANCE SCHEME

Alfreds Way, By-Pass Road, Barking, Essex

THE MANGAVOX Continued

Secretary W.W.Lloyd

Employees 542

MAGNET & SOUTHERNS LTD

Sasco House, Mill Lane, Widnes,
Cheshire WA8 0UJ
Telephone: 051-424 5500

Company Secretary R.G.Briggs, FCA

Pensions Secretary G.L.Thomas

Trustees Magnet & Southerns Trustees Ltd.

Investment Advisers Hill Samuel Investment Management Ltd.

Pension Fund Consultants Lowndes Associated Pensions Ltd.

Company Employees 4,219

MAGNOLIA GROUP (MOULDINGS) LTD PENSION FUND

Sutton Road Rochford, Essex SS4 1NA
Telephone: 0702-547121

Secretary J.Clark, CA

Trustees R.J.Wallrock, D.A.Arnold, I.A.Ferguson

Insured with Sun Life Assurance Society Ltd

Company Employees 350

Members 95

Annual Contributions £70,000

MAKRO SELF SEVICE WHOLESALERS LTD.

Charles House, Albert Street, Eccles,
Manchester M30 0LJ

Secretary N.J.Shepherd

Employees 2,392

MALLINSON-DENNY GROUP PENSION & LIFE ASSURANCE FUND

130 Hackney Road, London E2 7QR
Telephone: 01-739 7654

Pension Fund Administrator (Accountant) G.F.Brind

Managed by Legal & General Assurance (Pensions Management) Ltd.

Pensions Fund Consultants Sedgwick Employee Benefits Consultants Ltd.

Company Employees 3,300

Members 1,400

Pensioners 200

MALLORY UK

See Duracell Batteries Ltd.

THE MANCHESTER SHIP CANAL CO STAFF SUPERANNUATION SCHEME AND GENERAL PENSION SCHEME

Ship Canal House, King Street,
Manchester M2 4WX
Telephone: 061-872 2411

Pensions Administrator C.Bowyer

Trustees Williams & Glyn's Trust Co. Ltd.

Investment Managers Williams & Glyn's Bank Ltd.

Property Advisers Dunlop, Heywood & Co.

Actuaries R.Watson & Sons

Auditors Peat Marwick Mitchell & Co

Company Employees 3,000

Members 2,000

Pensioners 600

	£000
Annual Contributions	1,700
Annual Investment Income	1,300
Annual Outflow	1,000
Capital Value	13,000
Summary of Investments	%
Equities	48
Fixed Interest	48
Property	1
Cash & Deposits	3

MANDER BROTHERS LTD. STAFF PENSION FUND AND GROUP PENSION FUND

PO Box 9, Mander House,
Wolverhampton WV1 3NH
Telephone: 0902-20601

Financial Director R.K.Mullett, FCA

Secretary R.G.Purshouse

Trustees Four for each fund split equally between members and management

Investment Advisers Rea Brothers Ltd

Actuarial Advice Obtained through Cubie Wood & Co. Ltd.

Pension Fund Consultants Noble Lowndes & Partners Ltd

Auditors Thomson McLintock & Co.

Company Employees 1,150

Members Staff 278, Group 561

Pensioners Staff 66, Group 122

Capital value Staff £1,900,000, Group £1,400,000

MANGANESE BRONZE HOLDINGS LTD

1 Love Lane, London EC2V 7HJ
Telephone: 01-606 0088

Secretary Miss M.Buist

Insured with Legal & General Assurance Society Ltd

Employees 2,458

MANN EGERTON & CO LTD EXECUTIVE PENSION & FAMILY INCOME PLAN

5 Prince of Wales Road, Norwich,
Norfolk NR1 1BB
Telephone: 0603-28383

Pension Fund Manager & Secretary Brian P.Back, FCCA

Trustees J.W.D.Campbell, B.J.Bleaney, J.W.Harris, M.J.Gotts, B.P.Back

Insured with Standard Life Assurance Co, Eagle Star Insurance Co Ltd

Pension Fund Consultants C.E. Heath Urquhart (Life & Pensions) Ltd

Auditors Deloitte Haskins & Sells

MANN EGERTON & CO LTD Continued

Company Employees 4,131
Members 500
Pensioners 200
Annual Contributions £468,000

MANOR NATIONAL GROUP MOTORS LTD.
Hathersage Road Corner, Oxford Road,
Manchester M13 0JD
Telephone: 061-225 3070

Secretary J.Willcock,FCA

Employees 1,066

R MANSELL LTD
13-27 Grant Road, East Croydon, Surrey CR9 6BU
Telephone: 01-654 8191

Secretary P.W.Young,FCA,ACCA

Employees 583

MANSFIELD BREWERY CO LTD
Littleworth, Mansfield, Nottingham NG18 1AB
Telephone: 0623-25691

Secretary V.M.Phillips

Insured with Commercial Union Assurance Co Ltd

Employees 1,395

THE MANUFACTURERS LIFE INSURANCE GROUP. STAFF & MANAGERS PENSION PLAN AND PENSION PLAN FOR LIFE UNDERWRITERS
ManuLife House, St.George's Way, Stevenage, Herts.SG1 1HP
Telephone: 0438-56101

Secretary P.Oliver

Pensions Officer P.Ashdown

Actuaries Hymans, Robertson & Co.

Auditors Arthur Young McClelland Moores & Co.

Employees 625

	Staff	Underwriters
Members	241	223
Pensioners	43	2
	£000	£000
Annual Contributions	315	267
Capital Value	2,272	690

MAPLE & CO. (HOLDINGS) LTD.
140 Hampstead Road, London NW1 2PU
Telephone: 01-387 2833

Secretary P.W.T.Cash

Insured with Legal & General Assurance Society Ltd.

Pension Fund Consultants Noble Lowndes & Partners Ltd., Sedgwick Employee Benefits Consultants Ltd.

Employees 703

MAPPIN & WEBB LTD
106 Regent Street, London W1R 6JH
Telephone: 01-734 5842

Secretary J.P.Jeffery

Employees 1,500

MARATHON KNITWEAR (NOTTINGHAM) LTD. RETIREMENT BENEFITS PLAN (1978)
P.O.Box 5, West P.D.O., Radford Boulevard, Nottingham NG7 3AE
Telephone: 0602-782221

Secretary W.P.L.Rogers

Trustees G.H.Bignall, R.G.Littlefair, A.C.Foulds

Managed by Commercial Union Managed Fund

Actuarial Advice Obtained through Cubie, Wood & Co.Ltd.

Pension Fund Consultants Noble Lowndes Pensions Ltd.

Auditors Pannell Fitzpatrick & Co.

Company Employees 1,000
Members 300
Pensioners 20
Deferred Pensions
Annual Contributions £150,000
Annual Outflow £30,000
Capital Value £850,000

Parent Company John Beales Associated Companies Ltd.

MARCHWIEL HOLDINGS LTD
See Sir Alfred McAlpine & Son Ltd.

MARGLASS LTD
Sherborne, Dorset
Telephone: 093-581 3722

Director J.A.Nightingale

Executive D.G.Hutchison

Employees 600

MARINE AND GENERAL MUTUAL LIFE ASSURANCE SOCIETY MGM ASSURANCE STAFF PENSION PLAN
MGM House, Heene Road, Worthing, West Sussex BN11 2DY
Telephone: 0903-204631

Pension Fund Manager A.M.Lamb,MA,FIA

Secretary C.W.Ford,FCIS,APMI

Assistant General Manager & Actuary J.L.Robertson,FIA,APMI

Auditors Thomson McLinctock & Co.

Company Employees 281
Members 278
Pensioners 44

	£000
Annual Contributions	351
Annual Investment Income	159
Annual Outflow	152
Capital Value	2,102

MARINE AND GENERAL MUTUAL LIFE ASSURANCE SOCIETY Continued

Summary of Investments
Equities	716
Fixed Interest	625
Property	567
Cash & Deposits	90
Others	104

MARKS & SPENCER PENSION SCHEME
Michael House, 47 Baker Street,
London W1A 1DN
Telephone: 01-935 4422

Pension Fund Manager & Secretary H.E.Stevenson, FPMI

Trustees Marks & Spencer Pension Trust Ltd

Investment Advisers N.M. Rothschild & Sons Ltd, Prudential Pension Ltd

Actuarial Advice Obtained through Cubie, Wood & Co.Ltd.

Auditors Deloitte Haskins & Sells

Solicitors Linklaters & Paine

Company Employees/Members (at 31.3.80) 45,000

Pensioners 5,291

	£000
Annual Contributions	22,252
Annual Investment Income	4,707
Annual Outflow	8,536
Capital Value	121,500
Summary of Investments	
Equities	57,000
Fixed Interest	28,500
Property	32,800
Cash & Deposits	3,200

ALFRED MARKS BUREAU LTD
Ambur House, 8-9 Frith Street, London W1 6AJ
Telephone: 01-437 7855

Secretary E.Sharp

Employees 1,175

MARLEY PENSION SCHEMES
London Road, Riverhead, Sevenoaks,
Kent TN13 2DS
Telephone: 0732-55255

Pensions Administrator T.A.Jones

Assistants to Pensions Administrator Mr Tinsley, Mr Lewis

Trustees Marley Pensions Ltd.

Directors O.A.Aisher, O.A.A.Aisher, J.E.Aisher, F.G.Hardy

Trustees Marley Pensions Ltd

Secretary H.C.James

Investment Advisers Hill Samuel Investment Management Ltd, N.M. Rothschild Asset Management Ltd

Employees 8,177

Members 2,500

Capital Value £8.5 million (1977)

MARLING INDUSTRIES LTD
14 Aylmer Parade, London N2 0PF
Telephone: 01-340 4687

Secretary A.Lacey

Insured with Legal & General Assurance Society Ltd.

Employees 841

J. MARR & SON LTD
228 Dock Street, Fleetwood, Lancashire
Telephone: 0993-3466

Secretary C.D.Bennett

Insured with Legal & General Assurance Society Ltd, Royal Insurance Co Ltd

Employees 1,378

ROBERT MARRIOTT GROUP
Rushden, Northants NN10 9EA
Telephone: 09334-3331

Secretary D.M.McLeod

Employees 901

MARRYAT GROUP LTD RETIREMENT BENEFITS PLAN (1972)
M.J.N.House, 11 Dingwall Road, Croydon, Surrey CR9 3DB
Telephone: 01-686 5577

Managed by Legal & General (Pensions Management) Ltd.

Company Employees 1,000

Members 400

Pensioners 40

MARS PENSION PLAN
266 Bath Road, Slough, Berks.SL1 4EB
Telephone: 0753-23932

Secretary D.C.Drake

Social Security Manager G.R.F.Wiltshire

Trustees Mars Ltd.,Trustee Division

Property Advisers Jones Lang Wootton

Actuaries Clay & Partners

Auditors Arthur Andersen & Co.

Company Employees/Members 9,000

Pensioners 1,100

Annual Contributions £8.9 million

Annual Investment Income £7.8 million

Annual Outflow £2.5 million

Capital Value (Est.31.12.79) £90.0 million

MARSHALL-ANDREW (HOLDINGS) LTD.
Box 308, Bruce House, Black Prince Road,
London SE1 7SL
Telephone: 01-735 9155

Secretary E.W.Purdy

Employees 700

MARSHALL CAVENDISH LTD.
58 Old Compton Street, London W1V 5PA
Telephone: 01-734 6710

Secretary P.Cox

Employees 580

MARSHALLS (HALIFAX) LTD
Hall Ings, Southowram, Halifax, Yorkshire HX3 9TW
Telephone: 0422-62651

Secretary G.B.Taylor

Insured with Standard Life Assurance Co

Employees 1,460

D.B. MARSHALL (NEWBRIDGE) LTD PENSION AND LIFE ASSURANCE SCHEME
Newbridge, Midlothian EH28 8SW
Telephone: 031-333 3341

Secretary F.C.H.McLeod,CA

Trustees D.E.Roberts, W.M.Marshall,F.C.H.McLeod

Managed by Scottish Amicable Pensions Investments Ltd. and Pensions Management (S.W.F.) Ltd.

Pension Fund Consultants Sedgwick Employee Benefits Consultants L

Auditors Cooper & Lybrand

Company Employees 2,078

Members 816

Pensioners 1

Annual Contributions £456,000

Capital Value £1,153,000

MARSHALL OF CAMBRIDGE (ENGINEERING) LTD.
18 Jesus Lane, Cambridge CB5 8BH
Telephone: 0223-61133

Secretary G.Bruce

Employees 3,163

THOMAS MARSHALL & CO (LOXLEY) LTD
MARSHALL MOLER (WORKS PENSION) LTD.
Storrs Bridge Works, Loxley, Sheffield S6 6SX
Telephone: 0742-343844

Pension Fund Manager C.B.Jackson

Secretary Miss B.Jones

Trustees J.R.Gledshill, R.D.Hart, C.B.Jackson, C.Bradwell, D.R.French R.A.Rudling

Stockbrokers Laing & Cruickshank

Pension Fund Consultants and Actuarial Advice Obtained through Sedgwick Employee Benefits Consultants Ltd.

Auditors Hawson & Co.

Company Employees 750

Members 700

Pensioners 72

	£000
Annual Contributions	130
Annual Investment Income	65
Annual Outflow	68
Capital Value	700
Summary of Investments	
Equities	185
Fixed Interest	475
Cash & Deposits	40

MARSHALL'S UNIVERSAL LTD.
468-472 Purley Way, Croydon CR9 4BL Surrey
Telephone: 01-681 2600

Secretary P.Whitehorn,FCA

Managed by Prudential Pensions Ltd

Employees 768

MARSTON, THOMPSON & EVERSHED LTD.
The Brewery, Shobnall Road, Burton-on-Trent, DE14 2BW
Telephone: 0283-65671

Secretary K.R.Brown

Employees 669

ALBERT MARTIN (HOLDINGS) LTD.
Lenton Lane, Nottingham NG7 2HZ
Telephone: 0602-866461

Secretary Miss W.E.Wood

Insured with Provident Mutual Life Assurance Association

Employees 2,793

MARTIN-BAKER (ENGINEERING) LTD.
Higher Denham, Uxbridge, Middx.
Telephone: 089-583 2214

Secretary Mrs.A.Mower

Insured with Gresham Life Assurance Society Ltd

Employees 1,035

MARTIN BLACK LTD
Speedwell Works, Coatbridge, Strathclyde ML5 4RS
Telephone: 0236-22566

Secretary I.G.Cumming

Managed by Pensions Management (SWF) Ltd, Scottish Amicable Pensions Investments Ltd

Employees 744

MARTIN THE NEWSAGENT LTD
1 Raven Road, London E18 1HE
Telephone: 01-504 9611

Employees 11,725

MARTONAIR INTERNATIONAL LTD
128 St Margarets Road, Twickenham, Middlesex TW1 1RJ
Telephone: 01-892 4411

Secretary D.J.Fincham

Insured with Prudential Assurance Co Ltd

Employees 1,433

MARWIN (HOLDINGS) LTD
Barkby Road, Leicester LE4 7LL
Telephone: 0533-760181

Chairman E.E.Hopwell

Insured with Sun Life Assurance Society Ltd.

Employees 889

MASIUS WYNNE-WILLIAMS & D'ARCY MACMANUS (HOLDINGS) LTD.
2 St.James's Square, London SW1Y 4JY
Telephone: 01-839 3422

Company Secretary R.W.Sewell

Trustees Maspar Services Ltd

Insured with Prudential Assurance Co.Ltd.

Company Employees 511

Members 209

Pensioners 55

Annual Contributions £437,000

MASSEY-FERGUSON & PERKINS GROUP WORKS SCHEME & GROUP STAFF SCHEME
33 Davies Street, London W1Y 2AE
Telephone: 01-491 7000

Pension Fund Manager D.J.Brown,FPMI,ACII

Secretary J.W.J.Collins

Pensions Accountant M.G.Jones

Trustees Massey-Ferguson Holdings Pension Trust Ltd

Investment Advisers Geoffrey Morley & Partners Ltd

Property Advisers Hillier Parker May & Rowden

Actuarial Advice Obtained through William M. Mercer Benefits Ltd.

Auditors Armitage & Norton

Company Employees 20,060

Members 19,860

Pensioners 3,618

	£000
Annual Contribution	9,600
Annual Investment Income	15,700
Annual Outflow	2,800
Capital Value	64,600
Summary of Investments	
Equities	55,361
Fixed Interest	2,140
Property	3,262
Cash & Deposits	3,819

There is also a Group Executive Scheme with 55 members, annual contributions of £184,000 and a capital value of £1,302,000.

MAT INTERNATIONAL GROUP LTD
36-41 Holywell Lane, London EC2P 2EQ
Telephone: 01-247 6500

Secretary H.F.Stupples,FCIS

Employees 1,037

MATHER & PLATT LTD STAFF RETIREMENT BENEFITS SCHEME (1974)
Park Works, Manchester M10 6BA
Telephone: 061-205 2321

Secretary C.W.Young

Trustees Ten Acre Securities Ltd.

Investment Advisers Hill Samuel Investment Management Ltd.

Actuarial Advice Obtained through Cubie, Wood & Co. Ltd.

Pension Fund Consultants Noble Lowndes Pensions Ltd.

Auditors Arthur Young McClelland Moores & Co.

Members (at 31.12.79) 2,157

Pensioners 355

	£000
Annual Contributions	1,327
Annual Investment Income	260
Annual Outflow	576
Capital Value	7,395
Summary of Investments (at 31.12.79)	
Equities	5,548
Fixed Interest	528
Property	1,313
Cash & Deposits	6

MATHESON GROUP PENSION PLAN AND JMIB SCHEME
3 Lombard Street, London EC3V 9AQ
Telephone: 01-480 6633

Pensions Administrator J.C.Winn

Actuarial Advice obtained through Towers, Perrin, Forster & Crosny Inc.

Pension Fund Consultants Jardine Matheson Life & Pensions Ltd.

Auditors Spicer & Pegler

Solicitors Linklaters & Paines

Employees 1,250

	Group Plan	JMIB Scheme
Members (at 31.3.80)	820	270
Pensioners	4	3
	£000	£000
Annual Contributions	540	250
Capital Value	2,400	1,012

THE BERNARD MATTHEWS PENSION FUND
Great Witchingham Hall, Norwich, Norfolk NR9 5QD
Telephone: 060-544-611

Pension Fund Manager J.G.Brown

Trustees B.T.Matthews, Mrs.J.K.Matthews, J.G.Brown, L.R.Temple

Insured with Norwich Union Life Assurance Society

Stockbrokers Grieveson Grant & Co.

THE BERNARD MATTHEWS Continued

Actuaries and Pension Fund Consultants Duncan C.Fraser & Co.

Auditors Deloitte, Haskins and Sells

Company Employees 1,700

Members 128

Pensioners 2

	£000
Annual Contributions	134
Annual Investment Income	50
Annual Outflow	11
Capital Value (at 31.12.79)	359
Summary of Investments	
Equities	207
Fixed Interest	108
Property	12
Cash & Deposits	14
Others	18

MATTHEWS GROUP PENSION SCHEME

19-31 Church Street, Epsom, Surrey KT17 4PL

Secretary E.J.Young, FCA

Management Committees Managed by Trustees 4 appointed by Company and 3 by Members

Investment Advisers S.G.Warburg & Co Ltd

Actuaries Bacon & Woodrow

Property Advisers Jones Lang Wootton

Pension Fund Consultants Sedgwick Employee Benefits Consultants Ltd.

Employees 4,862

Members 500

Annual Contributions £400,000

Annual Investment Income £125,000

Annual Outflow £100,000

Capital Value £6 million

MAY & BAKER LTD STAFF PENSIONS FUND (A) AND PENSION PLAN FOR WAGE-EARNING EMPLOYEES (B)

Dagenham, Essex RM10 7XS
Telephone: 01-952 3060

Secretary P.D.G.Blake

Trustees (a) 8 trustees, 4 appointed by the company and 4 fund members nominated by the company's 4 common interest groups/Staff Unions. (b) 6 trustees, 3 nominated by the company and 3 nominated by Trade Union representatives who are members.

Managed by Standard Life Pension Funds Ltd., and (for part of Staff Fund) Clerical, Medical & General Life Assurance Society

Pension Fund Consultants Hogg Robinson (Benefit Consultants) Ltd

Auditors Howard, Tilly & Co.

Company Employees 4,550

Members (a) 2,200, (b) 2,150

Pensioners (a) 500, (b) 700

Capital Value (a) £12 million, (b) £2.5 million

MAY & HASSELL LTD RETIREMENT BENEFITS PLAN (1966)

3/8 Redcliffe Parade West, Bristol BS99 7PH
Telephone: 0272-298505

Secretary P.J.Ball, FCA

Trustees Lowndes Associated Pensions Ltd

Part managed by Legal & General (Pensions Management) Ltd

Investment Advisers Hill Samuel & Co Ltd and Brown Shipley & Co Ltd

Actuarial Advice obtained through Cubie Wood & Co Ltd

Pension Fund Consultants Noble LoWndes & Partners Ltd.

Auditors Price Waterhouse & Co.

Company Employees 1,530

Members (2 schemes) 890

Pensioners 82

Annual Contributions £500,000

Annual Investment Income £45,000

Annual Outflow £200,000

Capital Value £2,500,000

MAY GUERNEY HOLDINGS LTD.

Holland Court, The Close, Norwich NR1 4DY
Telephone: 0603-20481

Secretary S.F.Utting

Employees 1,081

MAYNARDS LTD. PENSION & LIFE ASSURANCE PLAN

Vale Road, Finsbury Park, London N4 1PH
Telephone: 01-800 4221

Administrator & Secretary D.M.Martin, FCIS, AIPM

Trustees R.W.Ramsdale, D.M.Martin, P.H.McGlaughlin, I.M.Peel

Insured with Scottish Widows' Fund & Life Assurance Society

Actuaries Clay & Partners

Pension Fund Consultants Metropolitan Pensions Association Ltd

Auditors Ernst & Whinney

Company Employees 2,263

Members 215

Pensioners 80

Annual Contributions £195,000

SIR ALFRED MCALPINE & SON LTD RETIREMENT BENEFITS PLAN (1973)

Hooton, South Wirral, Cheshire L66 7ND
Telephone: 051-339 4141

Pensions Administrator J.Holroyd, AIB

Company Secretary J.D.P.Walker, FCA

Part Managed by English Insurance (Pensions Management) Ltd.

SIR ALFRED MCALPINE & SON LTD Continued

Investment Managers Hill Samuel Investment Management Ltd.

Pension Fund Consultants Noble Lowndes & Partners Ltd

Auditors Touche Ross & Co.

Company Employees (UK) 7,598

Members 1,600

Pensioners 350

	£000
Annual Contributions	2,138
Annual Investment Income	1,293
Annual Outflow	612
Capital Value	12,801
Summary of Investments	
Equities	6,813
Fixed Interest	4,040
Property	1,301
Cash & Deposits	646

SIR ROBERT MCALPINE & SONS LTD STAFF PENSION & LIFE ASSURANCE SCHEME

40 Bernard Street, London WC1N 1LG
Telephone: 01-837 3377

Secretary J.B.Beldham

Trustees M.H.McAlpine, K.McAlpine, D.B.Jennings

Investment Advisers Lazard Brothers & Co Ltd

Stockbrokers Seligmann, Rayner & Co

Actuaries Clay & Partners

Property Advisers Strutt & Parker

Pension Fund Consultants Metropolitan Pensions Association Ltd

Members 1,129 (1978)

Pensioners 337

	£000
Annual Contributions (1978)	660
Annual Investment Income	1,120
Gross Annual Outflow	510
Capital Value	15,000
Summary of Investments	
Equities	6,300
Fixed Interest	3,900
Property	2,600
Cash & Deposits	2,200

ROBERT MCBRIDE (MIDDLETON) LTD.

171 Victoria Street, London SW1E 5NL

Secretary P.Marsh,ACCA,ACIS

Employees 569

MCCAIN INTERNATIONAL LTD PENSION & LIFE ASSURANCE SCHEME

Havers Hill, Eastfield, Scarborough, N.Yorks.YO11 3BS
Telephone: 0723-584141

Financial Director H.Kinder,FSCA

Investment Advisers N.M.Rothschild (Asset Management) Ltd.

Pension Fund Consultants William M.Mercer (Benefits) Ltd.

Auditors Coopers & Lybrand

Company Employees 1,500

Members 550

Pensioners 6

Annual Contributions £220,000

Capital Value £750,000

MCCANN-ERICKSON ADVERTISING LTD

McCann Erickson House, 36 Howland Street, London W1
Telephone: 01-580 6690

Managing Director W.A.Murphy

Managed by Providence Capitol Life Assurance Co Ltd

Employees 510

MCCLEERY L'AMIE GROUP LTD

Lamont House, Purdy's Lane, Belfast BT8 4DD
Telephone: 0232-640031

Secretary W.D.Bell

Insured with Legal & General Assurance Society Ltd

Employees 1,087

MCCLELLAND ENGINEERS

319 Pinner Road, Harrow, Middx.HA1 4XX
Telephone: 01-863 8666

Executive R.A.Sullivan

Employees 500

MCCORQUODALE GROUP (1) PENSION FUND, (2) PENSION SCHEME,(3) COX & WYMAN PENSION PLAN

McCorquodale House, PO Box 66, Telford Road, Basingstoke,Hants.RG21 2YA
Telephone: 0256-65811

Pension Fund Manager M.J.Hammond

Secretary H.N.McCorquodale,FCA

Pensions Administrator M.Startup

Trustees (1) Pension Fund Mccorquodale Group Pension Fund Trustees Ltd.

Directors J.R.Wood (Chairman), G.T.Dee, G.Garwood N.D.Paget

Trustees (2) Pension Scheme McCorquodale Group Pension Scheme Trustees Ltd.

Directors G.T.Dee, E.N.C.Eustance, N.Heroys, H.H.Ley, R.J.Reid, J.G.Finley

Trustees (3) Cox & Wyman Pension Trustees Ltd.

Directors J.L.Wood, N.Heroys, G.M.Russell, B.Wasley

(3) Managed by Prudential Pensions Ltd.

Investment Advisers (1) Baring Brothers & Co.Ltd. (2) Robert Fleming & Co.Ltd.

Actuarial Advice Obtained through Godwins (Central Services) Ltd.

Pension Fund Consultants Godwins (Central) Ltd.

MCCORQUODALE GROUP Continued

Auditors Edward Moore & Sons

Solicitors Sacker & Partners

Company Employees 5,000 (Works & Staff), 350 (Cox & Wyman)

	Pension Fund (1)	Pension Scheme (2)
Members (at 5.4.80)	1,031	2,948
Pensioners	279	57
	£000	£000
Annual Contributions	885	1,362
Annual Investment Income	522	141
Annual Outflow	461	311
Capital Value	6,403	2,183
Summary of Investments		
UK Equities	3,400	993
Overseas Securities	350	153
Fixed Interest	1,500	622
Property	1,025	306
Cash & Deposits	128	109

The Cox & Wyman Pension Plan commenced on 6.4.80 with 173 members and Annual Contributions of £40,000

THOMAS MCINERNEY & SONS LTD

McInerney House, The Green, Croxley Green, Richmansworth, Herts.WD3 3HN
Telephone: 09237-76622

Director A.McInerney

Employees 594

A.H. MCINTOSH & CO LTD

Mitchelston Industrial Estate, Kirkcaldy, Fife
Telephone: 0592-52551

Director R.W.Parker

Employees 500

MCKECHNIE BROTHERS LTD GROUP PENSION & LIFE ASSURANCE SCHEME

PO Box 8, Leighswood Road, Aldridge, Walsall, West Midlands WS9 8DS
Telephone: 0922-55887

Secretary E.Corker, BA, FCA

Director G.G.Howarth

Investment Advisers County Bank Investment Services Ltd.

Actuaries Clay & Partners

Pension Fund Consultants Metropolitan Pensions Association Ltd

Auditors Arthur Young McClelland Moores & Co

Company Employees 5,717

Members 2,305

Pensioners 668

Annual Contributions £1,506,000

Annual Investment Income £529,000

Capital Value £7,880,000

F.B. MCKEE & CO LTD

9 Shore Road, Belfast BT15 3PJ
Telephone: 0232-776 201

Secretary G.K.Armstrong

Employees 600

MCKELLAR WATT LTD.

17 Old Shettlesdon Road, Glasgow G32 7ES
Telephone: 041-778 9123

Secretary D.R.Kesson

Employees 615

MCLAUGHLIN & HARVEY LTD.

Caslteton Building Works, 34-42 York Road, Belfast BT15 3HU

Secretary C.A.Denny,ACIS

Employees 1,456

MCMULLEN & SONS LTD. HERTFORD BREWERY SUPERANNUATION FUND

26 Old Cross, Hertford SG14 1RD
Telephone: 54911

Secretary T.H.Brock, FCIS, ACMA

Actuaries Lane Clark & Peacock

Auditors Howard Tilly & Co

Company Employees 1,218

Pensioners 70

M.D.W.GROUP STAFF PENSION FUND

21 Blythswood Square, Glasgow G2 4AT
Telephone: 041-248 2681

Secretary J.A.Fulton,ACCA,ACMA

Trustees H.A.Whitson, J.C.K.Murray, G.R.MacDonald, W.W.Shearer, D.A.Hall, J.T.Lawlor

Insured with Scottish Mutual Assurance Society

Pension Fund Consultants Reed Stenhouse Benefit Consultants Ltd.

Auditors Thomsom McLintock & Co.

Company Employees 1,032

Members 155

Pensioners 33

Annual Contributions £100,000

THOMAS MEADOWS INTERNATIONAL LTD

36 Grosvenor Gardens, London SW1W 0ED
Telephone: 01-730 0266

Director S.J.Fetherston

Secretary F.T.Morgan

Insured with Clerical, Medical & General Life Assurance

Employees 1,467

MEARS BROTHERS HOLDINGS LTD SUPERANNUATION FUND

Dorcan House, Dorcan Way, Swindon
Wiltshire SN3 3TS
Telephone: 0793-40111

MEARS BROTHERS HOLDINGS LTD Continued

Pensions Manager T.G.Thackwray, APMI
Company Secretary P.A.Hall
Trustees Mears Bros.Group Pensions Ltd.
Actuaries R.Watson & Sons
Company Employees 1,435
Members 580
Pensioners 39
Annual Contributions £425,000
Capital Value £1,600,000

MEDCO GROUP OF COMPANIES
137A North End, Croydon, Surrey
Telephone: 01-681 7331
Director R.J.Orsman
Employees 1,000

MEDICAL RESEARCH COUNCIL MRC PENSION TRUST LTD.
20 Park Crescent, London W1N 4AL
Telephone: 01-636 5422
Secretary J.M.Jeffs, FCCA
Trustees Lord Shepherd, Sir Arnold Burgen, P.G.Daly, Dr.J.J.Harvey, A.W.Hemmings, F.Rushton, D.G.Sanders, Dr.R.Sanger, D.D.Vonberg
Investment Advisers N.M.Rothschild Asset Management Ltd.
Actuaries The Government Actuary
Auditors Coopers & Lybrand
Employees 4,200
Members 3,180
Pensioners 234

	£000
Annual Contributions	3,886
Annual Investment Income	1,362
Annual Outflow	1,027
Capital Value	25,350
Summary of Investments	
Equities	13,776
Fixed Interest	
Property	4,734
Cash & Deposits	749

GEORGE MELLIS & SON LTD.
30 Craigshaw Drive, Aberdeen
Telephone: 0224-871296
Secretary J.A.Donald
Employees 715

MELVILLE, DUNDAS & WHITSON LTD.
See MDW Group

MENTMORE MANUFACTURING CO LTD
Platignum House, Six Hills Way, Stevenage, Herts.SG1 2AY
Telephone: 0438-2488
Managing Director F.G.Sexton

Insured with National Mutual Life Assurance Society
Employees 833

JOHN MENZIES (HOLDINGS) LTD
Hanover Buildings, Rose Street, Edinburgh EH2 2YQ
Telephone: 031-225 2491
Pension Fund Manager J.S.Sloan, MA
Insured with Scottish Widows' Fund & Life Assurance Society
Pension Fund Consultants Martin Paterson Associates Ltd
Employees 7,225
Capital Value Over £2 million

MEPC LTD.
Brook House, 113 Park Lane, London W1Y 4AY
Telephone: 01-629 9022
Secretary A.L.Crowe
Employees 512

THE MERCANTILE & GENERAL REINSURANCE CO.LTD. STAFF SUPERANNUATION & WIDOWS FUND
Moorfields House, Moorfields, London EC2Y 9AL
Telephone: 01-628 7070
Personnel Manager T.W.Manley
Auditors Peat, Marwick, Mitchell & Co.
Employees 720
Members 600
Pensioners 39

MERCEDES-BENZ (UNITED KINGDOM) LTD RETIREMENT & DEPENDANTS BENEFIT PLAN
Mercedes-Benz Centre, Millingotn Road, Hayes, Middx.
Telephone: 01-573 7777
Pensions Administrator Miss P.J.Fosh, BA
Investment Advisers J.Henry Schroder Wagg & Co Ltd
Pension Fund Consultants Metropolitan Pensions Association
Auditors Ernst & Whinney
Company Employees 900
Members 640
Pensioners 16
Capital Value £1,800,000

THE MERCHANT NAVY (A) OFFICERS' PENSION FUND, (B) RATINGS' PENSION FUND
Ebbisham House, Church Street, Epsom, Surrey KT17 4QF
Telephone: 03727-24567
Chief Executive P.N.Evanson, FCA
Secretary (A) B.J.Glossop, FCA, (B) J.M.Bird
Investment Manager G.C.Musson
Trustees (a) Merchant Navy Officers Pension Fund Trustees Ltd. (b) Merchant Navy Ratings' Pension Fund Trustees Ltd.

THE MERCHANT NAVY Continued

Property Advisers (a) St.Quintin, (b) George Trollope & Sons
Actuaries R.Watson & Sons
Auditors Touche Ross & Co.
Solicitors Hill, Dickinson & Co.

	Officers	Ratings
Members (at 5.4.79)	33,269	30,000
Pensioners	6,825	2
Deferred Pensioners	25,614	-
	£000	£000
Annual Contributions	35,904	8,764
Annual Investment Income	20,629	188
Annual Outflow	8,188	251
Capital Value		
Book Value	265,583	8,681
Market Value	311,302	9,550
Summary of Investments		
UK Equities	160,419	4,309
Overseas Equities	10,039	338
Fixed interest	116,382	2,957
Property	15,859	-
Cash & Deposits	3,198	405
Others	5,405	1,541

MERCK SHARP & DOHME (HOLDINGS) LTD. PENSION SCHEME

Hertford Road, Hoddesdon, Herts EN11 9BU
Telephone: 61-67272
Pension Fund Manager & Secretary R.A.D.Newman, FCA
Trustees The MSD Pension Trustee Ltd.
Managed by Legal & General (Pensions Management) Ltd
Actuaries Bacon & Woodrow
Pension Fund Consultants Richards Longstaff Ltd
Auditors Arthur Andersen & Co
Company Employees 1,250
Members 1,200
Pensioners 240

	£000
Annual Contributions	1,180
Annual Investment Income	100
Capital Value	5,000
Summary of Investments	%
Equities	50%
Fixed Interest	20%
Property	30%

MERCURY SECURITIES LTD

30 Gresham Street, London EC2P 2EB
Telephone: 01-600 4545
Secretary I.B.Marshall
Employees 1,329

Subsidiaries include S.G.Warburg & Co.Ltd., Metropolitan Pensions Association Ltd.

D. MEREDEW LTD

Dunhams Lane, Letchworth, Herts SG6 1LG
Telephone: 046-26 4151
Director N.A.G.Brooks
Employees 975

MERRILL LYNCH HOLDINGS LTD. RETIREMENT BENEFIT PLAN

3 Newgate House, London EC1A 7DA
Telephone: 01-236 1030
Managing Director J.L.Owen
Company Employees 450
Members 350

MERSEY DOCKS & HARBOUR CO SALARIED OFFICERS PENSION FUND(A), WEEKLY STAFF PENSION FUND (B), PRE 63 STAFF SUPERANNUATION FUND (C)

Port of Liverpool Building, Pier Head, Liverpool L3 1BZ
Telephone: 051-200 2020
Personnel Services Manager R.L.S.Cumpstey, APMI
Trustees 3 Company Directors & 3 Members' Representatives
Stockbrokers & Investment Advisers Pember & Boyle
Actuaries A.G.MacG.Fraser,FIA, A.C.Baker,FIA
Auditors Deloitte, Haskins & Sells
Company Employees 3,500

	Salaried Officers	Weekly Staff
Members	835	2,043
Pensioners	239	1,096
	£000	£000
Annual Contributions	744	1,012
Annual Investment Income	482	259
Annual Outflow	568	760
Capital Value	5,831	3,313
Summary of Investments		
Equities	2,958	1,466
Fixed Interest	1,865	1,109
Property	658	338
Cash & Deposits	350	400

	Pre 63 Staff
Members	160
Pensioners	65
	£000
Annual Contributions	452
Annual Investment Income	84
Annual Outflow	520
Capital Value	1,023
Summary of Investments	

MERSEY DOCKS & HARBOUR CO *Continued*

Equities	548
Fixed Interest	356
Property	99
Cash & Deposits	20

MERSEY INSULATION CO LTD

58-64 Strand Road, Bootle 20, Merseyside
Telephone: 051-922 5281

Managing Director S.R.Silcock

Employees 680

MERSEYSIDE COUNTY COUNCIL SUPERANNUATION FUND

Metropolitan House, Old Hall Street,
Liverpool L69 3EL
Telephone: 051-227 5234

Treasurer P.W.Jenkins, IPFA

Investment Advisers Hambros Bank Ltd. (and Stockbrokers)

Stockbrokers Phillips & Drew, Grieveson Grant & Co., Tilney & Co.

Property Advisers Edmund Kirby & Sons

Actuaries Duncan C.Fraser & Co.

Auditors District Auditor

Members 40,000

Pensioners 14,000

	£000
Annual Contributions	34,617
Annual Investment Income	13,124
Annual Outflow	23,207
Capital Value (at 31.3.80)	174,127
Summary of Investments	
Equities	102,174
Fixed Interest	46,795
Property	18,614
Cash & Deposits	6,544

MERZ & MCLELLAN

Amberley, Killingworth,
Newcastle upon Tyne NE12 0RS
Telephone: 0632-683838

Partner G.G.R.Argent

Employees 580

THE METAL BOX PENSION SCHEME

Queens House, Forbury Road, Reading RG1 3JH
Telephone: 0734-581177

Pension Fund Manager and Secretary D.M.James, FPMI

Trustees Metal Box Pension Trustees Ltd.

Investment Advisers Robert Fleming Investment Management Limited

Actuaries R.Watson & Sons

Auditors Hodgson Harris & Co

Solicitors Rowe & Maw

Company Employees 34,151

Members 20,494

Pensioners 4,204

Deferred Pensions 3,011

	£000
Annual Contributions	22,100
Annual Investment Income	9,400
Annual Outflow	5,400
Capital Value	122,700
Summary of Investments	
Equities	56,000
Fixed Interest	35,500
Cash & Deposits	4,500
Others	26,700

METAL CASTINGS DOEHLER LTD

Droitwich Road, Worcester

Managing Director R.P.Bryan

Employees 859

METAL CLOSURES GROUP LTD STAFF SCHEME AND WORKS SCHEME

Bromford Lane, West Bromwich,
West Midlands B70 7HY
Telephone: 021-553 2900

Director M.J.Mann, ACCA

Company Secretary R.M.Daniels

Trustees Metal Closure Group Trustees Ltd

Part Managed by Legal & General (Pensions Management) Ltd.

Investment Advisers Cazenove & Co

Actuaries Bacon & Woodrow

Auditors Peat Marwick Mitchell & Co

Company Employees 2,960

	Staff	Works
Members	709	1,100
Pensioners	200	260
	£000	£000
Annual Contributions	597	45
Annual Investment Income	300	25
Capital Value	4,000	300

METALRAX (HOLDINGS) LTD

Ardath Road Kings Norton, Birmingham B38 9PN
Telephone: 021-458 6571

Secretary E.S.Moore

Insured with Clerical, Medical & General Life Assurance

Employees 1,315

METHODIST MINISTERS RETIREMENT FUND

1 Central Buildings, Westminster,
London SW1H 9NP
Telephone: 01-222 8868

General Secretary Finance Rev.D.R.Farrow, BA

Property Advisers Donaldson & Sons

Actuaries Bacon & Woodrow

Auditors Clay Ratnage Strevens & Hills

The Major UK Pension Funds MET/MIL

METHODIST MINISTERS Continued

Members 2,126
Pensioners 2,040
Annual Contributions £1,048,000
Annual Investment Income £935,000
Capital Value £9,571,000

THE METTOY CO.LTD. 1973 PENSION SCHEME
Queensway, Swansea Industrial Estate, Fforestfach, Swansea SA5 4EU
Telephone: 0792-32223

Secretary B.W.Lillyman, FCCA

Insured with Sun Life Assurance Society Ltd.

Employees 3,458

MONTAGUE L. MEYER LTD
Villiers House, 41-47 Strand, London WC2N 5JG
Telephone: 01-839 7766

Pension Fund Manager M.A.Holmes, APMI

Company Secretary A.R.Yeates

Managed by Eagle Pension Funds Ltd, Legal & General (Pensions Management) Ltd

Investment Advisers de Zoete & Bevan

Employees 8,397

M.F.I. FURNITURE GROUP LTD.
New Stadium Works, North End Road, Wembley, Middx HA9 0AY
Telephone: 01-903 1366

Secretary S.C.Moodley

Insured with Clerical, Medical & General Life Assurance

Employees 2,830

M G D GRAPHIC SYSTEMS LTD
Greenbank Street, Preston, Lancs.PR1 7LA
Telephone: 0772-57571

Director L.Putze

Employees 1,235

MICHELIN TYRE CO LTD PENSION AND LIFE ASSURANCE PLANS FOR MONTHLY STAFF AND WEEKLY STAFF
Campbell Road, Stoke-on-Trent, Staffs.ST4 4EY
Telephone: 0782-48101

Pension Fund Manager H.Gisbourne, FPMI

Trustees Michelin Pension Trust (No.1) Ltd., Michelin Pension Trust (No.2) Ltd.

Managed by Legal & General (Pensions Management) Ltd.

Investment Advisers Ivory & Sime Ltd., N.M.Rothschild & Sons Ltd., Warburg Investment Management Ltd.

Actuaries Clay & Partners

Pension Fund Consultants and Actuarial Advice for Weekly Staff Obtained through Metropolitan Pensions Association Ltd.

Auditors Binder Hamlyn

Company Employees 18,000

	Monthly Staff	Weekly Staff
Members	4,600	13,500
Pensioners	500	1,700
	£million	£million
Annual Contributions	6	8
Capital Value	38	39

MID GLAMORGAN COUNTY COUNCIL SUPERANNUATION FUND
Mid Glamorgan County Hall, Cathays Park, Cardiff
Telephone: 0222-28033

Treasurer R.K.Lacey, IPFA, DPA

Actuaries R.Watson & Sons

Auditor District Auditor

Employees (at 31.3.79) 24,331

Members 16,500

Pensioners 6,821

Annual Contributions £7.6 million

Capital Value £70 million

MIDLAND BANK LTD. PENSION SCHEME
27/32 Poultry, London EC2P 2BX
Telephone: 01-606 9911

Manager, Pensions E.C.Wells,APMI

Assistant to Manager, Pensions K.W.Bennett,APMI

Secretary B.M.Cocup,JP

Investment Manager K.L.Watling

Trustees Midland Bank Pension Trust Ltd.

Actuaries R.Watson & Sons

Company Employees 65,600

Capital Value
Book Value £340.0 million
Market Value £352.0 million

MIDLAND CONTRACT CLEANERS LTD
Cleveland Street, Wolverhampton, West Midlands
Telephone: 0902-21369

Director R.T.Hall

Employees 500

MIDLAND INDUSTRIES LTD
Heath Town Works, Wolverhampton, West Midlands WV10 0QD
Telephone: 0902-56234

Secretary R.J.Burns

Insured with Standard Life Assurance Co

Employees 1,190

THE MIDLAND NEWS ASSOCIATION LTD.
Queen Street, Wolverhampton WV1 3BU
Telephone: 0902-22351

MIDLAND SHIRES FARMERS LTD.
County Mills, Worcester
Telephone: 0905-25541

Secretary A.R.Cockhill,FCA

Employees 650

MILES LABORATORIES LTD RETIREMENT BENEFITS PLAN (1972)

Stoke Court, Stoke Poges, Slough, Berks.SL2 4LY
Telephone: 369-2151

Financial Director B.V.Gordon, FCA

Company Secretary G.C.Tuck

Trustees Lowndes Associated Pensions Ltd

Managed by Legal & General (Pensions Management) Ltd.

Actuarial Advice Obtained through Cubie, Wood & Co.Ltd.

Pension Fund Consultants Noble Lowndes & Partners Ltd.

Auditors Price Waterhouse & Co

Company Employees 728

Members 508

Pensioners 62

	£000
Annual Contributions	363
Capital Value	3,500
Summary of Investments	
Equities	2,390
Property	931

MILK MARKETING BOARD PENSION FUND AND PENSION SCHEMES A AND B

Thames Ditton, Surrey KT7 0EL
Telephone: 01-398 4101

Pensions Officer P.S.Marchant

Part Insured with Legal & General Assurance Society Ltd.

Investment Advisers Warburg Investment Management Ltd

Actuaries Clay & Partners

Pension Fund Consultants Metropolitan Pensions Association Ltd

Auditors Ernst & Whinney

Company Employees 13,500

	Pension Fund	Pension Scheme A
Members	9,100	2,625
Pensioners	1,750	12
	£000	£000
Annual Contributions	5,000	380
Annual Investment Income	539	87
Capital Value	15,946	875

	Pension Scheme B
Members	650
Pensioners	6
	£000
Annual Contributions	450
Annual Investment Income	220
Capital Value	2,225

JAMES MILLER & PARTNERS LTD PENSION SCHEME

Miller House, 18 South Groathill Avenue, Edinburgh EH4 2LW
Telephone: 031-332 2585

Secretary W.J.Brand

Director Personnel Services J.A.Ross,BSc,MIPM

Insured with Norwich Union Life Insurance Society

Pension Fund Consultants Norman Frizzell Life & Pensions Ltd.

Company Employees 2,689

Members 342

Pensioners 64

F. MILLER (TEXTILES) LTD

63 Raithburn Avenue, Castlemilk, Glasgow G45
Telephone: 041-634 1137

Secretary W.McRae,MA,LLB

Insured with Scottish Amicable Life Assurance Society

Employees 634

STANLEY MILLER HOLDINGS LTD

Great Lime Road East,
Newcastle Upon Tyne NE12 9UD
Telephone: 0632-663891

Director & Secretary R.A.Soan,FCIS

Insured with Legal & General Assurance Society Ltd

Employees 895

MILLERS (COCKERMOUTH) HOLDINGS LTD

Derwent Mills, Cockermouth, Cumbria CA13 0HT
Telephone: 0900-3031

Secretary P.Hutchinson

Employees 1,045

MILLETTS LEISURE SHOPS LTD.

Millett House, Summerhouse Road, Moulton Park
Northants.NN3 1XQ
Telephone: 0604-43687

Secretary J.A.Summerhayes,FCA

Employees 920

MILLS & ALLEN INTERNATIONAL LTD

Broadwick House, 15-17 Broadwick Street,
London W1V 1FP
Telephone: 01-439 9541

Secretary C.Gregson

Investment Advisers Kleinwort, Benson Investment Management Ltd

Employees 1,074

MILTON KEYNES DEVELOPMENT CORPORATION

Wavendon Tower, Waverton, Milton Keynes, Bucks.MK17 8LX
Telephone: 0908-74000

Pension Fund Manager County Treasurer

Managed by Buckinghamshire County Council

The Major UK Pension Funds MIL/MON

MILTON KEYNES DEVELOPMENT CORPORATION
Continued

Managed by Buckinghamshire County Council Superannuation Scheme and New Towns Pension Fund

Company Employees 1,400

MINE SAFETY APPLIANCES LTD
East Shawhead, Coatbridge, Lanarkshire ML5 4TD
Telephone: 0236-24966

Secretary W.D.Holland

Employees 611

MINET HOLDINGS LTD
Minet House, 100 Leman Street, London E1 8HG
Telephone: 01-481 0707

Secretary B.B.Chapple

Investment Advisers Geoffrey Morley & Partners

Employees 1,517

Subsidiaries Include J.H.Minet Life & Pensions Ltd.

MINEWORKERS AND ANCILLARY WORKERS PENSION SCHEMES
See National Coal Board

MINING SUPPLIES LTD
Hillcrest Works, Carr Hill, Balby, Doncaster, S.Yorks DN4 8DH
Telephone: 0302-22111

Secretary P.M.Urwin

Employees 1,264

MINORIES LTD
Benton Road, Newcastle Upon Tyne, Tyne & Wear NE9 1DS
Telephone: 0632-666361

Secretary T.M.Middleton

Employees 684

MINSTER ASSETS LTD
Minster House, Arthur Street, London EC4R 9BH
Telephone: 01-623 1050

Secretary A.E.Ward

Director J.N.Fuller-Shapcott

Company Employees 1,986

There are several schemes, the capital value of the self administered ones aggregating some £10 million

MITCHELL COTTS GROUP EXECUTIVE PENSION PLAN AND PENSION FUND
Cotts House, Camomile Street, London EC3A 7BJ
Telephone: 01-283 1234

Pension Fund Executive R.N.F.Glennie

Trustees Stewart Wrightson (Trustees) Ltd.

Part Insured with Legal & General Assurance Society Ltd

Actuaries Clay & Partners

Pension Fund Consultants Stewart Wrightson Assurance Consultants Ltd.

Auditors Touche Ross & Co.

Company Employees (UK) 2,000

Members 1,500 Approx.

Pensioners 150

Annual Contributions £1,400,000

MITCHELL SOMERS LTD
Haywood Forge, Prospect Road, Halesowen, West Midlands B62 8DZ
Telephone: 021-550 4741

Secretary A.S.Beaumont,FCA

Trustees Six

Managed by Metropolitan Pensions Association Ltd.

Investment Advisers Hill Samuel & Co. Ltd.

Auditors Touche Ross & Co.

Company Employees 1,500

WILLIAM MITCHELL (SINKERS) LTD
Warley, West Midlands B66 4HW
Telephone: 021-558 2614

Employees 600

MIXCONCRETE (HOLDINGS) LTD.
Little Billing, Northampton NN3 4AH
Telephone: 0604-409622

Secretary J.D.Cox

Insured with Legal & General Assurance Society Ltd

Employees 1,097

MK ELECTRIC HOLDINGS LTD PENSION FUND
Shrubbery Road, Edmonton, London N9 0PB
Telephone: 01-803 3355

Company Secretary G.A.Fry,FCIS,APMI

Investment Advisers Kleinwort Benson Investment Management Ltd

Actuaries Bacon & Woodrow

Auditors Coopers & Lybrand

Company Employees 5,832

Members 2,000

Pensioners 350

Annual Contributions £1,098,000

Annual Investment Income £360,000

Capital Value £4,806,000

MKR HOLDINGS LTD. RETIREMENT BENEFITS SCHEME AND PENSION SCHEME
6 Park Terrace, Worcester Park, Surrey KT4 7JZ
Telephone: 01-337 4444

Secretary Miss B.C.Fuller

Managed by Scottish Widows' Fund & Life Assurance Society

Pension Fund Consultants Sedgwick Employee Benefits Consultants Ltd.

Auditors Edward Moore & Sons

Company Employees 1,430

MKR HOLDINGS LTD. Continued

	Retirement Scheme	Pension Scheme
Members (at 5.4.80)	426	60
Pensioners	13	17
Annual Contributions	£121,000	£47,000
Capital Value	£923,000	£552,000

M.L. HOLDINGS LTD

M.L. Building, Ajax Avenue Trading Estate, Slough, Berks. SL1 4BQ
Telephone: 23838

Secretary A.P.Smith,ACMA

Managed by Standard Life Pension Fund Ltd

Employees 1,275

3 M UNITED KINGDOM LTD
See under Three M

MOBEN GROUP LTD.

41 Blackfriars Road, Salford, Manchester M3 7BB
Telephone: 061-834 5756

Secretary J.E.D.Ware

Employees 820

MOBIL PENSION & DEPENDANTS' BENEFIT PLAN

Mobil House, 54-60 Victoria Street,
London SW1E 6QB
Telephone: 01-828 9777

Pension Administration Manager A.D.Brann

Secretary C.J.Rumsey

Trustees Mobil Trustee Co.Ltd.

Investment Advisers Morgan Grenfell & Co.Ltd., N.M.Rothschild Asset Management Ltd., Warburg Investment Management Ltd., Lazard Securities Ltd.

Property Advisers Debenham Tewson & Chinnocks

Actuaries Bacon & Woodrow

Pension Fund Consultants Metropolitan Pensions Association Ltd

Auditors Arthur Young McClelland Moores & Co

Solicitors Allen & Overy

Company Employees 3,993

Members 1,208

Pensioners £3,700,000

Annual Contributions £3,266,000

Capital Value £36,700,000

MOLINS PENSION FUND

2 Evelyn Street, London SE8 5DH
Telephone: 01-237 4581

Secretary and Pensions Manager E.A.Claydon, FCA, APMI

Trustees The Molins Pension Trust Ltd

Investment Advisers Gartmore Investment Ltd

Actuaries R.Watson & Sons

Property Advisers Edward Erdman & Co

Auditors Baker Rooke & Amsdons

Employees 5,010

Members 4,570

Pensioners 1,640

Annual Contributions £2.3 million

Annual Investment Income £3.4 million

Annual Outflow £2.2 million

Capital Value £38.4 million

A. MONK & COMPANY LTD
SUPERANNUATION SCHEME

PO Box 43, Green Lane, Padgate, Warrington, Cheshire WA1 4JB
Telephone: 0925-812000

Secretary M.J.Anderson

Trustees A.Monk & Co (Pension Trust) Ltd

Stockbrokers R.Nivison & Co

Actuaries R.Watson & Sons

Auditors Bowman, Grimshaw & Co

Company Employees 3,935

Members 838

Pensioners 273

	£000
Annual Contributions	455
Annual Investment Income	466
Annual Outflow	225
Capital Value	7,372
Summary of Investments	
Equities	4,126
Fixed Interest	2,230
Property	949
Cash & Deposits	67
Others	15

MONO CONTAINERS (U.K.) LTD

Malt House, Field End Road, Eastcote, Ruislip, Middx.HA4 9LY
Telephone: 01-868 7242

Director J.Neasom

Secretary G.N.Dunnings

Employees 856

MONO PUMPS LTD.

Arnfield Works, Audenshaw, Manchester M34 5JA
Telephone: 061-330 3031

Secretary S.Maddison

Employees 989

MONOTYPE CORPORATION LTD

Salfords, Redhill, Surrey RH1 5JP
Telephone: 65959

Secretary A.G.Chelmick

Employees 2,000

MONSANTO LTD PENSION PLANS FOR SALARIED EMPLOYEES AND FOR HOURLY PAID EMPLOYEES

Monsanto House, 10-18 Victoria Street, London SW1H 0NQ
Telephone: 01-222 5678

Pension Fund Managers B.D.Hill (Financial), P.J.P.Aris (Benefits)

Secretary R.P.Hutton

Trustees Barclays Bank Trust Company Ltd.

Investment Advisers Robert Fleming Investment Management Ltd., Ivory & Sime Ltd., Pensions Management (S.W.F.) Ltd., Legal & General (Pensions Management) Ltd.

Pension Fund Consultants and Actuarial Advice Obtained through Towers Perrin Forster and Crosby Inc

Auditors Deloitte Haskins and Sells

Company Employees 3,515

Members 3,474

Pensioners 1,025

	£000
Capital Value	26,900
Summary of Investments	
Equities	15,900
Fixed Interest	7,600
Property	2,300
Cash & Deposits	1,100

SAMUEL MONTAGU & CO LTD STAFF PENSION SCHEME

114 Old Broad Street, London EC2P 2HY
Telephone: 01-588 6464

Pension Fund Director B.K.Barber

Trustees Montagu Executor and Trustee Co. Ltd.

Investment Advisers Drayton Montagu Portfolio Management Ltd

Actuaries Duncan C.Fraser & Co.

Auditors Coopers & Lybrand

Company Employees 600

Members 578

Pensioners 54

	£000
Annual Contributions	1,224
Annual Investment Income	1,091
Annual Outflow	227
Capital Value	10,906
Summary of Investments	
Equities	4,849
Fixed Interest	3,517
Property	1,967
Cash & Deposits	573

MONTFORT (KNITTING MILLS) LTD

PO Box 24, Tudor Road, Leicester LE3 5JS
Telephone: 0533-29112

Secretary B.R.Dennard

Insured with Scottish Widows Fund & Life Assurance Society

Employees 1,089

MOORE BUSINESS FORMS LTD. PENSION FUND

75-79 Southwark Street, London SE1 0HY
Telephone: 01-928 9022

Pensions Manager W.T.Buxey,FPMI,FCCA

Pension Fund Consultants Towers, Perrin, Forster & Crosby

Employees 1,882

GEO. A. MOORE & CO LTD

Queen Mary House, Avenue D, Thorp Arch Trading Estate, Wetherby, LS23 7BR
Telephone: 0937-843125

Pension Fund Manager and Secretary B.Todhunter, ACMA

Trustees Moores Furniture Group Ltd.

Managed by Prudential Pensions Ltd.

Investment Advisers Prudential Pensions Ltd.

Pension Fund Consultants Stewart Wrightson (North Eastern) Ltd.

Auditors Coopers & Lybrand

Company Employees 844

Members 710

Pensioners 21

	£000
Annual Contributions	330
Annual Outflow	45
Capital Value	1,072
Summary of Investments	
Equities	448
Fixed Interest	358
Property	266

MORFAX LTD

Willow Lane, Mitcham, Surrey CR4 4TD
Telephone: 01-648 7040

Director F.J.Frost

Executive J.Rooke

Employees 1,000

MORGAN CRUCIBLE CO LTD (THE)

98 Petty France, London SW1H 9EG
Telephone: 01-222 7121

Secretary A.M.Davis

Pensions Administrator Miss R.E.Adamson,APMI

Insured with Legal & General Assurance Society Ltd

Pension Fund Consultants Sedgwick Employee Benefits Consultants Ltd.

Employees 5,210

DAVID MORGAN LTD

26 The Hayes, Cardiff
Telephone: 0222-21011

Secretary F.R.Cempriere

Employees 700

MORGAN EDWARDS LTD
Sundorne House, Featherbed Lane, Shrewsbury, Salop SY1 4NS
Telephone: 0743-4674

Secretary D.G.C.Webster

Investment Advisers Hill Samuel Investment Management Ltd

Employees 598

MORGAN-GRAMPIAN LTD PENSION FUND
30 Calderwood Street, London SE18 6QH
Telephone: 01-855 7777

Pensions Manager J.C.Swaffield, APMI

Insured with Clerical, Medical and General Life Assurance Society

Pension Fund Consultants Willis Faber Advisory Services Ltd.

Company Employees 920

Members 570

MORGAN GRENFELL HOLDINGS LTD. STAFF PENSION SCHEME AND SENIOR GROUP PENSION SCHEME
23 Great Winchester Street, London EC2P 2AX
Telephone: 01-588 4545

Secretary M.C.Evans

Pension Fund Consultants Willis Faber Advisory Services Ltd.

Auditors Spicer & Pegler

Solicitors Slaughter & May

Company Employees 639

Members (Total) 671

Pensioners 107

MORLEY'S STORES LTD.
6-14 High Road, Ilford, Essex IG1 2DB

Secretary W.J.Hughes

Employees 725

JOHN MORRELL & CO LTD STAFF PENSION SCHEME AND WAGE EARNERS RETIREMENT & DEATH BENEFITS SCHEME
PO Box 100, Spinney House, Church Street, Liverpool L69 1AT
Telephone: 051-709 9483

Secretary R.L.Hollowood

Insured with Friends' Provident Life Office

Pension Fund Consultants Edward P.Matchett & Partners Ltd.

Company Employees 474

Members Staff 86, Wage Earners 135

Pensioners Staff 40, Wage Earners 10

Annual Contributions Staff £97,000, Wage Earners £59,000

MORRIS & BLAKEY WALLPAPERS LTD
159-161 Camden High Street, London NW1 7JP
Telephone: 01-485 0661

Secretary D.K.Tarling

Insured with Guardian Royal Exchange Assurance Group Ltd

Employees 501

MORRIS & COMPANY (SHREWSBURY) LTD PENSION SCHEME
Welsh Bridge, Shrewsbury, Salop SY3 8LH
Telephone: 0743-62005

Secretary C.B.Hancock

Trustees Morris & Co Trust Fund Ltd

Stockbrokers Tilney & Co.

Actuaries Duncan C.Fraser & Co.

Pension Fund Consultants Alsop Stevens Batesons

Auditors Whittingham Riddell & Co

Company Employees 511

Members 296

Pensioners 88

	£000
Contributions (15 months to 31.3.80)	199
Investment Income	174
Outflow	91
Capital Value	1,454
Summary of Investments	
Equities	288
Fixed Interest	925
Property	169
Others	60

HERBERT MORRIS LTD.
P.O.Box 7, Loughborough, Leics.LE11 1RL
Telephone: 0509-63123

Secretary G.M.Murray

Employees 2,000

PHILIP MORRIS GROUP PENSION PLAN
Great West House, Great West Road, Brentford, Middx.TW8 9DF
Telephone: 01-560 4191

Administration Director P.M.Steele, ACIS

Company Employees 1,000

Members 681

Pensioners 418

WM. MORRISON SUPERMARKETS LTD PENSION FUND
Hilmore House, Thornton Road, Bradford, Yorkshire BD8 9AX
Telephone: 0274-494166

Pension Fund Manager & Secretary H.E.Watkinson

Other Pension Management M.Ackroyd

Trustees H.E.Watkinson, K.D.Morrison, J.Rhodes

Managed by Prudential Pensions Ltd.

Company Employees 3,700

Members 700

Pensioners 100

Annual Contributions £400,000

MORSE EUROPE
Jubilee Road, Letchworth, Herts.
Telephone: 04626-5256
Director G.C.Hartman
Employees 500

MOSS BROS LTD
21-26 Bedford Street, London WC2E 8JB
Telephone: 01-240 4567
Secretary A.Inglis
Insured with Guardian Royal Exchange Assurance Co Ltd
Employees 660

MOSS ENGINEERING LTD.
Shenstone Hall, Shenstone, Lichfield,
Staffs.WS14 0JS
Telephone: 0543-480222
Secretary R.K.Jakeman,ACIS
Employees 979

THE WILLIAM MOSS GROUP LTD PENSION AND LIFE ASSURANCE SCHEME FOR PERMANENT STAFF
North Circular Road, London NW2 7AD
Telephone: 01-452 8080
Secretary H.C.Marshall
Trustees T.F.James, E.A.G.Woods, M.B.Bailey, A.J.Bower, H.C.Marshall, K.J.A.Chelu, N.England, N.Weil
Insured with Scottish Widows' Fund & Life Assurance Society
Pension Fund Consultants Willis Faber Advisory Services Ltd
Company Employees 1,667
Members 390
Pensioners 70

THE MOSSLEY WOOL COMBING & SPINNING CO.LTD. PENSION FUND
Milton Mills, Mossley, nr.Ashton-under-Lyme, Lancs.OL5 9AU
Telephone: 04575-2802
Financial Director & Secretary P.W.Harding,FCIS, FCCA
Trustees Milbrun Trustees Ltd.
Stockbrokers Henry Cooke Lumsden & Co.
Actuaries Duncan C.Fraser & Co.
Auditors Carter Chaloner & Kearns
Company Employees 800
Members 100
Pensioners 40

	£000
Annual Contributions	50
Annual Investment Income	50
Annual Outflow	40
Capital Value	550
Summary of Investments	
Equities	155
Fixed Interest	245
Property Unit Trusts	49
Cash & Deposits	100

MOTHERCARE LTD PENSION FUND
Cherry Tree Road, Watford,
Hertfordshire WD2 5SH
Telephone: 33577
Secretary T.P.Goddard
Trustees S.K.Zilkha, B.Goodman, A.Mowlem
Stockbrokers L.Messel & Co
Actuaries Lane Clark & Peacock
Auditors Peat, Marwick, Mitchell & co
Company Employees 4,985
Members 385
Pensioners 29

MOTHERWELL BRIDGE (HOLDINGS) LTD
Motherwell Bridge Works, Motherwell,
Lanarkshire ML1 3NP
Telephone: 0698-66111
Secretary J.Lumsden
Employees 3,137

MOTOR AGENTS ASSOCIATION NATIONAL MOTOR INDUSTRY PENSION FUND
201 Great Portland Street, London W1N 6AB
Telephone: 01-580 9122
Administration of MAA Pension Plan Motor Agents Pensions Administrators Ltd.
17 Market Square, Leighton Buzzard, Bedfordshire
Telephone: 0525-378237
Secretary J.R.Boast, FCIS
Trustees MAA Pension Plan Trustees Ltd.
Investment Advisers Wood Mackenzie & Co.
Stockbrokers de Zoete & Bevan
Pension Fund Consultants and Actuarial Advice Obtained through EBS (Management) Ltd
Auditors Couch Bright King & Co.
Companies belonging to MAA Pension Plan (at 1.4.80) 473
Members 9,642
Pensioners 75

	£000
Annual Contributions	2,758
Annual Investment Income	2,193
Annual Outflow	565
Capital Value	4,043
Summary of Investments	
Equities	2,449
Fixed Interest	1,262
Property	96
Others	264

MOTOROLA LTD PENSION FUND & LIFE ASSURANCE PLAN
Colvilles Road, Kelvin Estate, East Kilbride,
Glasgow G75 0TG
Telephone: 03552-39101

MOTOROLA LTD Continued

Pension Fund Manager Ian McConnell

Trustees Brian Bedford, John Dalby, Mike Phillips, Mike Alderson

Managed by Scottish Amicable Pensions Investments Ltd.

Pension Fund Consultants and Actuarial Advice Obtained through William M.Mercer Benefits Ltd.

Auditors Peat, Marwick, Mitchell & Co.

Company Employees 2,000

Members 1,600

Pensioners 17

Annual Contributions £500,000

Annual Outflow £80,000

Capital Value £1,600,000

MOTT, HAY & ANDERSON
St.Anne House, 20-26 Wellesley Road, Croydon, Surrey CR9 2UL
Telephone: 01-686 5041

Director J.V.Bartlett

Executive A.N.Palmer

Employees 600

MOUNT CHARLOTTE INVESTMENTS LTD
2 The Calls, Leeds, W.Yorks.LS2 7JU
Telephone: 0532-39111

Chairman S.C.Smith Cox

Insured with Sun Life Assurance Society Ltd.

Employees 1,164

JOHN MOWLEM & CO.LTD. STAFF PENSION & LIFE ASSURANCE SCHEME
Westgate House, Ealing Road, Brentford, Middlesex TW8 0QZ
Telephone: 01-568 9111

Pension Fund Manager Peter R.Cox

Secretary M.G.Tomkys

Trustees P.R.Cox, A.L.Charlesworth, K.R.Stancombe, E.A.Walker, T.H.Robinson, D.E.Glyn-Woods, M.Marsh

Part Managed by Prudential Pensions Ltd

Investment Advisers & Stockbrokers Hoare Govett Ltd

Actuarial Advice obtained through Cubie Wood & Co Ltd

Pension Fund Consultants Noble Lowndes & Partners Ltd

Auditors Dearden Farrow

Company Employees Staff 2,300, Operatives (not eligible for pension scheme) 4,000

Members 1,540

Pensioners 276

	£000
Annual Contributions (1980)	1,440
Annual Investment Income	450
Annual Outflow	420
Capital Value	8,560
Summary of Investments	
Equities	4,200
Fixed Interest	2,813
Property	1,247
Cash & Deposits	300

M P B CORPORATION
Cores End Road, Bourne End, Bucks.SL8 5AS
Telephone: 062-85 25222

Director T.M.Begel

Executive D.C.Shepperson

Employees 1,800

MUIRHEAD LTD PENSION AND ASSURANCE SCHEME
34 Croydon Road, Beckenham, Kent BR3 4BE
Telephone: 01-650 4888

Secretary D.Buchanan

Other Pension Management D.Buchanan

Trustees Sir Raymond Brown, E.G.Atkins, P.E.Gough, D.Buchanan

Insured with Friends' Provident Life Office

Company Employees 1,300

Members 700

Annual Contributions £600,000

MULTITONE ELECTRIC CO.LTD.
12-20 Underwood Street, London N1 7JT
Telephone: 01-253 7611

Secretary Mrs. D.Schuler

Employees 520

MUNRO & MILLER LTD.
Sighthill, Edinburgh EH11 4DU
Telephone: 031-443 6181

Secretary G.Stuart

Employees 541

J. MURPHY & SONS LTD
Highbury House, Highbury Corner, London N5 1RL
Telephone: 01-607 6711

Secretary T.Barron

Employees 2,685

MUSIC HIRE GROUP LTD
Low Lane, Horsforth, Leeds, West Yorkshire
Telephone: 0532-42201

Secretary H.C.Horton

Employees 600

M.Y. DART GROUP SALARIED STAFF PENSION SCHEME
Moxon street, Barnet, Herts.EN5 5TR
Telephone: 01-440 8441

Pensions Fund Manager & Secretary M.H.Speller

Trustees Lowndes Associated Pension Ltd

Investment Advisers Hill Samuel Investment Management Ltd

M.Y. DART GROUP Continued

Pension Fund Consultants Noble Lowndes & Partners Ltd

Company Employees 1,155

Members 120

Pensioners 6

Annual Contributions £50,000

HORATIO MYER & CO LTD PENSION & LIFE ASSURANCE SCHEME

83-97 Vauxhall Walk, London SE11 5EN
Telephone: 01-735 8191

Pension Fund Manager & Secretary H.C.Jeffrey

Trustees J.S.Myer, R.E.Myer, H.C.Jeffrey, P.Tyler

Insured with National Provident Institution

Pension Fund Consultants Hogg Robinson (Benefit Consultants) Ltd.

Company Employees 760

Members 491

Annual Contributions £300,000

M. MYERS & SON LTD

Vicarage Street, Langley Green, Oldbury, Warley, West Midlands B68 8HF
Telephone: 021-552 3322

Secretary J.E.Horwell

Executive K.Strawford

Employees 500

MYOTT SON & CO LTD

Alexander Potteries, Hanley, Stoke on Trent, Staffs.ST6 5HN
Telephone: 0782-87161

Secretary D.B.Jack

Employees 1,554

MYSON GROUP 1975 PENSION SCHEME

Industrial Estate, Ongar, Essex CM5 9RE
Telephone: 0277-362222

Company Secretary R.J.Humphreys,FCA

Pensions Officer & Assistant Secretary M.Maxwell

Trustees Myson Pension Trustees Ltd

Directors R.E.Myson (Chairman), N.Bend, R.J.Humphreys, R.H.Martin, B.E.Whichello

Investment Advisers and Stockbrokers E.B.Savory Milln & Co

Actuaries Duncan C.Fraser & Co

Property Advisers J.A. & M.A.Carter Consultants Ltd

Auditors Kidsons Elliot

Solicitors Nabarro Nathanson

Company Employees 2,600

Members 770

Number of Pensioners 35

Annual Contributions £430,000

Annual Investment Income £140,000

Annual Outflow £3,000

Capital Value £1,950,000

NAAFI PENSION FUND (1973)

Imperial Court, London SE11 5QX
Telephone: 01-735 1200

Pensions Manager and Secretary to the Trustees J.N.Connor

Secretary to P.F.Committee J.Crawley

Property Investment H.Legg

Trustees B.E.Whitaker, J.Morgan, N.W.Furse, T.J.Booth

Investment Advisers Guardian Royal Exchange Assurance

Auditors Deloitte, Haskins & Sells

Members 3,300

Pensioners 2,400

	£000
Annual Contributions	2,574
Annual Investment Income	2,260
Annual Outflow	1,601
Capital Value	24,590
Summary of Investments	
Equities	9,828
Fixed Interest	9,320
Property	5,319
Cash & Deposits	123

NABISCO LTD PENSION FUND

Bridge Road East, Welwyn Garden City, Herts.
Telephone: 96-25100

Secretary A.C.Clifford

Trustees Lowndes Associated Pensions Ltd.

Investment Advisers Bankers Trust Ltd., Kleinwort Benson Investment Management Ltd.

Actuarial Advice Obtained through Cubie, Wood & Co.Ltd.

Pension Fund Consultants Lowndes Associated Pensions Ltd.

Auditors Price Waterhouse & Co.

Company Employees 2,250

Members 1,798

Pensioners 429

	£000
Annual Contributions	1,114
Annual Investment Income	504
Annual Outflow	428
Capital Value	5,835
Summary of Investments	
Equities	4,535
Fixed Interest	1,953
Property	465
Cash & Deposits	420

NACANCO LTD

Salhouse Road, Norwich, Norfolk NR7 9AT
Telephone: 0603-47313

NACANCO LTD Continued

Secretary D.H.Geaves

Employees 920

J.F. NASH SECURITIES LTD
9 Station Road, Kettering, Northants NN15 7HY
Telephone: 0536-85921

Chairman J.F.Nash

Secretary P.J.R.Sawfoot

Employees 2,094

B. & I. NATHAN LTD.
Angel Road, Edmonton, London N18 3AO
Telephone: 01-803 4241

Secretary A.T.Cranch

Company Employees 569

NATIONAL & LOCAL GOVERNMENT OFFICERS ASSOCIATION STAFF SUPERANNUATION FUND
NALGO House, 1 Mabledon Place,
London WC1H 9AJ
Telephone: 01-388 2366

Senior Superannuation Officer D.J.Mayhew,APMI

Superannuation Officer J.Pitts,APMI

Legal Officer Miss P.Grant,LLB

Investment Advisers & Stockbrokers Fiske & Co, Pember & Boyle

Actuaries Bacon & Woodrow

Property Advisers E.W.Wallaker & Co

Auditors Clark Pixley & Co.

Employees 662

Members 611

UK Pensioners 114

Annual Contributions £959,000

Capital Value £4,317,000

NATIONAL BUS EMPLOYEES SUPERANNUATION TRUST (BEST) AND PENSION FUND
25 New Street Square, London EC4A 3AP
Telephone: 01-730 0368

Group Pensions Manager W.A.Walker, APMI

Secretary National Bus Employees Superannuation Trust L.W.Brown, APMI

Secretary National Bus Pension Fund R.B.F.Ingham, MA,FCA

Trustees National Bus Management Ltd.

Investment Advisers Robert Fleming Investment Management Ltd. (BEST), Henderson Administration Ltd. (Pension Fund)

Property Advisers Healey & Baker

Actuaries Government Actuary

Auditors Ernst & Whinney (BEST), Deloitte Haskins & Sells (Pension Fund)

	BEST	Pension Fund
Company Employees	58,000	4,500
Members	52,000	4,000
Pensioners	2,500	1,500
	£000	£000
Annual Contributions	16,000	4,000
Annual Investment Income	6,000	1,500
Annual Outflow	2,500	2,000
Capital Value	80,000	35,000
Summary of Investments		
Equities	35,000	11,500
Fixed Interest	23,000	8,000
Property	18,000	3,000
Cash & Deposits	4,000	500
Managed Fund	-	12,000

NATIONAL CARBONISING GROUP PENSION SCHEME
c/o NCC Energy Ltd. Fullarton Lodge,
Crow Hill Drive, Mansfield, Notts NG19 7AZ
Telephone: 0623-22644

Company Secretary A.Dodd,FCA

Pensions Secretary Miss J.M.Colton,BA

Directors R.Middleton, A.Dodd, M.A.Gaze, Sir James Whitaker, Bt

Trustees National Carbonising (Trustees) Ltd

Investment Advisers Arbuthnot Latham Investment Management Ltd

Actuaries Duncan C. Fraser & Co

Auditors Binder Hamlyn

Solicitors Sacker & Partners

Company Employees 613

Members 200

Pensioners 60

	£000
Annual Contributions	164
Annual Investment Income	76
Annual Outflow	31
Capital Value	1,660
Summary of Investments	
Equities	781
Fixed Interest	529
Property	24

NATIONAL CAR PARKS LTD
60 Charlotte Street, London W1P 2BB
Telephone: 01-637 9191

Secretary A.E.Bromfield

Managed by Provident Mutual Managed Pension Funds Ltd

Employees 2,843

NATIONAL COAL BOARD STAFF SUPERANNUATION SCHEME AND MINEWORKERS' PENSION SCHEME

Staff Superannuation Scheme Hobart House, Grosvenor Place, London SW1X 7AE
Telephone: 01-235 2020

Mineworkers' Pension Scheme Pensions and Insurance Centre, Queen's House, 105 Queen's St., Sheffield, S.Yorkshire S1 1GN54
Telephone: 0742-753754

Investment Department 10 Bouverie Street, London EC4Y 8BA
Telephone: 01-353 1500

Officials and Consultants

Staff Scheme

Secretary and Head of Superannuation and Retirement Branch G.W.H.Ferguson, LLB, MIPM, APMI

Assistant Secretary J.Henderson

The Staff Scheme also has 7 regional offices

Mineworkers' Pension Scheme

Director of Pensions and Insurance P.Stafford, MBE, FCII

Joint Secretaries J.McCallum (NCB), D.O'Connor (NUM)

Pensions Officer H.D.Ash

Investment Department

Director-General Superannuation Investments H.R.Jenkins,FRICS,FPMI

Deputy Director-General and Director (Industrial Finance) L.T.Anthony,MA

Director (Marketable Securities) D.J.Prosser,FIA

Director (Property) R.K.Juddery,FRICS

Director (Finance) J.L.Robb,CA

Accountant T.E.Chisholm, FCA

Consultants

Property Consultant A.E.Orchard-Lisle, CBE, FRICS (Healey & Baker)

Consulting Actuary E.A.Johnston, CB (Government Actuary's Dept)

Solicitor R.V.Cowles

Auditors Thomson McLintock & Co

Investment Advisory Panel W.Campbell Allan, J.F.G.Emms, A.W.John, Sir Oliver Chesterton, P.D.Tindley, D.M.Clement, W.Govett

Committees of Management

Staff Scheme 4 Board's Committee-Men and 4 Contributors' Committee-Men

Chairman N.Siddall, CBE

Deputy Chairman F.B.Harrison, FCA

Mineworkers Scheme 5 NCB Representatives and 5 NUM Representatives

Chairman J.R.Cowan, OBE

Joint Deputy Chairmen F.B.Harrison, J.Gormley

Joint Investment Sub-Committee 9 members

Chairman F.B.Harrison

	Staff (at 5.4.80)	Mineworkers (at 30.9.79)
Membership		
Contributors	59,062	251,285
Pensioners	49,281	253,863
	£million	£million
Annual Contributions	95.2	184.3
Annual Investment Income	94.8	53.7
Expenditure	69.7	88.3
Capital Value		
Book Value	970.8	636.3
Market Value	1,426.1	941.3
Summary of Investments		
Fixed Interest Securities Listed	179.6	98.6
Fixed Interest Securities Unlisted	7.3	2.0
Ordinary Shares Listed	346.0	219.7
Ordinary Shares Unlisted	5.7	4.2
British Investment Trust Ltd.	43.7	44.0
Property	314.0	190.8
Money on Deposit	43,734	39,866
Other Investments	14.1	26.3
Net Current Assets	60.4	50.7

It is estimated that by April 1981 the total assets of the two schemes will amount to about £2,650 million

These schemes also provide investment finance for industry through CIN Industrial Finance Ltd.

NATIONAL DOCK LABOUR BOARD PENSION SCHEME

Registered Office, 22-26 Albert Embankment, London SE1 7TE
Telephone: 01-735 7271

Administrative Office Argosy House, 31-39 Kingston Hill, Kingston upon Thames, Surrey KT2 7PU
Telephone: 01-549 9651

Secretary C.J.Normandale,FCA,APMI

Assistant Secretary R.W.E.Belcher

Accounting Officer J.B.Brown

Trustees National Dock Labour Board Pension Fund Trustees Ltd.

Chairman C.H.Blyth,O.B.E.

Investment Advisers Mullens & Co

Actuaries R.Watson & Sons

Auditors Deloitte Haskins & Sells

Legal Adviser Roy G.Hill, Hill, Dickinson & Co.

Members (at 31.12.79) 392

Pensioners 221

	£000
Annual Contributions	501
Annual Investment Income	467
Annual Outflow	331
Capital Value	

NATIONAL DOCK LABOUR BOARD *Continued*

Book Value	5,334
Market Value	5,298

Summary of Investments
Equities	3,118
Fixed Interest	1,940
Cash & Deposits	188
Others	52

See also Port Employers and Registered Dock Workers Pension Fund Trustees Ltd.

NATIONAL ENGINEERING LABORATORY

East Kilbride, Strathclyde G75 0QU
Telephone: 035-52 20222

Director D.H.Mallinson

Executive M.T.Watkins

Employees 875

THE NATIONAL FARMERS UNION MUTUAL INSURANCE SOCIETY LTD. RETIREMENT BENEFITS SCHEME

Church Street, Stratford-upon-Avon, Warwickshire CV37 6HL
Telephone: 0789-4211

Chief Accountant T.M.Barlow, FCA, FCII

Actuaries R.Watson & Sons

Auditors Attlee Edge & Lambert

Company Employees 2,200

Members 1,370

Pensioners 265

NATIONAL FEDERATION OF BUILDING TRADES EMPLOYERS PENSION SCHEME

82 New Cavendish Street, London W1M 8AD
Telephone: 01-580 5588

General Manager B.W.Crossland, APMI

Trustees National Federation of Building Trades Employers Pension Trustees Ltd.

Part Managed by Legal & General (Pensions Management) Ltd.

Actuaries R.Watson & Sons

Pension Fund Consultants Stewart Wrightson Assurance Consultants Ltd.

Auditors Binder Hamlyn

Members 3,430 (Pension Schemes), 2,570 (Death Benefit Scheme)

Pensioners 900

Annual Contributions £2.2 million

Capital Value £14.0 million

NATIONAL FREIGHT CORPORATION (A) (SALARIED STAFF) PENSION FUND AND (B) (WAGES GRADES) PENSION FUND

238 City Road, London EC1V 2ND
Telephone: 01-253 7677

Chief Pensions Officer J.E.Ager, FIA, FPMI

Secretary J.W.Robinson, APMI

Management Committee Management Committee comprising 8 Management Representatives and 8 Member Representatives

Chairmen J.D.Mather (Wages grades) and R.H.Teager (Staff)

Trustees N.F.C.Trustees Ltd

Investment Advisers Baring Brothers & Co Ltd

Property Advisers Strutt & Parker

Actuaries Duncan C.Fraser & Co.

Auditors Peat, Marwick, Mitchell & Co. (Wages Grades), Ernst & Whinney (Salaried Staff)

	Salaried Staff	Wages Grades
Company Employees (at 31.3.80)	8,283	25,597
Members	8,435	25,934*
Pensioners and Dependents	3,545	6,916
	£000	£000
Annual Contributions	5,392	9,325
Annual Investment Income	6,127	4,855
Annual Outflow	5,313	6,701
Capital Value (at Cost)	64,846	52,576
Summary of Investments		
Equities	30,523	26,162
Fixed Interest	18,790	14,320
Property	12,433	11,190
Cash & Deposits	2,015	1,785

*Includes members now with British Rail

NATIONAL INDUSTRIAL FUEL EFFICIENCY SERVICE LTD. SUPERANNUATION FUND

Orchard House, 14 Great Smith Street, London SW1P 3BU
Telephone: 01-222 0961

Secretary R.B.F.Chatham, FCA

Trustees F.N.Beveridge, W.Short, H.B.Weston, A.E.Wright

Investment and Property Advisers Ansbacher Investment Management Limited

Pension Fund Consultants and Actuarial Advice obtained through Sedgwick Employee Benefits Consultants Ltd.

Auditors Fryer, Whitehill & Co.

Solicitors Lovell White & King

Company Employees 191

Members 170

Pensioners 91

	£000
Annual Contributions	168
Annual Investment Income (includes Profit on Sales)	402
Annual Outflow	100
Capital Value	3,106

Summary of Investments

NATIONAL INDUSTRIAL FUEL EFFICIENCY SERVICE LTD. Continued

Equities	997
Fixed Interest	1,088
Property	213
Cash & Deposits	207

NATIONAL PORTS COUNCIL PENSION SCHEME

Commonwealth House, 1-19 New Oxford Street, London WC1A 1DZ
Telephone: 01-242 1200

Director of Finance and Secretary Dr. P.J.K.Webster, FCA, IPFA

Trustees National Ports Council Pensions Trustees Ltd

Investment Advisers J.Henry Schroder Wagg & Co Ltd

Actuaries R.Watson & Sons

Auditors Deloitte, Haskins & Sells

Employees 69

Members 66

Pensioners 17 (including 11 deferred)

	£000
Annual Contributions	174
Annual Investment Income	118
Annual Outflow	112
Capital Value	1,524
Summary of Investments	
Equities	798
Fixed Interest	367
Property	204
Cash & Deposits	145

NATIONAL PROVIDENT INSTITUTION STAFF SUPERANNUATION FUND

48 Gracechurch Street, London EC3P 3ER
Telephone: 01-623 4200

Assistant Secretary R.F.G.Poerscout-Edgerton,FIA

Auditors Deloitte Haskins & Sells

Company Employees 900

Members 522

Pensioners 58

Annual Contributions £778,000

Capital Value £5,400,000

NATIONAL RESEARCH DEVELOPMENT CORPORATION PENSION FUND

P.O.Box 236, Kingsgate House, 66/74 Victoria Street, London SW1E 6SL
Telephone: 01-828 3400

Personnel Manager Miss B.G.Winch,MIPM,APMI

Investment Advisers Phillips & Drew

Actuaries Bacon & Woodrow

Auditors Peat, Marwick, Mitchell & Co.

Company Employees 235

Members 160

Pensioners 56

Annual Contributions £343,000

Annual Investment Income £433,000

Capital Value £4,200,000

NATIONAL SOCIETY FOR THE PREVENTION OF CRUELTY TO CHILDREN PENSION SCHEME

1 Riding House Street, London W1P 8AA
Telephone: 01-580 8812

Secretary J.D.W.Low,FCIS

Accountant/Administrator E.J.Bermingham,FAIA, ACIS

Trustees NSPCC Pension Scheme Ltd.

Chairman Guy Edmiston

Investment Advisers & Stockbrokers Fielding, Newson-Smith & Co.

Actuaries Lane Clark & Peacock

Auditors Ernst & Whinney

Employees 800

Members (at 30.11.79) 369

Pensioners 102

	£000
Annual Contributions	283
Annual Investment Income	283
Annual Outflow	83
Capital Value (Market Value)	3,017
Summary of Investments	
Equities	1,572
Fixed Interest	1,279
Cash & Deposits	89

NATIONAL STANDARD CO LTD STAFF AND WORKS PENSION FUNDS

Stourport Road, Kidderminster, Worcs.DY11 7QX
Telephone: 0562-455

Pensions Manager A.R.Randle

Investment Advisers Barclays Bank Trust Co.Ltd. (Staff Fund), Kleinwort Benson Investment Management Ltd. (Works Fund)

Actuaries Duncan C.Fraser & Co.

Auditors Peat, Marwick, Mitchell & Co.

Company Employees 964

	Staff	Works
Members	209	667
Pensioners	16	39
	£000	£000
Annual Contributions	240	433
Annual Investment Income	146	136
Capital Value	1,303	1,590

NATIONAL SUPPLY CO (UK) LTD PENSION PLAN

Bird Hall Lane, Cheadle Heath, Stockport, Cheshire SK3 0SA
Telephone: 061-428 2214

Secretary N.H.Walker,ACMA

NATIONAL SUPPLY CO (UK) LTD *Continued*

Investment Advisers Bankers Trustee & Executor Co Ltd

Actuarial Advice Obtained through Cubie, Wood & Co.Ltd.

Pension Fund Consultants Lowndes Associated Pensions Ltd.

Auditors Deloitte Haskins & Sells

Company Employees 738

Members 660

Pensioners 171

Annual Contributions £350,000

Annual Investment Income £118,000

Capital Value £1,500,000

THE NATIONAL TRUST RETIREMENT & DEATH BENEFIT SCHEME

Western Way, Melksham, Wilts.SN13 8DZ
Telephone: 01-930 0211

Head Office 42 Queen Anne's Gate, London SW1H 9AS

Controller D.J.Gould,IPFA,FCCA,FCIS

Pension Fund Consultants Martin Paterson Associates Ltd.

Employees 1,374

Members 1,200

Pensioners 240

Annual Contributions £840,000

Capital Value £3,267,000

NATIONAL UNION OF PUBLIC EMPLOYEES STAFF SUPERANNUATION FUND

8 Aberdeen Terrace, London SE3 0QX
Telephone: 01-852 2842

Treasurer W.H.Bull,APMI

Deputy Treasurer R.Humphrey,APMI

Investment Advisers N.M.Rothschild Asset Management Ltd.

Actuaries Clay & Partners

Auditors Touche Ross & Co.

Employees 500

Members (at 31.12.79) 184

Pensioners 34

Annual Contributions £223,000

Annual Investment Income £111,000

Capital Value £1,390,000

NATIONAL UNION OF RAILWAYMEN 1946 SUPERANNUATION FUND AND EMPLOYEES SUPERANNUATION FUND

Unity House, Euston Road, London NW1 2BL
Telephone: 01-387 4771

Secretary P.J.King

Investment Advisers Grenfell & Colegrave

Actuaries R.Watson & Sons

Pension Fund Consultant R.W.Mountjoy

Auditors Stoy Hayward & Co

Employees 125

Members 90

Pensioners 18

Annual Contributions £102,000

Annual Investment Income £200,000

Capital Value £1,525,000

NATIONAL WATER COUNCIL SUPERANNUATION FUND

St.Peter's House, Hartshead, Sheffield S1 1EU
Telephone: 0742-737331

Secretariat 1 Queen Anne's Gate, London SW1H 9BT
Telephone: 01-222 8111 Telex: 918518

Direct Investment Management Unit 40-42 Cannon Street, London EC4N 6JJ
Telephone: 01-248 4384

Director of Finance A.R.Porter,FCA,IPFA

Superannuation Officer J.C.Richards,IPFA,APMI

Pensions Manager E.R.Ellam,IPFA,APMI

Administration & Finance Manager B.Wood,IPFA

Chairman Investment Management Panel Sir Robert Marshall,KCB,MBE

Investment Manager C.W.Crowther

Deputy Investment Manager J.W.Gibbon

Investment Secretary G.V.May

Investment Advisers County Bank Ltd, Phillips & Drew

Actuaries Duncan C.Fraser & Co

Property Advisers Jones Lang Wootton

Auditors Deloitte Haskins & Sells

Employees 65,000

Members (at 31.3.80) 56,440

Pensioners 10,910

Deferred Pensions 961

	£000
Annual Contributions	57,097
Annual Investment Income	27,710
Annual Outflow	19,015
Capital Value	
Book value	324,336
Market Value	351,500
Summary of Investments	
UK Equities	133,301
Foreign Equities	33,574
Fixed Interest	87,883
Property	55,213
Cash & Deposits	15,273
Net Current Assets	3,770

NATIONAL WESTMINSTER BANK PENSION FUND

Investment Department, 41 Lothbury, London EC2P 2BP
Telephone: 01-606 6060

Pension Fund Office 1st Floor, Wettern House, 56 Dingwall Road, Croydon CR9 3HB
Telephone: 01-686 9327

The Major UK Pension Funds NAT/NEW

NATIONAL WESTMINSTER BANK *Continued*

Company Secretary C.F.Green
Investment Manager E.A.Barnes
Property Adviser J.Strickland
Investment Advisers County Bank Ltd.
Actuaries R.Watson & Sons
Auditors Spicer & Pegler
Solicitors Wilde Sapte
Company Employees 64,000
Members 63,000
Pensioners 15,350

	£000
Annual Contributions	76,700
Capital Value	641,945
Summary of Investments	
Equities	420,601
Fixed Interest	4,425
Property	158,090
Cash & Deposits	46,558
Others	12,271

NATIONWIDE BUILDING SOCIETY SUPERANNUATION FUND

New Oxford House, High Holborn,
London WC1V 6PW
Telephone: 01-242 8822

General Manager (Finance) B.H.Phillips

Secretary J. del Strother

Trustees R.J.Sheppard, Sir Herbert Ashworth, P.G.Barron, E.P.Cessford, A.J.Ullathorne

Investment Advisers B.H.Phillips and Scrimgeour Kemp-Gee & Co.

Stockbrokers Scrimgeour Kemp-Gee & Co.

Actuaries Bacon & Woodrow

Auditors Touche Ross & Co.

Company Employees (at 30.9.80) 4,014

Members 1,419

Pensioners 192

	£000
Annual Contributions	1,408
Annual Investment Income (to 30.9.80)	1,988
Annual Outflow	535
Capital Value	20,800
Summary of Investments (Book Values)	
Equities	8,852
Fixed Interest	10,101
Property	527
Cash & Deposits	1,291

NCR LTD PENSION PLAN

206 Marylebone Road, London NW1 6LY
Telephone: 01-723 7070

Pension Fund Manager E.Richardson,APMI

Trustees A.J.Robertson (Chairman), P.Smith, D.S.Collins, O.C.Keltie, R.D.Louden

Investment Advisers Lloyds Bank Ltd

Actuaries R.Watson & Sons
Auditors Price Waterhouse & Co
Solicitors Richards, Butler & Co.
Company Employees 4,200
Members (at 5.4.80) 4,041
Pensioners 1,818
Deferred Pensions 5,606

	£000
Annual Contributions	2,002
Annual Investment Income	4,498
Gross Annual Outflow	1,493
Capital Value	
Book Value	46,592
Market Value	51,255
Summary of Investments	
Equities	19,726
Fixed Interest	14,709
Property	8,236
Cash & Deposits	2,800
Others	1,121

HARRY NEAL LTD

117 Baker Street, London W1M 2EE
Telephone: 01-935 8544

Secretary D.R.Hill

Employees 974

NEEPSEND STAFF PENSION FUND

Lancaster Street, Sheffield S3 8AQ
Telephone: 0742-23231

Assistant Secretary A.C.Farmer

Secretary & Director R.Hague

Trustees S.L.Speight OBE, K.Jacques, R.Hague, E.Quinn, F.B.Wright, D.M.King, A.Osborne, A.C.Farmer, D.A.Hopkins, Mrs D.J.Whiteley

Investment Advisers Neepsend Pension Fund Investment Committee

Stockbrokers E.B.Savory Milln & Co., Pidgeon de Smit

Property Advisers Fuller Peiser & Co.

Pension Fund Consultants and Actuarial Advice Obtained through Metropolitan Pensions Association

Auditors Pannell Fitzpatrick & Co

Company Employees 1,758

Members 431

Pensioners 211

	£000
Annual Contributions	419
Annual Investment Income	132
Gross Annual Outflow	76
Capital Value	1,980
Summary of Investments	
Equities	607
Fixed Interest	726
Cash & Deposits	32
Others	19

NEGRETTI & ZAMBRA LTD.
Stocklake, Aylesbury, Bucks.HP20 1DR
Telephone: 0296-5931
Secretary C.J.R.Weiss
Employees 794

NEIL & SPENCER HOLDINGS LTD.
Station Road, Leatherhead, Surrey KT2 7AJ
Telephone: 75441
Secretary J.Wade West,FCA,ACMA
Employees 693

JAMES NEILL HOLDINGS LTD. STAFF AND WORKS RETIREMENT BENEFIT PLANS
Napier Street, Sheffield, S.Yorks.S11 8HB
Telephone: 0742-760571
Secretary G.H.N.Peel,BA
Other Pension Management V.M.Shireby, FCIS
Trustees J.H.Neill, M.J.Mallett, A.H.Connell
Investment Advisers Hill Samuel Investment Management Ltd.
Actuarial Advice Obtained through Cubie, Wood & Co. Ltd.
Pension Fund Consultants Noble, Lowndes & Partners Ltd.
Auditors Barber, Harrison & Platt
Group Employees 4,150

	Staff	Works
Members	1,068	2,242
Pensioners	370	439
	£000	£000
Annual Contributions (to 31.12.79)	622	935
Annual Investment Income	309	103
Annual Outflow	343	352
Capital Value	7,085	2,469

NENE INDUSTRIES LTD
Carrington Works, Carrington Street, Kettering, Northants
Secretary M.J.Middleton
Employees 572

NEOSID GROUP LTD.
Edward House, Brownfields, Welwyn Garden City, Herts AL7 1AN
Telephone: 96-25011
Secretary R.C.Shead
Employees 508

NESTLE CO LTD PENSION FUND AND SUPERANNUATION FUND
St George's House, Park Lane, Croydon, Surrey CR9 1NR
Telephone: 01-686 3333
Pension Fund Manager J.J.Peachey, APMI
Secretary D.A.H.Bourke,APMI

Trustees Nestles Pension Trust Ltd and The Nestle Superannuation Trust Ltd
Investment Advisers J.P.P.Tindall, Warburg Investment Management Ltd.
Property Adviser J.P.P.Tindall
Actuaries Lane, Clarke & Peacock
Auditors Peat, Marwick, Mitchell & Co.
Company Employees 8,924

	Pension Fund	Superannuation Fund
Members	6,935	799
Pensioners	2,487	633
	£000	£000
Annual Contributions	6,491	166
Annual Investment Income	2,669	231
Annual Outflow	1,700	149
Capital Value	40,000	3,450

THE NEW TOWNS PENSION FUND
P.O.Box 102, Bletchley, Milton Keynes MK2 2AY
Telephone: 0908-79739
Secretary J.T.Jew,IPFA,FCIS
Trustees 5 Employer, 4 Employee Representatives
Partly Managed by Pension Management (SWF) Ltd.
Stockbrokers Hoare Govett Ltd., Laurie,Milbank & Co.
Actuarial Advice Obtained through Scottish Widows' Fund and Life Assurance Society
Auditors Deloitte Haskins & Sells
Members 2,750
Pensioners 180
Annual Contributions £3,000,000
Annual Investment Income £200,000
Annual Outflow £250,000
Capital Value £12,000,000

THE NEWALL MACHINE TOOL CO.LTD.
Oundle Road, Orton Longueville, Peterborough PE2 0BL
Telephone: 0733-67400
Secretary D.Kelly
Employees 874

NEWBOLD & BURTON HOLDINGS LTD PENSION & LIFE ASSURANCE SCHEME
Premier Works, Brook Street, Sileby, Leicester LE12 7RF
Telephone: 050981-2412
Secretary M.E.G.Lewis
Trustees H.Burton, N.R.Loxley, C.D.Wain, M.E.G.Lewis
Insured with Scottish Amicable Life Assurance Society
Company Employees 1,141
Members 112

NEWBOLD & BURTON HOLDINGS LTD *Continued*

Pensioners 37
Annual Contributions £107,000

THE NEWCASTLE & GATESHEAD WATER CO.
P.O.Box 10, Allendale Road,
Newcastle upon Tyne NE6 2SW
Telephone: 0632-654144

Secretary D.B.Newbold

Employees 574

NEWEY GROUP PENSION FUND
P.O.Box 277, Robin Hood Lane, Hall Green,
Birmingham B28 0JG
Telephone: 021-744 6681

Secretary & Financial Director B.C.Whitehouse
Trustees Newey Group Pension Fund Ltd
Investment Advisers M. & G. Investment Management Ltd
Stockbrokers Albert E.Sharp & Co
Actuaries Bacon & Woodrow
Auditors Peat Marwick Mitchell & Co
Company Employees 1,078
Members 664
Pensioners 476
Annual Contributions £152,000
Annual Investment Income £263,000
Annual Outflow £86,000
Capital Value £3,350,000

NEWHOME-VERITAS LTD.
Riverside House, Corney Road, London W4 2SL
Telephone: 01-995 4101

Secretary S.T.Hammond

Employees 1,408

NEWMAN INDUSTRIES LTD
Yate, Bristol BS17 5HG
Telephone: 0454-313311

Secretary P.G.Gollop
Insured with Prudential Assurance Co Ltd
Employees 4,998

NEWMAN-TONKS GROUP LTD. PENSION SCHEMES
Hospital Street, Birmingham B19 2YG
Telephone: 021-359 3221

Secretary B.R.Lewis
Insured with Standard Life Assurance Co., Scottish Equitable Life Assurance Co.
Employees 2,472

LOUIS NEWMARK LTD PENSION PLAN
80 Gloucester Road, Croydon, Surrey CR9 2LD
Telephone: 01-684 3696

Pensions Officer W.S.Cook
Secretary G.C.Taylor

Trustees Stewart Wrightson Trustees Ltd
Insured with Eagle Star Insurance Co Ltd
Company Employees 1,983
Members 975
Pensioners 171
Annual Contributions £680,000

NEWROYD LTD
Bank Top, Salem, Oldham, Lancs.OL4 3AB
Telephone: 061-624 6261

Secretary F.Leadbetter
Director J.Barnes
Executive A.R.Barnes
Employees 800

NEWS GROUP NEWSPAPERS LTD. (A) 1972 PENSION & LIFE ASSURANCE PLAN, (B) PENSION & LIFE ASSURANCE PLAN FOR EDITORIAL & ADMINISTRATIVE STAFF
30 Bouverie Street, London EC4Y 8EX
Telephone: 01-353 3030

Pensions Administrator A.A.Brace, APMI
Trustees (a) NGN Staff Pension Plan Trustees Ltd. and (b) NGN Editorial Pension Trustees Ltd.
(a) Managed by Prudential Pensions Ltd
(b) Insured with Commercial Union Assurance Co.Ltd.
Pension Fund Consultants Metropolitan Pensions Association Ltd
Auditors Arthur Andersen & Co.
Company Employees (at 1.7.80) 4,658

	(a)	(b)
Members	3,250	248
Pensioners	770	25
Annual Contributions	£2,014,000	£518,000
Annual Investment Income	£1,266,000	
Capital Value (at 30.6.79)		£9,112,000

NEWTON CHAMBERS ENGINEERING LTD GROUP PENSION SCHEME
Thorncliffe, Chapeltown, Sheffield,
S.Yorks.S30 4PY
Telephone: 07415-3181

Secretary R.J.V.Wheeler
Director L.J.Thomas
Employees 500

J. & W. NICHOLSON & CO. (HOLDINGS) LTD.
Windsor House, 83 Kingsway, London WC2B 6RF
Telephone: 01-405 3621

Secretary M.W.Nicholson
Employees 753

A.C.NIELSEN CO LTD PENSION PLAN
Nielsen House, Headington, Oxford OX3 9RX
Telephone: 0865-64851

Secretary D.A.Brooks,FCIS

A.C.NIELSEN CO LTD Continued

Pensions Administrator Miss P.J.Stephenson
Trustees The A.C.Nielsen Pension Plan Trust Ltd.
Investment Advisers Clerical Medical & General Life Assurance Society
Actuarial Advice Obtained Through Wyatt Harris Graham Ltd.
Pension Fund Consultants Wyatt Harris Graham Ltd.
Auditors Price Waterhouse & Co
Company Employees 1,200
Members (at 5.4.80) 766
Pensioners 61

	£000
Contributions (19 months to 5.4.80)	589
Investment Income	1,348
Gross Outflow	195
Capital Value	
Book Value	4,804
Market Value	5,400
Summary of Investments	%
Equities	43.8
Fixed Interest	30.2
Property Unit Trusts	8.6
Cash & Deposits	17.4

NORCROS SECURITY PLAN

Reading Bridge House, Reading RG1 8PP
Telephone: 0734-580861

Pension Fund Manager and Secretary A.J.Titmarsh, FCA,APMI
Pensions Administrator B.R.Jones
Trustees Norcros (Trustees) Ltd., RBH Trustees Ltd.
Investment Advisers N.M.Rothschild Asset Management Ltd.
Actuaries Clay & Partners
Auditors Peat Marwick Mitchell & Co
Solicitors Macfarlanes
Company Employees 14,300
Members 5,200
Pensioners 816

	£000
Annual Contributions	3,100
Annual Investment Income	1,940
Annual Outflow	1,270
Capital Value (Market Value)	20,400
Summary of Investments	
Equities	7,462
Fixed Interest	5,441
Property	5,189
Cash & Deposits	770
Others	1,538

NORFOLK CAPITAL GROUP LTD

2-10 Harrington Road, London SW7 3ER
Telephone: 01-581 0601

Secretary G.B.Baker,FCA
Employees 1,245

NORFOLK COUNTY COUNCIL SUPERANNUATION FUND

County Hall, Martineau Lane, Norwich NR1 2DH
Telephone: 0603-611122

Treasurer G.M.Ellis,IPFA
Superannuation Officer P.D.Sissen,APMI
Actuaries Hymans, Robertson & Co.
Auditors District Auditor
Employees 27,000
Members (at 31.3.80) 9,968
Pensioners 3,947
Annual Contributions £9,367,000
Annual Investment Income £4,959,000
Capital Value £55,686,000

NORMAND ELECTRICAL HOLDINGS LTD

3 East Street, Havant, Hants.PO9 1AA
Telephone: 0705-476012

Secretary A.J.Smith
Insured with Prudential Assurance Co Ltd
Employees 1,218

NORTH BRITISH MARITIME GROUP LTD.

King William House, Market Place, Hull HU1 1RB
Telephone: 0482-224181

Secretary H.J.Baker
Employees 917

NORTH BRITISH STEEL GROUP (HOLDINGS) LTD

Balbardie Steel Works, Bathgate, W.Lothian EH48 2RB
Telephone: 0506-52341

Secretary R.D.Cochrane,ACCA
Pension Fund Consultants Noble Lowndes & Partners Ltd
Employees 860

NORTH EASTERN CO-OPERATIVE SOCIETY LTD. EMPLOYEES SUPERANNUATION FUND

Jackson Street, Gateshead, Tyne & Wear NE8 1HR
Telephone: 0632-770291

Superannuation Officer W.Waton,APMI
Pension Fund Consultants Co-operative Insurance Society Ltd.
Auditors Appleby, English & Partners
Employees 6,900
Members 1,810
Pensioners 1,750
Annual Contributions £507,000
Annual Investment Income £1,151,000
Capital Value £11,117,000

M.F.NORTH LTD HOTEL STAFF PENSION FUND

58 Cromwell Road, South Kensington,
London SW7 5BZ
Telephone: 01-589 1212

Secretary D.J.Dowds

Employees 620

NORTH OF SCOTLAND HYDRO-ELECTRIC BOARD HYDROBOARD SUPERANNUATION FUND

16 Rothesay Terrace, Edinburgh EH3 7SE
Telephone: 031-225 1361

Secretary Andrew Innes

Other Pension Management Joint Committee, 4 members appointed by Board and 4 elected by contributors

Investment Advisers J.Henry Schroder Wagg & Co.Ltd.

Actuaries Robertson, Hymans & Co.

Auditors Thomson McLintock & Co.

Company Employees 4,146

Members 3,837

Pensioners 921

	£000
Annual Contributions	4,508
Annual Investment Income	3,076
Annual Outflow	1,536
Capital Value	42,639
Summary of Investments	
Equities	19,507
Fixed Interest	12,562
Property	1,270
Cash & Deposits	2,042
Others	7,257

NORTH YORKSHIRE COUNTY COUNCIL LOCAL GOVERNMENT SUPERANNUATION FUND

County Hall, Northallerton, North Yorks DL7 8AD
Telephone: 0609-3123

County Treasurer K.R.Hounsome,IPFA

Superannuation Accountant J.Pelter,IPFA

Secretary Chief Executive and Clerk of the County Council

Management Committee and Trustees Investment Panel of Finance, Sub-committee of Policy and Resources Committee of North Yorkshire County Council

Investment Advisers Gartmore Investment Ltd

Stockbrokers Pember & Boyle (Gilt Edged), de Zoete & Bevan (Equities)

Property Advisers Norman Fearn

Actuaries R.Watson & Sons

Auditor District Auditor

Employees (at 31.3.80) 12,887 (Full time), 12,317 (Part time)

Members 10,420

Pensioners 3,714

	£000
Annual Contributions	7,248
Annual Investment Income	7,320
Annual Outflow	5,255
Capital Value	42,736
Summary of Investments	
Equities	17,353
Fixed Interest	16,462
Property	3,643
Cash & Deposits	4,561

NORTHAMPTONSHIRE COUNTY COUNCIL SUPERANNUATION FUND

County Hall, Northampton NN1 1DN
Telephone: 0604-34833

Treasurer F.Fielding,BSc,IPFA

Superannuation Officer N.F.Bull,APMI

Investment Advisers Hoare Govett Ltd.

Actuaries R.Watson & Sons

Auditors Price Waterhouse & Co.

Employees 16,500

Members (at 31.3.80) 8,500

Pensioners 2,300

Annual Contributions £6.0 million

Annual Investment Income £3.0 million

Capital Value £30.0 million

NORTHERN BANK LTD PENSION SCHEME AND WIDOWS' PENSION SCHEME

Donegall Square, West, Belfast BT1 6JS
Telephone: 0232-45277

Assistant Staff Manager (Pensions) H.A.McC.Knott

Actuaries R.Watson & Sons

Auditors Thomson McLintock & Co.

Solicitors Sacker & Partners

Company Employees 2,845

	Pension	Widows
Members	2,530	1,300
Pensioners	288	28

	£000	£000
Annual Contributions	3,230	1,180
Capital Value	27,000	8,600

NORTHERN CLUBS FEDERATION BREWERY LTD

Forth Street, Newcastle-upon-Tyne NE99 1PT
Telephone: 0632-610591

Secretary W.L.Hutchinson,OBE,FCIS

Employees 565

NORTHERN ENGINEERING INDUSTRIES LTD

NEI House, Regent Centre,
Newcastle upon Tyne NE3 3SB
Telephone: 0632-843191

Director NEI Pensions J.W.Nicholson,FCA

Staff Pensions Manager A.R.Main,APMI

NORTHERN ENGINEERING INDUSTRIES LTD Continued

Works Pensions Manager W.Jones,APMI

Trustees NEI (Staff Pension Trustees) Ltd., Clarke Chapman (Works Pension Trustees) Ltd., NEI (Works Pension Trustees) Ltd.

Investment Advisers Hill Samuel Investment Management Ltd., Lloyds Bank Ltd.

Actuaries Duncan C.Fraser & Co.

Actuarial Advice also Obtained through Cubie, Wood & Co. Ltd.

Auditors Peat, Marwick, Mitchell & Co.

Company Employees 31,429

	Staff	Works
Members	8,942	11,561
Pensioners	2,750	508
	£million	£million
Annual Contributions	6.9	3.6
Annual Investment Income	5.3	0.5
Annual Outflow	5.0	0.9
Capital Value	58.1	6.0

NORTHERN FOODS SUPERANNUATION FUND

Beverley House, St. Stephen's Square, Hull HU1 3XG
Telephone: 0482-25432

Pension Fund Administrator C.J.R.Bedford

Secretary D.G.Simpson

Pensions Administration Manager G.E.Farlowe

Trustees Northern Foods Trustees Ltd.

Chairman Nicholas Horsley

Actuaries Bacon and Woodrow

Auditors Ernst & Whinney

Company Employees 16,400

Members (at 31.3.80) 5,177

Pensioners 331

	£000
Annual Contributions	4,002
Annual Investment Income	1,045
Annual Outflow	1,054
Capital Value	17,494
Summary of Investments	
Equities	6,492
Fixed Interest	2,048
Property	6,434
Cash & Deposits	698
Others	1,568

NORTHERN GAS

Norgas House, Killingworth, Newcastle-upon-Tyne
Telephone: 0632-683000

Pensions Officer Mrs.M.S.Rewcastle

NORTHERN IRELAND ELECTRICITY SERVICE SUPERANNUATION SCHEME

120 Malone Road, Belfast BT9 5HT
Telephone: 0232-661100

Secretary R.Brown,APMI

Investment Advisers Darbishire Malcolmson & Coates, R.Nivison & Co, Pidgeon de Smitt

Actuaries Bacon and Woodrow

Property Advisers Richard Ellis

Auditors Atkinson & Boyd

Solicitors Allen & Overy

Company Employees 6,400

Members 6,150

Pensioners 1,050

	£000
Annual Contributions	5,536
Annual Investment Income	4,606
Annual Outflow	1,839
Capital Value	53,158
Summary of Investments	
Equities	25,141
Fixed Interest	18,623
Property	6,599
Cash & Deposits	2,795

NORTHERN IRELAND LOCAL GOVERNMENT OFFICERS SUPERANNUATION COMMITTEE

114 Holywood Road, Belfast BT4 1NX
Telephone: 0232-658631

Secretary R.W.Nesbitt,IPFA,APMI

Stockbrokers Fielding, Newson-Smith & Co.

Actuaries Bacon & Woodrow

Members 26,500

Pensioners 3,700

	£000
Annual Contributions	14,719
Annual Investment Income	6,365
Annual Outflow	5,497
Capital Value	69,595
Summary of Investments	
Equities	33,765
Fixed Interest	26,532
Property	6,028
Cash & Deposits	1,500
Others	1,770

NORTHERN ROCK BUIDING SOCIETY

Northern Rock House, P.O.Box 2, Gosforth, Newcastle upon Tyne NE3 4PL
Telephone: 0632-857191

Staff Controller D.Urwin

Insured with Legal & General Assurance Society Ltd.

Company Employees 724

Members 372

Pensioners 24

NORTHUMBERLAND COUNTY COUNCIL LOCAL GOVERNMENT SUPERANNUATION FUND

County Hall, Morpeth, Northumberland NE61 2EF
Telephone: 0670-514343

Treasurer R.Wolstenholme IPFA

Superannuation Officer M.D.Edridge

Investment Advisers Hill Samuel Investment Management Ltd.

Stockbrokers Scrimgeour Kemp-Gee & Co., Wise Speke

Actuaries R.Watson & Sons

Auditors District Auditor

Employees 15,000

Members (at 31.3.80) 6,100

Pensioners 3,050

	£000
Annual Contributions	4,100
Annual Investment Income	2,200
Annual Outflow	2,800
Capital Value	27,900
Summary of Investments	
Equities	17,500
Fixed Interest	7,700
Property	2,200
Cash & Deposits	500

NORTON ABRASIVES LTD

Bridge Road East, Welwyn Garden City, Herts
Telephone: 96-23484

Secretary R.N.Lawton

Investment Advisers N.M.Rothschild Asset Management Ltd

Employees 1,448

NORVIC SECURITIES LTD

St. Georges Plain, Norwich, Norfolk NR3 1DB
Telephone: 0603-23171

Secretary A.L.Pitman

Investment Advisers Hoare Govett Ltd

Employees 1,842

NORWEST HOLST LTD GROUP STAFF PENSION SCHEME

P.O.Box 1, Ruthven Road, Seaforth, Liverpool L21 2QB
Telephone: 051-920 8100

Secretary to Trustee Company Miss D.Whittle

Company Secretary J.A.Bosdet

Trustees Norwest (Pensions) Ltd

Investment Advisers Rowan Investment Management Services

Actuaries Duncan C.Fraser & Co

Auditors Price Waterhouse & Co

Solicitors Alsop Stevens Batesons & Co.

Company Employees 5,556

Members 1,233

Pensioners 195

Deferred Pensions 71

Annual Investment Income £703,000

Capital Value £8,142,000

NORWICH UNION GROUP STAFF PENSIONS & LIFE INSURANCE NON-CONTRIBUTORY PLAN (1971)

P.O.Box 4, Surrey Street, Norwich NR1 3NG
Telephone: 0603-22200

Secretary H.H.Scurfield

Deputy Actuary R.Elven,MA,FIA,FPMI

Auditors Ernst & Whinney

Company Employees 8,400

Members 5,500

Pensioners 1,600

Annual Contributions £5,800,000

Capital Value £68,000,000

NOTTINGHAM MANUFACTURING CO.LTD.

Botany Avenue, Mansfield, Nottinghamshire NG18 5NF
Telephone: 0623-22661

Pensions Manager Mr.Watson

Secretary J.E.Christian

Insured with Prudential Assurance Co.Ltd.

Employees 13,889

NOTTINGHAMSHIRE COUNTY COUNCIL

County Hall, West Bridgford, Nottinghamshire NG2 7QP
Telephone: 0602-863366

Treasurer G.E.Daniel,IPFA,FCA,FRVA

NSS NEWSAGENTS LTD. SUPERANNUATION AND LIFE ASSURANCE FUND

Ryde House, Chobham Road, Woking, Surrey GU21 1JQ
Telephone: 04862-66771

Secretary D.I.Pennington

Trustees P.H.Byam-Cook, R.O.G.Gardner, V.E.G.Tagliavini, E.D.Sheehan

Insured with Legal & General Assurance Society Ltd

Company Employees 4,500

Members 250

Pensioners 22

Annual Contributions £250,000

NUCLEAR POWER GROUP STAFF PENSION FUND

Warrington Road, Risley, Warrington, Cheshire WA3 6BZ
Telephone: 0925-51291

Pension Fund Manager B.Jerams,ACIS

Investment Advisers J.Carrington & Co.Ltd.

Stockbrokers Henry Cooke Lumsden & Co.

Actuaries R.Watson & Sons

Auditors Touche Ross & Co

Company Employees 2,310

NUCLEAR POWER GROUP Continued

Members (at 6.4.80) 972
Pensioners 127
Annual Contributions £870,000
Annual Investment Income £840,000
Capital Value £10,000,000

NURDIN & PEACOCK LTD RETIREMENT BENEFIT FUND
Bushey Road, Raynes Park, London SW20 0JJ
Telephone: 01-946 9111

Pension Fund Manager D.G.Rowley
Company Secretary N.E.Kerry
Managed by Scottish Widows' Fund & Life Assurance Society
Employees 1,970
Members 1,250
Pensioners 90
Annual Contributions £800,000
Capital Value £3,500,000

NU-SWIFT INDUSTRIES LTD
Nu-Swift Factory, Elland, West Yorks HX5 9DS
Telephone: 0422-72852

Secretary K.Wood
Insured with Legal & General Assurance Society Ltd
Employees 820

EDWARD NUTTALL HOLDINGS LTD. (MANCHESTER) LTD
22 Grosvenor Gardens, London SW1W 0DR
Telephone: 01-730 0036

Secretary J.R.T.Hockin,FCA
Employees 1,061

O & K LIFTS LTD
Dryart Works, Dalton Lane, Keighley, W.Yorks.BD21 4JN
Telephone: 0535-605533

Director C.H.Gray
Employees 828

THE OBSERVER HOLDINGS LTD.
8 St.Andrew's Hill, London EC4V 5JA
Telephone: 01-236 0202

Secretary J.C.K.Steel
Employees 920

OCCIDENTAL INTERNATIONAL OIL INC PENSION FUND
16 Palace Street, London SW1E 5BQ
Telephone: 01-828 5600

Pension Fund Manager and Secretary R.M.Blamey
Part Insured with Swiss Life Insurance & Pension Co.
Pension Fund Consultants Frank B. Hall & Co. Consultants Inc.

Company Employees 1,200
Members 833
Pensioners 6
Annual Contributions £1,000,000
Annual Investment Income £152,000
Annual Outflow £17,500
Capital Value £2,700,000

OCEAN NESTOR PENSION FUND
c/o Ocean Transport & Trading Ltd.Water Street, Liverpool L2 0RB
Telephone: 051-236 9292

Secretary and Pensions Manager Derrick Colby
Assistant Pensions Manager J.W.G.Meredith
Trustees The Law Debenture Corporation Ltd
Investment Managers Baring Brothers & Co Ltd
Property Advisers Jones Lang Wootton
Actuaries and Pension Fund Consultants Duncan C. Fraser & Co.
Auditors Chalmers, Impey & Co.
Company Employees 10,343 (U.K.)
Members 4,665
Pensioners 2,638

	£000
Annual Contributions	5,000
Annual Investment Income	6,000
Annual Outflow	4,500
Capital Value (July 1980)	100,531
Summary of Investments	
UK Equities	51,531
Overseas Equities	12,000
Fixed Interest	15,000
Property	21,000
Cash & Deposits	1,000

There are also 4 other smaller Schemes:
Wm.Cory Oil Distribution Tanker Drivers Pension Scheme
Ocean Odyssey Pension Scheme
Cory Ship Towage Pension Scheme
James W.Cook (Wivenhoe) Ltd. Pension Scheme

Total Members 2,015
Pensioners 280
Annual Contributions £1,100,000
Annual Investment Income £215,000
Annual Outflow £336,000
Capital Value (at July 1980) £5,500,000

OCEAN WILSONS (HOLDINGS) LTD.
Regina House, 5 Queen Sreet, London EC4N 1SP
Telephone: 01-236 0488

Secretary E.C.Teidman
Insured with Legal & General Assurance Society Ltd
Employees 881

O.C.L.I.EUROPE
621 London Road, High Wycombe, Bucks.HP1 1ET
Telephone: 0494-36286

O.C.L.I.EUROPE Continued

Director R.F.Illsley
Executive R.J.Wales
Employees 900

OFFICE CLEANING SERVICES LTD
28-34 Eagle Street, London WC1
Telephone: 01-242 8800

Secretary F.Williams
Insured with Eagle Star Insurance Co Ltd
Employees 15,000

OFREX GROUP LTD PENSION PLAN
Ofrex House, Stephen Street, London W1A 1EA
Telephone: 01-636 3686

Secretary N.J.Buckingham
Trustees Ofrex Group Trustee Co. Ltd.
Stockbrokers Sheppards & Chase
Pension Fund Consultants Hogg Robinson (Benefit Consultants) Ltd.
Auditors Geo. Little, Sebire & Co.
Company Employees 2,700
Members 1,040
Pensioners 95

	£000
Annual Contributions	660
Annual Investment Income	316
Annual Outflow	169
Capital Value	2,900
Summary of Investments	
Equities	1,150
Fixed Interest	1,400
Property	22
Cash & Deposits	320

D.& J.OGILVIE (BUILDERS) LTD.
Pirnhill Works, Whins of Milton, Stirling
Telephone: 078681-2273

Secretary H.P.Simpson
Employees 570

OGILVY AND MATHER LTD 1972 PENSION & LIFE ASSURANCE PLAN
Brettenham House, Lancaster Place,
London WC2E 7EZ
Telephone: 01-836 2466

Treasurer J.O.Nettleton,FCA,FIPA
Company Secretary A.G.Lenton
Investment Advisers N.M.Rothschild & Sons Ltd
Pension Fund Consultant & Actuarial Advice Obtained through Metropolitan Pensions Association Ltd.
Auditors Price Waterhouse & Co
Company Employees 778
Members 300
Pensioners 215
Annual Contributions £800,000
Annual Investment Income £300,000
Capital Value £5,000,000

THE OILGEAR CO
Shuttleworth Road, Goldington, Bedford,
Bedfordshire
Telephone: 0234-51791

Executive R.J.Skirton
Employees 500

OLDHAM BATTERIES LTD.
Nelson Street, Denton, Manchester M34 3AT
Telephone: 061-336 2431

Secretary C.N.Snape
Employees 1,106

GEORGE OLIVER (FOOTWEAR) LTD.
Murrayfield Road, Braunstone, Leics.LE3 1UU
Telephone: 0533-87350

Secretary M.Tebbatt,FCA
Insured with Legal & General Assurance Society Ltd.
Employees 920

OLIVERS LTD
9 Courtleigh Gardens, London NW11 9PF
Telephone: 01-458 1607

Secretary P.Allen
Investment Advisers Keyser Ullmann Pensions Management Ltd.
Actuaries Clay & Partners
Company Employees 1,040
Members 350

THE OPEN UNIVERSITY
Walton Hall, Walton, Milton Keynes, Bucks.
Telephone: 0908-74066

Assistant Chief Accountant S.K.Mohindra,ACIS

A.OPPENHEIMER & CO LTD
38 Finsbury Square, London EC2A 1SJ
Telephone: 01-606 9121

Secretary J.E.Maxwell
Managed by Pensions Management (SWF) Ltd.
Employees 1,040

ORIEL FOODS GROUP PENSION & LIFE ASSURANCE PLANS
West Africa House, 25 Water Street,
Liverpool L2 0TE
Telephone: 051-236 9181

Group Secretary P.B.Holden
Pensions Secretary L.H.Vague
Trustees Oriel Foods Group Pension Trustees Ltd
Investment Advisers and Stockbrokers Grievson Grant & Co
Actuarial Advice obtained through Actuarial Advice Obtained through
Pension Fund Consultants William M.Mercer (Benefits) Ltd

ORIEL FOODS GROUP *Continued*

Auditors Arthur Young McClelland Moores & Co.
Company Employees 2,400
Members 500
Pensioners 300
Annual Contributions £240,000
Annual Investment Income £210,000
Gross Annual Outflow £163,000
Capital Value (Market Value) £2,500,000

ORKNEY ISLANDS COUNCIL SUPERANNUATION FUND

Council Offices, Kirkwall, Orkney LW15 1NY
Telephone: 0856-3535
Director of Finance R.H.Gilbert
Actuaries Robertson, Hymans & Co
Members 401
Pensioners 90
Annual Contributions £185,000
Annual Investment Income £85,000
Gross Annual Outflow £106,000
Capital Value £1,000,000

ORMEAU BAKERY LTD

307-317 Ormeau Road, Belfast BT7 3GN
Telephone: 0232-641241
Secretary J.A.L.Tolland
Employees 1,287

OTIS ELEVATOR CO.LTD. SALARIED STAFF SECURITY PLAN AND HOURLY PAID EMPLOYEES PENSION SCHEME

The Otis Building, 43-59 Clapham Road,
London SW9 0JZ
Telephone: 01-735 9131
Company Secretary P.C.Jones,ACIS
Trustees J.N.Cunningham, H.A.W.Pettinger, M.C.A.Holt, J.H.Paige
Insured with Crown Life Insurance Co, Crusader Insurance Co Ltd (Staff Plan), Phoenix Assurance Co Ltd (hourly paid employees scheme), Prudential Assurance Co Ltd
Actuarial Advice obtained through Stewart Wrightson Assurance Consultants and the Prudential Assurance Co Ltd
Pension Fund Consultants Stewart Wrightson Assurance Consultants Ltd.
Company Employees 3,304
Members 1,650
Pensioners 407
Annual Pension Contributions Approx £0.75 million (hourly paid), £0.75 million (staff)
Capital Value Approx £4.5 million (combined fund)

OTTER CONTROLS LTD

Otters Ole, Market Street, Buxton,
Derbyshire SK17 6LA
Telephone: 0298-71177

Secretary K.Elliott
Director I.G.M.Parker
Employees 600

OTTERMILL LTD

Ottery St Mary, Devon EX11 1AG
Telephone: 040-481 2131
Secretary D.H.Boutland
Employees 1,100

OVERSEAS CONTAINERS LTD PENSION SCHEME

Beaufort House, St.Botolph Street,
London EC3A 7DX
Telephone: 01283 8000
Secretary P.J.Hinton, FPMI
Company Secretary H.W.Perring,APMI
Investment Advisers Lazard Securities Ltd.
Actuaries R.Watson & Sons
Auditors Coopers & Lybrand
Company Employees 2,100
Members 1,832
Pensioners 53

	£000
Annual Contributions	1,500
Annual Investment Income	1,100
Annual Outflow	100
Capital Value	13,600
Summary of Investments	
Equities	7,400
Fixed Interest	4,300
Cash & Deposits	1,900

See also P. & O. Group

OWEN OWEN PENSION FUND

Stafford House, 105 London Road,
Liverpool L69 1BD
Telephone: 051-207 2677
Pensions Secretary S.B.Reid
Company Secretary W.Stothart,MA,FCIS,APMI
Trustees Owen Owen Pension Trustees Ltd
Investment Advisers John Govett & Co Ltd
Actuaries Duncan C.Fraser & Co
Auditors Coopers & Lybrand
Company Employees 4,434
Members 1,000
Pensioners 750

OXFORD UNIVERSITY PRESS GROUP PENSION SCHEME

Walton Street, Oxford OX2 6DP
Telephone: 0865-56767
Pensions & Insurance Manager J.E.K.Hassell
Investment Advisers Warburg Investment Management Ltd.
Pension Fund Consultants and Actuarial Advice Obtained through Metropolitan Pensions Association Ltd.

OXFORD UNIVERSITY PRESS Continued

Auditors Critchley, Ward & Pigott
Company Employees 1,600
Members (at 31.3.80) 1,212
Pensioners 390
Annual Contributions £1,123,000
Capital Value £3,346,000

OXFORDSHIRE COUNTY COUNCIL
County Hall, Oxford OX1 1ND
Telephone: 0865-722422

Treasurer B.P.Harty

OXLEY PRINTING GROUP LTD
55 Conduit Street, London W1R 0NY
Telephone: 01-434 1281

Secretary P.R.Wright, FCIS

Investment Advisers Robert Fleming Investment Management Ltd

Employees 2,017

OZALID GROUP HOLDINGS LTD
Langston Road, Loughton, Essex IG10 3TH
Telephone: 01-508 5544

Secretary J.A.T.Wedgwood

Employees 4,195

P.A.MANAGEMENT CONSULTANTS PENSION PLAN
Hyde Park House, 60A Knightsbridge,
London SW1X 7LE
Telephone: 01-235 6060

Secretary Miss B.Hicks, ACIS

Trustees P.A.Management Consultants Pension Trustees Ltd.

Investment Advisers Geoffrey Morley & Partners Ltd.

Actuaries R.Watson & Sons Ltd.

Auditors Ernst & Whinney

Company Employees 897

Members 624

Pensioners 111

Deferred Pensioners 741

Annual Contributions £1,800,000

Annual Investment Income £1,200,000

Annual Outflow £310,000

Capital Value £21,000,000

P.& O. GROUP PENSION SCHEME
Beaufort House, St. Botolph Street,
London EC3A 7DX
Telephone: 01-283 8000

Secretary P.J.Hinton, FPMI

Group Pensions Manager J.W.Grant, ACIS, FPMI

Trustees P & O Pension Fund Investments Ltd

Investment Advisers and Stockbrokers Hoare Govett Ltd

Property Advisers Internal (Bovis Ltd.)
Actuaries R.Watson & Sons
Auditors Deloitte Haskins & Sells
Employees 14,800
Members 9,350
Pensioners 4,000

	£ million
Annual Contributions	8.9
Annual Investment Income	9.3
Annual Outflow	5.3
Capital Value	96.1
Summary of Investments	
Equities	47.2
Fixed Interest	32.7
Property	6.0
Cash & Deposits	10.2

See also Overseas Containers

G.W.PADLEY LTD SUPERANNUATION SCHEME
Anwick Village, Sleaford, Lincs. NG34 9SL
Telephone: 0526-832661

Personnel Director J.Brown

Company Secretary R.Derry

Insured with Yorkshire General Insurance Co.

Company Employees 1,329

Members 111

Annual Contributions £41,000

PAGAN LTD
Faringdon Avenue, Harold Hill, Romford, Essex
Telephone: 45-4951 1

Company Secretary K.C.Cooper

Employees 694

ALAN PAINE LTD PENSION AND ASSURANCE SCHEME
Riverside, Godalming, Surrey
Telephone: 04868-5511

Administrator P.Dawes, FCA

Trustees R.A.Paine, A.J.Adams, M.A.Green

Insured with Legal & General Assurance Society Ltd.

Company Employees 570

Members 292

PAKAMAC LTD
Middleton Road, Chadderton, Oldham, Lancs
Telephone: 061-652 5111

Director L.Cohen

Employees 500

PALMER & HARVEY LTD.
Vale House, Vale Road, Portslade,
Brighton BN4 1HG
Telephone: 0273-420042

Secretaries P.C.Lock, J.R.Crook

Employees 3,535

PANNELL FITZPATRICK & CO
Lee House, London Wall, London EC2Y 5AL
Telephone: 01-606 7051

Employees 806

PAPWORTH AND ENHAM PENSION SCHEME (1978)
The White House, Enham-Alamein, Andover, Hants. SP11 6HJ
Telephone: 0264-51551

Pension Fund Administrator P.J.Bennett, FCA

Trustees Papworth Village Settlement

Insured with Provident Mutual Life Assurance Association, Legal and General Assurance Society Ltd.

Investment Advisers Barclays Insurance Services Ltd.

Company Employees 850

Members 90

Pensioners 3

PARK BROS LTD
Bankfield Works, Ordnance Street, Blackburn, Lancs BB1 3JB
Telephone: 0254-52561

Chairman D.G.Park

Employees 900

FREDERICK PARKER LTD
Viaduct Works, Cannon Street, Leicester LE4 6HD
Telephone: 0533-65999

Secretary R.Judkins

Insured with Crusader Insurance Co Ltd, Prudential Assurance Co Ltd

Employees 1,698

PARKER-HANNIFIN (UK) LTD
Parker House, P.O.Box 170, 6 Grey Lane Road, Watford, Herts.WD2 4QA

Managing Director C.F.Ackerman

Employees 613

PARKER KNOLL
The Courtyard, Frogmoor, High Wycombe, Bucks HP13 5DJ
Telephone: 0494-21144

Secretary P.R.Bolding

Managed by Pensions Management (SWF) Ltd.

Pension Fund Consultants J.H.Minet Life & Pensions Ltd.

Company Employees 1,224

Members 310

Pensioners 20

Annual Contributions £330,000

Capital Value £2,000,000

THE PARKER PEN CO LTD PENSION FUND
15 Grosvenor Gardens, London SW1W 0BL
Telephone: 01-834 4641

Secretary & Director J.L.R.Moller

Finance & Administration Manager R.H.Barnsley

Managed by Sun Life Pensions Management Ltd

Property Advisers Strutt & Parker

Pension Fund Consultants Antony Gibbs Pension Services Ltd.

Auditors Arthur Andersen & Co

Company Employees 982

Members 728

Pensioners 143

Annual Contributions £400,000

Capital Value £3,400,000

PARKER TIMBER GROUP LTD
Parker House, 144 Evelyn Street, London SE8 5DE
Telephone: 01-692 7181

Pension Fund Manager P.A.Nelson

Trustees Lowndes Associated Pensions Ltd.

Insured with English Insurance Co. Ltd.

Company Employees 1,600

Members 800

Pensioners 50

Annual Contributions £350,000

F.PARKINSON LTD.
Mowbray Drive, Blackpool, Lancs.
Telephone: 0253-34411

Secretary T.V.Austin

Employees 514

PARKLAND TEXTILE (HOLDINGS) LTD.
Albion Mills, Greengates, Bradford, W.Yorks.BD10 9TQ
Telephone: 0274-611161

Secretary D.Holmes FCA

Trustees Parkland Pensions Trust Ltd

Employees 1,958

PARSONS CONTROLS HOLDINGS LTD.
Stourport-on-Severn, Worcs.DY13 9AT
Telephone: 02993-2551

Director B.C.Jones

Secretary D.T.Watson

Employees 1,410

F.J.PARSONS LTD
Cambridge Road, Hastings, East Sussex
Telephone: 0424-428231

Director The Duke of Atholl

Executive R.Wild

Employees 500

THE RALPH M.PARSONS CO.LTD. STAFF PENSION & LIFE ASSURANCE SCHEME
Parsons House, Kew Bridge Road, Brentford, Middlesex TW8 0EH
Telephone: 01-995 1322

Company Secretary K.S.Solomons,FCA

THE RALPH M.PARSONS CO.LTD. *Continued*

Actuarial Advice Obtained through Cubie, Wood & Co.Ltd.

Pension Fund Consultants Noble Lowndes International Ltd

Auditors Price Waterhouse & Co

Solicitors Slaughter & May

Company Employees 602

Members 450

Pensioners 6

Annual Contributions £250,000

Capital Value £1,600,000

PATERSON, ZOCHONIS & CO LTD

Bridgewater House, 60 Whitworth Street, Manchester M1 6LU
Telephone: 061-236 7111

Secretary B.Lindley

Trustees Paterson Zochonis Provident Trust Ltd.

Insured with Prudential Assurance Co Ltd, Scottish Equitable Life Assurance Society

Employees 2,540

PATON, CALVERT & CO LTD

201 Binns Road, Liverpool L13 1BU
Telephone: 051-228 2721

Secretary A.H.Aiken

Employees 760

PATRICK MOTORS LTD

Patrick House, 180 Lifford Lane, Birmingham B30 3NT
Telephone: 021-459 4471

Secretary G.Wem

Stockbrokers Fyshe Horton Finney & Co.

Employees 730

PAULING & CO LTD

Pauling House, 100 Rochester Row, London SW1
Telephone: 01-828 4355

Secretary C.J.Manning

Employees 2,500

PAULS & WHITES PENSION SCHEME (MONTHLY PAID) AND RETIREMENT FUND (HOURLY PAID)

P.O.Box 39, Key Street, Ipswich, Suffolk IP4 1BX
Telephone: 0473-56711

Pension Fund Manager & Secretary S.Middleton

Trustees Individual Trustees

Stockbrokers Phillips & Drew

Actuaries Lane Clark & Peacock

Auditors Robson Rhodes

Company Employees 2,313

	Pension Scheme	Retirement Fund
Members	1,134	740
Pensioners	210	165
	£000	£000
Annual Contributions	925	224
Annual Investment Income	565	192
Annual Outflow	342	120
Capital Value	8,081	1,720
Summary of Investments		
Equities	4,248	795
Fixed Interest	2,678	693
Property	412	42
Cash & Deposits	743	125
Others	-	84

W.L.PAWSON & SON LTD.

71 Union Street South, Halifax, W.Yorks.HX1 2LA
Telephone: 0422-58444

Secretary D.Thompson

Employees 1,668

PEABODY LTD

Duke of York Street, London SW1Y 6LA
Telephone: 01-839 6843

Secretary T.R.Wicking

Managed by Scottish Amicable Pensions Investments Ltd.

Employees 1,139

C.H.PEARCE & SONS LTD. (CONTRACTING) LTD

Hambrook Lane, Stoke Gifford, Bristol BS12 6QU
Telephone: 0272-693951

Secretary K.D.Pearce

Insured with Eagle Star Insurance Co Ltd

Employees 728

PEARCE GROUP HOLDINGS LTD.

Insignia House, New Cross Road, London SE14 6AB
Telephone: 01-692 6611

Secretary F.R.Allen

Employees 727

PEARL ASSURANCE CO LTD STAFF SUPERANNUATION FUND

252 High Holborn, London WC1V 7EB
Telephone: 01-405 8441

Secretary A.W.Davies ACIS

Assistant Secretary D.A.Young

Trustees PAT (Pensions) Ltd

Actuary D.M.Gordon FIA

Auditors Clark Pixley

Company Employees (at 31.12.79) 9,111

Members 8,960

Pensioners 3,738

Deferred Pensions 3,570

PEARL ASSURANCE CO LTD *Continued*

	£000
Annual Contributions	10,112
Annual Investment Income	9,036
Annual Outflow	5,338
Capital Value	105,059
Summary of Investments	
Equities	48,755
Fixed Interest	38,860
Property & Property Unit Trusts	13,912
Cash & Deposits	2,023
Others	1,509

G.M.PEARSON & SON LTD.

19 Front Street, Helston le Hole, Houghton le Spring, Tyne & Wear DH5 9PD

Director L.G.Pearson

Employees 926

S.PEARSON & SON PENSION FUND

Millbank Tower, Millbank, London SW1P 4QZ
Telephone: 01-828 9020

Secretary D.A.Sampson

Trustees S.Pearson & Son Pension Trust Ltd

Directors M.J.Hare, P.D.A.Clarke, E.P.Emmerson, J.Prince, A.A.Whitaker

Investment Advisers Lazard Securities Ltd

Actuaries Bacon and Woodrow

Pension Fund Consultants Bain Dawes & Partners Ltd

Auditors Deloitte Haskins & Sells

Company Employees 64

Members 60

Pensioners 68

	£000
Annual Contributions (to 31.12.79)	230
Annual Investment Income	215
Gross Annual Outflow	170
Capital Value (Market Value)	2,640
Summary of Investments	
Equities	989
Fixed Interest	789
Property	255
Cash & Deposits	324
Others	283

PEARSON LONGMAN LTD

Millbank Tower, Millbank, London SW1P 4QZ
Telephone: 01-828 9020

Secretary G.A.S.Collett

There are numerous pension schemes which are managed within the five major operating subsidiaries

PEAT MARWICK MITCHELL & CO STAFF PENSION FUND

1 Puddle Dock, Blackfriars, London EC4V 3PD
Telephone: 01-236 8000

Pension Fund Manager E.A.L.Frost

Secretary R.L.Matthew

Investment Advisers & Stockbrokers Cazenove & Co.

Actuaries Bacon & Woodrow

Auditor J.Boyd-Barratt,FCA

Company Employees 3,357

Members 1,800

Pensioners 166

	£000
Annual Contributions	834
Annual Investment Income	875
Annual Outflow	550
Capital Value	11,300
Summary of Investments	
Equities	8,000
Fixed Interest	3,000
Cash & Deposits	300

H.T.H.PECK (HOLDINGS) LTD

West Bridge, Leicester LE3 5NR
Telephone: 0533-50081

Director G.H.Camamile

Insured with Royal Insurance Co Ltd, UK Provident

Employees 900

PECKSTON GROUP LTD

Dundas House, Middlesbrough, Cleveland TS1 IHZ
Telephone: 0642-245141

Director N.R.M.Moir

Employees 500

PEDIGREE PETFOODS

Mill Street, Melton Mowbray, Leics.LE13 1BB
Telephone: 0664-4141

Employees 2,700

PEERLESS STAMPINGS LTD.

Priory Road, Aston, Birmingham B6 7LF

Secretary I.Taylor

Employees 1,509

PEGLER-HATTERSLEY STAFF PENSION FUND AND WORKS PENSION FUND

St.Catherine's Avenue, Doncaster,
South Yorks DN4 8DF
Telephone: 0302-68581

Pension Fund Manager and Secretary J.E.Hepburn ACIS APMI

Assistant Manager L.J.Fry

Trustees Pegler-Hattersley Trustees Ltd

Investment Advisers Touche Remnant & Co

Actuaries Duncan C.Fraser & Co

Auditors Peat Marwick Mitchell & Co

Company Employees 6,273

Members 4,520

Pensioners 1,120

PEGLER-HATTERSLEY STAFF PENSION FUND
Continued

	£000
Annual Contributions	2,345
Annual Investment Income	1,312
Annual Outflow	637
Capital Value	13,900
Summary of Investments	
Equities	8,344
Fixed Interest	4,090
Property	560
Cash & Deposits	470
Others	436

PEMBROKE PACKAGING LTD
Paycocke Road, Basildon, Essex SS14 3HP
Telephone: 0268-20272

Secretary R.E.Smith

Employees 586

PENFOLD GOLF LTD
13 Romford Lane, Ward End, Birmingham B8 2SA
Telephone: 021-327 1318

Managing Director A.G.Penfold

Employees 600

PENGUIN PENSION SCHEME /THE LANE TRUST
Bath Road, Harmondsworth, Middlesex UB7 0DA
Telephone: 01-759 1984

Secretary J.B.Hart

Trustees Penguin Pension Trustees Ltd

Investment Advisers J.Henry Schroder Wagg & Co.Ltd.

Actuaries R.Watson & Sons

Joint Auditors Peat, Marwick, Mitchell & Co., Wall, Ward & Co.

Company Employees 500

Members 350

Pensioners 52

	£000
Annual Contributions	300
Annual Investment Income	200
Annual Outflow	150
Capital Value	2,700
Summary of Investments	
Equities	1,343
Fixed Interest	872
Property	424
Cash & Deposits	6

PENNWALT HOLDINGS PENSION PLAN
Priory Works, Tonbridge, Kent TN11 0QL
Telephone: 0732-364481

Secretary to the Trustees H.E.Mayo

Investment Advisers J.Henry Schroder Wagg & Co Ltd

Pension Fund Consultants Towers, Perrin, Forster & Crosby

Auditors Arthur Andersen & Co.

Plan Employees 1,420

Members 1,000

Pensioners 140

Annual Contributions £600,000

Capital Value £4,300,000

This Plan Covers the Employees of:- Wallace & Tiernan Ltd., Pennwalt Ltd., S.S.White Ltd., Pennwalt Chemicals Ltd.

PENTOS GROUP PENSION FUND
New Bond Street House, 1-5 New Bond Street, London W1Y 0SB
Telephone: 01-499 3484

Secretary E.J.Cater,FCIS

Trustees Pentos Pension Trustees Ltd.

Investment Advisers Robert Fleming Investment Management Ltd

Actuaries Bacon & Woodrow

Auditors Neville Russell & Co

Company Employees 3,340

Members 919

Pensioners 25

Annual Contributions £720,000

Annual Investment Income £125,000

Capital Value £2,200,000

PERGOMAN PRESS LTD
Headington Hill Hall, Oxford, Oxon
Telephone: 0865-64881

Secretary R.S.Evern

Employees 872

PERKIN-ELMER LTD PENSION FUND
Post Office Lane, Beaconsfield, Bucks
Telephone: 04946-6161

Company Secretary S.G.Wretoro

Trustees W.A.Lee, A.R.Gilson, G.M.Feast

Insured with Friends' Provident Life Office

Auditors Price Waterhouse & Co.

Company Employees 712

Members 502

Pensioners 19

Annual Contributions £234,800

DOROTHY PERKINS LTD
P.O.Box 5, Wokingham Road, Bracknell, Berks
Telephone: 0364-3131

Personnel Director & Secretary S.G.Nicholls

Company Secretary P.C.Smith

Employees 2,642

PERRING FURNISHINGS LTD.
Avenue House, Malden Road, Worcester Park, Surrey
Telephone: 01-337 0951

Secretary G.Voss,FCA

PERRING FURNISHINGS LTD. *Continued*

Investment Advisers Lazard Securities Ltd.
Employees 895

HAROLD PERRY MOTORS LTD. PENSION & ASSURANCE SCHEME 1978
2a Alexandra Grove, North Finchley,
London N12 8NS
Telephone: 01-446 1456

Pension Fund Manager R.J.Hoare FCA
Secretary H.W.Clarke
Trustees Lowndes Associated Pensions Ltd
Managed by Legal & General Assurance (Pensions Management) Ltd.
Auditors Price Waterhouse & Co.
Company Employees 1,200
Members 537
Pensioners 200
Annual Contributions £412,000
Capital Value £1,686,000

PETERS STORES LTD.
Julius House, Norham Roell, Northumberland

Secretary W.L.Campbell
Employees 529

PETROFINA PENSION SCHEME
Petrofina House, York Road, London SE1 7NT
Telephone: 01-928 8000

Pensions Co-ordinator E.R.Figes APMI
Assistant Manager, Pensions W.J.Hawthorne
Trustees 5 appointed individual trustees
Investment Advisers Lloyds Bank Ltd and Eagle Star Pension Funds Ltd (investment fund only)
Actuaries & Pension Advisers Bacon & Woodrow
Auditors Peat Marwick Mitchell & Co
Solicitors Turner Peacock
Company Employees 1,138
Members 943
Pensioners 659
Deferred Pensions 151

	£000
Annual Contributions	1,337
Annual Investment Income	1,984
Capital Value	18,787
Summary of Investments	%
Equities	49.1%
Fixed Interest	40.5%
Property	4.5%
Cash & Deposits	5.0%

PFIZER GROUP PENSION SCHEME
Pfizer Ltd, Ramsgate Road, Sandwich,
Kent CT13 9NJ
Telephone: 03046-3511

Pensions Manager B.May,ACIS

Trustees Pfizer Pension Trustees Ltd
Investment Advisers N.M.Rothschild Asset Management Ltd
Actuaries Bacon & Woodrow
Auditors McLintock Main Lafrentz & Co
Solicitors Allen & Overy
Company Employees 1,750
Members 1,650
Pensioners 800
Annual Contributions £1,310,000
Annual Investment Income £795,000
Gross Annual Outflow £250,000
Capital Value £9,245,000

PHICOM LTD PENSION PLAN
Centre Point, 103 New Oxford Street,
London WC1A 1ED
Telephone: 01-379 6090

Pension Fund Manager and Secretary J.D.Smith
Trustees S.W.Livesey, A.K.S.Franks, J.R. Ostler
Investment Advisers Baring Brothers & Co Ltd
Actuarial Advice obtained through S.Wright of Antony Gibbs Pension Services Ltd
Pension Fund Consultants Antony Gibbs Pension Services Ltd
Auditors Peat Marwick Mitchell & Co
Company Employees 2,032
Members 1,300
Pensioners 100

	£000
Annual Contributions	900
Annual Investment Income	800
Annual Outflow	100
Capital Value	4,400
Summary of Investments	
UK Equities	2,800
Overseas Equities	400
Fixed Interest	1,100
Cash & Deposits	200

PHILIPS AND PYE PENSION FUND
P.O.Box 298, City House, 420-430 London Road,
Croydon CR9 3QR
Telephone: 01-689 2166

Investment Dept. 8 Arundel Street, London WC2A 3DT
Telephone: 01-836 4360

Pension Fund Manager R.J.Amy
Investment Manager R.A.Downard
Property Manager R.M.Well, ARICS
Actuaries Bacon & Woodrow
Auditors Coopers & Lybrand
Company Employees 38,000
Members 33,000
Pensioners 8,500

PHILIPS AND PYE *Continued*

	£ million
Annual Contributions	20.0
Annual Investment Income	17.0
Annual Outflow	10.0
Capital Value	229.0
Summary of Investments	
Equities	85.0
Fixed Interest	72.0
Property	70.0
Cash & Deposits	2.6

PHILLIPS PATENTS (HOLDINGS) LTD.

Dantzic Street, Manchester M4 4JH
Telephone: 061-834 5854

Secretary R.Butterworth

Insured with Friends Provident Life Office

Employees 518

PHILLIPS PETROLEUM 1972 U.K. STAFF PENSION SCHEME

Portland House, Stag Place, London SW1E 5DA
Telephone: 01-828 9766

Manager Employee Relations R.D.Yonge

Trustees Phillips Petroleum Pension Trustees Ltd.

Investment Advisers Morgan Grenfell & Co Ltd

Pension Fund Consultants Wyatt Harris Graham Ltd.

Auditors Arthur Young McClelland Moores & Co

Company Employees 1,452

Members 1,157

Pensioners 4

	£000
Annual Contributions	656
Annual Investment Income	119
Annual Outflow	672
Capital Value	2,540
Summary of Investments	
Equities	1,110
Fixed Interest	788
Property	486
Cash & Deposits	63

PHILLIPS RUBBER LTD. STAFF PENSION SCHEME

Dantzic Street, Manchester M4 4JH
Telephone: 061-834 5854

Company Secretary R.Butterworth

Insured with Friends' Provident Life Office

Pension Fund Consultants Towry Law (Pension Services) Ltd.

Auditors Deloitte Haskins & Sells

Company Employees 500

Members 58

Pensioners 26

Annual Contributions £30,000

PHOENIX STAFF PENSION FUND (1978)

Phoenix House, 4-5 King William Street, London EC4P 4HR
Telephone: 01-626 9876

Pensions Department Phoenix House, Redcliff Hill, Bristol BS1 6SQ Tel. 0272-294941

Secretary A.H.G.Simmonds

Manager Pensions Department J.Walker,FIA

Trustees R.K.Bishop, R.K.Bishon, J.Brawley, M.H.Field, J.O.Hambro, A.R.Matanle, P.S.Seymour, R.G.Street

Actuary J.Walker,FIA

Auditors Touche Ross & Co.

Solicitors Slaughter & May

Company Employees 3,490 (at 1.4.79)

Members 2,970

Pensioners 913

	£000
Annual Contributions (to 1.4.79)	3,083
Annual Investment Income	2,306
Annual Outflow	1,240
Capital Value	24,276
Summary of Investments	
Equities	10,400
Fixed Interest	12,100
Property	600
Cash & Deposits	700

PHOENIX TIMBER PENSIONS TRUST LTD

Phoenix House, New Road, Rainham, Essex RM13 8RJ
Telephone: Rainham 53311

Financial Director & Secretary D.S.Cook,FCA

Trustees H.F.Hillman, H.G.Grainge, P.Abrams

Investment Advisers Drayton Montagu Portfolio Management Ltd

Actuaries Duncan C.Fraser & Co

Company Employees 1,231

Members 470

Pensioners 40

PHONOTAS CO LTD

102 College Road, Harrow HA1 1JD
Telephone: 01-863 2377

Director B.G.C.Becker

Employees 1,750

WILLIAM PICKLES PENSION & PROVIDENT SCHEME

101 Portland Street, Manchester M60 1EH
Telephone: 061-236 2182

Secretary Harry Tyass

Trustees N.F.Garrett, A.M.Hadfield, H.Tyass, J.T.M.Connolly, A.Slater, P.Plowright

Insured with Clerical, Medical & General Life Assurance Society

Company Employees 1,500

Members 398

PILKINGTON BROTHERS LTD (A) SUPERANNUATION SCHEME, (B) WORKMEN'S PENSION FUND, (C) RETIREMENT BENEFITS SCHEME, (D) VOLUNTARY PENSION SCHEME

Prescot Road, St. Helens, Merseyside WA10 3TT
Telephone: 0744-28882

Group Pensions Adviser A.F.Bennett,FCIS

Secretary Staff Funds A.Littler,APMI

Secretary Non Staff Funds J.Roughley

Investment Manager D.A.Budgett

Actuaries Bacon & Woodrow

Property Advisers Herring Son & Daw (Commercial), William H.Brown & Son (Agricultural)

Auditors Coopers and Lybrand

Company Employees (at 30.4.79) 22,826

	(a)	(b)
Members	7,165	11,350
Pensioners	2,519	5,180
	£000	£000
Annual Contributions	6,226	8,500
Annual Investment Income	5,761	500
Annual Outflow	4,213	-
Capital Value	70,760	4,900
Summary of Investments		
U.K. Equities	33,841	-
Overseas Equities	4,867	-
Fixed Interest	12,888	-
Property	15,563	-
Cash & Deposits	3,029	-
Others	572	-

	(c)	(d)
Members	11,291	8,538
Pensioners	-	2,906
	£000	£000
Annual Contributions	1,500	900
Capital Value	3,200	9,900

THE PILOTS' NATIONAL PENSION FUND

Colchester House, Pepys Street, London EC3N 4AY
Telephone: 01-481 1131

Secretary A.M.Alcock

Acting Secretary Mrs.P.Thumwood

Investment Advisers Lazard Securities Ltd

Actuaries R.Watson & Sons

Auditors Ernst & Whinney

Solicitors Rowe & Maw

Members 1,458

Pensioners 970

Annual Contributions £3,500,000

Annual Investment Income £2,464,000

Capital Value £27,846,000

PIONEER CONCRETE (HOLDINGS) LTD

Pioneer House, 56-60 Northolt Road, Harrow, Middx HA2 0EY
Telephone: 01-864 6611

Secretary F.H.P.Offer

Managed by Sun Life Pensions Management Ltd

Employees 810

PIONEER MUTUAL INSURANCE CO.LTD. EMPLOYEES PENSION FUND

16 Crosby Road North, Waterloo, Liverpool L22 0NY
Telephone: 051-928 6655

Pension Fund Manager & Secretary D.Bleazard,BA, FCIS,ACII

Trustees Pioneer Mutual Pension Trust Ltd.

Stockbrokers W.Greenwell & Co.

Actuaries Duncan C.Fraser & Co.

Auditors Arthur Young McClelland Moores & Co

Company Employees 949

Members 385

Pensioners 430

	£000
Annual Contributions	132
Annual Investment Income	143
Annual Outflow	236
Capital Value	2,072
Summary of Investments	
Equities	746
Fixed Interest	1,323
Cash & Deposits	(4)
Others	7

PIRELLI LTD.

Derby Road, Burton-on-Trent, Staffs.DE13 0BH
Telephone: 0283-66301

Secretary D.T.C.Pollock

Employees 4,674

PITMAN LTD

39-41 Parker Street, London WC2B 5PB
Telephone: 01-242 1655

Secretary J.H.T.Roger

Insured with Legal & General Assurance Society Ltd

Employees 1,327

THE PITNEY BOWES PENSION FUND

The Pinnacles, Harlow, Essex CM19 5BD
Telephone: 0279-26731

Secretary P.C.Sharp

Trustees Lloyds Bank International Trust Co

Stockbrokers Phillips & Drew

Actuaries Bacon & Woodrow

Auditors Price Waterhouse & Co

Solicitors Allen & Overy

Company Employees 1,765

Members 1,749

The Major UK Pension Funds PIT/POR

THE PITNEY BOWES Continued

Pensioners 96

	£000
Annual Contributions	767
Annual Investment Income	322
Annual Outflow	124
Capital Value	4,165
Summary of Investments (at cost)	
Equities	1,738
Fixed Interest	1,346
Property	16
Cash & Deposits	265

PITTARD GROUP LTD

Sherborne Road, Yeovil, Somerset BA21 5BA
Telephone: 0935-4321

Managing Director N.F.Wood

Secretary D.J.Foote

Insured with Commercial Union Assurance Co.Ltd., Standard Life Assurance Co.

Employees 863

PLATIGNUM LTD.

Platignum House, Six Hills Way, Stevenage, Herts.SG1 2AY
Telephone: 0438-2488

Secretary A.R.Montgomery

Employees 841

PLAXTON'S (SCARBOROUGH) LTD

P.O.Box 2, Castle Works, Seamer Road, Scarborough, N.Yorks.YO12 4DQ
Telephone: 0723-63311

Secretary D.P.Suffell FCA

Insured with Standard Life Assurance Co

Employees 1,770

PLAYBOY CLUB OF LONDON LTD

45 Park Lane, London W1
Telephone: 01-629 6666

Secretary L.J.Simmons

Employees 1,036

PLAYTEX LTD

Port Glasgow, Renfrewshire
Telephone: 0505-21402

Secretary D.W.Booth

Managed by R.S.Blincow

Employees 1,348

PLEASURAMA LTD

7 Welbeck Street, London W1M 7PB
Telephone: 01-486 2446

Secretary G.Martin

Insured with Sun Life Assurance Society Ltd

Employees 1,083

PLESSEY PENSION FUND

2-60 Vicarage Lane, Ilford, Essex IG1 4AQ
Telephone: 01-478 3040

Pension Fund Manager & Secretary K.J.Linford, APMI

Assistant Secretary D.E.Griffin,APMI

Trustees Plessey Pension Trust Ltd.

Investment Advisers Morgan Grenfell & Co.Ltd., Geoffrey Morley & Partners Ltd.

Property Advisers Gerald Eve & Co.

Actuaries Bacon & Woodrow

Auditors Thomson McLintock & Co.

Solicitors Sacker & Partners

Company Employees 38,326

Members 24,000

Pensioners 6,500

Annual Contributions £11.5 million

Annual Investment Income £8.7 million

Annual Outflow £4.3 million

Capital Value £115.0 million

PLUMBS (MAIL ORDER) LTD STAFF PENSION & LIFE ASSURANCE PLAN

Salmon Street, Preston, Lancashire PR1 6NY
Telephone: 0772-57584

Secretary & Director B.H.Spink,FCIS

Chief Accountant S.R.Jones,ACA

Insured with Standard Life Assurance Co.

Pension Fund Consultants Allison & Co

Auditors Thornton Baker & Co

Company Employees 1,144

Members 206

PLYMOUTH & SOUTH DEVON CO-OPERATIVE SOCIETY LTD. EMPLOYEES SUPERANNUATION FUND

Co-operative House, Derry's Cross, Plymouth, Devon PL1 1HA

Deputy Chief Executive V.R.Barton

Investment Advisers Westlake & Co.

Pension Fund Consultants Co-operative Insurance Society Ltd.

Auditors Appleby English & Partners

Company Employees 2,600

Members (at 5.4.80) 1,032

Pensioners 503

Annual Contributions £329,000

Annual Investment Income £400,000

Capital Value £3,700,000

PLYSU LTD

120 Station Road, Woburn Sands, Milton Keynes, Bucks MK17 8SE
Telephone: 0908-582311

Secretary N.A.Slocock

PLYSU LTD Continued

Investment Advisers Anderson & Co

Employees 882

P.M.A.HOLDINGS LTD
Hawkhurst House, Headley Road East, Woodley,
Reading, Berks. RG5 4SP
Telephone: 0734-692731

Secretary H.J.M.Price

Employees 1,500

POLAROID (UK) LTD
Ashley Road, St. Albans, Herts AL1 5PR
Telephone: 59191

Secretary H.Allen

Insured with Commercial Union Assurance Co.Ltd.

Employees 1,964

FREDERICK POLLARD & CO LTD
Corona Works, St. Saviours Road,
Leicester LE5 4HP
Telephone: 0533-767534

Chairman F.Pollard

Employees 500

POLYGRAM LEISURE LTD.
15 St.George Street, London W.1
Telephone: 01-499 3751

Secretary A.Roberts

Employees 1,509

THE PORT EMPLOYERS AND REGISTERED DOCK WORKERS PENSION SCHEME
Registered Office 22-26 Albert Embankment,
London SE1 7TE
Telephone: 01-735 7271

Administrative Office Argosy House, 31-39
Kingston Hill, Kingston upon Thames, Surrey KT2 7PU

Secretary C.J.Normandale,FCA,APMI

Assistant Secretary R.W.E.Belcher

Accounting Officer J.B.Brown

Trustees The Port Employers and Registered Dockworkers Pension Fund Trustees Ltd

Chairman J.P.Davidson,CBE

Investment Advisers Robert Fleming Investment Management Ltd

Actuaries R.Watson & Sons

Auditors Deloitte Haskins & Sells

Legal Adviser Roy G. Hill of Hill, Dickinson & Co.

Members (at 31.3.79) 25,317

Pensioners 17,294

	£000
Annual Contributions (to 1.4.78)	11,665
Annual Investment Income	4,521
Annual Outflow	4,005
Capital Value	
Book Value	58,968
Market Value	76,508
Summary of Investments	
Equities	40,835
Fixed Interest	22,581
Property	1,108
Property Unit Trusts	9,999
Cash & Deposits	1,638
Unit Trusts	793
Others	(446)

See also National Dock Labour Board Pension Fund Trustees Ltd.

PORT OF LONDON AUTHORITY PENSION FUND
Basin South, North Woolwich, London E16 2QF
Telephone: 01-476 6900

Secretary N.S.J.Coles

Trustees Hill Samuel Ltd

Investment Advisers Hill Samuel Investment Managers Ltd

Stockbrokers Capel-Cure Myers

Actuaries R.Watson & Sons

Property Advisers Weatherall, Green & Smith

Auditors Deloitte, Haskins & Sells

Company Employees 7,000

Members (at 31.3.80) 3,450

Pensioners 2,650

	£000
Annual Contributions	7,100
Annual Investment Income	3,900
Annual Outflow	4,300
Capital Value Book Value	48,200
Market Value	47,600
Summary of Investments	
Equities	24,800
Fixed Interest	11,200
Property	5,300
Cash & Deposits	3,000

PORT OF TYNE AUTHORITY
Bewick Street, Newcastle-upon-Tyne NE1 5HS
Telephone: 0632-25541

Director G.V.Carr

Executive J.H.H.Gillespie

Employees 800

PORTALS GROUP 1978 PENSION PLAN
Laverstoke Mill, Whitchurch, Hants RE28 7NR
Telephone: 025682-2360

Pension Fund Manager B.Plenderleith

Secretary A.Pike

Other Pension Management Minet Trustees Ltd.

Trustees Portals Group Trustees Ltd.

Managers Minet Trustees Ltd.

Investment Advisers Rowan Investment Management Services

Stockbrokers Rowe & Pitman

Actuaries Clay & Partners

PORTALS GROUP Continued

Property Advisers Lane Fox & Partners

Pension Fund Consultants Minet Consultancy Services Ltd.

Auditors Peat, Marwick, Mitchell & Co.

Company Employees 4,250

Members 3,015

Pensioners 600

	£000
Annual Contributions	2,500
Annual Investment Income	1,475
Annual Outflow	1,270
Capital Value	17,750
Summary of Investments	
Equities	8,950
Fixed Interest	5,550
Property	1,700
Others	1,550

PORTER CHADBURN LTD

Park Lane Works, Bootle, Merseyside L30 4UP
Telephone: 051-525 4155

Secretary J.M.Mickle,FCA

Employees 1,174

PORTH TEXTILES LTD.

Tonypandy, Glamorgan CF20 2SE
Telephone: 044371-3391

Secretary R.A.Freebody

Employees 772

PORTSEA ISLAND MUTUAL CO-OPERATIVE SOCIETY LTD. EMPLOYEES SUPERANNUATION FUND

110 Fratton Road, Portsmouth PO1 5DB
Telephone: 0705-22211

Secretary/Financial Controller M.C.Holden, ACIS

Committee 5 Directors, 4 Employees

Managed by Robert Fleming Investment Management Ltd.

Actuary P.D.Johnson (Co-operative Insurance Society Ltd.)

Pension Fund Consultants Godwins Ltd.

Auditors Appleby, English & Partners

Company Employees 3,864

Members 1,607

Pensioners 489

	£000
Annual Contributions	398
Annual Investment Income	564
Annual Outflow	256
Capital Value (Book Value)	5,585
(Market Value)	5,984
Summary of Investments	
Fixed Interest	1,252
Cash & Deposits	1,991
Others	2,344

PORTSMOUTH & SUNDERLAND NEWSPAPERS LTD.

85 Fleet Street, London EC4Y 1EA
Telephone: 01-353 4696

Secretary K.B.Parkinson

Insured with Legal & General Assurance Society Ltd.

Employees 1,230

PORTSMOUTH WATER CO RETIREMENT BENEFITS SCHEME

P.O.Box 8, West Street, Havant, Hampshire PO9 1LG
Telephone: 0705-486333

Secretary & Treasurer F.A.Bailey,FCIS,FSCA

Stockbrokers & Investment Advisers Seymour, Pierce & Co

Actuaries Lane Clark & Peacock

Auditors Thornton Baker & Co

Company Employees 407

Members 217

Pensioners 102

Annual Contributions £340,000

Annual Investment Income £343,000

Capital Value £3,000,000

POST OFFICE STAFF SUPERANNUATION FUND

47-51 King William Street London EC4R 9DD
Telephone: 01-626 4577

Chief Executive R.N.Quartano

Secretary F.B.Davis TD

Director of Securities Investment G.J.J.Dennis

Director of Property Investment D.E.Jackson

Director of Finance R.A.Padgett

Trustees Sir Daniel Pettit (Chairman), A.S.Ashton, C.E.Beauchamp,CBE, G.R.E.Leach, N.Stagg, K.R.Thomas, I.D.T.Vallance, E.A.Webb,OBE, A.H.Willitt,MBE

Custodian Trustees National Westminster Bank Ltd.

External Investment Managers J.Henry Schroder Wagg & Co Ltd, S.G.Warburg & Co Ltd, Morgan Grenfell & Co Ltd

Property Advisers Bernard Thorpe & Partners, Jones Lang Wootton, Schroder's Real Estate Corp., Heitman Group

Actuaries R.Watson & Sons

Auditors Ernst & Whinney

Internal Auditors Coopers & Lybrand

Solicitors Maxwell Batley & Co.

Employees 420,000

Members 405,000

Pensioners (at 31.3.80) 175,000

Deferred Pensioners 19,000

Annual Income (to 31.3.80)

POST OFFICE Continued

	£ million
Contributions	261
Investment Income	216
Amounts received from Post Office	230
From Secretary of State for Industry	45
Total Income	752
Annual Expenditure	301
Capital Value	
Book Value	2,438
Market Value	2,742
Summary of Investments (Market Value)	
Equities	1,274
Fixed Interest	528
Property	895
Cash & Deposits	66

It is estimated that by April 1981 the total assets of the Fund will amount to about £3,200 million

POTATO MARKETING BOARD PENSION & LIFE ASSURANCE SCHEME

50 Hans Crescent, Knightsbridge,
London SW1X 0NB
Telephone: 01-589 4874

Principal Finance Officer I.B.Rogers

Insured with Equity & Law Life Assurance Society Ltd.

Pension Fund Consultants Sydney Placketts & Sons Ltd.

Company Employees (at 31.5.80) 549

Members 380

Pensioners 233

Annual Contributions £426,000

T.POTTER & SONS LTD

Llewellyn's Quay, Port Talbot, West Glamorgan
Telephone: 06396-4951

Director T.Potter

Employees 550

POWELL DUFFRYN (A) RETIREMENT BENEFITS SCHEME, (B) PENSION PLAN, (C) HAMWORTHY RETIREMENT BENEFITS SCHEME

Imperial House, Kingsway, London WC2B 6TH
Telephone: 01-836 9864

Group Pensions Controller D.F.Richens APMI

Pensions Manager D.W.G.Shirley-Rollison, MA, FCII

Trustees (A) P.D. Superannuation Trust Ltd., (B) P.D.Pension Trust Ltd., (C) Hamworthy Engineering Pension Trust Ltd.

Investment Advisers (Pension Plan) J.Henry Schroder Wagg & Co.Ltd.

Investment Advisers (Retirement Benefits Scheme and Hamworthy Scheme) Phillips & Drew

Property Advisers Richard Ellis

Actuaries Bacon & Woodrow

Auditors Deloitte Haskins & Sells

Solicitors Slaughter & May

Company Employees 10,200

	Retirement Scheme	Pension Plan
Members	3,450	3,450
Pensioners	130	1,100
	£000	£000
Annual Contributions	1,150	3,040
Annual Investment Income	250	2,500
Annual Outflow	205	2,000
Capital Value	2,800	32,500
Summary of Investments		
Equities	1,800	17,100
Fixed Interest	1,000	8,300
Property	-	6,200
Others	-	1,100

	Hamworthy Scheme
Members	1,700
Pensioners	230
	£000
Annual Contributions	750
Annual Investment Income	87
Annual Outflow	140
Capital Value	1,900
Summary of Investments	
Equities	1,100
Fixed Interest	600
Others	200

POWYS COUNTY COUNCIL

County Hall, Llandrindod Wells LD1 5LE
Telephone: 0597-3711

Treasurer S.V.Woodhouse,IPFA

F.PRATT ENGINEERING CORP. LTD.

Park Works, Halifax, W.Yorks.HX1 5JH
Telephone: 0422-66371

Secretary D.Hillier,FCA

Insured with Norwich Union Life Insurance Society

Employees 1,650

ALFRED PREEDY & SONS LTD. EMPLOYEES' PENSION FUND

Burnt Tree House, Burnt Tree, Tipton,
West Midlands
Telephone: 021-557 3988

Pension Fund Manager & Secretary J.W.Palmer

Trustees S.L.Preedy, J.W.Palmer, D.C.May

Investment Advisers Fraser Green Ltd.

Actuaries Duncan C.Fraser & Co

Auditors Clement Keys & Co.

Company Employees 3,000

Members 750

Pensioners 125

ALFRED PREEDY & SONS LTD. *Continued*

	£000
Annual Contributions	225
Annual Investment Income	150
Annual Outflow	90
Capital Value	1,500

Summary of Investments %
Equities 65
Fixed Interest 30
Cash & Deposits 5

THE PRESS & JOURNAL
Lang Stracht, Mastrick, Aberdeen AB9 8AF
Telephone: 0224-690222

Employees 780

THE PRESS ASSOCIATION ANNUITY FUND
85 Fleet Street, London EC4P 4BE
Telephone: 01-353 7440

Pension Fund Manager & Secretary John Purdham, FCCA

Trustees P.A.Annuity Fund Trust Ltd.

Investment Advisers & Stockbrokers Phillips & Drew

Actuaries Lane Clark & Peacock

Auditors Robson Rhodes

Solicitors Biddle & Co.

Company Employees (at 31.12.79) 773

Members 627

Pensioners 167

	£000
Annual Contributions	701
Annual Investment Income	491
Annual Outflow	514
Capital Value	5,907

Summary of Investments
Equities 3,801
Fixed Interest 1,840
Cash & Deposits 266

WILLIAM PRESS & SON LTD GROUP PENSION & LIFE INSURANCE PLAN
28 Essex Street, London WC2R 3AU
Telephone: 01-353 6544

Group Pensions Manager C.A.H.Garstang

Assistant Pensions Manager G.H.Jeffrey

Company Secretary L.G.Pattle,FSCA

Investment Manager J.P.Bickley

Trustees William Press Group Pensions Trust Ltd

Pension Fund Consultants Wyatt Harris Graham Ltd.

Auditors Arthur Andersen & Co.

Solicitors Simmons & Simmons

Company Employees 12,700

Members (at 16.8.80) 3,200

Pensioners 300

Annual Contributions £1.3 million
Annual Investment Income £1.2 million
Capital Value £7.3 million

PRESSAC HOLDINGS LTD.
Acton Grove, Long Eaton, Nottingham NG10 1FW
Telephone: 06076-60141

Managing Director J.B.Wagstaff

Secretary J.Spindler,ACMA

Managed by Prudential Pensions Ltd

Employees 792

PRESTIGE GROUP LTD (THE)
Prestige House, 14-18 Holborn, London EC1N 2LQ
Telephone: 01-405 6711

Secretary J.B.Dykes

Insured with Clerical, Medical & General Life Assurance

Employees 2,877

PRICE & PIERCE GROUP PENSION SCHEME
51 Aldwych, London WC2B 4AZ
Telephone: 01-283 3122

Pension Fund Manager and Secretary F.A.Collinson

Trustees Price & Pierce Group Pension Trust Ltd

Investment Advisers Fraser Green Ltd

Investment Advisers (Overseas) Morgan Guaranty Trust Co. of New York

Actuaries Duncan C.Fraser & Co

Property Advisers Debenham Tewson & Chinnocks

Auditors Deloitte Haskins & Sells

Solicitors Sacker & Partners

Company Employees 1,600

Members (at 31.12.79) 962

Pensioners 166

Deferred Pensioners 167

	£000
Annual Contributions	959
Annual Investment Income	400
Annual Outflow	420
Capital Value (Market Value)	5256

Summary of Investments
UK Equities 1,937
USA Equities 155
Fixed Interest 1,973
Property 826
Cash & Deposits 351
Others 13

PRICE WATERHOUSE & CO PW (UK) PENSION FUND
Southwark Towers, 32 London Bridge Street, London SE1 9SY
Telephone: 01-407 8989

Pension Fund Manager and Secretary R.M.Bankes-Jones

Trustees 5 Partners and 4 members

Investment Advisers Hill Samuel Investment Management Ltd., Geoffrey Morley & Partners Ltd.

PRICE WATERHOUSE & CO *Continued*

Property Advisers Richard Ellis
Actuaries Clay & Partners
Auditor A.G.Whalley, FCA
Employees/Members 2,750 approx.
Pensioners 250 approx.
Annual Contributions Over £2,000,000
Capital Value £15,000,000 approx.

PRICKETTS LTD

30 Staines Road, Hounslow, Middlesex

Secretary D.W.Prickett

Employees 552

BENJAMIN PRIEST & SONS (HOLDINGS) LTD

Old Hill Works, Priest Street, Cradley Heath,
Warley, West Midlands B646JW
Telephone: 0384-66501

Secretary H.J.Baker

Employees 2,700

See also under Warne Wright Group

PRIMECUT FOODS LTD

Windmill Avenue, Kettering, Northants.NN16 0TQ
Telephone: 0536-4981

Director W.B.Wright

Employees 550

PRINCE OF WALES HOTELS LTD

Prince of Wales Hotel, Lord Street, Southport,
Merseyside PR8 1JS
Telephone: 0704-36688

Chairman A.M.Clayman

Insured with Norwich Union Life Insurance Society

Employees 850

PRITCHARD SERVICES GROUP LTD

Pritchard House, South Hill Avenue, South Harrow,
Middlesex HA2 0NS
Telephone: 01-864 4421

Director Corporate Affairs H.R.N.Jamieson

Insured with Commercial Union Assurance Co Ltd

Pension Fund Consultants Noble Lowndes & Partners Ltd.

Employees 15,178

PROCTER & GAMBLE LTD STAFF PENSION FUND AND MANUAL EMPLOYEES PENSION FUND

Newgate House, Newgate Street,
Newcastle upon Tyne NE99 1SH
Telephone: 0632-611900

Pension Fund Manager and Secretary D.R.Trousdale

Investment Advisers Morgan Grenfell & Co Ltd

Actuaries Bacon & Woodrow

Auditors Deloitte Haskins & Sells

Company Employees 3,400

Members 3,200
Pensioners 975

	£000
Annual Contributions	1,676
Annual Investment Income	3,142
Annual Outflow	1,486
Capital Value	31,375
Summary of Investments	
Equities	17,763
Fixed Interest	11,186
Property	998
Cash & Deposits	1,438

THE PROPRIETORS OF HAYS WHARF LTD

St. Olaf House, Tooley Street, London SE1 2PJ
Telephone: 01-407 7101

Pensions Secretary J.Hootton

Company Secretary N.H.Chase,DFC,FCA

Insured with Provident & Mutual Life Assurance Association

Employees 3,553

Capital Value £10 million

PROSPER DE MULDER GROUP PENSION FUND

c/o Cook & Co., 87 Lord Street, Liverpool L2 6PH
Telephone: 051-236 7551

Pension Fund Manager Cook & Co

Trustees K.C.Cook and D.J.Page

Stockbrokers Tilney & Co., Ashton Tod McLaren

Actuaries Duncan C.Fraser & Co

Pension Fund Consultants Cook & Co

Auditors Cook & Co.

Members 550

Pensioners 50

	£000
Annual Contributions	300
Annual Investment Income	285
Annual Outflow	63
Capital Value	3,486
Summary of Investments	
Equities	2,217
Fixed Interest	786
Cash & Deposits	211
Others	550

PROVIDENT FINANCIAL GROUP LTD. PENSION & ASSURANCE SCHEME FOR STAFF EMPLOYEES

Colonnade, Sunbridge Road, Bradford,
West Yorkshire BD1 2LR
Telephone: 0274-33321

Manager-Salaries & Pensions W.Holden

Company Secretary/Trustee P.W.Bretherton

Trustees 6 Company Representatives, 5 Union Representatives

Insured with Legal & General Assurance Society Ltd.

Actuarial Advice Obtained through Legal & General Assurance Society Ltd.

PROVIDENT FINANCIAL GROUP LTD. *Continued*

Pension Fund Consultants Martin Paterson Associates Ltd.

Auditors Coopers & Lybrand

Company Employees 4,100

Members 2,420

Pensioners 537

Annual Contributions £436,000

PROVIDENT LIFE ASSOCIATION OF LONDON PENSION SCHEME

266 Bishopsgate, London EC2M 4QP
Telephone: 01-247 3200

Assistant General Manager & Actuary B.E.Radley, FIA,ASA

Secretary F.W.Lee

Trustees J.D.Fox, E.E.Holland, R.K.Muddle

Auditors Deloitte Haskins & Sells

Company Employees (at 31.12.79) 619

Members 567

Pensioners 105

	£000
Annual Contributions	489
Annual Investment Income	453
Annual Outflow	176
Capital Value	4,159
Summary of Investments	
Equities	1,637
Fixed Interest	2,482
Cash & Deposits	39

PROVIDENT MUTUAL LIFE ASSURANCE ASSOCIATION

25-31 Moorgate, London EC2R 6BA
Telephone: 01-628 3232

Secretary G.W.Stirling, CA

Actuary P.Norton,FIA

Managed by Provident Mutual Managed Pension Fund Ltd.

Company Employees/Members 990

Pensioners 134

Annual Contributions (1979) £754,000

Annual Outflow £334,000

Capital Value (at 31.12.79) £4,828,000

PROVINCIAL BUILDING SOCIETY PENSION FUND

Provincial House, Bradford, W.Yorks.BD1 1NL
Telephone: 0274-33444

Secretary P.Clough, FCIS, FCBSI

Property Manager R.Watson

Investment Advisers Martin Currie & Co

Actuary R.W.Watson, FRICS, ARVA

Property Advisers Provincial Building Society

Auditors Deloitte Haskins & Sells

Company Employees 1,700

Members 890

Pensioners 80

	£000
Annual Contributions	584
Annual Investment Income	760
Annual Outflow	223
Capital Value	7,600
Summary of Investments	
Equities	2,840
Fixed Interest	1,060
Property	2,690
Cash & Deposits	1,080

PROVINCIAL INSURANCE COMPANY PENSION FUND

Sand Aire House, Stramongate, Kendal, Cumbria LA9 4BE
Telephone: 0539-23415

Secretary D.G.Blyth FCII APMI

Trustees C.F.E.Shakerley (Chairman), G.Griffin, H.T.W.Janson, G.Randall, B.Shippen, H.V.Walker, C.A.White

Actuaries R.Watson & Sons

Auditors Peat Marwick Mitchell & Co

Company Employees 1,954

Members 1,381

Pensioners 359

	£000
Annual Contributions	1,665
Annual Investment Income	1,101
Gross Annual Outflow	1,001
Capital Value	15,320
Summary of Investments	
Equities	8,254
Fixed Interest	3,523
Property	2,968
Cash & Deposits	575

PRUDENTIAL ASSURANCE COMPANY LTD STAFF PENSION SCHEME

142 Holborn Bars, London EC1N 2NH
Telephone: 01-405 9222

Staff Pensions Manager & Secretary P.F.Hall,ACII, APMI

Assistant Secretary R.P.Garratt,APMI

Trustees Prudential Nominees Ltd.

Auditors Deloitte, Haskins & Sells

Company Employees 20,000

Members 18,000

Pensioners 13,000

	£million
Annual Contributions	30.9
Annual Investment Income	29.7
Annual Outflow	21.1
Capital Value	312.1
Summary of Investments	

PRUDENTIAL ASSURANCE COMPANY LTD *Continued*

Equities	101.7
Fixed Interest	131.1
Property	70.9
Cash & Deposits	17.9
Net Current Liabilities	(9.5)

THE PULLMAN KELLOGG LTD. PENSION PLAN

The Pullman Kellogg Building, Stadium Way, Wembley, Middx.HA9 0EE
Telephone: 01-903 8484

Pension Fund Manager and Secretary A.R.Thurlow

Trustees 6

Managed by Scottish Amicable Pensions Investments Ltd.

Investment Advisers General Revisionary Investment Co.

Pension Fund Consultants Hogg Robinson (Benefit Consultants) Ltd.

Company Employees 1,600

Members 600

R.& J.PULLMAN LTD.

Pullman House, 42-50 York Way, London N1 9AB
Telephone: 01-278 8121

Secretary D.E.Helliar,ACIS

Employees 1,023

BERNARD PUMFREY GROUP LTD.

Lea Road, Gainsborough, Lincs.

Director P.W.R.Pumfrey

Employees 528

QUAKER OATS LTD

Bridge Road, Southall, Middlesex UB2 4AG
Telephone: 01-574 2388

Secretary B.P.H.Bryson

Pension Fund Consultants Alexander Howden Insurance Brokers Ltd.

Managers Prudential Pensions Ltd

Employees 1,702

QUEENS MOAT HOUSES LTD

Queens Moat House, St.Edwards Way, Romford, Essex RM1 4DD
Telephone: 70-25814

Secretary D.M.Hersey,FCA

Insured with Provident Mutual Life Assurance Association

Employees 1,339

H. & J. QUICK GROUP LTD

660 Chester Road, Old Trafford, Manchester M16 0GU
Telephone: 061-872 2201

Secretary L.J.Ellison

Employees 1,066

RACAL GROUP STAFF PENSION & LIFE ASSURANCE SCHEME

Western Road, Bracknell, Berks RG12 1RG
Telephone: 0344-3244

Group Pension Officer R.A.Potts

Investment Advisers Hill Samuel Investment Management Ltd

Actuarial Advice Obtained through Cubie Wood & Co Ltd

Pension Fund Consultants Noble Lowndes & Partners Ltd

Company Employees 6,700

Members 2,500

Pensioners 70

RADIO RENTALS (HOLDINGS) LTD.

Seymour Mews House, Wigmore Street, London W1H 0AA
Telephone: 01-935 9191

Secretary E.W.Clark,FCIS

Employees 8,208

RADYNE LTD

Molly Millars Lane, Wokingham, Berks.RG11 2PX
Telephone: 0734-783333

Secretary O.R.Browning

Employees 563

RAINE ENGINEERING INDUSTRIES LTD. STAFF PENSION & LIFE ASSURANCE SCHEME

St.Peters House, Hartshead, Sheffield S1 2EL
Telephone: 0742-750191

Secretary M.Ward

Insured with Prudential Assurance Co.Ltd.

Pension Fund Consultants Metropolitan Pensions Association Ltd.

Employees 1,000

Members 120

Annual Contributions £128,000

RAMAR TEXTILES LTD

New Main Road, Crook, Co Durham DL15 8AA
Telephone: 038882-2122

Secretary R.Chapman

Employees 998

THE RAMONEUR CO LTD

16 and 18 Denbigh Street, London SW1V 2ET
Telephone: 01-834 1321

Chairman A.B.Barclay

Director R.D.Hogan

Employees 2,000

RANCO EUROPE LTD

Southway Drive, Southway, Plymouth, Devon PL6 6QT

Secretary D.H.McElney

Pension Fund Consultants Reed Stenhouse Benefit Consultants Ltd.

Employees 1,496

THE RANK ORGANISATION PENSION PLAN

11 H1ll Street, London W1X 8AE
Telephone: 01-629 7454

Group Pensions Manager M.J.Evans,FCII,APMI

Deputy Pensions Manager T.N.London,ACII

Secretary B.C.Owers

Part Insured with Eagle Star Insurance Co Ltd

Part Managed by Eagle Pensions Ltd.

Actuarial Advice Obtained through Cubie, Wood & Co.Ltd.

Auditors Peat, Marwick, Mitchell & Co.

Solicitors Richards Butler & Co.

Company Employees 30,533

Members 13,291

Pensioners 4,700

Annual Contributions £7,500,000

Annual Investment Income £6,500,000

Capital Value £8,125,000

THE RANK XEROX PENSION SCHEME

Middlesex House, 4 Mercer Walk, Uxbridge, Middx.UB8 1UD
Telephone: 89-38230

Secretary and Pensions Manager A.C.Chapman, ACIS,FPMI

Accountant D.N.Harris,FAAI

International Pensions Manager R.R.Cobley,FIA, FPMI (at 338 Euston Road, London NW1 3BH, Telephone: 01-387 1244)

Trustees R.X.Pensions Ltd

Investment Advisers Grieveson Grant & Co., N.M. Rothschild & Sons Ltd., de Zoete & Bevan

Actuaries R.Watson & Sons

Property Advisers Richard Ellis

Auditors Peat, Marwick, Mitchell & Co.

Solicitors Slaughter & May

Company Employees 12,745

Members 10,077

Pensioners 1,409

	£000
Annual Contributions	14,494
Annual Investment Income	4,580
Annual Outflow	3,390
Capital Value	67,862
Summary of Investments	
Equities	42,153
Fixed Interest	14,712
Property	8,771
Cash & Deposits	2,688
Net Current Liabilities	(462)

RANKS HOVIS MCDOUGALL LTD. THE RHM PENSION FUND AND OPERATIVES PENSION FUND

Pembroke House, 44 Wellesley Road, Croydon, Surrey CR9 3PA
Telephone: 01-686 2551

Pensions Manager D.A.C.Miles,FPMI,FCIS

Secretary J.T.W.Botting,ACIS,APMI

Administration Manager D.G.Davey

Accountant E. Hart

Trustees RHM Pension Fund: J.Rank, D.W.Nutting, D.A.C.Miles, R.G.Rogerson
RHM Operatives Pension Fund: RHM Operatives Pensions Ltd. (Directors: D.W.Nutting, D.A.C.Miles, R.G.Rogerson)

Investment Advisers Morgan Grenfell & Co.Ltd. (Pension Fund), Hill Samuel Investment Management Ltd. (Operatives Fund)

Actuarial Advice Obtained through Cubie Wood & Co Ltd

Agricultural Land Advisers Edwin Thompson & Co.

Property Advisers Richard Ellis

Pension Fund Consultants Noble Lowndes & Partners Ltd

Auditors Hodgson Harris & Co.

Solicitors Richards Butler & Co.

Company Employees 49,575

	Operatives Fund	Pension Fund
Members	17,470	15,650
Pensioners	500	4,500
	£000	£000
Annual Contributions	6,000	12,000
Annual Investment Income	1,000	7,000
Gross Annual Outflow	1,000	6,000
Capital Value	9,663	90,000
Summary of Investments		
UK Equities	5,929	40,139
Overseas Equities	894	5,092
Fixed Interest	1,691	17,427
Property	995	23,108

RANSOME HOFFMANN POLLARD STAFF PENSION SCHEME AND WORKS PENSION SCHEME

Stanley Works, Newark, Notts NG24 2JF
Telephone: 0636-705123

Pension Fund Manager R.F.Rawlingson,APMI

Assistant Pensions Manager & Secretary D.H.O.Shawl,APMI

Trustees RHP Staff Pension Trust Ltd, RHP Works Pension Trust Ltd

Part Insured with Commercial Union Assurance Co.Ltd., Friends' Provident Life Office, Legal & General Assurance Society Ltd.

Investment Advisers County Bank Ltd

Stockbrokers Hoare Govett Ltd., Wood, Mackenzie & Co.

Actuaries-Staff Lane Clark & Peacock

Pension Fund Consultants-Works Metropolitan Pensions Association Ltd.

Auditors Peat Marwick Mitchell & Co

RANSOME HOFFMANN POLLARD Continued

Company Employees 9,464

	Staff	Works
Members	2,024	4,365
Pensioners	1,860	862
	£000	£000
Annual Contributions	1,146	792
Annual Investment Income	553	283
Annual Outflow	732	285
Capital Value	10,901	5,556
Summary of Investments		
Equities	5,561	2,981
Fixed Interest	765	405
Property	4,085	1,854
Cash & Deposits	490	316

RANSOMES, SIMMS & JEFFERIES LTD
Nacton Works, Ipswich, Suffolk IP3 9QG
Telephone: 0473-72222

Secretary L.W.Bryant

Investment Advisers Morgan Grenfell & Co.Ltd., J.Henry Schroder Wagg & Co.Ltd.

Employees 2,781

RATCLIFFS (GREAT BRIDGE) LTD PENSION SCHEME
Great Bridge, Tipton, West Midlands DY4 7BN
Telephone: 021-557 1212

Director & Secretary R.D.Ash,FCA

Trustees Ratcliffs (Greatbridge) Pensions Management Ltd.

Managed by Pensions Management (SWF) Ltd

Actuaries Clay & Partners

Pension Fund Consultants Glanvill Enthoven Life & Pensions Brokers Ltd.

Auditors Ernst & Whinney

Company Employees 825

Members 779

Pensioners 133

Annual Contributions £480,000

Annual Outflow £146,000

Capital Value £1,952,000

RATNERS (JEWELLERS) LTD.
19-21 Great Portland Street, London W1N 6HN
Telephone: 01-580 9853

Secretary M.Hussain

Employees 943

RAYBECK LTD
309 Oxford Street, London W1R 2LE
Telephone: 01-629 9756

Secretaries H.C.Seigal,MA, R.Penkethman,FCIS

Employees 4,769

RAYCHEM PENSION & ASSURANCE SCHEME
Faraday Road, Dorcan, Swindon, Wilts. SN3 5HH
Telephone: 0793-28171

Benefits Administration Manager P.H.Griffiths

Investment Advisers Morgan Grenfell & Co.Ltd.

Actuaries R.Watson & Sons

Auditors Arthur Young McClelland Moores & Co.

Company Employees 1,200

Members 1,100

Pensioners 8

Annual Contributions £800,000

Annual Investment Income £215,000

Capital Value £2,648,000

H.B.RAYLOR & CO LTD
Thomas Street, York YO1 3DT
Telephone: 0904-59855

Secretary J.C.Riley

Director H.B.Raylor

Employees 562

RAYNER & KEELER LTD.
Sheraton House, Lower Road, Chorleywood, Herts.

Secretary E.D.Terry

Employees 614

RCA LTD
Lincoln Way, Windmill Road, Sunbury on Thames, Middx TW16 7HW
Telephone: 76-85511

Secretary G.J.Jenkins

Investment Advisers Bankers Trustee & Executor Co Ltd

Pension Fund Consultants Sedgwick Employee Benefits Consultants Ltd.

Employees 1,512

R.C.F.HOLDINGS LTD.
Intersection House, 110-120 Birmingham Road, West Bromwich, West Midlands B70 6RP
Telephone: 021-525 7766

Secretary D.A.McCalman

Insured with Legal & General Assurance Society Ltd, Prudential Assurance Co Ltd

Company Employees 1,410

THE READER'S DIGEST 1967 PENSION SCHEME
25 Berkeley Square, London W1X 6AB
Telephone: 01-629 8144

Manager Financial Services E.T.Pearce,FCA

Company Secretary B.C.Gray

Trustees The Reader's Digest Pension Trustees Ltd.

Investment Advisers Ivory & Sime

Actuaries Bacon & Woodrow

Auditors A.T.Chenhalls & Co.

Company Employees 1,100

Members 655

THE READER'S DIGEST Continued

Pensioners 72

	£000
Annual Contributions	480
Annual Investment Income	230
Annual Outflow	102
Capital Value	3,500
Summary of Investments	
Equities	1,770
Fixed Interest	860
Property	178
Cash & Deposits	210
Others	482

READICUT INTERNATIONAL LTD. PENSION FUND

Terry Mills, Horbury, Wakefield, W.Yorks.WF4 6HD
Telephone: 0924-275241

Company Secretary K.F.Parry FCA

Pension Fund Director H.Morrell,FCA

Trustees H.Morrell,FCA, G.M.L.Hirst, G.Senior, M.Fielden,FCA, J.Littlewood,FCA

Part Managed by Legal & General (Pensions Management) Ltd.

Investment Advisers Ivory & Sime Ltd

Pension Fund Consultants Bain Dawes & Partners Ltd.

Auditors Wheawill & Sudworth

Company Employees 5,070

Members 1,878

READSON LTD RETIREMENT BENEFITS PLAN 1974

Orient House, Granby Row, Manchester M1 7AJ
Telephone: 061-228 3422

Managing Director T.Weatherby,FCA,FCMA,ATII

Secretary J.O.Alexander FCIS

Investment Advisers Hill Samuel Investment Managers Ltd

Actuarial Advice Obtained through Cubie, Wood & Co.Ltd.

Pension Fund Consultants Noble Lowndes & Partners Ltd

Auditors Price Waterhouse & Co.

Company Employees 3,498

Members 403

Pensioners 38

Annual Contributions £314,000

Annual Investment Income £121,000

Capital Value £2,043,000

READY MIXED CONCRETE GROUP PENSION FUND

RMC House, High Street, Feltham, Middlesex TW13 4HA
Telephone: 01-890 1313

Secretary & Group Pensions Manager P.H.F.Bullard APMI

Trustees RMC Pension Trust Ltd

Chairman J.W.Gauntlett

Stockbrokers Phillips & Drew

Property Advisers Richard Ellis

Actuaries R.Watson & Sons

Auditors Linklaters & Paines

Solicitors Linklaters & Paines

Employees 9,683

REARDON SMITH PENSION FUND

P.O.Box 90, Devonshire House, Greyfriars Road, Cardiff CF1 3JT
Telephone: 0222-28077

Pension Fund Manager and Secretary L.S.Williams FCIS

Other Pension Management D.J.Matthews, A.Morgan

Trustees Reardon Smith Pension Trustees Ltd

Investment Advisers & Stockbrokers Hoare Govett Ltd

Actuaries Duncan C.Fraser & Co

Auditors Touche Ross & Co.

Company Employees 611

Members (at 31.3.80) 360

Pensioners 78

	£000
Annual Contributions	471
Annual Investment Income	529
Annual Outflow	211
Capital Value (Market Value at 31.3.80)	5,920
Summary of Investments (Book Value)	
Equities	1,642
Fixed Interest	2,304
Property Unit Trusts	564
Cash & Deposits	816
Others	179

RECKITT & COLMAN PENSION FUND

Dansom Lane, Hull HU8 7DS
Telephone: 0482-26151

Pension Fund Director K.Cole,BA,FIA,FPMI

Secretary R.C.White

Comptroller C.W.Ward

Investment Advisers Baring Bros & Co Ltd

Stockbrokers Cazenove & Co

Actuaries R.Watson & Sons

Property Advisers Knight Frank & Rutley

Auditors Hodgson Harris & Co

Company Employees 16,000

Members 7,400

Pensioners 3,000

Annual Contributions £6.5 million

Annual Investment Income £4.5 million

Gross Annual Outflow £3.25 million

Capital Value £58 million

RECORD RIDGWAY LTD
Parkway Works, Sheffield, S.Yorks.S9 3BL
Telephone: 0742-449066

Secretary S.D.Woolass,FCA

Employees 1,825

REDDITCH DEVELOPMENT CORPORATION
Holmwood, Plymouth Road, Redditch,
Worcs.B97 4PD
Telephone: 0527-64200

Director Professor D.Hinton

Executive W.C.Evans

Employees 500

REDFEARN NATIONAL GLASS LTD
Fishergate, York YO1 4AD
Telephone: 0904-31371

Secretary M.C.Whatley,MA,FCA

Personnel Director A.Hirst

Insured with Prudential Assurance Co Ltd

Employees 2,623

REDIFFUSION LTD PENSION SCHEME
Carlton House, Lower Regent Street,
London SW1Y 4LS
Telephone: 01-930 0221

Group Pensions Manager & Secretary J.R.Heard, APMI

Trustees (at 1.9.79) R.F.G.Dennis (Chairman), J.C.Goodwin, D.A.Smith, H.L.Baker

Actuaries Clay & Partners

Pension Fund Consultants Metropolitan Pensions Association Ltd.

Auditors Fryer Whitehill & Co.

Company Employees 12,700

REDLAND STAFF PENSION SCHEME AND WORKS PENSION SCHEME
Redland House, Reigate, Surrey RH2 0SJ
Telephone: 07372-42488

Employment Administration Manager I.Hamilton

Pensions Administration Manager D.L.Fearnley,ACII

Senior Pensions Administrator Mrs. H.Phillips

Trustees Staff 11, Works 7

Investment Advisers Staff: Baring Bros Ltd & Robert Fleming Investment Management Ltd, Works: M&G Investment Management Ltd

Actuaries R.Watson & Sons

Auditors Binder Hamlyn

Solicitors Slaughter & May

Employees 6,874

	Staff	Works
Members	1,774	3,600
Pensioners	447	173
	£000	£000
Annual Contributions	1,271	1,349

Annual Investment Income	514	115
Capital Value	8,475	2,400

REDMAN HEENAN PENSION SCHEME
PO Box 29, Shrub Hill Road, Worcester WR4 9EQ
Telephone: 0905-23461

Secretary and Group Pensions Manager R.Hickling, APMI

Trustees R.H.I.Pensions Ltd

Stockbrokers Hoare Govett Ltd

Actuaries Duncan C.Fraser & Co.

Auditors Peat, Marwick, Mitchell & Co.

Company Employees 2,300

Members 2,100(at 5.4.80)

Pensioners 270

	£000
Annual Contributions (at 5.4.80)	758
Annual Investment Income	447
Annual Outflow	369
Capital Value	3,972
Summary of Investments	
Equities	1,399
Fixed Interest	842
Property	910
Cash & Deposits	821

REED & SMITH HOLDINGS LTD
Silverton Mills, Hele, Exeter, Devon EX5 4PX
Telephone: 039288-601

Secretary H.S.Levinger

Insured with English Insurance Co Ltd

Employees 1,572

Capital Value £3,600,000

REED EXECUTIVE LTD PENSION FUND
15 Sheet Street, Windsor, Berks.SL4 1AY
Telephone: 95-68277

Company Secretary C.J.Ison,ACMA,ACIS

Trustees C.J.Ison, D.J.Cooke

Insured with Prudential Assurance Co.Ltd.

Pension Fund Consultants J.H.Minet Life & Pensions Ltd

Auditors Coopers & Lybrand

Company Employees 1,002

Members 65

Annual Contributions £79,600

REED INTERNATIONAL LTD PENSION SCHEME
Registered Office Reed House, 83 Piccadilly, London W1A 1EJ
Telephone: 01-499 4020

Administration Mill Hale Centre, Aylesford, Maidstone, Kent
Telephone: 0622-77777

Director of Pensions K.G.Smith, FPMI, FIA

Chief Pensions Executive E.A.Flower,FPMI

Secretary A.H.Hilton

REED INTERNATIONAL LTD Continued

Investment Manager J.C.Woodward, BSc, FIA
Trustees Reed Pension Trusts Ltd.
Property Advisers Richard Ellis
Actuaries R.Watson & Sons
Auditors Champness Cowper & Co
Solicitors Sacker & Partners
Group Employees 61,000
Members 25,548
Pensioners 4,366
Annual Contributions £18.6 million
Annual Investment Income £8.3 million
Annual Outflow £5.9 million
Capital Value £110 million

REED PUBLISHING PENSION SCHEME

88 Kingsway, London WC2B 6AB
Telephone: 01-242 9311

Chief Pension Executive and Secretary P.R.Swann, BSc,FCA,APMI
Director of Pensions K.G.Smith,FPMI,FIA
Investment Manager J.C.Woodward
Trustees Reed Publishing Pension Trustee Ltd
Directors L.A.Carpenter (Chairman), A.D.Long, J.C.Bygrave, P.R.Phillips, K.G.Smith, P.R.Swann
Property Advisers Richard Ellis
Actuaries R.Watson & Sons
Auditors Deloitte Haskins & Sells
Solicitors Nicholson Graham & Jones
Company Employees 20,755
Members (at 5.4.80) 17,281
Pensioners 7,007
Deferred Pensioners 7,694

	£ millions
Annual Contributions	20.3
Annual Investment Income	11.3
Annual Outflow	7.2
Capital Value Market value	140.0
Summary of Investments(Market value)	
Equities	72.6
Fixed Interest	42.9
Property	15.7
Cash & Deposits	7.3
Others	1.5

REES & KIRBY LTD

PO Box 308, Foundry Road, Morriston, Swansea SA6 8EN
Telephone: 0792-71751

Secretary D.Samuel
Employees 728

REFUGE ASSURANCE CO LTD SUPERANNUATION FUND

103 Oxford Street, Manchester M60 7HA
Telephone: 061-236 9432

Secretary J.H.Sutcliffe,FCIS
Fund Actuary G.D.Shirley,BSc,FIA
Company Employees 3,975
Members (at 5.4.80) 3,865
Pensioners 2,620
Annual Contributions £930,000
Annual Investment Income £4,980,000
Capital Value £44,454,000

REGISTERED DOCK WORKERS PENSION SCHEME

See Port Employers and Registered Dock Workers Pension Fund Trustees Ltd.

RELIANCE KNITWEAR GROUP LTD

Hare Street Mills, Hare Street, Halifax, West Yorkshire HX1 4DL
Telephone: 0422-62171

Secretary F.O.Kirk,FCIS
Insured with Scottish Widows' Fund & Life Assurance Society
Employees 1,571

RELIANCE MUTUAL INSURANCE SOCIETY LTD PENSION SCHEME

Reliance House, Tunbridge Wells, Kent TN4 8BL
Telephone: 0892-22271

Joint Secretaries D.M.Collier, M.A.Robinson,MA,FIA
Trustees H.J.Brown, R.T.Kingsmill
Actuaries Bacon & Woodrow
Property Advisers Idris Jones & Partners
Auditors Hill Vellacott
Company Employees 602
Members 393
Pensioners 247

	£000
Annual Contributions	110
Annual Investment Income	267
Capital Value	2,748
Summary of Investments	
Equities	1,208
Fixed Interest	839
Property	603
Cash & Deposits	54

RELIANCE NAMEPLATES LTD

Cambridge Road, Twickenham, Middlesex TW1 2HW
Telephone: 01-891 1300

Secretary & Director Mrs.M.M.Cameron
Employees 520

RELIANT MOTOR GROUP LTD 1978 RETIREMENT FUND

Two Gates, Tamworth, Staffs B77 1HN
Telephone: 0827-4151

Secretary M.E.Smith,MBA,ACMA
Insured with Sun Alliance & London Insurance Ltd

RELIANT MOTOR GROUP LTD *Continued*

Pension Fund Consultants Hodge Insurance (Life & Pensions) Ltd

Company Employees 1,500

Members 700

Pensioners 2

Annual Contributions £350,000

P.B.W.S.RELYON LTD.

South Street, Wellington, Somerset
Telephone: 082-347 2216

Secretary D.P.Stocks,FCA

Stockbrokers Panmure Gordon & Co., Laing & Cruickshank

Employees 676

REMPLOY LTD

Remploy House, 415 Edgware Road,
London NW2 6LR
Telephone: 01-452 8020

Secretary W.L.Jacob

Pensions Executive J.P.D.Pickford, FCIS, APMI

Employees 7,910

RENAULT U.K. LTD PENSION FUND

Western Avenue, Acton, London W3 0RZ
Telephone: 01-992 3481

Secretary M.A.Currey

Trustees M.A.Currey, J.L.H.Young, Mrs. E.E.Singleton, O.Brown

Insured with Norwich Union Life Insurance Society

Pension Fund Consultants Sedgwick Employee Benefits Consultants Ltd.

Company Employees 1,011

Members 605

Pensioners 38

Annual Contributions £737,000 (at 1.4.80)

RENDEL, PALMER & TRITTON

61 Southwark Street, London SE1 1SA
Telephone: 01-928 8999

Secretary J.E.G.Palmer

Employees 575

RENOLD LTD. STAFF AND HOURLY RATED PENSION SCHEMES

Renold House, Wythenshawe,
Manchester M22 5WL
Telephone: 061-437 5221

Head of Pensions Department F.W.Donbavand

Secretary E.J.Murfin

Insured with Royal Insurance Co Ltd

Employees 8,383

RENTOKIL GROUP LTD STAFF PENSION & LIFE ASSURANCE PLAN

Felcourt, East Grinstead, West Sussex RH19 2JY
Telephone: 0342-833022

Secretary B.L.Banks

Trustees E.M.Buchan, K.A.Bridgman, B.McGillivray, D.A.Hackett, Mrs.M.P.Johnston, M.R.Morgan

Managed by Scottish Mutual Pension Funds Investments Ltd.

Actuarial Advice Obtained through Godwins (Central Services) Ltd.

Pension Fund Consultants Godwins (Central Services) Ltd.

Auditors Price Waterhouse & Co.

Company Employees (UK) 3,557

Members (at 1.4.80) 1,969

Pensioners 184

	£000
Annual Contributions	1,023
Annual Investment Income	1,500
Annual Outflow	350
Capital Value	7,412
Summary of Investments	
Equities	4,601
Fixed Interest	1,875
Property	641
Cash & Deposits	250
Others	45

THE RENWICK GROUP LTD.

Renwick House, Brixham Road, Paignton, Devon TQ4 7BN
Telephone: 0803-55261

Secretary M.A.C.Winterton

Insured with Equitable Life Assurance Society

Employees 1,815

RESTMOR GROUP LTD

Restmor Way, Hackbridge Road, Hackbridge, Wallington, Surrey SM6 7AQ
Telephone: 01-669 4333

Secretary P.A.Grove

Employees 647

REUTERS PENSION FUND

85 Fleet Street, London EC4P 4AJ
Telephone: 01-353 6060

Pension Fund Manager G.V.Dunk, ACII, FPMI

Secretary of Fund N.L.Judah, FCA

Trustees Reuters Pension Fund Ltd

Investment Advisers J. Henry Schroder Wagg & Co Ltd

Actuaries Bacon & Woodrow

Pension Consultants Noble Lowndes International Ltd

Auditors Binder Hamlyn

Solicitors Walker Martineau & Co.

Company Employees 2,600

Members 1,403

Pensioners 193

REUTERS Continued

	£000
Annual Contributions	1,836
Annual Investment Income	1,538
Gross Annual Outflow	696
Capital Value (at 30.6.80)	17,300
Summary of Investments	
Equities	7,500
Fixed Interest	5,700
Property Unit Trusts	1,400
Cash & Deposits	1,000
Others	1,700

REVERTEX GROUP PENSION FUND

Temple Fields, Harlow, Essex CM20 2AH
Telephone: 0279-29555

Secretary K.R.F.Bird

Other Pension Management R.C.A.Fitzgerald, A.J.Marsh

Trustees Dr.J.Stewart, G.Stott

Insured with Norwich Union Life Insurance Society

Company Employees 1,130

Members 1,070

Pensioners 78

REVLON INTERNATIONAL CORPN

PO Box 1, Maesteg, Bridgend, Mid-Glamorgan
Telephone: 0656-732345

Executive W.D.Williams

Employees 950

REXMORE LTD GROUP PENSION PLAN

Regent House, Rexmore Way, Liverpool L15 0HZ
Telephone: 051-733 4080

Pension Fund Manager R.G.Handley, ACIS

Secretary W.Redman

Trustees R.G.Handley, M.E.J.Ball,ACIS, J.Barlow, T.Plenderleith,ACMA, E.D.Beaumont,FCA, R.Craven

Stockbrokers Blankstone Sington & Co

Pension Fund Consultants and Actuarial Advice Obtained through Wyatt Harris Graham Ltd.

Auditors Deloitte Haskins & Sells

Company Employees 1,600

Members 400

Pensioners 25

	£000
Annual Contributions	130
Annual Investment Income	80
Annual Outflow	15
Capital Value	800
Summary of Investments	
Equities	220
Fixed Interest	300
Cash & Deposits	50
Managed Funds	280

R.F.D. GROUP LTD

Catteshall Lane, Godalming, Surrey GU7 1LH
Telephone: 04868-4122

Group Pensions Manager J.A.Gunner

Company Secretary P.C.Landsborough,FCCA

Insured with Friends' Provident Life Office and Phoenix Assurance Co. Ltd.

Pension Fund Consultants Hogg Robinson (Benefit Consultants) Ltd.

Auditors Touche Ross & Co.

Company Employees 1,763

Members 900

Pensioners 80

RHEEM BLAGDEN LTD

16-18 Hatton Garden, London EC1N 8FJ
Telephone: 01-242 6571

Secretary W.J.Chiddicks

Employees 2,034

RICARDO CONSULTING ENGINEERS LTD. SUPERANNUATION FUND

Bridge Works, Shoreham-by-Sea,
W.Sussex BN4 5FG
Telephone: 07917-5611

Secretary G.S.Tibbitts

Trustees D.R.Dixon, G.H.Harker, C.J.Walder

Investment Advisers Hambros Investment Management Services Ltd

Stockbrokers James Capel & Co.

Pension Fund Consultants Godwins (Central Services) Ltd.

Auditors Touche Ross & Co.

Company Employees 525

Members 504

Pensioners 79

	£000
Annual Contributions	389
Annual Investment Income	237
Annual Outflow	181
Capital Value	
Book Value	2,718
Market Value	3,513
Summary of Investments (at Cost)	
Equities	1,080
Fixed Interest	1,011
Cash & Deposits	326
Others	265

RICHARDS LTD

Broadford Works, 62 Maberly Street,
Aberdeen AB9 8DT
Telephone: 0224-630243

Secretary & Financial Director C.A.S.Low,CA,FCMA

Pension Fund Consultants Scottish Pension Trustees Ltd

Employees 1,017

RICHARDS & WALLINGTON GROUP PENSION FUND
Wharf Road, Tyseley, Birmingham B11 2DY
Telephone: 021-706 6181

Secretary C.H.Jacob

Company Secretary A.M.O.Davis,FSCA

Trustees W.R.Richards, A.M.O.Davis, R.Brantingham, T.F.Wellings

Insured with Scottish Widows Fund and Life Assurance Society

Pension Fund Consultants Godwins (Midlands & West) Ltd

Company Employees 2,177

Members 850

Pensioners 40

CHARLES RICHARDS FASTENERS LTD
PO Box 23, Heath Road, Darlaston, Wednesbury, West Midlands WS10 8LR
Telephone: 021-526 3188

Secretary P.H.Taylor

Employees 766

RICHARDSON-MERRELL LTD
20 Queensmere, Slough, Berkshire SL1 1LA
Telephone: 75-34688

Secretary P.R.Nicholson

Investment Advisers Robert Fleming Investment Management Ltd

Employees 863

RICHARDSONS, WESTGARTH & CO LTD
Wallsend, Tyne & Wear NE28 6QL
Telephone: 0632-628392

Secretary D.F.R.Foord

Pension Fund Consultants Godwins Ltd

Employees 2,307

RIGID CONTAINERS HOLDINGS LTD.
Rushton Road, Desborough, Kettering, Northants.NN14 2RY
Telephone: 0536-760266

Secretary J.E.Bailey

Employees 1,117

RIKER LABORATORIES
Head Office, Morley Street, Loughborough, Leics.LE11 1EP
Telephone: 0509-68181

Director N.A.Wolfstein

Employees 600

E.J.RILEY LTD.
1 Commodore Parade, Streatham High Road, London S.W.16
Telephone: 01-764 9468

Secretary M.Glyn,FCA

Employees 513

RILEYS POTATO CRISPS
Cottage Beck Road, Scunthorpe, South Humberside
Telephone: 0724-55001

Director R.J.Curgenven

Employees 700

RINGTONS LTD
Algernon Road, Newcastle upon Tyne NE6 2YN
Telephone: 0632-656181

Secretary J.Rutherford

Employees 655

R.T.Z. PENSION FUND AND R.T.Z.PENSION PLAN
The Rio Tinto-Zinc Corporation Ltd. P.O.Box 133, 6 St.James's Square, London SW1Y 4LD
Telephone: 01-930 2399

Pensions Manager D.W.B.Wood, FPMI

Secretary & Deputy Pensions Manager I.G.Lukins, APMI

Trustees R.T.Z. Pension Fund Trustees Ltd., R.T.Z. Pension Plan Trustees Ltd.

Investment Advisers N.M.Rothschild Asset Management Limited, Warburg Investment Management Limited

Actuaries Lane, Clark & Peacock

Property Advisers Jones, Lang, Wootton

Auditors Spicer & Pegler

UK Employees 13,500

Members 10,000

Pensioners 1,700

	£000
Annual Contributions	10,100
Annual Investment Income	4,100
Gross Annual Outflow	2,700
Capital Value (at 31.3.80)	54,400
Summary of Investments	
Equities	29,800
Fixed Interest	11,100
Property	7,300
Cash & Deposits	6,000
Others	200

Note: Some employees are members of three smaller schemes which for simplicity have been excluded from the data.

RIPAULTS LTD
Southbury Road, Enfield, Middx.EN1 1UE
Telephone: 01-804 8181

Financial Director D.F.Alexander

Employees 1,700

RIPOLIN LTD
Balfour Road, Southall, Middx.UB2 5BT
Telephone: 01-574 4353

Secretary D.W.Arundale

Trustees P.Jeffrey, D.W.Arundale

Insured with Sun Life Assurance Society Ltd.

RIPOLIN LTD *Continued*

Pension Fund Consultants Stewart Wrightson Assurance Consultants Ltd
Company Employees 820

RICHARD ROBERTS HOLDINGS LTD
PO Box 124, Vaughan Way, Leicester LE1 9JE
Telephone: 0533-51231
Secretary S.Kacher
Insured with Legal & General Assurance Society Ltd
Employees 1,973

THOMAS ROBERTS (WESTMINSTER) LTD
Eling House, 100 Eling Lane, Totton, Southampton,Hants.SO4 4TP
Telephone: 0703-867011
Secretary J.W.T.Saunders
Employees 1,906

ROBERTSON FOODS LTD. GROUP PENSION SCHEME (1978) AND GROUP MANAGEMENT PENSION SCHEME
Forest Lodge, Westerham Road, Keston, Kent BR2 6HE
Telephone: 66-50421
Company Secretary N.A.McBrien,FCA
Pensions Officer B.D.Mason
Stockbrokers Cazenove & Co.
Actuaries Hymans, Robertson & Co.
Employees 3,599
Members (at 29.7.80) 700
Pensioners 500

H H ROBERTSON (UK) LTD RETIREMENT BENEFITS PLAN (1978) AND LIFE ASSURANCE & RETIREMENT BENEFIT SCHEME
27 Newgate Street, Chester, Cheshire CH1 1DE
Telephone: 0244-41175
Secretary E.J.Bushell, MA, FCIS
Managed by Eagle Pension Funds Ltd and Legal & General (Pensions Management) Ltd
Actuarial Advice Obtained through Cubie, Wood & Co.Ltd.
Pension Fund Consultants Noble Lowndes & Partners Ltd.
Auditors Price Waterhouse & Co
Solicitors Clifford-Turner
Company Employees 1,650
Members (total two schemes) 1,570
Pensioners 137
Annual Contributions £660,000
Capital Value £4,500,000

ROBIN WOOLS LTD
Robin Mills, Idle, Bradford, W.Yorks.BD10 9TE
Telephone: 0274-612561

Director G.N.Hunter
Employees 500

ROBINSON & SONS LTD. PENSION FUND
Wheat Bridge, Chesterfield, Derbyshire,S40 2AD
Telephone: 0246-31101
Director & Secretary F.Rhodes,ACIS
Stockbrokers Phillips & Drew
Actuaries Bacon & Woodrow
Auditors Carlines
Company Employees 3,562
Members (at 5.4.80) 798
Pensioners 275
Annual Contributions £279,000
Annual Investment Income £320,000
Capital Value £3,946,000

ROBINSON BROTHERS LTD. STAFF AND WORKS PENSION & ASSURANCE SCHEMES
Phoenix Street, West Bromwich, West Midlands B70 0AH
Telephone: 021-553 2451
Secretary F.D.Robinson
Investment Advisers County Bank Ltd.
Pension Fund Consultants Noble Lowndes & Partners Ltd.
Company Employees 601

	Staff	Works
Members	179	283
Pensioners	7	25
Annual Contributions	£208,000	£195,000
Capital Value	£595,000	£253,000

FREDERICK ROBINSON LTD.
Unicorn Brewery, Lower Hillgate, Stockport, Cheshire
Secretary & Director P.B.Robinson
Employees 535

THOMAS ROBINSON & SON LTD
Railway Works, Rochdale, Lancashire OL16 5NB
Telephone: 0706-47811
Secretary K.Stanaway, FCIS
Employees 685

ROBISON & DAVIDSON LTD.
St.Catherines, 35-39 Annan Road, Dumfries
Telephone: 0287-2151
Secretary E.L.Grierson
Employees 570

ROBOSERVE LTD
19-21 Aintree Road, Perivale, Greenford, Middlesex UB6 7LG
Telephone: 01-998 2828
Managing Director E.S.Fattal
Employees 592

ROCHE PRODUCTS LTD PENSION FUND AND WORKS PENSION FUND

40 Broadwater Road, Welwyn Garden City, Herts. AL7 3AV
Telephone: 96-28128

Secretary K.Lavanchy, FCIS, APMI

Investment Advisers Royal Trust Company of Canada

Pension Fund Consultants and Actuarial Advice Obtained through Metropolitan Pensions Association Ltd

Auditors Rawlinson & Hunter

Company Employees 1,737

Members 1,600

Pensioners 350

ROCKWARE GROUP LTD & ASSOCIATED COMPANIES STAFF & WORKS PENSION FUNDS

Rockware House, 13-23 Victoria Street, Windsor, Berks.SL4 1HG
Telephone: 95-57421

Group Compensation Manager J.E.Lockwood,FCIS

Pensions Officer E.A.Lockyer

Company Secretary R.I.Andrews,MA

Investment Advisers N.M.Rothschild & Sons Ltd

Actuaries Bacon & Woodrow

Auditors Spicer & Pegler

Solicitors Beachcroft Hyman & Isaacs

Company Employees 7,321

	Staff	Works
Members (at 31.3.80)	1,487	3,920
Pensioners	407	784
	£000	£000
Annual Contributions	1,661	1,821
Annual Investment Income	541	525
Capital Value	7,636	7,657

ROCKWELL INTERNATIONAL LTD

23 Grafton Street, London W1P 5LG
Telephone: 01-409 0291

Managing Director W.L.Neely

Employees 3,631

JOHN RODWELL LTD

199-209 Hornchurch Road, Hornchurch, Essex RM12 4TJ
Telephone: 04024-48877

Director J.Rodwell

Employees 500

ROHM AND HAAS (UK) LTD. PENSION & LIFE ASSURANCE SCHEME (1975)

Lennig House, 2 Mason's Avenue, Croydon, Surrey CR9 3NB
Telephone: 01-686 8844

Pension Fund Manager & Secretary J.A.Pound APMI

Trustees W.G.Anderson, Dr.E.J.Cullen, A.I.Ferguson, L.A.Shearman

Investment Advisers Baring Bros. & Co.Ltd

Actuarial Advice Obtained through Cubie, Wood & Co.Ltd.

Pension Fund Consultants Lowndes Associated Pensions Ltd.

Auditors Peat, Marwick, Mitchell & Co.

Company Employees 750

Members (at 30.6.80) 745

Pensioners 58

	£000
Annual Contributions	665
Annual Investment Income	294
Annual Outflow	214
Capital Value	4,162
Summary of Investments	
Equities	2,556
Fixed Interest	886
Property	547
Cash & Deposits	173

ROLLS ROYCE MOTORS PENSION FUND

Pyms Lane, Crewe, Cheshire CW1 3PL
Telephone: 0270-55155

Pension Fund Manager G.White,APMI

Secretary J.H.Dodd

Trustees T.Neville (Chairman) plus 6 members and 5 company trustees

Investment Managers Warburg Investment Management Ltd, Touche, Remnant & Co

Actuaries Bacon & Woodrow

Property Advisers Chestertons

Auditors Touche Ross & Co

Company Employees 10,095

Members 8,554

Pensioners 1,568

	£000
Annual Contributions	6,200
Annual Investment Income	4,093
Annual Outflow	3,034
Capital Value	31,684
Summary of Investments	
Equities	16,526
Fixed Interest	8,728
Property	2,843
Net Current Assets	3,587

ROLLS-ROYCE WORKS AND STAFF PENSION FUNDS

P.O.Box 31, Derby DE2 8BJ
Telephone: 0332-367921

Pension Fund Manager C.Cook,FPMI

Secretary D.E.Haynes, FCCA, ACIS

Assistant Secretary J.E.Davis

Treasurer G.D.Muckelroy

ROLLS-ROYCE Continued

Trustees Chairman (H.E.Trevan-Hawke) plus 4 members and 4 company trustees

Custodian Trustees Rolls-Royce Pension Trust Ltd

Investment Advisers Hill Samuel Investment Management Ltd., Robert Fleming Investment Management Ltd.

Forestry Advisers Tilhill Forestry Advisory Ltd

Property Advisers N.M.Rothschild Asset Management Ltd.

Actuaries Bacon & Woodrow

Pension Fund Consultants Noble Lowndes & Partners Ltd

Auditors Coopers & Lybrand

Solicitors Claremont Haynes & Co.

	Staff	Works
Company Employees	28,145	30,288
Members (at 5.4.80)	27,018	29,446
Pensioners	5,721	9,155
	£000	£000
Annual Contributions	20,048	15,632
Annual Investment Income	11,150	6,630
Annual Outflow	8,591	7,865
Capital Value (Market)	154,072	91,098
Summary of Investments		
Equities	81,991	49,277
Fixed Interest	25,802	15,594
Property	41,606	23,233
Cash & Deposits	4,673	2,994
Net current assets	1,578	791

RONSON PRODUCTS LTD PENSION FUND

Randalls Road, Leatherhead, Surrey KT22 7TF
Telephone: 53-74444

Pension Fund Manager P.C.F.Rayment

Company Secretary J.I.McLean

Trustees R.I.Graham, J.H.Cape, J.I.McLean, P.S.Jackson, J.K.Scholey, M.Waugh

Investment Advisers Kleinwort Benson Investment Management Ltd

Property Advisers St. Quintin

Actuaries R. Watson & Sons

Auditors Ernst & Whinney

Solicitors Lawrence Jones & Co.

Company Employees 2,100

Members 1,932

Pensioners 398

	£000
Annual Contributions	1,100
Annual Investment Income	650
Annual Outflow	400
Capital Value	8,100
Summary of Investments	
Equities	3,740
Fixed Interest	3,000
Property	620
Cash & Deposits	740

THE ROOFF GROUP LTD.

Bushey House, 679 Barking Road, London E13 9ET
Telephone: 01-472 0106

Secretary W.J.Cole

Employees 546

ROPNER HOLDINGS LTD

140 Coniscliffe Road, Darlington, Co.Durham DL3 7RP
Telephone: 0325-62811

Secretary R.Vart

Employees 1,160

ROSSER & RUSSELL LTD

Queens Wharf, Queen Caroline Street, London W6 9RJ
Telephone: 01-748 4161

Secretary D.J.Thorburn, MA

Employees 1,049

JOHN ROSTRON & SONS LTD

Denison Road, Selby, North Yorkshire
Telephone: 0757-5151

Secretary A.J.Bannister

Employees 1,000

ROTAPRINT

Rotaprint House, Honeypot Lane, London NW9 9RE
Telephone: 01-204 3355

Secretary M.A.Lassman,LLB,FCA

Insured with Royal Assurance Co Ltd

Employees 1,169

ROTHMANS INTERNATIONAL LTD

See Carreras

ROTHSCHILDS CONTINUATION LTD.

New Court, St.Swithin's Lane, London EC4P 4DU
Telephone: 01-626 4356

Investment Director James Roe

Employees 893

Subsidiaries include N.M.Rothschild Asset Management Ltd. and Gresham Life Assurance Society Ltd.

ROUSSEL LABORATORIES LTD PENSION & LIFE ASSURANCE SCHEME (1975)

Roussel House, Wembley Park, Middlesex HA9 0NF
Telephone: 01-903 1454

Pension Fund Administrator Mrs.G.A.Crawford

Secretary D.M.S.Lumb

ROUSSEL LABORATORIES LTD Continued

Trustees G.E.Powderham, D.M.S.Lumb, J.Hawkins
Managed by Pensions Management (SWF) Ltd
Pension Fund Consultants Sedgwick Employee Benefits Consultants Ltd.
Company Employees 1,009
Members 916
Pensioners 75
Annual Contributions £1,200,000
Capital Value £4,600,000

ROWAN & BODEN LTD
1 Edison Street, Hillington Industrial Estate, Glasgow G52 4UF
Telephone: 041-882 9031

Secretary C.M.Thompson, FCMA
Employees 817

ROWE & CO.LTD.
Cardrew Road, Redruth, Cornwall
Telephone: 0209-215681

Secretary W.C.Jenkin
Employees 550

ROWNTREE MACKINTOSH PENSION FUND
York YO1 1XY
Telephone: 0904-53071

Pension Fund Manager & Secretary D.A.Jarrett
Assistant Investment Manager G.Thompson
Trustees Rowntree Mackintosh Pension Trust Limited
Actuary R.G.Lauener, FFA, FPMI
Property Advisers Hillier Parker May & Rowden, Kenneth Ryden & Partners, Smiths Gore
Auditors Price Waterhouse & Co.
Company Employees (UK) 22,600
Members 10,140
Pensioners 3,264

	£000
Annual Contributions	6,453
Annual Investment Income	5,710
Annual Outflow	3,364
Capital Value	
Book Value	61,794
Market Value(est)	63,000
Summary of Investments (Book Value)	
Equities	15,437
Fixed Interest	34,108
Property	8,734
Cash & Deposits	1,505
Others	2,010

ROWTON HOTELS LTD
Bondway House, 3-9 Bondway, London SW8 1SJ
Telephone: 01-735 7133

Secretary P.Harris,FCA

Insured with Yorkshire General Life Assurance Co Ltd
Employees 864

ROYAL ARSENAL CO-OPERATIVE SOCIETY LTD EMPLOYEES SUPERANNUATION FUND
147 Powis Street, London SE18 6JN
Telephone: 01-854 2000

Secretary R.A.Roffey,CSD,MBIM
Trustees RACS Employees Superannuation Trustee Co.Ltd.
Stockbrokers Sheppards & Chase, de Zoete & Bevan
Actuary P.D.Johnson,MA,FIA
Pension Fund Consultants Co-operative Union Ltd.
Auditors Appleby & Wood
Company Employees F/T 5,093, P/T 2,659
Members 1,422
Pensioners 1,763

	£000
Annual Contributions	569
Annual Investment Income	827
Annual Outflow	971
Capital Value	12,637
Summary of Investments	
Equities	2,309
Fixed Interest	9,476
Property	26
Cash & Deposits	825

THE ROYAL BANK OF SCOTLAND LTD STAFF PENSION SCHEME
42 St Andrew Square, Edinburgh EH2 2YE
Telephone: 031-556 8555

Pensions Manager W.G.D.Abbott,AIB,APMI
Investment Manager R.J.Herkes
Senior Assistant Investment Manager R.W.Taylor
Trustees Sir Michael Herries, Sir Donald Cameron of Lochiel, P.E.G.Balfour, A.M.Aitchison, W.W.Archibald, J.B.Burke, R.C.Cumming, P.N.Forsyth, J.C.R.Inglis
Investment Advisers The Royal Bank of Scotland Ltd. Trustee and Investment Office
Actuary D.W.A.Donald,OBE,TD,FFA
Auditors Thomson McLintock & Co
Company Employees 9,568
Members 6,228
Pensioners 2,538
Annual Contributions £17,984,000
Annual Investment Income £6,876,000
Annual Outflow £7,895,000
Capital Value £91,208,000

ROYAL BRIERLEY CRYSTAL
North Street, Brierley Hill, West Midlands DY5 3SJ
Telephone: 0384-77054

Director R.S.Williams-Thomas
Employees 500

ROYAL DOULTON
See Doulton & Co.Ltd.

ROYAL INSURANCE GROUP PENSION SCHEME
PO Box 144, New Hall Place, Liverpool L69 3EN
Telephone: 051-227 4422

Secretary to the Scheme I.C.Hill,MBA,FCII

Pensions Actuary A.C.Baker, FIA, FFA

Management Committee 10; Chairman W.Scanlan

Trustees 7; Chairman D.Meinertzhagen

Company Employees 9,426

Members 8,725

Pensioners 4,524

	£000
Annual Contributions	16,000
Annual Investment Income	11,500
Annual Outflow	9,300
Capital Value	
Book Value	103,800
Market Value	141,400

ROYAL LIVER FRIENDLY SOCIETY SUPERANNUATION FUND
Royal Liver Building, Pier Head, Liverpool L3 1HT
Telephone: 051-236 1451

Deputy Personnel Manager P.J.Cullen,ACII

Actuaries R.Watson & Sons

Auditors Deloitte Haskins & Sells

Solicitors Bremner Sons & Corlett

Company Employees 2,565

Members (at 31.12.79) 2,015

Pensioners 2,032

Annual Contributions £1,280,000

Annual Investment Income £2,222,000

Capital Value £24,571,000

THE ROYAL LONDON STAFF PENSION FUND
Royal London Mutual Insurance Soc.,
Finsbury Square, London EC2A 1DP
Telephone: 01-606 3044

Pension Fund Manager & Secretary D.L.Read MA FIA (Administrator)

Actuary to the Fund B.R.Jones,FIA

Trustees B.G.Skinner, W.H.Forsey, I.J.Pickard

Actuary B.R.Jones FIA

Auditors Howard, Tilly & Co.

Company Employees (at 31.12.79) 3,500

Members (at 5.4.80) 2,694

Pensioners 2,800

	£000
Annual Contributions	1,729
Annual Investment Income	3,488
Annual Outflow	2,454
Capital Value	30,916
Summary of Investments	
Equities	6,977
Fixed Interest	22,512
Property	651
Others	776

ROYAL SCHOLTEN HONIG (HOLDINGS) LTD
Stadex Works, Middle Green Road, Langley, Slough, Berks.

Chairman Dr.W.L.Hoefnagels

Employees 656

ROYAL SEAMEN'S PENSION FUND
58 High Street, Sutton, Surrey SM1 1HD

Secretary R.F.van Houten

ROYAL WORCESTER SPODE LTD. STAFF AND WORKS PENSION & LIFE ASSURANCE SCHEMES
Royal Porcelain Works, Severn Street, Worcester
Telephone: 0905-23221

Group Head Office 24 Old Burlington Street, London W1X 1RL. Telephone: 01-434 1428

Pension Fund Manager & Secretary D.Rutter

Group Pensions Manager A.M.V.Marshall

Trustees L.T.Davies, T.B.Miller, A.M.V.Marshall

Insured with Staff: Norwich Union Life Insurance Society, Works: Prudential Assurance Co.Ltd.

Actuaries Clay & Partners

Pension Fund Consultants Metropolitan Pensions Association Ltd.

Auditors Peat, Marwick, Mitchell & Co.

Company Employees (1978) 2,350

	Works	Staff
Members (6.4.79)	802	365
Pensioners	65	52
Annual Contributions	£206,000	£226,000

The Group also includes several other schemes as follows:
Royal Worcester Ltd. Executive Pension Plan (at London Address, Pension Fund Manager, A.M.V.Marshall)
RWIC Pension & Life Assurance Scheme (Worcester, Pension Fund Manager D.Rutter)
Welwyn Electric Ltd. See separate entry

	Executive	RWIC
Members	54	155
Pensioners	8	5
Annual Contributions	£200,000	£75,000
Capital Value (1979)	£759,000	-

W.R.ROYLE & SON LTD
Royle House, Wenlock Road, London N1 7ST
Telephone: 01-253 7654

Director E.V.Royle

Secretary R.T.Fleetham

Employees 631

RUBEROID LTD
1 New Oxford Street, London WC1A 1PE
Telephone: 01-405 8797

Secretary D.S.Morris,FCA

Insured with Legal & General Assurance Society Ltd

Employees 1,620

RUBERY OWEN GROUP STAFF PENSION SCHEME
Darlaston, PO Box 10, Wednesbury,
West Midlands WS10 8JD
Telephone: 021-526 3131

Pensions Secretary J.H.Whitehouse

Trustees Owen Organization Pensions Ltd

Investment Advisers Fraser Green Ltd., Phillips & Drew, Stock Beech & Co.

Actuaries Duncan C. Fraser & Co

Property Advisers Edwards, Bigwood & Bewlay

Auditors Coopers & Lybrand

Company Employees 6,576

Members 1,350

Pensioners 880

	£000
Annual Contributions	1,327
Annual Investment Income	1,297
Gross Annual Outflow	1,000
Capital Value Book Value	13,500
Market Value	15,200
Summary of Investments	
Equities	7,923
Fixed Interest	4,309
Property	1,008
Cash & Deposits	1,253
Others	503

HELENA RUBINSTEIN LTD PENSION PLAN
76 Oxford Street, London W1A 1EN
Telephone: 01-580 2030

Pension Fund Manager & Secretary P.J.Beazley

Trustees J.M.A.Barker, J.McLean, P.J.Pilzer, A.Nimmey

Part Managed by Legal & General (Pensions Management) Ltd.

Investment Advisers Kleinwort Benson Investment Management

Actuarial Advice Obtained through Cubie, Wood & Co.Ltd.

Pension Fund Consultants Noble Lowndes International Ltd.

Auditors Arthur Andersen & Co.

Company Employees 770

Members 570

Pensioners 30

Annual Contributions £216,000

see also Colgate-Palmolive

RUGBY PORTLAND CEMENT COMPANY LTD MONTHLY STAFF RETIREMENT BENEFIT SCHEME, HOURLY & WEEKLY STAFF RETIREMENT BENEFIT SCHEME AND SENIOR EXECUTIVES RETIREMENT BENEFIT SCHEME
Crown House, Rugby, Warks.CV21 2DT
Telephone: 0788-2111

Company Secretary D.Lindop

Administration Assistant Miss J.M.Scarratt

Managed by Prudential Pensions Ltd.

Stockbrokers Phillips & Drew

Actuaries Bacon & Woodrow

Auditors Leech Peirson Evans & Co.

Solicitors Slaughter & May

Company Employees 3,278

Members (3 schemes) 2,128

WALTER RUNCIMAN & CO LTD
52 Leadenhall Street, London EC3A 2BN
Telephone: 01-481 1461

Secretary F.Jobson

Employees 1,542

RUSH & TOMPKINS GROUP RETIREMENT BENEFITS SCHEME
Marlowe House, 109 Station Road, Sidcup, Kent
Telephone: 01-300 3338

Secretary P.G.Watson, FCIS

Trustees K.P.Rush, V.H.O'Brien, L.Andrews

Managed by Sun Life Pension Managers Ltd

Pension Fund Consultants R.D.& P.E.Sheppard

Auditors Deloitte, Haskins & Sells

Company Employees 2,173

Members 800

Pensioners 50

Annual Contributions £390,000

Capital Value £1,600,000

RUSSELL & BROMLEY LTD
24-34 Farwig Lane, Bromley, Kent
Telephone: 01-460 1122

Secretary A.R.G.Christie

Employees 1,050

RUST CRAFT GREETING CARDS (U.K.) LTD
Mill Street East, Dewsbury,
West Yorkshire WF12 9AW
Telephone: 0924-465200

Financial Director E.G.Siddons

Secretary J.S.Craven

Employees 619

RUSTON-BUCYRUS STAFF PENSION SCHEME AND WORKS PENSION SCHEME (1974)
Excavator Works, Lincoln LN6 7DJ
Telephone: 0522-25261

Pension Fund Manager G.N.Hill

Secretary I.McNish

RUSTON-BUCYRUS Continued

Trustees Lowndes Associated Pensions Ltd
Managed by Lowndes Associated Pensions Ltd (Trustees)
Investment Advisers Robert Fleming Investment Management Ltd, J.Henry Schroder Wagg & Co Ltd
Actuarial Advice Obtained through Cubie Wood & Co Ltd
Pension Fund Consultants Noble Lowndes & Partners Ltd
Auditors Price Waterhouse & Co.
Company Employees (at 6.4.79) 2,128

	Staff	Works
Members	638	1,183
Pensioners	116	198
Deferred Pensioners	82	1,156
	£000	£000
Annual Contributions	469	778
Annual Investment Income	239	229
Gross Annual Outflow	274	274
Capital Value	2,778	2,707
Summary of Investments		
Equities	180	-
Fixed Interest	2,355	2,668
Property Unit Trusts	273	-
Cash & Deposits	30	39

RYLAND VEHICLE GROUP LTD.

Ryland House, Ryland Street, Birmingham B16 8BT
Telephone: 021-455 7171

Secretary S.Roden

Employees 1,349

SAATCHI & SAATCHI COMPANY LTD. PENSION & ASSURANCE SCHEME

80 Charlotte Street, London W1A 1AQ
Telephone: 01-636 5060

Group Chief Accountant P.A.Richards,FCCA

Budget Controller Mrs.P.Cook

Managed by Legal & General (Pensions Management) Ltd.

Stockbrokers Phillips & Drew

Auditors Thomson McLintock & Co.

Company Employees 644

Members 220

Pensioners 3

Annual Contributions £207,000

Capital Value £1,326,000

SABRE INTERNATIONAL TEXTILES LTD

Windmill Road, Sunbury on Thames, Middlesex
Telephone: 76-86111

Secretary P.A.Williams,FCA

Employees 500

SAFEWAY RETIREMENT BENEFITS PLAN (1973)

Beddow Way, Aylesford, Nr Maidstone, Kent ME20 7AT
Telephone: 0622-77822

Pensions Administrator G.F.Norton

Secretary G.Hemsley - Lowndes Associated Pensions Ltd.

Trustees P.Benstead, D.M.Bristow, A.Graham, J.A.Wilson, Lowndes Associated Pensions Ltd.

Managed by Lowndes Associated Pensions Ltd

Investment Advisers Hill Samuel Investment Management Ltd

Actuarial Advice obtained through Cubie Wood & Co Ltd

Pension Fund Consultants Lowndes Associated Pensions Ltd.

Auditors Price Waterhouse & Co

Company Employees 8,939

Members 2,079

Pensioners 58

	£000
Annual Contributions	1,372
Annual Investment Income	545
Annual Outflow	66
Capital Value	7,553
Summary of Investments	
Equities	5,419
Fixed Interest	1,376
Property	715
Cash & Deposits	43

SAGA HOLIDAYS LTD.

Enbrook House, Sandgate, Folkestone, Kent CT20 3AX
Telephone: 0303-30311

Secretary P.C.de Haan

Employees 628

J. SAINSBURY PENSION & DEATH BENEFIT SCHEME

Stamford House, Stamford Street, London SE1 9LL
Telephone: 01-921 6649

Pensions Manager P.J.A.Fryer,BSc,MIPM

Secretary N.F.Matthews

Departmental Director Personnel R.A.Clark

Trustees J.Sainsbury Trustees Ltd

Investment Advisers Warburg Investment Management, Rowan Investment Management Services

Property Advisers Healey & Baker

Actuaries R.Watson & Sons

Auditors Clark Pixley

Company Employees 37,267

Members 20,000 Approx.

Pensioners 2,597

J. SAINSBURY Continued

	£000
Annual Contributions	10,326
Annual Investment Income	4,865
Annual Outflow	4,445
Capital Value	66,906

ST CUTHBERT'S CO-OPERATIVE ASSOCIATION LTD EMPLOYEES' SUPERANNUATION FUND

92 Fountainbridge, Edinburgh EH3 9QE
Telephone: 031-229 2424

Pension Fund Manager Ian Miller

Secretary Joseph H.Currie

Trustees G.R.Gay, R.Thomson, J.Durkin, D.Allan

Investment Advisers Baring Bros.& Co.Ltd.

Pension Fund Consultants & Actuarial Advice Obtained through Antony Gibbs Pension Services Ltd

Auditors R.W.Cessford,CA, W.K.Geddes,CA

Company Employees 1,751

Members 985

Pensioners 611

	£000
Annual Contributions	280
Annual Investment Income	225
Annual Outflow	410
Capital Value of Fund	2,980
Summary of Investments	
Equities	1,445
Fixed Interest	1,008
Property	414
Cash & Deposits	113

SAINT PIRAN LTD.

13 Hill Street, Berkeley Square, London W1X 8DS
Telephone: 01-629 8865

Secretary D.M.P.Burford

Employees 901

ST REGIS GROUP PENSION SCHEME

Bridge House, 10 Bridge Street, Cambridge CB2 1UE
Telephone: 0223-64445

Secretary Miss M.Park, APMI

Trustees 6 Management Trustees, 6 Employee Trustees

Investment Advisers Morgan Grenfell & Co Ltd

Actuaries Duncan C.Fraser & Co.

Auditors Cooper Adamson & Co

Company Employees 2,184

Members 1,833

Pensioners 390

	£000
Annual Contributions	*1,400
Annual Investment Income	879
Annual Outflow	363
Capital Value	10,340
Summary of Investments	
Equities	4,999
Fixed Interest	2,828
Property	1,150
Cash & Deposits	836
*Estimate	

SALE TILNEY & CO.LTD.

28 Queen Anne's Gate, London SW1H 9AB
Telephone: 01-222 1771

Secretary M.P.M.Ollard

Employees 728

CHRISTIAN SALVESEN LTD

50 East Fettes Avenue, Edinburgh EH4 1EQ
Telephone: 031-552 7101

Company Secretary M.W.Gow

Pension Fund Consultant Godwins Ltd

Employees 6,583

H. SAMUEL LTD

Hunters Road, Birmingham B19 1DS
Telephone: 021-554 3871

Secretary A.M.Dealey

Investment Advisers Hill Samuel Investment Management Ltd., N.M.Rothschild Asset Management Ltd.

Employees 4,477

SANACO PENSION FUND

c/o Smith & Nephew Associated Companies Ltd. 2 Temple Place, Victoria Embankment, London WC2R 3BP
Telephone: 01-836 7922

Secretary J.W.Marshall, A.Brown(Joint)

Trustees J.N.Hillman, A.Brown, P.A.Rooker

Stockbrokers Buckmaster & Moore

Actuaries G. Waugh,FFA and T.Young,FFA

Pension Fund Consultants Alexander Howden Insurance Brokers Ltd

Auditors Ernst & Whinney

Company Employees (at 29.12.79) 10,664

Members (at 30.9.79) 4,732

Pensioners 615

	£000
Annual Contributions	2,100
Annual Investment Income	900
Annual Outflow	500
Capital Value	15,900
Summary of Investments	
Equities	10,400
Fixed Interest	5,500

SANDELL PERKINS LTD

Cobtree House, Forstal Road, Aylesford, Maidstone, Kent ME20 7AG
Telephone: 0622-70111

Company Secretary A.L.Gurney

SANDELL PERKINS LTD Continued

Insured with Scottish Widows' Fund & Life Assurance society
Pension Fund Consultants Metropolitan Pensions Association Ltd
Company Employees 1,089
Members 163
Pensioners 14

	£000
Annual Contributions	119
Annual Investment Income	70
Annual Outflow	6
Capital Value	850
Summary of Investments	
Equities	600
Fixed Interest	200
Cash & Deposits	50

GEO.G.SANDEMAN SONS & CO.LTD.

37 Albert Embankment, London SE1 7UA
Telephone: 01-735 7971

Secretary R.I.Howard,FCA

Employees 740

SANDERSON KAYSER STAFF PENSION SCHEME AND WORKS PENSION SCHEME

P.O.Box 6, Newall Road, Sheffield, S.Yorks.S9 2SD
Telephone: 0742-44994

Secretary & Director H.Baron,FCA,FCIS

Trustees Sanderson Kayser Trustees Ltd.

Part Insured with Legal & General Assurance Society Ltd.

Investment Advisers Drayton Montagu Portfolio Management Ltd.

Actuaries Duncan C.Fraser & Co.

Auditors John Watson Sons & Wheatcroft

Employees 1,277

Members 612

Pensioners 343

	£000
Annual Contributions	74
Annual Investment Income	101
Annual Outflow	113
Capital Value	1,683
Summary of Investments	
Equities	837
Fixed Interest	469
Cash & Deposits	83
Others	62

SANDOZ PRODUCTS LTD. RETIREMENT BENEFIT PLAN

Calverley Lane, Horsforth, Leeds LS18 4RP
Telephone: 0532-584646

Secretary & Pensions Manager D.T.Kemp,FCIS, APMI

Stockbrokers Grieveson Grant & Co.

Actuaries Duncan C.Fraser & Co.

Auditors Everett Pinto & Co.

Company Employees 890

Members 660

Pensioners 125

	£000
Annual Contributions	550
Annual Investment Income	450
Annual Outflow	300
Capital Value	5,000
Summary of Investments	%
Equities	45
Fixed Interest	40
Property	15

SANDVIK (UK) LTD. PENSION & DISABILITY PLANS 1978

Manor Way, Halesowen, West Midlands B62 8QZ
Telephone: 021-550 4700

Secretary G.Wrangenberg

Assistant Company Secretary G.R.Neville

Managed by Standard Life Pension Funds Ltd.

Pension Fund Consultants Noble Lowndes & Partners Ltd.

Auditors Chalmers, Impey & Co.

Company Employees 2,572

Members 653

Pensioners 53

Annual Contributions £275,000

Capital Value £1,750,000

SANGAMO WESTON LTD PENSION FUND

580 Great Cambridge Road, Enfield, Middlesex EN1 3RX
Telephone: 01-366 1100

Company Secretary S.E.Cole,FCA

Group Personnel Manager B.W.Simmonds

Division Manager E.F.May

Personnel Officer G.J.Head

Insured with Standard Life Assurance Co., Eagle Star Insurance Co.Ltd.

Pension Fund Consultants C.T.Bowring & Layborn Ltd.

Auditors Arthur Young McClelland Moores & Co

Company Employees 2,119

Members 1,700

Pensioners 500

SANGERS GROUP LTD (THE)

Cinema House, 225 Oxford Street, London W1R 1AE
Telephone: 01-734 9751

Secretary K.G.Dibble

Insured with Sun Life Assurance Society Ltd

Employees 2,498

J H SANKEY & SON LTD RETIREMENT BENEFITS SCHEME

Station House, Harrow Road, Wembley, Middlesex HA9 6DB
Telephone: 01-902 8838

Finance Director & Group Secretary M.F.S.Broad, FCA

Assistant Group Secretary G.A.Yeomans, ACIS, AIARB

Investment Advisers J. Henry Schroder Wagg & Co Ltd

Actuaries Duncan C. Fraser & Co

Pension Fund Consultants Hogg Robinson (Benefit Consultants) Ltd

Auditors Garvin Cantor & Co.

Company Employees 2,293

Members 1,600

Pensioners 90

Annual Contributions £600,000

Capital Value £1,850,000

SAVE & PROSPER GROUP LTD 1953 STAFF PENSION & LIFE ASSURANCE SCHEME

4 Great St Helens, London EC3P 3EP
Telephone: 01-588 1717

Personnel Manager G.Davies

Investment Advisers Baring Brothers & Co Ltd

Actuaries Bacon & Woodrow

Auditors Ernst & Whinney

Company Employees 611

Members 626

Pensioners 48

Annual Contributions £732,000

Annual Investment Income £356,000

Capital Value £4,880,000

THE SAVOY HOTEL LTD

1 Savoy Hill, London WC2R 0BP
Telephone: 01-836 1533

Secretary F.C.Sawford

Insured with Legal & General Assurance Society Ltd., Scottish Widows' Fund & Life Assurance Society

Employees 3,490

SCAPA GROUP (UK COMPANIES) RETIREMENT BENEFITS SCHEME FOR WEEKLY CONTRACT EMPLOYEES AND PENSION FUND FOR SENIOR CONTRACT STAFF

52 Preston New Road, Blackburn, Lancs.BB2 6AH
Telephone: 0254-50123

Pensions & Insurance Officer R.Lofthouse

Pensions Officer J.R.Taylor

Trustees 5

Managed by Pensions Management (S.W.F.) Ltd

Pension Fund Consultants and Actuarial Advice Obtained through Martin Paterson Associates Ltd

Auditors Dearden Farrow

Company Employees 3,156

Members 1,353 and 221

Pensioners 540 and 76

Annual Contributions £320,000

There are also 3 other smaller schemes in the Group:
Senior Executives Retirement Benefits Scheme, 66 members
Bury & Masco (Holdings) Ltd. Pension Plan, Myrtle Grove, Waterfoot, Rossendale, Lancs. BB4 7JL Pension Fund Manager Mrs.J.M.Roberts, Members 180
Cooper & Co. (Birmingham) Ltd. Pension Scheme, (Rossendale), Members 60

SCHLEGEL (UK) LTD

Ring Road, Seacroft, Leeds, W.Yorks.LS14 1LY
Telephone: 0532-734891

Secretary B.Millgate

Employees 675

SCHOFIELDS (YORKSHIRE) LTD SUPERANNUATION FUND

The Headrow, Leeds LS1 6LS
Telephone: 0532-35235

Financial Director & Secretary J.Barritt

Trustees 8

Investment Advisers Royal Trust Co of Canada

Actuaries Duncan C. Fraser & Co

Auditors Coopers & Lybrand

Company Employees 1,400

Members 561

Pensioners 220

	£000
Annual Contributions	225
Annual Investment Income	136
Gross Annual Outflow	211
Capital Value	1,702
Summary of Investments	
Equities	681
Fixed Interest	629
Property Unit Trusts	268
Cash & Deposits	59
Others	65

GEORGE H.SCHOLES & CO.LTD. PENSION FUND

Wylex works, Wythenshawe, Manchester M22 4RA
Telephone: 061-998 5454

Secretary A.M.Mackenzie

Insured with Norwich Union Life Insurance Society

Pension Fund Consultants Sedgwick Employee Benefits Consultants Ltd.

Auditors Touche Ross & Co.

Company Employees 1,407

SCHOLL (UK) LTD

182-204 St. John Street, London EC1P 1DH
Telephone: 01-253 2030

SCHOLL (UK) LTD Continued

Secretary M.J.Green
Employees 1,789

SCHREIBER INDUSTRIES PENSION SCHEME

Edinburgh Way, Harlow, Essex CM20 2EQ
Telephone: 02796-26881

Secretary C.L.Lathan,FCA
Employees 2,478

SCHRODER WAGG RETIREMENT BENEFITS SCHEME

120 Cheapside, London EC2V 6DS
Telephone: 01-588 4000

Pensions Manager R.F.Thurgood,APMI
Secretary R.Badrock
Investment Advisers J.Henry Schroder Wagg & Co.Ltd.
Property Advisers Schroder Properties Ltd.
Actuaries Bacon & Woodrow
Auditors Deloitte Haskins & Sells
Solicitors Allen & Overy
Company Employees 975
Members 709
Pensioners 141
Annual Contributions £1,459,000
Annual Investment Income £805,000
Capital Value £11,762,000

SCM (UNITED KINGDOM) LTD

Kenrick Way, West Bromwich,
West Midlands B71 4JW
Telephone: 021-553 2331

Secretary R.Smith
Investment Advisers Barclays Bank Trust Co Ltd
Pension Fund Consultants Willis Faber (Midlands) Ltd.
Employees 792

SCOTCROS RETIREMENT BENEFITS SCHEME

3 Woodside Place, Glasgow G3 7QF
Telephone: 041-332 7166

Pension Fund Manager Ian C.Campbell
Secretary to the Trustees John Woods
Trustees I.C.Campbell, T.P.Wallace, N.A.Macleod, D.W.Biggart, Mrs. A.Binnie, W.McGregor
Insured with Scottish Widows' Fund & Life Assurance Society
Pension Fund Consultants Hogg Robinson (Benefit Consultants) Ltd
Auditors Deloitte, Haskins & Sells
Company Employees 700
Members 615
Pensioners 86
Annual Contributions £434,000

SCOTT & ROBERTSON LTD

Park Mill, Dundee DD1 9NA
Telephone: 0382-23100

Secretary D.Cunningham
Insured with Commercial Union Assurance Co Ltd
Employees 1,461

ANDREW SCOTT HOLDINGS LTD

The Grange, Margam, Port Talbot,
West Glamorgan
Telephone: 06396-4971

Secretary J.F.Reynish
Employees 1,035

DAVID SCOTT GROUP LTD.

Church Street, Irthlingborough, Northants.NN9 5SF
Telephone: 0933-650206

Secretary M.J.Chittock
Investment Advisers Hambros Investment Management Services Ltd.
Employees 850

JAMES SCOTT ENGINEERING GROUP LTD

80-110 Finnieston Street, Glasgow G3 8LA
Telephone: 041-221 3866

Secretary M.R.Hart
Employees 2,745

SCOTT WILSON KIRKPATRICK & PARTNERS

Scott House, Basing View, Basingstoke,
Hants.RG21 2JG
Telephone: 0256-61161

Partner G.M.J.Williams
Employees 900

SAI STAFF PENSION FUND & SAI PENSION FUND (1972)

Scottish Agricultural Industries Ltd.,
25 Ravelston Terrace, Edinburgh EH4 3ET
Telephone: 031-332 2481

Secretary I.A.Ross
Investment Advisers I.C.I. Investments Dept
Stockbrokers R.C.Greig
Actuaries R.Watson & Sons
Auditors Thomson McLintock & Co.
Company Employees 1,385
Members 1,385
Pensioners 778

	£000
Annual Contributions	1,441
Annual Investment Income	1,182
Annual Outflow	942
Capital Value	15,169
Summary of Investments	
Equities	8,626
Fixed Interest	3,229
Property	3,085
Cash & Deposits	329

SCOTTISH AMICABLE LIFE ASSURANCE SOCIETY RETIREMENT BENEFIT & LIFE ASSURANCE SCHEME

150 St. Vincent St., Glasgow G2 5NQ
Telephone: 041-221 8844

Assistant General Manager (service) K.J.Hurry, FIA, FPMI

Investment Manager W.G.Knox

Managed by Scottish Amicable Pensions Investments Ltd.

Auditors Arthur Young McClelland Moores & Co.

Company Employees 1,117

Capital Value £15,360,000

SCOTTISH & NEWCASTLE BREWERIES LTD. 1972 PENSION & LIFE ASSURANCE SCHEME AND STAFF PENSION & LIFE ASSURANCE SCHEMES

Abbey Brewery, 111 Holyrood Road, Edinburgh EH8 8YS
Telephone: 031-556 2591

Secretary F.D.Patterson,CBE,FCA

Pensions Manager Miss M.V.Wood

Staff Schemes Managed by Pensions Management (SWF) Ltd., Standard Life Pension Funds Ltd.

1972 Scheme Managed by J.Henry Schroder Wagg & Co. Ltd., Scottish Amicable Pensions

Investment Advisers N.M.Rothschild & Sons Ltd., J.Henry Schroder Wagg & Co.Ltd.

Pension Fund Consultants & Actuarial Advice Obtained through Metropolitan Pensions Association Ltd.

Auditors Scott Oswald & Co.

Company Employees 27,830

	1972 Scheme	Staff Schemes
Members	7,124	5,700
Pensioners	969	1,144
	£000	£000
Annual Contributions	1,900	4,600
Capital Value	8,600	39,400

SCOTTISH DEVELOPMENT AGENCY STAFF & LIFE ASSURANCE SCHEME

120 Bothwell Street, Glasgow G2 7JP
Telephone: 041-332 6582.

Chief Accountant W.A.Campbell

Managed by Pensions Management (SWF) Ltd.

Actuarial Advice Obtained through Cubie, Wood & Co.Ltd.

Pension Fund Consultants Scottish Pension Trustees Ltd.

Auditors Arthur Young McClelland Moores & Co.

Company Employees 700

Members 676

Pensioners 70

Annual Contributions £589,000

Capital Value £2,934,000

SCOTTISH, ENGLISH & EUROPEAN TEXTILES LTD

12 Hope Street, Charlotte Square, Edinburgh EH2 4DD
Telephone: 01-836 9261

Secretary W.R.L.Leigh

Employees 588

SCOTTISH EQUITABLE LIFE ASSURANCE SOCIETY

28 St.Andrew Square, Edinburgh EH2 1YF
Telephone: 031-556 9101

Pensions Manager D.A.Berridge,BSc,FFA

Employees 542

SCOTTISH FARM DAIRY FOODS LTD.

190 Helen Street, Glasgow G51 3HJ
Telephone: 041-445 4551

Director G.L.Wilson

Employees 1,000

SCOTTISH LAW ASSISTANTS' PENSION FUND

26 Drumsheugh Gardens, Edinburgh EH3 7YR
Telephone: 031-226 7411

Secretary R.B.Lauries,OBE,WS

Trustees R.K.Watson and others

Investment Advisers Edinburgh Fund Managers Ltd

Actuaries and Pension Fund Consultants A.R.H.Collins & Co.

Auditors Arthur Young McClelland Moores & Co

Members 323

Pensioners 241

	£000
Annual Contributions	135
Annual Investment Income	235
Annual Outflow	220
Capital Value	2,325
Summary of Investments	
Equities	875
Fixed Interest	1,300
Cash & Deposits	145

THE SCOTTISH LEGAL LIFE ASSURANCE SOCIETY

95 Bothwell Street, Glasgow G2 7HY
Telephone: 041-248 6251

Director J.M.Chalmers

Executive W.Paterson

Employees 930

SCOTTISH LIFE ASSURANCE COMPANY OFFICERS' RETIREMENT BENEFIT SCHEME

19 St. Andrew Square, Edinburgh EH2 1YE
Telephone: 031-225 2211

Pension Fund Manager A.P.Limb, FIA

Managed by Scottish Life Pensions Annuity Co.Ltd.

Company Employees 550

Pensioners 86

SCOTTISH LIFE ASSURANCE COMPANY Continued

	£000
Annual Contributions (1978)	680
Annual Outflow	270
Capital Value	4,687

Summary of Investments	%
Equities	37
Fixed Interest	54
Cash & Deposits	9

THE SCOTTISH PROVIDENT INSTITUTION
6 St. Andrew Square, Edinburgh EH2 2YA
Telephone: 031-556 9181

Company Secretary W.A.B.Scott, MA, FFA
Pensions Manager H.W.Gillon, FFA, FPMI
Employees 589

SCOTTISH ROAD SERVICES LTD.
Carron House, Town Centre, Cumbernauld, Glasgow G67 1HT
Telephone: 02367-37511

Secretary W.D.M.Leithead, CA
Employees 1,175

SCOTTISH SPECIAL HOUSING ASSOCIATION SUPERANNUATION FUND
15/21 Palmerston Place, Edinburgh EH12 5AJ
Telephone: 031-225 1281

Chief Finance Officer B.A.Gillard, IPFA
Secretary J.B.Fleming
Trustees Council of Management
Investment Advisers Royal Bank of Scotland Ltd.
Actuaries Government Actuary
Pension Fund Consultants Wood Mackenzie & Co.
Auditors Arthur Young McClelland Moores & Co
Company Employees 3,100
Members (at 31.3.80) 2,094
Pensioners 234

	£000
Annual Contributions	1,468
Annual Investment Income	848
Annual Outflow	797
Capital Value Market Value	10,715

Summary of Investments	
UK Equities	3,401
Overseas Equities	1,072
Fixed Interest	3,663
Property Unit Trusts	1,630
Cash & Deposits	731
Others	218

SCOTTISH TELEVISION LIMITED RETIREMENT BENEFITS SCHEME
Cowcaddens, Glasgow G2 3PR
Telephone: 041-332 9999

Pensions Administrator J.W.Baxter, APMI
Secretary L.J.M.Hynd, OBE

Trustees C.S.Waters (Chairman), J.W.Baxter, F.E.Morris, J.McLean, Miss E.Moriarty
Insured with Scottish Widows' Fund & Life Assurance Society
Pension Fund Consultants H.Clarkson (Scotland) Ltd
Auditors Deloitte Haskins & Sells
Company Employees 556
Members 513
Pensioners 47

SCOTTISH TRANSPORT GROUP STAFF PENSION FUND AND TRANSPORT OPERATIVES PENSION SCHEME
Carron House, 114/116 George Street, Edinburgh EH2 4LX
Telephone: 031 226-7491

Secretary & Group Pensions Officer J.M.Cowan, ACIS, APMI
Assistant Group Pensions Officer A.M.Denholme
Trustees Staff: I.S.Irwin, W.L.Sword, A.M.Newman, T.Marsden, R.McLeod; Operatives: I.S.Irwin, W.L.Sword, A.M.Newman, T.Marsden, N.J.D.Whittle
Investment Advisers The Royal Bank of Scotland Ltd
Actuary A.U.Lyburn
Employees 14,000

	Staff	Operatives
Members	1,907	4,290
Pensioners	733	43
	£000	£000
Annual Contributions	2,187	2,060
Annual Investment Income	745	444
Annual Outflow	836	232
Capital Value	12,949	8,470
Summary of Investments		
Equities	8,867	5,952
Fixed Interest	3,766	2,474
Cash & Deposits	316	44

SCOTTISH & UNIVERSAL INVESTMENTS LTD
4 Park Gardens, Glasgow G3 7YE
Telephone: 041 332-6081

Secretary A.D.Peebles
Insured with Legal & General Assurance Society Ltd
Pension Fund Consultant Godwins Ltd.
Employees 4,418

SCOTTISH WIDOWS' FUND AND LIFE ASSURANCE SOCIETY STAFF RETIREMENT BENEFITS SCHEME
15 Dalkeith Road, Edinburgh EH16 5XA
Telephone: 031-655 6000

Pensions Manager J.A.Cairns, FFA
Assistant General Manager A.Neill, MA MS FFA
Investment Manager D.C.Ritchie, FFA
Managed by Pensions Management (SWF) Ltd.

SCOTTISH WIDOWS' FUND AND LIFE ASSURANCE SOCIETY Continued

Company Employees 1,640
Members 1,400
Pensioners 200
Annual Contributions £2.1 million
Annual Outflow £0.7 million
Capital Value £15 million

SCOTTISH WORSTEDS & WOOLLENS LTD

Ladylaw Mills, Hawick, Roxboroughshire
Telephone: 0450-2241

Secretary D.Ballantyne
Employees 1,039

SEAFORTH MARITIME LTD PENSION & LIFE ASSURANCE SCHEME (1978)

30 Waterloo Quay, Aberdeen AB2 1BS
Telephone: 0224-573401

Group Personnel Manager J.D.Mullenger
Secretary Mrs.V.S.Griffin
Insured with Phoenix Assurance Co.Ltd.
Pension Fund Consultants Lyle Gibson & Co.Ltd.
Employees 849
Members 626
Pensioners 12

SEAGRAM DISTILLERS LTD

111-113 Renfrew Road, Paisley PA3 4DY
Telephone: 041-887 9131

Company Secretary J.B.Wark
Group Personnel Manager D.J.Godfrey
Trustees National Westminster Bank Ltd.
Investment Advisers Hill Samuel Investment Management Ltd
Pension Fund Consultants and Actuarial Advice Obtained through William M. Mercer Benefits Ltd.
Auditors Price Waterhouse & Co.
Employees 2,247

G. D. SEARLE & CO LTD (UK) PENSION FUND

Lane End Road, High Wycombe, Bucks HP12 4HI
Telephone: 0494-21124

Secretary J.Gardner,FCIS,APMI
Pensions Officer G.J.Britt
Trustees Chemical Bank Trustee Co.Ltd.
Investment Advisers Robert Fleming Investment Management Ltd
Pension Fund Consultants Metropolitan Pensions Association Ltd.
Auditors Arthur Andersen & Co.
Employees 1,294
Members (at 31.3.80) 800
Pensioners 170
Annual Contributions £802,000
Annual Investment Income £426,000

Capital Value £4,554,000
Each company in the group manages its own pension fund - some insured, some not

SEARS HOLDINGS LTD

40 Duke Street, London W1M 6AN
Telephone: 01-408 1180

Company Secretary D.J.R.Ward,FCA,ACCA
Group Pension Manager M.S.Kennish, APMI
Pensions Manager BSC Footwear R.E.Skinner,FPMI
Head of Pensions Dept., Bentley Engineering Group Miss J.F.Taylor
Total Group Employees 59,000

Each Company in the Group is responsible for its own pension Arrangements

There are 14 Insured schemes
Members 7,500
Annual Contributions £2.7 million

3 schemes are Self-administered
Members 18,000
Pensioners 6,000
Annual Contributions £4.3 million
Capital Value £25 million

SECOND CITY PROPERTIES LTD

Second City House, Oxford street, Bilston, West Midlands WV14 7DU
Telephone: 0902-43131

Secretary J.H.Bennett
Insured with Clerical, Medical, & General Life Assurance
Employees 503

SECURICOR GROUP LTD

24 Gillingham Street, London SW1V 1HZ
Telephone: 01-828 5611

Secretary D.O.Blanks
Insured with Norwich Union Life Insurance Society
Employees 23,573

SEDDON HOLDINGS LTD.

Coronation Building, Armitage Avenue, Lityle Hulton, Manchester
Telephone: 061-790 2223

Secretary A.J.Brown,BA
Employees 1,675

SEDDON DIESEL VEHICLES LTD SEDDON GROUP 1972 STAFF PENSION SCHEME & SCHEME FOR WORKS EMPLOYEES

Woodstock Factory, Oldham, Lancs OL2 6HP
Telephone: 061-624 6041

Secretary E.G.Caygill
Trustees S.Husband, W.A.Crombie, J.N.Davis
Managed by Reed Stenhouse Benefit Consultants Ltd.
Investment Advisers Ivory & Sime Ltd.
Actuaries Duncan C. Fraser & Co.

SEDDON DIESEL VEHICLES LTD *Continued*

Auditors Thomson McLintock & Co.
Company Employees 1,945
Members 1,600
Pensioners 130

SEDDON (STOKE) LTD.
55 Duke Street, Stoke on Trent, Staffs.ST4 3NN
Telephone: 0782-321511

Secretary R.S.Spooner
Employees 800

SEDGWICK GROUP LTD.
Sedgwick Forbes House, 33 Aldgate High Street, London EC3N 1AJ
Telephone: 01-377 3456

Secretary B.W.Burnett
Employees 4,346

SEISMOGRAPH SERVICE LTD
Holwood, Westerham Road, Keston, Kent
Telephone: 66-53355

Chairman E.D.Wilson
Investment Advisers Morgan Grenfell & Co Ltd
Employees 510

SELECTION TRUST LTD
Selection Trust Building, Masons Avenue, London EC2V 5BU
Telephone: 01-606 6000

Fund Secretary R.W.Macleod
Trustees Selection Pension Trustees Ltd.
Investment Advisers Kleinwort Benson Investment Management Ltd.
Actuary P.J.Shore, BSc, FFA
Pension Fund Consultants C.T.Bowring & Layborn Ltd.
Auditors Dearden Farrow
Company Employees 4,103
Members 500
Pensioners 200

SELINCOURT LTD. GROUP PENSION FUND
74/80 Camden Street, London NW1 0EL
Telephone: 01-387 3132

Pension Manager W.J.F.Benton
Secretary K.O.Goodchild
Employees 3,358

IRVINE SELLARS LTD
Sellar House, Lancelot Road, Wembley, Middx.HA0 2BJ
Telephone: 01-903 1466

Personnel Director I.Roberts
Employees 1,000

SENIOR ENGINEERING GROUP LTD STAFF AND WORKS PENSION SCHEMES
Senior House, 21 Derby Road, Watford, Herts.WD1 1LT
Telephone: 38411

Secretary F.H.Fermor, FCA, ATII
Pensions Manager M.Brewis
Insured with Prudential Assurance Co.Ltd., Crusader Insurance Co., Crown Life Group
Pension Fund Consultants Godwins Ltd
Auditors Arthur Andersen & Co.
Company Employees 3,523
Members Staff 800, Works 1,250
Pensioners Staff 120, Works 100

SERCK PENSION SCHEME
Serck House, 737 Warwick Road, Solihull, West Midlands B91 3DG
Telephone: 021-704 2511

Pension Fund Manager and Secretary D.F.Webb
Trustees J.M.Pinckard, R.H.Baird, I.T.W.Shearman, L.J.Ainsley, J.H.Gilbertson
Investment Advisers Robert Fleming Investment Management Ltd
Stockbrokers Smith, Keen Cutler
Property Advisers Grimley & Son
Actuaries Duncan C.Fraser & Co.
Auditors Price Waterhouse & Co
Company Employees 4,500
Members 3,800
Pensioners 390

	£000
Annual Contributions	2,500
Capital Value	12,300
Summary of Investments	
Equities	6,000
Fixed Interest	3,400
Property	1,900
Cash & Deposits	1,000

SERVISYSTEM LTD
92 Albert Street, Birmingham B5 5LN
Telephone: 021-643 8831

Company Secretary T.A.Halls
Pension Fund Consultants Hogg Robinson Benefit Consultants Ltd.
Employees 5,000

SEVALCO LTD (1971) PENSION & LIFE ASSURANCE SCHEME
Severn Road, Avonmouth, Bristol BS11 0YL
Telephone: 02752-2611

Company Secretary H.F.Gould
Assistant Secretary C.F.Northcott
Insured with Guardian Royal Exchange
Pension Fund Consultants Bain Dawes & Partners Ltd.
Auditors Price Waterhouse & Co.

SEVALCO LTD Continued

Company Employees 513
Members 501
Pensioners 93
Annual Contributions £350,000

SGB GROUP STAFF PENSION & FAMILY SECURITY SCHEME
23 Willow Lane, Mitcham, Surrey CR4 4TQ
Telephone: 01-640 3393

Director & Secretary R.D.Halsall

Trustees Sir Edgar Beck, N.L.Clifford-Jones, R.D.Halsall, APMI (Financial Director), Clive Beck

Investment Advisers Hill Samuel Investment Management Ltd

Actuarial Advice obtained through Cubie Wood & Co Ltd

Pension Fund Consultants Noble Lowndes & Partners Ltd

Auditors Rowley Pemberton Roberts & Co.

Company Employees 6,349
Members 2,212
Pensioners 250

	£000
Annual Contributions	1,800
Annual Investment Income	450
Annual Outflow	450
Capital Value	6,500
Summary of Investments (1979)	
Equities	3,094
Fixed Interest	406
Property	668
Cash & Deposits	60

SGS INSPECTION SERVICES LTD RETIREMENT BENEFITS PLAN (1976)
Orchard Lea, Winkfield, nr.Windsor, Berks.
Telephone: 03447-4111

Pension Fund Manager R.H.Peel

Secretary Mrs. S.Lockyer

Trustees & Administrators Lowndes Associated Pensions Ltd.

Insured with Crusader Insurance Co.Ltd. (Deposit Administration contract)

Actuarial Advice Obtained through Cubie, Wood & Co.Ltd.

Pension Fund Consultants Lowndes Associated Pensions Ltd.

Auditors Price Waterhouse & Co.

Company Employees 590
Members 356
Annual Contributions £183,000
Annual Investment Income £136,000
Annual Outflow £46,000

JOSEPH SHAKESPEARE & CO LTD
Cox's Lane, Old Hill, Warley,
West Midlands B64 5NX
Telephone: 0384-66151

Secretary W.J.R.Jones,FCCA

Employees 505

ALEXANDER SHAND (HOLDINGS) LTD PENSION & LIFE ASSURANCE PLAN
Normanhurst, Matlock, Derbyshire DE4 3AF
Telephone: 062983-4441

Secretary R.Gratton

Insured with Standard Life Assurance Co

Auditors Touche Ross & Co.

Employees 2,025
Members 280
Pensioners 20

SHANKS & MCEWAN LTD
22 Woodside Place, Glasgow G3 7QY
Telephone: 041-332 8834

Secretary A.J.N.Fowler

Insured with Scottish Widows' Fund & Life Assurance Society

Employees 1,189

SHAPLAND & PETTER LTD
Barnstable, Devon EX31 2AA
Telephone: 0271 72561

Secretary A.J.Gracie, MA, ACMA

Employees 550

SHARNA WEAR LTD.
Lumb Mill, Droylsden, Manchester M35 7LD
Telephone: 061-370 3467

Secretary J.H.Robinson

Employees 508

SHARPE & FISHER LTD
Gloucester Road, Cheltenham, Glos.GL51 8PT
Telephone: 0242-21477

Secretary J.N.Bays, FCA

Assistant Secretary M.G.Towey

Trustees K.J.Fisher, J.J.West, D.Mitton

Insured with Eagle Star Insurance Co.Ltd.

Pension Fund Consultants Willis Faber Champness Ltd.

Auditors Deloitte Haskins & Sells

Employees 678

W.N.SHARPE HOLDINGS LTD.
Bingley Road, Heaton, Bradford, W.Yorks.BD9 6SD
Telephone: 0274-41365

Secretary D.J.Snowden

Employees 656

SHAW CARPETS LTD
Dearne Mills, Darton, Barnsley, Yorks.S75 5NH
Telephone: 022678-3311

SHAW CARPETS LTD *Continued*

Secretary J.Scott
Managed by Standard Life Pension Funds Ltd.
Employees 844

FRANCIS SHAW & CO.LTD. STAFF PENSION FUND AND WORKS PENSION SCHEME

PO Box 12, Corbett Street, Ashton New Road, Manchester M11 4BB
Telephone: 061-223 1313

Secretary and Pension Manager A.Roberts, ACIS
Insured with Norwich Union Life Insurance Society
Pension Fund Consultants Estridge & Ropner Life and Pensions Services Ltd.
Company Employees 672
Members 217 (staff), 248 (works)
Pensioners 65 (staff)

SHEEPBRIDGE ENGINEERING LTD STAFF SUPERANNUATION FUND AND RETIREMENT & DEATH BENEFITS PLAN FOR HOURLY WORKERS

Sheepbridge Works, Chesterfield, Derbyshire S41 9QD
Telephone: 0246-450471

Secretary P.Howarth
Works Scheme Insured with Scottish Life Assurance Co.
Investment Advisers Rowan Investment Management Services
Actuaries Bacon & Woodrow
Pension Fund Consultants Willis Faber Advisory Services Ltd.
Auditors Thomson McLintock & Co.
Employees 5,391
Members Staff 950, Works 1,900
Pensioners Staff 112
Annual Contributions Staff £350,000, Works £150,000
Capital Value Staff £3,400,000

SHEERNESS STEEL CO LTD GROUP PENSION FUND

Sheerness, Kent ME12 1TH
Telephone: 07956-3333

Company Secretary M.J.Shirley,FCA
Investment Advisers Midland Bank Trust Co
Actuaries Bacon & Woodrow
Pension Fund Consultants Richards Longstaff (Pension & Trustee) Ltd.
Auditors Coopers & Lybrand
Company Employees 800
Members 780
Pensioners 6
Annual Contributions £650,000
Capital Value £1,200,000

THE SHEFFIELD INSULATING CO LTD

Hillsborough Works, Langsett Road, Sheffield, S.Yorks.S6 2LW
Telephone: 0742-349311

Director W.N.Adsetts
Employees 550

THE SHEFFIELD SMELTING CO.LTD.

Royds Mills, Windsor Street, Sheffield, S.Yorks.S4 7WD
Telephone: 0742-20966

Secretary S.F.Norton
Insured with Legal & General Assurance Society Ltd
Investment Advisers Warburg Investment Management Ltd
Employees 910

SHEFFIELD TWIST DRILL & STEEL CO LTD (THE) WORKS PENSION PLAN (1978) AND STAFF RETIREMENT BENEFITS PLAN

Summerfield Street, Sheffield, S.Yorks.S11 8HL
Telephone: 0742-78633

Secretary S.L.Elkington
Financial Controller G.W.D.Fox,ACMA
Investment Advisers Robert Fleming Investment Management Ltd, Hill Samuel Investment Management Ltd
Actuarial Advice Obtained through Cubie, Wood & Co.Ltd.
Pension Fund Consultants Noble Lowndes & Partners Ltd.
Auditors Finnie Ross Allfields
Company Employees 2,363

	Staff	Works
Members	624	1,170
Pensioners	47	85
	£000	£000
Annual Contributions	400	378
Annual Investment Income	127	75
Capital Value	1,288	779

SHELL CONTRIBUTORY PENSION FUND

Shell Centre, London SE1 7NA
Telephone: 01-934 6480

Secretary and Administrator W.M.C.Mackenzie
Assistant Secretary E.A.Risley,APMI
Investment Manager A.V.Hall,AIA,FSS,FPMI (01-934 6261)
Deputy Investment Manager G.C.Whaley
Head of Pensions Policy C.R.Hopkins,BA,FIA,APMI
Trustees Shell Pensions Trust Ltd.
Investment Advisers Shell International Petroleum Co Ltd
Property Advisers Hiller Parker May & Rowden
Actuaries Bacon & Woodrow
Auditors Price Waterhouse & Co

SHELL Continued

UK Employees 27,900
Members 26,500
Pensioners 15,700

	£ million
Annual Contributions	58
Annual Investment Income	61
Gross Annual Outflow	27
Capital Value (Book cost)	604
Summary of Investments	
Equities	177
Fixed Interest	258
Property	99
Cash & Deposits	70

SHEPHARD, HILL & CO LTD
Cedar House, Vine Lane, Hillingdon, Middx UB10 0BX
Telephone: 36471

Secretary B.C.Sharp

Employees 620

SHEPHERD BUILDING GROUP LTD PENSION FUND
Blue Bridge Lane, York YO1 4AS
Telephone: 0904-53040

Secretary W.James, LLB

Trustees The Shepherd Group Pension Trust Ltd.

Actuaries Duncan C.Fraser & Co.

Auditors Armitage & Norton

Employees 5,040

SHERWOOD MEDICAL INDUSTRIES LTD
London Road, County Oak, Crawley, Sussex RH10 2TA
Telephone: 0293-34501

Secretary J.P.Madley

Employees 567

SHETLAND REGIONAL COUNCIL
4 Market Street, Lerwick ZE1 0HB
Telephone: 0595-3535

Director Finance C.V.B.E.Ennis

SHILOH SPINNERS LTD.
Holden Fold, Royton, Oldham, Lancs.OL2 5ET
Telephone: 061-624 8161

Secretary L.Holland

Employees 847

C.SHIPPAM LTD.
East Walls, Chichester, West Sussex
Telephone: 0243-85191

Secretary F.H.Moore

Employees 687

SHOPFITTERS (LANCASHIRE) LTD
Oswaldtwistle, Accrington, Lancs.BB5 3ET
Telephone: 0254-31133

Secretary J.Lawson

Employees 546

SHORROCK SECURITY SYSTEMS LTD.
Shadsworth Road, Guide, Blackburn, Lancs.BB1 2PR
Telephone: 0254-63644

Director S.Shorrock

Employees 750

SHORT BROTHERS PENSION LTD.
Airport Road, Belfast BT3 9DZ
Telephone: 0232-58444

Pension Fund Manager H.A.Curran,BA

Secretary R.Milnes, ACIS, APMI

Investment Advisers J.Henry Schroder Wagg & Co.Ltd

Pension Fund Consultants Willis Faber Advisory Services Ltd.

Auditors Price Waterhouse & Co.

Company Employees 6,700

Members 6,400

Pensioners 2,400

SHROPSHIRE COUNTY COUNCIL SUPERANNUATION FUND
Shirehall Abbey, Foregate, Shrewsbury, Shropshire SY2 6ND
Telephone: 0743-222243

County Treasurer R.Renville,FCA,IPFA

Investment Advisers Baring Bros. & Co.Ltd.

Actuaries Duncan C.Fraser & Co.

Auditors District Auditor

Employees 14,200

Members (at 31.3.80) 5,900

Pensioners 1,500

Annual Contributions £4,831,000

Annual Investment Income £2,417,000

Capital Value £31,671,000

SIDLAW INDUSTRIES LTD
Meadow Place Buildings, Dundee DD1 9QN
Telephone: 0382-23161

Secretary C.M.Nichol

Manager Secretary's Dep. A.Brown,CA

Managed by Pensions Management (SWF) Ltd, Standard Life Pension Funds Ltd

Employees 3,013

SIEBE GORMAN HOLDINGS LTD
Leworth House, 14/16 Sheet Street, Windsor, Berks.SL4 1BG
Telephone: 95-55411

Secretary P.G.Lockley,FCIS

Insured with Scottish Amicable Life Assurance Society

Employees 2,704

SIEMENS LTD
Siemens House, Windmill Road,
Sunbury on Thames, Middx.TW16 7HS
Telephone: 76-85691

Secretary P.V.Lush

Employees 1,093

SIEMSSEN, HUNTER LTD. & SUBSIDIARIES RETIREMENT BENEFITS SCHEME
10 Snow Hill, London EC1A 2EB
Telephone: 01-236 1907

Finance Director & Secretary P.B.Clarke

Insured with Sun Life Assurance Society Ltd.

Pension Fund Consultants C.E.Heath Urquhart (Life & Pensions) Ltd.

Auditors Hill Vellacott

Employees 602

Members 169

Pensioners 10

Annual Contributions £139,000

SIGNODE LTD
9 Queensway, Fforestfach, Swansea SA5 4ED
Telephone: 0792-32811

Secretary J.N.Clement

Insured with Standard Life Assurance Co

Employees 561

SILCOCK & COLLING LTD
Essex House, Ripple Road, Barking, Essex
Telephone: 01-592 6666

Executive D.J.R.Ward

Employees 1,300

SILENT CHANNEL PRODUCTS LTD PENSION & LIFE ASSURANCE SCHEME
Ferrars Road, Huntingdon,
Cambridgeshire PE18 7HN
Telephone: 0480-52191

Company Secretary K.S.Chamberlain

Insured with Guardian Royal Exchange Group

Pension Fund Consultants Willis Faber Advisory Services Ltd

Company Employees 680

Members 112

Pensioners 49

Annual Contributions £37,500

SILENTNIGHT HOLDINGS LTD. STAFF RETIREMENT BENEFITS SCHEME
Wellhouse Road, Barnoldswick, Colne,
Lancashire BB8 6DR
Telephone: 0282-815888

Secretary R.A.Faulding, ACIS

Trustees T.Clarke, J.Clarke, A.Beattie

Insured with Scottish Widows' Fund & Life Assurance Society

Company Employees 2,900

Members 400

SILHOUETTE (LONDON) LTD
84 Baker Street, London W1M 2AU
Telephone: 01-486 2681

Secretary E.J.Edwards

Stockbrokers W.Greenwell & Co

Employees 1,785

SILVER LINE LTD
43 Fetter Lane, London EC4A 1BA
Telephone: 01-353 0262

Director R.G.Crawford

Employees 500

SIME DARBY PENSION SCHEME
52-54 Leadenhall Street, London EC3A 2AB
Telephone: 01-488 2444

Pension Fund Manager and Secretary C.R.Shilling

Investment Advisers Prudential Assurance Co. Ltd., Legal & General Assurance Society Ltd.

Stockbrokers James Capel & Co.

Pension Fund Consultants and Actuarial Advice Obtained through Wyatt Harris Graham Ltd.

Auditors Price Waterhouse & Co.

Company Employees Approx.500

Members 339

Pensioners 18

	£000
Annual Contributions	380
Annual Outflow	240
Capital Value	3,322
Summary of Investments	
Equities	1,188
Fixed Interest	1,094
Property	938
Cash & Deposits	100

SIMON ENGINEERING STAFF PENSION FUND AND WORKS PENSION FUND
PO Box 31, Cheadle Heath, Stockport,
Cheshire SK3 0RT
Telephone: 061-428 3600

Director of Pensions & Employee Benefits A.Royle, FPMI

Pensions Administration Manager R.Nichols,APMI

Investment Manager M.J.Bishop

Trustees Simon Engineering Pension Trust Ltd

Investment Advisers Lloyds Bank Ltd.

Stockbrokers Greene & Co., Kemp-Gee & Co., Rowe & Pitman

Property Advisers W.H.Robinson & Co.

Actuaries Duncan C.Fraser & Co.

Auditors Peat, Marwick, Mitchell & Co.

Company Employees 6,377

	Staff Fund	Works Fund
Members (at 5.4.80)	3,258	2,133
Pensioners	1,031	232

SIMON ENGINEERING Continued

	£000	£000
Annual Contributions	2,483	934
Annual Investment Income	2,545	194
Capital Value	29,578	2,688

SIMONS CONSTRUCTION GROUP PENSION SCHEME

401 Monks Road, Lincoln LN3 4NU
Telephone: 0522-32160

Secretary G.McIntyre, FCA

Trustees P.G.Hodgkinson, G.McIntyre, D.J.Mander

Insured with Royal Insurance Co. Ltd.

Auditors Prior & Palmer

Company Employees 1,100

Members 110

Pensioners 10

Annual Contributions £100,000

SIMPLEX-GE HOLDINGS LTD. STAFF PENSION & LIFE ASSURANCE SCHEME AND GENERAL PENSION & LIFE ASSURANCE SCHEME

PO Box 102, Ash Hall, Stoke on Trent, Staffs.ST2 9QD
Telephone: 0781-303505

Director J.D.Johnson

Benefits Manager R.E.Jacques,FPMI

Actuarial Advice Obtained through Cubie, Wood & Co.Ltd.

Pension Fund Consultants Noble Lowndes & Partners Ltd.

Auditors Peat, Marwick, Mitchell & Co.

Solicitors Slaughter & May

Company Employees 4,500

	Staff	General
Members	1,200	2,100
	£000	£000
Annual Contributions	1,000	1,000
Annual Investment Income	250	125
Capital Value	5,000	2,500

SIMPLICITY PATTERNS LTD

39-45 Tottenham Court Road, London W1P 9RD
Telephone: 01-580 7082

Director H.Cooper

Employees 768

S. SIMPSON LTD

92-100 Stoke Newington Road, London N16
Telephone: 01-254 1212

Secretary C.G.Campbell

Insured with Pearl Assurance Co Ltd

Employees 1,959

WILLIAM SINCLAIR HOLDINGS LTD.

Wybert on Park, Church Lane, Wyberton, Boston, Lincs.PE21 7AF
Telephone: 0205-65244

Secretary K.Dobson

Employees 674

SINDALL GROUP PENSION FUND

347 Cherry Hinton Road, Cambridge CB1 4DJ
Telephone: 0223 48091

Secretary C.L.Pratt

Other Pension Management M.L.Steele

Trustees Mrs.C.Ridgeon, D.J.Holmes, M.Grieve

Investment Advisers and Stockbrokers Fyshe Horton Finney & Co

Actuaries Duncan C. Fraser & Co

Auditors Spicer & Pegler

Company Employees 1,223

Members 163

Pensioners 14

	£000
Annual Contributions	119
Annual Investment Income	70
Gross Annual Outflow	6
Capital Value	850
Summary of Investments	
Equities	600
Fixed Interest	200
Cash & Deposits	50

THE SINGER CO (UK) LTD CLYDEBANK PENSION FUND

Clydebank Factory, Clydebank G81 2XS
Telephone: 041-352 2055

Pensions Manager J.A.C.Craig, APMI

Secretary C.A.Williams

Part Insured with Prudential Assurance Co.Ltd.

Investment Advisers Morgan Grenfell & Co Ltd

Actuaries Clay & Partners

Pension Fund Consultants Metropolitan Pensions Association Ltd.

Auditors Peat Marwick Mitchell & Co

Employees 5,856

Members 4,652

Pensioners 1,800

Annual Contributions £1,400,000

Capital Value £6,700,000

SINGLO GROUP LTD.

Empire House, 123 Kennington Road, London SE11 6SF
Telephone: 01-582 4030

Secretary R.B.Drummond

Employees 813

SIRDAR LTD STAFF RETIREMENT BENEFIT PLAN

Bective Mills, Alverthorpe, Wakefield, W.Yorks.WF2 9ND
Telephone: 0924-71501

Managing Director F.G.Lumb,FCA

Financial Director N.A.Harrison,FCA

Managed by Legal & General (Pensions Management) Ltd

Pension Fund Consultants Lowndes Associated Pensions Ltd.

Auditors Price Waterhouse & Co.

Company Employees 1,278

Members (at 16.6.80) 220

Pensioners 60

Annual Contributions £300,000

Annual Investment Income £100,000

Capital Value £1,000,000

THE 6CO STAFF PENSION FUND AND COBORN PENSION SCHEME

600 Wood Lane, London W12 7RL
Telephone: 01-743 2070

Group Pension Manager & Secretary W.G.Blanket

Trustees The 600 Group Pension Trustees Ltd, Coborn Pension Trustees Ltd.

Investment Advisers J. Henry Schroder Wagg & Co Ltd

Actuaries Bacon and Woodrow

Property Advisers Gerald Eve & Co

Auditors Peat, Marwick, Mitchell & Co.

Solicitors Simmons & Simmons

Company Employees 6,000

	600 Fund	Coborn Scheme
Members	1,450	1,500
Pensioners	750	45
	£000	£000
Annual Contributions	1,100	1,100
Annual Investment Income	1,500	108
Annual Outflow	910	150
Capital Value	18,541	1,825
Summary of Investments		
Equities	9,412	856
Fixed Interest	3,581	488
Property	1,970	-
Cash & Deposits	699	163
Unit Trusts	2,879	318

SKELMERSDALE DEVELOPMENT CORPORATION

Pennylands, Skelmersdale, Lancs.
Telephone: 0695-24242

Director A.J.E.Taylor

Employees 649

SKETCHLEY LTD STAFF SECURITY PLAN AND SENIOR MANAGEMENT PENSION SCHEME

PO Box 7, Rugby Road, Hinckley, Leicestershire LE10 2NE
Telephone: 0455-38133

Pensions Officer G.A.Odell

Secretary P.G.F.Lancaster, FCIS, FIAM, APMI

Investment Advisers Morgan Grenfell & Co Ltd

Actuaries Clay & Partners

Pension Fund Consultants Metropolitan Pensions Association Ltd.

Auditors Peat Marwick Mitchell & Co

Company Employees 5,753

Members Staff 602, Management 37

Pensioners Staff 281, Management 23

Annual Contributions £409,000

Capital Value £2,265,000

SKF (UK) LTD STAFF & WORKS RETIREMENT & DEATH BENEFITS PLAN

Sundon Park Road, Luton, Beds.LU3 3BL
Telephone: 0582-21244

Pensions Manager B.J.Woods, JP, ACIS

Secretary P.A.Champion

Insured with Standard Life Assurance Co

Company Employees 2,627

Members 2,500

Pensioners 1,600

THE SLAG REDUCTION STAFF PENSION SCHEME AND COMPANY PENSION SCHEME

Asphalt House, Palace Street, London SW1E 5HH
Telephone: 01-828 2741

Secretary R.C.de L.Walters

Trustees E.C.Prest, J.S.Prest, J.M.Boardman, W.Jones, J.A.Hanley

Investment Advisers and Stockbroker James Capel & Co

Actuaries R.Watson & Sons

Auditors Westcott Wilson

Company Employees 1,000 approx.

	Staff	Company
Members (at 31.12.79)	190	924
Pensioners	59	253
	£000	£000
Annual Contributions	344	432
Annual Investment Income	175	83
Annual Outflow	267	145
Capital Value	2,138	1,220
Summary of Investments		
Equities	1,319	596
Fixed Interest	716	449
Cash & Deposits	103	175

SLOUGH ESTATES (1957) PENSION SCHEME

234 Bath Road, Slough SL1 4EE
Telephone: 75-37171

Director/Secretary E.A.Brooks, ACCA

Trustees G.N.Mobbs,W.J.Mackenzie, J.C.Harding, E.A.Brooks

Managed by Prudential Pensions Ltd

Pension Fund Consultants Sedgwick Employee Benefits Consultants Ltd.

Auditors Cocke, Vellacott & Hill

Company Employees 228

Members 214

Pensioners 84

	£000
Annual Contributions	517
Capital Value	1,877
Summary of Investments	
Equities	760
Fixed Interest	650
Property	467

SMALL & CO (LOWESTOFT) LTD

Waveney Chambers, Lowestoft, Suffolk NR32 1BP
Telephone: 0502-2301

Secretary F.O.Hillman,FCIS

Investment Advisers Brown, Shipley & Co Ltd

Employees 625

R.SMALLSHAW (KNITWEAR) LTD.

Druid Street, Hinckley, Leics.LE10 1QG
Telephone: 0455-36736

Secretary M.W.Pope

Employees 603

J. SMART & CO (CONTRACTORS) LTD

28 Cramond Road South, Edinburgh EH4 6AB
Telephone: 031-336 2181

Secretary D.McIntyre, CA

Insured with Guardian Royal Exchange Assurance Group Ltd

Employees 728

JOHN SMEDLEY LTD

Lea Mills, Matlock, Derbyshire DE4 5AG
Telephone: 062984-571

Secretary D.A.Elliott

Employees 900

SMITH & NEPHEW ASSOCIATED COMPANIES

See Sanaco Pension Fund

SMITH ANDERSON & CO LTD

Fettykil Mills, Leslie, Glenrothes, Fife KY6 3AQ
Telephone: 0592-741521

Secretary G.M.Colman,CA

Employees 935

FREDERICK SMITH & CO

Anaconda Works, Tenax Road, Trafford Park, Manchester M17 1PH
Telephone: 061-872 4444

Director K.Bennett

Employees 600

G.T.SMITH & SONS LTD.

22 Market Place, Pontefract, Yorks.WF8 1AR
Telephone: 0977-3176

Secretary H.G.Smith

Employees 702

SMITH KLINE & FRENCH LABORATORIES LTD. PENSION FUND

Mundells, Welwyn Garden City, Herts AL7 1EY
Telephone: 96-25111

Pension Fund Manager D.C.Reeves,BA,FCA

Secretary P.G.House, FCA

Trustees Smith Kline & French Pension Trustees Ltd

Investment Advisers J. Henry Schroder Wagg & Co Ltd

Actuaries Clay & Partners

Property Advisers Strutt & Parker

Pension Fund Consultants Metropolitan Pensions Association Ltd

Auditors Peat Marwick Mitchell & Co

Company Employees 1,580

Members 1,430

Pensioners 131

	£000
Annual Contributions	1,037
Annual Investment Income	541
Annual Outflow	198
Capital Value	8,250
Summary of Investments	
Equities	3,571
Fixed Interest	2,408
Property	1,748
Cash & Deposits	523

SAML. SMITH OLD BREWERY (TADCASTER) LTD

The Old Brewery, Tadcaster, N.Yorks.LS24 9SB
Telephone: 0937-83225

Personnel Controller B.Askew

Secretary D.W.Thirkill

Employees 1,399

THE W.H.S. PENSION TRUST

c/o W.H.Smith & Sons (Holdings) Ltd.
Strand House, 10 New Fetter Lane,
London EC4A 1AD
Telephone: 01-353 0277

Pensions Director & Secretary J.Chapman

Trustees W.H.Smith Pension Trustees Ltd

Investment Advisers & Stockbrokers Cazenove & Co

THE W.H.S. PENSION TRUST Continued

Actuaries Bacon & Woodrow
Property Valuers Cluttons
Property Advisers Edward Erdman & Co
Pension Fund Consultants Bacon & Woodrow
Auditors Touche Ross & Co
Company Employees 22,337
Members 8,976
Pensioners 2,858

	£ Million
Annual Contributions	4.0
Annual Investment Income	5.7
Annual Outflow	2.7
Capital Value	70.0
Summary of Investments	
Equities	36.9
Fixed Interest	23.1
Property	8.0
Cash & Deposits	1.3

SMITHFIELD & ZWANENBERG GROUP LTD

2 Lindsey Street, London EC1A 9HN
Telephone: 01-488 3211

Secretary C.Hackworth

Employees 1,233

SMITHS FOOD GROUP PENSION PLAN FOR HOURLY AND WEEKLY PAID EMPLOYEES AND PENSION PLAN FOR MONTHLY PAID EMPLOYEES

111 Mortlake Road, Kew, Surrey
Telephone: 01-876 3414

Investment Advisers J.Henry Schroder Wagg & Co.Ltd.

Actuaries Hymans, Robertson & Co.

Auditors Price Waterhouse & Co.

Company Employees

	Hourly Paid	Weekly Paid
Members	1,189	482
Pensioners	249	24
	£000	£000
Annual Contributions	500	500
Capital Value	2,280	2,260

SMITHS INDUSTRIES PENSION SCHEME 1972

47 High Street, Rickmansworth, Herts.WD3 1TE
Telephone: 01-452 3333

Pension Manager & Secretary K.Melia
Investment Administration Manager G.M.Lloyd
Trustees S.I. Pension Trustees Ltd
Directors Sir Roy Sisson (Chairman), A.K.Hornsby, F.R.Hurn, W.A.Mallinson, G.F.Mortimer, R.Tulip
Stockbrokers Phillips & Drew, L. Messel & Co
Actuaries Bacon & Woodrow

Auditors Fryer Whitehill & Co.
Solicitors Sacker & Partners
Company Employees 17,164
Members (at 5.4.80) 11,530
Pensioners 3,476

	£000
Annual Contributions	5,660
Annual Investment Income	4,579
Gross Annual Outflow	3,816
Capital Value (Market Value)	63,417
Summary of Investments	
U.K.Equities	10,378
U.S.Equities	1,459
Fixed Interest	9,356
Property	32,635
Cash & Deposits	9,573
Others	16

SMURFIT UK PENSION FUND

Bridge Mills, Holland Street, Pendleton, Manchester

Head Office Beech Hill,Clonskeagh, Dublin 4 (Telephone: 696622)

Pension Fund Manager G.P.Langford, FPMI
Secretary W.N.J.Russell, FCA
Trustees Smurfit UK Pension Trustees Ltd.
Investment Advisers Morgan Grenfell & Co Ltd, Warburg Investment Management Ltd
Stockbrokers Rowe & Pitman, Phillips & Drew
Property Advisers Hassett & Associates Ltd.
Actuaries Duncan C. Fraser & Co
Pension Fund Consultants Smurfit Group Pension Trustees Ltd
Auditors Stokes Kennedy Crowley
Employees 4,730
Members 4,538
Pensioners 363

	£000
Annual Contributions	2,061
Annual Investment Income	890
Annual Outflow	596
Capital Value	10,088
Summary of Investments	
Equities	4,600
Fixed Interest	2,239
Property	1,936
Cash & Deposits	880
Others	432

SOBRANIE (HOLDINGS) LTD

Sobranie House, Chichester Road, London N6 9DJ
Telephone: 01-807 0141

Secretary E.A.Rochford,FCA
Employees 533

SOCIAL WORKERS PENSION FUND

93-95 Borough High Street, London SE1 1NL
Telephone: 01-403 0301

SOCIAL WORKERS Continued

Pensions Manager & Secretary R.K.Stroud,BA,APMI
Trustees SocPen Trustees Ltd.
Chairman R.S.Connelly, ACIS
Investment Advisers J. Henry Schroder Wagg & Co Ltd
Property Advisers Schroder Properties Ltd., Wilks Head & Eve
Actuaries R.Watson & Sons
Auditors Touche Ross & Co.
Solicitors Rowe & Maw

897 employers contribute to Fund
Members (30.9.79) 4,797
Pensioners 1,819
Deferred Pensioners 1,541

	£000
Annual Contributions	2,445
Annual Investment Income	2,422
Annual Outflow	1,905
Capital Value (Market Value)	34,037
Summary of Investments	%
UK Equities	45
Overseas Equities	4
Fixed Interest	35
Property	16

SOLICITORS' LAW STATIONERY SOCIETY LTD PENSION SCHEME
Oyez House, P O Box 55, 237 Long Lane, London SE1 4PU
Telephone: 01-407 8055

Group Executive (Personnel) P.Mallett
Secretary Pension Scheme J.Peake
Investment Advisers Britannia Fund Managers Ltd., Tower Fund Managers Ltd.
Actuarial Advice Obtained through Cubie, Wood & Co.Ltd.
Auditors Touche Ross & Co.
Solicitors Slaughter & May
Company Employees 1,566
Members 700
Pensioners 300
Annual Contributions £650,000
Annual Investment Income £450,000
Capital Value £5,700,000

THE SOLICITORS STAFF PENSION FUND
Baryta House, 29 Victoria Avenue, Southend-on-Sea, Essex SS2 6AF
Telephone: 0702-354024

Secretary J.D.Watkins, FCIS, FPMI
Committee of Management 13 members, E.J.Winterbotham (Chairman)
Trustees The Law Society

Solicitors Allen & Overy (Rules), Slaughter & May (Property)
Stockbrokers and Investment Advisers de Zoete & Bevan
Actuaries Bacon & Woodrow
Property Advisers Mellersh & Harding
Auditors Peat, Marwick, Mitchell & Co.
Members 2,068
Pensioners 1,387

	£000
Annual Contributions	939
Annual Investment Income	1,912
Gross Annual Outflow	918
Market Value	20,871
Summary of Investments	
Equities	9,276
Fixed Interest	5,382
Property	5,367
Cash & Deposits	595
Others	2

SOMERSET COUNTY COUNCIL SUPERANNUATION FUND
County Hall, Taunton, Somerset TA1 4DY
Telephone: 0823-3451

Treasurer B.M.Tanner, BA, IPFA
Trustees Somerset County Council
Investment Advisers Touche Remnant & Co.
Stockbrokers de Zoete & Bevan
Actuaries R.Watson & Sons
Auditors Thomson McLintock & Co.
Employees 7,000
Members 6,800
Pensioners 3,142

	£000
Annual Contributions	6,312
Annual Investment Income	3,486
Annual Outflow	4,459
Capital Value	38,389
Summary of Investments	
Equities	24,373
Fixed Interest	11,345
Property	759
Cash & Deposits	1,912

SONY (UK) LTD.
Pyrene House, Sunbury Cross, Sunbury-on-Thames, Middx.
Telephone: 76-87644

Secretary C.Beams
Employees 1,070

SOTHEBY PARKE BERNET & CO. PENSION SCHEME
34 New Bond Street, London W1A 2AA
Telephone: 01-493 8080

Director of Personnel D.K.Coombs
Trustees G.D.Llewellyn, R.P.T.Came, D.K.Coombs

SOTHEBY PARKE BERNET & CO. *Continued*

Actuaries Clay & Partners
Auditors Deloitte Haskins & Sells
Company Employees 890
Members 730
Pensioners 47

SOUTH CROFTY LTD (1978) PENSION SCHEME
Pool, Redruth, Cornwall RT15 3QH
Telephone: 0209-714821
Secretary W.D.Kneebone
Trustees 9
Insured with The Prudential Assurance Co.Ltd.
Pension Fund Consultants Metropolitan Pensions Association Ltd.
Company Employees 577
Members 456
Pensioners 9
Capital Value £386,000

SOUTH GLAMORGAN COUNTY COUNCIL SUPERANNUATION FUND
County Headquarters, Newport Road, Cardiff CF2 1XA
Telephone: 0222-499022
Treasurer R.G.Tettenborn, MA,IPFA
Trustees South Glamorgan County Council
Stockbrokers de Zoete & Bevan
Actuaries R. Watson & Sons
Auditors District Auditor
Members 8,500
Pensioners 3,565

	£000
Annual Contributions (to 31.3.80)	4,486
Annual Investment Income	3,064
Capital Value (Market Value)	34,471
Summary of Investments	
Equities	17,414
Fixed Interest	16,111
Property	63
Cash & Deposits	882

SOUTH OF SCOTLAND ELECTRICITY BOARD SUPERANNUATION SCHEME
Cathcart House, Spean Street, Glasgow G44 4BE
Telephone: 041-637 7177
Secretary T.Goodfellow, FCIS, APMI
Management Accountant (Investment & Borrowing) A.T.Roy, CA
Executive Officer (Superannuation) M.K.Higgins
Management Committee 5 Board's and 5 Contributors' Committee Members
Investment Advisers Lazard Bros & Co Ltd, The Royal Bank of Scotland Ltd Investment Department
Actuaries A.R.H. Collins & Co
Property Advisers Richard Ellis

Auditors Deloitte, Haskins & Sells
Company Employees 13,658
Members 12,127
Pensioners 3,273

	£000
Annual Contributions	13,728
Annual Investment Income	10,645
Annual Outflow	5,489
Capital Value	131,981
Summary of Investments	
Equities	48,390
Fixed Interest	49,285
Property	32,686
Others	1,620

THE SOUTH STAFFORDSHIRE WATERWORKS CO SUPERANNUATION FUND
50 Sheepcote Street, Birmingham B16 8AR
Telephone: 021-643 8131
Pension Fund Manager R.G.Clarke, APMI
Secretary I.E.Wallis,FCA,IPFA
Trustees 3 Directors
Investment Advisers Hill Samuel Investment Management Ltd
Actuaries Duncan C.Fraser & Co.
Auditors Binder Hamlyn & Co.
Solicitors Nabarro Nathanson & Co.
Company Employees 823
Members (at 31.3.80) 424
Pensioners 285

	£000
Annual Contributions	649
Annual Investment Income	336
Annual Outflow	284
Capital Value	5,451
Summary of Investments	
Equities	3,650
Fixed Interest	624
Cash & Deposits	25
Others	973

SOUTH YORKSHIRE COUNTY COUNCIL SUPERANNUATION FUND
Regent Street, Barnsley, South Yorks S70 2HG
Telephone: 0226-86141
Treasurer D.B.Chynoweth, BA, IPFA, AMBIM
Superannuation Officer L.Brooks, DPA, MLLGA, APMI
Investment Officer J.T.Smith,IPFA
Investment Advisers J.M.Corlett, L.G.Hall, G.Heywood, S.D.Hughes
Actuaries Duncan C. Fraser & Co
Property Advisers Edward Erdman & Co
Auditors District Audit
Members (at 31.3.80) 32,000
Pensioners 6,000

SOUTH YORKSHIRE COUNTY COUNCIL Continued

	£000
Annual Contributions (at 31.3.80)	23,400
Annual Investment Income	11,400
Gross Annual Outflow	8,650
Capital Value (Market Value)	127,700

Summary of Investments	%
Equities	51
Fixed Interest	37
Property	12

JAMES SOUTHALL & CO LTD
Crome Road, Norwich, Norfolk NR3 4RD
Telephone: 0603-43841

Secretary E.H.E.Cooper

Trustees J.L.Hanly, G.B.Menzies, D.J.H.White, A.G.Holmes

Insured with Norwich Union Life Insurance Society

Auditors Peat, Marwick, Mitchell & Co.

Employees 850

Members 70

Pensioners 34

Annual Contributions £83,000

SOUTHERN CONSTRUCTIONS (HOLDINGS) LTD.
204 London Road, Waterlooville, Hants.PO7 7AW
Telephone: 07014-4499

Secretary M.J.Stallard,ACCA

Investment Advisers Kleinwort Benson Investment Management Ltd.

Employees 568

SOUTHERN COUNTIES AGRICULTURAL TRADING SOCIETY LTD.
Northgate House, Staple Garden, Winchester, Hants.
Telephone: 0962-2311

Secretary Miss C.V.Bryant

Trustees J.R.Ward, E.D.Hodgkinson, R.W.Shepherd

Insured with Phoenix Assurance Co. Ltd.

Pension Fund Consultants Bowring Rose Ltd.

Auditors Appleby, English & Partners

Company Employees 620

Members 400

Pensioners 110

SOUTHERN NEWSPAPERS
45 Above Bar Street, Southampton, Hants.SO9 7BA
Telephone: 0703-34134

Secretary M.W.Stone,FCIS,FCCA

Employees 1,560

SOUTHERN TELEVISION LTD STAFF RETIREMENT SCHEME
Northam, Southampton, Hants.SO9 4YQ
Telephone: 0703-28582

Director of Finance F.W.Letch,FCA

Secretary D.R.Baker

Insured with Eagle Star Insurance Co Ltd

Employees 591

Members 480

Pensioners 32

SPAFAX LTD
Mill Lane, Box, Corsham, Wiltshire SN14 9PL
Telephone: 0225-742721

Director R.J.Adamson

Employees 500

SPANSET LTD
Stanley Estate, Stanley Road, Knutsford, Cheshire WA16 0DD
Telephone: 0565-52424

Director E.Ehnimb

Employees 500

G.W. SPARROW & SONS LTD
Lower Bristol Road, Bath, Avon BA2 9ET
Telephone: 0225-21201

Secretary M.D.Flatley,FCA

Insured with Legal & General Assurance Society Ltd

Employees 732

SPARTAN RUDHEUGH LTD
Spartan Works, St. Stephens Street, Birmingham B46 4RE
Telephone: 021-359 3115

Managing Director B.A.Nisbitt

Employees 529

SPEAR & JACKSON INTERNATIONAL LTD STAFF PENSION & LIFE ASSURANCE SCHEME
Aetna Works, Savile Street East, Sheffield, S.Yorks.S4 7UR
Telephone: 0742-77471

Administration Office Millbrook, Guildford, Surrey GU1 3YB (Telephone: 0483-35131)

Secretary B.H.Jackson

Company Secretary J.L.Palmer

Insured with Equity & Law Life Assurance Society Ltd.

Property Advisers Fuller Peiser

Pension Fund Consultants Metropolitan Pensions Association Ltd.

Auditors Coopers & Lybrand

Company Employees 1,794

Members 600

Pensioners 400

Annual Contributions £210,000

J.W. SPEAR & SONS LTD (1967) PENSION SCHEME
Green Street, Enfield, Middx.EN3 7SF
Telephone: 01-366 0261

Secretary J.W.B.Estall

J.W. SPEAR & SONS LTD Continued

Other Pension Management W.J.Hall

Trustees J.W.B.Estall, F.A.Spear, J.Rubens

Insured with Prudential Assurance Co Ltd

Pension Fund Consultants Superannuation Advisory Services Ltd.

Company Employees 636

Members 68

Pensioners 8

SPEEDO (EUROPE) LTD

Ascot Works, Ascot Road, Nottingham NG8 5AJ
Telephone: 0602-296131

Director E.P.Tew

Employees 500

SPENCE, BRYSON & CO LTD

41 Great Victoria Street, Belfast BT2 7AJ
Telephone: 0232-26464

Chairman J.B.Bryson

Employees 1,000

GEORGE SPENCER LTD

Wimborne House, Bar Lane, Basford,
Nottingham NG6 0HZ
Telephone: 0602-789484

Secretary G.R.Norwood, FCA

Insured with Equity & Law Life Assurance Society Ltd

Employees 1,194

SPERRY LTD. PENSION PLAN

Sperry House, 78 Portsmouth Road, Cobham,
Surrey KT11 1JZ
Telephone: 0936-7333

Pension Fund Manager Miss D.G.Powell, APMI

Secretary R.Mantel,FCA,APMI

Trustees Sperry Rand Trustees Limited

Part Managed by Prudential Pensions Ltd.

Investment Advisers Robert Fleming Investment Management Ltd, Morgan Grenfell & Co Ltd, Prudential Pensions Ltd

Actuarial Advice Obtained through Wyatt Harris Graham Ltd. (R.Machin,FIA,ASA,FPMI)

Pension Fund Consultants Wyatt Harris Graham Ltd.

Auditors Arthur Young McClelland Moores & Co

Company Employees 8,023

Members 5,745

Pensioners 578

	£000
Annual Contributions (to 31.3.80)	2,252
Annual Investment Income	1,060
Gross Annual Outflow	731
Capital Value	17,143
Summary of Investments	
Equities	4,588
Fixed Interest	2,463
Cash & Deposits	4,007
Others	400
Insurance Policies	2,688

SPICER & PEGLER PENSION PLAN

St. Mary Axe House, 56-60 St. Mary Axe,
London EC3A 8BJ
Telephone: 01-283 3070

Secretary M.H.Waller

Company Employees 1,100

SPILLERS SUPERANNUATION FUND (1952)

New Malden House, 1 Blagdon Road, New Malden,
Surrey KT3 4TB
Telephone: 01-248 5700

Pensions Manager R.J.Emsden,APMI

Secretary F.H.V.Beazley

Assistant Group Pensions Manager G.W.Macrow, APMI

Trustees Spillers Trustees Ltd

Investment Advisers John Govett & Co.Ltd.

Actuary R.W.A.Fowler,FIA

Property Advisers David C. Hunter & Co

Auditors Touche Ross & Co.

Company Employees 18,356

Members (at 31.12.79) 5,068

Pensioners 2,146

	£000
Annual Contributions	2,736
Annual Investment Income	3,676
Gross Annual Outflow	2,640
Capital Value	
Book Value	37,561
Market Value	42,242
Summary of Investments	
Equities	17,625
Fixed Interest	13,500
Property	10,403
Cash & Deposits	1,950
Others	(1,236)

SPIRAX-SARCO ENGINEERING LTD

Charlton House, Cheltenham,
Gloucestershire GL53 8ER
Telephone: 0242-21361

Secretary S.J.Harris,FCA

Stockbrokers Phillips & Drew

Employees 1,795

SPOONERS (HULL) LTD

Glebe Road, Stoneferry, Hull
Telephone: 0482-43221

Secretary J.P.Spooner

Employees 714

SPUN GLASS LTD

Westbury, Sherborne, Dorset DT9 3RB
Telephone: 093581-3722

SPUN GLASS LTD Continued

Secretary D.G.Hutchinson

Employees 543

SQUARE D LTD

Windsor House, High Street, Esher, Surrey
Telephone: 78-67021

Secretary A.H.Beddoes

Insured with Scottish Widows' Fund & Life Assurance Society

Employees 1,093

E.R. SQUIBB & SONS LTD 1965 PENSION & LIFE ASSURANCE SCHEME

Squibb House, Staines Road, Hounslow, Middx. TW3 3JB
Telephone: 01-572 7422

Secretary A.T.Nadal

Administrative Director & Company Secretary C.O.J.Miller

Investment Advisers Morgan Grenfell Trustee Services Ltd

Actuaries Bacon & Woodrow

Auditors Peat Marwick Mitchell & Co

Company Employees 1,250

Members 960

Pensioners 38

Annual Contributions £650,000

Annual Investment Income £345,000

Capital Value £3,512,000

STADIUM LTD RETIREMENT BENEFITS PLAN (1974)

36 Queensway, Enfield, Middlesex EN3 4SD
Telephone: 01-804 4343

Director/Secretary A.J.Hinds, CA

Other Pension Management Miss E.Wells

Trustees A.E.Wiseman, A.J.Hinds, Miss D.M.Turner

Investment Advisers Legal and General Assurance Society Ltd

Actuarial Advice Obtained through Cubie, Wood & Co.Ltd.

Pension Fund Consultants Noble Lowndes & Partners Ltd.

Auditors Peat, Marwick, Mitchell & Co.

Company Employees 800

Members 325

Pensioners 20

	£000
Annual Contributions	175
Annual Outflow	55
Capital Value	1,000
Summary of Investments	
Equities	300
Fixed Interest	250
Property	450

STAFFORDSHIRE BUILDING SOCIETY

PO Box 66, 84 Salop Street, Wolverhampton WV3 0SA
Telephone: 0902-772611

Personnel & Training Manager C.L.Williams, ACIS, MIPM

STAFFORDSHIRE COUNTY COUNCIL SUPERANNUATION FUND

County Buildings, Eastgate Street, Stafford ST16 2LH
Telephone: 0785-3121

Treasurer G.Woodcock, FCA, IPFA

Investment Advisers Hill Samuel Investment Management Ltd.

Property Adviser C.W.Jonas, FRICS

Actuaries Robertson, Hymans & Co.

Auditors District Auditor

Members (at 31.3.80) 16,250

Pensioners 5,000

Annual Contributions £7,044,000

Annual Investment Income £12,789,000

Capital Value £84,000,000

STAFFORDSHIRE POTTERIES (HOLDINGS) LTD. RETIREMENT BENEFITS PLAN (1975)

Meir Park, Stoke-on-Trent ST3 7AA
Telephone: 0782-315251

Secretary G.H.Cashmore

Trustees C.W.Bowers, E.C.Bowers, G.T.Basnett

Managed by English Insurance (Pensions Management) Ltd

Pension Fund Consultants Noble Lowndes & Partners Ltd

Employees 1,526

STAG FURNITURE HOLDINGS LTD

Haydn Road, Nottingham NG5 1DU
Telephone: 0602-605007

Secretary I.C.McKenzie, FCA

Investment Advisers Hill Samuel Investment Management Ltd

Employees 1,678

THE REO STAKIS ORGANISATION RETIREMENT BENEFITS SCHEME

443 Parliamentary Road, Glasgow G4 0AE
Telephone: 041-332 9711

Secretary A.Lang, CA

Trustees R.Stakis, J.F.Loughray, A.Lang

Managed by Standard Life Pension Funds Ltd

Pension Fund Consultants Metropolitan Pensions Association Ltd

Company Employees 4,000

Members 340

Pensioners 7

Annual Contributions £275,000

Capital Value £800,000

STANDARD BRANDS LTD
Feature Road, Thurmaston, Leicester
Telephone: 051-525 5107

Chairman A.R.Pendry

Insured with Legal & General Assurance Society Ltd

Employees 1,130

STANDARD CHARTERED BANK FUND & CHARTERED BANK PENSION FUND
10 Clements Lane, London EC4N 7AB
Telephone: 01-623 7500

Investment Manager W.Agate

Company Secretary L.R.Bishop

Deputy Manager B.J.Royal

Pensions Manager S.P.West, APMI

Investment Management Standard Chartered Bank Investment Dept

Employees 6,179

STANDARD FIREWORKS LTD
Standard House, Half Moon Street, Huddersfield, W.Yorks. HD12JH
Telephone: 0484-31538

Secretary M.Howlett, ACIS

Employees 589

STANDARD INDUSTRIAL GROUP LTD.
Shelley House, 3 Noble Street, London EC2V 7DL
Telephone: 01-628 5641

Secretary A.M.Harvey

Employees 637

STANDARD LIFE ASSURANCE COMPANY STAFF PENSION FUND
3 George Street, Edinburgh EH2 2XZ
Telephone: 031-225 7971

Asst. General Manager & Pensions Manager A.U.Lyburn, MA FFA

Secretary G.C.Philip, FFA

Trustees 4 Directors and 3 Members of Staff

Managed by Standard Life Pension Funds Ltd.

Auditors Thomson McLintock & Co

Company Employees 1,978

Members 2,456

Pensioners 239

	£000
Annual Contributions	1,976
Gross Annual Outflow	707
Capital Value	22,585
Summary of Investments	
Pooled Mixed Fund	17,392
Pooled Property Fund	5,193

STANDARD TELEPHONES AND CABLES LTD ITT (UK) PENSION PLANS
STC House, 190 Strand, London WC2R 1DU
Telephone: 01-836 8055

Pension Fund Manager and Acting Secretary P.A.Baker, CA

Investment Advisers Midland Bank Trust Co Ltd

Actuaries R.Watson & Sons

Pension Fund Consultants Metropolitan Pensions Association Ltd

Auditors Arthur Andersen & Co

Company Employees 32,000

Members 22,400

Pensioners 7,600

Annual Contributions £14.5 million

Annual Investment Income £7.9 million

Annual Outflow £6.9 million

Capital Value £88.3 million

A.G. STANLEY HOLDINGS LTD
Stanley House, Cray Avenue, Orpington, Kent BR5 3PW
Telephone: 66-71521

Secretary D.K.Brown

Insured with Legal & General Assurance Society Ltd

Employees 1,484

STANLEY (U.K.) PENSION & LIFE INSURANCE PLANS
Woodside, Sheffield, S.Yorks. S3 9DD
Telephone: 0742-78678

Pension Management D.G.Burton

Trustees S.H.Davies, J.M.Cross, J.S.Drinkhall

Managed by Reed Stenhouse Pension Services Ltd.

Investment Advisers Ivory & Sime Ltd.

Actuaries Duncan C. Fraser & Co.

Company Employees 2,146

Members 1,334

Pensioners 301

	£000
Annual Contributions	830
Annual Investment Income	168
Annual Outflow	281
Capital Value	3,695
Summary of Investments	
Equities	3,370
Fixed Interest	281
Cash & Deposits	44

STAPLES PRINTERS PENSION TRUSTEES LTD
94 Wigmore Street, London W1H 08R
Telephone: 01-935 0665

Pension Administrator F.W.Pitt

Secretary H.M.Whalley

Company Employees 778

STAR GROUP OF COMPANIES
Cavendish House, The Headrow, Leeds 1 W.Yorks.
Telephone: 0532-38561

STAR GROUP OF COMPANIES Continued

Secretary F.G.Cox

Employees 1,811

STAR PAPER CO LTD
Feniscowles, Blackburn, Lancs.BB2 5HX
Telephone: 0254-22011

Secretary F.W.Ormerod

Insured with Standard Life Assurance Co.Ltd.

Employees 1,418

STATES OF JERSEY PUBLIC EMPLOYEE CONTRIBUTORY RETIREMENT SCHEME (AND OTHERS)
States Treasury, 31 Broad Street, St Helier, Jersey
Telephone: 0534-25521

States Treasurer J.Clennett, FCA, ACMA

Deputy Treasurer R.Lee,BA,IPFA

Management Services Officer B.P.Le Geyt

Investment Advisers Hambros Investment Management Services Ltd., Le Mesurier James & Chinn

Actuaries Bacon & Woodrow

Auditors Turquand Barton Mayhew

Employees 5,704

Members 3,725

Pensioners 815

Annual Contributions £3,518,000

Annual Investment Income £2,323,000

Capital Value £25,918,000

STATUS DISCOUNT LTD
375 Anlaby Road, Hull, N.Humberside HU3 6AB
Telephone: 0482-562141

Secretary D.A.Dawson

Insured with Legal & General Assurance Society Ltd

Employees 565

STAVELEY INDUSTRIES LTD RETIREMENT BENEFITS SCHEME (1978)
Portland House, Stag Place, London SW1E 5RU
Telephone: 01-828 6311

Pension Fund Manager and Secretary R.Shaw, APMI

Trustees 6 Company appointed, 5 Member appointed

Part Managed by Equity & Law (Managed Funds) Ltd

Investment Advisers Hill Samuel Investment Management Ltd.

Pension Fund Consultants Willis Faber Advisory Services Ltd.

Auditors Coopers & Lybrand

Company Employees 7,340

Members 4,000

Pensioners 880

	£000
Annual Contributions	2,900
Annual Outflow	1,073
Capital Value	10,445
Summary of Investments	
Equities	3,017
Fixed Interest	871
Property	347
Cash & Deposits	444
Managed Fund Units	5,766

STAVERTON CONTRACTING GROUP LIMITED
Staverton, Totnes, Devon
Telephone: 0803-863663

Secretary D.A.Bignold

Employees 850

STEAD & SIMPSON LTD
Fosse Way, Syston, Leicester LE7 8PG
Telephone: 053723-5981

Secretary S.J.Harvey

Insured with Prudential Assurance Co Ltd

Employees 1,853

STEECHAN LTD
Ferrars Road, Huntingdon,
Cambridgeshire PE18 7HN

Chairman K.Beaton

Employees 868

STEEL BROTHERS SUPERANNUATION FUND
Sondes Place, Dorking, Surrey RH4 3EF
Telephone: 0306-5901

Secretary C.A.Prudden,FCIS

Trustees J.T.Wishart, A.P.F.Malcolm, A.M.French, D.E.W.Thomas, C.A.Prudden

Stockbrokers W.Greenwell & Co

Actuaries Lane, Clark & Peacock

Auditors Deloitte Haskins & Sells

Company Employees 777

Members 278

Pensioners 165

	£000
Annual Contributions	185
Annual Investment Income	492
Gross Annual Outflow	307
Capital Value (Market Value)	4,907
Summary of Investments	
Equities	2,304
Fixed Interest	2,480
Cash & Deposits	84
Others	39

W. STEEL & CO LTD
Palmers Road, Roman Road, London E2 0SG
Telephone: 01-980 4848

Director L.G.Hall

Employees 500

THE STEETLEY COMPANY LTD.

PO Box 6, Gateford Hill, Worksop, Notts.S81 8AF
Telephone: 0909-474551

Pensions & Insurance Manager R.Hardstaff

Assistant to Company Secretary J.A.Bower, ACII, APMI

Company Secretary J.D.Ridley, FCIS

Company Employees 3,997

STEINBERG GROUP LTD

Steinberg House, Kiln Farm, Milton Keynes, Bucks.MK11 3EE
Telephone: 0908-565758

Secretary R.C.Barklett

Insured with Legal & General Assurance Society Ltd

Employees 2,532

STEINER PRODUCTS LTD

Cottrell Cottages, The Broadway, Stanmore, Middx
Telephone: 01-954 6121

Secretary I.W.Wisely

Employees 740

STENHOUSE INSURANCE DIVISION PENSION SCHEME & VOLUNTARY EQUITY SCHEME

145 St. Vincent Street, Glasgow G2 5NX
Telephone: 041-248 5070

Secretary W.M.Docherty

Trustees Reed Stenhouse Benefit Consultants Ltd.

Investment Advisers Ivory & Sime, Reed Stenhouse Benefit Consultants Ltd.

Actuaries Duncan C. Fraser & Co

Pension Fund Consultants Reed Stenhouse Benefit Consultants Ltd.

Auditors Adam Ker & Sangster

Group Employees 4,268

Members 1,100

Pensioners 125

	£000
Annual Contributions	700
Annual Investment Income	300
Gross Annual Outflow	400
Capital Value	6,000
Summary of Investments	
Equities	75%
Fixed Interest	16%
Property	5%
Cash & Deposits	4%

GROVEHILL,

Grove Hill, Beverley, North Humberside
Telephone: 0482-885173

Secretary A.Abrahamson

Employees 593

STERLING-WINTHROP GROUP PENSION FUND AND IZAL GROUP PENSION FUND

Sterling-Winthrop House, Surbiton-upon-Thames, Surrey KT6 4PH
Telephone: 01-399 5252

Pensions Controller L.C.Williams, APMI

Trustees Sterling Group Pension Trustees Ltd

Directors E.E.Barber, R.Brown, H.R.Burrell, H.G.C.Carter, Lord Porritt

Investment Advisers Warburg Investment Management Ltd

Actuarial Advice obtained through Cubie, Wood & Co.

Auditors Price Waterhouse & Co.

Solicitors Slaughter & May

Company Employees 4,000

	SWG	IZAL
Members (at 5.4.80)	2,568	636
Pensioners	326	83
	£000	£000
Annual Contributions	1,760	277
Annual Investment Income	808	138
Annual Outflow	532	113
Capital Value	9,651	1,641
Summary of Investments		
Equities	4,231	669
Fixed Interest	4,212	802
Cash & Deposits	1,027	128
Others	181	42

STEVIN CONSTRUCTION (U.K.) LTD

Stevin House, Springwell Road, Springwell, Gateshead, Tyne & Wear NE9 7SP
Telephone: 0632-462011

Secretary K.A.Anderson

Employees 539

WILLIAM STEWARD GROUP

Nash Works, 75 Agincourt Road, London NW3
Telephone: 01-267 1151

Director M.A.Sothers

Employees 1,000

JAMES STEWART & SONS LTD

3 Brunswick Street, Manchester M13 9TT
Telephone: 061-273 2292

Secretary D.Stewart

Insured with Scottish Widows' Fund & Life Assurance Society

Employees 1,095

STEWART PLASTICS LTD

Canford Works, Purley Way, Croydon, Surrey CR9 4HS
Telephone: 01-686 2231

Secretary E.C.Gray

STEWART PLASTICS LTD *Continued*

Insured with Eagle Star Insurance Co Ltd

Employees 595

STEWART WRIGHTSON PENSION FUND
1 Camomile Street, London EC3A 7HJ
Telephone: 01-623 7511

Pension Administrator H.J.Burfitt

Secretary J.R.Sicely

Trustees I.G.B.Wardle, D.P.Tayler, B.V.Hitchcock, C.J.Gysin, W.Tresadern

Part Insured with Standard Life Assurance Co.

Part Managed by Standard Life Management Co.

Investment Advisers Warburg Investment Management Ltd.

Actuary G.N.Woolfenden

Pension Fund Consultants Stewart Wrightson Assurance Consultants Ltd.

Auditors Ernst & Whinney

Company Employees 2,400

Members 2,200

Pensioners 300

	£000
Annual Contributions	2,600
Annual Investment Income	2,200
Annual Outflow	600
Capital Value	12,600
Summary of Investments	
Equities	6,517
Fixed Interest	4,187
Property	1,448
Cash & Deposits	468
Others	44

STIRLING KNITTING GROUP LTD
Stakehill Lane, Bentley Avenue, Middleton, Manchester M24 2RY
Telephone: 061-643 9211

Secretary W.Lachs

Employees 1,048

STIRLING'S (GLASGOW) LTD
28-34 Argyle Street, Glasgow G2 8AU
Telephone: 041-248 2626

Secretary M.A.Robinson

Employees 787

THE STOCK EXCHANGE
London EC2N 1HP
Telephone: 01-588 2355

Secretary to the Council N.S.M.Kemp

Employees 1,092

THE STOCK EXCHANGE CLERKS PENSION FUND
The Stock Exchange, London EC2N 1HP
Telephone: 01-588 3015

Secretary R.W.S.Hunwick, APMI

Trustees Sexpen Trustees Ltd.

Chairman Gerald W.Ashfield

Actuaries Bacon & Woodrow

Auditors Deloitte Haskins & Sells

Solicitors Linklaters & Paines

Members (at 25.3.80) 452

Pensioners 1,923

Deferred Pensions 635

	£000
Annual Contributions	178
Annual Investment Income	824
Gross Annual Outflow	508
Capital Value	
Book Value	7,435
Market Value	9,458
Summary of Investments (Market Value)	
Equities	6,744
Fixed Interest	1,797
Mortgages	81
Cash & Deposits	772
Others	64

STODDARD HOLDINGS LTD
Glenpatrick Works, Elderslie, Johnstone, Renfrewshire PA5 9UJ
Telephone: 0505-21121

Finance Director M.J.R.Townsend

Company Secretary A.Rennison, CA

Insured with Scottish Widows' Fund & Life Assurance Society

Pension Fund Consultants Reed Stenhouse Benefit Consultants Ltd.

Employees 1,662

STONE & WEBSTER ENGINEERING LTD
Stone and Webster House, 236 Gray's Inn Road, London WC1X 8HA
Telephone: 01-837 2855

Managing Director M.G.Cataford

Employees Over 700

STONE-PLATT PENSION FUND
10 Grafton Street, London W1X 3LA
Telephone: 01-493 7000

Pension Fund Manager & Secretary L.Pollard, APMI

Trustees Stone-Platt Trustees Ltd

Investment Advisers N.M.Rothschild Asset Management Ltd and Morgan Grenfell & Co Ltd

Pension Fund Consultants & Actuarial Advice obtained through Willis Faber Advisory Services Ltd

Auditors Price Waterhouse & Co

Company Employees 7,993

Members 4,784

Pensioners 1,511

	£000
Annual Contributions	3,231

STONE-PLATT Continued

Annual Investment Income	1,544
Annual Outflow	1,941
Capital Value	22,000
Summary of Investments	
Equities	12,200
Fixed Interest	5,300
Property	3,300
Cash & Deposits	950
Others	450

STONEHILL HOLDINGS LTD

Lea Valley Trading Estate, Angel Road,
London N18 3LP
Telephone: 01-807 1020

Secretary A.C.Landsman,FCA

Insured with Sun Alliance & London Insurance Ltd

Employees 905

STOTHERT & PITT LTD

PO Box 25, 166 Lower Bristol Road, Bath,
Avon BA2 3DJ
Telephone: 0225-314400

Secretary J.A.Terry

Investment Advisers Rea Brothers Ltd.

Employees 1,773

STRATHCLYDE REGIONAL COUNCIL SUPERANNUATION FUND

20 India Street, Glasgow G2 4PF
Telephone: 041-204 2900

Director of Finance K.R.Paterson, IPFA, ACCA

Management Committee Regional Council Committee/Department of Finance

Trustees Strathclyde Regional Council

Investment Advisers Investment Managers, Murray Johnstone Ltd and three advisers

Property Advisers Richard Ellis

Actuaries Robertson, Hymans & Co.

Auditors Controller of Audit

Employees 122,000

Members 72,000

Pensioners 22,000

	£000
Annual Contributions	42,255
Annual Investment Income	23,633
Annual Outflow	20,540
Capital Value	269,957
Summary of Investments	
Equities	130,660
Overseas Equities	27,000
Fixed Interest	98,000
Property	8,000
Cash & Deposits	6,297

STRATOFLEX (UK) LTD

5 Watt Road, Glasgow G52 4RX
Telephone: 041-882 3276

Administrative Manager D.F.Chalmers

Employees 3,000

STRONG & FISHER (HOLDINGS) LTD

100 Irchester Road, Rushden,
Northants NN10 9XQ
Telephone: 09334-53131

Secretary T.Body

Insured with Scottish Amicable Life Assurance Society

Employees 1,260

STUART & SONS LTD

Red House Glassworks, Stourbridge,
West Midlands DY8 4AA
Telephone: 0384-77391

Company Secretary B.J.Richens,ACMA

Trustees Stuart Crystal Pensions Ltd.

Director F.G.Stuart

Managed by Friends' Provident Managed Pension Funds Ltd

Actuaries Duncan C. Fraser & Co

Auditors Pannell Fitzpatrick & Co.

Company Employees 630

Members 150

Pensioners 70

Annual Contributions £38,000

Annual Investment Income £29,000

Capital Value £450,000

STYLO SHOES LTD

Harrogate Road, Apperley Bridge, Bradford,
West Yorks BD10 0LX
Telephone: 0274-617761

Secretary D.Lloyd Hughes,FCA

Insured with Equity & Law Life Assurance Society Ltd

Employees 2,354

SUFFOLK COUNTY COUNCIL SUPERANNUATION FUND

P.O.Box 38, Milner House, Rope Walk, Ipswich,
Suffolk IP4 2JP
Telephone: 0473-55801

Treasurer C.Stephenson, BSc, IPFA

Trustees Suffolk County Council

Investment Advisers Hill Samuel Investment Management Ltd.

Actuaries R.Watson & Sons

Auditors District Audit

Employees 23,000

Members 7,500

Pensioners 2,200

	£000
Annual Contributions	5,700
Annual Investment Income	3,037
Annual Outflow	3,747
Capital Value	33,825

The Major UK Pension Funds STO/SUN

SUFFOLK COUNTY COUNCIL Continued

Summary of Investments
Equities	21,106
Fixed Interest	8,704
Property	2,748
Cash & Deposits	1,267

SUFLEX LTD
Newport Road, Risca, Newport, Gwent NP1 6YD
Telephone: 0633-612212

Secretary H.W.Stapleton

Employees 500

SULZER STAFF PENSION SCHEME
Westmead, Farnborough, Hampshire
Telephone: 0252-44311

Pensions Administrator J.B.Martin

Secretary O.M.E.Pelczer

Trustees Sulzer Pension Trustees Ltd.

Stockbrokers & Investment Advisers Phillips & Drew

Actuaries R. Watson & Sons

Auditors Touche Ross & Co.

Company Employees 1,700

Members 700

Pensioners 200

	£000
Annual Contributions	419
Annual Investment Income	318
Annual Outflow	281
Capital Value	4,200

Summary of Investments (1979)
Equities	1,578
Fixed Interest	1,120
Property	138
Cash & Deposits	188
Others	517

FRANCIS SUMNER (HOLDINGS) LTD
Cross Street, Leek, Staffs.ST13 5AR
Telephone: 0538-383261

Secretary T.E.Ratcliffe

Employees 1,566

SUMRIE CLOTHES LTD
Sumrie House, York Road, Leeds, W.Yorks.LS9 6TB
Telephone: 0532-458526

Secretary F.Rains

Employees 656

SAL PENSION SCHEME
Sun Alliance Insurance Group,
1 Bartholomew Lane, London EC2N 2AB
Telephone: 01-588 2345

Pension Fund Manager H.Silver (Administrator)

Assistant to Administrator R.A.Pointer,FCAA,APMI

Superintendent Pensions & Benefits O.G.Fellows, ACIS,APMI

Actuary S.L.Smaller,MA,FIA FPMI

Trustees Alliance Assurance Co Ltd

Auditors Deloitte, Haskins & Sells

Solicitors Sacker & Partners

Company Employees 9,600

Active Members 8,868 (at 31.3.79)

Pensioners 3,582

	£million
Annual Contributions (to 31.3.80)	14
Annual Investment Income	14.3
Gross Annual Outflow	8.6
Capital Value (Market value)	186

Summary of Investments
Equities	79
Fixed Interest	52
Property	45
Cash & Deposits	9
Others	1

SUN LIFE STAFF PENSION AND WIDOWS & ORPHANS FUND
107 Cheapside, London EC2V 6DU
Telephone: 01-606 7788

Secretary W.J.Amos

Pensions Actuary D.H.Kingston,FIA,APMI

Trustees P.G.Walker, R.F.C.Zamboni, D.H.Kingston

Auditors Gane, Jackson & Walton

Company Employees 2,333

Members 2,208

Pensioners 545

Annual Contributions £1.7 million

Capital Value £19 million

SUN VALLEY POULTRY LTD
Shobdon Leominster, Herefordshire HR6 9NA
Telephone: 056881-395

Secretary W.A.Brailsford

Investment Advisers Kleinwort Benson Investment Management Ltd

Employees 2,318

SUNBEAM ELECTRIC (HOLDINGS) LTD
14-16 Old Quebec Street, London W1H 8AG
Telephone: 03552-20255

Chairman W.E.Haward

Managed by Scottish Amicable Pensions Investment Ltd

Employees 1,261

SUNDERLAND FORCE & ENGINEERING CO LTD
PO Box 41, Pallin Yard, Neville Road, Sunderland, Tyne and Wear SR4 6PZ
Telephone: 0783-74452

Managing Director W.J.Rose

Employees 700

BERNARD SUNLEY INVESTMENT TRUST LTD
Berkeley Square House, Berkeley Square,
London W1X 6DY
Telephone: 01-493 7200

Secretary B.Williams,FCA

Insured with Eagle Star Insurance Co.Ltd.

Employees 599

SUNLIGHT SERVICE GROUP LTD
204 South Park Road, Wimbledon,
London SW19 8TE
Telephone: 01-542 9011

Secretary N.C.Davis

Insured with Eagle Star Insurance Co Ltd

Employees 4,093

SUPERDRUG STORES LTD
Felnex Trading Estate, 190 London Road,
Wallington, Surrey SM6 7EG
Telephone: 01-669 2151

Secretary R.Goldstein

Employees 1,600

SURREY COUNTY COUNCIL
County Hall, Penrhyn Road,
Kingston upon Thames, Surrey KT1 2DN
Telephone: 01-546 1050

Treasurer D.J.Thomas

Members (at 31.3.80) 12,637 members from 11 District Councils and 692 members from 40 admitted bodies

Pensioners 4,421

	£000
Annual Contributions	10,767
Annual Investment Income	6,678
Gross Annual Outflow	8,655
Capital Value (Market Value)	67,302
Summary of Investments	
Equities	7,389
Fixed Interest	41,616
Property	10,580
Cash & Deposits	5,457
Others	2,260

SURRIDGE DAWSON (HOLDINGS) LTD.
AMP House,6th Floor, Dingwall Road, Croydon,
Surrey CR9 2AP

Secretary W.D.Clark

Employees 1,046

L.S.& J.SUSSMAN LTD
Albany Hse, 12 Albany Road, London E10
Telephone: 01-539 8373

Director H.Sussman

Employees 850

SUTCLIFFE CATERING GROUP LTD PENSION FUNDS 3A,3B,3C
40 The Mall, Ealing, London W5 3TJ
Telephone: 01-579 3261

Company Secretary R.B.Martin

Pension Fund Manager Sun Life Assurance Society

Trustees J.D.Stirling Gallacher, J.K.R.Graveney,
K.Morris, P.W.Davies, Mrs.L.Lynch, Mrs.B.M.Drew

Pension Fund Consultants Wigham Polan Pension Consultants Ltd.

Auditors Peat Marwick Mitchell & Co.

Company Employees 7,000 approx.

Members (A) 107, (B) 132, (C) 500 approx.

Pensioners Total 30

	£000
Annual Contributions A & B	120
Capital Value A & B (at 31.7.80)	1,382
Summary of Investments A & B	%
Equities	43.0
Fixed Interest	41.1
Property	4.9
Cash & Deposits	10.0

SUTCLIFFE SPEAKMAN & CO LTD
Guest Street, Leigh, Lancs.WN7 2HE
Telephone: 0942-672101

Secretary A.Flint

Insured with Prudential Assurance Co Ltd

Employees 550

SWIFT PENSION TRUST
10 Charterhouse Square, London EC1P 1AX
Telephone: 01-253 7600

Pension Fund Manager G.S.Moyse

Trustees G.S.Moyse, B.M.Jeffrey, V.N.Wright

Managed by Legal & General (Pensions Management) Ltd., Pensions Management (SWF) Ltd.

Pension Fund Consultants C.T.Bowring and Layborn Ltd

Auditors Arthur Young McLelland Moores

Company Employees 1,500

Members 600

Annual Contributions £350,000

Annual Outflow £75,000

Capital Value £2,600,000

SWIZZELS MATLOW LTD
Carlton House, New Mills, Stockport SK12 3HA
Telephone: 0663-44144

Secretary N.S.Menzies

Employees 860

SYBRON LTD
35 St Thomas Street, London SE1
Telephone: 0438-2366

Chairman D.A.Gaudion

Managed by Legal & General (Pensions Management) Ltd

Employees 2,412

HENRY SYKES LTD
Sykes House, 445 Woolwich Road, Charlton, London SE7 7AP
Telephone: 01-858 8121

Secretary A.F.Potts,FCA

Managed by Legal & General (Pensions Management) Ltd

Pension Fund Consultants Godwins Ltd

Employees 1,317

SYLTONE LTD RETIREMENT BENEFITS SCHEME
Park Gate House, Church Bank, Bradford, W.Yorks.BD1 5BS
Telephone: 0274-307588

Secretary M.G.Ingham, ACA

Managed by Scottish Life Pensions Annuity Co Ltd

Pension Fund Consultants Sedgwick Employee Benefits Consultants Ltd.

Auditors Stirk Lambert Kidsons

Employees 653

SYSTIME LTD.
432 Dewsbury Road, Leeds LS11 7DF

Secretary J.Parkinson

Employees 657

TACK INDUSTRIES LTD
Tack House, Longmore Street, London SW1V 1JJ
Telephone: 01-834 5001

Secretary E.F.Tuffrey

Employees 741

TAGGARTS (MOTOR HOLDINGS) LTD.
Knowetop, Motherwell,Lanarkshire
Telephone: 0698-66133

Secretary D.B.Clark,CA

Employees 622

TALBEX GROUP LTD
12a Golden Square, London W1R 3AF
Telephone: 01-734 6220

Secretary D.G.Falconer

Employees 1,049

TALBOT MOTOR COMPANY LTD. VARIOUS PENSION PLANS
Administrative Centre, P.O.Box 122A, Abbey Road, Whitley, Coventry CV3 4GB
Telephone: 0203-303505

Pensions Manager B.D.Caucutt, APMI

Managed by Barclays Bank Trust Co. Ltd., Prudential Pensions Ltd., Warburg Investment Management Ltd.

Actuaries R.Watson & Sons

Auditors Touche Ross & Co.

Members 19,000

Pensioners 3,500

Annual Contributions £12.4 million

Annual Investment Income £5.5 million

Capital Value (at 30.6.80) £72 million

TALLEY GENERAL TIME LTD.
Strathleven, Dumbarton, Strathclyde G82 3PL
Telephone: 0389-822531

Secretary J.B.Miller

Insured with Scottish Amicable Life Assurance Society

Employees 709

TAMPAX LTD
Dunsbury Way, Leigh Park, Havant, Hants PO9 5DG
Telephone: 0705-474141

Secretary J.P.Dodgson

Managed by Legal & General (Pensions Management) Ltd

Employees 737

JOHN TAMS LTD
Longton, Stoke on Trent, Staffs.ST3 2PG
Telephone: 0782-312226

Director P.Tams

Employees 500

TANGENT INDUSTRIES LTD.
New Roman House, 10 East Road, London N1 6AJ
Telephone: 01-251 1533

Secretary P.B.Harding

Employees 881

JOHN TANN HOLDINGS LTD
Stuart Works, Stirling Corner, Boreham Wood, Herts WD6 2AB
Telephone: 01-953 2021

Secretary W.E.G.Manning

Employees 807

TANSLEY WITT
28 Ely Place, London EC1P 1JE
Telephone: 01-242 1666

Employees 979

TAPP & TOOTHILL LTD
Contury Works Swinnow Road, Bramley, Leeds, W.Yorks.LS13 2TE
Telephone: 0532-579991

Secretary D.C.Fordham

Employees 529

TARGET TRUST GROUP LTD PENSION & ASSURANCE PLAN
72/80 Gatehouse Road, Aylesbury, Bucks.HP19 3EB
Telephone: 0296-5981

Pension Fund Manager T.C.Brooks, FCA

Pension Fund Consultants Metropolitan Pensions Association Ltd

Auditors Thomson McLintock & Co

Company Employees 400

TARGET TRUST GROUP LTD *Continued*

Members 114
Pensioners 7
Annual Contributions £135,000
Capital Value £1,351,000

TARMAC STAFF PENSION SCHEME

Tarmac Ltd, Ettingshall, Wolverhampton WV4 6JP
Telephone: 0902-41101

Group Pensions Manager A.B.Shufflebotham, APMI

Group Pensions Adviser M.Kendal, FCA, APMI

Trustees Tarmac Pensions Ltd

Investment Advisers Robert Fleming Investment Management Ltd, Charterhouse Japhet Ltd, Phillips & Drew

Actuaries Duncan C.Fraser & Co

Auditors Peat Marwick Mitchell & Co.

Solicitors Sacker & Partners

Company Employees 23,688

Members 5,072

Pensioners 2,969

Annual Contributions £4,901,000

Annual Investment Income £2,687,000

Capital Value £29,002,000

There is also a Tarmac Divisions Retirement Plan with 2,714 members and 73 pensioners. This is insured with The London Life Association Ltd.

TATE & LYLE GROUP PENSION SCHEME

Sugar Quay, Lower Thames Street,
London EC3R 6DQ
Telephone: 01-626 6525

Secretary P.W.White

Director of Group Pensions D.E.Green, ACIS, FPMI

Trustees J.Forbes, D.E.Green, L.E.Fenn, J.C.R.Scott, J.E.Wright

Investment Advisers S.G.Warburg & Co Ltd, Baring Brothers & Co Ltd

Actuaries R.Watson & Sons

Property Advisers Richard Ellis

Auditors Price Waterhouse & Co.

Company Employees 10,772

Members 8,832

Pensioners 4,777

	£million
Annual Contributions	12.2
Annual Investment Income	6.7
Annual Outflow	7.3
Capital Value	92.5
Summary of Investments	
Equities	46.2
Fixed Interest	14.0
Property	18.7
Cash & Deposits	12.0
Others	1.6

TATE PIPE LINING PROCESSES LTD

Manchester M12 4SA
Telephone: 061-273 3971

Director M.K.Watson

Employees 600

TAYLOR INSTRUMENT LTD.

Gunnels Wood Road, Stevenage, Herts.SG1 2EL
Telephone: 0438-2366

Secretary B.D.Jarvis

Employees 1,347

TAYLOR WOODROW GROUP PENSION & LIFE ASSURANCE FUND

345 Ruislip Road, Southall, Middlesex UB1 2QX
Telephone: 01-575 4445

Company Secretary R.Christie, FCIS

Pension Fund Manager Martin G.Bailey, APMI, FCII

Insured with Standard Life Assurance Company

Auditors Mann Judd

Company Employees 10,062

Members 3,523

Pensioners 500

Annual Contributions £3,000,000

TAYLORPLAN CATERING LTD

9 The Quadrant, Richmond, Surrey TW9 1BS
Telephone: 01-940 6080

Secretary P.A.Hooper

Employees 1,936

TAYSIDE REGIONAL COUNCIL

Tayside House, 28 Crichton Street,
Dundee DD1 3RF
Telephone: 0382-23281

Director Finance L.H.Burdge

Superannuation Officer J.Crosbie, APMI

TECALEMIT LTD. PENSION & LIFE ASSURANCE SCHEME

Old Court, Cox Green, Maidenhead,
Berkshire SL6 3AQ
Telephone: 0628-26167

Pension Fund Manager M.C.Oughton, FCIS

Secretary to Trustees E.Broadbridge

Trustees M.C.Oughton, FCIS, D.H.V.Chapman, FCA, L.Daley, R.C.Palmer, R.W.A.Richards

Part Managed by Legal & General Assurance (Pensions Management) Ltd

Investment Advisers Kleinwort Benson Investment Management Ltd

Actuaries R.Watson & Sons

Pension Fund Consultants Holmwoods & Crawford (Life & Pension Brokers) Ltd

Auditors Peat, Marwick, Mitchell & Co.

Company Employees 2,697

Members 2,250

Pensioners 619

TECALEMIT LTD. Continued

	£000
Annual Contributions	530
Annual Investment Income	12
Annual Outflow	315
Capital Value	5,218
Summary of Investments	
Equities	213
Fixed Interest	120
Property Units	1,681
Mixed Fund Units	3,198
Cash & Deposits	4

TEES & HARTLEPOOL PORT AUTHORITY PENSION SCHEME

Queen's Square, Middlesbrough, Cleveland TS2 1AH
Telephone: 0642-241121

Director Personnel Services J.K.Beckton

Personnel Officer J.R.Cummings

Investment Advisers Kleinwort Benson Investment Management Ltd.

Actuaries R.Watson & Sons

Auditors Peat, Marwick, Mitchell & Co.

Employees 1,673

Members 754

Pensioners 315

Annual Contributions £920,000

Annual Investment Income £350,000

Capital Value £5,700,000

TEKTRONIX LTD

PO Box 69, Coldharbour Lane, Harpenden AL5 4UP
Telephone: 05827-63141

Secretary F.L.Beckwith

Employees 727

TELEFLEX MORSE LTD

Christopher Martin Road, Basildon, Essex SS14 3ES
Telephone: 0268-22861

Finance Director L.Jackson

Employees 650

TELEFUSION GROUP PENSION FUND & LIFE ASSURANCE SCHEME

Telefusion House, Preston New Road, Blackpool, Lancs.FY4 4QY
Telephone: 0253-66111

Director & Secretary John Hayhurst, LLB

Insured with Norwich Union Life Insurance Society

Pension Fund Consultants Metropolitan Pensions Association Ltd

Company Employees 3,245

Members 300

Pensioners 30

Annual Contributions £80,000

T.R.PENSION FUND

c/o **Telephone Rentals Ltd.** TR House, Bletchley, Milton Keynes, Bucks.MK3 5JL
Telephone: 0908-71200

Secretary K.H.Francis,ACIS,FCCA

Trustees Eight Directors/Employees

Managed by Commercial Union Assurance Co Ltd, Legal & General Assurance Society Ltd

Actuaries Clay & Partners

Pension Fund Consultants Clay & Partners

Auditors Baker Rooke & Amsdons

Company Employees 1,861

Members 1,320

Pensioners 189

Annual Contributions £1,232,000

Capital Value £9,750,000

TEMPERED GROUP LTD

P.O.Box 20, Park Works, Foley Street, Sheffield, W.Yorks.S4 7WS
Telephone: 0742-20031

Secretary G.W.Bridge

Stockbrokers Phillips & Drew, Buckmaster & Moore

Property Advisers Fuller Peiser

Auditors Pannell Fitzpatrick & Co.

Company Employees 832

Members 546

Pensioners 137

Annual Contributions £303,000

Annual Investment Income £194,000

Capital Value £2,519,000

HOWARD TENENS SERVICES LTD

Parsonage Road, Stratton St.Margaret, Wilts.SN3 4RJ
Telephone: 0793-822831

Secretary A.W.Baxendale

Employees 1,399

C.TENNANT SONS & CO.LTD. STAFF PENSION SCHEME

9 Harp Lane, London EC3R 6DR
Telephone: 01-626 4533

Executive Trustee G.L.Hellier,FPMI

Insured with Prudential Assurance Co.Ltd.

Auditors Ernst & Whinney

Company Employees 600

Members 251

Pensioners 90

Annual Contributions £562,000

TENNANTS CONSOLIDATED LTD. PENSION FUND

69 Grosvenor Street, London W1X 0BP
Telephone: 01-493 5451

Pension Fund Secretary R.S.Sears,FCA

TENNANTS CONSOLIDATED LTD. *Continued*

Company Secretary J.V.Dawson, FCA

Employees 1,234

Members 648

Pensioners 177

R.TERLEY LTD
Farmloan Industrial Estate, Rutherglen, Lanarkshire
Telephone: 041-647 9231

Secretary M.Paul

Employees 600

HERBERT TERRY & SONS LTD
Millsbro Road, Redditch, Worcs.B98 7BU
Telephone: 0527-64261

Managing Director B.C.Jessop

Executive R.J.Smith

Employees 518

TESCO STORES (HOLDINGS) LTD STAFF PENSION SCHEME
Tesco House, Delamare Road,
Cheshunt, Waltham Cross, Herts.EN8 9SL
Telephone: 97-32222

Pension Fund Manager P.G.Uttley

Secretary M.J.Boxall

Trustees Tesco Pension Trustees Ltd.

Investment Adviser Phillips & Drew

Actuaries Duncan C. Fraser & Co.

Auditors Hogg Bullimore & Co.

Solicitors Stallard & Co.

Company Employees 52,829

Members 11,990

Pensioners 600

TEXACO PENSION PLAN
1 Knightsbridge Green, London SW1X 7QJ
Telephone: 01-584 5000

Pension Fund Manager & Secretary
P.D.C.Woollerton, FCA, FPMI

Trustees Texaco Trustees Ltd.

Investment Advisers J.Henry Schroder Wagg & Co.Ltd., Warburg Investment Management Ltd.

Bankers National Westminster Bank Ltd

Actuaries Duncan C.Fraser & Co

Auditors Arthur Andersen & Co

Solicitors Lovell, White & King

Company Employees (at 31.3.80) 2,940

Members 2,751

Pensioners 1,299

	£000
Annual Contributions (at 31.3.80)	3,468
Annual Investment Income	2,383
Gross Annual Outflow	1,248
Capital Value Market Value	27,783

Summary of Investments

Equities	13,405
Fixed Interest	9,421
Property	2,476
Cash & Deposits	1,880

TEXAS INSTRUMENTS LTD. PENSION PLAN
Manton Lane, Bedford MK41 7PA
Telephone: 0234-67466

Company Secretary J.R.Hewell

Compensation Manager R.J.Hill

Investment Advisers Morgan Grenfell & Co.Ltd.

Pension Fund Consultants Metropolitan Pensions Association Ltd.

Auditors Arthur Young McClelland Moores & Co.

Company Employees 2,552

Members 2,000

Pensioners 150

Annual Contributions £700,000

Annual Investment Income £500,000

Capital Value £7,000,000

TEXTRON LTD
Station Road, Edenbridge, Harpenden,
Herts.AL5 4UP
Telephone: 0533-51122

Secretary M.W.Parker

Managed by 784

Employees 3,468

CHAS F.THACKRAY LTD
PO Box 171, 10 Park Street, Leeds,
W.Yorks.LS1 1RQ
Telephone: 0532-42321

Secretary R.B.Gray

Employees 707

THAMES TELEVISION LTD
Teddington Studios, Teddington Lock, Teddington,
Middlesex TW11 9NT
Telephone: 01-977 3252

Secretary B.E.Marr

Employees 1,832

THAMES VALLEY EGGS LTD
Foxhall Rd, Didcot, Oxon OX11 7AE
Telephone: 0235-814103

Director J.H.Jennings

Executive D.Watts

Employees 620

THERMAL SYNDICATE LTD
PO Box 6, Wallsend, Tyne & Wear NE8 6DG
Telephone: 0632-625311

Secretary F.O.Moran

Employees 906

THERMOS LTD
Ongar Road, Brentwood, Essex CM15 9AY
Telephone: 0277-213404

THERMOS LTD Continued

Secretary D.E.Weston
Insured with Clerical, Medical & General Life Insurance
Employees 781

EDWARD THOMPSON GROUP
Richmond Street, Sunderland SR5 1BQ
Telephone: 0783-44199/77
Director F.S.Cronin
Employees 600

J.WALTER THOMPSON GROUP LTD GROUP PENSION & LIFE ASSURANCE SCHEME
40 Berkeley Square, London W1X 6AD
Telephone: 01-629 9496
Company Secretary J.R.Page
Financial Accountant J.C.Maulkin
Pension Fund Consultants Willis Faber Advisory Services Ltd
Insured with Scottish Provident Institution
Company Employees (at 1.4.79) 969
Members 492
Pensioners 160
Annual Contributions £800,000

THOMSON PUBLICATIONS LTD (1977) PENSION SCHEME
Elm House, 10-16 Elm Street, London WC1X 0BP
Telephone: 01-278 2345
Pension Fund Manager K.S.Goatham
Stockbrokers Cazenove & Co.
Actuaries Bacon & Woodrow
Pension Fund Consultants Wigham Poland Pension Consultants Ltd.
Auditors Price Waterhouse & Co
Employees 800
Members 330
Pensioners 12
Annual Contributions £125,000
Capital Value £650,000

TBF THOMPSON (GARVAGH) LTD
Garvagh, Co Londonderry
Telephone: 026652-353
Secretary J.L.Baxter
Employees 2,000

D.C.THOMSON & CO LTD PROVIDENT FUND
Courier Building, Albert Square, Dundee DD1 9QJ
Telephone: 0382-23131
Secretary A.McDougall
Employees 3,036

THOMSON MCLINTOCK & CO
70 Finsbury Pavement, London EC2A 1SZ
Telephone: 01-638 2777

Partner A.M.C.Morison, MA, CA
Employees 1,365

THE THOMSON ORGANISATION (1968) PENSION FUND
44 Bedford Square, London WC1B 3DU
Telephone: 01-631 9072
Secretary C.R.Jones, APMI
Group Pensions Administration Manager C.P.Brown, FCA
Trustees The Thomson Organisation Pension Trust Ltd
Directors J.Evans, T.E.Hayes, C.R.Jones, J.White
Investment Advisers S.G.Warburg & Co.Ltd., Cazenove & Co.
Actuaries Bacon & Woodrow
Property Advisers Jones, Lang, Wootton
Forestry Advisers Fountain Forestry Ltd.
Auditors Price Waterhouse & Co
Company Employees 14,400
Members 7,077
Pensioners 1,928

	£000
Annual Contributions	5,400
Annual Investment Income	2,900
Annual Outflow	2,800
Capital Value (Book Value)	35,200
Summary of Investments	
Equities	21,500
Fixed Interest	8,100
Property	1,900
Cash & Deposits	2,900
Others	800

THORN GROUP PENSIONS FUND
Group Pension Dept, 91A High Street, Crawley, Sussex RH10 1BA
Telephone: 0293-24208
Investment Dept. Cambridge House, Great Cambridge Road, Enfield, Middx. EN1 1UL
Telephone: 01-363 5353
Group Pension Fund Manager & Secretary R.A.Parrett, APMI
Investments Manager R.P.Good, BSc, FCIS, ACII, APMI, ASIA
Deputy Investment Manager T.L.Croft
Property Manager K.O.Wakeling, FRICS
Trustees T.E.I.Pension Trust Ltd
Actuaries R.Watson & Sons
Auditors Ernst & Whinney
Company Employees 68,460
Members (at 30.9.80) 25,337
Pensioners 5,594

	£000
Annual Contributions	15,500
Annual Investment Income	15,189
Annual Outflow	8,686

THORN GROUP Continued

Capital Value
Book Value 123,841
Market Value 183,600
Summary of Investments
Equities 49,552
Fixed Interest 16,507
Property 36,383
Cash & Deposits 5,974
Managed Fund 16,022

THORNHILL & SONS LTD

Great Longstone, Bakewell, Derbyshire DE4 1TD
Telephone: 062-987 351

Secretary L.Cohen

Employees 1,000

THORNTON BAKER PENSION FUND

Fairfax House, Fulwood Place, London WC1V 6DW
Telephone: 01-405 8422

Pension Fund Manager Mrs A.Hearn

Financial Controller D.A.Jerrett

Actuaries R.Watson & Sons

Auditors Spicer & Pegler

Solicitors Allen & Overy

Company Employees 2,750

Members 930

Pensioners 55

Annual Contributions £2,473,000

Capital Value £5,013,000

J.W.THORNTON LTD. NON-CONTRIBUTORY PENSION FUND

Archer Road, Sheffield S8 0JH
Telephone: 0742-583751

Pension Fund Manager & Secretary M.S.Thornton, FCIS

Trustees F.J.Kershaw, J.S.Thornton, A.H.Thornton, R.E.Smith

Investment Advisers Kershaw, Tudor & Co.

Stockbrokers Walter Ward & Co

Actuaries Duncan C.Fraser & Co

Auditors Pannell Fitzpatrick & Co.

Company Employees 1,442

Members 303

Pensioners 24

	£000
Annual Contributions	90
Annual Investment Income	113
Gross Annual Outflow	5
Capital Value	790
Summary of Investments	
Equities	239
Fixed Interest	231
Property	82
Cash & Deposits	142

3M UNITED KINGDOM LTD PENSION & LIFE ASSURANCE SCHEME

3M House, PO Box 1, Bracknell, Berks.RG12 1JU
Telephone: 0344-58329

Pension Fund Manager D.Yarrow,BSc,APMI

Company Secretary W.T.S.Digby-Seymour

Part Managed by Prudential Pensions Ltd.

Investment Advisers Hill Samuel & Co.Ltd., J.Henry Schroder Wagg & Co.Ltd. Morgan Grenfell & Co.Ltd., N.M.Rothschild Asset Management Ltd.

Property Advisers Davies Knight & Partners

Actuaries Clay & Partners

Pension Fund Consultants Metropolitan Pensions Association Ltd.

Auditors Deloitte Haskins & Sells

Company Employees (at 6.4.80) 4,504

Members 4,154

Pensioners 362

Annual Contributions £3,462,000

Capital Value (at 31.3.80) £19,823,000

DANIEL THWAITES 1959 PENSION SCHEME

Star Brewery, Blackburn, Lancs.BB1 5BU
Telephone: 0254-54431

Company Secretary G.J.Hacking,FCA,ACMA

Secretary G.J.Hacking

Trustees G.J.Hacking, T.Kay, R.Cunliffe, J.M.A.Yerburgh

Investment Advisers Prudential Assurance Co. Ltd.

Pension Fund Consultants Godwins (North) Ltd.

Auditors Cooper, Basden and Adamson

Company Employees 1,022

Members 470

Pensioners 98

THYSSEN (GREAT BRITAIN) LTD.

Bynea, Llanelli, Glamorgan SA14 9SU
Telephone: 05542-2244

Pension Fund Manager J.Davies

Company Secretary H.Heinrich

Company Employees 2,311

Members 350

TIBBETT & BRITTEN LTD.

691-697 High Road, Tottenham, London N17
Telephone: 01-808 3040

Director J.H.Tibbett

Employees 868

JACK TIGHE LTD

Redbourne Mele, Kirton Lindsey, Gainsborough, Lincs DN21 4NN
Telephone: 06524-441

Secretary E.H.Cherry

Employees 1,494

TILBURY CONTRACTING GROUP LTD

Tilbury House, Rusper Road, Horsham,
W Sussex RH12 4BB
Telephone: 0403-69031

Pension Fund Secretary A.J.Tonking,APMI

Investment Advisers J.Henry Schroder Wagg & Co.Ltd.

Employees 1,952

TILGHMAN WHEELABRATOR LTD

PO Box 60, Broadheath, Altrincham,
Cheshire WA14 5ED
Telephone: 061-928 6388

Secretary M.L.Buckley

Employees 500

THOMAS TILLING GROUP PENSION SCHEME

Crewe House, Curzon Street, London W1Y 8AX
Telephone: 01-499 4151

Pension Fund Manager A.W.C.Davey,FPMI,FCIS

Deputy Pension Fund Manager J.Meredith, APMI

Trustees Thomas Tilling Pension Trust Co Ltd

Investment Advisers N.M.Rothschild Asset Management Ltd, J.Henry Schroder Wagg & Co Ltd

Company Employees 35,300

Members 13,000

Capital Value (1977) £32 million

TIME PRODUCTS LTD SUPERANNUATION FUND

81/89 Farringdon Road, London EC1M 3LH
Telephone: 01-242 8899

Financial Director H.A.Chesterman

Pensions Officer Miss S.Taylor

Investment Advisers Hill Samuel Investment Management Ltd.

Pension Fund Consultants Sedgwick Employee Benefit Consultants Ltd.

Auditors Spicer & Pegler

Solicitors Paisner & Co.

Company Employees 1,300

Members 320

Pensioners 6

Annual Contributions £150,000

Capital Value £1,000,000

TIMES NEWSPAPERS LTD

New Printing House Square, Gray's Inn Road,
London WC1X 8EZ
Telephone: 01-837 1234

Pension Fund Manager R.E.Gobbett, APMI

Secretary W.Macleod

Employees 4,437

TIMEX CORPORATION U.K. RETIREMENT BENEFITS PLAN

Harrison Road, Dundee DD2 3XL
Telephone: 0382-819211

Secretary Miss A. McKay, FCII

Trustees W.G.Hay, J.A.Keay, F.W.Ralston

Investment Advisers N.M.Rothschild Asset Management Ltd., S.C.A.M.P.I.

Actuaries Clay & Partners

Auditors Peat, Marwick, Mitchell & Co.

Members 4,411

Capital Value £9 million

TIOXIDE INTERNATIONAL LTD 1959, 1973 AND 1978 PENSION FUNDS

10 Stratton Street, London W1A 4XP
Telephone: 01-499 6070

Pension Fund Manager J.P.Harrington

Secretary D.J.Busby

Investment Advisers Hill Samuel Investment Management Ltd., N.M.Rothschild & Sons Ltd.

Actuaries Duncan C. Fraser & Co.

Pension Fund Consultants Noble Lowndes & Partners Ltd.

Auditors Deloitte Haskins & Sells

Company Employees 2,800

Members 2,760 (at 1.1.80)

Pensioners 495

Annual Contributions £3,103,000

Annual Investment Income £2,000,000

Capital Value £19,064,000

TOBLER SUCHARD LTD

PO Box 72, Miller Road, Bedford, Beds.MK42 9PB
Telephone: 0234-55161

Secretary G.C.Howlett

Employees 787

TOLLEMACHE & COBBOLD BREWERIES LTD. RETIREMENT BENEFITS PLAN

Cliff Brewery, Ipswich, Suffolk IP3 0AZ
Telephone: 0473-56751

Secretary C.H.Pratt,FCIS

Trustees Lowndes Associated Pensions Ltd.

Managed by English Insurance (Pensions Management) Ltd.

Actuarial Advice Obtained through Cubie Wood & Co. Ltd.

Pension Fund Consultants Noble Lowndes & Partners Ltd.

Employees 1,109

F.H.TOMKINS LTD

PO Box 22, All Saints Road, Wednesbury,
West Midlands WS10 9LN
Telephone: 021-526 3166

Secretary R.N.Marchant,FCA

Insured with Legal & General Assurance Society Ltd

Employees 763

TOMKINSONS CARPETS LTD
Duke Place, Kidderminster, Worcs DY10 2JR
Telephone: 0562-745771

Pension Fund Manager B.J.Spittle

Insured with Legal & General Assurance Society Ltd

Employees 735

TOM'S FOODS LTD
111 Mortlake Road, Richmond, Surrey TW9 4RH
Telephone: 01-876 3414

Director J.W.Feighner

Employees 4,000

TOOTAL STAFF PENSION SCHEME
56 Oxford Street, Manchester M60 1HJ
Telephone: 061-228 1144

Group Pension Fund Manager & Secretary M.Ainsworth, APMI

Assistant Pension Fund Manager B.L.Dean

Trustees Tootal Pension Trust Ltd

Investment Advisers J.Henry Schroder Wagg & Co. Ltd.

Actuaries Duncan C.Fraser & Co

Auditors Spicer & Pegler

Company Employees 17,500

Members (at 31.3.80) 4,000

Pensioners 2,800

	£000
Annual Contributions	4,100
Annual Investment Income	2,300
Annual Outflow	3,200
Capital Value	27,800
Summary of Investments (Cost)	
Equities	14,449
Fixed Interest	8,372
Property Unit Trusts	4,005
Cash & Deposits	1,162

TORRINGTON CO LTD
Torrington Avenue, Coventry CV4 9AF
Telephone: 0203-74241

Secretary H.T.Clark

Employees 1,612

TORVALE HOLDINGS LTD.
Torvale Industrial Estate, Pembridge, Hereford.
Telephone: 05447-262

Secretary G.C.J.Ellis

Employees 743

TOTAL OIL GREAT BRITAIN LTD PENSION SCHEME
33 Cavendish Square, London W1M 0JE
Telephone: 01-499 6393

Pension Fund Manager E.E.Snow, ACIS, APMI

Investment Advisers Cazenove & Co

Actuaries Bacon & Woodrow

Auditors Spicer & Pegler

Company Employees 1,111

Members (at 31.12.79) 1,090

Pensioners 28

	£000
Annual Contributions	1,509
Annual Investment Income	601
Gross Annual Outflow	215
Capital Value	
Book Value	6,637
Market Value	8,867
Summary of Investments	
U.K.Equities	4,043
Overseas Equities	866
Fixed Interest	1,507
Property	143
Others	716

TOUCHE, REMNANT GROUP PENSION FUND
Winchester House, 77 London Wall, London EC2N 1BH
Telephone: 01-638 1737

Pension Fund Manager C.J.Kirman

Secretary E.S.Lewis

Trustees Touche, Remnant Group Trustees Ltd.

Investment Advisers Touche, Remnant & Co.

Actuaries Bacon & Woodrow

Auditors Touche Ross & Co.

Company Employees/members 70

Pensioners 10

	£000
Annual Contributions	218
Annual Investment Income	250
Annual Outflow	18
Capital Value	3,261
Summary of Investments	
Equities	2,402
Fixed Interest	705
Cash & Deposits	108
Others	46

TOUCHE ROSS & CO PENSION FUND
3 London Wall Buildings, London EC2M 5PH
Telephone: 01-588 3678

Partner P.C.Macnamara, MA, FCA

Supervisor Insurance & Pensions L.R.Vost

Investment Advisers Touche Remnant & Co

Actuaries Bacon & Woodrow

Auditors W.J.Findlay

Company Employees 1,200

Members 516

Pensioners 77

Annual Contributions £230,000

Capital Value £2,300,000

TOWERS & CO.LTD.
Canterbury House, 1-4 Giltspur Street, London EC1P 1EJ
Telephone: 01-248 7112

TOWERS & CO.LTD. Continued

Secretary D.J.Seabrook

Employees 572

TOWLES LTD
Queen's Road, Loughborough, Leics.LE11 1HE
Telephone: 0509-213555

Secretary M.Walpole

Insured with English Insurance Co Ltd

Employees 1,055

TOWN & CITY PROPERTIES PENSION & LIFE ASSURANCE SCHEME
220-222 Tottenham Court Road,
London W1P 0HH
Telephone: 01-637 1400

Secretary Miss E.R.Osborne

Administrator W.Wade

Trustees W.Wade (Managing), J.M.Sterling, B.D.MacPhail, P.H.Gimson, S.Velupillai

Investment Advisers William Wade and Oliver Marriott

Stockbrokers Panmure Gordon & Co.

Actuarial Advice Obtained through Cubie, Wood & Co.Ltd.

Pension Fund Consultants William Wade, IPFA, ACMA, FCIS, FRVA, Barrister in association with Noble Lowndes & Partners Ltd

Auditors Peat, Marwick, Mitchell & Co.

Company Employees 2,780

Members (at 1.4.80) 162

Pensioners 24

	£000
Annual Contributions	176
Annual Investment Income	283
Annual Outflow	231
Capital Value	1,906
Summary of Investments	
Equities	567
Fixed Interest	471
Property	832
Cash & Deposits	73
Others	(37)

J.R.TOWNSON INVESTMENTS LTD.
Higher Swan Lane, Bolton BL3 3AH
Telephone: 0204-62121

Secretary K.J.Hardcastle

Employees 655

TOYE & COMPANY LTD
Regalia House, 19-21 Great Queen Street,
London WC2B 5BE
Telephone: 01-242 0471

Secretary L.M.Johnson

Employees 600

TOZER, KEMSLEY & MILLBOURN (HOLDINGS) LTD: TKM PENSION SCHEME
28 Great Tower Street, London EC3R 5DE
Telephone: 01-283 3122

Pension Fund Manager & Secretary D.W.Peffer

Trustees D.R.Spray(Chairman), R.O.A.Keel, W.H.Maciver, D.W.Peffer, K.T.Roberts, I.W.Sanderson, R.Schofield

Investment Advisers J.Henry Schroder Wagg & Co Ltd

Actuaries R.Watson & Sons

Auditors Deloitte Haskins & Sells

Group Employees 11,003 (includes members of Price & Pierce Pension Scheme and Wadham Stringer Pension Fund)

Members 1,400

Pensioners 126

	£000
Annual Contributions	1,200
Annual Investment Income	600
Annual Outflow	330
Capital Value	11,067
Summary of Investments	
UK Equities	4,900
Overseas	1,300
Fixed Interest	3,500
Property Unit Trusts	1,100
Cash & Deposits	300

TPT LTD RETIREMENT BENEFITS PLAN
Oakwood Avenue, Romiley, Stockport,
Cheshire SK6 4LP
Telephone: 061-430 6061

Secretary D.Illingworth, FCA, ACMA

Investment Advisers M & G Investment Management Ltd

Actuarial Advice Obtained through Cubie, Wood & Co.Ltd.

Pension Fund Consultants Noble Lowndes & Partners Ltd.

Auditors Wheawill & Sudworth

Employees 1,023

TRADAX ENGLAND LTD.
Staple Hall, Stone House Court, London EC3A 7AX
Telephone: 01-283 5272

Secretary D.B.Hobday

Employees 587

TRAFALGAR HOUSE GROUP PENSION FUND (A), AND CUNARD PENSION FUND (B)
Trafalgar House Group Pensions Dept.,
Mitcham House, 681 Mitcham Road,
Croydon Surrey CR9 3AP
Telephone: 01-689 2266

Pension Fund Manager & Secretary H.T.Watkins, FPMI

Investment Manager D.J.C.Berens (at 1 Berkeley Street, London W1X 6NN)

Trustees (a) Trafalgar House Trustees Ltd (b) Cunard Group Pension Trustees Ltd

TRAFALGAR HOUSE GROUP Continued

Actuaries Lane Clark & Peacock
Auditors Touche Ross & Co.
Group Employees 25,698

	(a)	(b)
Members	5,000	1,000
Pensioners	500	1,000
	£000	£000
Annual Contributions	4,100	1,500
Annual Investment Income	2,300	1,300
Annual Outflow	1,900	1,900
Capital Value	28,700	15,800

TRANS WORLD AIRLINES INC.
200 Piccadilly, London W1V 0DH
Telephone: 01-636 4090

Director T.P.Fennessey
Executive J.Cooper
Employees 620

TRANSPARENT PAPER LTD
Bridge Hall Mills, Bury, Lancs BL9 7PA
Telephone: 061-764 5441

Secretary G.P.Cooper,LLB,FCIS,FCMA
Insured with Sun Life Assurance Society Ltd
Employees 1,401

TRANSPORT & GENERAL WORKERS UNION OFFICIALS & STAFF SUPERANNUATION FUND
Transport House, Smith Square,
London SW1P 3JB
Telephone: 01-828 7788

Financial Secretary H.Timpson
Stockbrokers Pember & Boyle
Actuaries Bacon & Woodrow
Auditors Hard Dowdy, Watson Collin & Co.
Employees 1,290
Members 1,176
Pensioners 726
Annual Contributions £1,000,000
Capital Value £18,000,000

TRANSPORT DEVELOPMENT GROUP LTD
Kingsgate House, 66-74 Victoria Street,
London SW1E 6SR
Telephone: 01-828 5051

Company Secretary R.D.Garwood
Pension Fund Manager B.Holden
Pension Fund Consultants Godwins Ltd
Employees 10,982

TRAVENOL LABORATORIES LTD PENSION PLAN
Caxton Way, Thetford, Norfolk
Telephone: 0842-4581

Pension Fund Manager J.Dutton
Part insured with Swiss Life Insurance Co.
Part managed by Legal & General (Pensions Management) Ltd.
Pension Fund Consultants Wyatt Harris Graham Ltd.
Auditors Arthur Andersen & Co.
Company Employees 1,600
Members 320
Pensioners 15
Annual Contributions £125,000
Annual Outflow £2,000
Capital Value £328,000

TRAVIS & ARNOLD LTD
Lodge Way House, Harleston Road,
Northampton NN5 7UG
Telephone: 0604-52424

Secretary T.W.Glover, FCA
Insured with Eagle Star Insurance Co Ltd
Employees 2,529

TREBOR GROUP PENSION SCHEME 1978
Trebor House, Woodford Green, Essex IG8 8EX
Telephone: 01-550 8800

Secretary E.G.Thorne
Trustees Trebor Group Trustees Ltd.
Investment Advisers County Bank Ltd.
Actuaries Duncan C.Fraser & Co.
Auditors Binder Hamlyn
Company Employees 3,593
Members 2,461
Pensioners 443
Annual Contributions £1.3 million
Capital Value £7.7 million

TREMLETTS HOLDINGS LTD.
Swan Court, Waterhouse Street,
Hemel Hempstead, Herts
Telephone: 0442-63934

Secretary D.W.Rigwell, ACIS
Employees 1,698

G.PERCY TRENTHAM LTD RETIREMENT BENEFITS PLAN
Head Office, Pangbourne, Reading,
Berkshire RG8 8AN
Telephone: 07357-3333

Company Secretary G.Hornby
Part Managed by Sun Alliance Fund Management Ltd
Investment Advisers Hill Samuel Investment Management Ltd
Actuarial Advice Obtained through Cubie, Wood & Co.Ltd.
Pension Fund Consultants Lowndes Associated Pensions Ltd.
Auditors Price Waterhouse & Co.

G.PERCY TRENTHAM LTD *Continued*

Company Employees 1,500
Members 380
Pensioners 24
Capital Value £2,500,000

TRIANGLE INTERNATIONAL LTD

PO Box 72, Wigan, Lancashire WN4 8EJ
Telephone: 0942-214513

Pension Fund Secretary D.J.L.Lems
Company Secretary J.L.Eagle
Trustees Trind Pension Trust Ltd
Investment Advisers Finance for Industry
Actuaries R.Watson & Sons
Auditors Parker Gradwell & Co
Company Employees 1,433
Members 195
Pensioners 296
Annual Contributions £67,000
Annual Investment Income £337,000
Capital Value £2,345,000

TRICENTROL INCREMENTAL PENSION SCHEME

Capel House, New Broad Street,
London EC2M 1JS
Telephone: 01-628 4951

Secretary H.R.Harlow
Treasurer R.B.Ambury
Trustees Tricentrol Pension Trustees Ltd
Stockbrokers & Investment Advisers de Zoete & Bevan
Actuaries Bacon & Woodrow
Auditors Deloitte Haskins & Sells
Solicitors Slaughter & May
Company Employees 2,337
Members 900
Pensioners 22

	£000
Annual Contributions	432
Annual Investment Income	233
Gross Annual Outflow	81
Capital Value	2,643
Summary of Investments	
Equities	1,079
Fixed Interest	874
Cash & Deposits	69
Others	57

TRICO-FOLBERTH LTD PENSION PLAN

Great West Road, Brentford, Middx.TW8 9HP
Telephone: 01-560 2111

Financial Executive & Company Secretary P.A.Green, CA
Trustees G.G.Cooke, J.F.Blackham

Insured with Standard Life Assurance Co
Pension Fund Consultants Wigham Poland Pension Consultants Ltd.
Auditors Touche Ross & Co.
Company Employees 1,660
Members 900
Pensioners 200

TRIDENT TELEVISION GROUP PENSION SCHEME

The Television Centre, Leeds LS3 1JS
Telephone: 0532-38283

Secretary L.T.Thornby, FCIS
Trustees Trident Television Group Pension Trust
Stockbrokers and Investment Advisers Hoare Govett Ltd.
Actuaries Duncan C.Fraser & Co.
Auditors Peat, Marwick, Mitchell & Co.
Group Employees (at 10.9.80) 2,122
Members 1,925
Pensioners 102

	£000
Annual Contributions (to 5.4.80)	2,056
Annual Investment Income	954
Annual Outflow	287
Capital Value	10,759
Summary of Investments	
Equities	5,386
Fixed Interest	3,962
Property	159
Cash & Deposits	1,281

TRIND LTD

See Triangle International Ltd

TRIPLEX HOLDINGS PENSION FUND AND SUPPLEMENTARY SCHEME

Eckersall Road, Kings Norton,
Birmingham B38 8SR
Telephone: 021-458 2031

Assistant Company Secretary F.W.Newell,BSc
Investment Advisers Drayton Montagu Portfolio Management Ltd.
Actuarial Advice Obtained through Cubie, Wood & Co.Ltd.
Pension Fund Consultants Noble Lowndes & Partners Ltd.
Auditors Coopers & Lybrand
Company Employees 2,900
Members 800
Pensioners 1,000
Annual Contributions £573,000
Annual Investment Income £555,000
Capital Value £6,943,000

TRIPLEX FOUNDRIES GROUP LTD

Upper Church Lane, Tipton,
West Midlands DY4 9PA
Telephone: 021-557 6211

TRIPLEX FOUNDRIES GROUP LTD *Continued*

Secretary W.C.Adams
Employees 3,000

TRUSTEE SAVINGS BANKS 1976 PENSION SCHEME

PO Box 33, 3 Copthall Avenue, London EC2P 2AB
Telephone: 01-588 9292

Pension Fund Secretary C.D.Willett
Pension Fund Controller R.Peacock,APMI
Trustees TSB Pension Trust Ltd.
Chairman R.T.Ellis,OBE
Investment Advisers Central Trustee Savings Bank
Property Advisers Hillier Parker May & Rowden
Actuaries R.Watson & Sons
Auditors Ernst & Whinney
Company Employees (at 30.11.79) 16,614
Members 15,457
Pensioners 2,907

	£000
Annual Contributions	14,099
Annual Investment Income	11,791
Annual Outflow	5,163
Capital Value	107,099
Summary of Investments	
Equities	41,661
Fixed Interest	48,072
Property	5,700
Cash & Deposits	11,666

TRUSTHOUSE FORTE LTD. GROUP PENSION FUND

7 Hanover Square, London W1R 0PS
Telephone: 01-493 8121

Head of Pensions N.J.Preston,APMI
Investment Advisers Hambros Investment Management Services Ltd., Hill Samuel Investment Management Ltd., Warburg Investment Management Ltd.
Actuaries Clay & Partners
Pension Fund Consultants Metropolitan Pensions Association Ltd.
Auditors Price Waterhouse & Co.
Solicitors Paisner & Co.
Company Employees 55,000
Members 7,700
Pensioners 1,800
Annual Contributions £2,073,000
Annual Investment Income £1,574,000
Capital Value £17,422,000

TRW CLIFFORD LTD. HOURLY PAID PENSION SCHEME

Dupont House, Vaughan Way,
Secretary L.T.Hall
Pensions Administrator P.D.Blakemore

Managed by Provident Mutual Managed Pension Funds Ltd.
Auditors Ernst & Whinney
Members 1,350
Pensioners 30
Annual Contributions £391,000

See also Clifford Group

W.S.TRY (HOLDINGS) LTD

Cowley, Uxbridge, Middlesex UB8 2AL
Telephone: 0895-51222

Secretary G.S.Whitmore
Employees 500

TUBE INVESTMENTS LTD STAFF PENSION SCHEME & TI GENERAL PENSION AND LIFE ASSURANCE SCHEME

TI House, Five Ways, Birmingham B16 8SO
Telephone: 021-454 4838

Pension Fund Manager and Secretary B.J.Solomon, APMI
Director of Pensions K.J.Austin, FPMI
Trustees 9 for each scheme
Investment Advisers J.Henry Schroder Wagg & Co Ltd, S.G.Warburg & Co Ltd
Actuaries Clay & Partners
Pension Fund Consultants Metropolitan Pensions Association Ltd
Auditors Price Waterhouse & Co
Company Employees 60,431

	Staff Scheme	General Scheme
Members	18,927	31,435
Pensioners	4,824	7,029
	£000	£000
Annual Contributions	15,145	14,717
Annual Investment Income	8,661	5,079
Annual Outflow	10,492	8,551
Capital Value (market value)	110,376	60,329
Summary of Investments		
UK Equities	50,585	35,322
Overseas Equities	6,672	2,970
Fixed Interest	28,402	10,170
Property	21,128	9,732
Cash & Deposits	3,589	2,135

TUFNOL INDUSTRIES LTD. STAFF PENSION FUND

P.O.Box 376, Perry Bar, Birmingham B42 2TB
Telephone: 021-356 9351

Director & Secretary J.M.Meek,ACMA
Investment Advisers Fraser Green & Co.
Actuaries Duncan C.Fraser & Co.
Auditors H.H.Sherwood & Co.
Company Employees 590
Members 324

TUFNOL INDUSTRIES LTD. Continued

Pensioners 211
Annual Contributions £185,000
Annual Investment Income £121,000
Capital Value £858,000

TULLIS RUSSELL STAFF & EMPLOYEES PENSION SCHEMES

Auchmuty & Rothes Paper Mills, Glenrothes, Fife KY7 6PB
Telephone: 0592-75311

Secretary W.G.Fletcher

Trustees Dr.D.F.O.Russell, W.G.Fletcher, R.J.Wylie, T.D.Murray, R.MacGregor

Insured with Scottish Widows' Fund & Life Assurance Society

Pension Fund Consultants Reed Stenhouse Benefit Consultants Ltd.

Company Employees 1,634

Members 950

Pensioners 250

Annual Contributions £600,000

TUNNEL HOLDINGS LTD. STAFF PENSION SCHEME & WORKS PENSION SCHEME

16 Old Queen Street, London SW1H 9HT
Telephone: 01-222 9080

Personnel Manager J.W.Blair,BA

Company Secretary G.A.A.Currie

Staff Scheme Part Insured with Standard Life Assurance Co.

Investment Advisers Cazenove & Co, Kleinwort Benson Investment Management Ltd

Actuaries Bacon & Woodrow

Auditors Price Waterhouse & Co.

Solicitors Biddle & Co.

Company Employees 1,481

	Staff	Works
Members	359	1,250
Pensioners	237	25
	£000	£000
Annual Contributions	445	513
Annual Investment Income	104	14
Capital Value	1,677	516

There is also a Workmens Pension Fund with 816 members and 480 pensioners. This is insured with The Standard Life Assurance Company

TUNNEL REFINERIES LTD

Thames Bank House, Tunnel Avenue, London SE10 0PA
Telephone: 01-858 3271

Secretary D.F.Scadeng

Employees 574

THOMAS TUNNOCK LTD.

34 Old Mill Road, Uddington, Lanarks.

Director T.M.Tunnock

Employees 706

TURNER & CO (GLASGOW) LTD

65 Brown Street, Glasgow G2 8PQ
Telephone: 041-221 9211

Director A.G.Turner

Employees 500

TURNER & NEWALL LTD. STAFF RETIREMENT BENEFITS SCHEME AND RETIREMENT BENEFITS SCHEME FOR HOURLY PAID PERSONNEL

20 St Mary's Parsonage, Manchester M3 2NL
Telephone: 061-833 9272

Group Pensions Controller N.J.Godden, BSc, FPMI

Secretary C.J.Dodson

Pensions Administration Manager C.Farrow, ACIS, APMI

Trustees Staff: Turner & Newall (Staff) Pension Trustees Ltd. Hourly Paid: Turner & Newall (Hourly Paid) Pension Trustees Ltd.

Chairman H.D.S.Hardie

Investment Advisers Staff: J.Henry Schroder Wagg & Co. Ltd., Phillips & Drew. Hourly Paid: Hoare Govett Ltd.

Property Advisers Weatherall Green & Smith

Actuaries Duncan C.Fraser & Co.

Auditors Deloitte, Haskins & Sells

Company Employees 22,456

	Staff Scheme	Hourly Paid
Members (at 31.12.79)	5,952	9,868
Pensioners	2,261	2,742
	£000	£000
Annual Contributions	7,178	5,114
Annual Investment Income	4,477	1,330
Annual Outflow	3,815	2,330
Capital Value		
Book Value	51,192	17,540
Market Value	60,789	18,308
Summary of Investments		
Fixed Interest	15,654	5,344
Equities	27,574	8,562
Unit Trusts & Managed Funds	4,104	510
Property	9,806	2,048
Short Term Loans	2,426	1,401
Others	1,225	443

W & E TURNER LTD

St Crispin's Way, The Roundabout, Thurmaston, Leicester LE4 8BR
Telephone: 0533-694701

Secretary E.W.G.Broughton

Employees 884

TURNER MANUFACTURING CO LTD

Wulfruna Works, Moorfield Road,
Wolverhampton WV2 4PD
Telephone: 0902-28231

Secretary P.J.Horrell

Trustees D.W.Evans, R.A.Joseph, G.Wollam, R.A.Hadley, K.J.Staves, P.J.Horrell

Investment Managed by Pensions Management (SWF) Ltd

Actuarial Advice obtained through Scottish Widows' Fund & Life Assurance Society

Pension Fund Consultant G.A.Bickley

Members 2,015

Pensioners 192

Annual Contributions £950,000

Capital Value £2,732,000

	£000
Annual Contributions	159
Annual Investment Income	136
Annual Outflow	206
Capital Value	2,231
Summary of Investments	
Equities	1,173
Fixed Interest	346
Property	321
Cash & Deposits	111
Others	232

TURRIFF CORPORATION LTD

Budbrooke Road, Warwick CV34 5XJ
Telephone: 0926-43400

Company Secretary P.D.Taylor

Insurance Manager E.C.Elmer

Insured with Scottish Widows' Fund & Life Assurance Society

Employees 1,245

TWENTIETH CENTURY SUPPLIERS LTD

187a Field End Road, Eastcote, Pinner, Middx HA5 1QU
Telephone: 01-868 7233

Secretary Mrs.B.Wagstaff

Employees 540

TWIL LTD. STAFF & WORKS PENSION FUND

PO Box 119, Shepcote Lane, Sheffield, S.Yorks.S9 1TY
Telephone: 0742-442741

Pension Fund Manager R.M.Hill, FSCA, APMI

Secretary A.M.Gillam

Insured with Guardian Royal Exchange Assurance Group Ltd

Employees 5,886

TWINLOCK PENSION SCHEME

36 Croydon Road, Beckenham, Kent BR3 4BH
Telephone: 01-650 4818

Secretary Mrs.M.M.Wells

Trustees M.J.H.Hale, R.B.Kemp, G.H.Goode, G.P.Shillinglaw, B.W.H.Croft

Investment Advisers N.M.Rothschild Asset Management Ltd

Pension Fund Consultants and Actuarial Advice obtained through Wyatt Harris Graham Ltd.

Auditors Touche Ross & Co

Company Employees 1,700

Members 474

Pensioners 117

JOHN TYLER & SONS LTD

Relyt Works, Humberstone Road, Leicester LE5 3AR
Telephone: 0533-22294

Secretary E.E.Egan

Employees 500

TYNE & WEAR COUNTY COUNCIL SUPERANNUATION FUND

Sandyford House, Archbold Terrace, Newcastle upon Tyne NE2 1ED
Telephone: 0632-816144

Treasurer P.J.Smith

Deputy County Treasurer E.S.Gill,IPFA

Actuaries R.Watson & Sons

Auditors Price Waterhouse & Co.

Members 31,987

Pensioners 6,586

Annual Contributions £11,640,000 (1979)

Capital Value (at 30.6.80) £135,118,000

TYNE PLYWOOD (HOLDINGS) LTD

Kingsway, Team Valley, Gateshead, Tyne & Wear NE11 0JX
Telephone: 0632-877231

Secretary K.Rollison

Employees 987

TYSONS (CONTRACTORS) LTD.

Dryden Street, Liverpool L5 5BU
Telephone: 051-207 4949

Secretary D.R.Perrett,FCA

Employees 765

UBM GROUP PENSION FUND

P.O.Box 78, County Gates, Ashton Road, Bristol BS99 7EW
Telephone: 0272 633315

Secretary J.H.Risdon, ACIS, APMI

Pension Fund Managers A.M.Dilleigh, FCIS, APMI (Director), C.K.Irwin, BA (Investment Manager)

Trustees UBM Pension Trust Ltd

Directors M.G.Phillips (Chairman), F.Brooksbank, D.Howroyd, A.M.Dilleigh, APMI, C.K.Irwin, BA

Actuaries R.Watson & Sons

Auditors Peat Marwick Mitchell & Co

Company Employees 6,500

Members 3,346

UBM GROUP *Continued*

Pensioners 1,681

	£000
Annual Contributions	2,300
Annual Investment Income	2,000
Gross Annual Outflow	1,600
Capital Value	28,000
Summary of Investments	
Equities	11,583
Fixed Interest	6,813
Property	9,604

UDS GROUP LTD

66-68 Seymour Street, London W1A 2BY
Telephone: 01-262 7755

Pension Fund Administrator Miss R. Sykes

Finance Director A.B.Wilson

Insurance Manager J.H.Tarry

Company Secretary M.S.Samuels,FCA

Investment Advisers Barclays Bank Trust Co.Ltd.

Property Advisers Michael Laurie & Partners

Actuaries Clay & Partners

Auditors Vinney Merrets

Company Employees 28,353

Members 5,400

Pensioners 900

Annual Contributions £1,300,000

Capital Value £9,650,000

UK PROVIDENT STAFF PENSION FUND

Dolphin House, New Street, Salisbury, Wilts.SP1 2QQ
Telephone: 0722-6242

Assistant General Manager Pensions J.D.Hammond,FIA,APMI

Stockbrokers de Zoete & Bevan

Auditors Deloitte, Haskins & Sells

Employees 650

Members 515

Pensioners 195

Annual Contributions £548,000

Annual Investment Income £323,000

Annual Outflow £520,000

Capital Value £3,878,000

UKF FERTILISERS LTD PENSION FUND

Ince, Chester CH2 4LB
Telephone: 09282-2777

Manager Personnel Services D.F.C.Pugh, LLB

Investment Advisers Robert Fleming Investment Management Ltd

Pension Fund Consultants Wyatt Harris Graham Ltd.

Auditors Price Waterhouse & Co

Company Employees 918

Members (at 31.12.79) 912

Pensioners 40

Annual Contributions £680,000

Annual Investment Income £915,000

Capital Value £8,750,000

UKO INTERNATIONAL LTD

Bittacy Hill, London NW7 1EN
Telephone: 01-346 2660

Secretary J.F.Gittus

Managed by Legal & General Assurance Society Ltd

Employees 3,546

ULSTER CARPET MILLS LTD

Castleisland Factory, Portadown BT62 1EE
Telephone: 0762-34433

Director W.O.Wilson

Employees 600

ULSTER LACES LTD

Loughgall Road, Portadown, Armagh BT62 4BY
Telephone: 0762-35111

Secretary S.D.Brown

Director K.Bloch

Employees 550

THE ULSTER WEAVING CO LTD

47 Linfield Road, Belfast BT12 5GL
Telephone: 0232-29494

Chairman K.T.Sturgess

Employees 1,000

UMECO HOLDINGS LTD.

99 Boston Road, Hanwell, London W7 3SB
Telephone: 01-567 6644

Secretary D.J.Webber

Employees 562

UNBRAKO LTD PENSIONS AND INSURANCE PLAN

Burnaby Road, Coventry, West Midlands CV6 4AE
Telephone: 0203-88722

Pensions and Benefits Administrator Miss E.McNamara

Trustees A.R.Cropper, G.M.Doyle, M.Dwyer, J.P.Rhein, D.Wales, R.A.Zeberlein

Investment Advisers Bankers Trustee and Executor Co. Ltd.

Pension Fund Consultants and Actuarial Advice Obtained through Towers, Perrin, Forster & Crosby Inc.

Employees 878

Members 821

Pensioners 176

	£000
Annual Contributions	363
Annual Investment Income	318

UNBRAKO LTD Continued

Annual Outflow	217
Capital Value	1,818
Summary of Investments	
Equities	923
Fixed Interest	603
Cash & Deposits	292

UNDERGROUND MINING MACHINERY LTD PENSION FUND

Horndale Avenue, Aycliffe Industrial Estate, Newton Aycliffe, Co. Durham
Telephone: 0325-312431

Secretary K.H.Asbeck

Pension Fund Manager Eric Lodge

Trustees K.H.Asbeck, A.J.Sanford, E.Lodge

Insured with Sun Life Assurance Society Ltd.

Auditors Peat, Marwick, Mitchell & Co.

Company Employees 510

Members 381

Pensioners 27

Annual Contributions £159,000

UNICHEM LTD PENSION AND ASSURANCE SCHEME

Crown House, Morden, Surrey SM4 5EF
Telephone: 01-542 8572

Secretary R.J.Hunt, FCA

Trustees P.J.Dodd,FCIS, R.E.Monaghan,FCCA, J.N.Thompson, N.Sampson

Insured with Legal & General Assurance Society Ltd.

Pension Fund Consultants C.E.Heath, Urquhart (Life & Pensions) Ltd.

Company Employees 1,600

Members 300

Annual Contributions £270,000

UNICORN INDUSTRIES LTD. PENSION PLAN

Castle Hill House, Windsor, Berks SL4 1LY
Telephone: 54231

Secretary J.J.F.Francis

Assistant Group Secretary Mrs. P.M.Kemp

Trustees Unicorn Industries Pension Fund Trustees Ltd

Managed by Pensions Management (SWF) Ltd

Pension Fund Consultants Wood and Steven Ltd

Company Employees 3,194

Members 3,200

UNIFLEX HOLDINGS LTD.

Lea Valley Trading Estate, Edmonton, London N18 3LH
Telephone: 01-807 1077

Secretary M.D.Lazarus

Employees 960

UNIGATE 'A' AND 'B' PENSION SCHEMES

Unigate House, Western Avenue, London W3 0SH
Telephone: 01-992 3400

Group Pensions Manager I.J.Ferguson

Company Secretary W.G.Cottrell

Trustees Unigate Staff Pension Scheme Trustees Ltd

Part Managed by Prudential Pensions Ltd.

Investment Advisers J.Henry Schroder Wagg & Co Ltd

Actuaries Bacon & Woodrow

Auditors Peat, Marwick Mitchell & Co.

Company Employees 37,800

	A Scheme	B Scheme
Members	4,492	16,643
Pensioners	2,273	150
	£000	£000
Annual Contributions	5,893	2,799
Annual Investment Income	1,819	669
Annual Outflow	4,962	1,281
Capital Value (Market Value)	40,631	9,304

UNILEVER SUPERANNUATION FUND

Unilever House, Blackfriars, London EC4P 4BQ
Telephone: 01-822 5252

Pensions Officer E.F.Rogers,BA,FIA,FPMI

Deputy Pensions Officer F.R.Langham, FIA, FPMI

UK Pension Fund Manager D.G.Hosegood,FPMI

Investment Controller R.Wilson, FPMI

Property Manager B.Rumway

Secretaries Ernest Allen, Nigel G.C.Wilson

Joint Actuaries Adrian S.Garner, FIA, F.R.Langham, FIA, FPMI

Trustees Unilever Superannuation Trustees Ltd

Directors 12 Nominated by Unilever and 12 Elected by Members' Delegates

Investment Managers Unilever Pension Investments Ltd (funds are registered in the name of USF Nominees Ltd)

Auditors Price Waterhouse & Co

Company Employees 85,000

Members 56,400

Pensioners 24,800

	£ million
Annual Contributions	40
Annual Investment Income	40
Annual Outflow	30
Capital Value (Market)	521
Summary of Investments	
Equities	270
Fixed Interest & Cash	64
Property	170
Cash & Deposits	16

UNION CARBIDE UK LTD. STAFF PENSION FUND AND WORKS PENSION SCHEME

8 Grafton Street, London W1A 2LR
Telephone: 01-629 8100

Pension Fund Manager A.C.Morris

Senior Pensions Officer L.A.W.Barrow

Insured with Staff: Standard Life Assurance Co., *Works:* Prudential Assurance Co.Ltd.

Pension Fund Consultants Staff: Holmwoods & Crawfurd (Life & Pension Brokers) Ltd., *Works:* Bain Dawes & Partners Ltd.

Auditors F.W.Stephens & Co.

Company Employees 1,951

Members Staff: 320, *Works:* 500

Pensioners Staff: 67, *Works:* 84

THE UNION-CASTLE LINE SUPERANNUATION SCHEME

2 & 4 St.Mary Axe, London EC3A 8BP
Telephone: 01-283 4343

Pension Fund Manager & Secretary A.H.Mitchell, APMI

Trustees Tendimus Pension Trustee Co.Ltd.

Investment Advisers Gartmore Investment Ltd.

Property Advisers St.Quintin

Actuaries R.Watson & Sons

Auditors Deloitte, Haskins & Sells

Company Employees 2,000

Members 1,300

Pensioners 1,750

	£000
Annual Contributions	2,590
Annual Investment Income	1,940
Annual Outflow	1,930
Capital Value	20,400
Summary of Investments	
Equities	11,200
Fixed Interest	5,700
Property	700
Cash & Deposits	1,200
Others	1,600

UNION CORPORATION (UK) LTD LONDON PENSION FUND

Princes House, 95 Gresham Street, London EC2V 7BS
Telephone: 01-606 3845

Pension Fund Manager L.C.Bartram

Company Secretary P.Hurst

Actuarial Advice Obtained through Cubie, Wood & Co.Ltd.

Auditors Price Waterhouse & Co

Members 35

Pensioners 61

Annual Contributions £87,000

Annual Investment Income £270,000

Capital Value £2,537,000

THE UNION INTERNATIONAL CO LTD STAFF PENSION FUND AND PENSION SCHEME FOR HOURLY & WEEKLY PAID EMPLOYEES

14 West Smithfield, London EC1A 9JN
Telephone: 01-248 1212

Pension Fund Manager R.W.C.Offwood, FPMI

Investment Advisers Alder Investment Management Ltd

Property Advisers Commercial Properties Ltd

Actuaries Bacon & Woodrow

Solicitors Rowe & Maw

Auditors Kidsons

Company Employees 16,680

Members 10,000

Pensioners 2,200

Capital Value £28 million

UNION OF SHOP DISTRIBUTIVE & ALLIED WORKERS USDAW STAFF SUPERANNUATION FUND

Oakley, 188 Wilmslow Road, Fallowfield, Manchester M14 6LJ
Telephone: 061-224 2804

Pension Fund Secretary A.W.Hilton

Management Committee 7

Trustees S.Tierney, W.H.P.Whatley

Investment Advisers & Stockbrokers Halliday Simpson & Co.

Actuaries Bacon & Woodrow

Auditors Appleby English & Partners

Employees 401

Members 394

Pensioners 126

	£000
Annual Contributions	355
Annual Investment Income	357
Annual Outflow	254
Capital Value (Market Value)	3,973
Summary of Investments	
Equities	1,321
Fixed Interest	2,300
Cash & Deposits	80
Others	11

UNIPORK LTD

Molesworth Road, Cookstown, Co Tyrone BT80 8PJ
Telephone: 06487-3321

Secretary K.S.McLennon

Employees 750

UNIROYAL LTD STAFF PENSION FUND

Newbridge, Midlothian EH28 8LG
Telephone: 031-333 2700

Secretary J.Edgar

Trustees J.Edgar, N.Little, D.Millar, D.Vickers, J.Ralph, T.Bartlett

Investment Advisers N.M.Rothschild & Sons Ltd., Warburg Investment Management Ltd.

UNIROYAL LTD *Continued*

Pension Fund Consultants and Actuarial Advice Obtained through Martin Paterson Associates Ltd.

Auditors Deloitte, Haskins & Sells

Company Employees 2,000

Members 400

Pensioners 250

UNIT CONSTRUCTION CO LTD
34 St James's Street, London SW1A 1JA
Telephone: 01-930 8383

Secretary E.W.Owens

Employees 1,910

UNITECH LTD
Phoenix House, Station Hill, Reading, Berks RG1 1NB
Telephone: 0734-57075

Secretary J.B.C.Lethbridge

Stockbrokers Buckmaster & Moore

Employees 2,397

UNITED ASSN FOR THE PROTECTION OF TRADE LTD
Zodiac House, 163 London Road, Croydon, Surrey CR9 2RP
Telephone: 01-686 5644

Executive C.McNeil Greig

Employees 850

UNITED BISCUITS PENSION PLAN
Syon Lane, Isleworth, Middlesex TW7 5NN
Telephone: 01-560 3131

Secretary D.R.J.Stewart,MA

Pensions Administration Manager H.G.Hunt, ACMA, APMI

Trustees United Biscuits (Pension Trustees) Ltd

Chairman M.A.Heller

Investment Advisers Morgan Grenfell & Co Ltd, Robert Fleming Investment Management Ltd

Stockbrokers Rowe & Pitman, Wood Mackenzie

Property Advisers Richard Ellis, Savills

Actuaries Bacon & Woodrow

Solicitors Slaughter & May, W. & J. Burness WS, Dale & Newbery

Auditor Arthur Young McClelland Moores & Co

Company Employees (UK) 32,000

Members (at 31.5.79) 10,970

Pensioners 2,919

Deferred Pensioners 531

	£000
Annual Contributions	7,128
Annual Investment Income	2,907
Annual Outflow	2,548
Capital Value	
Book Value	34,362
Market Value	42,818

Summary of Investments	
Ordinary Shares & Unit Trusts	15,435
Fixed Interest	8,965
Overseas Shares & Bonds	2,484
Property & Property Shares	14,136
Cash & Deposits	1,505
Net Current Assets	293

UNITED-CARR PENSION FUND
Buckingham Road, Aylesbury, Bucks HP19 3QA
Telephone: 0296-26171

Secretary Miss M.Redman

Financial Director P.G.Martin, APMI

Trustees W.Clarke, P.G.Martin, APMI, D.J.Miller, R.G.McCarty

Investment Advisers Warburg Investments Management Ltd

Pension Fund Consultants Towers Perrin Forster & Crosby Inc

Auditors Ernst & Whinney

Company Employees 252

Members 215

Pensioners 88

	£000
Annual Contributions	64
Annual Investment Income	228
Annual Outflow	20
Capital Value	2,600
Summary of investments	
Equities	1,400
Fixed Interest	354
Others	80

UNITED CARRIERS LTD
Turnell's Mill Lane, Wellingborough, Northants NN8 2QQ
Telephone: 0933-225461

Secretary T.M.Smith

Insured with Scottish Equitable Life Assurance Society

Employees 2,582

UNITED CITY MERCHANTS LTD GROUP PENSION SCHEME
U.C.M. House, 3-5 Swallow Place, Princes Street, London W1A 1BB
Telephone: 01-629 8424

Pension Fund Manager K.Farrant

Investment Advisers Arbuthnot Investment Management Services Ltd

Stockbrokers Vickers Da Costa Ltd.

Actuarial Advice Obtained through Cubie, Wood & Co. Ltd.

Pension Fund Consultants Noble Lowndes & Partners Ltd.

Auditors Hill, Vellacott

UNITED DOMINIONS TRUST LTD GROUP RETIREMENT BENEFITS SCHEME
51 Eastcheap, London EC3P 3BU
Telephone: 01-623 3020

UNITED DOMINIONS TRUST LTD *Continued*

Pension Fund Manager P.A.Wilthew, APMI
Secretary P.W.S.Rowland
Investment Advisers Barclays Bank Trust Co Ltd
Actuaries R.Watson & Sons
Solicitors Simmons & Simmons
Auditors Price Waterhouse & Co
Company Employees 6,500
Members 3,250
Pensioners 500
Annual Contributions £2,887,000
Annual Investment Income £1,165,000
Capital Value £20,500,000

UNITED ENGINEERING INDUSTRIES LTD.

Chronicle Buildings, 74 Corporation Street,
Manchester M4 2DD
Telephone: 061-832 9075

Secretary E.Bridgehouse,FCA
Employees 642

THE UNITED GAS INDUSTRIES PENSION FUND

U.G.I.House, 3-4 Bentinck Street,
London W1M 6DH
Telephone: 01-486 4781

Pensions Officer & Secretary N.H.Redman
Associate Director & Group Secretary E.Milner, FCIS, APMI
Trustees UGI Pension Fund Trustees Ltd
Managed by Prudential Pensions Ltd., Pensions Management (SWF) Ltd.
Stockbrokers Scrimgeour, Kemp-Gee & Co.
Pension Fund Consultants and Actuarial Advice obtained through Godwins Ltd
Auditors Deloitte, Haskins & Sells
Company Employees 3,471
Members 870
Pensioners 550 approx.
Annual Contributions £490,000
Capital Value £4,000,000

UNITED GLASS LTD (A) HOURLY PAID PENSION SCHEME, (B) STAFF PENSION FUND AND (C) SENIOR MANAGEMENT STAFF PENSION FUND

79 Kingston Road, Staines, Middx.TW8 1AD
Telephone: 51321

Employee Benefits Manager P.Armitage, MA, APMI, AMBIM
Company Secretary J.E.Oliver, FCA, ACIS
Trustees (A) United Glass Hourly Paid Scheme (Pension Trustee) Ltd., (B) United Glass Staff Scheme (Pension Trustee) Ltd., (C) United Glass Senior Management Staff Scheme (Pension Trustee) Ltd.
Investment Advisers (A) Legal & General (Investment Management) Ltd. (B) Warburg Investment Management Ltd. (C) Grieveson Grant & Co.
Actuaries Clay & Partners
Pension Fund Consultants Godwins Ltd.
Auditors Peat, Marwick, Mitchell & Co.
Company Employees 9,875
Members 8,550
Pensioners 3,550
Annual Contributions £8,200,000
Capital Value £29,950,000

UNITED KINGDOM ATOMIC ENERGY AUTHORITY (A) PRINCIPAL NON-INDUSTRIAL SUPERANNUATION SCHEME, (B) INDUSTRIAL SUPERANNUATION SCHEME AND (C) PROTECTED PERSONS SUPERANNUATION SCHEME

11 Charles II Street, London SW1Y 4QP
Telephone: 01-930 5454

Pension Officer K.Longson
Actuary Government Actuary
Members (at 31.3.80) (a) 20,403, (b)12,765, (c) 813
Pensioners (at 31.3.80) (a) 5,079, (b) 2,670, (c) 2,807
Annual Contributions £35 million approx.

Not funded but notional values at 31.3.79 (a) £248 million, (b)£36 million, (c) £10 million

(a)includes employees of:
(i) British Nuclear Fuels Ltd
(ii) The Radiochemical Centre Ltd
(iii) The Science Research Council
(iv) The National Radiological Protection Board
(v) The Ministry of Defence (Procurement Executive) Aldermaston
(b) and (c) includes employees of
(i) BNFL and (ii) TRC

UNITED KINGDOM PROPERTY CO LTD

19 Hanover Square, London W1A 1DU
Telephone: 01-409 3100

Managing Director M.S.Gorvy
Company Secretaries Hanover Management Services Ltd.
Investment Advisers Schlesinger Investment Management Services Ltd.
Employees 615

UNITED NEWSPAPERS LTD

23-27 Tudor Street, London EC4Y 0HR
Telephone: 01-583 9199

Secretary K.F.C.Elgar
Insured with Eagle Star Insurance Co Ltd, Scottish Widows' Fund & Life Assurance Society
Employees 5,603

UNITED SCIENTIFIC HOLDINGS LTD

140 Tottenham Court Road, London W1P 0JD
Telephone: 01-387 7224

UNITED SCIENTIFIC HOLDINGS LTD Continued

Secretary A.M.Jackson
Employees 913

UNITED SPRING & STEEL GROUP LTD
Hawthorn Works, Oldbury Road, Smethwick, West Midlands B66 1NQ
Telephone: 021-558 2791
Secretary M.R.Pye
Employees 684

UNITED STERLING CORPORATION LTD
Borax House, Carlisle Place, London SW1P 1HT
Telephone: 01-734 7080
Financial Director D.J.G.Shaw
Secretary N.L.Foskett
Employees 940

UNITED TRANSPORT CO LTD GROUP PENSION & ASSURANCE SCHEME
Mounton Chambers, Chepstow, Gwent NP6 5XB
Telephone: 02912-2222
Pension Fund Manager S.C.Hatchard, APMI
Director P.A.Brown, FCA, APMI
Insured with Legal & General Assurance Society Ltd
Pension Fund Consultants Notcutt Life & Pensions Ltd.
Auditors Peat, Marwick, Mitchell & Co.
Company Employees 3,370
Members 452
Pensioners 97
Annual Contributions £835,000
Capital Value £3,000,000

UNITED WIRE GROUP LTD
Granton Park Avenue, Edinburgh EH5 1HT
Telephone: 031-552 6241
Secretary E.Mullholland, LLB
Insured with Standard Life Assurance Co
Employees 670

UNIVERSITIES SUPERANNUATION SCHEME
Richmond House, Rumford Place, Liverpool L3 9FD
Telephone: 051-227 4711
Chief Executive Officer & Secretary P.Stirrup, MA, FIA, FPMI, FBCS
Deputy Chief Executive Officer T.J.McHugh, BA, FCII, APMI
Pensions Officers J.A.Howarth,BA, A.G.Smith,BSc
Trustees Universities Superannuation Scheme Ltd
Stockbrokers Phillips & Drew, Rowe & Pitman
Property Advisers Jones Lang Wootton
Actuaries Duncan C,Fraser & Co.
Legal Advisers Alsop Stevens Batesons & Co
Auditors Chalmers Impey & Co
Total Academic Staff 60,000

Members (at 31.3.80) 56,000
Pensioners 2,968

	£ million
Annual Contributions	85
Annual Investment Income	28
Other Income	31
Annual Outflow	47
Capital Value	623
Summary of Investments	
Equities	109
Fixed Interest	85
Property	75
Cash & Deposits	28
Managed Funds	106
Individual Life Assurance Policies	219

The figures include those of the associated Universities Supplementary Dependents Pension Scheme which has the same membership

THE UNIVERSITY COLLEGE OF NORTH WALES PENSION SCHEME
College Road, Bangor, Gwynedd
Telephone: 0248-51151
Accountant J.Cherry, DPA IPFA
Insured with Legal & General Assurance Society Ltd.
Pension Fund Consultants Noble Lowndes & Partners Ltd
Employees (June 1980) 1,350
Members 518
Pensioners 35
Annual Contributions £350,000
Capital Value £1,400,000

UNIVERSITY COLLEGE OF SWANSEA PENSION FUND
Singleton Park, Swansea SA2 8PP
Telephone: 0792-25678
Secretary to the Trustees W.F.D.Harrison
Pensions Administrators Lowndes Associated Pensions Ltd.
Trustees Professor R.W.Steel (Principal), A.Davies (Registrar), DR.D.J.Young (Treasurer), D.Boorman (Academic Secretary) Trade Union Representatives (full trustees) G.Phillips, A.Williams
Managed by Legal & General (Pensions Management) Ltd.
Actuarial Advice Obtained through Cubie, Wood & Co.Ltd.
Pension Fund Consultants Lowndes Associated Pensions Ltd.
Auditors Deloitte, Haskins & Sells
Employees/Members 565 (at 31.7.79)
Pensioners 129

	£000
Annual Contributions (to 31.7.79)	297
Annual Outflow	148
Capital Value	1,339

UNIVERSITY COLLEGE OF SWANSEA Continued

Summary of Investments
Mixed Fund	842
Property	388
Cash & Deposits	37
Others	84

THE UNIVERSITY COLLEGE OF WALES PENSION & ASSURANCE SCHEME

1 King Street, Aberystwyth, Dyfed SY23 2AX
Telephone: 0970-3177

Accountant W.L.Smart, BA, IPFA

Managed by Legal & General Assurance (Pension Management) Ltd.

Investment Advisers C.W.Jacob

Actuarial Advice Obtained through Cubie, Wood & Co.Ltd.

Pension Fund Consultants Noble Lowndes & Partners Ltd

Auditors Fraser, Threlford & Co.

Employees 1,400

Members 450

Pensioners 50

	£000
Annual Contributions	285
Annual Investment Income	237
Annual Outflow	67
Capital Value	1,590

Summary of Investments
	%
Equities	40
Fixed Interest	31
Property	28
Cash & Deposits	1

UNIVERSITY OF ABERDEEN SUPERANNUATION & LIFE ASSURANCE SCHEME

University Office, Regent Walk, Aberdeen AB9 1FX
Telephone: 0224-40241

Secretary T.B.Skinner

Insured with Scottish Amicable Life Assurance Society

Pension Fund Consultants D.L.Bloomer & Partners

Employees 939

Members 144

Pensioners 123

Annual Contributions £499,000

UNIVERSITY OF ASTON IN BIRMINGHAM RETIREMENT BENEFITS SCHEME

Gosta Green, Birmingham B4 7ET
Telephone: 021-359 3611

Pensions Officer J.R.Edgar

Insured with Scottish Widows' Fund & Life Assurance Society

Pension Fund Consultants Hogg Robinson (Benefit Consultants) Ltd.

Auditors Deloitte Haskins & Sells

Employees 2,200

Members 406

Pensioners 10

Annual Contributions £253,000

UNIVERSITY OF BRISTOL PENSION & ASSURANCE SCHEME

Senate House, Tyndall Avenue, Bristol BS8 1TH
Telephone: 0272-24161

Pension Fund Manager G.H.Edgington,IPFA

Pension Fund Consultants Noble Lowndes & Partners Ltd.

Members 1,187

Pensioners 98

Annual Contributions £672,000

Capital Value £3,437,000

UNIVERSITY OF CAMBRIDGE CONTRIBUTORY PENSION FUND

The Old Schools, Cambridge CB2 1TS
Telephone: 0223-358933

University Treasurer T.C.Gardner

Administrative Assistant M.J.Atkin

Stockbrokers Buckmaster & Moore

Actuaries and Pension Fund Consultants Burton & Co

Auditors Spicer & Pegler

Employees 2,700 (non-academic)

Members 2,000

Pensioners 650

Annual Contributions £1,269,000

Capital Value £14,000,000

UNIVERSITY OF DURHAM RETIREMENT BENEFITS PLAN (1969)

Old Shire Hall, Durham
Telephone: 0385-64466

Treasurer A.McWilliam, BA IPFA

Trustees Lowndes Associated Pensions Ltd.

Managed by Legal & General Assurance (Pensions Management) Ltd.

Pension Fund Consultants Lowndes Associated Pensions Ltd

Auditors Price Waterhouse & Co.

Employees 2,100

Members 573

Pensioners 49

	£000
Annual Contributions	226
Annual Investment Income	90
Annual Outflow	65
Capital Value of Fund (Market Value)	1,298

Summary of Investments
Equities	805
Fixed Interest	142
Property	351

UNIVERSITY OF EAST ANGLIA STAFF SUPERANNUATION SCHEME

The Registry, University Plain, Norwich, Norfolk NR4 7TJ
Telephone: 0603-56161

Finance Officer R.A.Newstead,FCCA,IPFA

Investment Advisers Lazard Securities Ltd.

Actuary M.E.Peters,FIA

Auditors Ensors

Employees 1,800

Members 572

Pensioners 72

Annual Contributions £304,000

Annual Investment Income £196,000

Capital Value £2,070,000

UNIVERSITY OF LEICESTER PENSION & ASSURANCE SCHEME

University Road, Leicester LE1 7RH
Telephone: 0533-50000

Assistant Accountant B.W.Pegg, ACMA, IPFA, AMBIM

Insured with Legal & General Assurance Society Ltd.

Pension Fund Consultants Bain Dawes & Partners Ltd.

Employees 1,900

Members 750

Pensioners 112

THE UNIVERSITY OF LIVERPOOL PENSION FUND

PO Box 147, Liverpool L69 3BX
Telephone: 051-709 6022

Pension Fund Administrator E.Bradshaw, CA

Secretary P.H.Gayward

Trustees University of Liverpool Pension Fund Trustees Ltd.

Stockbrokers Ashton Tod McLaren, Rowe & Pitman, Tilney & Co.

Actuaries Duncan C. Fraser & Co

Auditors Deloitte, Haskins & Sells

Employees 6,000

Members 1,437

Pensioners 215

	£000
Annual Contributions	969
Annual Investment Income	545
Capital Value	6,739
Summary of Investments	
Equities	4,482
Fixed Interest	2,257

SUPERANNUATION ARRANGEMENTS OF THE UNIVERSITY OF LONDON(SAUL)

Senate House, Malet Street, London WC1E 7HU
Telephone: 01-636 8000

Secretary & Superannuation Officer N.A.Ryan,BA, FPMI

Deputy Secretary Mrs V.A.Walters, BA

Other Pension Management Mrs M.E.Hawkesworth, BSc, Miss M.C.Steed,BSc

Trustees University of London

Investment Advisers Charterhouse Japhet Ltd, Legal & General Assurance (Pensions Management) Ltd

Actuaries Duncan C.Fraser & Co

Legal Advisers Alsop Stevens Batesons & Co

Auditors Knox Cooper

Total Employees 12,500

Members 11,500

Pensioners 1,000 (including deferred)

	£000
Annual Contributions	8,917
Annual Investment Income	1,362
Annual Outflow	3,294
Capital Value	32,214
Summary of Investments	
Equities	16,419
Fixed Interest	10,090
Property	493
Cash & Deposits	774

Some 50 independent employers participate in SAUL. They, together with recognised Trade Unions, appoint members to the Council, which has general oversight of the scheme, and elects the Executive and Investment Committees. SAUL applies to non-academic or related staff of the University of London and certain associated Institutions. For academic and related staff, see Universities Superannuation Scheme.

UNIVERSITY OF MANCHESTER SUPERANNUATION SCHEME

Oxford Road, Manchester M13 9PL
Telephone: 061-273 3333

Personnel Officer P.R.Jackson,BA,MIPM

Actuaries Duncan C.Fraser & Co.

Employees 3,400

Members 2,000

Pensioners 250

Annual Contributions £1,111,000

Annual Investment Income £797,000

Capital Value £8,609,000

UNIVERSITY OF NEWCASTLE UPON TYNE RETIREMENT BENEFITS PLAN

Kensington Terrace,
Newcastle upon Tyne NE1 7RU
Telephone: 0632-28511

Assistant Finance Officer W.Lawson,ACA

Trustees Lowndes Associated Pensions Ltd.

Employees 2,500

Members (approx) 2,100

THE UNIVERSITY OF NOTTINGHAM CONTRIBUTORY PENSION & ASSURANCE SCHEME

University Park, Nottingham NG7 2RD
Telephone: 0602-56101

Assistant Bursar and Secretary to the Trustee G.W.Baxendale-Baine, APMI

Insured with Legal & General Assurance Society Ltd.

Pension Fund Consultants Bain Dawes and Partners Ltd

Auditors Singleton, Carter & Co.

Employees 1,386

Members 899

Pensioners 56

Annual Contributions £640,000

UNIVERSITY OF OXFORD STAFF PENSION SCHEME

University Offices, Wellington Square,
Oxford OX1 2JD
Telephone: 0865-56747

Managed by Legal and General Managed Funds

Actuaries Bacon & Woodrow

Auditors Deloitte Haskins & Sells

Employees 5,100

Members 1,570

Pensioners 62

	£000
Annual Contributions	620
Annual Investment Income	620
Capital Value	3,800
Summary of Investments	
Equities	1,200
Fixed Interest	1,300
Property	1,300

UNIVERSITY OF READING EMPLOYEES' PENSION FUND

Whiteknights, Reading, Berks.RG6 2AH
Telephone: 0734-85123

Pension Fund Manager and Bursar R.H.Giddings, FCCA

Trustees The University of Reading

Investment Advisers Kleinwort Benson Investment Management Ltd.

Actuaries Duncan C. Fraser & Co.

Auditors Ernest Francis & Son

Employees 3,000

Members 520

Pensioners 85

	£000
Annual Contributions	293
Annual Investment Income	216
Annual Outflow	96
Capital Value	2,766
Summary of Investments	
Equities	1,216
Fixed Interest	1,244
Cash & Deposits	307

UNIVERSITY OF ST ANDREWS SUPERANNUATION & LIFE ASSURANCE SCHEME

College Gate, St Andrews, Fife KY16 9AJ
Telephone: 0334-76161

Quaestor and Factor C.P.Gordon, CA

Managed by S.C.A.M.P.I.

Pension Fund Consultants James M.MacAlaster & Alison Ltd.

Auditors Thomson McLintock & Co

Employees (at 1.8.80) 1,500

Members 382

Pensioners 69

Annual Contributions £203,000

UNIVERSITY OF SOUTHAMPTON NON-ACADEMIC STAFF PENSION & ASSURANCE SCHEME

University Road, Highfield, Southampton SO9 5NH
Telephone: 0703-559122

Clerk to the Trustees P.C.Payne, ACCA

Trustees J.M.Roberts,MA,D.Phil, D.A.Schofield,MA, J.H.Dalby,MA,FCA

Managed by Legal & General (Pensions Management) Ltd.

Actuarial Advice obtained through Cubie, Wood & Co. Ltd.

Pension Fund Consultants Noble Lowndes & Partners Ltd.

Auditors Peat, Marwick, Mitchell & Co.

Employees 2,068

Members 890

Pensioners 111

	£000
Annual Contributions	477
Annual Investment Income	31
Annual Outflow	163
Capital Value	2,856
Summary of Investments	
Fixed Interest	113
Cash & Deposits	164
Managed Fund Units	2,524

UNIVERSITY OF SUSSEX PENSION & ASSURANCE SCHEME

Sussex House, Falmer, Brighton BN1 9RH
Telephone: 0273-606755

Superannuation Officer R.W.Griffin,FIAA

Insured with Legal & General Assurance Society Ltd.

Pension Fund Consultants Noble Lowndes & Partners Ltd.

Employees 2,200

Members 600

Pensioners 50

UNIVERSITY OF SUSSEX Continued

Annual Contributions £356,000

In addition there are 742 members of the Universities Superannuation Scheme, and 18 pensioners

UNIVERSITY OF YORK

Heslington, York YO1 5DD
Telephone: 0904-59861

Finance Officer and Secretary of Pension Trust T.R.Bradley, IPFA

Trustees University of York Pension Trust Ltd.

Actuaries Duncan C. Fraser & Co

Auditors Barron & Barron

Solicitors Allen & Overy

Employees 1,500

Members 416

Pensioners 36

Annual Contributions £213,000

Capital value £900,000

UNOCHROME INDUSTRIES LTD.

1 Imperial Square, Cheltenham, Glos GL50 1QB
Telephone: 0242-34653

Secretary J.Gilbert,FCA

Insured with Equity & Law Life Assurance Society Ltd.

Pension Fund Consultants Godwins (Midlands & West) Ltd.

Auditors Robson Rhodes

Company Employees 885

Members 426

Pensioners 14

THE UNWINS WINE GROUP LTD.

35 Park Road, Chislehurst, Kent BR7 6BJ
Telephone: 01-468 7941

Secretary R.C.Burnes

Employees 1,035

UPJOHN LTD

PO Box 8, Fleming Way, Crawley, Sussex RH10 2NJ
Telephone: 0293-31133

Secretary J.W.Emerson,FCIS

Employees 548

URWICK ORR & PARTNERS LTD. PENSION SCHEME

Urwick House, 50 Doughty Street, London WC1N 2LS
Telephone: 01-405 4683

Managing Director J.R.Armstrong

Part Managed by Eagle Star Insurance Co.Ltd.

Investment Advisers Robert Fleming Investment Management Ltd.

Stockbrokers Capel-Cure Myers Ltd.

Actuaries Clay & Partners

Pension Fund Consultants Metropolitan Pensions Association Ltd., The Herriot Group

Auditors Cocke Vellacott & Hill

Company Employees 196

Members 166

Pensioners 142

Annual Contributions £233,000

Annual Investment Income £211,000

Capital Value £4,000,000

USMC INTERNATIONAL LTD 1950 STAFF PENSION FUND AND PENSION FUND FOR HOURLY RATED EMPLOYEES

British United House, PO Box 88, Belgrave Road, Leicester LE4 5BX
Telephone: 0533-61551

Pensions Department Manager D.C.Hairs

Trustees 6 for each fund

Stockbrokers Cazenove & Co.

Property Advisers Richard Ellis, Fisher & Co (Agricultural)

Pension Fund Consultants and Actuarial Advice Obtained through Metropolitan Pensions Association Ltd.

Auditors Deloitte Haskins & Sells

Company Employees 5,146

Members 4,780

Pensioners 2,656

	£000
Annual Contributions	2,840
Annual Investment Income	1,605
Annual Outflow	1,892
Capital Value	25,000
Summary of Investments (Book Values)	
Equities	12,535
Fixed Interest	7,519
Property	4,424
Cash & Deposits	522

U U TEXTILES LTD

35 King Street, Leicester LE1 9HH
Telephone: 0533 541242

Secretary C.Chambers

Employees 572

VACU-LUG TRACTION TYRES LTD. PENSION FUND

Spitalgate Mill, Bridge End Road, Grantham, Lincs.NG31 7HY
Telephone: 0476-2424

Secretary Mrs.D.J.Parker

Insured with Norwich Union Life Insurance Society

Employees 676

VALOR CO.LTD.

Riverside House, Corney Road, Chiswick, London W4 2SL
Telephone: 01-995 4010

VALOR CO.LTD. *Continued*

Secretary S.T.Hammond,ACIS

Insured with Equity & Law Life Assurance Society Ltd.

Employees 2,447

VAN LEER (UK) LTD
Edmund House, 12/22 New Hall Street, Birmingham B3 3DX
Telephone: 021-236 9898

Secretary C.Hoareau

Insured with Prudential Assurance Co Ltd

Pension Fund Consultants Godwins Ltd

Employees 2,118

VANTONA GROUP LTD PENSION & DEATH BENEFIT PLAN
Bank House, Charlotte Street, Manchester M1 4ET
Telephone: 061-427 2802

Pension Fund Manager J.Webb

Secretary S.M.Norton

Trustees Vantona Trustee Co.Ltd.

Investment Advisers Phillips & Drew, N.M. Rothschild Asset Management Ltd

Pension Fund Consultants & Administrators Godwins Ltd.

Auditors Spicer & Pegler

Employees 9,968

VAUX BREWERIES LTD. 1978 PENSION SCHEME
The Brewery, Sunderland, Tyne & Wear SR1 3AN
Telephone: 0783-76277

Secretary C.J.Storey

Trustees A.Mills, J.M.Webb, P.D.Nicholson

Managed by Prudential Pensions Ltd

Actuarial Advice obtained through Prudential Pensions Ltd

Pension Fund Consultants E.H.Foster & Co Ltd

Company Employees 2,500 Full-time

Members 850

Pensioners 350

Annual Contributions £300,000

Capital Value £3.3 million

VAUXHALL & ASSOCIATED COMPANIES PENSION FUND
P.O.Box 3, Kimpton Road, Luton, Beds.LU2 2BR
Telephone: 0582-21122

Pension Fund Manager C.V.F.Jowitt,FPMI

Secretary L.W.Watson

Pensions Board G.E.Moore (Chairman), J.K.Frankish, (Secretary, Vauxhall Motors Ltd.), 5 Members Representatives, and 5 Company Representatives, including C.V.Jowitt and D.T.Young (Vice-Chairman)

Investment Advisers Kleinwort Benson Ltd., Lloyds Bank Ltd., Lazard Brothers & Co.Ltd., Barclays Bank Trust Co.Ltd., County Bank Investment Services Ltd., Schlesinger Investment Management Services Ltd.

Property Advisers Hillier Parker May & Rowden, Savills Wimborne, Merryweather, Corbett & Dawson

Actuaries Bacon & Woodrow

Members 37,086 (and 3,063 Lump Sum Death Benefits only)

Pensioners 10,064

	£000
Annual Contributions	28,412
Annual Investment Income	17,363
Annual Outflow	12,498
Capital Value	
Book Value at 5.4.80	205,197
Market Value	245,521

Summary of Investments (Book Value)
Equities	68,656
Fixed Interest	80,702
Property	23,026
Agricultural	11,194
Property Unit Trusts	5,927
Cash & Deposits	13,799
Others	1,894

Participating Companies General Motors Ltd., General Motors Acceptance Corporation (UK) Ltd., Park Street Luton, The Stampings Alliance Ltd., Nechells, Birmingham, Fisher Body Ltd., (N.Ireland), Vauxhall Motors Ltd.

VEEDER INDUSTRIES UK RETIREMENT PLAN
Kilspindie Road, Dundee, Tayside
Telephone: 0382-84161

Pensions Administrator F.Mackay

Pension Fund Manager N.P.Key

Trustees N.P.Key, M.L.Hovey, W.Esplin

Managed by S.C.A.M.P.I.

Pension Fund Consultants William M.Mercer Benefits Ltd.

Auditors Arthur, Young, McClelland & Moores

Company Employees 1,420

Members 800

Pensioners 32

Annual Contributions £208,000

Annual Outflow £8,000

Capital Value £1,174,000

VERNON-CARUS LTD PENSION & ASSURANCE SCHEME
Penwortham Hills, Preston, Lancs.PR1 9SN
Telephone: 0772-44493

Secretary R.R.Morris

Insured with Legal & General Assurance Society Ltd

Pension Fund Consultants John Reynolds (Life & Pensions) Ltd.

Auditors Moore & Smalley

Employees 1,106

VERNON-CARUS LTD Continued

Members 535
Pensioners 40

VERNON ORGANISATION LTD.
1 Basnett Street, Liverpool L1 1DL
Telephone: 051-709 2562
Company Secretary P.J.Hobson
Insured with Scottish Amicable Life Assurance Society
Employees 2,474

VERO ELECTRONICS PENSION FUND
School Close, Chandlers Ford Industrial Estate, Eastleigh, Hampshire SO5 3ZR
Telephone: 04215-69911
Pension Fund Manager R.W.Varley, AAIA, ACIS
Secretary Mrs.S.Rice
Trustees D.E.Hedger, R.C.Bennett, R.W.Varley
Insured with Sun Life Assurance Society
Pension Fund Consultants F.E.Wright & Co.(Life & Pensions) Ltd.
Auditors Deloitte, Haskins & Sells
Company Employees 580
Members 288
Pensioners 4
Annual Contributions £247,000

VIBROPLANT HOLDINGS LTD
Prospect Road, Starbeck, Harrogate, N.Yorks HG2 7PW
Telephone: 0423 886341
Secretary R.J.Reeve
Insured with Commercial Union Assurance Co Ltd
Employees 667

VICKERS DA COSTA LTD SUPERANNUATION FUND
Regis House, King William Street, London EC4R 9AR
Telephone: 01-623 2494
Director & Secretary D.W.James,FCA
Principal D.W.Bartlett,FCIS,APMI
Actuaries Bacon & Woodrow
Pension Fund Consultants City Financial Administration Ltd.
Auditors Touche Ross & Co
Solicitors Freshfields
Company Employees 250
Members 110
Pensioners 50
Annual Contributions £220,000
Capital Value £2,400,000

VICKERS GROUP PENSION SCHEME
P.O.Box 177, Vickers House, Millbank Tower, Millbank, London SW1P 4RA
Telephone: 01-828 7777
Manager Salaries & Pensions K.H.Edwards
Investment Managers Standard Life Pension Fund
Property Advisers Jones Lang Wootton
Actuaries R.Watson & Sons
Pension Fund Consultants Rowe & Maw
Auditors Deloitte Haskins & Sells
Group Employees 13,000

VICTOR PRODUCTS (WALLSEND) LTD
Church Bank Offices, Wallsend, Tyne & Wear NE28 6PP
Telephone: 0632-628331
Secretary R.Davidson
Investment Advisers Investment Intelligence Ltd, Midland Bank Trust Co Ltd
Employees 910

VICTORIA CARPET HOLDINGS LTD.
Green Street, Kidderminster, Worcs.DY10 1HL
Telephone: 0562-2278
Secretary M.W.Allman
Employees 513

VINERS LTD
Broomhall Street, Sheffield, S.Yorks.S3 7SN
Telephone: 0742-21391
Secretary D.Bullers
Insured with Scottish Life Assurance Co.
Employees 514

VIRGIN HOLDINGS LTD.
2 Vernon Yard, Portobello Road, London W.11
Telephone: 01-727 8070
Secretary N.M.Powell
Employees 595

VISCOSE DEVELOPMENT CO.LTD.
185 London Road, Croydon, Surrey CR9 2TT
Telephone: 01-686 3241
Secretary T.Williams
Employees 513

VLI GROUP LTD
VLI House, 68-69 St Martins Lane, London WC2N 4JS
Telephone: 01-836 8411
Director M.J.Bayfield
Employees 600

VOLKSWAGEN (GB) LTD PENSION FUND
Yeomans Drive, Blakelands, Milton Keynes, Bucks MK14 5AN
Telephone: 0908-679121
Secretary Paul A.Campion
Trustees M.J.G.Knox, J.Thompson, P.N.Duxbury, D.Smallwood, P.Burke

VOLKSWAGEN (GB) LTD *Continued*

Stockbrokers Grievson Grant & Co.
Actuaries Hymans, Robertson & Co., Prudential Pensions Ltd.
Property Advisers Prudential Pensions Ltd.
Auditors Peat, Marwick, Mitchell & Co.
Company Employees 1,023
Members 811
Pensioners 67

	£000
Annual Contributions	790
Annual Investment Income	152
Annual Outflow	166
Capital Value	2,801
Summary of Investments	
Equities	1,151
Fixed Interest	945
Property	567
Cash & Deposits	138

VOLVO TRUCKS (GREAT BRITAIN) LTD.

Kilwinnng Road, Irvine, Ayrshire KA12 8TB
Telephone: 0294-74120

Secretary W.Gordon

Employees 523

'W' RIBBONS HOLDINGS LTD. 1973 PENSION FUND

12 Commerce Way, Purley Way, Croydon, Surrey CR9 4HH
Telephone: 01-688 6032

Secretary S.R.Earl

Trustees S.R.Earl, P.J.Kelly, F.Maynard

Insured with Norwich Union Life Insurance Society

Pension Fund Consultant W.R.Shiel

Employees 744

JOHN WADDINGTON LTD.

Wakefield Road, Leeds, W.Yorks.LS10 3TP
Telephone: 0532-712244

Secretary P.B.Stephens,BA,FCA

Investment Advisers Kleinwort Benson Investment Management Ltd., N.M.Rothschild Asset Management Ltd.

Pension Fund Consultants Noble Lowndes & Partners Ltd.

Employees 3,293

WADE POTTERIES LTD. RETIREMENT & DEATH BENEFITS SCHEME

Manchester Pottery, Burslem, Stoke-on-Trent ST6 4AE
Telephone: 0782-89321

Secretary J.Johnston, ACCA

Trustees G.A.J.Wade, J.Johnston, J.McBratney, G.Stanyer

Managed by Friends' Provident Managed Funds Ltd.

Actuaries Clay & Partners

Pension Fund Consultants C.E.Heath, Loades & Co Ltd

Employees 1,117

WADHAM STRINGER PENSION FUND

Hambledon Road, Waterlooville, Hampshire PO7 7TY
Telephone: 07014-4411

Pensions & Insurance Manager J.R.Lanham

Trustees 11

Stockbrokers and Investment Advisers Panmure Gordon & Co

Actuaries R. Watson & Sons

Pension Fund Consultants Reed Stenhouse Benefit Consultants Ltd.

Auditors Henry Malpas & Son

Company Employees 4,965

Members 3,384

Pensioners 124

Annual Contributions £1,511,000

Capital Value £5,826,000

WADKIN GROUP LTD. SECURITY PLAN

Green Lane Works, Leicester LE5 4PF
Telephone: 0533-769111

Secretary Mrs. P.A.Walker, FCA

Finance Director J.J.Catterson,FCCA

Trustees Wadkin Pension Fund Trust Ltd.

Stockbrokers Cazenove & Co.

Actuaries Clay & Partners

Pension Fund Consultants Metropolitan Pensions Association Ltd.

Auditors Price Waterhouse & Co.

Company Employees 1,891

Members 1,175

Pensioners 204

	£000
Annual Contributions (at 31.12.78)	621
Annual Investment Income	84
Annual Outflow	668
Capital Value	
Book Value	997
Market Value	1,142
Summary of Investments	
Equities	493
Cash & Deposits	615
Others	34

WAGON INDUSTRIAL HOLDINGS LTD

Haldane House, Halesfield, Telford, Salop TF7 4LN
Telephone: 0952-586811

Secretary A.J.Smith

Insured with Legal & General Assurance Society Ltd

Pension Fund Consultants Godwins Ltd

Employees 2,006

THE WAKEFIELD SHIRT CO.LTD. GROUP PENSION SCHEME

P.O.Box 1, Wakefield, W.Yorks. WF1 5RQ
Telephone: 0924-75651

Pension Management R.N.Thorp

Trustees R.J.Donner, D.R.Sugden, R.N.Thorp

Insured with Norwich Union Life Insurance Society

Company Employees 1,200

Members 131

Pensioners 8

Annual Contributions £43,000

WAKEFIELD STORES (MIDLANDS) LTD.

Kirky Folly Road, Sutton-in-Ashfield,
Notts. NG17 5LP
Telephone: 0623-56565

Secretary J.P.Wakefield

Employees 961

C.&.W.WALKER HOLDINGS LTD. 1973 PENSION FUND & LIFE ASSURANCE SCHEME

Walker House, Malinslee, Telford, Salop TF3 4HA
Telephone: 0952-501848

Pension Fund Manager & Secretary T.Tufnell

Trustees G.Lewis, T.B.Madden, K.C.Norton

Investment Adviser G.W.S.Miskin

Stockbrokers Dunkley Marshall

Pension Fund Consultants Antony Gibbs Pension Services Ltd.

Auditors Arthur Young McClelland Moores & Co.

Company Employees 656

Members 104

Pensioners 19

	£000
Annual Contributions (to 31.1.79)	100
Annual Investment Income	58
Annual Outflow	34
Capital Value (Market Value)	707
Summary of Investments	
Equities	504
Fixed Interest	130
Cash & Deposits	20

C. WALKER & SONS LTD PENSION & LIFE ASSURANCE SCHEME

Walker Road, Walker Industrial Estate, Guide, nr.Blackburn, Lancs.
Telephone: 0254-55161

Secretary & Finance Director D.M.Brown

Insured with Guardian Royal Exchange Assurance Group Ltd

Pension Fund Consultants Hogg Robinson (Benefit Consultants) Ltd.

Auditors Arthur, Young, McClelland, Moores & Co.

Company Employees 1,237

Members 900

Pensioners 40

WALKER CROSWELLER & CO LTD RETIREMENT BENEFITS SCHEME

Whaddon Works, Cromwell Road, Cheltenham, Gloucestershire GL52 5EP
Telephone: 0242-27953

Group Pensions and Insurance Manager Miss M.A.Higham, MIPM

Company Secretary D.A.Launchbury, FCIS

Insured with Sun Life Assurance Society Ltd.

Company Employees 655

Members 584

Pensioners 74

Annual Contributions £340,000

HIRAM WALKER & SONS (SCOTLAND) LTD. 1961 PENSION SCHEME

3 High Street, Dumbarton G82 1ND
Telephone: 0389-65111

Secretary R.I.Roxburgh, CA

Trustees Morgan Grenfell Trustee Service Ltd

Investment Advisers Morgan Grenfell & Co Ltd

Actuarial Advice obtained through Cubie Wood & Co Ltd

Pension Fund Consultants Scottish Pension Trustees Ltd.

Auditors Price Waterhouse & Co

Employees 1,950

Members 1,650

Pensioners 400

Annual Contributions £1.5 million

Capital Value £11.5 million

JAMES WALKER & CO LTD

Lion Works, Woking, Surrey
Telephone: 04862-5951

Secretary G.Hayes

Employees 2,373

JAMES WALKER GOLDSMITH & SILVERSMITH LTD RETIREMENT BENEFITS PLAN

Century House, Streatham High Road, London SW16 6ER
Telephone: 01-769 2001

Secretary J.S.Cushnie

Stockbrokers Vickers da Costa Ltd.

Actuaries R.Watson & Sons

Auditors Finnie Ross Allfields

Company Employees 2,350

Members 440

Pensioners 150

WALKERS CRISPS LTD.

Feature Road, Thurmaston, Leicester LE4 8BS
Telephone: 0533-695151

Secretary J.H.Bending

Employees 1,045

WALL PAPER MANUFACTURERS LTD.
King's House, 42 King Street West, Manchester M3 2WT
Telephone: 061-833 9292

Company Secretary E.F.Baverstock

Trustees The WPM Employees Pension Trust Ltd

Employees 10,000

WALLIS FASHION GROUP LTD
Wallis House, Claremont Road, London NW2 1SY
Telephone: 01-450 8989

Secretary J.E.D.Ware

Insured with National Provident Institution

Employees 1,321

G. E. WALLIS & SONS LTD
2-6 Homesdale Road, Bromley, Kent BR2 9TN
Telephone: 01-464 3377

Secretary E.A.Pywell

Insured with Eagle Star Insurance Co Ltd

Employees 1,279

E.WALTERS (HOLDINGS) LTD.
Old Street, Ludlow, Salop

Director E.B.Walters

Employees 1,162

WANDER LTD. PENSION FUND
Station Road, Kings Langley, Herts WD4 8LJ
Telephone: 66122

Secretary E.H.Nurse

Pension Administrators & Trustees G.W.Cooper, R.W.Peevers

Stockbrokers & Investment Advisers Grieveson Grant & Co.

Actuaries R. Watson & Sons

Auditors Futcher Head & Gilberts

Company Employees 700

Members 379

Pensioners 180

	£000
Annual Contributions	241
Annual Investment Income	262
Annual Outflow	173
Capital Value (Market Value)	2,454
Summary of Investments	
Equities	1,104
Fixed Interest	1,006
Property	221
Cash & Deposits	123

WARBURTONS LTD
Back o'th'Bank House, Blackburn Road, Bolton, Manchester BL1 8HJ
Telephone: 0204-23551

Company Secretary C.Wood,FCIS

Trustees H.D.Warburton, S.Jones, C.Wood

Managed by Scottish Mutual Pension Funds Investment Ltd

Investment Advisers Ivory & Sime Ltd.

Pension Fund Consultants and Actuarial Advice Obtained through Reed Stenhouse Benefit Consultants Ltd.

Auditors Thomson McLintock & Co.

Company Employees 3,400

Members 1,150

Pensioners 126

	£000
Annual Contributions	750
Annual Investment Income	300
Annual Outflow	260
Capital Value	3,000
Summary of Investments	
Equities	1,700
Fixed Interest	650
Property	100
Cash & Deposits	550

WARD & GOLDSTONE LTD
Sampson Works, Frederick Road, Salford, Manchester M6 6AP
Telephone: 061-736 5822

Secretary W.E.Gardiner

Actuaries Duncan C. Fraser & Co

Employees 5,790

WARD BLENKINSOP & CO LTD PENSION PLAN
Fulton House, Empire Way, Wembley, Middlesex HA9 0LX
Telephone: 01-902 8686

Company Secretary J.H.Awdry, FCA

Insured with Legal & General Assurance Society Ltd.

Pension Fund Consultants Bain Dawes & Partners Ltd

Company Employees 600 approx.

Members (at 31.3.80) 527

Pensioners (at 1.7.79) 89

Annual Contributions £276,000

WARD BROTHERS (SHERBURN) LTD. EXECUTIVE PENSION SCHEME, MANAGED PENSION PLAN AND PENSION AND ASSURANCE SCHEME
Widespan Works, Sherburn, Malton, N.Yorks.YO17 8PQ
Telephone: 09444-421

Secretary R.P.Metcalfe

Investment Advisers and Stockbrokers Boys-Stones, Simpson & Spencer

Actuaries Clay & Partners

Auditors Price Waterhouse & Co.

Company Employees 539

Members (Total for three Schemes) 395

Pensioners 1

THOS. W. WARD LTD
Albion Works, Sheffield, S.Yorks.S4 7UL
Telephone: 0742-26311
Pension Fund Manager J.Senior
Company Secretary A.C.Boydell,LLB
Investment Advisers & Stockbrokers Phillips & Drew
Employees 6,716
Capital Value £11.5 million (1977)

WARD WHITE GROUP LTD
Midland Road, Higham Ferrers, Wellingborough, Northants NN9 8DW
Telephone: 09334-57533
Group Secretary S.W.Iliffe
Group Pension Executive D.W.Ablett
Investment Advisers Barclays Bank Pension Advisory Service Ltd
Actuaries Duncan C. Fraser & Co
Employees 4,943

BERNARD WARDLE & CO LTD
Wardle House, 82 King Street, Knutsford, Cheshire WA16 6HL
Telephone: 0565-54881
Secretary K.S.Hooper,FCA
Insured with Equity & Law Life Assurance Society Ltd
Employees 1,457

WARING & GILLOW PENSION FUND
The Mount, Glossop Road, Sheffield S10 2PZ
Telephone: 0742-686970
Secretary T.G.Hutton, FCA
Trustees M.Cussins, T.G.Hutton, J.G.Etchells, F.J.Kershaw
Stockbrokers Broadbridge Lawson & Co
Actuaries Duncan C. Fraser & Co
Pension Fund Consultants Kershaw Tudor & Co (Solicitors)
Auditors Cobden Board & Co.
Company Employees 2,200
Members 650
Pensioners 105
Annual Contributions 2% of Salaries
Annual Investment Income £115,000
Annual Outflow £40,000
Capital Value £1,050,000

WARNE WRIGHT GROUP RETIREMENT BENEFITS PLAN
P.O.Box 38, Priest Street, Cradley Heath, Warley, West Midlands B64 6JW
Telephone: 0384-66501
Pension Fund Manager H.J.Baker
Secretary Lowndes Associated Pensions Ltd.
Trustees R.D.Young, J.H.Cook, H.J.Baker, Lowndes Associated Pensions Ltd.

Managed by Gartmore Pension Fund Managers Ltd.
Actuarial Advice Obtained through Cubie, Wood & Co. Ltd.
Pension Fund Consultants Lowndes Associated Pensions Ltd
Company Employees 1,350
Members 1,140
Pensioners 66

	£000
Annual Contributions	600
Capital Value	1,719
Summary of Investments	
Equities	602
Fixed Interest	439
Property	352
Cash & Deposits	62
Others	264

WARNER ELECTRIC LTD
St Helen Auckland, Bishop Auckland, Co.Durham DL14 9AA
Telephone: 0388-4000
Managing Director M.P.Nutting
Employees 600

WARNER HOLIDAYS LTD
Warner House, North Street, Havant, Hants.PO9 1SQ
Telephone: 0705-483531
Secretary P.R.Holmes
Insured with Legal & General Assurance Society Ltd
Employees 1,127

WARNER-LAMBERT (UK) LTD THE WHL PENSION SCHEME AND PARKE DAVIS PENSION PLAN
Chestnut Avenue, Eastleigh, Hampshire SO5 3ZQ
Telephone: 0703-613131
Company Secretary J.C.Burt
Pensions & Administration Manager J.E.Borrow
Pensions Executive R.Smith
Investment Advisers Morgan Grenfell & Co Ltd
Pension Fund Consultants Willis Faber Advisory Services Limited
Auditors Price Waterhouse & Co

	WHL	Parke Davis
Company Employees	1,386	1,100
Members	900	750
Pensioners	-	214
	£000	£000
Annual Contributions	576	420
Capital Value	5,000	2,000

WARRINGTON CO-OPERATIVE SOCIETY LTD EMPLOYEES PENSION FUND

79 Winwick Road, Warrington WA2 7PF
Telephone: 0925-34432

Secretary W.P.Smith

Trustees A.V.Worby, W.E.Williams, P.Conroy, W.E.Leatherwood, W.Hoult, M.Dean, C.Cartwright

Investment Managers Cooperative Investment Management Ltd.

Actuary P.D.Johnson,FIA (Co-operative Insurance Society)

Pension Fund Consultants B.Holden at Cooperative Union

Auditors Appleby English & Partners

Company Employees 1,100

Members (Nov.80) 419

Pensioners 273

	£000
Annual Contributions (Apr.80)	112
Annual Investment Income	154
Annual Outflow	128
Capital Value	1,800
Summary of Investments	
Equities	868
Fixed Interest	726
Cash & Deposits	197
Others	10

WARWICK ENGINEERING INVESTMENTS LTD

66 High Street, Henley-in-Arden, Warks
Telephone: 05642-3800

Secretary M.R.Watson

Employees 1,813

WARWICKSHIRE COUNTY COUNCIL SUPERANNUATION FUND

Shire Hall, Warwick CV34 4RR
Telephone: 0926-43431

Treasurer J.P.Hunt, IPFA

Investment Advisers Lloyds Bank Ltd.

Actuaries Duncan C.Fraser & Co.

Auditors District Auditor

Members 6,500

Pensioners 2,080

Annual Contributions £4,494,000

Capital Value £41 million

WATES LTD SUPERANNUATION FUND

1260 London Road, Norbury, London SW16
Telephone: 01-764 5000

Secretary M.Nicholls

Investment Advisers Drayton Montagu Portfolio Management Ltd., Martin Curries & Co

Actuaries Bacon & Woodrow

Auditors Slater Chapman & Cooke

Company Employees 2,500

Members 685

Pensioners 180

Annual Contributions £432,000

Annual Investment Income £250,000

Capital Value £2,400,000

WATMOUGHS (HOLDINGS) LTD RETIREMENT BENEFITS SCHEME

High Street, Idle, Bradford, W.Yorks.BD10 8NL
Telephone: 0274-612111

Secretary C.Maughan

Trustees C.Maughan, B.Topham, P.G.Walker, J.E.Watmough

Insured with Scottish Widows' Fund & Life Assurance Society

Company Employees 800

Members 600

WATNEY MANN & TRUMAN BREWERS

The Brewery, 91 Brick Lane, London E1 6QN
Telephone: 01-377 0020

Company Secretary A.H.F.Ewell

Pension Officers B.R.Hanks, APMI, R.F.J.Bacon, APMI

WATSON & PHILIP LTD RETIREMENT AND DEATH BENEFITS PLAN

P.O.Box 89, Blackness Road, Dundee, Tayside DD1 9PU
Telephone: 0382-27501

Assistant Company Secretary M.F.McGregor

Trustees J.C.Hadden, H.V.Gardner, I.D.R.Philip, D.J.T.Shentall, F.D.Keanie, E.H.Thompson

Insured with Standard Life Assurance Co.

Pension Fund Consultants Scottish Pension Trustees Ltd.

Auditors Arthur Young McClelland & Moores

Company Employees 780

Members 215

Pensioners 41

Annual Contributions £133,000

WATSON NORIE LTD

Wincomblee Road, Walker,
Newcastle upon Tyne NE6 3PL
Telephone: 0632-627411

Director N.Calvert

Employees 600

W. & J. R. WATSON LTD

Romans House, Station Road, Corstorphine, Edinburgh EH12 7AQ
Telephone: 031-334 9871

Secretary A.F.Thomson

Employees 760

WATTS, BLAKE, BEARNE & COMPANY LTD

Park House, Courtenay Park, Newton Abbot, Devon TQ12 4PS
Telephone: 0626-2345

Secretary D.A.Norman

WATTS, BLAKE, BEARNE & COMPANY LTD *Continued*

Insured with Scottish Widows' Fund & Life Assurance Society

Employees 771

WATTS OF LYDNEY GROUP LTD.
High Street, Lydney, Glos.
Telephone: 05944-2481

Secretary G.P.Quinn,FCA

Employees 711

WAVIN PLASTICS LTD STAFF AND WORKS PENSION SCHEMES
Rigby Lane, Dawley Road, Hayes, Middx.UB3 1EY
Telephone: 01-573 7799

Administration Officer A.H.Nayler, ACMA

Insured with Legal & General Assurance Society Ltd., Provident Mutual Life Assurance Association

Pension Consultants Metropolitan Pensions Association Ltd

Auditors Spain Bros. & Co.

Company Employees 1,100

Members 1,000

Pensioners 36

Annual Contributions £450,000

THE WEBSTERS GROUP LTD.
79 Temple Chambers, Temple Avenue, London EC4Y OEX
Telephone: 01-353 5681

Secretary E.R.Framp

Insured with Guardian Royal Exchange Assurance Group Ltd

Employees 1,031

ENOCH WEDGWOOD (TUNSTALL) LTD
Brownhills, Tunstall, Stoke on Trent, Staffs.
Telephone: 0782-84165

Secretary Mrs A.Broad

Employees 1,434

JOSIAH WEDGWOOD & SONS LTD. 1978 EXECUTIVE MANAGEMENT PENSION SCHEME, 1G78 STAFF PENSION SCHEME, AND 1978 WORKS PENSION SCHEME
Barlaston, Stoke on Trent, Staffs.ST12 9ES
Telephone: 078139-2141

Group Pensions Manager W.J.Wilkinson

Secretary J.Moffat, MA, BCom, CA

Trustees P.Williams, J.Moffat, W.J.Wilkinson & others

Managed by Friends' Provident Managed Pension Funds Ltd

Investment Advisers Hambros Investment Management Services Ltd.

Actuaries Duncan C. Fraser & Co

Auditors Peat, Marwick, Mitchell & Co.

Company Employees 10,154

Members Executive 196, Staff 976, Works 3,796

Pensioners 286

Annual Contributions Executive £385,000, Staff £613,000, Works £1,104,000

Annual Outflow Executive £317,000, Staff £558,000, Works £754,000

WEEKS ASSOCIATES LTD.
Ferry Road, Hessle,N.Humberside HU13 0DZ
Telephone: 0482-64917

Secretary D.Butterfield

Insured with Eagle Star Insurance Co.Ltd.

Employees 613

WEETABIX LTD. STAFF PENSION SCHEME AND WORKS PENSION SCHEME
Weetabix Mills, Burton Latimer, Kettering, Northants NN15 5JR
Telephone: 053672-2181

Secretary I.P.Clarke

Other Pension Management (Works) Miss P.A.Bettles

Trustees W.A.George, R.W.George, P.Amos, I.P.Clarke

Staff Scheme Insured with Equity & Law Assurance Society

Works Scheme Managed by Scottish Life Pensions Annuity Ltd.

Pension Fund Consultants Staff: Bain Dawes & Partners Ltd., Works: Hogg Robinson (Benefit Consultants) Ltd.

Company Employees 2,040

Members Staff 447, Works 439

Pensioners Staff 54, Works 8

ANDREW WEIR & CO LTD
21 Bury Street, London EC3A 5AU
Telephone: 01-283 1266

Secretary R.C.Yarham

Insured with Legal & General Assurance Society Ltd.

Employees 586

THE WEIR GROUP LTD,
149 Newlands Road, Cathcart, Glasgow G44 4EX
Telephone: 041-637 7111

Pensions Manager J.M.Graft

Pensions & Salaries Officer J.McL.McKenzie,CA, APMI

Investment Advisers Robert Fleming Investment Management Ltd, N.M.Rothschild Asset Management Ltd

Employees 8,539

WELDON & WILKINSON LTD
Rawson Street, New Basford, Nottingham NG7
Telephone: 0602-785041

Director L.A.Weldon

Executive B.C.Weldon

Employees 800

WELLA (GT. BRITAIN) LTD ASSOCIATED COMPANIES PENSION SCHEME

Wella Road, Basingstoke, Hampshire RG22 4AF
Telephone: 0256-20202

Secretary J.H.Hobbs

Trustees J.H.Hobbs, P.A.Batten, F.Davies

Insured with Sun Life Assurance Society Ltd.

Pension Fund Consultants Noble Lowndes & Partners Ltd.

Auditors Brooking, Knowles & Lawrence

Company Employees 660

Members 461

Pensioners 33

THE WELLCOME GROUP PENSION FUND

42 Gower Place, London WC1A 6BN
Telephone: 01-387 4477

Secretary & Group Pensions Manager K.P.Collins, ACIS, FPMI

Investment Advisers Baring Bros. & Co. Ltd., Warburg Investment Management Ltd.

Actuaries R. Watson & Sons

Auditors Touche Ross & Co.

Company Employees 6,830

Members 5,880

Pensioners 1,754

	£000
Annual Contributions	7,086
Annual Investment Income	5,912
Annual Outflow	2,376
Capital Value	73,741
Summary of Investments	
Equities	50,770
Fixed Interest	20,577
Property	255
Cash & Deposits	2,139

WELLMAN ENGINEERING CORP.LTD. STAFF SUPERANNUATION FUND

Parnell House, 25 Wilton Road,
London SW1V 1LS
Telephone: 01-834 6800

Secretary A.G.Docherty

Company Secretary N.F.Reynolds

Managed by Legal & General (Pensions Management) Ltd

Employees 1,040

WELLTRADE INTERNATIONAL LTD

International House, Tamworth Road,
Hertford SG13 7DQ
Telephone: 0992-58121

Director S.J.Bond

Employees 1,500

WELWYN ELECTRIC LTD. RETIREMENT & DEATH BENEFIT SCHEME

Bedlington, Northumberland
Telephone: 0670-822181

Pension Fund Manager & Secretary R.Mather

Trustees J.E.Herrin, J.Browning, A.M.V.Marshall, R.Mather

Actuaries Clay & Partners

Pension Fund Consultants Metropolitan Pensions Association Ltd.

Auditors Peat, Marwick, Mitchell & Co.

Company Employees 1,820

Members (at 5.4.79) 575

Pensioners 148

Annual Contributions £319,000

Capital Value £1,485,000

See also Royal Worcester Ltd. (Parent Company)

WESLEYAN & GENERAL ASSURANCE SOCIETY

Colmore Circus, Birmingham B4 6AR
Telephone: 021-236 7894

Director J.D.W.Field

Executive E.Butler

Employees 2,000

WEST CUMBERLAND FARMERS LTD

PO Box 11, Catherine Street, Whitehaven,
Cumbria CA28 7QU
Telephone: 0946-3191

Managing Director N.E.L.Hill

Employees 1,800

WEST GLAMORGAN COUNTY COUNCIL

The Guildhall, Swansea SA1 4PG
Telephone: 0792-50821

Treasurer S.G.Dunster, MA, IPFA

Other Pension Management Investment Panel appointed by Policy and Resources Committee

Stockbrokers Phillips & Drew, Fielding Newson Smith Ltd.

Actuaries R.Watson & Sons

Auditors District Audit

Employees 15,000

Members 8,500

Pensioners 2,000

	£million
Annual Contributions	4.5
Annual Investment Income	2.5
Annual Outflow	2.5
Capital Value (at 31.3.80)	35.0
Summary of Investments	
Equities	20.0
Fixed Interest	10.0
Property Units	3.5
Cash & Deposits	1.5

WEST MIDLANDS COUNTY COUNCIL SUPERANNUATION FUND

County Hall, 1 Lancaster Circus, Queensway,
Birmingham B4 7DJ
Telephone: 021-300 5151

County Treasurer K.E.Rose, IPFA

WEST MIDLANDS COUNTY COUNCIL Continued

Chief Superannuation Officer J.W.Bannister,IPFA, APMI

Investment Manager D.Woodward,IPFA

Investment Advisers County Bank

Property Agents Healey & Baker

Actuaries Duncan C.Freser & Co.

Members 61,500

Pensioners 18,800

	£ million
Annual Contributions	45
Annual Investment Income	27
Annual Outflow	18
Capital Value	305
Summary of Investments	
Equities	170
Fixed Interest	90
Property	30
Cash & Deposits	15

THE WEST OF ENGLAND TRUST LTD.

18 Canynge Road, Bristol BS99 7UA
Telephone: 0272-32241

Secretary D.J.Brewster

Employees 603

WEST RIDING WORSTED & WOOLLEN MILLS LTD.

West Riding House, Ghyll Road, Guiseley, West Yorks.LS20 9NB
Telephone: 0943-77121

Secretary M.J.Cotton,FCA,ACIS,ACMA

Employees 2,892

WEST SUSSEX COUNTY COUNCIL SUPERANNUATION FUND

County Hall, Chichester PO19 1RG
Telephone: 0243-85100

County Treasurer B.Fieldhouse,MA,IPFA

Actuaries R.Watson & Sons

Auditors District Auditor

Employees 19,000

Members 9,100

Pensioners 2,500

Annual Contributions £7,108,000

Annual Investment Income £4,178,000

Capital Value £45,266,000

WEST YORKSHIRE METROPOLITAN COUNTY COUNCIL SUPERANNUATION FUND

County Hall, Wakefield WF1 2QN
Telephone: 0924-67111

Director of Finance G.S.Pollard, IPFA, FCA

Management Committee Panel appointed by the Policy and Finance Committee of the County Council

Actuaries Duncan C. Fraser & Co

Members 47,000

Pensioners 17,000

Annual Contributions £31 million

Annual Investment Income £19 million

Gross Annual Outflow £18 million

Capital Value £197 million

WESTBRICK PRODUCTS LTD PENSION & ASSURANCE SCHEME

Chancel Lane, Pinhoe, Exeter, Devon EX4 8JB
Telephone: 0392-68151

Pension Fund Manager & Secretary E.D.Dyer,FCIS

Trustee of Pension Fund S.J.Saunders

Insured with Legal & General Assurance Society Ltd

Pension Fund Consultants Martin Paterson Associates Ltd.

Auditors Ernst & Whinney

Employees 959

Members 210

Pensioners 24

WESTERN ISLES COUNCIL

County Offices, South Beach, Stornoway, Isle of Lewis PA87 2BW
Telephone: 0851-3773

Director Finance D.G.Macleod

WESTERN MOTOR HOLDINGS LTD GROUP PENSION FUND

Drake House, Laira Bridge Road, Plymouth, Devon PL4 9LS
Telephone: 0752-68411

Secretary R.Davey,ACIS

Investment Advisers Fraser Green Ltd

Property Advisers Body Son & Fleury

Actuaries Duncan C.Fraser & Co.

Auditors Cullum White & Pawley

Company Employees 1,347

Members (at 31.3.80) 1,177

Pensioners 80

Annual Contributions £664,000

Annual Investment Income £198,000

Capital Value £1,975,000

WESTERN UNITED INVESTMENT CO.LTD.

13-16 West Smithfield, London EC1A 9JN
Telephone: 01-248 1212

Secretary C.H.Carrell

Employees 16,600

WESTINGHOUSE BRAKE & SIGNAL CO.LTD.

3 John Street, London WC1N 2ES
Telephone: 01-405 5971

Secretary H.R.Baines, BA

Employees 4,865

WESTLAND AIRCRAFT LTD STAFF PENSION SCHEME AND WORKS PENSION SCHEME

Westland Works, Yeovil, Somerset BA20 2YB
Telephone: 0935-5222

Group Pensions & Insurance Manager N.M.Malpass,ACII,FPMI

Investment Advisers J. Henry Schroder Wagg & Co Ltd

Property Advisers King & Co.

Actuaries Bacon & Woodrow

Auditors Turquands Barton Mayhew & Co.

Solicitors Slaughter & May

Company Employees 12,380

	Staff Scheme	Works Scheme
Members	7,000	5,000
Pensioners	1,600	150
	£000	£000
Annual Contributions (to 5.4.80)	5,682	2,951
Annual Investment Income	2,640	456
Annual Outflow	2,228	368
Capital Value		
Book Value	33,636	6,929
Market Value	37,743	6,964
Summary of Investments		
Equities	11,504	2,051
Overseas Equities	3,798	801
Fixed Interest	6,857	2,516
Property	5,611	382
Others	3,102	-

WESTMINSTER CITY COUNCIL

PO Box 240, Westminster City Hall, Victoria Street, London SW1E 6QP
Telephone: 01-828 8070

City Treasurer John W.Bamford, IPFA, FRVA

Property Advisers Hampton & Co

WESTMINSTER DREDGING GROUP

See Bos Kalis Westminster

WESTMINSTER PRESS PENSION SCHEMES

Chansitor House, 37/38 Chancery Lane, London WC2A 1EL
Telephone: 01-242 7221

Pension Fund Manager & Secretary G.Spence, FPMI, AAAI

Assistant Manager M.Slowe

Trustees Westminster Press Pension Trust Ltd.

Investment Advisers Lazard Bros.& Co.Ltd.

Property Advisers Goodman Mann Associates

Actuaries R.Watson & Sons

Auditors Chalmers, Impey & Co.

Company Employees 7,600

Members 4,700Ø

Pensioners 1,000

	£000
Annual Contributions	4,015
Annual Investment Income	3,528
Annual Outflow	1,502
Capital Value	33,602
Summary of Investments	
Equities	9,781
Fixed Interest	11,608
Property	6,569
Cash & Deposits	5,199

WEYBURN ENGINEERING CO LTD

Weyburn, Eashing, Surrey
Telephone: 04868-4373

Secretary A.W.Hyams

Employees 900

WEYROC LTD

Weybridge, Surrey
Telephone: 0932-45599

Director V.Roine

Employees 600

W.G.I. LTD STAFF SUPERANNUATION FUND AND SUPERANNUATION FUND FOR WEEKLY AND HOURLY PAID EMPLOYEES

Lloyds House, Alderley Road, Wilmslow, Cheshire SK9 1QA
Telephone: 0625-527488

Financial Controller & Secretary G.Butterworth

Chairman, Committee of Managers D.R.Brooks

Trustees W.G.I. Trustees Ltd

Chairman F.P.S.Stammers

Works Fund Insured with Clerical, Medical & General Assurance Society

Investment Advisers Warburg Investment Management Ltd.

Actuaries Duncan C. Fraser & Co

Auditors Spicer and Pegler

Company Employees 2,358

Members (at 5.4.80) 716

Pensioners 184

	£000
Annual Contributions	297
Annual Investment Income	204
Annual Outflow	168
Capital Value	2,173
Summary of Investments	
Equities	1,598
Fixed Interest	468
Cash & Deposits	63
Others	26

WHATLINGS LTD.

North Claremont Street, Glasgow G3 7LF
Telephone: 041-331 2151

Secretary R.G.Lawson

Insured with Standard Life Assurance Co.

WHATLINGS LTD. *Continued*

Pension Fund Consultants Godwins Ltd.
Employees 960

WHATMAN REEVE ANGEL UK PENSION SCHEME

Springfield Mill, Maidstone, Kent ME14 2LE
Telephone: 0622-61681

Pensions Manager D.W.Eddison,FCA

Management Committee Six employees including Pensions Manager

Trustee W.R.A.Trustee Ltd

Investment Advisers Warburg Investment Management Ltd.

Pension Fund Consultants and Actuarial Advice obtained through Metropolitan Pensions Association Ltd

Auditors Baker, Rooke & Amsdons

Solicitors Kenneth Brown Baker & Baker

Company Employees (at 30.3.80) 735 worldwide, (U.K. 501)

Members 399 (full) and 30 (Life Assurance only)

Pensioners 17

	£000
Annual Contributions	268
Annual Investment Income	30
Annual Outflow	118
Capital Value (at 5.4.79)	1,294
Summary of Investments	
Equities	413
Fixed Interest	117
Globe Managed Fund	646
Cash & Deposits	56
Others	62

WHEATSHEAF DISTRIBUTION & TRADING LTD. PENSION SCHEME

St.George's House, St. George's Street, Winchester, Hampshire SO23 8BG
Telephone: 0962-68351

Pension Fund Manager Mr Dowson

Company Secretary G.D.Neely

Insured with National Mutual Life Assurance Society

Employees 6,532

Members 1,250

Pensioners 300

Annual Contributions £600,000

WHESSOE LTD STAFF PENSION SCHEME AND WORKS PENSION SCHEME

Brinkburn Road, Darlington, Co.Durham DL3 3DS
Telephone: 0325-60188

Secretary G.Renwick

Company Registrar A.Green

Insured with Clerical, Medical & General Life Assurance

Pension Fund Consultants Hogg Robinson (Benefit Consultants) Ltd.

Auditors Peat, Marwick, Mitchell & Co.

Company Employees 2,941

Members Staff 973, Works 828

Pensioners Staff 200, Works 300

WHEWAY WATSON HOLDINGS LTD

101 Sutton New Road, Erdington, Birmingham
Telephone: 021-382 3100

Secretary G.Young

Investment Advisers Drayton Montagu Portfolio Management Ltd

Employees 732

L.WHITAKER & SONS LTD.

Holme Spring Hill, Haslingden, Rossendale, Lancs.
Telephone: 07062-4761

Secretary J.W.Whitaker

Employees 515

WHITBREAD GROUP PENSION FUND

The Brewery, Chiswell Street, London EC1Y 4SD
Telephone: 01-606 4455

Pension Fund Manager and Secretary A.H.Hallen, FCA, APMI

Trustees Whitbread Pension Trustees Ltd

Investment Advisers J.H.Schroder Wagg & Co. Ltd., Cazenove & Co., Robert Fleming Investment Management Ltd.

Actuaries Bacon & Woodrow

Auditors Ernst & Whinney

Solicitors Field Fisher & Martineau

Company Employees 23,476 (Full-time)

Members 17,365

Pensioners 4,491

	£million
Annual Contributions	11.9
Annual Investment Income	6.8
Annual Outflow	5.5
Capital Value	89.4
Summary of Investments	
Equities	43.7
Fixed Interest	21.3
Property	16.8
Cash & Deposits	4.7
Others	2.9

WHITECROFT GROUP PENSION SCHEME

Blackfriars House, Parsonage, Manchester M3 2HX
Telephone: 061-834 8181

Secretary E.S.Bailey,FCA

Trustees Whitecroft Pension Trustee Ltd

Investment Advisers Williams & Glyn's Bank Ltd.

Stockbrokers Henry Cooke Lumsden & Co

Actuaries R.Watson & Sons

Solicitors Rowe & Maw

Auditors Spicer & Pegler

WHITECROFT GROUP Continued

Company Employees 4,300
Members 3,100
Pensioners 300
Annual Contributions £1,200,000
Annual Investment Income £560,000
Annual Outflow £410,000
Capital Value £6,000,000

W. & J. WHITEHEAD (LAISTERDYKE) LTD.

P.O.Box 340, New Lane Mills, Laisterdyke,
Bradford, W.Yorks.BD4 8BD
Telephone: 0274-664241

Secretary A.Bentley

Trustees Noble Lowndes & Partners Ltd.

Insured with Legal & General Assurance Society Ltd.

Employees 675

WHITELEY ELECTRICAL RADIO CO LTD

Radio Works, Victoria Street, Mansfield, Notts
Telephone: 0623-24762

Secretary R.D.Manterfield, FCA

Employees 500

WHITTAKER ELLIS BULLOCK LTD RETIREMENT BENEFITS PLAN

Northgate, Aldridge, Walsall,
West Midlands WS9 8TU
Telephone: 0922-58311

Director D.G.Austin, MBIM, MinstM

Secretary R.Wilcox

Investment Advisers Warburg Investment Management Ltd.

Actuarial Advice Obtained through Cubie, Wood & Co.Ltd.

Pension Fund Consultants Noble Lowndes & Partners Ltd.

Auditors Price Waterhouse & Co.

Company Employees 620
Members 250
Pensioners 40
Capital Value £1,340,000

WILLIAM WHITTINGHAM (HOLDINGS) LTD STAFF RETIREMENT BENEFITS PLAN

PO Box 60, Ettingshall Road, Wolverhampton,
West Midlands WV2 2JT
Telephone: 0902-53891

Secretary H.W.T.Birks

Trustees H.W.T.Birks, P.J.Howells, Lowndes Associated Pensions Ltd.

Managed by Hill Samuel Investment Management Ltd

Actuarial Advice obtained through Cubie Wood & Co Ltd

Pension Fund Consultants Noble Lowndes & Partners Ltd

Auditors Price Waterhouse & Co
Company Employees 350 approx.
Members 70
Pensioners 2

	£000
Annual Contributions (to 29.2.80)	103
Annual Investment Income	20
Annual Outflow	5
Capital Value	246
Summary of Investments	
Equities	182
Fixed Interest	46
Property	10
Cash & Deposits	8

WHITWORTHS HOLDINGS LTD.

Victoria Mills, Wellingborough, Northants NN8 2DT
Telephone: 093376-351

Secretary F.N.Jones

Employees 1,469

HENRY WIGFALL & SON, LTD.

Rutland Road, Sheffield, S.Yorks.S3 9PQ
Telephone: 0742-24055

Financial Director G.L.Myers

Secretary E.R.Dickinson

Investment Advisers Drayton Montagu Portfolio Management Ltd, Schlesinger Investment Management Services

Actuaries Clay & Partners

Employees 2,342

WIGGINS CONSTRUCT LTD MANAGED PENSION PLAN

57 Hart Road, Thundersley, Benfleet,
Essex SS7 3PD
Telephone: 03745-2591

Secretary J.A.Sterry

Company Secretary M.J.Rowles

Managed by Colonial Mutual Life Assurance Society Ltd.

Auditors Griffin Stone Moscrop & Co.

Company Employees 836
Members 400
Pensioners 40
Annual Contributions £144,000
Capital Value £383,000

WIGGINS TEAPE PENSION SCHEME

Gateway House, Basing View, Basingstoke,
Hampshire RG21 2EE
Telephone: 0256-20262

Secretary & Manager Pensions Dept G.W.Bennett, APMI

Assistant Secretary A.T.Clapshaw

Trustees Wiggins Teape Pensions Ltd

Investment Advisers Bankers Trust International Ltd

Actuaries Bacon & Woodrow

WIGGINS TEAPE Continued

Auditors Dearden Farrow

Solicitors Richards Butler

Company Employees 10,400

Members 9,238

Pensioners 3,225

	£000
Annual Contributions	5,352
Annual Investment Income	2,866
Annual Outflow	2,243
Capital Value	43,832
Summary of Investments	
Equities	28,608
Fixed Interest	12,387
Property	1,100
Cash & Deposits	1,737

WIGHT GROUP PENSION FUND

PO Box 1, Polmont, Falkirk FK2 0PP
Telephone: 0324-711 271

Secretary A.R.Nicol, CA

Insured with Friends' Provident Life Office

Pension Fund Consultants James M. Macalaster & Alison Ltd.

Auditors Scott Oswald & Co.

Company Employees 600

Members 150

Pensioners 10

Annual Contributions £100,000

W.J.WILD MANUFACTURING CO

PO Box 103, Floodgate Street,
Birmingham B5 5SJ
Telephone: 021-643 9611

Secretary P.J.Wild

Executive R.J.McLachlan

Employees 500

JAMES WILKES LTD (A) PENSION AND LIFE ASSURANCE SCHEME AND (B) RETIREMENT AND DEATH BENEFIT SCHEME FOR WORKS EMPLOYEES

146 Oxford Street, Bilston,
West Midlands WV41 7DW
Telephone: 0902-42961

Secretary T.A.Sealey

Trustees (a) T.A.Sealey, W.G.Pearce, R.Leaver, M.Woodward, (b) W.G.Pearce, R.Leaver, P.Bailey, A.Baker

Insured with (a) Commercial Union Assurance Co. Ltd., (b) Standard Life Assurance Co.

Pension Fund Consultants Godwins (Midlands and West) Ltd.

Auditors Binder Hamlyn

Company Employees 565

Members (a) 195, (b) 203

Annual Contributions (a) £212,000, (b) £80,000

J. & D. WILKIE LTD

Gairie Works, Kirriemuir, Tayside DD8 4BL
Telephone: 057-52 2502

Managing Director and Secretary A.R.Lindsay

Employees 520

WILKINS & MITCHELL LTD.

Richard Street, Darlaston, Wednesbury,
West Midlands WS10 8AN
Telephone: 021-526 3111

Secretary D.Leach

Insured with Clerical, Medical & General Life Assurance Society

Pension Fund Consultants Harold Yates Burges & Co. (Birmingham) Ltd.

Employees 3,267

WILKINSON GROUP RETIREMENT BENEFITS SCHEME

Lawn Road, Carlton-in-Lindrick, Worksop,
Notts.S81 9LB
Telephone: 0909-731001

Pension Fund Manager & Secretary G.F.Jackson, FCA

Trustees Wilkinson Hardware Stores Ltd.

Insured with Norwich Union Life Insurance Society

Pension Fund Consultants Sedgwick Employee Benefits Consultants Ltd.

Company Employees 475

Pensioners 17

Annual Contributions £116,500

Capital Value £490,000

WILKINSON MATCH LTD. (5 SCHEMES)

Langley Hall, Station Road, Langley,
Slough,Berks.SL3 8BZ
Telephone: 44212

Group Pensions Manager M.R.Beaumont,ACII,FPMI

Pensions Administration Manager R.J.Braber

Trustees 5 different companies

Investment Advisers Lazard Securities Ltd.
Warburg Investment Management Ltd.

Pension Fund Consultants and Actuarial Advice Obtained through Metropolitan Pensions Association Ltd

Auditors Deloitte Haskins & Sells

Company Employees 4,756

Members 3,605

Pensioners 1,250

Annual Contributions £2,000,000

Capital Value £12,325,000

The figures above cover the following Funds:
Wilkinson Pension Fund
Brymay Pension Fund

WILKINSON MATCH LTD. *Continued*

Wilkinson Match (Safety & Protection Division) Pension Fund
Wilkinson Match (Packaging Companies) Pension Fund
Match Importers Pension Fund

WILKINSON WARBURTON LTD

Caressa House, Pudsey, W.Yorks.LS28 7FD
Telephone: 0532-578234

Secretary T.W.Sullivan

Insured with National Employers Life Assurance Co. Ltd., Phoenix Assurance Co. Ltd.

Employees 587

WILLIAMS & GLYN'S BANK LTD STAFF PENSION SCHEME

45 Mosley Street, Manchester M60 2BE
Telephone: 061-236 8585

Pension Fund Manager D.Olroyd,APMI

Secretary M.H.J.Thomas

Investment Manager L.J.Gant

Investment Advisers Williams & Glyn's Bank Ltd.Investment Division

Actuaries Duncan C. Fraser & Co

Auditors Peat, Marwick, Mitchell & Co.

Company Employees 6,189

Members 4,600

Pensioners 1,500

Annual Contributions £7.6 million

Annual Investment Income £6.5 million

Capital Value £62.0 million

EDWARD WILLIAMS HOLDINGS LTD

Windsor House, Temple Row, Birmingham B2 5LD
Telephone: 021-472 5391

Secretary E.R.Bosley

Insured with Scottish Widows' Fund & Life Assurance Society

Employees 1,346

WILLIAMS (HOUNSLOW) LTD

Greville House, Hibernia Road, Hounslow, Middlesex TW3 3RX
Telephone: 01-570 7766

Secretary G.T.Puttock

Employees 500

WILLIAMS HUDSON GROUP LTD. GROUP SUPERANNUATION FUND (1974)

8 Maltravers Street, London WC2R 3EQ
Telephone: 01-836 4433

Pension Fund Manager D.C.Howorth

Company Secretary J.W.Jones

Insured with Prudential Assurance Co Ltd

Pension Fund Consultants Stewart Wrightson Assurance Consultants Ltd.

Auditors Thomson McLintock & Co.

Company Employees 1,370

Members 550

Pensioners 190

JOHN WILLIAMS OF CARDIFF LTD RETIREMENT BENEFITS PLAN

PO Box 27, Williams Way, Cardiff CF1 1UH
Telephone: 0222-388 555

Secretary N.F.C.Phillips

Personnel Manager H.Davies

Finance Director D.A.Cavell

Managed by Prudential Pensions Ltd.

Pension Fund Consultants Lowndes Associated Pensions Ltd.

Auditors Price Waterhouse & Co.

Company Employees 933

Members 198

Pensioners 21

Annual Contributions £206,000

Capital Value £1,106,000

WILLIAMS LEA GROUP LTD

Clifton House, Worship Street, London EC2A 2EJ
Telephone: 01-247 4366

Secretary R.C.Cole,FCCA

Employees 561

W. WILLIAMS & SONS (HOLDINGS) LTD

Pontygwindy Industrial Estate, Caerphilly, Glamorgan CF8 2XG
Telephone: 0222-885941

Secretary F.T.Davies

Insured with English Insurance Co Ltd

Employees 556

WILLIS, FABER & DUMAS LTD. PENSION AND LIFE ASSURANCE SCHEME

Ten Trinity Square, London EC3P 3AX
Telephone: 01-488 8111

Pension Fund Director S.A.Phillips, FCII, FPMI

Trustees Eastern Trustees Ltd. (a subsidiary of Willis Faber Ltd.)

Actuaries Lane, Clark & Peacock

Pension Fund Consultants Willis Faber Advisory Services Ltd.

Auditors Ernst & Whinney

Company Employees 2,719

Members 1,983

Pensioners 435

Annual Contributions £2,200,000

Annual Investment Income £1,500,000

Annual Outflow £1,000,000

Capital Value £20,000,000

JOHN WILLMOTT HOLDINGS LTD

Hitchin Road, Shefford, Bedfordshire
Telephone: 0462-814 455

JOHN WILLMOTT HOLDINGS LTD *Continued*

Secretary J.Bayliss

Employees 900

ARNOLD WILLS & CO LTD
10 Station Road, Uppingham,
Leicestershire LE15 9TZ
Telephone: 057-282 2261

Director R.H.W.Wills

Employees 600

WALTER WILLSON LTD
Auckland House, Team Valley Estate, Gateshead,
Tyne & Wear
Telephone: 0632-875086

Secretary D.C.Robson

Employees 1,282

WILMOT BREEDEN GROUP STAFF PENSION SCHEME
PO Box 173, Amington Road,
Birmingham B25 8EW
Telephone: 021-707 5333

Pension Fund Manager W.D.Wilkinson, APMI

Secretary A.E.L.Olphin

Pensions Administration Manager S.G.Medlicott

Investment Manager D.H.Bayley

Trustees Wilmot Breeden Employees Trust Ltd

Committee of Management D.L.Breeden (Chairman), M.L.Breeden, D.L.Milne, H.D.Kettle, A.E.L.Olphin

Stockbrokers Phillips & Drew, Smith Keen Cutler, Spiers & Jeffrey, Capel-Cure Myers Ltd.

Actuaries Clay & Partners

Property Advisers Grimley & Son

Pension Fund Consultants Metropolitan Pensions Association Ltd

Auditors Thornton Baker & Co

Company Employees 3,730

Members (at 5.4.80) 3,023

Pensioners 2,306

	£000
Annual Contributions	2,791
Annual Investment Income	2,078
Annual Outflow	1,090
Capital Value	20,929
Summary of Investments (1979)	
Equities	3,681
Fixed Interest	9,620
Property	1,738
Cash & Deposits	213
Others	280

WILSON (CONNOLLY) HOLDINGS LTD
Thomas Wilson House, Tenter Road, Moulton Park,
Northampton NN3 1QJ
Telephone: 0604-46121

Director and Secretary F.H.Clowes, FSCA

Member of National Federation of Building Trades Employers Pension Scheme

Company Employees 531

THE WILTON ROYAL CARPET FACTORY LTD
THE WILTON GROUP PENSION FUND
Wilton, Salisbury, Wilts. SP2 0AY
Telephone: 072274-2441

Joint Managing Director I.W.Green, FCIS

Secretary A.J.Pilcher (Deloitte Haskins & Sells)

Other Pension Management Employees' and Employers' Advisory Committee

Trustees Solent Pensions Ltd.

Directors G.Wardle, MBE, I.W.Green, FCIS, M.P.G.Lamacraft

Investment Advisers A.H.Cobbold & Co

Actuaries Hymans Robertson & Co

Auditors Ernst & Whinney

Company Employees (at 5.4.80) 841

Members 432

Pensioners 60

	£000
Annual Contributions	241
Annual Investment Income	144
Annual Outflow	67
Capital Value	2,122
Summary of Investments	
Equities	1,726
Fixed Interest	283
Property	61
Cash & Deposits	27

WILTSHIRE COUNTY COUNCIL SUPERANNUATION FUND
County Hall, Trowbridge, Wiltshire BA14 8JG
Telephone: 02214-3641

Treasurer R.L.W.Moon, IPFA

Secretary County Solicitor and Clerk

Trustees Wiltshire County Council

Investment Advisers Lazard Securities Ltd.

Actuaries R.Watson & Sons

Auditors District Auditor

Employees 17,000

Members 7,500

Pensioners 2,700

	£000
Annual Contributions	6,500
Annual Investment Income	3,500
Annual Outflow	4,500
Capital Value	34,598
Summary of Investments	
UK Equities	5,685
N.American Equities	3,089
Fixed Interest	12,899
Property Unit Trusts	3,772
Cash & Deposits	6,008
Others	3,145

WIMPEY (A) STAFF PENSION FUND, (B) WIMPEY PENSION FUND AND (C) THE SECOND WIMPEY PENSION FUND

27 Hammersmith Grove, London W6 7EN
Telephone: 01-748 2000

Secretary D.M.Penton, MA, FCIS

Pension Fund Manager G.A.Calloway,APMI

Trustees Wimpey Pension Trustees Ltd

Investment Advisers J.Henry Schroder Wagg & Co.Ltd. & in house committee

Actuaries Duncan C. Fraser & Co

Auditors Deloitte, Haskins & Sells

Company Employees 27,000

	(A)	(B)
Members (at 5.4.80)	9,453	368
Pensioners	294	938
	£000	£000
Annual Contributions	4,710	329
Annual Investment Income	2,998	772
Capital Value	42,679	7,250
Summary of Investments (1979)		
Equities	24,169	-
Fixed Interest	5,072	-
Property	8,743	-
Cash & Deposits	689	-
Others	66	-

	(C)
Members	1,319
Pensioners	98
	£000
Annual Contributions	277
Annual Investment Income	315
Capital Value	2,825

WINDSMOOR (HOLDINGS) LTD

Windsmoor House, Lawrence Road, London N15 4EP
Telephone: 01-800 8022

Chairman A.D.Green

Employees 1,087

WIPAC GROUP (HOLDINGS) LTD

London Road, Buckingham MK18 1BH
Telephone. 02802-3031

Secretary N.F.Brazell

Employees 575

THOMAS WITTER & CO LTD

Water Street, Chorley, Lancashire PR7 1EY
Telephone: 02572-3031

Company Secretary J.G.Ritchie, FCA

Insured with Phoenix Assurance Co.Ltd.

Employees 1,108

W.L.SHAREHOLDINGS LTD.

6 King Edward Street, Oxford

Director C.R.Dick

Employees 576

WOLF ELECTRIC TOOLS (HOLDINGS) LTD PENSION FUNDS

Pioneer Works, Hanger Lane, London W5 1DS
Telephone: 01-998 2911

Secretary & Financial Director B.Robinson, FCA

Managed by Sun Life Pensions Management Ltd

Pension Fund Consultants Sedgwick Employee Benefits Consultants Ltd.

Auditors Mann Judd

Company Employees 906

Members 292

WOLSELEY-HUGHES LTD.

18 Vines Lane, Droitwich, Worcs.WR9 8ND
Telephone: 09057-8181

Finance Director & Secretary R.Ireland,FCIS

Investment Advisers Hill Samuel Investment Management Ltd.

Pension Fund Consultants Noble Lowndes & Partners Ltd.

Employees 5,357

WOLVERHAMPTON & DUDLEY BREWERIES LTD.

Park Brewery, Lovatt Street, Wolverhampton WV1 4NY
Telephone: 0902-772411

Secretary R.B.Houle,FCA

Insured with Standard Life Assurance Co.

Employees 5,429

WOMBWELL FOUNDRY & ENGINEERING CO.LTD.

Hough Lane, Wombwell, Barnsley, S.Yorks.S73 0LT

Secretary P.S.Barrett,MA,ACA

Employees 602

WOOD & SONS (HOLDINGS) LTD.

Trent Pottery, Burslem, Stoke on Trent, Staffs.ST6 3LF
Telephone: 0782-87201

Secretary I.E.Ingram

Insured with Scottish Widows' Fund & Life Assurance Society

Employees 902

WOOD BROTHERS GLASS CO.LTD.

Borough Flint Glass Works, Pontefract Road, Barnsley, S.Yorks.S71 1HL
Telephone: 0226-203637

Secretary Mrs.I.P.Holloway

Employees 650

WOOD HALL TRUST LTD GROUP PENSION FUND

St.Martin's House, 140 Tottenham Court Road, London W1P 9LN
Telephone: 01-387 0791

WOOD HALL TRUST LTD *Continued*

Pension Fund Manager J.West, FCIS
Secretary H.Harle, FCA
Trustees H. S. Trustees Ltd
Insured with Provident Mutual Life Assurance Association
Pension Fund Consultants Godwins Ltd
Auditors Deloitte, Haskins & Sells
Company Employees 1,605
Members 780
Pensioners 220
Annual Contributions £504,000
Annual Outflow £152,000
Capital Value £1,814,000

JOHN WOOD GROUP (ABERDEEN) LTD

Raik Road, Aberdeen AB9 8AG
Telephone: 0224-29288

Secretary E.C.Garrett
Insured with Sun Life Assurance Society Ltd.
Employees 2,027

JONAS WOODHEAD & SONS LTD

177 Kirkstall Road, Leeds, W.Yorks.LS4 2AQ
Telephone: 0532-41202

Secretary G.M.McIntosh,FCA
Managed by Legal & General (Pensions Management) Ltd, Prudential Pensions Ltd
Employees 4,211

WOODHOUSE & RIXSON (HOLDINGS) LTD STAFF PENSION PLAN (A), AND WORKS PENSION PLAN (B)

PO Box 74, Sheffield, S.Yorks.S9 3XS
Telephone: 0742-669283

Secretary C.B.Cotton
Investment Advisers Keyser Ullmann Pensions Management Ltd
Pension Fund Consultants EBS (Management) Ltd
Employees 650
Members (a) 163, (b) 275

WOODVILLE RUBBER CO LTD

Alton Lane, Ross on Wye, Herefordshire

Chairman D.J.Camille
Employees 817

WOOLWICH EQUITABLE BUILDING SOCIETY PENSION FUND

Equitable House, Woolwich, London SE18 6AB
Telephone: 01-854 2400

Pensions Manager D.J.Hutson
Secretary M.E.Tuke,FCCA
Investment Advisers National Westminster Bank Ltd.
Actuaries Duncan C.Fraser & Co.
Auditors Clark Pixley

Company Employees 2,465
Members 1,802
Pensioners 293
Annual Contributions £1,100,000
Capital Value £8,000,000

F.W. WOOLWORTH & CO LTD PENSION PLAN

Woolworth House, 242-246 Marylebone Road, London NW1 6JL
Telephone: 01-262 1222

Pension Fund Manager J.D.Burke, BA, APMI
Investment Advisers Warburg Investment Management Ltd.
Stockbrokers Phillips & Drew
Actuaries Bacon & Woodrow
Auditors Ernst & Whinney
Company Employees 41,500

Members (at 1.4.80)	16,500
Pensioners 4,895	
	£000
Annual Contributions	7,969
Annual Investment Income	3,510
Annual Outflow	2,533
Capital Value (Book Value)	53,400
Market Value	48,613
Summary of Investments	
Equities	33,900
Fixed Interest	13,100
Property	2,500
Cash & Deposits	1,000
Eagle Managed Fund	2,900

WORCESTER CONTROLS (UK) LTD.

Burrell Road, Haywards Heath, West Sussex RH16 1TL

Chairman E.A.Norris
Employees 755

WORTHINGTON-SIMPSON LTD.

Lowfield Works, P.O.Box 17, Newark, Notts.NG24 3EN
Telephone: 0636-5151

Secretary K.Keegan
Insured with Prudential Assurance Co.Ltd.
Employees 1,164

FRANK WRIGHT SHOES LTD.

Avondale Works, Connaught Street, Kettering, Northants

Secretary R.D.Moore
Employees 692

F.WRIGHTON & SONS (ASSOC.COMPANIES) LTD.

Brampton Works, Billet Road, London E17 5DW
Telephone: 01-527 5521

Secretary J.Sharman
Employees 588

THE WRIGLEY CO.LTD. PENSION & LIFE INSURANCE PLAN

Estover, Plymouth, Devon PL6 7PR
Telephone: 0752-701107

Secretary A.C.Ogle

Managed by Eagle Pension Funds

Actuaries Clay & Partners

Pension Fund Consultants Reed Stenhouse Benefit Consultants Ltd.

Auditors Arthur Young McClelland Moores & Co.

Company Employees 600

Members 450

Pensioners 54

Annual Contributions £250,000

Capital Value £700,000

JOHN WYETH & BROTHER LTD.

Huntercombe Lane South, Taplow, Maidenhead, Berkshire
Telephone: 0628-28311

Secretary D.E.Gibbens

Insured with Legal & General Assurance Society Ltd

Employees 1,198

YALE SECURITY PRODUCTS

Wood Street, Willenhall,
West Midlands WV13 1LA
Telephone: 0902-66911

Director C.G.Smith

Employees 1,700

YARROW GROUP BENEFITS PLAN

Charing Cross Tower, Glasgow G2 4UN
Telephone: 041-226 4192

Secretary W.McMillan,CA

Part Insured with Prudential Assurance Co Ltd

Part Managed by Prudential Pensions Ltd.

Pension Fund Consultants Sedgwick Employee Benefits Consultants Ltd.

Employees 1,300

Members (at 1.7.80) 1,064

Pensioners 60

YATES BROS WINE LODGES LTD YATES-ADDISON STAFF PENSION FUND

54 Carnarvon Street, Manchester M3 1HB
Telephone: 061-834 4691

Secretary J.C.Dickson

Accountant T.P.Fletcher,FCA

Investment Advisers Robert Fleming & Son Ltd

Actuaries Duncan C. Fraser & Co

Auditors Thornton Baker & Co

Company Employees 665

Members 178

Pensioners 103

Annual Contributions £65,000

Annual Investment Income £80,000

Capital Value £841,000

YORK TRAILER HOLDINGS LTD 1960 STAFF PENSION FUND

Northallerton, W.Yorks.LS1 2NS
Telephone: 0609-3155

Secretary S.Beckett

Finance Director G.Barker,ACCA

Insured with Norwich Union Insurance Group

Auditors Arthur Andersen & Co.

Company Employees 1,779

Members 114

Pensioners 10

YORKSHIRE BANK LTD SUPERANNUATION FUND (A), AND PENSIONS AND ANNUITIES FUND (B)

20 Merrion Way, Leeds LS2 8NZ
Telephone: 0532-441244

Pensions Manager T.M.Cocker, AIB

Secretary J.Crossley, FIB

Trustees YB Trust Co Ltd

Investment Advisers Morgan Grenfell & Co Ltd

Auditors Ernst & Whinney

Company Employees 3,511

	(A)	(B)
Members	145	1,900
Pensioners	337	57
	£000	£000
Annual Contributions	852	2,326
Annual Investment Income	1,632	885
Annual Outflow	1,069	42
Capital Value	15,250	11,569
Summary of Investments		
Equities	6,640	4,909
Fixed Interest	5,502	3,220
Cash & Deposits	1,659	2,470
Others	1,449	970

YORKSHIRE CHEMICALS (PENSION TRUST) LTD

20 Black Bull Street, Leeds, W.Yorks.LS10 1HP
Telephone: 0532-36591

Secretary G.H.Williamson

Managed by Legal & General (Pensions Management) Ltd

Investment Advisers Barclays Bank Trust Co Ltd

Actuaries Clay & Partners

Pension Fund Consultants Bain Dawes & Partners Ltd.

Employees 854

YORKSHIRE SWITCHGEAR GROUP LTD.

Meanwood Road, Leeds, West Yorkshire LS6 2BN
Telephone: 0532-757121

YORKSHIRE SWITCHGEAR GROUP LTD. *Continued*

Secretary G.D.Smith,FCA

Employees 796

YOUNG & CO'S BREWERY LTD
The Ram Brewery, Wandsworth,
London SW18 4JD
Telephone: 01-870 0141

Secretary J.R.Lawes

Insured with Provident Mutual Life Assurance Association

Employees 978

ARTHUR YOUNG MCCLELLAND MOORES & CO
Rolls House, 7 Rolls Buildings, London EC4A 1NL
Telephone: 01-831 7130

Employees 1,384

CECIL M. YUILL LTD
Cecil House, Loyalty Road, Hartlepool, Cleveland
Telephone: 0429-66620

Secretary D.Grieveson

Employees 750

ZECOL HOLDINGS LTD.
Lombard Road, Merton, London SW19 3UU
Telephone: 01-542 2283

Secretary M.H.Zeal

Employees 626

THE ZENITH CARBURETTER CO LTD GORDON RICAHARDS PENSION SCHEME
Honeypot Lane, Stanmore, Middlesex HA7 1LG
Telephone: 01-204 3388

Company Secretary F.W.Sumner,FCA

Trustees P.Arnold, E.E.Coombs, I.G.Mortimer, G.W.Sumner

Insured with Norwich Union Life Insurance Society

Pension Fund Consultants Godwins Ltd.

Auditors Touche Ross & Co.

Company Employees 1,455

Members 820

Pensioners 280

Annual Contributions £300,000

ZETTERS GROUP LTD.
86-88 Clerkenwell Road, London EC1
Telephone: 01-253 5376

Secretary A.Lubich

Insured with Crusader Insurance Co.Ltd.

Employees (Full-Time) 508

ZURICH INSURANCE CO UK PENSION FUND
Zurich House, Stanhope Road, Portsmouth, Hampshire PO1 1DU
Telephone: 0705-22200

Actuary C.Redman, BSc, FFA

Auditors Thornton Baker & Co

Company Employees 1,700
Pensioners 140
Annual Contributions £990,000
Capital Value £11 million

Major US and Canadian Pension Funds

The following section gives details of the major US and Canadian pension funds and their advisers. The pension funds listed include all companies with funds in excess of $500 million and public organisations with pension and retirement funds exceeding $750 million.

The information for this section has been extracted from the 1981 edition of the Money Market Directory and the January 19th, 1981 edition of Pensions & Investment Age, with the permission of their publishers. This information has also been updated with data extracted from the Pension Directory published with the January 1981 issue of Institutional Investor. The publisher of Pension Funds and Their Advisers thanks them for their help in ensuring the accuracy of the information. The list of money managers has been extracted from the same sources and includes details of all firms managing tax-exempt funds (including charitable foundations etc.) of over $1,500 million. Substantial differences however appear on occasion between amounts shown in the Money Market Directory, as employee benefits accounts, and those shown in Pensions & Investments Age, as tax exempt funds. Most of the amounts shown are taken from Pensions & Investments Age.

The Major USA Pension Funds

RETIREMENT SYSTEM OF ALABAMA

135 South Union Street, Montgomery, Ala 36130
Telephone: 205-832 6950

Contacts David G.Bronner, (Secretary & Treasurer), Warren J.Fredericks (Director, Investment Research), William C.Walsh (Benefits Administrator)

Funds	$million
Teachers' Retirement System of Alabama	1,475
Employees' Retirement System of Alabama	664
Judicial Retirement Fund	14
Total Assets	2,153
Summary of Investments	%
Equities	4
Fixed Interest	72
Mortgages	13
Cash	10
Real Estate	1
	$million
Employer Contributions	286
Benefit Payments	120

ALLIED CHEMICAL CORP.

Columbia Road & Park Avenue, Morristown, N.J.07960
Telephone: 201-455 5681

Contacts Harold W.Burke (Senior Vice President Planning & Finance), Nicholas A.Cameron (Treasurer), R.W.Hawkins (Director Employee Benefits)

Funds	$million
Pension Plan for Salaried & Hourly Employees	500
Stock Purchase & Savings Plan	80
Total Assets	70
Est.Assets Sept.1980	700
Summary of Investments	%
Equities	70
Fixed Interest	25
Cash	5
	$million
Employer Contributions	70

ALUMINIUM CO OF AMERICA

1501 Alcoa Building, Pittsburgh, Pa 15219
Telephone: 412-553 3595

Contact Joseph C.Pellegrino (Assistant Treasurer), Richard J.Forester (Manager, Pension Fund Investments & Analysis)

Funds	$million
Employees Retirement Plans	842
Savings Plan Salaried Employees	148
Total Assets	990
Est.Assets Sept. 1980	1,079

Is your pension fund a loss making subsidiary?

Any Finance Director knows that poor performance of his pension fund will entail an expensive "topping-up" sometime in the future. International diversification of assets is a key to achieving a total real return on the value of the pension fund. With funds under management in excess of £450 million the G.T. Management group, through offices in London, Hong Kong and San Francisco, offers a professional international investment management service.

For further information
contact D.F. Lay or H.J. Birch,
Park House, 16 Finsbury Circus,
London EC2M 7DS
Tel: 01-628 8131 Telex 886100

G.T. Pension Services Co. Ltd.

ALUMINIUM CO OF AMERICA *Continued*

Summary of Investments	%
Equities	60
Fixed Interest	21
Cash	15
Real Estate	4
Others	1

	$million
Employer Contributions	175
Benefit Payments	87

AMERICAN AIRLINES INC

Dallas Fort Worth Airport, P.O.Box 61616, Dallas, Texas 75261
Telephone: 214-630 5100

Contacts John C. Pope (Vice-President & Treasurer), John J.Tierney (Director of Trust Investments), T.F.Quinn (Vice President Tax & Insurance)

Funds	$million
Fixed Benefit Plans	931
Supplemental Variable Annuity Plans	472
Total Assets	1,403

Summary of Investments	%
Cash	22
Equities	54
Fixed Income	21
Others	3

	$million
Employer Contributions	116
Benefit Payments	60

AMERICAN CAN CO

American Lane, Greenwich, Ct 06830
Telephone: 203-552 2620

Contacts E.C.Ecker (Director, Pension & Group Insurance Funds), L.N. Sterling (Senior Vice President Finance), D.E.Rubinstein (Manager Pension Investment)

Funds	$million
American Can Company Master Trust	530
American Can Co Retirement Plan Trust for Salaried Employees	25
Canadian Plans	58
3 other funds	7
Total Assets	620
Est.Assets Sept.1980	670

Summary of Investments	%
Cash	9
Equities	38
Fixed Income	13
Mortgages	2
Others	38

	$million
Employer Contributions	90
Benefit Payments	51

AMERICAN TELEPHONE & TELEGRAPH CO

195 Broadway, New York, NY 10007
Telephone: 212-393 5025

Contacts David Feldman (Assistant Vice President), Robert Angelica (Manager, Pension Fund Planning), John English (Director, Investment Management Administration)

Fund	$million
Retirement Plans	31,100
Est.Assets Sept.1979	1,261
Total Assets	33,700

Summary of Investments	%
Equities	56
Fixed Interest	30
Cash	12
Real Estate	2

	$million
Employer Contributions	1,750
Benefit Payments	1,200

33 separate funds for A.T.& T. and Bell System were merged in Summer 1980 to form the above scheme

ARIZONA STATE RETIREMENT SYSTEM

1777 West Camelback Road, Phoenix, Ariz 85067
Telephone: 602-255 5131

Contacts C.M.Sullivan (Director), John Hendicks (Cash Manager)

Fund	$million
Benefit Fund	1,713
Total Assets June 1980	1,713

Summary of Investments	%
Equities	18
Fixed Income	51
Mortgages	8
Cash	23

	$million
Employer Contributions	212
Benefit Payments	85

ARMCO INC.

703 Curtis Street, Middletown, Ohio 45042
Telephone: 513-425 5238

Contacts J.Robert Whitehurst (Vice President, Pension Fund), Alan B.Cooper (Director, Benefits Administrator), Fund), Paul G.Chenault (Director, Investments)

Funds	$million
Consolidated Retirement Plans	748
Thrift Plan for Salaried Employees	232
Other Funds	10
Total Assets	1,090
Est.Assets Sept.1908	1,172

Summary of Investments	%
Cash	17
Equities	49
Fixed Income	27
Property	6
Foreign	1

	$million
Employer Contributions	104
Benefits Payments	76

ATLANTIC RICHFIELD CO

515 South Flower Street, Los Angeles, Calif 90071
Telephone: 213-486 0163

ATLANTIC RICHFIELD CO Continued

Contacts Howard H.Ocklemann (Investment Officer), Walter J.Milner (Benefit Administrator), Marie L.Lafond (Manager Investor Relations)

Funds	$ million
Retirement Plan	770
Anaconda Company Retirement Plan	226
Thrift Plan	308
7 other funds	257
Total Assets	1,561
Est.Assets Sept.1980	1,750

Summary of Investments	%
Cash	20
Equities	45
Fixed Income	35

	$ million
Employers Contributions	140
Benefit Payments	80

BAKERY & CONFECTIONERY WORKERS UNION

1828 L Street,N.W., Suite 3800, Washington, D.C.20036
Telephone: 202-857 4510

Contact John S.Fleming (Administrator & Director)

Funds	$ million
Retirement Fund	600

Summary of Investments	%
Equities	37
Fixed Interest	51
Cash	8
Mortgages	3

	$ million
Employer Contributions	105
Benefit Payments	75

BENDIX CORPORATION

Bendix Center, Southfield, Mich.48037
Telephone: 312-352 5000

Contacts Bernard Winograd (Treasurer), John W.Kemble (Director), Robert J.Gillette (Director, Pension Investment)

Fund	$ million
Master Retirement Trust	1,000

Summary of Investments	%
Equities	50
Fixed Interest	38
Real Estate	12

BETHLEHEM STEEL CORPORATION

Bethlehem, Pa 18016
Telephone: 215-694 2424

Contacts Davis T.Dunbar (Pension Fund Manager), David Kempken (Manager, Employee Benefit Programmes)

Funds	$ million
Pension Plan	1,872
4 other funds	7
Total Assets	1,879
Est.Assets Sept.1980	1,900

Summary of Investments	%
Cash	6
Equities	69
Fixed Interest	25

	$ million
Employers Contributions	321
Benefit Payments	258

BOEING COMPANY

7755 East Marginal Way, PO Box 3707, Seattle, Wash 98124
Telephone: 206-655 2546

Contacts Gary B.Bland (Manager, Trust Investments), J.B.L.Pierce (Treasurer)

Funds	$ million
Employees Retirement Plans	1,250
Voluntary Savings Plans	750
Employees' Financial Security Plan	122
Total Assets	2,122
Est.Assets Sept.1980	2,700

Summary of Investments	%
Equities	60
Fixed Interest	30
Cash	10

	$ million
Employers Contributions	85
Benefit Payments	36

BOILERMAKERS, IRON, SHIPBUILDERS PENSION FUND

522 Old Brotherhood Building, Kansas City, Kansas 66101
Telephone: 913-342 6555

Contacts T.Lusk Wands (Administrator), David Lewis (Secretary & Treasurer)

Funds	$ million
Pension Fund	800

Summary of Investments	%
Equities	60
Fixed Interest	40

	$ million
Employer Contributions	80
Benefit Payments	36

CALIFORNIA EMPLOYEES' RETIREMENT SYSTEMS

PO Box 1953, Sacramento, Calif 95809
Telephone: 916-445 7700

Contact Melvin W.Petersen (Chief of Investments)

Funds	$ million
California Public Employees' Retirement System	12,400
California State Teachers Retirement System	7,000
California Legislators' Retirement System	35
Total Assets	19,435

Summary of Investments	%
Equities	23
Fixed Interest	77

	$ million
Employer Contributions	2,200
Benefit Payments	1,452

CATERPILLAR TRACTOR CO.
100 NE Adams Street, Peoria, Ill.61629
Telephone: 309-675 5000

Contact M.W.Coon (Manager Employee Benefit Funds)

Funds	$ million
Non-Contributory Pension Plan	540
Retirement Income Plan	690
Employees' Investment Plan	335
Total Assets	1,565
Est.Assets Sept. 1980	1,700

Summary of Investments	%
Cash	11
Equities	56
Fixed Income	28
Mortgages/Real Estate	5

CELANESE CORP.
1211 Avenue of the Americas, New York, N.Y.10036
Telephone: 212-764 8760

Contacts Charles S.Stephens (Asset Controller), Ms.F.McCarthy (Pension Analyst), K.G.Anderson (Vice President Employee Affairs)

Funds	$ million
Retirement Income Plans	390
Stock Bonus & Investment Plan	187
Total Assets	577
Est.Assets Sept. 1980	650

Summary of Investments	%
Equities	70
Fixed Interest	16
Cash	4
Real Estate	10

	$ million
Employer Contributions	61
Benefit Payments	6

CHICAGO TEACHERS RETIREMENT FUND
228 North LaSalle Street, Chicago, Ill.60601
Telephone: 312-641 4464

Contact James F.Ward (Executive Director)

Funds	$ million
Public School Teachers Pension & Retirement Fund	830

Summary of Investments	%
Equities	20
Fixed Interest	52
Cash	28

	$ million
Employer Contributions	106
Benefit Payments	69

CHRYSLER CORPORATION
PO Box 1919, Detroit, Mich.43288
Telephone: 313-956 6548

Contacts R.K.Alverson (Manager, Pension Fund Administration), Roy S.Good (Manager Investment Review)

Funds	$ million
U.A.W. Pension Plan	780
Salaried Employees' Retirement Plan	467
C.C. Employees Pension Plan	244
Thrift Stock Ownership Program	74
4 other funds	39
Total Assets	1,604

Summary of Investments	%
Cash	18
Equities	62
Fixed Income	20
Mortgages/Real estate	3
Others	1

	$ million
Employer Contributions	270
Benefit Payments	210

CITIBANK N.A.
One Citicorp Center, 153 East 53rd Street, N.Y.10043
Telephone: 212-559 9700

Contact Peter H.Vermilye (Senior Vice President)

Funds	$ million
Retirement Plan	517
Staff Incentive Plan	66
Total Assets	583

CITIES SERVICE COMPANY
P.O.Box 300, Tulsa, Okla.74102
Telephone: 918-586 4211

Contacts W.K.Witmer (Treasurer), R.W.Woollen (Assistant Treasurer)

Funds	$ million
Retirement Plan	370
Employees Thrift Plan	219
8 Other Plans	151
Total Assets	740
Est.Assets Sept. 1980	831

Summary of Investments	%
Cash	9
Equities	44
Fixed Interest	47

	$ million
Employers Contributions	53
Benefit Payments	25

COLORADO PUBLIC EMPLOYEES RETIREMENT ASSOCIATION
1300 Logan Street, Denver, Col 80203
Telephone: 303-832 9750

Contacts Kenneth E.Peterson (Assistant Executive Secretary Investments), Joseph P.Natale (Executive Secretary)

Funds	$ million
Benefit Fund	2,059
Total Assets Sept. 1980	2,059

Summary of Investments	%
Cash	3
Equities	27
Fixed Income	56
Mortgages	14

	$ million
Employer Contributions	235
Benefit Payments	92

497

COMMONWEALTH EDISON CO.

One First National Plaza, P.O.Box 767, Chicago, Ill.60690
Telephone: 312-294 2946

Contacts Ernest Roth (Treasurer), Bill Jenkins (Financial Advisor)

Funds	$million
Service Annuity Fund	712
Employees Stock Ownership Plan	18
Total Assets	730
Employer Contributions	78

STATE OF CONNECTICUT TRUST FUNDS

20 Trinity Street, Hartford, Ct 06115
Telephone: 203-566 2166

Contacts Lee van Meter (Deputy Treasurer-Investments), Henry Parker (Treasurer)

Funds	$million
Teachers Retirement Fund	1,109
State Employees Retirement Fund	342
Municipal Employees Retirement Fund	113
Total Assets	1,564

Summary of Investments	%
Cash	27
Equities	27
Fixed Income	58

	$million
Employer Contributions	395
Benefit Payments	200

CONSOLIDATED EDISON CO.OF N.Y.

4 Irving Place, New York, N.Y.10003
Telephone: 212-460 4600

Contacts John V.Thornton (Senior Vice President), Alfred R.Wassler (Treasurer), Donald L.Miller (Vice President Personnel)

Funds	$million
Retirement Fund	631

Summary of Investments	%
Equities	41
Fixed Interest	47
Cash	10
Real Estate	2

	$million
Employer Contributions	117
Benefit Payments	58

CONTINENTAL GROUP

1 Harbour Plaza, Stamford, Conn.06902
Telephone: 203-964 6252

Contacts Walter R.Good (Vice President Asset Management), William J.Corbett (Director Pension Investment Management), J.Connolly (Director Employee Benefits)

Funds	$million
Retirement Fund	729

Summary of Investments	%
Equities	59
Fixed Interest	17
Cash	16
Real Estate	8

	$million
Employer Contributions	62
Benefit Payments	53

CONTINENTAL OIL COMPANY (CONOCO)

High Ridge Park, Stamford, Conn 06904
Telephone: 203-359 3500

Contacts Roland F.Hartman (Manager Pension Investment), William H.Smith (Co-ordinator, Pension Investment)

Funds	$million
Retirement Plan Master Trust	457
Thrift Plan	391
Total Assets	848
Est.Assets Sept.1980	982

Summary of Investments	%
Cash	9
Equities	58
Fixed Income	24
Real Estate	9

	$million
Employer Contributions	55
Benefit Payments	30

CROWN ZELLERBACH

One Bush Street, San Francisco, Calif.94104
Telephone: 415-823 5445

Contacts Charles S.LaFollette (Vice President), Susan Tohbe (Manager Treasury Operations), R.C.Farr (Benefit Administrator)

Funds	$million
Retirement Plan	300
Salaried Employees Savings Plan	80
Total Assets	380
Est.Assets Sept.1980	530

Summary of Investments	%
Equities	57
Fixed Interest	37
Cash	1
Real Estate	5

	$million
Employers Contributions	35
Benefit Payments	22

DEERE & CO.

John Deere Road, Moline, Ill.61265
Telephone: 309-752 4857

Contact Greta E.Marshall (Director, Investments)

Funds	$million
Retirement Plan for Hourly Employees	389
Retirement Plan for Salaried Employees	380
Total Assets	769
Est.Assets Sept.1980	850

Summary of Investments	%
Cash	3
Equities	69
Fixed Income	27
Real Estate	1

DEERE & CO. *Continued*

	$million
Employer Contributions	120
Benefit Payments	50

DETROIT RETIREMENT SYSTEMS

510 City-County Building, Detroit, Mich 48226
Telephone: 313-224 3360

Contact Fred Murphy (Executive Secretary)

Funds	$million
City of Detroit Retirement System	796
Policemen & Firemen Retirement System	717
Total Assets	1,513

Summary of Investments	%
Cash	18
Equities	19
Fixed Income	37
Mortgages	10
Others	16

	$million
Employer Contributions	160
Benefit Payments	99

THE DOW CHEMICAL CO.

2030 E.Dow Center, Midland, Mich.48640
Telephone: 517-636 1455

Contacts Eugene C.Yehle (Director of Pension Investment), J.Frank Whitley (Manager, Pension Investment), T.E.Burtch (Administration Manager)

Funds	$million
Retirement Plan Trust	890
Total Assets	890
Est.Assets Sept.1979	790

Summary of Investments	%
Equities	80
Fixed Income	10
Cash	10

	$million
Employers Contributions	85
Benefit Payments	40

E.I.DUPONT DE NEMOURS & CO.INC.

1055 Wilmington Trust Building, Wilmington, Del.19898
Telephone: 302 774 4543

Contacts David F.Marvin (Director, Pension Fund Investment), A.H.Nehrling (Director Employee Compensation)

Funds	$million
E.A.DuPont de Nemours & Co.Pension Trust Fund	2,720
Employees Thrift Plan	709
4 other funds	233
Total Assets	4,425
Est.Assets Sept.1980	4,425

Summary of Investments	%
Equities	68
Fixed Interest	30
Cash	2

	$million
Employer Contributions	562
Benefit Payments	227

EASTERN AIRLINES INC.

Miami International Airport, Miami, Florida 33148
Telephone: 305-873 2211

Contacts Wayne A.Yeoman (Senior Vice President Finance), Bill Ott (Director Personnel), Speros G. Drelles (Director Pension Asset Management)

Funds	$million
Fixed Benefit & Retirement Fund	528
Variable Benefit Retirement Plan for Pilots	396
Variable Benefit Retirement Plan (Ground)	72
Total Assets	996

Summary of Investments	%
Cash	2
Equities	59
Fixed Income	31
Real Estate	8

	$million
Employer Contributions	99
Benefit Payments	25

EASTMAN-KODAK CO.

343 State Street, Rochester, N.Y.14650
Telephone: 716-724 4325

Contacts Donald Snyder (Treasurer), Russell L.Olson (Administrative Assistant), Robert R.Ross (Assistant Vice President, Corporate Compensation & Benefits)

Funds	$million
Retirement Income Plan	2,247
Employees' Savings & Investment Plan	406
Total Assets	2,653

Summary of Investments	%
Cash	4
Equities	49
Insured/Fixed Interest	45
Real Estate	2

	$million
Employer Contributions	230
Benefit Payments	95

INTERNATIONAL BROTHERHOOD OF ELECTRICAL WORKERS

1125 15th Street,N.W., Washington, D.C.20005
Telephone: 202-833 7000

Contacts Ken Maddox

Funds	$million
Retirement Fund	878

Summary of Investments	%
Equities	7
Fixed Interest	79
Cash	4
Real Estate	10

	$million
Employer Contributions	140
Benefit Payments	40

EPISCOPAL CHURCH PENSION FUND
800 2nd Avenue, New York, N.Y.10017
Telephone: 212-661 6700

Contacts Robert A.Robinson (President), Walter F.Donnelly, Rev.Craig W.Casey (Vice Presidents)

Funds	$million
Pension Fund	524

Summary of Investments	%
Equities	67
Fixed Interest	29
Cash	4

	$million
Employer Contributions	27
Benefit Payments	15

EXXON CORPORATION
1251 Avenue of the Americas, New York, NY 10020
Telephone: 212-398 3000

Contacts G.B.McCullough (Administrator of Benefits), Allan Hamilton (Administrator of Finance), Vincent J.Motto (Assistant Treasurer)

Funds	$million
Trusteed Annuity Fund	3,000
Thrift Fund (Savings Programs)	1,339
Total Assets	4,339

Summary of Investments	%
Cash	4
Equities	53
Fixed Income	7
Real Estate	13
Insurance	23

	$million
Employers Contributions	362
Benefit Payments	142

FIRESTONE TIRE & RUBBER COMPANY
1200 Firestone Parkway, Akron, Ohio 44317
Telephone: 216-379 7000

Contact W.L.Strong (Vice President Finance), L.M.Jones (Benefit Administrator), T.A.Lesher (Manager Pension Fund Administration)

Funds	$million
Non Contributory Pension Plan	412
Retirement Plan	504
1 other fund	15
Total Assets	932

Summary of Investments	%
Cash	7
Equities	67
Fixed Income	25
Real Estate	1

	$million
Employer Contributions	57
Benefit Payments	71

FLORIDA STATE BOARD OF ADMINISTRATION
2005-135 Apalachee Parkway, PO Drawer 5318, Tallahassee, Fla.32301
Telephone: 904-488 4406

Contacts Leo Bailey (Executive Director), A.J. McMullian (Retirement Director)

Funds	$million
Florida Retirement System	4,000
Total Assets	4,000

Summary of Investments	%
Equities	6
Fixed Interest	84
Cash	5
Mortgages	5

	$million
Employer Contributions	300
Benefit Payments	225

FMC CORP.
200 East Randolph Drive, Chicago, Ill.60601
Telephone: 312-861 6172

Contacts B.K.Van Eck (Vice President,Treasurer), Robert B.Hoffman (Vice President Finance)

Funds	$million
Master Retirement Trust	520
Thrift & Stock Purchase Plan	80
Total Assets	600

Summary of Investments	%
Equities	83
Fixed Interest	11
Cash	6

	$million
Employer Contributions	39

FORD MOTOR CO
The American Road, Dearborn, Mich 48121
Telephone: 313-322 8035

Contacts R.C.White (Assistant Treasurer), Maurice Maertens (Manager Trust Investment Analysis)

Funds	$million
Ford Motor Co General Retirement Plan	1,845
Ford Motor Co U.A.W. Retirement Plan	1,347
Ford Motor Co Savings & Stock Investment Plan	946
Aeronutronic-Ford Corporation various plans	157
Ford Motor Co-U.A.W. Supplemental Unemployment Benefit Plan	172
Total Assets	4,467
Est Assets Dec.1978	5,100

	$million
Employer Contributions	600
Benefit Payments	300

GENERAL DYNAMICS CORPORATION
7733 Forsyth, St Louis, Mo 63105
Telephone: 314-862 2440

Contacts John P.Maguire (Secretary & Fund Administrator), C.D.Walbrandt (Director Employee Benefit Trust Investments)

Funds	$million
Retirement Plan for Salaried Employees	650
Employees' Savings & Stock Investment Plan	400
Total Assets	1,050
Est.Assets Sept.1980	1,560

GENERAL DYNAMICS CORPORATION Continued

Summary of Investments	%
Equities	36
Fixed Interest	64

	$million
Employer Contributions	73
Benefit Payments	14

GENERAL ELECTRIC CO
112 Prospect Street, PO Box 7900, Stamford, Ct 06904
Telephone: 203-357 4100

Contact Edward H.Malone (Vice President - Trust Investments, Chairman of Trustees) W.R.Fulljames (Treasurer)

Funds	$million
Pension Trust	4,706
Savings & Security Plan	443
Elfun Trusts	209
6 other Funds	287
Total Assets	5,645
Est. Assets Sept.1980	7,184

Summary of Investments	%
Equities	64
Fixed Interest	18
Cash	12
Real Estate	5
Others	1

	$million
Employer Contributions	556
Benefit Payments	551

GENERAL FOODS CORP.
250 North Street, White Plains, N.Y.10625

Contacts Douglas A.Smith (Senior Vice President, Chief Finance Officer), Richard A.Aszling (Vice President)

Funds	$million
Retirement Fund	550

GENERAL MOTORS CORPORATION
767 Fifth Avenue, New York, NY 10022
Telephone: 212-486 3585

Contacts R.Charles Tschampion (Director, Pension Fund Analysis), Richard Dugan (Director, Employee Benefit Plan Analysis)

Funds	$million
Hourly rate Employees Pension Plan	5,333
Retirement Program for Salaried Employees (non insured portion)	3,105
Retirement Program for Salaried Employees (insured portion)	2,500
Savings & Stock Purchase Program for Salaried Employees	1,672
Supplemental Unemployment Benefit Plans	1,183
2 other funds	48
Total Assets	13,841

Summary of Investments	%
Equities	60
Fixed Interest	34
Cash	6

	$million
Employer Contributions	2,069
Benefit Payments	956

GENERAL TELEPHONE & ELECTRONICS CORPORATION
One Stamford Forum, Stamford, Ct 06904
Telephone: 203-357 2170

Contacts James M. Dunn, Jr (President of Pension Fund Administration), William P.Marshall (Manager of Pension Fund Evaluation), W.L.Hyland (Director, Insurance & Pensions)

Funds	$million
GTE & Subsidiaries Pension Trust	3,000

Summary of Investments	%
Equities	65
Fixed Interest	19
Cash	15
Real Estate	1

	$million
Employer Contributions	220
Benefit Payments	72

GEORGIA STATE RETIREMENT SYSTEMS
Two Northside 75, Suite 400, Atlanta, Ga 30318
Telephone: 404-656 2151

Contacts Graham R.Lynch (Director-Division of Investment Services), C.W.Cary (Assistant Director), Wesley Rucker, Abe Domain (Benefit Administrators)

Funds	$million
Teachers Retirement System of Georgia	1,610
Employees Retirement System of Georgia	654
Total Assets	2,264

Summary of Investments	%
Cash	4
Equities	32
Fixed Income	62
Mortgages/Real Estate	2

	$million
Employer Contributions	259
Benefit Payments	139

GETTY OIL CO.
3810 Wilshire Boulevard, Los Angeles, Calif.90010
Telephone: 213-381 7151

Contacts Duane A.Bland (Vice President Finance), Hugh M.Slawson (Treasurer)

Funds	$million
Pension Plan	404
Thrift Plan	166
Total Assets	575
Est.Assets Sept.1980	614

Summary of Investments	%
Equities	63
Fixed Interest	20
Cash	12
Real Estate	1
Others	5

GETTY OIL CO. *Continued*

	$million
Employer Contributions	52
Benefit Payments	32

GOODYEAR TIRE & RUBBER CO

1144 East Market Street, Akron, Ohio 44316
Telephone: 216-794 4625

Contacts Bennett H.Shaver (Assistant Treasurer), D.R.Kronenberger (Vice President & Treasurer)

Funds	$million
Pension Plans	1,245

Summary of Investments	%
Equities	61
Fixed Income	31
Real Estate	8

	$million
Employer Contributions	146
Benefit Payments	92

GREYHOUND CORPORATION

Greyhound Towers, Phoenix, Ariz 85077
Telephone: 602-248 5659

Contacts Richard B.Zoller (Director of Investments), Rhodes M.Barbarick (Director Pension Investment), B.Brody (Director Employee Benefits)

Funds	$million
Retirement & Disability Plan	265
Armour & Co Salaried Employees' Pension Plan	179
Western Greyhound Lines Pension Plan	101
Armour & Co Labor Pension Plan	86
Retirement Income Trust	64
Total Assets	695

Summary of Investments	%
Equities	61
Fixed Interest	25
Cash	10
Others	4

	$million
Employers Contributions	55

GRUMMAN CORPORATION

1111 Stewart Avenue, Bethpage, NY 11714
Telephone: 516-575 7987

Contacts Robert W.Bradshaw (Benefits Secretary) Robert G.Freese (Vice President & Treasurer), William Parmentier (Assistant Treasurer)

Funds	$million
Employee Retirement Plan	580
Employee Investment Plan	191
Total Assets	771

Summary of Investments	%
Cash	20
Equities	50
Fixed Interest	23
Real Estate	5
Others	2

	$million
Employers Contributions	60
Benefit Payments	30

GULF OIL CORPORATION

Gulf Building, Pittsburgh, Pa 15230
Telephone: 412-263 5304

Contacts Robert A. McKean (Pension Fund Investments Manager), J.C.Irwin (Supervisor, Pensions Plan Administration), P.E.Lintner (Director Compensation)

Funds	$million
Pension Plan	1,146
Savings & Stock Bonus Plan	105
Other Funds	114
Total Assets	1,365

Summary of Investments	%
Cash	16
Equities	45
Fixed Interest	25
Others	14

	$million
Employers Contributions	166
Benefit Payments	90

HALLIBURTON SERVICES

P.O.Box 1431, Duncan, Oklahoma 73533
Telephone: 405-251 3760

Contacts Charles S.Storms (Financial Manager), William T.Sheets (Benefits Administrator)

Funds	$million
Employees Benefit Fund	628

Summary of Investments	%
Equities	63
Fixed Interest	24
Cash	9
Mortgages	4

	$million
Employer Contributions	37
Benefit Payments	28

HAWAII EMPLOYEES' RETIREMENT SYSTEM

888 Mililani Street, Suite 502, Honolulu, Hawaii 96813
Telephone: 808-548 7593

Contact Stanley Siu (Executive Secretary)

Funds	$million
Benefit Fund	1,300

Summary of Investments	%
Equities	14
Fixed Interest	60
Cash	16

	$million
Employer Contributions	67
Benefit Payments	71

HERCULES INC.

910 Market Street, Wilmington, Delaware 19899
Telephone: 302-575 5250

Contact Priscilla M.Wellford (Manager Pension Trust)

Funds	$million
Pension Plan	447
Savings Plan	77
2 other plans	78
Total Assets	610

HERCULES INC. *Continued*

Summary of Investments	%
Equities	38
Fixed Interest	34
Cash	18
Real Estate	10

	$million
Employer Contributions	60
Benefit Payments	25

HONEYWELL INC.

Honeywell Plaza, Minneapolis, Minn.55408
Telephone: 612-870 2750

Contacts Sandy Wendler (Manager Pension Policy), Glenn H.Kent (Manager Pension Funding)

Funds	$million
Master Trust Fund	580
Savings & Security Program	24
Total Assets	604

Summary of Investments	%
Equities	72
Fixed Interest	24
Cash	2
Real Estate	2

	$million
Employer Contributions	93
Benefit Payments	34

HUGHES AIRCRAFT CO

Centineal and Teale, Culver City, Calif.90230
Telephone: 213-391 0711

Contacts T.V.Keene (Vice President Finance), Gary B. Helms (Director Investment Management)

Funds	$million
Pension Plan	1,127
Savings Plan	307
Total Assets	1,434
Employer Contributions	100
Benefit Payments	30

IBM CORPORATION

Old Orchard Road, Armonk, NY 10504
Telephone: 914-765 1900

Contacts Robert Schultz (Director of US Retirement Trust Fund), William V.Hoyt (Director)

Funds	$million
IBM Retirement Plan	5,200

Summary of Investments	%
Equities	62
Fixed Interest	25
Cash	13

	$million
Employer Contributions	520
Benefit Payments	80

ILLINOIS STATE UNIVERITIES RETIREMENT SYSTEM

50 Gerty Drive, Champaign, Ill.61820
Telephone: 217-333 3860

Contacts Donald Hoffmeister (Director), Charles Hundley (Assistant Director)

Funds	$million
Retirement System	907

Summary of Investments	%
Equities	45
Fixed Interest	49
Cash	4
Others	2

	$million
Employer Contributions	120
Benefit Payments	42

ILLINOIS MUNICIPAL RETIREMENT FUND

100 South Wacker Drive, Chicago, Ill 60606
Telephone: 312-346 6722

Contacts Hiroshige Mori (Investment Manager), R.W.Kausch (Benefits Administrator)

Funds	$million
Retirement Fund	1,108

Summary of Investments	%
Cash	2
Equities	33
Fixed Interest	65

	$million
Employers Contributions	129
Benefit Payments	85

ILLINOIS STATE BOARD OF INVESTMENT

180 North LaSalle Street, Room 905, Chicago, Ill 60601
Telephone: 312-793 5710

Contact Robert Harmon (Director)

Funds	$million
State Employees Retirement Fund	867
State Judges Fund	53
General Assembly Fund	12
Total Assets	932

Summary of Investments	%
Equities	20
Fixed Interest	61
Cash	18

	$million
Employers Contributions	103
Benefit Payments	51

ILLINOIS TEACHERS' RETIREMENT SYSTEM

2815 West Washington Street, Springfield, Ill 62706
Telephone: 217-753 0311

Contact Samuel W. Anderson (Director)

Funds	$million
Benefit Fund	2,233

Summary of Investments	%
Cash	11
Equities	27
Fixed Interest	57
Mortgages	5

	$million
Employer Contributions	213
Benefit Payments	193

INDIANA PUBLIC EMPLOYEES RETIREMENT FUND

143 West Market Street, Indianapolis, Indiana 46204
Telephone: 317-232 1620

Contacts Harold J.Egenes (Secretary), Louis S.Eggert (Manager Investment Department)

Funds	$million
Benefit Fund	713
Policemen & Firefighters Pension Fund	80
2 other funds	9
Total Assets	810

Summary of Investments	%
Fixed Interest	75
Cash	11
Mortgages	14

	$million
Employer Contributions	82

INLAND STEEL COMPANY

30 West Monroe Street, Chicago, Ill 60603
Telephone: 312-346 0300

Contacts Robert J.Greenbaum (Treasurer), Richard J.Schutter (Manager Pension Investment)

Funds	$million
Pension Plan	698
Thrift Plan	85
Total Assets	783

Summary of Investments	%
Equities	68
Fixed Interest	19
Cash	8
Real Estate	5

	$million
Employer Contributions	80
Benefit Payments	50

INTERNATIONAL HARVESTER COMPANY

401 North Michigan Avenue, Chicago, Ill 60611
Telephone: 312-670 2000

Contacts James C.Cotting (Senior Vice President, Finance), Robert C.Lannert (Vice President & Treasurer), W.Grant Chandler (Director) Human Resources)

Funds	$million
Retirement Plan for Salaried Employees	627
Non-contributory Retirement Plan	455
2 other funds	18
Total Assets	1,190

Summary of Investments	%
Equities	39
Fixed Interest	26
Real Estate	9
Cash	10
Others	16

	$million
Employer Contributions	215
Benefit Payments	162

INTERNATIONAL PAPER COMPANY

220 East 42nd Street, New York, NY 10017
Telephone: 212-490 6000

Contacts John A.McDonough (Treasurer), Jose A.Colls (Manager Pension Fund)

Funds	$million
Employee Retirement Plan	673
Savings Investment Plan	78
Total Assets	751
Est.Assets Sept.1980	817

Summary of Investments	%
Cash	10
Equities	55
Fixed Interest	30
Real Estate	5

INTERNATIONAL TELEPHONE & TELEGRAPH CORP.

320 Park Avenue, New York, NY 10022
Telephone: 212-752 6000

Contacts Edwin J.Ehrlich (Director Pension Fund Trust), A.J.Montegari (Manager Pension Fund Trust)

Funds	$million
Master Retirement Trusts	427
I.T.T. Investment & Saving Plan	157
Hartford Insurance Group Retirement Plan	125
Total Assets	709
Est.Assets Sept.1980	1,009

Summary of Investments	%
Equities	60
Fixed Interest	40

	$million
Employer Contributions	100

IOWA PUBLIC EMPLOYEES' RETIREMENT SYSTEM

1000 East Grand Avenue, Des Moines, Iowa 50319
Telephone: 515-281 5800

Contacts Edward R.Longnecker (Director), Doyle Sales (Assistant Director)

Funds	$million
Benefit Fund	1,300

Summary of Investments	%
Cash	14
Equities	9
Fixed Interest	71
Mortgages	6

	$million
Employer Contributions	151
Benefit Payments	58

JOHNS-MANVILLE CORP.

Ken Caryl Ranch, P.O.Box 5108, Denver, Colorado 80217
Telephone: 303-979 1000

Contact J.L.Neill (Manager Benefit Funds)

Funds	$million
Master Trust and other funds	551

Summary of Investments	%
Equities	70
Fixed Interest	14
Cash	12
Real Estate	3

JOHNS-MANVILLE CORP. *Continued*

	$million
Employer Contributions	43
Benefit Payments	23

KANSAS PUBLIC EMPLOYEES RETIREMENT SYSTEM

400 First National Bank Tower, Townsite Plaza,
Topeka, Kansas 66603
Telephone: 913-296 3921

Contacts John K.Corkhill (Secretary), Ronald J.Bleidissel (Chief Accountant)

Fund	$million
Benefit Fund	922

Summary of Investments	%
Equities	36
Fixed Interest	33
Cash	31

	$million
Employer Contributions	128
Benefit Payments	47

KENTUCKY TEACHERS RETIREMENT SYSTEM

216 West Main Street, Frankfort, Kentucky 40601
Telephone: 502-564 2057

Contacts Pat N.Miller (Secretary), Charles L.Bratton (Investment Officer)

Funds	$million
Retirement System	837

Summary of Investments	%
Equities	69
Fixed Interest	20
Cash	4

	$million
Employers Contributions	123
Benefit Payments	76

KRAFT INC.

Kraft Court, Glenview, Ill.60025
Telephone: 312-998 2408

Contact William B.Jordan

Funds	$million
Pension Plan	500

LOCKHEED AIRCRAFT CORPORATION

2555 North Hollywood Way, Burbank, Calif 91520
Telephone: 213-847 1926

Contacts George C.Weintz (Investment Counselor), A.J.Ratto (Director Retirement & Savings Plan)

Funds	$million
Retirement Plan Funds	1,575
Savings and basic benefit plans	584
Total Assets	2,159
Employer Contributions	200
Benefit Payments	65

LOS ANGELES COUNTY EMPLOYEES' RETIREMENT ASSOCIATION

500 West Temple Street, Room 437, Los Angeles, Calif 90012
Telephone: 213-974 2101

Contacts H.B.Alvord (Treasurer & Tax Collector), Betty Mulkern (Investment Officer)

Funds	$million
Employees Retirement Fund	2,875

Summary of Investments	%
Cash	5
Equities	25
Fixed Interest	50
Mortgages	5
Others	15

	$million
Employer Contributions	275
Benefit Payments	195

LOS ANGELES FIRE & POLICE PENSION SYSTEM

111 East First Street, City Hall South, Los Angeles, Calif.90012
Telephone: 213-485 2833

Contacts James S.Muhlstein (Manager,Secretary), Kathleen L.Thorton (Investment Officer)

Funds	$million
Retirement Plan	799

Summary of Investments	%
Equities	17
Fixed Interest	77
Cash	6

	$million
Employer Contributions	182
Benefit Payments	117

LOUISIANA TEACHERS' RETIREMENT SYSTEM

PO Box 44123, Capitol Station, Baton Rouge, La 70804
Telephone: 504-925 6470

Contacts Dr Carleton C. Page (Secretary & Treasurer), Jerald J.Juneau (Assistant Secretary & Treasurer)

Funds	$million
Benefit Fund	1,245

Summary of Investments	%
Cash	11
Equities	3
Fixed Interest	85
Others	1

	$million
Employer Contributions	149
Benefit Payments	142

THE LTV CORPORATION

1525 Elm Street, PO Box 225003, Dallas, Texas 75265
Telephone: 214-746 7793

Contacts W.E. Meyer (Vice President Personnel), George H.Simon (Director Employee Trust Administration)

Funds	$million
Consolidated Retirement Trust	1,106
Jones & Laughlin Steel Corp Savings Plan	41
1 other fund	39
Total Assets	1,186
Employer Contributions	121
Benefit Payments	40

MARATHON OIL CO.

539 South Main Street, Findlay, Ohio 45840
Telephone: 419-422 2121

Contacts Charles E.Merzbacher (Vice President & Tax Counsel), Charles K.Morgan (Treasurer)

Funds	$ million
Retirement Plan	356
Thrift Plan	247
Employee Stock Ownership	20
Total Assets	623
Summary of Investments	%
Equities	65
Fixed Interest	25
Cash	10

	$ million
Employer Contributions	58
Benefit Payments	15

MARCOR

619 West Chicago Avenue, Chicago, Ill 60607
Telephone: 312-467 3408

Contacts Lawrence A.Ward (Assistant Treasurer), R.W.Berry (Benefits Administration)

Funds	$ million
Montgomery Ward & Co Retirement Plan	529
Container Corp Retirement Plan	177
Container Stock Bonus Plan	78
Total Assets	784
Summary of Investments	%
Equities	58
Fixed Interest	27
Cash	15

	$ million
Employer Contributions	66

MARTIN MARIETTA CORP.

6801 Rockledge Drive, Bethesda, Md.20034
Telephone: 301-897 6454

Contact Wayne H.Shaner (Director Pensions Investment)

Funds	$ million
Master Retirement Trust	676
Summary of Investments	%
Equities	60
Fixed Interest	40

	$ million
Employer Contributions	50
Benefit Payments	20

MARYLAND STATE RETIREMENT SYSTEM

301 West Preston Street, Baltimore, Md.21201
Telephone: 301-383 3798

Contacts Howard J.France (Investment Administrator), Chris Christis (Benefits Administrator)

Funds	$ million
Retirement Fund	2,400
Summary of Investments	%
Equities	54
Fixed Interest	43

	$ million
Employer Contributions	350
Benefit Payments	200

MASSACHUSETTS STATE EMPLOYEES & TEACHERS RETIREMENT SYSTEM

1 Ashburton Place, Boston, Mass 02108
Telephone: 617-727 2010

Contacts Donald P.Frary (Deputy State Treasurer), Philip D.Kett (Assistant Director)

Funds	$ million
Teachers' Retirement Fund	887
State Employees' Retirement Fund	763
Total Assets	1,650
Summary of Investments	%
Equities	8
Fixed Interest	66
Cash	4
Mortgages	20
Others	2

J.RAY MCDERMOTT INC.

1010 Common Street, P.O.Box 60035, New Orleans, Louisiana 70160
Telephone: 504-587 4411

Contacts Nicholas E.Mezey (Director Benefit Funds), M.W.Rohm (Manager Employee Benefit Funds)

Funds	$ million
Group Trust	389
Employees Thrift Fund	100
2 other funds	4
Total Assets	493
Est.Assets Sept.1980	545
Summary of Investments	%
Equities	30
Fixed Interest	55
Cash	15

	$ million
Employer Contributions	59
Benefit Payments	25

MCDONNELL DOUGLAS CORPORATION

Department H322-H, Q Building, PO Box 516, St Louis Mo 63166
Telephone: 314-232 5903

Contacts Ralph R.Di Fiore (Director-Retirement Funds Management), Donald J.Homan (Plan Administrator)

Funds	$ million
Salaried Employees Retirement Income Plan	972
Salaried Employees' Savings Plan	443
Hourly Employees' Pension Plan - West Coast	370
Hourly Employees' Pension Plan-St Louis	298
3 other Funds	59
Total Assets	2,142
Summary of Investments	%
Cash	6
Equities	52
Fixed Income	42

MCDONNELL DOUGLAS CORPORATION *Continued*

	$million
Employer Contributions	244
Benefit Payments	75

METROPOLITAN LIFE INSURANCE COMPANY
One Madison Avenue, New York, N.Y.10010
Telephone: 212-578 2937

Contact J.Robert Bloom (Vice President)

Funds	$million
Retirement Plan	1,351
Savings & Investment Plan	264
Total Assets	1,615

MICHIGAN STATE EMPLOYEES RETIREMENT SYSTEMS
Michigan Department of Treasury, PO Box 15128, Lansing, Mich 48901
Telephone: 517-373 3140

Contacts William A.Amerman (Director-Bureau of Finance), Curtis O.Townsend (Deputy Treasurer), Stephen Van Note (Director, Retirement Systems)

Funds	$million
Public School Employees Retirement Fund	3,027
State Employees Retirement Fund	1,009
Public School Employees Chapter 11 Retirement Fund	404
3 other funds	119
Total Assets	4,559

Summary of Investments	%
Cash	18
Equities	19
Fixed Interest	48
Mortgages	15

	$million
Employer Contributions	619
Benefit Payments	292

MINEWORKERS PENSION TRUST
2021 K Street, N.W., Washington, D.C.20008
Telephone: 202-452 5055

Contacts Robert Boylan (Director), Barrie R.Cohen (Treasurer)

Funds	$million
1974 Pension Trust	700
1950 Pension Trust	60
Total Assets	768

Summary of Investments	%
Equities	50
Fixed Interest	35
Cash	10
Real Estate	

	$million
Employers Contributions	225

MINNESOTA MINING & MANUFACTURING CO.
3-M Center, St.Pauls, Minn.55101
Telephone: 612-733 6198

Contacts J.J.Erdman (Assistant Treasurer), Harry H.Vernon (Director of Investments)

Funds	$million
Employees Retirement Income Fund	643

Summary of Investments	%
Equities	59
Fixed Interest	28
Cash	13

	$million
Employer Contributions	47

MINNESOTA STATE BOARD OF INVESTMENT
Room 105, MEA Building, 55 Sherburne Avenue, St.Paul,Minn.55103
Telephone: 612-296 3328

Contacts Jonathan White (Executive Director), Howard J.Bicker (Assistant Director)

Funds	$million
Minnesota Adjustable Fixed Benefit Fund	1,033
Teachers' Retirement Fund	671
Public Employees' Retirement Fund	584
State Employees' Retirement System	337
Permanent School Fund	273
Public Employees' Police & Fire Fund	102
Supplemental Retirement Fund-Income Share Account	67
Minnesota Variable Annuity Fund	62
4 other Funds	81
Total Assets	3,210
Est.Assets Sept.1980	4,122

Summary of Investments	%
Cash	11
Equities	43
Fixed Interest	46

	$million
Employer Contributions	200
Benefit Payments	105

MISSISSIPPI PUBLIC EMPLOYEES RETIREMENT SYSTEM
1704 Sillers State Office Building, Jackson, Mi.39021
Telephone: 601-354 6737

Contact Charles D.Wilkinson (Investment Manager)

Funds	$million
Public Employees Retirement Fund	963
Highway Patrol System	27
Other Funds	9
Total Assets	1,000

Summary of Investments	%
Equities	6
Fixed Interest	94

	$million
Employer Contributions	150
Benefit Payments	60

MISSOURI PUBLIC SCHOOL RETIREMENT SYSTEM
PO Box 268, Jefferson City, Mo.65102
Telephone: 314-751 3414

Contact Warren M.Black (Secretary)

MISSOURI PUBLIC SCHOOL RETIREMENT SYSTEM
Continued

Fund	$million
Benefit Fund	1,224

Summary of Investments	%
Equities	15
Fixed Interest	61
Cash	13
Others	11

	$million
Employer Contributions	166
Benefit Payments	100

MOBIL OIL CORPORATION
150 East 42nd Street, New York, NY 10017
Telephone: 212-883 4242

Contacts Charles J.Clune (Manager of Corporate Investments), R.B.Hahnen (Assistant Manager), Robert B.Peters (Benefit Administrator)

Funds	$million
Retirement Plan of Mobil Oil Corp (Insured Portion)	480
Retirement Plan of Mobil Oil Corp (Trusteed Portion)	955
Employees Savings Plan (Equity-oriented)	711
Employees Savings Plan (Fixed-income Portion)	210
Total Assets	2,355
Est.Assets Sept.1980	2,623

Summary of Investments	%
Equities	40
Fixed Interest	55
Cash	5

	$million
Employer Contributions	166
Benefit Payments	97

MONSANTO CO
800 North Lindbergh Boulevard, St Louis, Mo 63166
Telephone: 314-694 1000

Contacts R.C.O'Sullivan (Treasurer), A.E.Wolfarth (Director Pension Assets), Walter R.Mulhall (Benefit Administrator)

Funds	$million
Salaried Employees Pension Plan	588
Hourly Paid Employees Pension Plan	251
1 other Fund	189
Total Assets	1,028
Est.Assets Sept.1980	1,290

Summary of Investments	%
Equities	65
Fixed Interest	14
Cash	15
Real Estate	6

	$million
Employer Contributions	97
Benefit Payments	40

NATIONAL RURAL ELECTRICAL COOPERATIVES ASSOCIATION
1800 Massachusetts Avenue, Washington, D.C.20036
Telephone: 202-857 9722

Contacts Peter R.Morris (Manager Pension Administration), Martin Wood (Director)

Funds	$million
Retirement Plan	420
Savings Plan	100
Total Assets	520

Summary of Investments	%
Equities	55
Fixed interest	30
Cash	15

	$million
Employer Contributions	73

NATIONAL STEEL CORPORATION
2800 Grant Building, Pittsburgh, Pa 15219
Telephone: 412-263 4100

Contacts W.J.Rust (Vice-President Finance), T.J.Rudd (Assistant Vice President Industrial Relations), D.W.Gingery (Manager Pension Fund Administration)

Funds	$million
Retirement Program	320
Pension Plan for Hourly Employees	146
Stock Investment Plan for Salaried Employees	109
10 other plans	53
Total Assets	628
Est.Assets Sept.1980	759

Summary of Investments	%
Equities	30
Fixed Interest	44
Cash	19
Real Estate	7

	$million
Employer Contributions	112
Benefit Payments	65

NEVADA PUBLIC EMPLOYEES RETIREMENT SYSTEM
693 West Nye Lane, Carson City, Nevada 89701
Telephone: 702-885 4206

Contact Vernon Bennett (Executive Officer)

Funds	$million
Benefit Fund	773

Summary of Investments	%
Equities	11
Fixed Interest	68
Cash	6

	$million
Employer Contributions	91
Benefit Payments	30

NEW JERSEY DIVISION OF INVESTMENT
349 West State Street, Trenton, NJ 08625
Telephone: 609-292 5106

Contacts Roland M.Machold (Director), William P.Mooney (Deputy Director), W.Joseph (Pension Director)

NEW JERSEY DIVISION OF INVESTMENT Continued

Funds	$million
Teachers' Pension & Annuity Fund	2,482
Public Employees' Retirement System	1,797
General Trust Fund	442
Police & Firemen's Retirement System	1,092
Consolidated Police & Firemen's Pension Fund	86
State Police Retirement System	106
Supplemental Annuity Collective Trust	55
1 other Fund	13
Total Assets	6,073
Est.Assets Sept.1980	7,570

Summary of Investments	%
Cash	24
Equities	8
Fixed Interest	68
Mortgages	

NEW MEXICO STATE PERMANENT FUND

PO Box 966, Santa Fe, N.M.87503
Telephone: 505-827 2120

Contact Stanley P.Hidalgo (Investment Officer)

Fund	$million
Permanent Fund	815

Summary of Investments	%
Cash	7
Equities	19
Fixed Income	52
Mortgages	22

NEW YORK CITY CONTROLLER'S OFFICE

Municipal Building, Chambers & Centre Streets, New York, N.Y.10007
Telephone: 212-566 6300

Contact Robert T.C. Wilson (Investment Bureau Chief), Jack R.Meyer (Deputy Controller)

Funds	$million
Retirement System Funds	12,703

Summary of Investments	%
Equities	12
Fixed Interest	70
Cash	16
Mortgages	2

	$million
Employer Contributions	1,443
Benefit Payments	1,023

NEW YORK CITY TEACHERS' RETIREMENT SYSTEM

40 Worth Street, New York, NY 10013
Telephone: 212-566 6668

Contacts Patrick Kiernan (Assistant Executive Director), Wally Sullivan (Executive Director)

Funds	$million
Fixed Annuity Program	3,164
Variable Annuity Program & Tax Deferred Annuity Program	1,544
Total Assets	4,608

Summary of Investments	%
Equities	29
Fixed Interest	67
Cash	4

	$million
Employer Contributions	60
Benefit Payments	52

NEW YORK STATE COMMON RETIREMENT FUND

Governor A.E.Smith, State Office Building, Albany, N.Y.12866
Telephone: 518-474 6398

Contacts Madelon Talley (Director), William Hay (Chief Investment Officer), John S.Mauhs (Deputy Comptroller), Thomas Flanigan (Investment Officer)

Funds	$million
Fixed Income Portion	11,797
Common Stock Portion	1,877
Total Assets	13,674

Summary of Investments	%
Cash	14
Equities	16
Fixed Interest	54
Mortgages	16

	$million
Employer Contributions	1,237
Benefit Payments	701

NEW YORK STATE TEACHERS' RETIREMENT SYSTEM

143 Washington Avenue, Albany, N.Y.12210
Telephone: 518-447 2666

Contacts Dr.Harold N.Langlitz (Executive Director), Edward J.Reno (Investment Officer)

Fund	$million
New York State Teachers Retirement System	7,914

Summary of Investments	%
Equities	32
Fixed Interest	60
Cash	4
Others	4

	$million
Employer Contributions	620
Benefit Payments	355

NORTH CAROLINA RETIREMENT SYSTEM

325 North Salisbury Street, Raleigh, North Carolina 27611
Telephone: 919-733 7273

Contacts Christopher S.Moore (State Investment Officer), Edwin T.Barnes (Benefits Administrator)

Funds	$million
Retirement Systems	3,640
State Treasurers Cash Management Program	1,102
Total Assets	4,742

Summary of Investments	%
Cash	2
Equities	15
Fixed Interest	81
Mortgages	2

	$million
Employer Contributions	278

NORTH CAROLINA RETIREMENT SYSTEM *Continued*

Benefit Payments	204

NORTHROP CORPORATION

1800 Century Park East, Los Angeles, Calif.90067
Telephone: 213-556 4564

Contacts Richard B.Lohrer (Treasurer), John B.Campbell (Vice President & Controller)

Fund	$million
Employee Benefit Plan	825

Summary of Investmnets	%
Equities	77
Fixed Interest	15
Cash	8

	$million
Employer Contributions	80
Benefit Payments	20

OHIO PUBLIC EMPLOYEES RETIREMENT SYSTEM

277 East Town Street, Columbus, Ohio 43215
Telephone: 614-466 5155

Contacts Robert A.McLaughlin (Assistant Director, Investment Officer), Greg Bauer, Richard Moore (Assistant Investment Officers)

Funds	$million
Benefit Fund	4,561

Summary of Investments	%
Cash	7
Equities	30
Fixed Interest	62
Mortgages	1

	$million
Employer Contributions	420
Benefit Payments	315

OHIO SCHOOL EMPLOYEES RETIREMENT SYSTEM

88 East Broad Street, Columbus, Ohio 43215
Telephone: 614-221 7012

Contact R.Jack Cooper (Investment Officer)

Funds	$million
Benefit Fund	900

Summary of Investments	%
Cash	10
Equities	20
Fixed Interest	45
Real Estate	4
Mortgages	21

	$million
Employers Contributions	118
Benefit Payments	95

THE STATE TEACHERS RETIREMENT SYSTEM OF OHIO

275 East Broad Street, Columbus, Ohio 43215
Telephone: 614-227 4006

Contacts Alan D.Browning (Director of Investment), C.James Grothaus (Director Member Benefits)

Funds	$million
Benefit Fund	4,902

Summary of Investments	%
Cash	11
Equities	37
Fixed Interest	52
Mortgages	1

	$million
Employer Contributions	358
Benefit Payments	335

INTERNATIONAL UNION OF OPERATING ENGINEERS

4115 Chesapeake Street,N.W., Washington, D.C.20016
Telephone: 202-362 1000

Contacts Jack E.Johnson (Assistant Administration Manager), Reese Hammond (Secretary), Frank Gould (Benefits Administrator)

Funds	$million
Central Pension Fund	517

Summary of Investments	%
Equities	35
Fixed Interest	52
Cash	13

	$million
Employer Contributions	81
Benefit Payments	25

OREGON PUBLIC EMPLOYEES RETIREMENT SYSTEM

State Capitol, Room 103, Salem, Oregon 97310
Telephone: 503-378 4111

Contacts James C.George (Investment Officer), James L.McGoffin (Director), Roger S.Meier (Chairman Advisory Council)

Funds	$million
Oregon Public Employees' Retirement System	1,700

Summary of Investments	%
Cash	3
Equities	33
Fixed Interest	40
Mortgages	24

OWENS-ILLINOIS INC

Madison Avenue, PO Box 1035, Toledo, Ohio
Telephone: 419-242 6543

Contacts R.D.Foster (Director Benefit Funds), Robert M.Ellis (Benefits Manager), Ronald C.Boller (Manager Portfolio Management & Benefit Funds)

Funds	$million
Salaried Retirement Plan	401
Hourly Retirement Plan	341
Employee Savings Plan	95
Total Assets	837

Summary of Investments	%
Cash	11
Equities	67
Fixed Interest	13
Real Estate	4
International	5

	$million
Employer Contributions	79
Benefit Payments	46

PACIFIC GAS & ELECTRIC CO

77 Beale Street, San Francisco, Calif 94106
Telephone: 415-781 4211

Contacts Stanley T.Skinner (Senior Vice-President), Michael J.Bonner (Employee Benefits Administrator)

Funds	$million
Retirement Plan	950
Savings Fund Plan	280
Total Assets	1,230

Summary of Investments	%
Equities	57
Fixed Interest	35
Cash	7
Real Estate	1

	$million
Employer Contributions	111
Benefit Payments	36

PACIFIC TELEPHONE & TELEGRAPH CO

140 New Montgomery Street, San Francisco, Calif 94105
Telephone: 415-542 9000

Contacts A.C.Cassidy (Vice President Finance & Secretary), P.K.Jennings (Treasurer)

Funds	$million
Plan for Employees Pension, Disability Benefits & Death Benefits	2,106
Est.Assets Sept.1979	2,500

Summary of Investments	%
Equities	46
Fixed Income	50
Real Estate	3
Others	1

	$million
Employer Contributions	318
Benefit Payments	94

PAN AMERICAN WORLD AIRWAYS INC

200 Park Avenue, New York, N.Y.10017
Telephone: 212-880 1834

Contacts Harold N.Friesen (Assistant Treasurer), Carl Stillwell (Director-Pensions)

Funds	$million
Co-operative Retirement Income Trust Plan for Pilots	447
Co-operative Retirement Income Plan	376
6 other funds	261
Total Assets	1,084

Summary of Investments	%
Cash	9
Equities	49
Fixed Interest	42

	$million
Employer Contributions	103
Benefit Payments	50

J.C.PENNEY CO.INC.

1301 Avenue of the Americas, New York, N.Y.10019
Telephone: 212-957 7157

Contacts E.George Matthew (Investment Manager), Paul Hubbard (Treasurer), A.J.Dennigan (Benefits Administrator)

Funds	$million
Pension Plan	293
Saving & Profit Sharing Plan	301
1 other plan	30
Total Assets	624

Summary of Investments	%
Equities	63
Fixed Interest	15
Cash	12
Real Estate	10

	$million
Employer Contributions	36

PENNSYLVANIA PUBLIC SCHOOL EMPLOYEES' RETIREMENT SYSTEM

301 Chestnut Street, Harrisburg, Pa 17108
Telephone: 717-787 8546

Contact Andrew Sheffler (Executive Director)

Funds	$million
Retirement Fund	4,544

Summary of Investments	%
Cash	5
Equities	18
Fixed Income	63
Mortgages	14

	$million
Employer Contributions	397
Benefit Payments	462

PENNSYLVANIA STATE EMPLOYEES' RETIREMENT SYSTEM

204 Labor & Industry Building, Harrisburg, Pa 17120
Telephone: 717-787 6780

Contact William J.Moran (Chairman of Trustees), Robert L.Cusma (Secretary), Frances M.Crimbly (Assistant Secretary)

Funds	$million
Retirement Fund	2,803

Summary of Investments	%
Equities	19
Fixed Interest	62
Mortgages	13
Cash	6

	$million
Employer Contributions	258
Benefit Payments	264

PHILLIPS PETROLEUM COMPANY

3A3 Phillips Building, Bartlesville, Okla 74004
Telephone: 918-661 6018

Contacts R.E.Bonnell (Treasurer), W.R.Thomas (Director Human Resources), Ron Sellers (Director Pensions Investment)

Funds	$million
Retirement Income Plan	900
Thrift Plan	450
2 other Plans	44
Total Assets	1,394

Summary of Investments	%
Equities	58

PHILLIPS PETROLEUM COMPANY *Continued*

Fixed Interest	35
Cash	7
	$million
Employer Contributions	120
Benefit Payments	30

PPG INDUSTRIES INC.
1 Gateway Center, Pittsburgh, Pa.15222
Telephone: 412-434 3345

Contacts E.H.Eaton (Vice President Investments), Elias E.Moses (Director Pension Investment), C.McLane (Benefits Administrator)

Funds	$million
Pension Assets	430
Security & Benefits Plans	140
Total Assets	570
Summary of Investments	%
Equities	55
Fixed Interest	45
	$million
Employer Contributions	100
Benefit Payments	38

PROCTOR & GAMBLE COMPANY
301 East Sixth Street, Cincinnati, Ohio 45202
Telephone: 513-562 1100

Contacts Edwin H.Eaton (Treasurer), Robert Bidwell (Treasury Dept.)

Funds	$million
Profit Sharing Trust Plan	950
Profit Sharing Dividend Plan	282
Other Plans	7
Total Assets	945
Employer Contributions	110
Benefit Payments	48

PRUDENTIAL INSURANCE CO OF AMERICA
745 Broad Street, Newark, N.J.07101
Telephone: 201-877 8000

Contact F.Hoenemeyer (Executive Vice-President)

Funds	$million
The Retirement System for Employees & Special Agents	1,744
The Prudential Investment Plan for Employees	387
Total Assets	2,131

RCA CORPORATION
30 Rockefeller Plaza, New York, NY 10020
Telephone: 212-621 6463

Contacts Robert D.Isinger (Secretary-Retirement Benefits Committee), Melvin Cornfield (V.P. & Treasurer)

Funds	$million
Retirement Plan for Employees	1,199
RCA Income Savings Plan	166
Other plans	162
Total Assets	1,528
Summary of Investments	%
Equities	42
Fixed Interest	45
Cash	9
Real Estate	4
	$million
Employer Contributions	194
Benefit Payments	100

REPUBLIC STEEL CORPORATION
25 West Prospect Avenue, N.W., P.O.Box 6778
Cleveland, Ohio 44101
Telephone: 216-574 7430

Contacts J.J.Loftus (Executive Vice-President), Eugene P.Walker (Director Investment), Robert Fisher (Benefits Administrator)

Funds	$million
Pension Trust	755
2 other Funds	98
Total Assets	853
Est.Assets Sept.1980	965
Summary of Investments	%
Cash	13
Equities	62
Fixed Interest	24
	$million
Employer Contributions	128
Benefit Payments	98

R.J.REYNOLDS INDUSTRIES INC.
4C World Headquarters Building, Winston-Salem, N.Carolina 27102
Telephone: 919-777 2617

Contacts Joseph F.Abely (Chief Investment Officer), Gene A.Hoots (Director Pension Fund Management), Thomas E.Quinn (Pension Fund Manager)

Funds	$million
Pension Plans	536
Profit Sharing & Savings Plan	36
Total Assets	536
Est.Assets Sept.1980	612
Employer Contributions	86
Benefit Payments	23

REYNOLDS METALS CO.
6601 West Broad Street, Richmond, Virginia 23218
Telephone: 804-281 3508

ROCKWELL INTERNATIONAL
600 Grant Street, Pittsburgh,Pa. 15219
Telephone: 412-565 2000

Contacts E.W.Altstaetter (Vice-President Pensions), Edwin C.McManus (Vice-President Employee Benefits)

Funds	$million
Master Fund	2,100
Savings Plan	630
Total Assets	2,730
Summary of Investments	%
Cash	12
Equities	57
Fixed Income	31

ROCKWELL INTERNATIONAL Continued

	$million
Employer Contributions	297
Benefit Payments	110

SAN FRANCISCO CITY & COUNTY EMPLOYEES' RETIREMENT SYSTEM

770 Golden Gate Avenue, San Francisco, Calif 94102
Telephone: 415-558 5061

Contacts Daniel Mattroce (General Manager), George B.Springman (Chief Investment Officer)

Funds	$million
Pension Fund	1,004

Summary of Investments	%
Equities	33
Fixed Interest	58
Cash	4
Real Estate	5

	$million
Employer Contributions	135
Benefit Payments	102

SEARS, ROEBUCK & CO

Sears Tower, Chicago, Ill 60684
Telephone: 312-875 5768

Contacts Jack F.Kincannon (Senior Vice-President-Finance), M.Douglas (Plan Administrator), David Dootson (President, Sears Investment Management Co.)

Funds	$million
Savings & Profit Sharing Fund	2,050
Supplement Pension Plan	950
Total Assets	3,000

Summary of Investments	%
Equities	67
Fixed Interest	12
Cash	21

	$million
Employer Contributions	405
Benefit Payments	136

SHELL OIL CO

One Shell Plaza, P.O.Box 2463, Houston, Texas 77002
Telephone: 713-241 4834

Contacts R.S.MacIntire (Administrator), Milton Planch (Investment Manager), J.L.Docherty (Benefit Administrator)

Funds	$million
Shell Pension Trust	1,230
Shell Provident Fund	1,580
Total Assets	2,810

Summary of Investments	%
Equities	63
Fixed Interest	25
Real Estate	12

	$million
Employer Contributions	140
Benefit Payments	50

SIGNAL COMPANIES INC

11255 North Torrey Pines Road, La Jolla, Calif.92037
Telephone: 714-457 3555

Contacts R.W.Rauch (Vice President Employee Relations), Andrew J.Chitiea (Senior Vice President), W.D.Sanborn (Vice President Manager Selection)

Funds	$million
Group Benefit Trust	610
Savings & Stock Purchase Plan	430
Total Assets	1,040

Summary of Investments	%
Cash	14
Equities	73
Fixed Interest	13

	$million
Employer Contributions	111

SOUTH CAROLINA RETIREMENT SYSTEM

P.O.Box 11778, Columbia, South Carolina 29211
Telephone: 803-758 2146

Contacts Grady L.Patterson (Treasurer), Raye Parrish (Investment Manager), Purvis W.Collins (Director, Benefit Administrator)

Funds	$million
State Employees, Teachers, Counties, Municipalities etc.	1,704
Police Officers' Retirement System	126
2 other funds	6
Total Assets	1,836
Est.Assets Sept.1980	1,952

Summary of Investments	%
Cash	28
Fixed Interest	72

	$million
Employer Contributions	123
Benefit Payments	90

SOUTHERN CALIFORNIA EDISON CO.

2244 Walnut Grove Avenue,P.O.Box 800, Rosemead, Ca.91770
Telephone: 213-572 1077

Contacts J.Raymond Walker (Director Pension Investment), Michael L.Noel (Vice President, Treasurer), C.E.Hathaway (Benefits Administrator)

Funds	$million
Retirement Plan	401
Employees Stock Purchasing Plan	106
Total Assets	507

Summary of Investments	%
Equities	49
Fixed Interest	42
Cash	9

	$million
Employer Contributions	51
Benefit Payments	12

SPERRY CORP.

1290 Avenue of the Americas, New York, N.Y.10019
Telephone: 212-956 2121

Contacts Alfred J.Moccia (Senior Vice-President &

SPERRY CORP. *Continued*

Chief Financial Officer), Raymond L.Colotti (Director, Pension Asset Management), Thomas V.Hirschberg (Benefit Administrator)

Funds	$million
Sperry Rand Retirement Program Part A	968
Sperry Rand Retirement Program Part B and Sperry Rand Retirement Investment Plan	329
Total Assets	1,297
Summary of Investments	%
Cash	18
Equities	43
Fixed Interest	13
Insurance	26
	$million
Employer Contributions	78
Benefit Payments	33

STANDARD OIL CO OF CALIFORNIA

225 Bush Street, San Francisco, Calif 94104
Telephone: 415-894 7700

Contacts Howard W.Bell (Vice-President-Finance & Director), Sellers Stough (Comptroller), R.K.Maggy (Manager Benefits Staff)

Funds	$million
Company Stock Purchase Plan for Employees	982
Annuity Plan	799
Total Assets	1,781
Est.Assets Sept.1980	2,288
Summary of Investments	%
Cash	26
Equities	48
Fixed Interest	21
Real Estate	5
	$million
Employer Contributions	153
Benefit Payments	73

STANDARD OIL CO (INDIANA)

200 East Randolph Drive, Chicago, Ill 60680
Telephone: 312-856 6370

Contacts Phillip W.Binzel (General Manager Fund Investments), David E.Tierney (Administration Manager Investments)

Funds	$million
Retirement Plan	1,462
Employees' Savings Plan (Company Stock Purchase)	580
Other Funds	59
Total Assets	2,759
Summary of Investments	%
Cash	13
Equities	68
Fixed Interest	12
Real Estate	3
International	4
	$million
Employer Contributions	135
Benefit Payments	80

SUN OIL COMPANY INC.

100 Matsonford Road, Radnor, Pa 19087
Telephone: 215-293 6536

Contacts William S.Woods (Treasurer), Ed Warwick (Manager Employee Investment Funds)

Funds	$million
Retirement Plan	834
Stock Purchase Plan	158
Other plans	41
Total Assets	1,033
Summary of Investments	%
Equities	55
Fixed Interest	22
Cash	13
Real Estate	10
	$million
Employer Contributions	67
Benefit Payments	30

TEXAS INSTRUMENTS INC.

13500 North Central Expressway, Dallas, Texas 75265
Telephone: 214-238 2267

Contacts William L.Green (Senior Investment Analyst), A.J.Bird (Manager Employee Benefits)

Funds	$million
Pension Plans	600
Summary of Investments	%
Equities	60
Fixed Interest	19
Cash	15
Real Estate	5
	$million
Employer Contributions	68
Benefit Payments	5

INTERNATIONAL BROTHERHOOD OF TEAMSTERS CENTRAL STATES, SOUTHEAST & SOUTHWEST AREAS

8550 West Bryn Mawr, Chicago, Ill 60631
Telephone: 312-693 5300

Contacts John L.Sherry (Director Financial Group), Jack Yarborough (Assistant Executive Director)

Funds	$million
Central States, Southeast & Southwest Areas Pension Fund	2,491
Summary of Investments	%
Cash	14
Equities	28
Fixed Interest	27
Mortgages	23
Real Estate	5
Others	3
	$million
Employer Contributions	606
Benefit Payments	349

TENNECO INC

1010 Milan, P.O.Box 2511 Houston, Texas 77001
Telephone: 713-757 4228

Contact E.M.White (Assistant Treasurer)

Fund	$million
General Employee Benefit Trust	455

TENNECO INC Continued

Thrift Plan	390
Insured Plan	100
Total Assets	945
Summary of Investments	%
Cash	18
Equities	27
Fixed Interest	55
	$million
Employer Contributions	122

TENNESSEE CONSOLIDATED RETIREMENT SYSTEM

P.O.Box 2867, 960 Capitol Building, Nashville, Tenn 37219
Telephone: 615-741 2643

Contact H.Swift Lipscomb Jr (Chief Investment Officer)

Funds	$million
Tennessee Consolidated Retirement System	1,339
Est.Assets Sept.1980	1,654
Summary of Investments	%
Equities	25
Fixed Interest	63
Cash	12
	$million
Employer Contributions	200
Benefit Payments	100

TENNESSEE VALLEY AUTHORITY

410 Millers Building, Knoxville, Tenn.37902
Telephone: 615-632 3391

Contact Eugene Stephens (Secretary & Administrator)

Funds	$million
Retirement System Pension Fund	780
Voluntary Savings Plan	25
Total Assets	805
Summary of Investments	%
Equities	59
Fixed Interest	34
Cash	5
Real Estate/Mortgages	2
	$million
Employer Contributions	86
Benefit Payments	32

TEXACO INC

2000 Westchester Avenue, White Plains, NY 10650
Telephone: 914-253 4000

Contacts J.D.Keough (Manager Benefit Funds), R.G.Brinkman (Vice President & Treasurer), W.K.Tell (Benefits Administrator)

Funds	$million
Group Pension Plan	1,038
Employees Savings Plan	419
1 other fund	22
Total Assets	1,479
Est.Assets Sept.1980	1,665
Employer Contributions	107
Benefit Payments	125

TEXAS EMPLOYEES RETIREMENT SYSTEM

Capitol Station, Box 12337, Austin, Texas 78711
Telephone: 512-476 6431

Contacts Joseph N.Murphy (Executive Secretary & Investment Officer), Gary Craig (Administrator)

Fund	$million
State Employees Retirement Fund	1,168
Summary of Investments	%
Equities	20
Fixed Income	74
Others	6
	$million
Employer Contributions	85
Benefit Payments	51

TEACHER RETIREMENT SYSTEM OF TEXAS

1001 Trinity Street, Austin, Texas 78701
Telephone: 512-477 9701

Contact Clark P.Manning (Investment Officer), Leonard Prewitt (Executive Secretary)

Fund	$million
Benefit Fund	5,300
Summary of Investments	%
Equities	29
Fixed Income	71
	$million
Employer Contributions	374
Benefit Payments	306

TEXTRON INC

40 Westminster Street, Providence, RI 02903
Telephone: 401-421 2800

Contacts Maurice G.Wilkins (Treasurer), Edward O.Handy (President Employee Benefits)

Funds	$million
Salaried Pension Plan	112
Employees Stock Saving Plan	155
Bell Pension Plan for Union Employees	78
Bell Helicopter Pension Plan for Salaried Employees	97
19 other funds	191
Total Assets	633
Est.Assets Sept.1980	687
Summary of Investments	%
Cash	18
Equities	19
Fixed Interest	56
Mortgages/Real Estate	7
	$million
Employer Contributions	89
Benefit Payments	36

TRANS WORLD AIRLINES INC.

605 Third Avenue, New York, NY 10016
Telephone: 212-557 3000

Contacts Frank L.Salizzoni (Vice-President & Treasurer), Edwin Burke (Director Pension Investment)

The Major US Pension Funds TRA/WES

TRANS WORLD AIRLINES INC. Continued

Funds	$million
Retirement Plan for Employees	575
Trust Annuity Plan for Pilots	320
IAM Trust Fund	66
5 other funds	46
Total Assets	1,007
Est.Assets Sept.1980	1,150

Summary of Investments	%
Equities	55
Fixed Interest	40
Cash	5

	$million
Employer Contributions	119
Benefit Payments	40

TRW INC.

23555 Euclid Avenue, Cleveland, Ohio 44117
Telephone: 216-383 2121

Contacts Edward Button (Investments President), William J.Newman (Vice President), S.M.Curry (Director Employee Benefits)

Funds	$million
Collective Trust Fund	1,031

Summary of Investments	%
Equities	65
Fixed Interest	15
Cash	20

	$million
Employer Contributions	80
Benefit Payments	47

UNION CARBIDE CORPORATION

270 Park Avenue, New York, NY 10017
Telephone: 212-551 3031

Contacts James A.O'Connell (Assistant Treasurer), James Tobin (Planning Manager)

Funds	$million
Non-Contributory Pension Plan for Employees	1,465
Savings Plan	258
Total Assets	1,723

Summary of Investments	%
Cash	53
Equities	18
Fixed Interest	1
Real Estate	1
Annuity	7

	$million
Employer Contributions	175
Benefit Payments	80

UNION METHODIST CHURCH GENERAL BOARD OF PENSIONS

1200 Davis, Evanston, Ill 60601
Telephone: 312-869 4550

Contacts Gerald K.Hornung (General Secretary), Donald R.McKee (Treasurer)

Fund	$million
Pension Fund	836

Summary of Investments	%
Cash	23
Equities	53
Fixed Interest	17
Mortgages	1
Others	6

	$million
Employer Contributions	92
Benefit Payments	70

UNION OIL COMPANY OF CALIFORNIA

PO Box 7600, Los Angeles, Calif 90051
Telephone: 213-486 6246

Contacts E.H.Powell (Assistant Treasurer), Paul K.Doyle (Vice President)

Funds	$million
Retirement Plan	444
Profit Sharing Plan	221
Total Assets	665
Est.Assets Sept.1980	878

Summary of Investments	%
Equities	35
Fixed Interest	48
Cash	11
Real Estate	6

	$million
Employer Contributions	56
Benefit Payments	24

UNITED AIRLINES INC.

PO Box 66100, Chicago, Ill 60666
Telephone: 312-952 4000

Contacts John M.Batten (Vice President & Treasurer), Ronald Nankervis (Benefits Administrator), Philip Schneider (Pensions Assistant Manager)

Funds	$million
Group Investment Trust	1,350
Variable Pension Plan for Pilots	413
Total Assets	1,763
Est.Assets Sept.1980	1,900

Summary of Investments	%
Cash	10
Equities	47
Fixed Income	7
GIC	36

	$million
Employer Contributions	197
Benefit Payments	40

UNITED NATIONS JOINT STAFF PENSION FUND

United Nations, New York, NY 10017
Telephone: 212-754 1234

Contacts E.Charles Stockmar (Senior Investment Officer), Arthur C.Liveran (Secretary)

Funds	$million
Benefit Fund	2,350

Summary of Investments	%
Cash	5
Equities	51
Fixed Interest	39
Real Estate	5

UNITED NATIONS JOINT STAFF PENSION FUND
Continued

	$million
Employer Contributions	290
Benefit Payments	180

UNITED TECHNOLOGIES CORPORATION

United Technologies Building, Hartford, Ct 06101
Telephone: 203-728 7000

Contacts Joseph A.Biernat (Treasurer), Raymond L.Willis, Charles Lard (Assistant Treasurers)

Fund	$million
Pension Fund	1,700
Est.Assets Sept.1979	2,100

Summary of Investments	%
Equities	35
Fixed Interest	57
Cash	7
Real Estate	1

	$million
Employer Contributions	130
Benefit Payments	90

UNIVERSITY OF CALIFORNIA

615 University Hall, Berkeley, Calif 94720
Telephone: 415-642 3251

Contact Herbert M.Gordon (Treasurer of the Regents)

Fund	$million
Pension Fund	1,118

US STEEL & CARNEGIE PENSION FUND

767 Fifth Avenue, New York, N.Y.10022
Telephone: 212-826 8420

Contacts Graham O.Harrison (President), John Van Deusen (Vice-President), Louis Valli (Plan Administrator)

Funds	$million
US Steel & Carnegie Pension Fund	4,897
Savings Plan for Salaried Employees	390
Other Funds	8
Total Assets	5,295
Est.Assets Sept.1980	5,540
Employers Contributions	434
Benefit Payments	450

UTAH STATE RETIREMENT SYSTEM

540 East 200th Street South, Salt Lake City, Utah 84102
Telephone: 801-533 5441

Contacts Bert D.Hunsaker (Executive Director), Reed E.Gunderson (Investment Officer)

Funds	$million
State Retirement Fund	835

Summary of Investments	%
Equities	25
Fixed Interest	53
Cash	16
Real Estate	6

The Major US Pension Funds TRA/WES

	$million
Employer Contributions	103
Benefit Payments	31

VIRGINIA SUPPLEMENTAL RETIREMENT SYSTEM

Seventh & Franklin Building, Richmond, Va.23214
Telephone: 804-770 3831

Contacts Robert H.Daniel (Investment Director), Glen Pond (Director)

Fund	$million
Retirement System Trust Fund	1,698

Summary of Investments	%
Cash	9
Equities	29
Fixed Interest	56
Others	6

	$million
Employer Contributions	286
Benefit Payments	142

WASHINGTON PUBLIC EMPLOYEES RETIREMENT SYSTEM

1025 East Union Avenue, Olympia, Wash 98504
Telephone: 206-753 0606

Contacts John Hitchman (Executive Secretary-Finance Committee), J.Hugh McKinny (Investment Officer), Robert Hollister (Benefits Director)

Funds	$million
Public Employees Retirement System	1,520
Teachers Retirement System	683
Teachers Reserve Fund	422
Police & Firemen's Benefit Fund	399
Total Assets	3,126

Summary of Investments	%
Cash	9
Equities	22
Fixed Interest	44
Mortgages	22
Others	3

	$million
Employer Contributions	365
Benefit Payments	220

WEST VIRGINIA EMPLOYEES RETIREMENT SYSTEMS

State Capitol Building, Charleston, W.Va 25305
Telephone: 304-348 2281

Contacts Larrie Bailey (State Treasurer), James L.Sims (Director of Investments), Lewis McManus (Executive Secretary)

Funds	$million
State Fund General Revenue	618
Workmens Compensation Fund	424
Public Employees Retirement System	310
State Teachers Retirement System	215
2 other Funds	18
Total Assets	1,585

Summary of Investments	%
Fixed Income	91
Mortgages	6
Others	3

WESTERN CONFERENCE OF TEAMSTERS

1212 Eastlake Avenue East, Seattle, Wash. 98102
Telephone: 206-329 4900

Contacts John H.Hughes (Fund Administrator),
Joseph Ballew (Executive Director)

Fund	$million
Pension Fund	3,110

Summary of Investments	%
Cash	1
Equities	86
Fixed Income	11
Others	1

	$million
Employer Contributions	450
Benefit Payments	350

WESTINGHOUSE ELECTRIC CORPORATION

Westinghouse Building, Pittsburgh, Pa 15222
Telephone: 412-255 3243

Contacts Thomas A.Gudiness (Director-Pension Funds & Corporate Investment), J.C.Mullen (Benefits Administrator)

Funds	$million
Westinghouse Master Trust	1,915
Personnel Investment Savings Plan	235
Total Assets	1,547

Summary of Investments	%
Cash	13
Equities	48
Fixed Interest	28
Mortgages/Real Estate	7

	$million
Employer Contributions	251
Benefit Payments	135

WISCONSIN INVESTMENT BOARD

244 West Washington Avenue, Madison, Wis 53702
Telephone: 608-266 2381

Contacts James M.LaFleur (Executive Director), Kenneth Codlin (Executive Director)

Funds	$million
Fixed Trust Fund	3,405
Short Term-State Investment Fund	1,713
Wisconsin Variable Trust Fund	639
Total Assets	5,757

Summary of Investments	%
Cash	33
Equities	31
Fixed Interest	25
Mortgages	4

	$million
Employer Contributions	341
Benefit Payments	165

XEROX CORPORATION

800 Long Ridge Road, Stamford, Conn 06904
Telephone: 203-329 8711

Contacts Robert R.Evans (Manager Treasury Projects), Donald F.Crowley (Benefits Administrator)

Funds	$million
Profit Sharing Retirement & Savings Plan	805
Est.Assets Sept.1980	914

Summary of Investments	%
Cash	15
Equities	67
Fixed Interest	13
Real Estate	5

	$million
Employer Contributions	115
Benefit Payments	45

Largest US Money Managers

AETNA LIFE & CASUALTY CO.

151 Farmington Avenue, Hartford, Conn 06156
Telephone: 203-273 0123

Contacts Donald G.Conrad (Executive Vice-President), John C.Lang (Assistant Vice-President)

Tax Exempt Assets Managed $15,400 million

Tax Exempt Clients 3,750

Portfolio Managers 24

Research Staff 54

ALLIANCE CAPITAL MANAGEMENT CORPORATION

140 Broadway, New York, NY 10005
Telephone: 212-635 3636

Contacts Dave H.Williams (Chairman), Clinton J. Kendrick (President)

Tax Exempt Assets Managed $7,900 million

Tax Exempt Clients 218

Portfolio Managers 28

Research Staff 10

Parent Company Donaldson,Lufkin & Jenrette

AMERICAN FLETCHER NATIONAL BANK

101 Monument Circle, Indianapolis, Indiana 46277
Telephone: 312-639 3000

Contacts William R.Fry (Chief Investment Officer), James W.Magee (Senior Investment Officer), J.William Rice (Vice President Investments)

Tax Exempt Assets Managed $2,207 million

Tax Exempt Clients 1,123

Portfolio Managers 11

Research Staff 5

AMERICAN NATIONAL BANK & TRUST CO OF CHICAGO

33 North LaSalle Street, Chicago, Ill 60690
Telephone: 312-661 5000

Contacts Harold I Arbit (Vice President), Edward D. Matz (Senior Vice President)

Tax Exempt Assets Managed $2,900 million

Tax Exempt Clients 250

Portfolio Managers 8

Research Staff 7

AMERICAN SECURITY BANK N.A.

1501 Pennsylvania Avenue, N.W., Washington, D.C.20013
Telephone: 202-624 4272

Contacts Michael B.Miller (Senior Investment Officer), Geoff Caldwell (Vice President)

Tax exempt Assets Managed $1,600 million

Tax exempt Clients 408

AMERICAN SECURITY BANK N.A. Continued

Portfolio Managers 18

Research Staff 7

AMERITRUST COMPANY

900 Euclid Avenue, Cleveland, Ohio 44101
Telephone: 216-687 5750

Contacts William S.Brooks (Senior Vice President), Robert C.Gebauer (Vice President)

Tax Exempt Assets Managed $2,935 million

Tax Exempt Clients 500

Portfolio Managers 12

Research Staff 14

BA INVESTMENT MANAGEMENT CORP

555 California Street, San Francisco, Calif.94104
Telephone: 415-622 5510

Contacts Jack H.Leylegian (President & Chief Executive Officer), Douglas E.Heidhorn (Senior Vice-President Marketing)

Tax Exempt Assets Managed $2,873 million

Tax Exempt Clients 42

Portfolio Managers 9

Research Staff 10

Parent Company Bank of America Corp.

DAVID L.BABSON INC

One Boston Place, Boston, Mass 02108
Telephone: 617-723 7540

Contacts David L.Babson (Chairman), H.Bradlee Perry (President), Robert C.Puff (Vice President)

Tax Exempt Assets Managed $2,300 million

Tax Exempt Clients 200

Portfolio Managers 18

Research Staff 10

THE BANK OF NEW YORK

48 Wall Street, New York, NY 10015
Telephone: 212-530 1784

Contacts Douglas F.Adams (Senior Vice President, Head Trust Sector), Douglas A.Leslie (Vice President, Employee Benefit Trust), David P.Ruley (Vice President)

Tax Exempt Assets Managed $2,200 million

Tax Exempt Clients 167

Portfolio Managers 12

Research Staff 20

BANKERS LIFE CO

711 High Street, Des Moines, Iowa 50307
Telephone: 515-247 5111

Contacts Roy W. Ehrle (Senior Vice-President, Chief Investment Officer), Ronald E.Keller (Director of Group Pension Marketing)

Tax Exempt Assets Managed $4,700 million

Tax Exempt Clients 12,000

Portfolio Managers 4

Research Staff 20

BANKERS TRUST CO

280 Park Avenue, New York, NY 10017
Telephone: 212-775 2500

Contacts H.Kent Atkins (Senior Vice-President, Chief Investment Officer), George W.Cowles (Senior Vice President), Frank Minard (Vice President) 2

Tax Exempt Assets Managed $12,000 million

Tax Exempt Clients 290

Portfolio Managers 28

Research Staff 29

BATTERYMARCH FINANCIAL MANAGEMENT CORP

600 Atlantic Avenue, Boston, Mass.02210
Telephone: 617-973 9300

Contacts Dean LeBaron (President, Chief Investment Officer), Alan J.Strassman (Executive Vice President)

Tax Exempt Assets Managed $3,400 million

Tax Exempt Clients 74

Portfolio Managers 8

BERNSTEIN-MACAULAY INC.

505 Park Avenue, New York, N.Y.10022
Telephone: 212-826 1500

Contacts Harold B.Ehrlich (Chairman), Heath B.McLendon (President)

Tax Exempt Assets Managed $1,700 million

Tax Exempt Clients 11

Parent Company Shearson Loeb Rhodes, Inc.

THE BOATMEN'S NATIONAL BANK OF ST.LOUIS

100 North Broadway, P.O.Box 7365, St.Louis, Mo.63102
Telephone: 314-425 7000

Contacts Russell W.Murphy (Chief Investment Officer), Robert W.Mainini (Marketing Representative)

Tax Exempt Assets Managed $2,000 million

Tax Exempt Clients 175

Portfolio Managers 12

Research Staff 4

THE BOSTON CO.INSTITUTIONAL INVESTORS INC.

One Boston Place, Boston, Mass.02106
Telephone: 617-722 7000

Contacts Peter Summers (President), A.Wagner (Executive Vice President)

Tax Exempt Assets Managed $3,800 million

Tax Exempt Clients 325

Portfolio Managers 35

Research Staff 9

Subsidiaries in Los Angeles, San Francisco, New Orleans

BROWN BROTHERS HARRIMAN & CO

59 Wall Street, New York, NY 10005
Telephone: 212-483 1818

BROWN BROTHERS HARRIMAN & CO *Continued*

Contacts Maarten van Hengel (Chairman Investment Policy Committee), Douglas McCartney (Manager for Equity and Balanced Portfolios), Eugene C.Rainis (Manager)

Tax Exempt Assets Managed $4,800 million

Tax Exempt Clients 365

Portfolio Managers 59

Research Staff 20

CAPITAL GUARDIAN TRUST CO
333 South Hope Street, Los Angeles, Calif 90071
Telephone: 213-486 9200

Contacts R.Michael Shanahan (President & Chief Investment Officer), Mitchell J.Milias (Vice-President)

Tax Exempt Assets Managed $5,673 million

Tax Exempt Clients 71

Portfolio Managers 10

Research Staff 29

CAPITAL SUPERVISORS INC.
135 South LaSalle Street, Chicago, Ill.60603
Telephone: 312-236 8271

Contacts A.Lee Thurow (President), James C.Seyfarth (Vice President)

Tax Exempt Assets Managed $1,798 million

Tax Exempt Clients 23

Portfolio Managers 6

CHASE INVESTORS MANAGEMENT CORP
1211 Avenue of the Americas, New York, N.Y.10036
Telephone: 212-730 3355

Contacts Stephen E.Canter (President), Thomas R.Jackson (Vice President, London), Lawrence F. Weber (Vice President)

Tax Exempt Assets Managed $6,500 million

Tax Exempt Clients 200

Portfolio Managers 24

Research Staff 20

CHEMICAL BANK
30 Rockefeller Plaza, New York, N.Y.10020
Telephone: 212-621 2323

Contacts Kenneth S.Rolland (Senior Vice-President, Investment Officer), William G.Gallaher (Vice-President)

Tax Exempt Assets Managed $5,372 million

Tax Exempt Clients 674

Portfolio Managers 16

Research Staff 18

CITIBANK, NA
One Citicorp Center, 153 East 53rd Street, New York, N.Y.10043
Telephone: 212-559 9700

Contacts Peter H.Vermilye (Chairman Investment Policy), Anthony Howkins (Vice President, Investments), Alexander Thomson (Vice President)

Tax Exempt Assets Managed $7,185 million

Tax Exempt Clients 435

Portfolio Managers 56

Research Staff 32

CITIZENS AND SOUTHERN NATIONAL BANK
34 Broad Street, PO Box 4114, Atlanta, Ga 30302
Telephone: 404 581 4870

Contacts David W. Meese (Chief Investment Officer), David F.Seng, T.Marion Slaton (Vice Presidents)

Tax Exempt Assets Managed $2,140 million

Tax Exempt Clients 775

Portfolio Managers 10

Research Staff 6

CONNECTICUT GENERAL LIFE INSURANCE CO
950 Cottage Grove Road, Hartford, Ct 06152
Telephone: 203-726 6000

Contacts Hartzel Z.Lebed (Executive Vice-President), W.E.Chapman (Second Vice President) Robert E.Hyatt (Vice President)

Tax Exempt Assets Managed $9,500 million

Tax Exempt Clients 8,013

Portfolio Managers 10

Research Staff 21

CONTINENTAL ILLINOIS NATIONAL BANK & TRUST CO
30 North LaSalle Street, Chicago, Ill.60693
Telephone: 312-828 7117

Contacts Joseph Alaimo (Chief Investment Officer), Richard W.Foss (Senior Vice President), Anthony P.Wilson (Vice President)

Tax Exempt Assets Managed $3,318 million

Tax Exempt Clients 805

Portfolio Managers 38

Research Staff 13

CROCKER INVESTMENT MANAGEMENT CORP
44 Montgomery Street, San Francisco, Calif 94104
Telephone: 415-983 2676

Contacts Robert G Wade (President, Chief Investment Officer), John Dracott (Vice President)

Tax Exempt Assets Managed $1,860 million

Tax Exempt Clients 43

Portfolio Managers 14

Research Staff 11

DELAWARE INVESTMENT ADVISERS
7 Penn Center Plaza, Philadelphia, Pa 19103
Telephone: 215-568 5880

Contacts Wayne A.Stork (Executive Vice President, Chief Investment Officer), James T.Blair (Senior Vice President)

Tax Exempt Assets Managed $2,700 million

Tax Exempt Clients 129

DELAWARE INVESTMENT ADVISERS *Continued*

Portfolio Managers 10

Research Staff 4

EBERSTADT ASSET MANAGEMENT, INC.
61 Broadway, New York, N.Y.10006
Telephone: 212-480 8600

Contacts John Hill (President), G.Peter Schieferdecker (Senior Vice President, Chairman Investment Policy Committee), Wayne W.D.Leizear (Vice President)

Tax Exempt Assets Managed $1,627 million

Tax Exempt Clients 21

Research Staff 8

Parent Company Marsh & McLennan

LIONEL D.EDIE & CO INC
530 Fifth Avenue, New York, NY 10036
Telephone: 212-575 4000

Contacts Fletcher Hodges (President & Chief Executive Officer), Willard Wheeler (Chief Investment Officer), Philip Metcalf (Director of Marketing)

Tax Exempt Assets Managed $6,680 million

Tax Exempt Clients 583

Portfolio Managers 40

Research Staff 14

EQUITABLE LIFE ASSURANCE SOCIETY OF THE UNITED STATES
1285 Avenue of the Americas, New York, NY 10019
Telephone: 212-554 1448

Contacts James Attwood (Chief Investment Officer), Thomas C.Gorman (Vice President), Robert M.Angland (Vice President, Pension Client Contact)

Tax Exempt Assets Managed $25,100 million

Tax Exempt Clients 2,600

Portfolio Managers 12

Research Staff 25

FIDUCIARY TRUST CO OF N.Y.
Two World Trade Center, New York, NY 10048
Telephone: 212-466 4100

Contacts Harry Fowler (Chairman), Landon Thomas (Executive Vice President), Peter V.Haight (Vice President)

Tax Exempt Assets Managed $3,726 million

Tax Exempt Clients 189

Portfolio Managers 18

Research Staff 12

FIRST NATIONAL BANK IN DALLAS
P.O.Box 83771, Dallas, Texas 75283
Telephone: 214-744 8323

Contacts Ted C.Newell (President, Chief Investment Officer), Nathan O.Finke (Vice President), Richard D.Frizzell (Executive Vice President)

Tax Exempt Assets Managed $2,191 million

Tax Exempt Clients 305

Portfolio Managers 12

Research Staff 8

THE FIRST NATIONAL BANK OF BOSTON
100 Federal Street, Boston, Mass 02110
Telephone: 617-434 4560

Contacts Edward G.Riley, Jr(Vice-President), Peter F.Tague (Vice President Director of Marketing)

Tax Exempt Assets Managed $4,902 million

Tax Exempt Clients 600

Portfolio Managers 17

Research Staff 22

FIRST NATIONAL BANK OF CHICAGO
One First National Plaza, Chicago, Ill.60670
Telephone: 312-732 6474

Contacts Gary Brinson (Vice-President Investment Officer), Charles M.Spear (Vice-President)

Tax Exempt Assets Managed $4,250 million

Tax Exempt Clients 440

Portfolio Managers 20

Research Staff 15

FIRST NATIONAL BANK OF MINNEAPOLIS
120 South 6th Street, Minneapolis, Minn.55480
Telephone: 612-370 4141

Contacts Denis E.Evans (Senior Vice-President), Randolph L.Kohn (Vice-President)

Tax Exempt Assets Managed $1,900 million

Tax Exempt Clients 30

Portfolio Managers 7

Research Staff 7

FISCHER, FRANCIS, TREES & WATTS INC
717 Fifth Ave, New York, N.Y.10022
Telephone: 212-350 8050

Contacts Richard Fischer (Chief Investment Officer), John H. Watts (Vice President)

Tax Exempt Assets Managed $2,250 million

Tax Exempt Clients 30

Portfolio Managers 11

Parent Company Philadelphia National Bank

FMR INVESTMENT MANAGEMENT SERVICE INC.
One Boston Place, Boston, Mass.02108
Telephone: 617-726 0555

Contacts Roger L.Clifton (President), Robert F.Johnston (Vice President)

Tax Exempt Assets Managed $1,600 million

Tax Exempt Clients 26

Portfolio Managers 6

Research Staff 4

GIRARD BANK
One Girard Plaza, Philadelphia, Pa.19101
Telephone: 215-585 2000

Contacts F.Joseph McDonald (Senior Vice

GIRARD BANK Continued

President), Charles E.Bradford (Senior Investment Officer)

Tax Exempt Assets Managed $2,559 million

Tax Exempt Clients 800

Portfolio Managers 10

Research Staff 12

JOHN HANCOCK MUTUAL LIFE INSURANCE CO

John Hancock Place, PO Box 111, Boston, Mass 02117
Telephone: 617-421 6000

Contacts Lewis Kleinrock (Chief Investment Officer), Richard P. Troy (Vice President)

Tax Exempt Assets Managed $8,000 million

Tax Exempt Clients 2,000

Portfolio Managers 11

Research Staff 30

HARRIS TRUST & SAVINGS BANK

111 West Monroe Street, Chicago, Ill.60603
Telephone: 312-461 6932

Contacts William S.Gray (Senior Vice-President, Chief Investment Officer), Richard C.Caldwell (Assistant Vice President)

Tax Exempt Assets Managed $8,036 million

Tax Exempt Clients 1,025

Portfolio Managers 11

Research Staff 18

IDS ADVISORY

3100 IDS Tower, Minneapolis, Mn.55402
Telephone: 612-372 3335

Contacts Eugene C.Sit (President), Peter Mitchelson (Vice President)

Tax Exempt Assets Managed $2,200 million

Tax Exempt Clients 39

Portfolio Managers 8

Research Staff 35

Parent Company Investors Diversified Services Inc.

IRVING TRUST CO

One Wall Street, New York, N.Y.10015
Telephone: 212-487 3225

Contacts Peter D. Richardson (Senior Vice-President), Allen R.Malcolm (Vice President)

Tax Exempt Assets Managed $1,400 million

Tax Exempt Clients 502

Portfolio Managers 7

Research Staff 15

JENNISON ASSOCIATES CAPITAL CORP.

270 Park Avenue, New York, N.Y.10017
Telephone: 212-421 1000

Contacts Spiros Segalas (Chief Investment Officer), H.Carnie Lawson (Senior Vice President)

Tax Exempt Assets Managed $3,000 million

Tax Exempt Clients 52

Portfolio Managers 8

Research Staff 5

LINCOLN NATIONAL LIFE INSURANCE CO.

1300 South Clinton, Fort Wayne, Indiana 46801
Telephone: 219-424 5421

Contacts Walter G.Gadient (Chief Investment Officer), W.L.Sanders (Second Vice President), Robert A.Nickels (Vice President)

Tax Exempt Assets Managed $2,100 million

LOOMIS, SAYLES & CO INC

225 Franklin Street, Boston, Mass 02110
Telephone: 617-482 2450

Contacts Robert L.Kemp (President & Investment Officer), Charles C.Thomas (Vice-President)

Tax Exempt Assets Managed $4,300 million

Tax Exempt Clients 357

Portfolio Managers 58

Research Staff 23

MACKAY-SHIELDS FINANCIAL CORP.

551 Fifth Avenue, New York, N.Y.10176
Telephone: 212-986 1100

Contacts William Grant (Chairman Investment Policy Committee), William H.Todd (Director)

Tax Exempt Assets Managed $2,000 million

Tax Exempt Clients 21

Research Staff 16

MANUFACTURERS HANOVER TRUST CO

600 Fifth Avenue, New York, NY 10020
Telephone: 212-957 0760

Contacts Victor J.Melone (Senior Vice-President, Investment Officer), William C.Petty (Vice-President)

Tax Exempt Assets Managed $6,499 million

Tax Exempt Clients 800

Portfolio Managers 15

Research Staff 22

MANUFACTURERS NATIONAL BANK OF DETROIT

Manufacturers Bank Tower,
100 Renaissance Center, Detroit, Mich 48243
Telephone: 313-222 4000

Contacts Benedict J.Smith (Chief Investment Officer), Otto G.Hinzman, Richard C.Van den Brul (Vice Presidents)

Tax Exempt Assets Managed $3,100 million

Tax Exempt Clients 1,451

Portfolio Managers 12

Research Staff 8

MASSACHUSETTS MUTUAL LIFE INSURANCE COMPANY

1295 State Street, Springfield, Mass.01111
Telephone: 413-788 8411

Contacts Richard G.Dooley (Chief Investment Officer), Peter J.Vogian (Second Vice President)

MASSACHUSETTS MUTUAL LIFE INSURANCE COMPANY Continued

Tax Exempt Assets Managed $2,430 million
Tax Exempt Clients 1,950
Portfolio Managers 3
Research Staff 16

MELLON BANK, N.A.
Mellon Square, Pittsburgh, PA 15230
Telephone: 412-232 4100

Contacts Lloyd W.Pedersen (Senior Vice-President, Investment Officer), John R. Gepfert (Vice-President)

Tax Exempt Assets Managed $9,206 million
Tax Exempt Clients 975
Portfolio Managers 13
Research Staff 13

MERCANTILE TRUST CO.
One Mercantile Tower, St.Louis, Mo.63166
Telephone: 314-425 2603

Contacts John H.Blixen (Chief Investment Officer), Edmund J.Thimme (Vice President)

Tax Exempt Assets Managed $1,562 million
Tax Exempt Clients 470
Portfolio Managers 6
Research Staff 14

METROPOLITAN LIFE INSURANCE CO
1 Madison Avenue, New York, NY 10010
Telephone: 212-578 2937

Contacts Robert Schwartz (Chief Investment Officer), John J.Creedon (President), J.Robert Bloom (Vice President)

Tax Exempt Assets Managed $17,958 million
Tax Exempt Clients 2,848
Portfolio Managers 19
Research Staff 51

MORGAN GUARANTY TRUST CO.OF NEW YORK
9 West 57th Street, New York, N.Y.10019
Telephone: 212-826 7357

Contacts Perry E.Hall (Senior Vice President), David L.Hopkins (Executive Vice President), Martin J.Dowd (Assistant Vice President)

Tax Exempt Assets Managed $19,200 million
Tax Exempt Clients 370
Portfolio Managers 24
Research Staff 70

MUTUAL OF NEW YORK
1740 Broadway, New York, N.Y.10019
Telephone: 212-586 4000

Contacts Floyd L.Smith (Chief Investment Officer), Peter J.Cross (Vice President,Pension Investment)

Tax Exempt Assets Managed $1,927 million
Tax Exempt Clients 3,025
Portfolio Managers 10
Research Staff 56

NATIONAL BANK OF DETROIT
PO Box 222-A, 611 Woodward Avenue, Detroit, Mich 48232
Telephone: 313-225 2633

Contacts William C.Rands (First Vice-President, Senior Investment Officer), Paul E. Jensen (Senior Vice President Marketing)

Tax Exempt Assets Managed $6,700 million
Tax Exempt Clients 1,050
Portfolio Managers 9
Research Staff 25

NEW ENGLAND MUTUAL LIFE INSURANCE CO
501 Boylston Street, Boston, Mass 02117
Telephone: 617-266 3700

Contacts Robert C.Jordan (Executive Vice-President, Finance Investment Officer), Edwin H.Tebbells (Second Vice President)

Tax Exempt Assets Managed $2,600 million
Tax Exempt Clients 25,500
Portfolio Managers 11
Research Staff 17

NEW YORK LIFE INSURANCE CO
51 Madison Ave, New York, N.Y.10010
Telephone: 212-576 7000

Contacts Harold K.Herzog Bundschuh (Senior Vice-President), William D.Calligan (Vice-President)

Tax Exempt Assets Managed $2,100 million
Tax Exempt Clients 2,640
Portfolio Managers 2
Research Staff 6

THE NORTHERN TRUST CO.
50 South LaSalle Street, Chicago, Ill.60638
Telephone: 312-630 6000

Contacts James N.van Germeten (Senior Vice-President, Chief Investment Officer), Luke C.Mazur Thomas H.Kalen (Vice Presidents)

Tax Exempt Assets Managed $2,882 million
Tax Exempt Clients 430
Portfolio Managers 31
Research Staff 14

OPPENHEIMER CAPITAL CORP.
1 New York Plaza, New York, N.Y.10004
Telephone: 212-825 4000

Contacts Herbert Gullquist (Chief Investment Officer), David Dewey (Vice President)

Tax Exempt Assets Managed $2,132 million
Tax Exempt Clients 89
Portfolio Managers 12
Research Staff 2

PACIFIC MUTUAL LIFE INSURANCE CO.

700 Newport Center Drive, Newport Beach, Ca.92663
Telephone: 714-640 3040

Contacts Ott Thompson (Senior Vice President Investments), Daryle Johnson (Second Vice President,Pension Sales), Neale A.Randle (Director-Pension Investments)

Tax Exempt Assets Managed $2,266 million

Tax Exempt Clients 1,262

Portfolio Managers 10

Research Staff 5

THE PRUDENTIAL INSURANCE CO OF AMERICA

Prudential Plaza, Newark, N.J.07101
Telephone: 201-877 7884

Contacts Meyer Meinikoff (Senior Vice President), James E.Ludlam (Pension Asset Manager), Robert H.Dunphy (Vice-President)

Tax Exempt Assets Managed $19,612 million

Tax Exempt Clients 4,200

Portfolio Managers 34

Research Staff 527

PUTNAM ADVISORY CO INC

265 Franklin Street, Boston, Mass 02110
Telephone: 617-423 4960

Contacts Norton H.Reamer (President & Investment Officer), John O.Parker John O. Parker (Chairman, Chief Officer)

Tax Exempt Assets Managed $4,700 million

Tax Exempt Clients 75

Portfolio Managers 13

Research Staff 14

REPUBLIC NATIONAL BANK OF DALLAS

PO Box 241, Dallas, Texas 75221
Telephone: 214-653 5881

Contacts J.Donald Squibb (Chairman, Chief Investment Officer), W.Humphrey Bogart (Senior Vice President), David Pitman (Vice President Corporate Services)

Tax Exempt Assets Managed $2,600 million

Tax Exempt Clients 1,800

Portfolio Managers 6

Research Staff 8

ROSENBERG CAPITAL MANAGEMENT

One Market Plaza, San Francisco, Calif.94105
Telephone: 415-777 5474

Contact Claude Rosenberg (Chief Investment Officer)

Tax Exempt Assets Managed $2,000 million

Tax Exempt Clients 56

Portfolio Managers 6

Research Staff 9

T.ROWE PRICE ASSOCIATES INC

100 East Pratt Street, Baltimore, Md 21202
Telephone: 301-547 2000

Contacts E.Kirkbride Miller (Chairman & Investment Officer), Curran W.Harvey (Vice-Chairman), Charles H.Salisbury, Jr(Vice-President)

Tax Exempt Assets Managed $5,100 million

Tax Exempt Clients 200

Portfolio Managers 32

Research Staff 23

Associated Company Rowe Price Fleming International Inc.

FAYEZ SAROFIM & CO

Two Houston Center, Suite 2907, Houston, Tx 77002
Telephone: 713-654 4484

Contacts Daniel A.Breen (Executive Vice-President), Fayez Sarofim (President & Chief Investment Officer)

Tax Exempt Assets Managed $6,600 million

Tax Exempt Clients 155

Portfolio Managers 15

SCUDDER, STEVENS & CLARK

345 Park Avenue, New York, N.Y.10154
Telephone: 212-350 8200

Contacts George S.Johnston (President), Cuyler Findlay (Vice President Marketing)

Tax Exempt Assets Managed $7,724 million

Tax Exempt Clients 300

Portfolio Managers 52

Research Staff 40

SECURITY PACIFIC INVESTMENT MANAGERS

333 S.Hope Street, Los Angeles, Calif.90017
Telephone: 213-613 7090

Contacts Edmund A.Mennis (Chief Investment Officer), Thomas R.Tuttle (Vice President)

Tax Exempt Assets Managed $2,209 million

Tax Exempt Clients 53

Portfolio Managers 6

Research Staff 12

SPRINGFIELD MARINE BANK

1 Old Capital Plaza East, Springfield, Ill.62701
Telephone: 217-753 6160

Contact Michael J.Provines (Vice President, Investments)

Tax Exempt Assets Managed $2,600 million

Tax Exempt Clients 210

ST LOUIS UNION TRUST CO

510 Locust Street, St Louis, Mo 63101
Telephone: 314-231 9300

Contacts Henry Johnston (Chief Investment Officer), Thomas S.Darnall (senior Vice President), William F.Florich (Pensions Marketing)

Tax Exempt Assets Managed $2,428 million

Tax Exempt Clients 240

ST LOUIS UNION TRUST CO *Continued*

Portfolio Managers 12
Research Staff 13

STATE STREET RESEARCH & MANAGEMENT
225 Franklin Street, Boston, Mass 02110
Telephone: 617-482 3920

Contacts Charles L.Smith (Managing Partner), George F.Bennett (Partner), Harry Sterling (Vice President)

Tax Exempt Assets Managed $6,200 million
Tax Exempt Clients 44
Portfolio Managers 34
Research Staff 16

STEIN ROE & FARNHAM
150 South Wacker Drive, Chicago, Ill 60606
Telephone: 312-368 7600

Contacts Alfred Kugel (Director of Research & Investment Officer), Marshall B.Front (Partner)

Tax Exempt Assets Managed $3,800 million
Tax Exempt Clients 463
Portfolio Managers 4
Research Staff 25

THORNDIKE, DORAN, PAINE & LEWIS INC
28 State Street, Boston, Mass 02109
Telephone: 617-742 8100

Contacts Robert W.Doran (President & Investment Officer), Dena W.Reed (Vice-President)

Tax Exempt Assets Managed $3,200 million
Tax Exempt Clients 160
Portfolio Managers 12
Research Staff 16

THE TRAVELERS INSURANCE CO
1 Tower Square, Hartford, Ct 06115
Telephone: 203-277 7777

Contacts Kevin J.Bradley (Chairman), Eliot P.Williams (Executive Vice President, Chief Operating Officer), Thomas E. Keating (Vice-President)

Tax Exempt Assets Managed $8,100 million
Tax Exempt Clients 7,000
Portfolio Managers 227

TRUST COMPANY OF THE WEST
800 West Sixth Street, Suite 1400, Los Angeles, Ca.90017
Telephone: 213-485 9500

Contacts Ernest O.Ellison (President), Thomas E.Larkin (Vice President)

Tax Exempt Assets Managed $2,500 million
Tax Exempt Clients 49
Portfolio Managers 6
Research Staff 9

UNITED STATES TRUST CO.OF NEW YORK
45 Wall Street, New York, N.Y.10005
Telephone: 212-425 4500

Contacts Frank Grady (Chief Investment Officer), Richard R.Smith (Vice President)

Tax Exempt Assets Managed $3,500 million
Tax Exempt Clients 300
Portfolio Managers 9
Research Staff 8

WACHOVIA BANK & TRUST CO, NA
PO Box 3099, Winston-Salem, NC 27103
Telephone: 919-748 5363

Contacts H.Vernon Winters, Ed Roberts (Senior Vice President), David E. Wyatt (Employee Benefits Sales Manager)

Tax Exempt Assets Managed $1,600 million
Tax Exempt Clients 1,670
Portfolio Managers 9
Research Staff 8

WELLS FARGO INVESTMENT ADVISORS
475 Sansome St, San Francisco, Calif. 94144
Telephone: 415-396 5951

Contacts James R.Vertin (Senior Vice-President and Chief Investment Officer), William F.Adam, William Jahnke (Vice-Presidents)

Tax Exempt Assets Managed $4,900 million
Tax Exempt Clients 132
Portfolio Managers 29
Research Staff 12

WERTHEIM ASSET MANAGEMENT SERVICES INC.
200 Park Avenue, New York, N.Y.10166
Telephone: 212-578 0780

Contacts Nicholas A.Marshall (President, Chief Investment Officer), Robert P.Follert (Executive Vice President)

Tax Exempt Assets Managed $1,502 million
Tax Exempt Clients 15

WESTERN ASSET MANAGEMENT CO.
707 Wilshire Boulevard, Los Angeles, Ca.90017
Telephone: 213-614 3156

Contacts James B.Fox (President), Richard A.Miller (Vice President)

Tax Exempt Assets Managed $2,400 million
Tax Exempt Clients 67
Portfolio Managers 16
Research Staff 6

WILMINGTON TRUST CO
10th & Market Streets, Wilmington, Del 19899
Telephone: 302-428 7000

Contacts Joseph Sieneski (Chief Investment Officer), Robert B. Landon (Vice President)

Tax Exempt Assets Managed $3,330 million
Tax Exempt Clients 173

WILMINGTON TRUST CO *Continued*

Portfolio Managers 32
Research Staff 16

In present times there is a greater need for obtaining inflation proof invesments than ever before. We can assist in the Irish property market.

Auctioneers, Valuers, Surveyors and Estate Agents
24 St. Stephen's Green, Dublin 2. Telephone (O1) 601222. Telex 25804.
Offices at Dun Laoghaire (O1) 806820. Cork (O21) 25079. Belfast (O84) 38955.

The Largest Canadian Pension Funds and Money Managers

PENSION FUNDS

The following are the largest Canadian Pension Funds listed in the 1981 Money Market Directory

AIR CANADA
Suite 3721, 1 Place Ville Marie,
Montreal H3B 3P7
Telephone: 514-874 4302

Contacts Thomas W.De Wolf (Director of Investments)

Fund	$million
Pension Trust Fund	630
Summary of Investments	%
Equities	29
Fixed Interest	50
Cash	14
Real Estate	7

CANADIAN PACIFIC LTD.
20 King Street West, Toronto M5H 1C4
Telephone: 416-360 3286

Contact G.H.Cloutier (Assistant Vice-President, Pension Investment)

Fund	$million
Pension Trust Fund	885

ONTARIO HYDRO
700 University, Toronto M5G 1X6
Telephone: 416-592 6347

Contacts Terence Staples (Assistant Treasurer), P.L.Baxter (Pension Fund Manager), W.G.Johnson (Manager Employee Benefits)

Fund	$million
Pension Plan	1,029
Summary of Investments	%
Cash	8
Equities	24
Fixed Interest	36
Real Estate	1
Mortgages	31

MONEY MANAGERS

The following are the largest Canadian Money Managers as listed in the 1980 Money Market Directory and the 14th April 1980 issue of Pensions & Investments

CANADA LIFE ASSURANCE CO
330 University Avenue, Toronto M5G 1R8
Telephone: 416-597 1456

Contacts R.D.Radford (Vice-President & Treasurer), J.G.Fleming (Financial Vice President), W.Taylor Eichlin (Group Pensions Investment)

Tax-Exempt Assets Managed $913 million
Total Assets Managed $3,021 million
Tax-Exempt Clients 790
Portfolio Managers 4
Research Staff 28

THE CANADA TRUST CO
110 Yonge Street, Toronto M5C 1T4
Telephone: 416-362 6161

Contacts W.James Blowers (Vice-President Investments), Liam O'Brian (Corporate Business Development), D.Baillie (Vice-President & Treasurer), Gary Rubacha (Manager, Pension Investment)

Tax-exempt Assets Managed $1,600 million
Total Assets Managed $2,300 million
Tax-exempt Clients 575
Portfolio Managers 9
Research Staff 5

CONFEDERATION LIFE INSURANCE CO
321 Bloor Street East, Toronto M4W 1H1
Telephone: 416-967 8111

Contacts John Watson (Vice-President, Investments), A.E.Hamblin (Vice-President, Pension Fund Investments), F.G.Ryan (Vice-President)

Tax Exempt Assets Managed $1,040 million
Total Assets Managed $3,036 million
Tax Exempt Clients 425
Portfolio Managers 8
Research Staff 13

GREAT WEST LIFE ASSURANCE CO.
60 Osborne Street North, Winnipeg, Manitoba R3C 3A5
Telephone: 204-946 9342

Contacts J.R.Crysdale (Senior Vice-President Investments), Gary Coopland (Pension Investment Manager)

Tax-exempt Assets Managed $1,100 million
Total Assets Managed $5,800 million
Tax-exempt Clients 1,600
Portfolio Managers 12
Research Staff 43

JARISLOWSKY,FRASER & CO.LTD.
1110 Sherbrooke Street W., Suite 2609, Montreal, Quebec H3A 1H1
Telephone: 514-842 2727

Contact Steven Jarislowsky (President)

Tax-Exempt Assets Managed $1,500 million
Tax-exempt Clients 54
Portfolio Managers 5

MONTREAL TRUST CO
15 King Street West, Toronto M5H 1B4
Telephone: 416-362 6363

Contacts Norman Cunningham (Vice-President, Investment), D.R.Plander, G.Coleman (Managers Pension Investment Depts)

MONTREAL TRUST CO *Continued*

Tax-Exempt Assets Managed $1,586 million

	$million
Discretionary - Tax-Exempt	2,851
Discretionary - Taxable	2,000

Research Staff 6

NATIONAL TRUST CO LTD

21 King Street East, Toronto M5C 1B3
Telephone: 416-364 9141

Contacts D.D.Landreville (Vice President Employee Benefits), Donald Dique (Vice President Finance)

Tax-exempt Assets Managed $1,610 million

Total Assets Managed $4,474 million

Tax-exempt Clients 700

Portfolio Managers 25

Research Staff 5

THE ROYAL TRUST CORP. OF CANADA

630 Dorchester Boulevard West, P.O.Box 1810, Station B, Montreal H3B 1S6
Telephone: 514-876 2525

Contacts G.Roger Otley (Group Vice-President, Investments), Fraser Blakeley (Assistant Vice-President, Pension Trust Services)

Tax-exempt Assets Managed $4,100 million

Total Assets Managed $9,260 million

Tax-exempt Clients 2,040

Portfolio Managers 20

Research Staff 18

Everything you ever wanted to know about pensions but didn't know who to ask.

*Benefit Planning; Scheme Design and Maintenance;
International and Multi-national Plans; Acquisitions & Mergers;
Actuarial Aspects; Investment Services and Portfolio Measurement;
Communications and Presentation; Administration & Trusteeship;
Legal & Documentary Aspects; Compensation for Executives;
Share Options & Incentives*

METROPOLITAN PENSIONS ASSOCIATION LTD
International Employee Benefit Consultants

Burwood House, 16 Caxton Street, LONDON SW1H 0QU
Metropolitan House, Northgate, Chichester, Sussex PO19 1BE
and at
Birmingham, Edinburgh, Glasgow, Leeds, Leicester, Manchester,
Brussels, Frankfurt, Hong Kong, Johannesburg, Melbourne, Sydney
and New York.

Major European Pension Funds

The following section includes details of the major Organisations involved with pension matters, and where relevant details of the Pension Funds or Largest Companies, in 6 of the major European countries. These countries are:-

(a) Belgium
(b) France
(c) West Germany
(d) Ireland
(e) Netherlands
(f) Switzerland

The amount of information included under each varies substantially depending on the pension structure of the country. More information on those countries can be found in the articles at the beginning of this book. Extra information on these and other countries can be found in 'Employee Benefits in Europe' published by Callund & Co Ltd or in the International Benefits Information Service (IBIS).

Belgium

Public Offices

MINISTRY OF ECONOMIC AFFAIRS

Service des Assurances rue de Mot 24, 1040 Brussels
Telephone: 02-233 6111

OFFICE DE CONTROLE DES ASSURANCES (OCA)

(O.C.A.) Square de Meeus 1, bte 8, 1040 Brussels
Telephone: 02-513 9851

President Mr. Dumortier

OFFICE NATIONAL DE SECURITE SOCIALE

(National Social Security Office)
Boulevard de Waterloo 76, 1000 Brussels
Telephone: 02-513 8520

OFFICE NATIONAL DES PENSIONS POUR TRAVAILLEURS SALARIES (O.N.P.T.S.)

Tour du Midi, 1060 Brussels
Telephone: 02-523 4040

Associations

ASSOCIATION BELGE DES FONDS DE PENSION

(Belgian Association of Pension Funds)
rue Montoyer 46, 1040 Brussels
Telephone: 02-233 0511

President Mr. T'Jampens

ASSOCIATION ROYALE DES ACTUAIRES BELGES

Boulevard Emile Jacqmain 53, 1000 Brussels
Telephone: 02-218 6010

President H.Rykers

UNION PROFESSIONNELLE DES ENTREPRISES D'ASSURANCES (U.P.E.A.)

Square de Meeus 29, 1040 Brussels
Telephone: 02-513 6845

Actuarial Matters J.Gabriel

Legal Matters R. van Gompel

Insurance Companies

GROUPE A.G. (COMPAGNIE BELGE D'ASSURANCES GENERALES)

Boulevard Emile Jacqmain 53, 1000 Brussels
Telephone: 02-218 6010

GROUPE ASSUBEL (ASSUBEL GAIN NETWORK)

rue de Laeken 35, 1000 Brussels
Telephone: 02-218 0400

ROYALE BELGE (AREA BENEFITS NETWORK)

Boulevard du Souverain 25, 1170 Brussels
Telephone: 02-673 6030

BELGIUM

Actuaries and Pension Consultants

AREA BENEFITS NETWORK
25 Boulevard de Souverain, 1170 Brussels
Telephone: 02-660 6613

MICHAEL DUNHILL FIA
124 rue du Commerce, Bte 6, 1040 Brussels
Telephone: 02-230 7477
Senior Partner M.Dunhill,FIA
Professional Staff Anne Claes, M.Thom,BA
Other Employees 3

INSUROPE
Boulevard Bischoffsheim 45, Bte 7, 1000 Brussels
Telephone: 02-217 8163
Executives F.Smolar, M.Connarty

METROPOLITAN PENSIONS ASSOCIATION SA
avenue des Arts 50, Bte 4, 1040 Brussels
Telephone: 02-512 0136

TOWERS, PERRIN, FORSTER & CROSBY
21 rue du Beausite, 1050 Brussels
Telephone: 02-648 7324
Principal E.Pinkert

WILLIAM M. MERCER-HENRIJEAN SA
rue de la Science 41, 1040 Brussels
Telephone: 02-230 4125
Director P.Goffin

Banks

BANQUE BRUXELLES LAMBERT SA
Pension Funds Division rue de la Regence 2, 1000 Brussels
Telephone: 02-513 8181
Director Mr.Koen de Ryck
Pension Fund Experts 2 actuaries, 1 legal adviser, 1 tax adviser, 4 investment managers
Employees 18
Value of Pension Funds Managed £160 million
Pension Fund Clients 51
Services Investment management, full custodian and banking service; actuarial valuations; plan design; administration; general employee benefit advice

KREDIETBANK
Arenbergstraat 7, 1000 Brussels
Telephone: 02-513 8050

SOCIETE GENERALE DE BANQUE
rue Montagne du Parc 3, 1000 Brussels
Telephone: 02-513 6600

The Largest Companies and Pension Funds

ACEC-ATELIERS DE CONSTRUCTIONS ELECTRIQUES DE CHARLEROI
6000 Charleroi
Telephone: 071-360020
Managing Director P.Uytdenhoef
Employees 16,600

AGFA - GEVAERT GROUP
27 Sepstraat, 2510 Mortsel
Telephone: 031-401940
Managing Director A.Leysen
Employees 32,300 (worldwide), 8,500 (Belgium)

BANQUE BRUXELLES LAMBERT SA ASBL, PENSIONS COMPLEMENTAIRES
rue de la Regence 2, 1000 Brussels
Telephone: 02-513 8181
Managing Director J.L.Delbar
Director and Secretary A.Orban
Chairman of the Board B.Peelman
Employees 12,300
Auditors Messrs P. Moulinasse & P. Bes
Employees/Members 12,300
Pensioners 3,300
Summary of Investments (at 31.10.80)
Fixed Interest 58%
Others 42%

BEKAERT SA
L. Bekaertstraat, 8550 Zwevagem
Telephone: 056-756111
Chairman and Managing Director J.Ch.Velge
Employees 13,300

BELL TELEPHONE MANUFACTURING COMPANY SA
Francis Wellesplein 1, 2000 Antwerpen
Telephone: 031-371717
Employees 11,200

COCKERILL SA
Avenue Adolphe Grenier, 4100 Seraing
Telephone: 041-340810
President C.Huriaux
Secretary X.Neve de Mevergnies
Employees 46,300

DELHAIZE SA
53 Osseghemstraat, 1080 Brussels
Telephone: 02-428 0010
Chairman L.Ameye
Employees 6,300

BELGIUM

EBES NV
Mechelsesteenweg 271, 2000 Antwerp
Telephone: 031-307800

Chairman J. van der Schueren

Employees 4,600

ESSO BELGIUM NV
101 Frankrijklei, Antwerp
Telephone: 031-319600

Chairman M.L.Coppen

Employees 2,000

FABRIQUE NATIONALE DE HERSTAL (FN)
Voie de Liege 33, 4400 Herstal
Telephone: 041-640800

Employees 9,405

FORD MOTOR COMPANY (BELGIUM)
200/204 Kanaaldok, 2030 Antwerp
Telephone: 031-410080

Chairman H.Daems

Employees 15,000

GB-INNO-BM
111 rue Neuve, 1000 Brussels
Telephone: 02-241 6560

Chairman F.Vaxelaire

Employees 27,400

GENERAL MOTORS CONTINENTAL
75 Noorderlaan, 2030 Antwerp
Telephone: 031-421100

Employees 10,500

IBM BELGIUM,
Fonds de Pensions et de Prevoyance
Square Victoria Regina 1, 1030 Brussels
Telephone: 02-2193880

Managing Director C. de Meyer

Employees 2,300

ICI BELGIAN PENSION FUND
Everslaan 45, 3078 Everberg
Telephone: 02-731 6900

Investment Advisers Banque Bruxelles Lambert, Assubel EG

Actuaries Michael Dunhill Consulting Actuary

Auditors Price Waterhouse

Employees 460

Members 409

Pensioners 19

	BF million
Annual Contributions	26
Annual Investment Income	10.5
Gross Annual Outflow	5.5
Capital Value	197.6
Summary of Investments (at July 1980) Equities	21.9
Fixed Interest	138.4
Properties	8.1
Cash & Deposits	29.2

INTERCOM SA (AND PENSIOBEL ASBL)
1 Troonplein, 1000 Brussels
Telephone: 02-511 7240

Chairman A.Thys

Employees 8,500

ITT EUROPE INC.
480 avenue Louise, 1050 Brussels
Telephone: 02-649 9620

Pension Executive G.Hobbs

KEMPENSE STEENKOOLMIJNEN
Grote Baan 27, 3530 Houthalen
Telephone: 011-534351

Employees 19,600

METALLURGIE HOBOKEN-OVERPELT NV
14 Adolf Greinerstraat, Hoboken
Telephone: 031-281000

Chairman P.E.Corbiau

Employees 7,000

MONSANTO EUROPE NV
Tervurenlaan 270-272, 1150 Brussels

NESTLE FONDS DE PENSIONS
rue de Birmingham 221, 1070 Brussels
Telephone: 02-523 0040

Pension Fund Manager J.P.Hainaut

Investment Advisers Societe Generale de Banque

Auditors E. van de Putte

Employees 283

Members 414

Pensioners 108

	BF million
Annual Contributions	12
Annual Investment Income	10
Gross Annual Outflow	7
Capital Value	184
Summary of Investments Equities	70
Fixed Interest	90
Property	14
Cash & Deposits	10

PETROFINA SA
33 rue de la Loi, 1040 Brussels
Telephone: 02-513 6900

Chairman J.Meeus

Employees 23,000

PHILIPS I.C.M. SA
2 Debrouckereplein, 1000 Brussels
Telephone: 02-219 1800

BELGIUM

PHILIPS I.C.M. SA *Continued*

Chairman D.Fallon

Employees 12,500

SABENA SA NV

rue Cardinal Mercier 35, 1000 Brussels
Telephone: 02-511 9060

Chairman C. van Rafelghem

Employees 10,200

SOCIETE GENERALE DE BANQUE

rue Montagne du Parc 3, 1000 Brussels
Telephone: 02-513 6600

Employees 15,600

SOLVAY & CIE SA

33 rue du Prince Albert, 1050 Brussels
Telephone: 02-511 5940

Chairman J.Solvay

Employees 45,000 (worldwide)

UCB SA (FONDS DE PREVOYANCE)

4 Chaussee de Charleroi, 1060 Brussels
Telephone: 02-537 1220

Chairman P.Foriers

Employees 9,200

UNILEVER PENSIOENFONDS 'UNION' BV

46 Montoyerstraat, 1040 Brussels

Director A.T'Jampens

WAGONS-LITS CIE INTERNATIONALE

Boulevard Clovis 53, 1040 Brussels
Telephone: 02-230 5455

Employees 23,000

France

Government Offices

AGENCE CENTRALE DES ORGANISATIONS DE SECURITESOCIALE

(Social Security) 67 Boulevard Richard-Lenoir, 75536 Paris Cedex 11
Telephone: 355 3120

APEC (ASSOCIATION POUR L'EMPLOI DES CADRES, INGENIEURS ET TECHNICIENS)

(Unemployment Office) 8 rue Duret, 75783 Paris Cedex 16
Telephone: 502 1350

MINISTERE DE L'ECONOMIE ET DES FINANCES, DIRECTION DES ASSURANCES

(Insurance Supervisory Bureau)
54 rue de Chateaudun, 75007 Paris
Telephone: 874 8603

MINISTERE DU TRAVAIL ET DE LA SECURITE SOCIAL

(Direction Generale de la Securite Sociale)
1 Place du Fonteroy, 75007 Paris

UNEDIC

(Unemployment Office) 77 rue de Miromesnit, 75008 Paris
Telephone: 296 1651

UNION DE CAISSE NATIONALES DE SECURITE SOCIALE

(Social Security) 110 rue de Flandre, 75951 Paris Cedex 19
Telephone: 203 9657

Associations

REUNION DES SOCIETES D'ASSURANCE SUR LA VIE

3 rue Meyerbeer, 75009 Paris
Telephone: 824 9612

FEDERATION FRANCAISE DES SOCIETES D'ASSURANCES

(National Association of Insurance Companies)
3 rue de la Chaussee d'Antin, 75009
Telephone: 770 8939

Retirement Pension Schemes

AGIRC (ASSOCIATION GENERALE DES INSTITUTIONS DE RETRAITES DES CADRES)

(Cadres Retirement Pensions Associates)
4 rue Leroux, 75116 Paris
Telephone: 503 5320

ARRCO (ASSOCIATION DES REGIMES DE RETRAITES COMPLEMENTAIRES)

(Non Cadre Retirement Pension System)
44 Boulevard de la Bastille, 75012 Paris
Telephone: 346 1320

Some Caisse de Retraites

CIRCIA	AGRR
CIPC	ANEP
CRICA	CRI
UPC	IRPSIMMEC
CAPIMMEC	UNIRS
ARRCO	IRICASE

Life Insurance Companies and Institutions

ABEILLE-PAIX

52 rue de la Victoire, 75009 Paris
Telephone: 280 7575

AGF (GROUPE DES ASSURANCES GENERALES DE FRANCE)

87 rue Richelieu, 75060 Paris Cedex 02
Telephone: 742 7010

AGP (ASSURANCES DU GROUPE DE PARIS)

21 rue de Chateaudun, 75447 Paris, Cedex 09
Telephone: 285 0437

COMPAGNIES D'ASSURANCES DU GROUPE DROUOT

Place Victorien Sardou, 78161 Marly-le-Roi
Telephone: 958 6214

Chief Actuary Artus de Lallembert

CREDIT MUTUEL

28 rue Hamelin, 75016 Paris
Telephone: 723 7280

FRANCE (CIE D'ASSURANCE LA)

7-9 Boulevard Haussmann, 75009 Paris
Telephone: 770 9569

GAN (GROUPE DES ASSURANCES NATIONALES)

Tour GAN, Cedex 13, 92082 Paris la Defense
Telephone: 776 4225

GENERALI

76 rue Saint Lazare, 75440 Paris Cedex 09
Telephone: 280 6293

IRICASE INSTITUTION DE RETRAITE INTERPROFESSIONEL DES CADRES SUPERIEURS

13 rue Bachaumont, 75002 Paris
Telephone: 508 5437

MGF (MUTUELLE GENERALE FRANCAISE ACCIDENTS ET VIE)

37 rue Chanzy, 72000 le Mans
Telephone: 284910

and at 17-21 Faubourg St. Honore, 75008 Paris (265 7290)

MONDIALE

37 rue Liege, 75008 Paris
Telephone: 387 6435

and at 32 rue Emile Zola, 59 Mons en Baroeul (557485)

France

UAP VIE

(l'Union des Assurances de Paris-Vie) Tour Assur,
Cedex 14, 92083 Paris la Defense
Telephone: 776 4215

Chief Actuary M.Mascombe

International Benefit Advisors

GRAS SAVOYE SA

(Correspondent of Johnson & Higgins)
19 rue Calais, 75009 Paris
Telephone: 285 7244

WILLIAM M. MERCER-FAUGERE & JUTHEAU SARL

26 Boulevard Malesherbes, 75008 Paris
Telephone: 266 3508

Representive G.A.F.Frechet

SECCAR

(Correspondent of Alexander & Alexander
25 rue Marbeuf, 75008 Paris
Telephone: 256 2090

Germany

Government Offices

DER BUNDESMINISTER FUR ARBEIT UND SOZIALORDNUNG
(Social Security Office, Ministry of Labour)
Bonnerstrasse 85, 5300 Bonn-Duisdorf

BUNDESVERBAND DEUTSCHER VERSICHERUNGSKAUFLEUTE
Kekulestrasse 12, 5300 Bonn
Telephone: 0221-633267

DER BUNDESMINISTER DES INNERN
(Insurance Supervisory Bureau)
Rheindorferstrasse 198, 5300 Bonn

Associations

ARBEITSGEMEINSCHAFT BETRIEBLICHE ALTERVERSORUNG
(Association for Company Sponsored Pension Programmes) Postfach 510770, 5000 Koln 51
Telephone: 0221-380038

President Prof.Dr.G.Heubeck

Secretariat Rohrbacherstrasse 12, Postfach 101108, 6900 Heidelberg (06221-214)

BUNDESVEREINIGUNG DER DEUTSCHEN ARBEITGEBERVERBANDE
(National Employers Association)
Postfach 510508, 5000 Koln 51
Telephone: 0221-380172

DEUTSCHER GEWERKSCHAFTSBUND
(National Association of Labour Unions)
Hans Bockler Haus, Stromstrasse 8,
4000 Dusseldorf

DEUTSCHER VERSICHERUNGS SCHUTZVERBAND
Breitestrasse 98, 5300 Bonn
Telephone: 02221-652857

GESAMTVERBRAND DE DEUTSCHEN VERSICHERUNGSWIRTSCHAFT
(Association of Insurance Companies)
Adenauerallee 209, 5300 Bonn 1
Telephone: 02221-216054

Insurance Companies

ALTE LEIPZIGER LEBENSVERSICHERUNGSGESELLSCHAFT AG
Alte Leipziger Platz 1, Postfach 1660,
6370 Oberursel 1
Telephone: 06171-2001

Directors Acting for Pension Funds J.Osburg, S.M.Slottko

Employees 1,200

Pension Fund Clients 3,500

Services Offered to Pension Funds Insurance, reinsurance

Other Offices 15 branch offices in West Germany

Other Information Member of INSUROPE

COLOHIA LEBENS-VERSICHERUNGS AG
Oppenheimstrasse 11, 5000 Koln 1
Telephone: 0221-77211

VICTORIA LEBENS-VERSICHERUNGS AG
Bahnstrasse 2, Postfach 1116, 4000 Dusseldorf 1
Telephone: 0211-8881

Pensions Director G.Roper

Actuaries & Pension Consultants

HANS DINTER
Bockenheimer Anlage 15, 6000 Frankfurt/Main
Telephone: 0611-71231

HANS-ALBERT ETZEL
Weingartenstrasse 24, 6234 Hattersheim

WERNER GASSNER
Herdweg 44, 7000 Stuttgart 1
Telephone: 0711 298819

PROF. DR. GEORG HEUBECK
Robert-Heuser-Strasse 16, 5000 Koln 51
Telephone: 0221 380038

HANS KESSEL
Stocker Weg 58, 5064 Rosrath
Telephone: 02205-3636

DIETER KLEYLEIN
Westendstrasse 24, 6000 Frankfurt

WERNER KLOSE
Rheidter Weg 19, 5025 Stommeln
Telephone: 02238-3274

DR. HANS LAUX
Lenbachstrasse 6, 7014 Kornwestheim
Telephone: 07154-3119

PROF. DR. EDGAR NEUBURGER
Schneeglockchenstrasse 103, 8000 Munchen 50
Telephone: 089-1501055

JOHANN PIEGER
Deutsche Treuhand-Gesellschaft, Uhlandstrasse 8,
8000 Munchen 2
Telephone: 089-51591

RITA PORTH
Towers, Perrin, Forster & Crosby
Munchener Strasse 1, 6000 Frankfurt/Main 1
Telephone: 0611-231421

Germany

GERHARD ROPER

VictoriaLebens-Vers AG, Bahnstrasse 2,
4000 Dusseldorf 1
Telephone: 0211-8281

DR. RUDOLF SCHNEIDER

Schleissheimerstrasse 270b, 8000 Munchen 40
Telephone: 089-300 9014

DR. KLAUS VINNEMAN

Krauskopfallee 3, 6229 Schlangenbad 5
Telephone: 06129-2350

The Largest Companies

AEG-TELEFUNKEN

Hohenzollerndamm 150, 1000 Berlin 33
Telephone: 030-8381

Chairman Dr.W.Cipa

Employees 158,400

BASF AG

6700 Ludwigshafen
Telephone: 0621-601

Chairman Dr.B.Timm

Pensions Executive G.Klugger

Employees 113,800

BAYER AG

5090 Leverkusen-Bayerwerk
Telephone: 02171-301,

Chairman Prof. H.Grunewald

Pensions Executive T.Zuhlsdorf

Employees 170,400

ROBERT BOSCH AG

Postfach 50, 7000 Stuttgart 1
Telephone: 0711-81111

Chairman H.L.Merkle

Employees 110,500

DAIMLER-BENZ AG

Mercedesstrasse 136, Postfach 202,
7000 Stuttgart 60
Telephone: 0711-3021

Chairman Prof.Dr.J.Zahn

Employees 169,200

FORD WERKE AG

5000 Koln 21

Employees 56,300

GUTEHOFFNUNGSHUTTE AKTIENVEREIN

Essenerstrasse, 4200 Oberhausen
Telephone: 0208-8201

Chairman M.Lennings

Employees 84,200

HOECHST AG

Postfach 800320, 6230 Frankfurt/Main 80
Telephone: 0611-3051

Chairman Dr.R.Sammet

Pensions Executive W.Dickfeld

Employees 180,900

FRIED KRUPP GMBH

Altendorferstrasse 103, 4300 Essen
Telephone: 0201-1881

Chairman H.Petry

Employees 86,600

MANNESMANN AG

Mannesmannufer 2, Postfach 5501,
4000 Dusseldorf
Telephone: 0211-8201

President Dr.E.Overbeck

Employees 106,000

RHEINISCHE-WESTFALISCHES ELEKTRIZITATSWERK

Kruppstrasse 5, 4300 Essen
Telephone: 0201-1851

Chairman Prof.H.Mandel

Employees 57,900

RUHRKOHLE AG

Rellinghauserstrasse, Postfach 5, 4300 Essen

Chairman Dr.K.Bund

Employees 136,600

SIEMENS AG

Wittelsbacherplatz 2, 8000 Munich 2
Telephone: 089-2341

Chairman Dr.P.von Siemens

Pensions Executive J.Keilbar

Employees 319,000

AUGUST THYSSEN-HUTTE AG

Kaiser Wilhelmstrasse 100, Postfach 11067,
4100 Duisburg 11
Telephone: 0203-5401

Chairman Dr.D.Spethmann

Employees 134,300

VEBA AG

Karl Arnold Platz 3, Postfach 300306,
4000 Dusseldorf 4
Telephone: 0211-45791

President R.V.Benningsenfoerder

Employees 66,500

VOLKSWAGENWERK

3180 Wolfsburg 1
Telephone: 05361-221

Chairman H.Birnbaum

Employees 191,900

Ireland

Major Irish Funds

ALLIED IRISH BANKS LTD
(Staff Pension Fund) Bank Centre, Ballsbridge, Dublin 4
Pensions Manager I.H.E.Johnston

ARNOTT'S STAFF PENSION FUND
PO Box 3, 12 Henry Street, Dublin 1
Secretary J.C.O'Sullivan

BANK OF IRELAND
(Staff Pension Fund) Lower Baggot Street, Dublin 2
Chief Pensions Officer G.E.Collier

BORD NA MONA SUPERANNUATION SCHEME
Clanwilliam House, Mount Street Bridge, Dublin 2
Secretary F.V.Haniver

P.J.CARROLL & COMPANY
Dublin Road, Dundalk
Pensions Manager D.P.Duffy

CIE SUPERANNUATION FUND
c/o Financial Controller's Office, Heuston Station, Dublin 8
Pensions Manager G.A.Wallace

CONSTRUCTION INDUSTRY FEDERATION
9 Leeson Park, Dublin 6
Secretary P.S.O'Riada

ELECTRICITY SUPPLY BOARD
Lower Fitzwilliam Street, Dublin 2
Secretary Superannuation Funds C.P.Kavanagh

HENRY FORD & SONS LTD
Marina, Cork
Pension Funds Administrator T.Healy

ARTHUR GUINESS SON & CO. (DUBLIN) LTD.
St. James's Gate, Dublin 8
Secretary Pension Fund P.Gallagher

INDEPENDENT NEWSPAPERS LTD
90 Middle Abbey Street, Dublin 1
Secretary J.Mitchell

IRISH AIRLINES SUPERANNUATION SCHEMES
PO Box 180, Dublin Airport
Pensions Manager M.L.Slater

IRISH SHIPPING LTD
Merrion Hall, Strand Road, Dublin 4

Personnel Secretary P.G.Devine

PFIZER CHEMICAL CORPORATION
Ringaskiddy, Co.Cork
Financial Controller A.R.Baker

PHILLIPS ELECTRICAL (IRELAND) LTD
Newstead, Clonskeagh, Dublin 14
Pensions Manager A.J.Cullen

RADIO TELEFIS EIREANN
Bonnybrook, Dublin 4
Secretary, Superannuation Scheme A.O'Braonain

ROADSTONE PENSION TRUST LTD
Saggart, Co. Dublin
Pensions Manager J.Hamilton

ROWNTREE-MACKINTOSH (IRELAND) LTD
34 Inchicore Road, Dublin 8
Director P.Marron

SMURFIT GROUP PENSION TRUSTEES LTD
Beech Hill, Dublin 4
Managing Director G.P.Langford

WATERFORD GLASS LTD
Kilbarry, Waterford

Pension Fund Consultants

This list includes the names of all the members of the Irish Association of Pension Funds

BOWEN KININMONTH GROUP LTD
40 Upper Fitzwilliam Street, Dublin 2
Telephone: 761936

BRENNAN INSURANCES LTD
1 Westmoreland Street, Dublin 2
Telephone: 778358

CONSOLIDATED INSURANCE BROKERS LTD.
71 Upper Leeson Street, Dublin 4
Telephone: 684743

COYLE HAMILTON LIFE & PENSIONS LTD
7 South Leinster Street, Dublin 2
Telephone: 687211

FBD LIFE & PENSIONS TRUST LTD
Irish Farm Centre, Bluebell, Dublin 12
Telephone: 501166

INDEPENDENT PENSION CONSULTANTS LTD
120 Lr. Kilmacud Road, Stillorgan, Co. Dublin
Telephone: 887253

INVEST & PROSPER LTD
11 Upper Pembroke Street, Dublin 2
Telephone: 760295

IRISH PENSIONS TRUST LTD
Hill Samuel House, Adelaide Road, Dublin 2
Telephone: 767591

LIFE & PENSIONS LTD
68 Lr. Baggot Street, Dublin 2
Telephone: 763665

MCDONAGH & BOLAND GROUP LTD
Hume House, Ballsbridge, Dublin 4
Telephone: 689288

METROPOLITAN PENSIONS ASSOCIATION (IRELAND) LTD.
90 Marlboro Road, Dublin 4
Telephone: 977852

M M & S LIFE & PENSIONS LTD.
10 South Leinster Street, Dublin 2
Telephone: 717151

JOHN O'BRIEN INSURANCE ASSOCIATES LTD
Bridge House, Baggot Street Bridge, Dublin 4
Telephone: 601033

MARTIN PATERSON ASSOCIATES (IRELAND) LTD
50 Northumberland Road, Dublin 4
Telephone: 682988

PENSION & INVESTMENT CONSULTANTS LTD
6 Harcourt Road, Dublin 2
Telephone: 681122

ROYAL TRUST BANK (IRELAND) LTD
10 Lansdowne Road, Dublin 4
Telephone: 603111

SEDGWICK DINEEN LIFE & PENSIONS LTD
19 Harcourt Street, Dublin 2
Telephone: 781599

SHERIDAN ASSURANCE ASSOCIATES LTD
53 Adelaide Road, Dublin 2
Telephone: 687466

Consulting Actuaries

BACON & WOODROW
58 Fitzwilliam Square, Dublin 2
Telephone: 762031

DUNCAN C.FRASER & COMPANY
6 Harcourt Road, Dublin 2
Telephone: 782399

R.WATSON & SONS
7 Fitzwilliam Square, Dublin 2
Telephone: 761923

Insurance Companies

CALEDONIAN INSURANCE COMPANY LTD
38 St. Stephens Green, Dublin 2
Telephone: 760651

CANADA LIFE ASSURANCE COMPANY
65 St. Stephens Green, Dublin 2
Telephone: 781522

FRIENDS PROVIDENT LIFE OFFICE
16 Suffolk Street, Dublin 2
Telephone: 771301

INSURANCE CORPORATION OF IRELAND (LIFE) LTD
Burlington Road, Dublin 4
Telephone: 601377

IRISH LIFE ASSURANCE COMPANY LTD
Irish Life Centre, Lower Abbey Street, Dublin 1
Telephone: 720288

LAW UNION & ROCK INSURANCE COMPANY LTD
18/19 College Green, Dublin 2
Telephone: 770881

LIFE ASSOCIATION OF IRELAND
4 Dawson Street, Dublin 2
Telephone: 776567

NEW IRELAND ASSURANCE COMPANY LTD
Dawson Street, Dublin 2
Telephone: 776881

NORWICH UNION LIFE ASSURANCE SOCIETY
60 Dawson Street, Dublin 2
Telephone: 717181

THE SCOTTISH PROVIDENT INSTITUTION
Scottish Provident House, 25 St. Stephens Green, Dublin 2
Telephone: 789633

STANDARD LIFE ASSURANCE COMPANY LTD
59 Dawson Street, Dublin 2
Telephone: 773996

SUN LIFE OF CANADA
Hawkins House, Hawkins Street, Dublin 2
Telephone: 778192

Netherlands

Government and Public Departments

MINISTRY OF SOCIAL AFFAIRS
Zeestraat 71A, Den Haag
Telephone: 070-183220

SOCIAL INSURANCE INFORMATION CENTRE
Rhijnspoorplein, Amsterdam

SOCIALE VERZEKERINGSBANK
(Social Security Office) Appollolaan 15, Amsterdam
Telephone: 020-572 9111

SOCIALE VERZEKERINGSRAAD
(Supervisory Council of Social Security)
President Kennedylaan 21, 2517 JK Den Haag
Telephone: 070-469370

VERZEKERINGSKAMER
(Insurance Supervisory Bureau)
John F. Kennedylaan 32, postbus 9029,
7300 EM Apeldoorn
Telephone: 055-550888

Associations

ACTUARIEEL GENOOTSCHAP
p/a Delta Lloyd, Spaklerweg 4, Amsterdam
Telephone: 020-5949111

Secretary Mr. Wapstra

ADVIESCOMMISSIE VAN PENSIOENEN
(Association of Private Pension Funds)
Prinses Beatrixlaan 5, Postbus 93093,
2509 AB Den Haag
Telephone: 070-814171

Director J.W.Janssen

Secretary F.W.M.Vloemans

CONTACTCOMMISSIE VAN BEDRIJFSPENSIOENFONDSEN
(Association of Industry Wide Pension Funds)
Prinsenvinkenpark 19, Postbus 1901,
2585 HK Den Haag
Telephone: 070-572111

Secretary Dr.W.L.van Leeuwen

K.O.R.A.
(Association of Self-Employed Actuaries)
Emmastraat 36 Amsterdam

Secretary B.Sinnema

KRING VAN NEDERLANDSCHE ACTUARISSEN
Engelsestraat 2, 8913 BH Leeuwarden
Telephone: 05100-24994

VERBOND VAN VERZEKEKERAARS IN NEDERLAND
Groot Hertoginnelaan 8, 2517 EG Den Haag
Telephone: 070-614731

This is also the address for several other organisations relating to the Insurance and Pensions industries e.g. Bedrijfslommissie Voor Het Verzekeringsbedrijk, Ombudsman Levensverzekering(R.J.Erdbrink)

Insurance Companies

AGO LEVENSVERZEKERING MAATSCHAPPIJ N.V.
Kortenaerhuis, Kortenaerkade 1, postbus16150,
2500 BD 's-Gravenhage
Telephone: 070-614511

AMEV
Archimedeslaan 10, 3845 HB Utrecht
Telephone: 030-579111

CENTRAAL BEHEER PENSIOENVERZEKERING N.V.
Prins Willem Alexanderlaan 651, postbus 700,
7300 HC Apeldoorn
Telephone: 055-799111

DELTA LLOYD LEVENSVERZEKERING N.V.
Spaklerweg 4, postbus 1000,
1000 BA Amsterdam
Telephone: 020-5949111

ENNIA LEVENSVERZEKERING N.V.
Churchillplein 1, postbus 5,
2501 AB 's-Gravenhage
Telephone: 070-727272

LEVENSVERZEKERING MAATSCHAPPIJ 'UTRECHT' N.V.
Archimedeslaan 10, postbus 2072,
3500 HB Utrecht

NEDERLANDEN VAN 1870
Herengracht 124-128, postbus 870,
1000 AW Amsterdam

PENSIOENVERZEKERINGSMAATSCHAPPIJ 'METALLICUS' N.V.
Mathenesserlaan 285, 3021 HH Rotterdam
Telephone: 010-775288

RVS LEVENSVERZEKERING N.V.
Westerstraat 3, 3016 DG Rotterdam
Telephone: 010-692722

WINTERTHUR LEVENSVERZEKERING MAATSCHAPPIJ
Prinses Irenestraat 33, 1077 AW Amsterdam

Actuaries

BRANS & COMPANY
van Leyenberghlaan 197, postbus 7312,
Amsterdam-Buitenveldert
Telephone: 020-440610

Partner H.Langhorst

NETHERLANDS

HEIJNIS & KOELMAN B.V.
Roemer Virscherstraat 41, postbus 60074,
1005 GB Amsterdam
Telephone: 020-188522

and at Gebouw Bouwcentrum, Weena 736,
postbus 20736, 3001 JA Rotterdam (010-118656)

TEN PAS
Lairessestraat 117, 1075 HH Amsterdam
Telephone: 020-736625

V/H SMIT & BUNSCHOTEN
Emmastraat 36, 1075 HW Amsterdam

Pension Consultants

CONSULTASS
Postbus 70, 8000 AB Zwolle
Telephone: 05200-30566

HUDIG LANGEVELDT
Grootebeckarstraat 74, 1013 KS Amsterdam
Telephone: 020-212325

MEES & ZONEN
van Volenhovenstraat 3, 3016 BA Rotterdam
Telephone: 010-366277

and at Postbus 505, 3000 AM Rotterdam

WILLIAM M MERCER BV
Jan van Nassaustraat 74, 2596 BV 's-Gravenhage
Telephone: 070-244424

Banks & Investment Managers

ABN
Vijzelstraat 68, 1000 AK Amsterdam
Telephone: 020-299111

AMROBANK
Herengracht 595, 1018 CE Amsterdam
Telephone: 020-289393

and at Coolsingel 119, postbus 949, 3000 DD Rotterdam, (010-304911)

BUREAU W.B.O. BV
Prof.J.H. Bavincklaan 5, 1183 AT Amstelveen
Telephone: 020-434636

NEDERLANDSE CREDIETBANK
Kijkerstraat 521, Amsterdam
Telephone: 020-212727

NEDERLANDSE MIDDENSTANDSBANK N.V.
Eduard van Beinumstraat 2, postbus 1800,
1000 BV Amsterdam
Telephone: 020-543 9111

RABOBANK
St. Jacobsstraat 30, postbus 8098,
3511 BT Utrecht
Telephone: 030-369111

Industry Wide Pension Funds

There are about 80 Occupational or Industry Wide Pension Funds covering about 1,400,000 employees

AGRICULTURE PENSION FUND
Buitenrustweg 3, 2517 KD 's-Gravenhage
Telephone: 070-609930

Directors T.Boersma, Dr.P.Mastenbroek

Members 75,000

Pensioners 44,085

Annual Income Dfl 59.9 million

Capital Dfl 686 million

BAKERS PENSION FUND
Ged. Zuiderdriep 31, 9711 HB Groningen
Telephone: 050-188545

Director E.D.Kruyswijk

Actuary W.G.J.ten Pas

Accountant Moret & Limperg

Pensioners 430

BUILDERS PENSION FUND
Basisweg 10, 1043 AA Amsterdam
Telephone: 020-583911

Director Drs. P.J. van Leersum

Assistant Director J.Bos

Secretaries Mevr.A. Kloeth-Zwennis, J.M.Pot

Investment Adviser B.Sinnema

Actuaries A.W. van der Lans

Auditors Reyn, De Blaey & Co.

Employees 256,933

Independents 43,117

Pensioners 132,542

	Dfl million
Annual Contributions	424.9
Annual Investment Income	261.7
Annual Outflow	436.5
Capital Value	3,811.2
Summary of Investments	
Equities	232.6
Fixed Interest	2,950.5
Property	618.3
Cash & Deposits	162.8

BUTCHERS PENSION FUND
Bankastraat 100, 2585 ES 's-Gravenhage
Telephone: 070-514361

Director J.Kramer

Assistant Director H.J.Vogt

Actuary W.G.J.ten Pas

Members (at 31.12.77) 11,829

Pensioners 1,677

CLEANING & WINDOW CLEANING PENSION FUND
Nijenoord 1, 3552 AS Utrecht
Telephone: 030-453911

Accountants Brans & Co

Administration Detam

Members 13,812

Pensioners 867

NETHERLANDS

CLOTHING PENSION FUND
Koningslaan 35, 1075 AB Amsterdam
Telephone: 020-763767

Director A.Greshof

Members 10,600

Pensioners 3,911

CONCRETE PENSION FUND
Bos en Lommerplantsoen 1, 1055 AA Amsterdam
Telephone: 020-879111

Secretary G.J.Zeewuster

Actuary Brans & Co

Accountant Klijnveld Kraayenhof & Co

Administration Vereniging Gemeenschappelijk Administratiekantoor

Members (at 31.12.78) 10,300

Pensioners 2,261

FURNITURE PENSION FUND
Bos en Lommerplantsoen 1, 1055 AA Amsterdam
Telephone: 020-879111

Actuary Drs. J.K.de Liefpe

Accountant Klijnveld Kraayenhof & Co

Administration Vereniging Gemeeschappetijk Administratiekantoor

Members (at 31.12.78) 20,531

Pensioners 867

HEALTH, MENTAL WELFARE & SOCIAL INTEREST (PENSIOENFONDS PGGM)
Kroostweg 149, Postbus 117, 3700 AC Zeist
Telephone: 03404-28322

Director B.Boertien

Secretary G.J.Sterk

Chairman Drs.G.J.M.Horbach

Actuaries Brans & Co.

Auditors Dijker en Doornbos

Members (at 31.12.79) 197,000

Pensioners 22,000

	Dfl million
Annual Contributions	1,440.6
Annual Investment Income	564.3
Capital Value	7,097.8
Summary of Investments	
Equities	959.5
Fixed Interest	4,567.0
Property	633.5
Mortgages	759.1
Cash & Deposits	173.9

HOTEL, RESTAURANT & CATERING PENSION FUND
(Administration) Bos en Lommerplantsoen 1, 1055 AA Amsterdam
Telephone: 020-879111

Secretariat Johan de Wittlaan 8, 's-Gravenhage

Actuary Brans & Co

Accountants Klijnveld Kraayenhof & Co

Administration Vereniging Gemeenschappelijk Administratiekantoor

Members (at 31.12.77) 25,000

Pensioners 6,200

HOUSEPAINTERS AND DECORATORS PENSION FUND
Polakweg 8, Plaspoelder, 2280 AA Rijswijk (ZH)
Telephone: 070-906878

Director G.v.d.Gaag

Assistant Director O.v.d.Woude

Actuary V/H Smit en Bunschoten

Members 49,043

Pensioners 10,138

MEDICAL SPECIALISTS & GENERAL PRACTITIONERS (2 FUNDS)
Lomanlaan 103, postbus 3047, Utrecht
Telephone: 030-887021,

Director J.J.G.Hoes

Secretary H. van Boxtel

Actuary V/H Smit en Bunschoten

Accountants Klynveld Kraayenhof & Co

Annual Contributions Dfl 75 million and Dfl 116 million

Capital Dfl 537 million and Dfl 877 million

MERCHANTS PENSION FUND
Bos en Lommerplantsoen 1, 1055 AA Amsterdam
Telephone: 020-879111

Chairmen D.Opmeer, A. Rook

Secretaries J.H.W.Habermehl, J.B. Meyer

Investment Advisers Drs. J.K. de Liefde, Actuaris A.G.

Actuary Drs. J.K.de Liefde

Accountants Klijnveld Kraayenhof & Co

Administration Vereniging Gemeenschappelijk Administratiekantoor

Members (at 31.12.78) 13,458

Pensioners 7,036

	Dfl million
Annual Contributions	50.3
Annual Investment Income	89.1
Annual Outflow	123.0
Capital Value	1,162.6
Equities	17.6
Fixed Interest	958.8
Property	32.5
Mortgages	77.1

METAL INDUSTRY (LARGE) PENSION FUND
Statenlaan 128, 2582 GW 's-Gravenhage
Telephone: 070-546700

Director H.Wagenvoort

Assistant Director J.A. van Opijnen

Actuary Drs.J.H.de Liefde

Auditors Moret & Limperg

NETHERLANDS

METAL INDUSTRY (LARGE) PENSION FUND Continued

Administration GAK-Bos en Lommerplantsoen 1, 1055 AA Amsterdam

Members (at 31.12.80) 129,603

Pensioners 33,083

	Dfl million
Annual Contributions	186.5
Annual Investment Income	328.8
Annual Outflow	296.8
Capital Value	4,106.6
Summary of Investments	
Equities	55.0
Fixed Interest	3,163.2
Property	431.8
Mortgages	288.6

METAL INDUSTRY (SMALL) PENSION FUND

Prinsevinkenpark 19, 2585 KH 's-Gravenhage
Telephone: 070-572111

Director W.L.van Leewen

Assistant Director A.T.J.Verkerk

Actuaries H.J. Bartelink (Internal), Actuarieel Bureau Dr.F.W.Nijhoff (External)

Auditors Dijker en Doornbos

Members (at 31.12.79) 186,700

Pensioners 21,980

	Dfl million
Annual Contributions	287.9
Annual Investment Income	265.7
Annual Outflow	514.8
Capital Value	3,596.0
Summary of Investments	
Equities	29.5
Fixed Interest	2,844.6
Property	400.2
Mortgages	102.5
Others	60.1

MINEWORKERS PENSION FUNDS

Beheer Pensionfondsen, 92 Akerstraat, 6401 CZ Heerlen
Telephone: 045-763333

Directors W.H.M.Klijberg, Dr.W.J.M.Schlosser

Actuaries Drs.W.J.M.Schlosser & M.W.Claassen

Accountants Moret & Limperg

Members (at 31.12.78) 2,308

Pensioners 19,602

Capital (at 31.12.78) Dfl 2,860 million

ONDERLING PENSION FUND

Lange Markstraat 12, 8911 AD Leewarden

Director Dr.H.Tjepkema

Assistant Director G.Volkers

Actuary Actuaries

Members 22,576

Pensioners 5,797

Capital Value Dfl 1,926.9 million

PRINTING PENSION FUND

Zwaansvliet 3, 1081 AP Amsterdam
Telephone: 020-541 8418

Director Th.S.L.Kwee

Financial Director S.J.Breeman

Actuaries V/H Smit en Blunschoten

Accountants Moret & Limperg

Members (at 31.12.78) 24,900

Pensioners 14,100

	Dfl million
Annual contributions	127.0
Annual Investment Income	161.3
Annual Outflow	154.5
Capital Value	1,866.5
Summary of Investments	
Equities	205.0
Fixed Interest	731.5
Property	516.3
Mortgages	225.5
Others	112.3

RETAIL TRADE PENSION FUND

Nijenoord 1, 3553 AS Utrecht
Telephone: 030-453911

Actuary Brans & Co.

Administration (Detam) Bedrijfsvereniging VoorDetailhandel, Ambachten en Huisvrouwen

Members 41,200

Pensioners 2,722

ROAD TRANSPORT PENSION FUND

Bos en Lommerplantsoen 1, 1055 AA Amsterdam
Telephone: 020-879111

Actuary V/H Smit en Bunshot

Accountants Klijnveld Kraayenhof & Co

Administration Vereniging Gemeenschappelijk Administratiekantoor

Members 54,500

Pensioners 2,200

TEXTILE INDUSTRY PENSION FUNDS (2 FUNDS)

Reitsplein 1, 5037 AA Tilburg
Telephone: 013-654133

Actuary Brans & Co.

Administration Stichting Bureau van Spaendonck

Members 20,853

Pensioners 16,029

Annual Contributions Dfl 18.9 million

Capital Value Dfl 296.8 million

TRANSPORT & HARBOUR PENSION FUND

Lombardkade 77, 3011 ZE Rotterdam
Telephone: 010-141988

Director J. de Vack

NETHERLANDS

TRANSPORT & HARBOUR PENSION FUND *Continued*

Secretary A.Koenderman
Actuary J.A.W.Hammer
Members (at 1.1.79) 16,634
Pensioners 4,342
Capital Value Dfl 884 million

TRANSPORT PENSION FUND

Prins Willem Alexanderlaan 651,
7311 PB Apeldoorn
Telephone: 055-792415

Members 13,918
Pensioners 2,096

The Largest Companies and Pension Funds

In total there are 20,000-30,000 Company Pension Funds covering 900,000 employees. Of these about 1,050 (covering 560,000 employees) are self administered (of which about half are reinsured) and the rest are directly insured with a life insurance company.

A.B.N. BANK PENSION FUND (ALGEMENE BANK NEDERLAND N.V.)

Vijzelstraat 32, Postbus 669, 1000 EG Amsterdam
Telephone: 020-299111

Secretaries D.Wessels, H.G.ten Cate
Chairmen J.Visser, R.J.A. van.der Veen
Actuaries Smit en Bunschoten
Employees 27,500
Members (at 31.12.78) 9,342
Pensioners 3,690

	Dfl million
Annual Contributions	51.5
Annual Investment Income	84.8
Capital Value	791.1
Summary of Investment	
Equities	46.0
Fixed Interest (Quoted)	107.2

AHOLD NV

Ankersmidplein 2, 1506 CK Zaandam,
Telephone: 075-599111

Secretary T.Baljon
Employees 22,200

AKZO STICHTING AKZO PENSIOEN FUNDS

Yssellaan 2, Postbus 186, 6800 LS Arnhem,
Telephone: 085-651911

Chairman W.J.Wolff
Secretary H.Hennis
Managers P.J.J.Gooris, H.R.Tierie
Investment Manager P.A.Van de Paverd
Actuaries V/H Smit en Bunschoten
Auditors Kijker en Doornbos
Employees 83,000 worldwide

Members (at 31.12.78) 25,000
Pensioners 8,100

	Dfl million
Annual Contributions	134
Annual Investment Income	98
Annual Outflow	180
Summary of Investments	
Equities	153
Fixed Ihterest	833
Property	443
Cash & Deposits	10
Others	41

AMRO BANK PENSION FUND

Coolsingel 19, Postbus 1800,
1000 BV Amsterdam
Telephone: 020-5439111

Director H.van der Helm
Secretary K.Mulder
Actuaries B.Smit
Auditors Moret & Limperg
Employees 23,200
Members (at 31.12.79) 14,213
Pensioners 4,300

	Dfl million
Annual Contributions	79.4
Annual Investment Income	75.2
Capital Value	1,025.4
Summary of Investments	
Equities	80.5
Fixed Interest	218.0
Loans	501.4
Mortgages	92.7
Others	58.8

DSM PENSIOENVERZEKERINGSMAATSCHAPPIJ

Van der Maesenstraat 2, Postbus 65,
6400 AB Heerlen
Telephone: 045-782250

Pension Fund Manager J.A.M.Dams
Secretary Th.F.Scheepers
Other Pension Management L.G. van Druten
Investment Advisers Dr.J.R.M. van den Brink, Dr.B.Pruijt, Dr.J.de Vries
Actuary J.M.G.Mennens
Auditors Moret & Limperg
Employees 31,750
Members 17,955
Pensioners 1,644

	Dfl million
Annual Contributions	113.5
Annual Investment Income	153.8
Capital Value	1,172.8
Summary of Investments	
Equities	84.9
Fixed Interest	1,048.5
Property	187.2
Cash & Deposits	1,147.8

NETHERLANDS

ESTEL HOOGOVENS NV HOGGOVENS PENSION FUND

Barbarossastraat 35, Postbus 401,
6500 AK Nijmegen
Telephone: 080-269111

Director Drs.J.P.A.van Casteren

Actuary Drs. G.H.Klein

Managers Drs.B.G.Djie, H.J.N.Rozemeijer

Actuaries Smit en Bunschoten

Auditors Klynveld Kraayenhof & Co.

Company Employees 79,000 (Worldwide), 26,500 (Netherlands)

Members (at 31.12.79) 21,213

Pensioners 5,317

	Dfl million
Annual Contributions	137.0
Annual Investment Income	106.5
Annual Outflow	40.7
Capital Value	1,591.9
Summary of Investments	
Equities	133.4
Fixed Interest	99.6
Loans	966.2
Property	314.1
Others	78.6

HEINEKEN PENSION FUND

2de Weteringplantsoen 21, 1017 ZD Amsterdam
Telephone: 020-709111

Director Drs. C.J.Melcherts

Managers J.Keller, E.H.Spenger

Actuaries Smit en Bunschoten

Auditors Klynveld Kraayenhof & Co.

Employees 20,300

Members (at 31.12.78) 5,534

Pensions 1,218

	Dfl million
Annual Contributions	27.7
Annual Investment Income	23.8
Capital Value	361.2
Summary of Investments	
Equities	88.7
Fixed Interest	47.3
Loans	146.0
Property	16.8
Cash & Deposits	15.0

INTERNATIO-MULLER

1 Westerlaan, 3000 AN Rotterdam
Telephone: 010-360100

Chairman H.F.Schenk

Secretary H.J.Kruisinga

Employees 15,800

KLM

PO Box 7700, Schiphol
Telephone: 020-492953

Secretary Mrs.Otten-Struben

Other Pension Management Drs.G.Hoogerwerf, J.F.L.v.d.Klein

Property Advisers Den Boer, Hartog, Hooft

Actuaries V/H Smit en Bunschoten

Employees 18,900

Members 10,350

Pensioners 4,150

	£ million
Annual Contributions	28
Annual Investment Income	33
Annual Outflow	9
Capital Value	396
Summary of Investments	
Equities	10
Fixed Interest	326
Property	60

NEDLLOYD PENSIOENFONDS

(Stichting Pensioenfonds van de Koninklijke Nedlloyd Groep) Houtlaan 21, 3016 DA Rotterdam
Telephone: 010-177911

Pension Fund Manager F.H.Lageman

Chairman of the Board of Trustees B.E.Ruys

Actuaries Actuarieel Bureau Dr.W.G.J. ten Pas

Auditors Klynveld Kraayenhof & Co.

Employees (at 31.12.79) 15,600

Members and Pensioners 14,700

	Dfl million
Annual Contributions	17.4
Annual Investment Income	61.8
Gross Annual Outflow	39.1
Capital Value	850.4
Summary of Investments	
Equities	86.2
Fixed Interest	553.3
Property	206.2
Cash & Deposits	4.7

OGEM HOLDINGS NV

Marconistraat 16, 3029 AK Rotterdam
Telephone: 010-898911

President Dr.B.J.Udink

Secretary T.J.C.Verduin

Employees 20,300

PHILIPS GLOEILAMPENFABRIEKEN NV PENSION FUND A AND PENSION FUND B

Tramstraat 62, 5600 MD Eindhoven
Telephone: 040-791111

Director Drs. A.D.J.van Riel

Assistant Directors W.A.F. van der Boor, J.van der Vliet

Investment Head A.D.J. van Riel

Actuaries Brans & Co.

Auditors Klynveld Kraayenhof & Co.

Employees 37,900 (worldwide), 82,000 (Netherlands)

NETHERLANDS

PHILIPS GLOEILAMPENFABRIEKEN NV *Continued*

	A Fund	B Fund
Members (at 31.12.79)	56,250	16,941
Pensioners	13,730	6,214
	Dfl million	Dfl million
Annual Contributions	131.3	330.7
Annual Pensions	56.9	142.2
Capital Value	2,488.6	4,746.4
Summary of Investments		
Equities	155.0	311.7
Fixed Interest	289.5	546.2
Loans		809.9
1,630.7		
Property	653.1	1,165.0
Overseas Property	62.7	115.6
Cash & Deposits	38.4	76.8
Others	83.5	269.3

RABOBANK PENSION FUNDS

St.Jacobsstraat 30, Postbus 8098, 3503 SE Utrecht
Telephone: 030-369111

Chairman C.G.A.Mertens

Secretaries Th.H.van Oort, J.de Hoop

Actuaries Brans & Co.

Auditors Moret & Limperg

Company Employees 25,300

Members (1977) 10,200

Annual Contributions Dfl 60 million

Annual Investment Income Dfl 36 million

Capital Value Dfl 600 million

RSV (RIJN SCHELDE VEROLME MACHINEFABRIEKEN)

Oostmaaslaan 59-65, 3000 BK Rotterdam
Telephone: 010-142811

Employees 26,500

SHELL PENSIOENFONDS

Carnegielaan 12, 2501 AN The Hague
Telephone: 070-779111

Director General Drs.J.J.de Kort

Directors Dr.A.Bier, Drs.A.C.Roodhuyzen, Drs.W.O.Wentges

Investment Head Drs.W.O.Wentges

Portfolio Managers E.R.A.Bolle, J. de Jonge, P.W.Knoester, A.W.Toole

Actuaries Smit en Bunschoten

Auditors Klynveld Kraayenhof & Co.

Employees 163,000 (worldwide), 19,400 (Netherlands)

Members (at 31.12.79) 16,059

Pensioners 10,211

	Dfl million
Annual Contributions	450

Annual Investment Income	350
Annual Outflow	250
Capital Value	5,100
Summary of Investments	
Equities	10%
Fixed Interest	53%
Property	37%

SHV PENSIOENFONDS

(4 Funds) 1 Rijnkade, 3511 LC Utrecht
Telephone: 030-338833

Pension Fund Administrator W.de Ruiter

Secretary Drs.C.A.P.M.de Beer

Other Pension Management Supervisory Board

Chairman of the Board of Trustees Drs.J.V.M.van Heeswijk

Trustees 8 members

Actuaries & Pension Fund Consultants Heijnis & Koelman BV; Jonker & Baars BV; Dr.W.G.J. ten Pas

Auditors Van Dien & Co

Members (at 31.12.79) 5,067

Pensioners 1,558

	Dfl million
Annual Contributions	20.6
Annual Investment Income	25.8
Gross Annual Outflow	13.3
Capital Value	327.7
Summary of Investments	
Equities	23.7
Fixed Interest	280.4
Property	15.0
Cash & Deposits	8.6

The details above cover 4 funds within the Group including those for:-
Pensioenfonds GRES, 55 Catharijnesingel, 3511 GD Utrecht (030-338833). Pension Fund Administrator-J.D.van Oenen, members 2,738

Pensioenfonds Nigoco, 2 Veerhaven, 3016 CJ Rotterdam (010-362322). Pension Fund Administrator-W.B.L.de Bijl, members-309

SPOORWEGPENSIOENFONDS

(Dutch Railways) Tiberdreef 4, postbus 2030, 3500 GA Utrecht
Telephone: 030-615561

Pension Fund Manager M.Buijense

Secretary E.E.W.Nooy

Investment Adviser P.C.Maas

Actuary Drs. W.H. van der Klink

Pension Fund Consultant P.R.Leopold

Auditors Moret & Limperg

Employees 85

Members 26,600

Pensioners 25,300

	Dfl million
Annual Contributions	195

547

NETHERLANDS

SPOORWEGPENSIOENFONDS *Continued*

Annual Investment Income	265
Gross Annual Outflow	245
Capital Value	4,900
Summary of Investments	3,055
Equities	200
Fixed Interest	2,460
Property	280
Cash & Deposits	30
Others	85

STICHTING UNILEVER PENSIOENFONDS 'PROGRESS'

's Gravelandseweg 555, 3119 XT Schiedam
Telephone: 010-737700

Pension Fund Managers Ph.Hordijk, G.O.J. van Tets

Secretary M.E.M.Aalsma

Other Pension Fund Management R.Clement, M.J.A. van der Krabben, H.P. van Soest

Chairman of Board of Trustees H.C.Wesseling

Trustees 8 members

Actuaries Smit & Bunschoten

Auditors Price Waterhouse & Co.

Employees 15,000 (Netherlands), 309,000 (Worldwide)

Members 21,000

Pensioners 6,300

	Dfl million
Annual Contributions	106
Annual Investment Income	108
Capital Value	1,553
Summary of Investments	£ million
Equities	85
Fixed Interest	137
Property	115

VROOM & DREESMAN

Spaklerweg 52, Amsterdam
Telephone: 020-595 9111

Employees 24,200

Switzerland

Government Offices

FEDERAL BUREAU OF INSURANCE
EIDGENOSSISCHE VERSICHERUNGSAMT
(Insurance Supervisory Bureau) Eigerstrasse 71, 3003 Bern 23
Telephone: 031-611111

THE FEDERAL SOCIAL INSURANCE OFFICE
(Social Security Office) Effingerstrasse 33, 3003 Bern

Associations

ASSOCIATION OF SWISS INSURANCE COMPANIES
Avenue de Rumine 13, Box 461, 1002 Lausanne
Telephone: 021-201811

INTERKANTONALER VERBAND FUR PERSONALVORSORGE
(Association of Public Sector Pension Funds)
Kornhausplatz 7, 3011 Bern
Secretary F.Haflinger

SCHWEIZERISCHER GEWERKSCHAFTSBUND
(Trade Union Association) Monbijoustrasse 61, 3000 Bern

SCHWEIZERISCHER VERBAND FUR PRIVATWIRTSCHAFTLICHE PERSONALVORSORGE
(Association of Private Company Pension Funds)
Seefeldstrasse 7, 8008 Zurich
Telephone: 01-347373
Secretary Dr.H.Walser
President V.Widmer
Members 1,000

SCHWEIZERISCHER ZENTRALVERBAND DER VERSICHERUNGSGENERALAGENTEN
Igelweid 9, 5000 Aarau
Telephone: 064-227575
and at CP 619, 1211 Geneva

VERSICHERUNGS INFORMATION
Christoffelgasse 3, 3001 Berne
Telephone: 031-226979

Insurance Companies

BASLER LEBENS-VERSICHERUNGS-GESELLSCHAFT
Dufourstrasse 38, 4002 Basel
Telephone: 061-224020

LA SUISSE LIFE INSURANCE COMPANY
Box 913, 13 Avenue de Rumine, 1001 Lausanne
Telephone: 021-201811

SWISS LIFE INSURANCE & PENSION COMPANY
General Guisan-Quai 40, 8002 Zurich 2

VITA LIFE INSURANCE COMPANY
Mythenquai 10, 8006 Zurich 2
Telephone: 01-360011

WINTERTHUR GROUP
General Guisan Strasse 40, 8401 Winterthur
Telephone: 052-851111

The Largest Companies

ALUSUISSE
Feldeggstrasse 4, 8034 Zurich
Telephone: 01-349090
Managing Director E.R.Meyer
Pensions Department Mr. Juchli

BROWN BOVERI & CIE AG
5400 Baden
Telephone: 056-751111
Chairman F.Luterbacher
Pensions Department Mr.Gamper
Employees 96,400 Switzerland 20,00

CIBA-GEIGY PENSIONSKASSE
PO Box, 4002 Basel
Telephone: 061-375915
Pension Fund Manager W. von Ehrenberg
Head of Superannuation Fund U.Kaufmann
Secretary E.Zingg
Trustees 7 company's representatives; 7 member's representatives
Employees 20,745 (Switzerland)
Members 19,241
Pensioners 5,567

	SF million
Annual Contributions	137
Annual investment Income	97
Gross Annual Outflow	87
Capital Value	2,301
Summary of Investments	
Equities	15%
Fixed Interest	43%
Property	38%

GEORG FISCHER AG
8201 Schaffhausen
Telephone: 053-8111
Managing Director R.Mayr
Employees 15,400

GEBR. SULZER AG
Zurcherstrasse 9, 8401 Winterthur
Telephone: 052-811122
Managing Director A.Schaffner
Pensions Department Dr.Schiess

Switzerland

F. HOFFMANN-LA ROCHE & COMPANY LTD

Grenzacherstrasse 124, 4002 Basel
Telephone: 061-271122

Chairman Dr.A.W.Jann

Personnel Department J.Richard

Employees 40,000

MIGROS

Limmatstrasse 152, Postfach 266, 8031 Zurich
Telephone: 01-444411

Chairman A.Gehring

Employees 35,000

OERLIKON-BUHRLE HOLDING

Hofwiesenstrasse 135, 8057 Zurich
Telephone: 01-604060

Managing Director Dr.D.Buhrie

Pensions Department Dr.Schaetzle

Employees 21,300

FONDS DE PENSIONS NESTLE

(Fondation Edouard Muller) PO Box 121,
1814 la Tour-de-Peilz
Telephone: 021-510112

Pension Fund Manager J.Golay

Secretary T.Munk

Other Pension Fund Management D.Chable,
J.F.Kunz, E.Locher, T.Munk, J.P.Steiner, J.Bomatter

Trustees 6 Company's representatives (Chairman J.Golay), 6 member's representatives

Actuaries NESTEC SA

Auditors Societe Fiduciaire Suisse

Members (at 1978) 5,018

Pensioners 2,165

	SF million
Annual Contributions	31.5
Annual Investment Income	24.0
Gross Annual Outflow	21.0
Capital Value	525.0

Summary of Investments	
Equities	5%
Fixed Interest	45%
Property	30%
Cash & Deposits	7%
Others	13%

SWISSAIR

PO Box, 8058 Zurich
Telephone: 01-8121212

Managing Director A.Baltensweiler

Pensions Department Mr.Peter

Employees 14,100

THE DIRECTOR'S GUIDE TO PENSIONS (4th edition)

Pensions are of immense importance to every organisation because they necessarily affect every employee; the choice of corporate superannuation scheme is a major responsibility for senior executives; and following a clear and judicious path through the tangle of pensions legislation is an exercise demanding caution and skill. For all these reasons, a comprehensive guide to the whole field of pensions is a necessity for any director.
The new issue of *The Director's Guide to Pensions,* to be published on July 20, is an authoritative collection of writings on the most important aspects of the subject, by a group of acknowledged experts. Among the topics they examine are such things as: pension schemes and inflation, the role of trustees, pensions for the self-employed, topping-up benefits, pensions equity plans, consultancies and the ramifications of present state schemes.

Edited by George Bull. Price: £2.00.
Free to members of the Institute of Directors

Other guides in this series include:
— Guidelines for Directors (£3.90)
— Director's Guide to Computing (£1.95)
— Director's Guide to Energy Saving (£1.00)
— Director's Guide to Storage, Handling, Freight and Distribution (£2.90)
— Director's Guide to Better Offices (£2.50)
— Director's Guide to the EEC (£1.00)

Copies available from: Miss Kate Holmes, Publications Department, Institute of Directors, 116 Pall Mall, London, SW1Y 5ED.

I enclose cheque/postal order for £
made payable to "Director Publications Ltd"'
Name
Company
Address

Compass.
You shouldn't enter the pension admin jungle without it.

Compass is the complete, flexible answer to pension administration problems.

All in one easy-to-implement computer package.

It handles all pension scheme requirements, maintains member records, and provides all information necessary to successfully control the scheme.

And it handles it quickly, accurately, securely, with the maximum reliability and the minimum work and cost.

If you're in the pension admin jungle, you need Compass.

BARIC

Please send me details of the BARIC Computerised Pensions and Superannuation System.

Name _____
Position _____
Company _____
Address _____
_____ Tel No _____

Baric Computing Services Limited,
Westfields, West Avenue, Kidsgrove,
Stoke-on-Trent ST7 1TL.
Telephone: Stoke-on-Trent (0782) 29681.

Advisers

Financial Advisers
555 (a) Banks and Merchant Banks
567 (b) Stockbrokers
579 (c) Other Financial Advisers
591 (d) Pooled Pension Funds

611 **Property Advisers**
659 **Forestry and Agricultural Land**

663 **Actuaries**

667 **Pension Fund Consultants**

689 **Insurance Companies**

709 **Miscellaneous**
(a) Associations and Professional Bodies
(b) Public Organisations
(c) Publications
(d) Employee Communications
(e) Computer and Administration Bureaux
(f) Investment Research

719 **Index of Advisers**

Funds of £1.9 billion.
What qualities stand behind our involvement?

* Performance
* Reliability
* Resources
* Personal Service
* Professionalism
* Experience
* Continuity

For further information on the full scope of our pension fund investment management services, please write to, or telephone, David Gamble.

COUNTY BANK
Merchant Bankers

11 Old Broad Street, London EC2N 1BB.
Telephone: 01-638 6000.

National Westminster Bank Group

Financial Advisers

(a) Banks & Merchant Banks
(b) Stockbrokers
(c) Other Financial Advisers
(d) Pooled Pension Funds

(a) Banks and Merchant Banks

The following section gives details of the major banks who actively advise or manage investments on behalf of Pension and Superannuation Funds. As such, this list includes all the major Merchant Banks as well as the Trustee or Investment departments of the main clearing banks and some of the larger American banks.

These details have in the main been based on information supplied by the respective banks named.

ANSBACHER INVESTMENT MANAGEMENT LTD.

Subsidiary of Henry Ansbacher & Co.Ltd.
One Noble Street, London EC2V 7JH
Telephone: 01-726 4931/4

Directors Acting for Pension Funds P.J.Duffy, R.A.Henley, R.D.Young

Employees 75

Total Value of Funds Managed £38 million

Number of Pension Fund Clients 10

Services Offered to Pension Funds Discretionary Investment management and total administrative package

Other Offices Guernsey, Bristol

Major Clients Grand Metropolitan Pension Trust Ltd., Giltspur Ltd., National Industrial Fuel Efficiency Services Ltd., Benjamin Priest & Sons (Holdings) Ltd.

ARBUTHNOT INVESTMENT MANAGEMENT SERVICES LTD.

37 Queen Street, London EC4R 1BY
Telephone: 01-236 5281

Directors Acting for Pension Funds Sir H.H.Trevor Dawson,Bt, P.Ashley Miller, FCA

Pension Fund Expert L.F.Heasman

Employees 20

Number of Pension Fund Clients 5

Services Offered to Pension Funds Investment Management

Associated Companies Arbuthnot Securities Ltd. (Unit Trust Managers) (both subsidiaries of Arbuthnot Latham Holdings Ltd)

BANK OF AMERICA INTERNATIONAL INVESTMENT MANAGEMENT SERVICE (IIMS)

St. Helen's, One Undershaft, London EC3A 8HN
Telephone: 01-236 5266

Senior Executive G.Wellesley

Director of Marketing D.H.Carter

Pension Fund Portfolio Managers M.Beckett, K.Brown, I.Datwiler

Employees 25 in London

Services Offered to Pension Funds Full range of

BANK OF AMERICA
IN LONDON

In addition to being one of the largest foreign exchange dealers in the United Kingdom, Bank of America's specialized group of investment professionals has, for more than ten years, provided clients around the world with an international investment management service.

For information on how the Bank can assist you in effectively diversifying your pension fund assets over a range of alternatives, including international stocks and bonds, precious metals and U.S. real estate, please contact:

David H. Carter or Michael Beckett,
International Investment Management Service,
Bank of America NT & SA.,
St. Helen's, One Undershaft, London EC3A 8HN.
Tel: (01) 236 5266

Hambros Investment Management Services Limited
would be delighted to make presentations to medium and large pension funds, demonstrating the advantages of using the investment ability of a large and highly experienced merchant bank.

Hambros Investment Management Services Limited

41 Bishopsgate, London EC2. 01-588 2851.

For further information, please contact Mr J. S. Cumming

(a) Banks and Merchant Banks

BANK OF AMERICA *Continued*

investment management services, both domestic and international, including fixed interest, equities, cash, property and custodianship

Other Offices and Affiliates Zurich, Luxembourg, Hong Kong, San Francisco

Other Information Investment management to captive insurance companies. Offshore trusteeship through affiliates in the Channel Islands, Bahamas, Cayman Islands and Hong Kong

BANKERS TRUST CO.

9 Queen Victoria Street, London EC4P 4DB
Telephone: 01-236 5030

Directors Acting for Pension Funds J.D.Webb (Vice President-Investments), M.J.Dwyer (Vice President-Trust Administration)

Employees 25

Total Value of Pension Funds Managed £150 million

Number of Pension Fund Clients 50

Services Offered to Pension Funds Investment Management, Trusteeship, Custodian, Administration

Other Offices U.S.A., Cayman Islands, Belgium, Germany, Switzerland, Australia

Associated Companies Bankers Trustee & Executor Co.Ltd., Bankers Trust International Ltd

BANK OF SCOTLAND INVESTMENT SERVICES

PO Box 41, 101 George Street,
Edinburgh EH2 3JH
Telephone: 031-225 1333

Manager I.A.Watt

Assistant Manager I.C.Rattray

Employees 29

Services Offered to Pension Funds Investment Management, Custodian, Trusteeship and Panel Membership

Other Offices Robert Hunter, London Representative, Bank of Scotland, 37 Threadneedle Street, London EC2R 8HH

Other Information Trustee Services, Tax Services, Unit Trust Department, Insurance Services

BARCLAYS BANK TRUST CO. LTD.

Juxon House, 94 St. Pauls Churchyard,
London EC4M 8EH
Telephone: 01-248 9155

Executive Directors D.S.G.Adam (Deputy Chairman), D.G.A.Moss, M.E.Emm

Pension Fund Experts Include D.G.A.Moss, D.Cottingham,APMI, W.H.Hilling, B.J.Cain, L.J.Juniper, A.E.Jordan, D.A.W.Killingbeck, D.G.Thomas, M.W.Phillips, B.T.Cassidy, H.L.Morgan, Miss S.J.Lamb

Gross Assets of Company £44 million. Company is a wholly owned subsidiary of Barclays Group

Total Value of Funds Managed £220 million plus

Total Value of Pension Funds Advised £200 million plus

Number of Pension Fund Clients 46

Services Offered to Pension Funds Investment management, full trusteeship, custodian trusteeship, panel membership, administration

Other Offices 28 offices situated in major centres throughout England and Wales

Parent Company Barclays Bank Ltd.

Associated Companies Barclays Merchant Bank Ltd., Barclays Unicorn Group Ltd., Barclaytrust International Ltd. (Channel Islands), Barclays Trident Management Ltd. (Hong Kong)

Areas of Specialization Money management, international investment management, unit trusts and unit linked life assurance

BARING BROTHERS & CO LIMITED

88 Leadenhall Street, London EC3A 3DT
Telephone: 01-588 2830

Directors Involved with Pension Funds E.M.P.Welman, C.W.Akers, T.G.Abell, J.A.Carwardine

Other Pension Fund Experts G.S.Cass (Assistant Director) plus 8 pension fund managers

Employees 412 (investment group 124)

Number of Pension Fund Clients 73

Amounts Involved £796 million (Pension Funds), £1,284 million (total funds under management)

Services to Pension Funds Full investment advisory and management services

Subsidiary Companies New York, Paris, Hong Kong, Singapore, Boston,

Affiliated Companies Argentina, Australia, Brazil, Guernsey, Lebanon, Malaysia, Nigeria, Switzerland, U.S.A.

Other Information Manages Funds specializing in the U.S.A., Far East, Japan and Pacific Basin, as well as exempt unit trusts for pension funds and charities

BROWN SHIPLEY & CO.LTD.

Founders Court, Lothbury, London EC2R 7HE
Telephone: 01-606 9833

Director Acting for Pension Funds T.M.Trowell

Pension Fund Experts Lord Harvey of Tasburgh, C.G.Bomford

Employees 224 (Investments 17)

Total Value of Funds Managed £70 million

Number of Pension Fund Clients 11

Services Offered to Pension Funds Investment management services, co-ordinated pension scheme service

Associated Companies Brown Shipley Asset Management Ltd. E.B. Consultants Ltd

Other Offices Jersey and Guernsey

CHARTERHOUSE JAPHET INVESTMENT MANAGEMENT LTD.

1 Paternoster Row, St. Paul's, London EC4M 7DH
Telephone: 01-248 3999

Directors Involved with Pension Funds C.W.Taylor-Young, B.C.Johnston, FPMI, N.McG. Moore

Other Pension Fund Experts N.G.Watson, E.W.Rowe, J.W.Clark

Employees 35 in investment department

Professional Management for your Pension Fund

Baillie, Gifford & Co. is an independent investment management firm engaged exclusively in the management of equity and fixed interest portfolios for institutional clients.

The firm has developed an expertise in managing the worldwide portfolios of investment trust companies, pension funds and large charities over a period of seventy years.

Baillie, Gifford & Co. provides a complete investment management service for pension funds in accordance with policies agreed with individual clients. For further information, please contact: J.G.C. White (Senior Partner) or G.J.N. Gemmell (Partner in charge of pension funds)

Baillie, Gifford & Co.
3 Glenfinlas Street, Edinburgh EH3 6YY
Telephone 031-225 2581

(a) Banks and Merchant Banks

CHARTERHOUSE JAPHET INVESTMENT MANAGEMENT LTD. *Continued*

Total Value of Pension Funds Managed £220 million

Number of Pension Fund Clients 32

Services Offered to Pension Funds Investment management (with related administrative services)

Other Offices Birmingham, Manchester, St. Helier (Jersey), Geneva, Paris, Frankfurt, Nassau, New York, Philadelphia

Associated Companies CJIM is a wholly-owned subsidiary of Charterhouse Japhet which is in turn part of the Charterhouse Group

Clients Include Allied Breweries, Civil Aviation Authority, Tarmac, University of London

CHEMICAL BANK TRUSTEE CO.LTD.

33 Old Broad Street, London EC2N 1HT
Telephone: 01-283 8171

Senior Trust Officer T.P.Carey

Value of Pension Funds Administered £85 million

Number of Pension Fund Clients 23

Services Offered to Pension Funds Fully comprehensive administration, accounting and pension payments service

Associated Companies Chemical Bank, International Investment Services; Pension Funds Investment Management

CONTINENTAL ILLINOIS LTD

Continental Bank House,
162 Queen Victoria Street, London EC4V 4BS
Telephone: 01-236 5292

Head of Investment Management and Services Division Geoffrey Osmint (Associate Director)

Services Offered to Pension Funds Investment management, international investment advisory and custodian services, short-term asset management, property advisory services, currency exchange agreements and parallel loans. In conjunction with Continental Bank Trust Department, Chicago, US Investment management, advisory and custodian services, including US Property and farm management services

COUNTY BANK LTD

11 Old Broad Street, London EC2N 1BB
Telephone: 01-638 6000

Directors Involved with Pension Funds D.Gamble, E.Barnes, M.Corlett

Pension Fund Experts 25

Employees Investment division 63

Number of Pension Fund Clients 47

Total Value of Pension Funds Managed £1.2 billion

Total Value of Pension Funds Advised £0.8 billion

Services Offered to Pension Funds Total Asset management

Parent Company National Westminster Bank Ltd

Other Offices Edinburgh, Manchester, Leeds, Birmingham, Dubai, New York

DRAYTON MONTAGU PORTFOLIO MANAGEMENT LTD

117 Old Broad Street, London EC2N 1AL
Telephone: 01-588 1750

Directors Involved with Pension Funds M.A.Vaughan-Lee, J.G.Stitt

Employees 130

Total Value of Funds Managed In excess of £900 million

Number of Pension Fund Clients 40

Services Offered to Pension Funds Complete range of investment advisory and management services, Exempt Funds for UK and overseas equities and property are available for all pension funds

Other Information Exempt Funds-equities: Midland Drayton Equity Exempt, London Fixed Interest Exempt, London North America, London Far East, London Continental, London Australian; property: see under entry for: Hanover Property, North American Property, PanEuropean Property

ROBERT FLEMING INVESTMENT MANAGEMENT LTD

8 Crosby Square, London EC3A 6AN
Telephone: 01-638 5858

Directors J.Burnett-Stuart, BA (Chairman), J.G.Archibald, CA, W.L.Banks, MA, J.D.Drysdale, BA, CA, J.R.K.Emly, FCIS, A.R.Fleming, Lord Mark Fitzalan Howard, FCIS, D.W.J.Garrett, BA, P.A.F.Gifford, BA, D.S.P.McEuen, J.A.Morrell, MA, C.K.R.Nunneley, CA, APMI, H.Shiozumi, N.G.Prowse, BA, J.E.Redwood, FCIS, W.N.Smith, FCIS, D.K. Thomas,BA,FCA

Pension Fund Investment Managers R.P.Ansell, N.W.A.Chapman, F.P.Hinks, T.G.Hyde,BA, G.K.Johns,BA, F.J.K.Ledwidge, Bsc (Econ), D.L.P.Lutyens, ACIS, C.Russell, ACA, R.G.Todd

Employees 80 (Group 350)

Total Value of Pension Funds £1,400 million; in addition, investment management covers large numbers of charities, overseas governments, unit trusts, investment trusts, insurance companies and private clients

Number of Pension Fund Clients 99

Services Offered to Pension Funds Investment management, custody of cash and securities, wide range of administrative and accounting services (but excluding pensions records and payments of pensions)

Other Offices New York, in association with Jardine Fleming & Co Ltd: Hong Kong, Tokyo, Singapore, Manila and Sydney; in association with AEGIS AG: Zurich; in association with Rowe Price-Fleming International Inc.: Baltimore

Associated Companies Robert Fleming & Co. Ltd. (100%) - corporate finance and banking; Robert Fleming Investment Trust Ltd. (100%); Robert Fleming Trustee Co. Ltd. (100%); Robert Fleming Insurance Brokers Ltd. (100%); Investment Trust Services Ltd. (100%); Rowe Price-Fleming International Inc. (50%) international investment management for U.S. clients; Tay & Thames Investment Services Ltd. (50%); Jardine Fleming & Co. Ltd. (50%) - Far East merchant bankers; AEGIS AG (25%) - international investment management from Zurich; IFA Banque (15%) - bankers

Other Information Robert Fleming Investment Management Ltd manages various specialised

Do you know someone in the City who knows about PENSION FUND MANAGEMENT SERVICE?

Do you know that we are one of the largest pension fund investment managers in Europe?

Do you know that we have a complete range of exempt unit trusts?

Do you know that our computerised administration is one of the most advanced that is available?

Do you know that our fees are as competitive as any in the market place?

Do you know that we have achieved a good consistent performance record?

Do you know that we will manage pension funds with assets or cash flow of £25,000 or above?

Do you know that you can contact Paul Talbot on 01-628 8011 for further information?

Hill Samuel Investment Management Limited
45 Beech Street London EC2P 2LX

(a) Banks and Merchant Banks

ROBERT FLEMING INVESTMENT MANAGEMENT LTD
Continued

funds investing in overseas markets, particularly US, Japan and Far East; (e.g. Fleming American Exempt Fund and Fleming Japanese Exempt Fund); Robert Fleming & Co Ltd manages Fleming Property Unit Trust; Robert Fleming Investment Management Ltd is a wholly owned subsidiary of Robert Fleming Holdings Ltd.

ANTONY GIBBS INVESTMENT MANAGEMENT LTD.

3 Frederick's Place, Old Jewry, London EC2R 8HD
Telephone: 01-588 4111

Director Acting for Pension Funds D.E.Franklin (Managing Director)

Pension Fund Expert N.L.Wilson

Employees 15

Total Value of Funds Managed £27 million

Total Value of Funds Advised £15 million

Number of Pension Fund Clients 11

Services Offered to Pension Funds Investment management, investment administration, banking services, tax claims, investment advisory services

Associated Company Antony Gibbs Holdings Ltd.

Other Information Specialists in investment management for gross funds

GUINNESS MAHON & CO LTD

32 St. Mary-at-Hill, London EC3P 3AJ
Telephone: 01-623 9333

Directors acting for Pension Funds Sir David B.Hill-Wood

Pension Fund Experts 2

Employees 8 (investment management)

Total Value of Funds Managed £40 million

Number of Pension Fund Clients 5

Services Offered to Pension Funds Trustee services, administration, full investment management service

Other Offices Guernsey, Dublin, Cayman, Zurich, Singapore

Associated Companies Lewis & Peat Group Ltd, Fenchurch Insurance Brokers Group Ltd

HAMBROS BANK LTD

41 Bishopsgate, London EC2P 2AA
Telephone: 01-588 2851

Directors acting for Pension Funds P.D.Hill-Wood, J.S.Cumming, M.St. Giles, D.P.Gibbs

Pension Fund Experts All Pension Fund Management Services are supplied by Hambros Investment Management Services Ltd, a wholly owned subsidiary of the Bank. The Director of HIMS Ltd responsible for services to Pension Funds is J.S.Cumming, BA (Cantab), CA

Employees 140 (total investment staff)

Total Funds Managed £660 million

Pension Funds Managed £410 million

Pension Funds Advised £250 million

Number of Pension Fund Clients 31

Services Offered to Pension Funds Full management services including administration, stock office services, banking and trustee functions. The Allied Hambro Group offers four exempt unit trusts for investment by pension funds-The Exempt Smaller Companies Fund, The U.S.A. Exempt Fund, The Far East Exempt Fund and The Income Exempt Fund

Other Offices of Hambros Bank Ltd 67 Pall Mall, London SW1Y 5EU, Jersey, Athens, Helsinki, Holland, Hong Kong, Milan, New York, Paris, Sydney and Zurich

Associated Companies Berkeley Hambro Property Co Ltd. Hambro Life Assurance Ltd, Mitsui Finance Europe Ltd.

Other Information Clients include the following: Hambros Bank Staff Pension Fund, Royal National Pension Fund for Nurses (an insurance company), British Airports Authority Superannuation Scheme and Civil Aviation Authority Superannuation Scheme, Furness Withy Pension Funds

HILL SAMUEL INVESTMENT MANAGEMENT LTD

45 Beech Street, London EC2P 2LX
Telephone: 01-628 8011

Directors Acting for Pension Funds G.R.H.Kitson, MA (Managing Director), D.S.Allison, MA, H.D.Andrews, BSc, P.C.Axten, R.D.Green, BA, R.W.Lewis, APMI, ACII, A.M.Summers,BA

Other Pension Fund Experts R.A.Cawdron, ACA, M.D.Gordon, FCA, R.J. Aldworth, AIB, G.M.Harvey, P.T.Bucknell, P.F.G.V. Sich, Miss E.C.Rae,MA, M.I.Henderson, BA, J.S.Wood

Employees 157

Total Value of Funds Managed £1,303 million

Total Value of Funds Advised £1,198 million

Number of Pension Fund Clients 150

Services Offered to Pension Funds Hill Samuel Investment Management Ltd. offers a complete range of investment management and advisory services

Other Office Dublin

Associated Companies Hill Samuel Investment Management Ltd. is part of the Hill Samuel Group which provides financial services worldwide. Together with another company in the Group, Hill Samuel Investment Management International, based in Switzerland, Hill Samuel Investment Management Ltd. is able to provide a full international investment management service

Other Information Hill Samuel Investment Management's pension fund service emphasises personal service and attention to individual requirements, with an administrative back-up designed to be comprehensive and straightforward. Funds managed vary widely in size, ranging from those having annual contributions in excess of £25,000 to nineteen having a portfolio value of more than £15 million. 5 exempt unit trusts are available. 1) Hill Samuel Property Unit Trust, 2) Hill Samuel Agricultural Property Unit Trust, 3) Hill Samuel Beech Street Trust, 4) Hill Samuel General Exempt Trust, 5) Hill Samuel Worldwide Trust

Lazards offer pension funds maximum potential for a good return. Our long experience, comprehensive service and personal attention are all reasons why.

Flexibility is also an important factor. Lazards emphasize flexibility in their management approach to allow each pension fund to develop strength by taking advantage of the changing character of many markets.

Be certain your pension fund receives this kind of attention with specific tailoring to your long-term needs. Ring Geoffrey Dutton at Lazards, 01-588 2721.

Lazard Brothers & Co., Limited

21 Moorfields, London EC2P 2HT
Telex: General 886438

Lazard Brothers & Co., Limited

(a) Banks and Merchant Banks

INDUSTRIAL & COMMERCIAL FINANCE CORPORATION LTD.

91 Waterloo Road, London SE1 8XP
Telephone: 01-928 7822

Investment Manager John Evans

Other Pension Fund Experts Pension Funds are managed by ICFC's Investment Department

Total Employees 8

Value of Pension Funds Managed £90 million

Pension Fund Clients 8

Services Offered to Pension Funds Discretionary investment management of pension funds and the administration of investments, if required

Other offices Nationwide

Other information Also management of two listed Investment Trusts. Specialists in investment in small and medium sized companies

KEYSER ULLMANN PENSIONS MANAGEMENT LTD

25 Milk Street, London EC2V 8JE
Telephone: 01-606 7070

Directors Acting for Pension Funds R.A.Good, P.H.Campbell, W.J.C.Douie R.W.Seabrook

Employees Approx 50 in investment functions

Total Value of Funds Managed Group manages £200 million

Services Offered to Pension Funds Investment management and professional and technical services associated with Pension Funds

Other Information Specialists in investment in smaller U.K. quoted companies

KLEINWORT BENSON INVESTMENT MANAGEMENT LTD

20 Fenchurch Street, London EC3P 3DB
Telephone: 01-623 8000

Directors Acting for Pension Funds J.F.H.Trott, S.B.Craig, D.A.C.Lawrence, A.C.Mortimer, R.N.Young

Pension Fund Experts 11 executives

Employees 143

Total Value of Funds Managed £600 million

Total Value of Funds Advised £110 million

Number of Pension Fund Clients 54

Services Offered to Pension Funds Full range of investment management services and supporting administrative services

Other Offices Network of offices in the main financial centres of the world. Investment management personnel in Bremen, Brussels, Geneva, Hong Kong, New York, Tokyo

Associated Companies Kleinwort Benson Unit Managers Ltd., Kleinwort Benson International Investment Ltd., Kleinwort Benson Farmland Trust (Managers) Ltd.

LAZARD SECURITIES LTD

21 Moorfields, London EC2P 2HT
Telephone: 01-588 2721

Directors Acting for Pension Funds Geoffrey P.Dutton, Dennis A.Roberts (Managing)

Pension Fund Experts David Ives, Tony Puckridge

Employees 25 (of these, 12 are predominantly involved in pension fund management)

Total Value of Funds Managed £500 million

Total Value of Funds Advised £1,250 million

Number of Pension Fund Clients 45

Services Offered to Pension Funds Full range of investment management and ancilliary administrative and taxation services

Parent Company S.Pearson & Son Ltd via Lazard Brothers & Co Ltd

Associated Companies Lazard Freres et Cie, Paris; Lazard Freres & Co, New York; Richard Daus & Co, Frankfurt; Lazards-Hong Kong; Lazards Seoul (Sth. Korea)

Other Information Exempt Unit Trusts for investment in North America and in the Far Eastern equity markets and also Property

LLOYDS BANK LTD, INVESTMENT DEPARTMENT

34 Threadneedle Street, London EC2R 8AX
Telephone: 01-623 1288

Directors Acting for Pension Funds H.E.S.Morris (Chief Investment Manager), M.L.Jones, B.T.Ackerman (Assistant Chief Investment Managers)

Pension Fund Experts Investment managers: 14 plus a team of 10 U.K. and Overseas research analysts

Employees 74

Total Value of Funds Managed £1,050 million

Total Value of Funds Advised £250 million

Number of Pension Fund Clients 35

Services Offered to Pension Funds Investment management of fixed interest, equities, property and cash. Exempt Unit Trust

Associated Companies Part of Lloyds Bank Group

MIDLAND BANK TRUST CO LTD

6 Threadneedle Street, London EC2R 8BB
Telephone: 01-606 9911

Director and General Manager P.S.Hargreaves

Pension Fund Specialists P.S.Roots (Manager, Corporate Services Branch), J.W.Hickman (Fund Manager), S.J.P.Reed (Assistant Investment Manager)

Total Employees 1,200

Total Value of Pension Funds £1,956 (including Custodianships)

Number of Pension Fund Clients 63

Services Offered to Pension Funds Full trusteeships, custodianship services, investment advice, investment management

Other Offices Complete national branch network

Associated Companies Part of Midland Bank Group

Other Information The custodianship and trustee services provided to Pension Funds are also available to other institutions, including Insurance Companies, Unit Trusts etc. The Company also provides a service as a trustee and administrator of Employee Profit Sharing Schemes.

(a) Banks and Merchant Banks

MORGAN GRENFELL & CO LTD

23 Great Winchester Street, London EC2P 2AX
Telephone: 01-588 4545

Directors Acting for Pension Funds H.G.Gorell Barnes (Head of Investment Division), J.H.L.Norton, P.J.Dawney, M.J.Meyrick

Senior Pension Fund Manager B.D.Wood

Employees 730 - 150 in investment division

Total Value of Pension Funds Managed Over £1.2 billion

Total Value of Pension Funds Advised Over £600 million

Number of Pension Fund Clients 76

Services Offered to Pension Funds Full range of investment management services

Other Offices Athens, Bogota, Cairo, Caracas, Edinburgh, Frankfurt, Geneva, Guernsey, Jersey Madrid, Manila, Milan, Moscow, New York, Paris, Quito, Singapore, Sydney, Tehran

Associated Companies Tokai Kyowa Morgan Grenfell Ltd., Eupic Services BV, MWP Incentives Ltd., Araven Finance Ltd.

Other Information Exempt unit trusts for pension funds and charities: Jersey Exempt International Fund, Industrial and Commercial Property Unit Trust, Morgan Grenfell Special Exempt Fund

Major Pension Fund Clients Include UK pension funds of international companies-Ford, International Nickel, Mobil Oil, UK Pension Funds of Allied Breweries, BICC, ICL, Post Office, Plessey, United Biscuits, Rank Hovis McDougall and London Transport

MORGAN GUARANTY TRUST CO OF NEW YORK

49 Berkeley Square, 30 Throgmorton Street, London EC2N 2DT
Telephone: 01-600 2300

Head of London Investment Division Martin E. Harrison

Pension Fund Experts 21 investment and research officers

Employees 70

Total Value of Funds Managed £558 million

Total Value of Funds Advised £27 million

Number of Pension Fund Clients 20

Services Offered to Pension Funds Full investment management service

Other Investment Offices 9 West 57th Street, New York, NY 10019; 14 Place Vendome, 75001 Paris; J.P.Morgan (Suisse) SA, 7 Rue des Alpes, 1201 Geneva; New Yuraku-cho Building, 12-1 1-chome, Yuraku-cho, Chiyoda-ku, Tokyo; Alexandra House, 16-20 Chater Road, Hong Kong

Other Information Emphasis on management of internationally diversified bond and equity portfolios in Europe, Pacific Basin economies and North America. Major corporate, national and international clients are drawn from 13 different countries

NATIONAL GIROBANK

Bootle, Merseyside GIR 0AA
Telephone: 051-966 2216

Directors S. Wainwright (Managing Director), A.K.Hanton (Senior Director), H.G.Robson,OBE, (Marketing Director), D.A.Baggaley (Finance Director)

Pension Payment Facilities Experts R.C.Marriott, J.H.N.Cheek, W.G.Partington, W.Guy, J.Slimon, D.Hindle, S.F.Underwood and over 50 consultant staff

Product Manager D.J.C.Sutton

Employees 5,500

Number of Pension Clients Over 200

Services Offered to Pension Funds Facilities for paying pensions by direct credits to personal bank accounts, or by open cheque, enabling beneficiaries to obtain cash at their local Post Office, Methods of input include credit transfer via BACS and usual documentation

Other Offices 10 Milk Street, London EC2V 8JH (01-600 6020); Edinburgh, Belfast, Leeds, Birmingham, Branches at over 20,000 Post Offices

Other Information Clients include many major organisations e.g. ICI, Ford, Marks & Spencer, Post Office, Rolls Royce, Rank Organisation. The facilities are used to make over 36 million payments per annum of wages, salaries or pensions

NATIONAL WESTMINSTER BANK LTD

Trustee and Income Tax Department, Chief Office, Little John Street, Bristol BS99 7NQ
Telephone: 0272 293841

Head of Department K.W.McGregor

Investment Manager J.F.Morton

Other Pension Fund Experts 7 Investment Managers and supporting staff

Employees 64 Investment staff plus administrative staff

Total Value of Funds Managed or Advised £2,500 million (including custodian functions)

Number of Pension Fund Clients 100 (including custodian functions)

Services Offered to Pension Funds Investment management, administrative, tax, custody of assets

Other Offices Country-wide branch network

Associated Companies Trust companies in the Channel Islands and the Isle of Man, Trust Corporation of Bahamas, Nassau

Other Information This type of business is mainly concerned with custodian functions. The Investment Management Service covers the provision of a complete package of investment management and custodian facilities.

N.M.ROTHSCHILD ASSET MANAGEMENT LTD

PO Box 185, New Court, St. Swithin's Lane, London EC4P 4DU
Telephone: 01-626 4356

Directors Acting for Pension Funds Nicolas McAndrew (Managing Director), James Roe, Richard Chandler, David Leathers, John Redwood

Pension Fund Experts 8 fund managers plus supporting research and administrative staff

Employees 150

Total Value of Pension Funds Managed £720 million

(a) Banks and Merchant Banks

N.M.ROTHSCHILD ASSET MANAGEMENT LTD *Continued*

Number of Pension Fund Clients 73

Services Offered to Pension Funds Day-to-day management, strategic reviews, valuations, performance data, full custodian and banking service, seminars, presentations to trustees and employee representations

Other Offices New York, Zurich, Hong Kong, Singapore, Guernsey

Other Information Specialist investment vehicles available for self managed funds include: (a) international-American, Japanese, Hong Kong, Commodities; (b) domestic-property, smaller companies, gilt-edged. Property services include creation and management of directly held property portfolios

ROYAL BANK OF SCOTLAND LTD

Trustee and Investment Office, PO Box 40, 31 St. Andrew Square, Edinburgh EH2 2PS
Telephone: 031-556 8555

Head Office: 42 St.Andrew Square, Edinburgh EH2 2YE

General Manager (Trustee & Investment) W.C.T.Crosby

Investment Manager R.J.Herkes

Senior Assistant Investment Manager R.W.Taylor

Employees 24 investment staff

Total Value of Pension Funds Managed Over £300 million

Number of Pension Fund Clients 6

Services Offered to Pension Funds Full Investment Management Service, Nominee Service and collection of dividends are included in normal service and charge. Tax reclamation normally charged at small percentage of amount recovered. Trusteeship of pension funds is undertaken at a negotiable fee within a maximum of 60p per cent per annum of value of fund. Payment of benefits can be undertaken-present charges 15p per pensioner subject to minimum of £15.00 per payment date plus a probable take-on charge according to work involved

Other Investment Offices London, Glasgow

THE ROYAL TRUST CO OF CANADA

Royal Trust House, 48-50 Cannon Street, London EC4N 6LD
Telephone: 01-236 6044

Managing Director R.S.Traquair

Associate Director (Investment) A.J.Hall

Investment Manager A.J.Albert

Senior Pensions Consultant T.J.Downing

Employees 125

Total Value of Pension Funds Managed £40 million

Total Value of Pension Funds Advised £11 million

Total Value of Funds Managed by Group £2.5 billion

Number of Pension Fund Clients 37

Services Offered to Pension Funds Investment management, trusteeship, employee benefit consultancy, administration, trust accountancy, staff liaison and education, documentation of schemes, broking advice on insured schemes

Other Offices Dublin, Jersey, Isle of Man (and offices throughout Canada and in Bahamas, Bermuda, Cayman Islands, Switzerland and the United States)

Associated Companies The Royal Trustco Ltd., The Royal Trust Corporation of Canada, The Royal Trust Co of Canada (CI) Ltd, The Royal Trust Bank (Isle of Man), The Royal Trust Bank (Ireland) Ltd, The Royal Trust Co Fund Management Ltd, The Royal Trust Co of Canada (CI)Fund Management Ltd, QUEST Fund Management Ltd, Bahamas International Trust Co Ltd, Cayman International Trust Co Ltd, The International Trust Co of Bermuda, The Royal Trust Company AG, The Royal Trust Bank Corporation, RoyTrust Financial Services Ltd.

Other Information Emphasis on international investment for Pension Funds where applicable. Royal Trust Exempt International Fund-a vehicle for international investment for UK pension funds

SAMUEL MONTAGU

See **DRAYTON MONTAGU PORTFOLIO MANAGEMENT LTD.**

J.HENRY SCHRODER WAGG & CO LTD

120 Cheapside, London EC2V 6DS
Telephone: 01-588 4000

Directors Acting for Pension Funds G.H.Popham, Sir Richard Baker Wilbraham,BT, J.A.de Havilland, J.A.Hill, R.C.E.Morgan, D.J.Mumford, D.Walters, C.J.Govett

Pension Fund Experts 10 pension fund managers

Employees 130 investment staff

Total Value of Funds Managed or Advised £1,388 million

Number of Pension Fund Clients 92

Services Offered to Pension Funds Full investment management, including nominee and related administrative services

Other Offices New York, Tokyo, Zurich

Associated Companies Schroders & Chartered Ltd. Hong Kong; Schroder Darling & Co Ltd, Australia; Singapore International Merchant Bankers Ltd

SINGER & FRIEDLANDER LTD

20 Cannon Street, London EC4M 6XA
Telephone: 01-248 9646

Other Offices Birmingham, Glasgow, Leeds and Nottingham

Associated Company Subsidiary of C.T.Bowring & Co. Ltd.

ULSTER BANK LTD

Investment Division, PO Box 233, Waring Street, Belfast BT1 2ER
Telephone: 0232 35232

Pension Fund Experts 5

Employees 13

Number of Pension Fund Clients 4

Services Offered to Pension Funds Complete investment and administration

(a) Banks and Merchant Banks

ULSTER BANK LTD Continued

Other Office College Green, Dublin 2

Parent Company National Westminster Bank Ltd

WARBURG INVESTMENT MANAGEMENT LTD

St. Albans House, Goldsmith Street,
London EC2P 2DZ
Telephone: 01-600 4555

Directors Acting for Pension Funds
A.R.W.Smithers, D.W.J.Price, R.S.Malnick, L.S.Licht, P.G.P.Dew, M.A.Oakeshott, J.C.Spink, S.A.Zimmerman

Other Pension Fund Experts 10 fund managers

Employees 135

Total Value of Pension Funds Managed £1,350 million

Number of Pension Fund Clients 99 clients, 115 pension funds

Services Offered to Pension Funds Complete management service for the investment of Pension Fund Assets

Associated Companies S.G.Warburg & Co Ltd, Warburg Investment Management Jersey Ltd, Warburg Investment Management (Isle of Man) Ltd, Warburg Investment Management Bermuda Ltd, Mercury Fund Managers Ltd, Warburg Investment Management International Ltd, Co-operative Investment Management Ltd

Other Information (1) Warburg Investment Management Ltd. manages 3 exempt unit trusts: Mercury Exempt Fund, Co-operative Pension Fund Unit Trust, Stewart Wrightson Exempt Funds. It also manages Common Market Trust Ltd. (£25.7 million), Transatlantic Market Trust Ltd. (£13.8 million), Selected Market Trust Ltd. (£8.7 million), all of which are open-ended Jersey funds.

(2) Warburg Investment Management International Ltd.'s major clients are U.S. tax exempt funds and captive insurance companies. It is registered with SEC. It offers U.S. tax clients specialist investment services in international bond and equity markets. It has 20 accounts, 9 of which are pension funds. The directors are A.R.W.Smithers, R.O.Bernays, Mrs.C.C.Brooke, A.W.Baker, B.J.Weiss. Total employees are 20 and there is a New York office

WILLIAM & GLYN'S BANK LTD

Investment Services, 20 Birchin Lane,
London EC3P 3DP
Telephone: 01-626 4356

Head of Investment Services L.J.Gant

Employees 55 investment services staff, 6,190 bank staff

Total Value of Funds Managed or Advised £450 million

Number of Pension Fund Clients 6

(b) Stockbrokers

The following list contains details of all the major firms of stockbrokers as well as certain smaller ones actively advising Pension Funds. As such it includes details of all the firms with 10 or more partners.
The information has been obtained either directly from the firms named or from the list of 'Firms and Companies' published by The Stock Exchange. It should be noted that some of these firms have a predominantly private clientele and only very few actively manage Pension Funds.

BEARDSLEY BISHOP ESCOMBE
21 New Street, London EC2M 4UN
Telephone: 01-283 2545

Senior Partner C.B.Vertue

Employees 108

Other Offices Worcester, Hereford, Cheltenham and Tunbridge Wells

Associated Company Beardsley Financial Services Ltd.

Areas of Specialisation Textiles, timber importers, carpet manufacturers, employment agencies, chemicals

BELL, LAWRIE, MACGREGOR & CO
PO Box 8, Erskine House, 68-73 Queen Street, Edinburgh EH2 2AE
Telephone: 031-225 2566

Senior Partner G.R.Simpson

Partners Acting for Pension Funds J.W.M.M.Richard, D.J.H.McIntosh

Manager, Management Services A.T.M.Henderson

Other Offices Dumfries

BREWIN DOLPHIN & CO
49 Gray's Inn Road, London WC1X 8PP
Telephone: 01-405 8711

Senior Partner G.E.Ruggles-Brise

Finance Partner G.S.Goodsir

BUCKMASTER & MOORE
The Stock Exchange, London EC2P 2JT
Telephone: 01-588 2868

Senior Partner O.N.Dawson

Partners Acting for Pension Funds O.N.Dawson, I.T.McEwan, J.R.Mathias

Other Pension Fund Expert Ian Wright, AIA

Employees 150

Number of Pension Fund Clients 15 discretionary funds, 1 advised fund

Value of Funds Managed £80 million

Value of Funds Advised £1 million

Associated Companies Cecogest (European research organisation based in Paris)

Other Information Specialists in most of the major overseas markets

CAPEL-CURE MYERS LTD
Bath House, Holborn Viaduct, London EC1A 2EU
Telephone: 01-236 5080

Chairman A.C.Hugh Smith

Director Acting for Pension Funds P.M.T.Jones

Other Pension Fund Experts D.I.A.McKechnie (Senior Fund Manager), R.H.Pain,FIA, D.B.Carlisle, FIA

Employees 230

Number of Pension Fund Clients 11 (Larger Discretionary Funds)

Value of Funds Managed or Advised £114 million

Other Offices Edinburgh

Associated Companies Capel-Cure Myers Financial Services Ltd, Capel-Cure Myers (Scotland) Ltd

Other Information Organisation of a pension scheme; review of existing benefits structure; updating service on changes in legislation; advice on individual or group schemes for senior management

JAMES CAPEL & CO
Winchester House, 100 Old Broad Street, London EC2N 1BQ
Telephone: 01-588 6010

Senior Partner D.K.F.Heathcote

Partners/Executives Acting for Pension Funds T.R.Winser, P.G.Foster, P.E.Cornish

Employees 400

Number of Pension Fund Clients 13 (Discretionary Funds);
5 (Advised Funds)

Value of Funds Managed £14 million

Value of Funds Advised £46 million

Other Offices Jersey, Hong Kong, Singapore, Luxembourg

Associated Companies James Capel Unit Trust Management Ltd

Services Offered to Pension Funds Comprehensive stockbroking service (UK and Overseas), portfolio management of small self administered Pension Funds

Other Information Research back-up in all areas including UK fixed interest and equities, Eurobonds and mining, overseas markets

CARR, SEBAG & CO.
Ocean House, 10-12 Little Trinity Lane, London EC4P 4LB
Telephone: 01-248 2090

Senior Partner A.C.Gilmour

Partners Acting for Pension Funds T.K.Thornton, M.P.J.Cotton

Other Pension Fund Experts A.W.Franks, B.D.Welch

Employees 350

Other Offices Geneva, Hong Kong, Manila, Tokyo, San Francisco

Services Offered to Pension Funds Complete discretionary or advisory service for the

Henry Cooke, Lumsden & Co.

MEMBERS OF THE STOCK EXCHANGE

OUR SPECIALIST RESEARCH COVERAGE
includes
ENGINEERING   TEXTILES
AGENCY MAIL ORDER
and NORTHERN BASED COMPANIES

PO BOX 369
ARKWRIGHT HOUSE
PARSONAGE GARDENS
MANCHESTER M60 3AH
Telephone: 061-834 2332
Telex: 667783

CITY WALL HOUSE
14/16 FINSBURY STREET
LONDON EC2Y 9DR
Telephone: 01-628 0411
Telex: 888417

SHEPPARDS AND CHASE

Members of The Stock Exchange since 1827

Investment managers and advisers to pension funds for over 25 years

Clements House, Gresham Street, London EC2V 7AU
Telephone: 01-606 8099

(b) Stockbrokers

CARR, SEBAG & CO. Continued

management and investment of pension fund money, including advice on investment policy and strategy, individual stock selection, dealing, settlement and registration, valuations and performance assessment

CAZENOVE & CO

12 Tokenhouse Yard, London EC2R 7AN
Telephone: 01-588 2828

Senior Partners J.Kemp-Welch, A.D.A.W.Forbes

Pension Fund Partners G.J.Chandler, Lord Faringdon, U.D.Barnett, H.de L. Cazenove, D.L.Mayhew, N.A.Gold

Other Offices Sydney, Johannesburg, Hong Kong, San Francisco, New York, Geneva

CHAMBERS & REMINGTON

85 New Hall Street, Birmingham B3 1LS
Telephone: 021-236 2577

Senior & Finance & Administration Partner K.J.Thurstans, FCA

Dealing Partner C.D.H.Blackshaw

Employees 16

Number of Pension Fund Clients 12 (approx)

Other Information Specialist contact and knowledge of Midlands companies

CHARLTON, SEAL, DIMMOCK & CO

76 Cross Street, Manchester M60 2EP
Telephone: 061-832 3488

Senior Partner J.Diggle, MA, TD

Partners Acting for Pension Funds G.Harrison, W.L.Beevers

Other Pension Fund Experts D.W.Youngman, J.B.Smith, J.M.Scott

Employees 60

Number of Pension Fund Clients 34

Other Office Austin Friars House, 2-6 Austin Friars, London EC2N 2EE (01-588 2686)

Associated Companies Mattinson Ginty & Partners Ltd, Four Yards Services Ltd, Four Yards Estates, Charlton Seal (Jersey)

CONI, GILBERT & SANKEY

15 Throgmorton Avenue, London EC2N 2DH
Telephone: 01-638 8871

Senior Partner M.F.Somerset Leeke

Other Offices 3 Athol Street, Douglas, Isle of Man (27134); 60 Waterloo Road, Wolverhampton (0902-28711); Grosvenor House, 14 Bennets Hill, Birmingham B2 5SE (021-643 7861); Britannic Assurance Building, 29 St. Nicholas Street, Bristol (0272-22171)

HENRY COOKE, LUMSDEN & CO.

P.O.Box 369, Arkwright House, Parsonage Gardens, Manchester M60 3AH
Telephone: 061-834 2332

Senior Partner David I.Hunter

Partners Acting for Pension Funds David I.Hunter, David H.Adams, Geoffry W.Furness, Julian R.Grice, David A.Pitt, David C.Walton

Other Pension Fund Experts Richard H.Prestwich, Edward J.Raphael, Richard V.Thompson

Employees 142

Number of Pension Fund Clients 25 (Advised Funds)

Value of Funds Advised £47 million

Other Offices City Wall House, 14-16 Finsbury Street, London EC2Y 9DR (01-628 0411)

Associated Companies Henry Cooke, Plan Invest Ltd., National Westminster House, Market Place, Macclesfield SK10 1EA; Henry Cooke, Estridge (Pensions) Ltd., Arkwright House, Parsonage Gardens, Manchester M60 3AH

Other Information Specialised research coverage of textiles, engineering, mail order and Northern based companies

DE ZOETE & BEVAN

25 Finsbury Circus, London EC2M 7EE
Telephone: 01-588 4141

Senior Partner S.J.Titcomb,FCA

Pension Fund Partners D.A.Foster,APMI, A.T.Grant, FFA,FIA, P.R.Withers Green

Employees 300 (the firm), 25 (pension fund department)

Number of Pension Fund Clients Significant

Value of Funds Managed and Advised Significant

Services Offered to Pension Funds A comprehensive investment advisory/management service tailored to suit the requirements of trustees

DUFF STOOP & CO.

Capital House, 22 City Road, London EC1Y 2AJ
Telephone: 01-628 5070

Senior Partner L.E.Marshall

Finance Partner A.E.C.Chapman

DUNKLEY MARSHALL

4 London Wall Buildings, London EC2M 5NX
Telephone: 01-638 1282

Senior Partner L.E.Marshall

EARNSHAW, HAES & SONS

17 Tokenhouse Yard, London EC2R 7LB
Telephone: 01-638 1282

Senior Partner L.E.Marshall

Finance Partner J.A.Redgrave

EASTON, WATSON & SMITH

26 West Nile Street, Glasgow G1 2PG
Telephone: 041-248 5781

Senior Partner J.C.S.A.Fleming

Finance Partner D.L.M.Stewart

Employees 60

Other Offices Edinburgh, Stirling, Perth

Associated Company E.W.S. Nominees

Areas of Specialisaztion Scottish Companies, Leisure Sector, Bond management

(b) Stockbrokers

FIELDING, NEWSON-SMITH & CO
Garrard House, 31 Gresham Street,
London EC2V 7DX
Telephone: 01-606 7711

Senior Partner J.Dundas Hamilton

Pension Fund Department Partners P.C.Curtis, C.S.Clayton, H.E.Fisher

Consultants R.A.Bourne, K.T.Kearney

Executive J.C.Whitaker

Employees 189

Other Information Exempt Property unit Trust Service Copies of 'The Investments of Pension Funds' are available on request

J.M.FINN & CO
Salisbury House, London Wall, London EC2M 5TA
Telephone: 01-626 9688

Senior Partner P.W.Freeman

Finance & Administration Partner G.W.Ball

FOSTER & BRAITHWAITE
22 Austin Friars, London EC2N 2BU
Telephone: 01-588 6111

Senior Partner J.N.Braithwaite

Finance Partner M.B.Savory

Dealing Member R.Wilby

Other Pension Fund Experts T.H.Williams, S.Lawson

Employees 60

Number of Pension Fund Clients 7

Services Offered to Pension Funds Investment Management

GALLOWAY & PEARSON
Warnford Court, Throgmorton Street, London EC2
Telephone: 01-628 8211

Senior Partner J.R.W.Lingard

Finance Partner D.H.Starling

GILBERT ELIOTT & CO
381-399 Salisbury House, London Wall,
London EC2M 5SB
Telephone: 01-628 6782

Senior Partner M.E.Hodge

Finance & Administration Partner G.M.S.Baylis

PANMURE GORDON & CO
9 Moorfields Highwalk, London EC2Y 9DS
Telephone: 01-638 4010

Chief Executive Partner J.G.Lithiby

Partners Acting for Pension Funds A.T.Jamieson, FFA, R.M.S.Parsons

Other Pension Fund Expert K.Davies

Employees 140

Number of Pension Fund Clients 100

Other Information Specialists in corporate finance, provision of investment research and management services

W.GREENWELL & CO.
Bow Bells House, Bread Street, London EC4M 9EL
Telephone: 01-236 2040

Joint Senior Partners R.H.Lawson, G.T.Pepper

Finance Partner N.S.King

R.C.GREIG & CO
139 St. Vincent Street, Glasgow G2 5JP
Telephone: 041-221 8103

Senior Partner D.C.Greig

Partners Acting for Pension Funds R.M.Sherriff, J.D.T.Greenall, C.H.Brown

Employees 45

Number of Pension Fund Clients 18

Other Office 13th Floor, The Stock Exchange, London EC2N 1HH

Specialisation Scottish companies, small companies, oil

GRENFELL AND COLEGRAVE
55/61 Moorgate, London EC2R 6OR
Telephone: 01-628 6044

Senior Partner T.H.Joly de Lotbiniere

Finance Partner S.N.B.Leishman

Administration Partner P.D.Dawkins

Employees 140

Number of Pension Fund Clients 15 wholly served

GRIEVESON GRANT & CO
PO Box 191, 59 Gresham Street,
London EC2P 2DS
Telephone: 01-606 4433

Senior Partner A.R.D.Rutherford

Partners Acting for Pension Funds P.J.Ellis, E.J.A.Vaughan, K.Barclay-Brown, M.B.Shortt, R.J.H.D.Palmer

Other Pension Fund Experts J.A.Willard, D.J.Harris, S.M.Butler, A.F.Cosgrove

Other Offices Union House, Tunbridge Wells, Kent, Guernsey C.I., Tokyo and Boston

Associated Companies Grieveson Management Co. Ltd., Grieveson Grant Financial Services Ltd, Grieveson Grant International Ltd

HALLIDAY, SIMPSON & CO.
P.O.Box 412, 98 King Street,
Manchester M60 2HA
Telephone: 061-832 8471

Partners in Charge of Institutional Sales D.M.Garner, G.M.Jackson

Other Pension Fund Expert R.L.Torr

Employees 90

Pension Fund Clients 14

Discretionary Funds 6

Advised Funds 20

Other Offices London, Colwyn Bay, Bexhill-on-sea, Ramsey,IOM, St.Helier,Jersey

Associated Companies Manchester Securities, J.F.Williams (Financial Mgt.) Ltd.

(b) Stockbrokers

HANSON & CO
6 Regent Terrace, South Parade,
Doncaster,S.Yorks.DN1 2EL
Telephone: 0302-23223

Senior Partner A.Mathews

Finance Partner A.Raymond Holt

HARRIS, ALLDAY, LEA & BROOKS
Stock Exchange Buildings,
33 Great Charles Street, Birmingham B3 3JN
Telephone: 021-233 1222

Senior Partner C.P.Harris, FCA

Partners Acting for Pension Funds A.J.Whitehead, J.E.B.Brooks, P.S.Watts

Other Pension Fund Experts A.W.Bond, P.M.Marks

Employees 62

Number of Pension Fund Clients 12 (advised funds)

Other Offices Warnford Court, Throgmorton Street, London EC2 (01-628 0261); Elgin House, West Bar, Banbury, Oxon (0295 2562)

Associated Company Halcyon Financial Services Ltd. (Investment & Insurance Advisory Service)

Areas of Specialization Midland Companies Electronics

HEDDERWICK, STIRLING, GRUMBAR & CO
1 Moorgate, London EC2R 6AA
Telephone: 01-600 4011

Senior Partner R.A.R.Hedderwick

Finance Partner C.B.Franklin

Administration Partner W.G.G.Hunt

Partners in Charge of Institutional Sales R.Althaus, C.H.Curtis, J.Garner, S.P.Meredith Hardy, Sir Peter Troubridge

HENDERSON CROSTHWAITE & CO
194-200 Bishopsgate, London EC2M 4LL
Telephone: 01-283 8577

Senior Partner A.K.Barlow

Partners Acting for Pension Funds K.A.Crosthwaite, K.M.H.Millar, J.A.Price, M.E.Clayton, M.R.Riley, P.E.Ross, M.F.Cartwright, B.W.M.Cowper, C.J.Heath, P.O.Crosthwaite

Other Pension Fund Experts R.N.Philipson-Stow, P.W.A.Henderson

Pension Fund Clients 40 approx, 2 Pension Funds to which firm acts as sole dealer

Areas of Specialization Engineering, Food Manufacturing and distribution Investment Trust, Oil, Distillers, Japan

HESELTINE MOSS & CO
Lawrence House, 3-4 Trump Street,
London EC2V 8DH
Telephone: 01-606 1401

Partners Acting for Pension Funds M.A.Ingram,LLB, B.G.A.Burton, MA

Employees 100

Number of Pension Fund Clients 50 (approx)

Services Offered to Pension Funds Computer valuations, Investment advice, research, dealing, underwriting, contacts with industry

Other Offices Reading, Gloucester, Newbury, Oxford

Market Sector Specialities Banks, defence, North Sea Oil, overseas traders, smaller regional companies

HOARE GOVETT LTD
Heron House, 319-325 High Holborn,
London WC1V 7PB
Telephone: 01-242 2848

Chairman R.K.Westmacott

Head of Fund Management Department M.O.P.Francis

Other Pension Fund Experts A team of executives handling funds under management and supporting staff

Employees 9

Number of Pension Fund Clients Discretionary Funds - 18; Advised Funds - 26

Other Offices 27 Throgmorton Street, London EC2N 2AN and Hong Kong

Other Information Charitable Funds also managed or advised

ILLINGWORTH & HENRIQUES
38-40 Kennedy Street, Manchester M60 2BP
Telephone: 061-236 8521

Senior Partner R.C.Mather

Finance & Administration Partner M.C.Mowat

Other Partners and Associates Acting for Pension Funds Magnus C.Mowat, Tom Tutton

Employees 50

Other Offices London and Bolton

Associated Company Illingworth & Henriques Rickitt Ltd

KEITH, BAYLEY, ROGERS & CO
194-200 Bishopsgate, London EC2M 4NR
Telephone: 01-623 2400

Senior Partner D.H.Covell

Partners Acting for Pension Funds D.H.Covell, W.Howard Saunders, W.K.Armstrong

Other Pension Fund Expert M.R.Dodd

Employees 50

Number of Pension Clients Numerous

Other Offices 49 Bank Street, Carlisle, Cumbria (Resident Manager D.Murray)

KEMP-GEE & CO
20 Copthall Avenue, London EC2R 7JS
Telephone: 01-600 7595

Senior Partner R.D.Fulford

Partners Acting for Pension Funds Advised Funds: (Equities) I.A.K.Dipple, J.B.Fisher and 12 other partners; (Gilt-Edged) H.H.Cove, A.M.Williams, Managed Funds W.J.Murden, J.H.Perry, I.Maxwell Scott, P.D.Roy

Employees 165 (including partners)

ADVISERS TO PENSION FUNDS

18 Finsbury Circus, London EC2M 7BH. Telephone 01-588 2311 Telex 888026
Members of the Stock Exchange

Carr, Sebag & Co.
Members of The Stock Exchange, London.
also in Geneva, Hong Kong, Manila, New York & Tokyo

Investment Managers
and Advisers to Pension Funds

Ocean House,
Little Trinity Lane,
London EC4P 4LB.

Telephone 01-236-5000
01-248-2090

(b) Stockbrokers

KEMP-GEE & CO *Continued*

Number of Pension Fund Clients Discretionary Funds-Significant

Advised Funds Almost all investment houses and a large number of self-administered funds

Value of Funds Managed Substantial

Value of Funds Advised Very Large

Other Offices Jersey

Associated Companies Bartlett, Kemp-Gee & Co; Kemp-Gee Holdings (Jersey) Ltd; Kemp-Gee Management (Jersey) Ltd

Other Information Specialists in life and pension insurance and retirement schemes

KITCAT & AITKEN

The Stock Exchange, London EC2N 1HB
Telephone: 01-588 6280

Senior Partner N.O.Taube

Partners Acting for Pension Funds K.G.Philpot, P.M.Evans Lombe, T.Ruck Keene, P.J.Willis, M.H.Cave, R.A.Edwards, G.R.C.Hubbard, N.W.Bagshawe, J.G.Doctor, A.H.Clifton, J.C.D.Goldschmidt, J.M.Y.Oliver, R.C.Borthwick, J.S.H.H.Motion, A.R.H.Thomas, P.V.Olsen, A.H.M.Kelsey

Employees 150 (approx)

Number of Pension Fund Clients All major investment houses specialising in pension fund management and additional direct contact with about 50 self-administered pension funds

Areas of Specialization Life Insurance, Composite Insurance, Insurance Brokers, Investment Trusts, Oils, Shipping, Paper and Packaging, Building Materials, Pharmaceuticals, Retail, Tobacco, Eurobonds, Traded Options, Australia, Europe, United States, Canada

LAING & CRUICKSHANK

The Stock Exchange, London EC2N 1HA
Telephone: 01-588 2800

Senior Partner R.A.Stormonth-Darling

Partner Responsible for Pension Fund Management Activities G.M.Powell

Partner in Charge of Institutional Sales G.C.Mordaunt

Employees 230

Other Offices Eastbourne, Taunton

Associated Companies Laing & Cruickshank Financial Services Ltd, L&C Unit Trust Management Ltd

LAURENCE, PRUST & CO

Basildon House, 7-11 Moorgate,
London EC2R 6AH
Telephone: 01-606 8811

Senior Partner P.W.Darwin CA

Finance Partner W.H.Keatley

Partners Acting for Pension Funds C.R.Holloway (Partner in charge of institutional department), W.R. Stuttaford (partner in charge of Fund Management), D.M.White, R.A.Bourne, A.B.Milford

Employees 200

Other Information Laurence, Prust & Co has acted as sole investment manager of the Framlington Unit Trusts since their inception

LAURIE,MILBANK & CO.

Portland House, 72/73 Basinghall Street,
London EC2V 5DP
Telephone: 01-606 6622

Senior Partner A.M.Everett

Partners Acting for Pension Funds K.E.Ayers, R.Warley Cummings (Gilts); C.G.H.Allen, G.F.Burnand, K.S.Perrett (Equities); A.P.Scott (Money Management, Treasury Bills, C.D.'s etc.)

Employees 200, including Partners

Number of Pension Fund Clients Contacts are maintained with and advice given to most major pension funds in the public and private sectors, as well as investment departments and merchant banks etc.

Other Offices Jersey

Associated Companies American Securities Corporation

Areas of Specialization Gilt edged, domestic and International bonds and equities

Other Information Publishers of and contributors to the ISIS Bulletin, which advises on domestic and International security and property markets

LE MARE, MARTIN & CO

Regina House, 5 Queen Street, London EC4N 1UH
Telephone: 01-236 2251

Senior Executive Partner Frank G.Martin

Partners Acting for Pension Funds Frank G.Martin, D.J.Rutter, P.Q.Rawlings, P.H.Gliss, R.J.Arthurell

Other Pension Fund Experts L.C.Little, J.M.Coburn

LYDDON & CO

113-116 Bute Street, Cardiff CF1 6TA
Telephone: 0222-33171

Senior Partner D.S.Box

Finance & Administration Partner E.W.Powell

Partners Acting for Pension Funds D.S.Box, D.R.W.Williams, A.D.Malcomson, E.W.Powell

Employees 54 (including Partners)

Number of Pension Fund Clients 12

Other Offices Swansea, London

Areas of Specialization South Wales companies, Textiles, Relative strength analysis

MCANALLY MONTGOMERY & CO

18 Finsbury Circus, London EC2M 7BH
Telephone: 01-588 2311

Senior Partner P.J.Ensor

Associated Company McAnally Company Services Ltd (Merger brokers)

Areas of Specialization Research in engineering, building and contracting, retailing, overseas traders and shipping

L. MESSEL & CO.

Winchester House, 100 Old Broad Street,
London EC2P 2HX
Telephone: 01-606 4411

Quilter Hilton Goodison & Co

Members of the Stock Exchange

Investment Decisions?

We can help you decide, with our specialist knowledge of

PROPERTY

ELECTRICAL

CHEMICAL

ENGINEERING

FINANCIAL

EUROPEAN

shares

Quilter Hilton Goodison & Co

Garrard House,
31-45 Gresham Street,
London EC2V 7LH,
Telephone: 01-600 4177

TAY & THAMES
investment services limited

PROVIDES A BROAD RANGE OF INVESTMENT SERVICES AND MANAGEMENT FOR COMPANIES, LOCAL AUTHORITIES, PENSION FUNDS, CHARITIES, TRUSTS AND PRIVATE INVESTORS

Directors
I R Guild, WS (Chairman), A K Aitkenhead, CA
D M C Donald, WS, FCIS, W D Marr, CA
C K R Nunneley, CA

Belsize House, West Ferry, Dundee DD5 1NF
Telephone (0382) 78244

(b) Stockbrokers

L. MESSEL & CO. Continued

Senior Partner J.D.Lloyd

Partners Acting for Pension Funds K.W.Wright, FIA, A.West, FIA, A.N.Haddon

Employees 220

Areas of Specialisation The UK Economy, British Government Securities, Debentures and Convertibles, Brewery, Building, Electricals, Insurance, Banking, Oils, Mining, Investment Trusts Retailing and Arbitrage

W. N. MIDDLETON & CO

Throgmorton House, 15 Copthall Avenue, London EC2
Telephone: 01-628 9481

Senior Partner M.N.Kemp-Gee

MONTAGU, LOEBL, STANLEY & CO

31 Sun Street, London EC2M 2QP
Telephone: 01-377 9242

Senior Partner The Hon N.Assheton

Partners Acting for Pension Funds C.A.Priestman

Associated Companies Montagu Loebl Stanley Financial Services Co.

Other Information A brochure detailing the pension fund management services is available on request

MULLENS & CO

15 Moorgate, London EC2B 6AN
Telephone: 01-638 4121

Senior Partner Sir Thomas Gore Browne

Finance & Administration Partner The Lord Cromwell

J.W.NICHOLSON & SONS

Fargate Court, Sheffield S1 1LE
Telephone: 0742 26651

Senior Partner J.A.H.Nicholson

Partner Responsible for Pension Funds N.P.Nicholson

Other Pension Fund Expert S.J.Harker

Employees 20

Number of Pension Fund Clients 5

Other Information Specialists in Sheffield District Securities

R.NIVISON & CO

25 Austin Friars, London EC2N 2JB
Telephone: 01-588 7244

Senior Partner The Lord Glendyne

Finance & Administration Partner P.R.Colville

NORTHCOTE & CO

P.O. Box 548, Copthall Close, London EC2P 2JJ
Telephone: 01-628 8121

Senior Partner F.H.Tavener

Partner in Charge of Institutional Sales H.W.Everett

Research Partner R.J.Tavener

Employees 120

Areas of Specialization Light Electronics, Leisure

PANMURE GORDON SEE GORDON PANMURE

PARSONS & CO

100 West Nile Street, Glasgow G1 2QU
Telephone: 041-332 8791

Senior Partner R.A.A.Gray

Finance & Administration Partner G.McL. Carrick

Other Offices Aberdeen, Dundee, Edinburgh, London

PEMBER & BOYLE

P.O. Box 435, 30 Finsbury Circus
London EC2P 2HB
Telephone: 01-638 6242

Senior Partner N.F.Althaus

Partners Acting for Pension Funds L.Needham, H.L.Johnston, R.P.Morris, R.S.Allen

Employees 100 (approx)

Number of Pension Fund Clients 40

Value of Pension Funds Managed or Advised In excess of £1,500 million

Pension Fund Services Advisory, broking or full management as required on fixed interest and equity portfolios at home and overseas

PENNEY, CASTELLO CARLEBACH & CO

24 George Square, Glasgow G2 1EB
Telephone: 041-248 4111

Senior Partner A.J.B.Agnew

Partner Acting for Pension Funds J.M.Tolmie

Other Offices Edinburgh, London

Associated Companies Kyle Financial Services Ltd., Kyle Employee Incentives Ltd.

Area of Specialization Employee Share Schemes

PHILLIPS & DREW

Lee House, London Wall, London EC2Y 5AP
Telephone: 01-628 4444

Senior Partner E.P.Bazalgette

Partners/Acting for Pension Funds M.G.Hall,AIA, A.R.P.Bird, H.H.Sparks,APMI, T.J.Cann

Other Pension Fund Experts 13 Fund Managers

Employees Firm 451 (42 partners), Pensions Department 37 (4 partners)

Other Information A brochure detailing the pension fund management services offered is available from the pension fund department

PIDGEON DE SMITT

Salisbury House, London Wall, London EC2M 5RT
Telephone: 01-588 6066

Senior Partner G.A.Cloake

Finance Partner J.E.Bury

Other Offices Lymington, Hants; Poole, Dorset; Truro, Cornwall

(b) Stockbrokers

QUILTER, HILTON, GOODISON & CO
Garrard House, 31-45 Gresham Street,
London EC2V 7LH
Telephone: 01-600 4177

Senior Partner N.P.Goodison

Managing Partner R.B.Blaxland

Employees 200

RAPHAEL, ZORN
10 Throgmorton Avenue, London EC2N 2DP
Telephone: 01-628 4000

Senior Partner A.G.A.T.Laing

Finance Partner M.H.Tollemache

RENSBURG & CO.
Silkhouse Court, Tithebarn Street,
Liverpool L2 2NH
Telephone: 051-227 2030

Senior Partner J.M.Rayner

Partners Acting for Pension Funds T.C.Jason Wood, S.P.H.Cookson, N.C.Williams, M.J.P.Cooke

Employees 60 (13 Partners)

Other Offices Bradford

Associated Company Tithebarn Financial Consultants Ltd.

ROWE & PITMAN
39-45 Finsbury Square, London EC2A 1JA
Telephone: 01-606 1066

Senior Partner A.D.Hurst-Brown

Finance Partner D.A.Innes

Employees 250 (34 partners)

Other Offices San Francisco, Johannesburg, Hong Kong, Tokyo

Associated Companies Rowe & Pitman International, Rowe & Pitman Inc, Rowe & Pitman Money Broking, Rowan Investment Management Services

E.B.SAVORY MILLN & CO
20 Moorgate, London EC2R 6AQ
Telephone: 01-606 4477

Senior Partner J.G.Milln

Partner/Manager Acting for Pension Funds W.A.C.Wield (partner), D.S.Maker (manager)

Employees 110

Number of Pension Fund Clients 1 (Discretionary Fund), 3 (Advised Funds)

Value of Funds £1.5 million (managed), £1 million (advised)

Areas of Specialisation include engineering, electrical, building, insurance and banking

PAUL E. SCHWEDER MILLER & CO
18 Finsbury Square, London EC2A 1LD
Telephone: 01-588 5600

Senior & Finance Partner S.Davis

SCOTT, GOFF, HANCOCK & CO
Salisbury House, London Wall, London EC2
Telephone: 01-628 4433

Senior Partner G.A.Reddington

Finance Partner C.H.James

SCRIMGEOUR, KEMP-GEE & CO.
20 Copthall Avenue, London EC2R 7JS
Telephone: 01-600 7595
Telex: 885171

Senior Partner R.D.Fulford

Partner Acting for Pension Funds R.S.Allen

Other Offices Jersey

SEYMOUR PIERCE & CO
10 Old Jewry, London EC2
Telephone: 01-628 4981

Senior & Finance Partner A.G.A.Pierce

ALBERT E. SHARP & CO
Edmund House, 12 Newhall Street,
Birmingham B3 3ER
Telephone: 021-236 5801

Senior Partner S.D.Sharp

Finance Partner K.G.Smellie, FCA

Partners Acting for Pension Funds G.K.Sharp, L.A.Goodenough, T.Morris-Jones, J.M.Macnair, D.Cashdan

Other Pension Fund Adviser N.E.E.Stephens

Associated Companies Sharp Unquoted Midland Investment Trust Ltd., Bowring Sharp Ltd.

Areas of Specialization Engineering, Motor and Midlands Companies

SHEPPARDS AND CHASE
Clements House, Gresham Street,
London EC2V 7AU
Telephone: 01-606 8099

Senior Partner J.L.M.Wilson

Partners Acting for Pension Funds J.E.Austin,FCA, R.M.Leach, J.A.Letchford, D.S.Sanderson

Other Offices Leeds and St. Helier, Jersey, CI

Associated Company Mayflower Management Co Ltd

Other Information The Firm manages investments on a discretionary basis for some Pension Funds and is sole adviser, or acts for, many other Funds. Full details of these services are available on request

SIMON & COATES
1 London Wall Buildings, London EC2M 5PT
Telephone: 01-588 3644

Senior Partner E.P.M.Brown

Partner Acting for Pension Funds H.Jackson,FCA

Employees 200 (Approx)

Number of Pension Funds Advised 5

Value of Funds Managed £40 million

Areas of Specialisation South African Arbitrage (Mining)

SMITH KEEN CUTLER
Exchange Buildings, Stephenson Place,
Birmingham B2 4NN
Telephone: 021-643 9977

(b) Stockbrokers

SMITH KEEN CUTLER *Continued*

Senior Partner D.K.Rowe-Ham, FCA

Partners Acting for Pension Funds P.J.Feeny, N.L.Rowland

Other Office 52 Cornhill, London EC3V 3NR (01-623 9483)

Areas of Specialisation Engineering, Midlands and smaller companies

SPIERS & JEFFREY

36 Renfield Street, Glasgow G2 1NA
Telephone: 041-248 4311

Senior Partner R.S.Waddell,CA

Partners Acting for Pension Funds R.S.Waddell,CA, A.A.W.Waddell,MBA, J.R.Gibb,FFA, P.C.M.Roger,CA

Employees 60

Number of Pension Fund Clients Firm acts for many but exclusively for only a few

STANCLIFFE, TODD & HODGSON

City House, 206-208 Marton Road, Middlesbrough TSA 2JE
Telephone: 0642 249211

Senior Partner Frank Taylor

Partners Acting for Pension Funds Frank Taylor, Alan Kitching, Andrew Priestley

Other Pension Fund Expert R.S.Thomson

Employees 65

Number of Pension Fund Clients 4 (advised funds)

Services Offered to Pension Funds Normal investment services

Other Offices Gibraltar, Carlisle, Sunderland, Harrogate, Hull

Associated Company Tees Investment Corporation Ltd

Specialisation Northern Companies, overseas taxation, Personal and Corporate

CHARLES STANLEY & CO

18 Finsbury Circus, London EC2M 7BL
Telephone: 01-638 5717

Senior Partner Sir Edward Howard, Bt

Finance & Administration Partner D.H.S.Howard

Employees 70

Other Office Gibralter

Areas of Specialisation Pharmaceuticals, consumer durables, chemical engineering, speciality chemicals, TV rental, plant hire, building and construction

STERNBERG, THOMAS CLARKE & CO.

Salisbury House, London Wall, London EC2M 5RU
Telephone: 01-588 6050

Senior Partner J.H.Leaman

Partner Acting for Pension Funds K.R.Smith

Employees 55

Number of Pension Fund Clients Advised 3

Value of Funds £50 million

Other Offices Brighton, Horsham

Areas of Specialization Traditional Options, Warrants, Convertibles

STIRLING, HENDRY & CO

Exchange House,16 Royal Exchange Square, Glasgow G1 3AD
Telephone: 041-248 6033

Senior & Finance Partner A.T.Hendry

Partners Acting for Pension Funds G.B.Stirling, D.Walton

Employees 25

Number of Pension Fund Clients 35-40

STOCK, BEECH & CO.

Bristol & West Building, Broad Quay, Bristol BS1 4DO
Telephone: 0272 20051

Senior & Finance Partner T.C.M.Stock

Other Offices 24 Bennetts Hill, Birmingham B2 5QY (021-643 7551); The Stock Exchange, London EC2N 1HE (01-638 8471)

STRAUSS, TURNBULL & CO

3 Moorgate Place, London EC2R 6HR
Telephone: 01-638 5699

Senior Partner R.Strauss

Finance & Administration Partner F.W.Watts

Other Offices Paris, Amstelveen (Holland)

TILNEY & CO

385 Sefton House, Exchange Building, Liverpool L2 3RT
Telephone: 051-236 6000

Senior Partner J.P.Bingham

Finance Partner A.C.Binks

Other Offices London, Shrewsbury

VICKERS DA COSTA LTD

Regis House, King William Street, London EC4R 9AR
Telephone: 01-623 2494

Chairman R.C.Vickers

Partners Acting for Pension Funds M.J.G.Hill, P.J.Brickell, B.C.Richardson

Other Pension Fund Experts D.W.Bartlett, P.G.R.Lyon

Total Employees 250

Other Offices Hong Kong, Tokyo, Manila

Associated Companies City Financial Administration Ltd, Bridge Fund Managers Ltd

VIVIAN, GRAY & CO

Ling House, 10-13 Dominion Street, London EC2M 2UX
Telephone: 01-628 9311

Senior Partner Sir Alastair F.S.Coats

Finance Partner R.Anderson

WILLIAMS DE BROE HILL CHAPLIN & CO

Pinners Hall, Austin Friars, London EC2P 2HS
Telephone: 01-588 7511

(b) Stockbrokers

WILLIAMS DE BROE HILL CHAPLIN & CO *Continued*

Senior and Finance Partner R.Pettman

Senior Partner P.Pettman

WISE, SPEKE & CO
Commercial Union House, 39 Pilgrim Way,
Newcastle upon Tyne NE1 6RQ
Telephone: 0632 611266

Senior Partner P.J.Orde

Partners and Other Experts Acting for Pension Funds N.H.R.Speke, C.J.Pumphrey, C.F.S.May, P.J.Orde, B.J.Gillespie, N.Sherlock, T.R.P.S.Norton

Employees 84

Number of Pension Fund Clients 7 Discretionary Funds and 11 Advised Funds

Value of Funds Managed £60 million

Value of Funds Advised £120 million

Other Offices 103 Albert Road, Middlesbrough, Cleveland TS1 2PA (0642 248431); (Dealing Office) Austin Friars House, 2-6 Austin Friars, London EC2N 2EE (01-638 0691/2)

WOOD, MACKENZIE & CO
62-3 Threadneedle Street, London EC2R 8HP
Telephone: 01-600 3600

Partners Involved with Pension Funds John Chiene (Senior Partner), Peter Derby (Chairman, Wood, Mackenzie Pension Trustees Ltd), Dugald Eadie and Ian Hogg, (Partners in Charge of Pension Fund Performance Measurement)

Other Pension Fund Experts Gordon M. Bagot, John M. Gillies

Employees 300

Number of Pension Fund Clients 600 (approx)

Amounts Involved £20 billion (approx) total assets of Pension Funds in measurement sample

Other Office Erskine House, 68-73 Queen Street, Edinburgh EH2 4NS (031-225 8525)

Other Information A booklet which describes the performance measurement services is available on request. The Firm does not manage Pension Fund investments

---

J. & E. DAVY

Members of the Stock Exchange

Specialists in Irish Government Stocks

and

Irish Equities

60 Dawson Street	Telephone 772416
Dublin 2	Telex 25865

(c) Other Financial Advisers

A large number of different types of organisations either act as financial advisers or serve as an intermediary for the investment needs of Pension Funds. Some of these are listed elsewhere in this book.

Among the other types of organisation coming into this category are the following:

Building Societies, Trustee savings banks, Other banks, Money brokers and discount brokers, Foreign exchange and currency deposit brokers, Investment Trusts, Unit trust managers, Offshore and overseas fund managers, Investment managers, Independent investment counsellors and managers, Commodity and bullion brokers

This Section does not aim to give a comprehensive list of these firms but includes details of some of those that are most active in dealing with Pension Funds. More comprehensive lists are available in various other directories (such as The City Director) or from various Trade and Professional Associations.

ALLIANCE CAPITAL MANAGEMENT INTERNATIONAL, INC.

319-325 High Holborn, London WC1V 7PB
Telephone: 01-404 0377

Directors Acting for Pension Funds C.J.Kendrick, CFA,MBA, G.Wellman,MBA

Employees 50 investment professionals, 70 supporting staff (worldwide)

Value of Funds Managed (Worldwide) Discretionary-$4 billion, Advisory-$5 billion

Pension Fund Clients 106

Services Offered to Pension Funds Investment management including the management of:- equity, fixed income, and balanced accounts in North America; multi-currency equity, fixed income, balanced accounts; US Dollar money market instruments
The Alliance group has available several pooled vehicles including funds which specialise in:- smaller capitalisation US equities (aggressively managed); US Dollar money market instruments (offshore, very conservative); multi-currency balanced instruments

Other Offices New York, Chicago, Cleveland, Dallas, Minneapolis, San Francisco

Parent Company Alliance Capital Management Corporation

Associated Company Alliance Capital Management Corporation is a wholly owned but operationally independent subsidiary of Donaldson, Lufkin & Jenrette Inc.

BAILLIE, GIFFORD & CO

3 Glenfinlas Street, Edinburgh EH3 6YY
Telephone: 031-225 2581

Senior Partner J.G.C.White, MA, BA

Directors Acting for Pension Funds G.J.N.Gemmell, CA, R.R.J.Burns,BA,LLB,WS

Employees 35

Number of Pension Fund Clients 10

Total Value of Funds Managed £105 million

Services Offered to Pension Funds Investment management, full administrative, and secretarial taxation services in connection with investments, if required

Other Information Total funds managed £340 million. Baillie, Gifford & Co. is an investment management firm engaged exclusively in the management of equity and fixed interest portfolios for institutional clients

BLYTHE EASTMAN DILLON

59A London Wall, London EC2M 5TP
Telephone: 01-638 3491

Partner Acting for Pension Funds A.I.Milne

Services Offered to Pension Funds Investment banking, both in U.S.A. and internationally and all aspects of stockmarket investments in U.S.A.

BRITANNIA INSTITUTIONAL FUND MANAGEMENT LTD.

Salisbury House, 31 Finsbury Circus,
London EC2M 5QL
Telephone: 01-588 2777
Telex:883781

Directors Acting for Pension Funds Peter Baker, MA,FCA, Vernon Harris,BSc,FCA

Pension Fund Experts 5

Employees 120

Total Value of Pension Funds Managed £28 million

Number of Pension Fund Clients 13

Services Offered to Pension Funds A full investment management service covering equities, gilts (and other fixed interest) and property in the U.K. and overseas. Whilst portfolios are individually structured, use is made, where appropriate, of exempt unit trusts for a part of the portfolio; particularly to achieve exposure to the smaller company sector and for overseas investment

Other Offices Britannia International Management Ltd. (P.O.Box 271, Queensway House, Queen Street, St.Helier, Jersey)

Associated Companies Britannia Group of Investment Companies

Other Information The Britannia Group, managing total funds in excess of £450 million, offers a wide range of investment and financial services including pensions advice for senior executives and directors.

BROMBARD FINANCIAL SERVICES LTD

Duke House, 32 Waterloo Street, Hove,
East Sussex BN3 1AN
Telephone: 0273-23136

Directors Acting for Pension Funds D.M.Rogers, F.J.Richardson, J.Willmot

Pension Fund Experts 6

Employees 14

Value of Pension Funds Managed and Advised £20 million

Murray Johnstone:
the single-minded approach to pension fund management

By concentrating exclusively on investment management Murray Johnstone can offer a pension fund management service that is fully professional and that gets results. We manage pension fund assets of over £200 million and are still small enough in numbers to give director-level attention to each account. We aim to limit the number of stocks in a portfolio, so that the investment manager can follow them closely as well as looking at new opportunities.

We maintain a worldwide approach: in addition to the UK, our principal areas of investment are North America, Europe, Japan and the Far East. We have funds specially designed for gross funds to invest with advantage in North America and Japan.

With our stress on broad-ranging research and the involvement of all our senior staff in day-to-day investment decisions, we believe that Murray Johnstone can provide pension funds of all sizes with the responsible and effective management service they are looking for.

For more information, please contact Nicholas Prescott, Murray Johnstone Limited, 163 Hope Street, Glasgow G2 2UH. Telephone: 041-221 5521. Telex: 778667.

BROMBARD FINANCIAL SERVICES LTD *Continued*

Pension Fund Clients 110

Services Offered to Pension Funds Full comprehensive service, including Administration, Actuarial & Investment Advice, Inland Revenue negotiations, preparation of Accounts, Pensioneer Trusteeship and general Tax Planning advice.

CAPITAL PARTNERS INTERNATIONAL

Westland House, 17c Curzon Street, London W.1
Telephone: 01-629 9928

Director Acting for Pension Funds Christoph von Luttitz, MBA

Other Pension Fund Expert Simon Bingham, FCA

Employees 7

Services Offered to Pension Funds Arranging investments, on behalf of private investors and institutional investors, in small companies internationally

Areas of Specialization Specialists in small company investment including start-ups. Up to £250,000 per investment. Can provide similar services as co-investor or manager of venture capital pool.

JOHN CARRINGTON & CO LTD

44a Bedford Row, London WC1R 4LL
Telephone: 01-242 5363

Directors Involved with Pension Funds John Carrington, Mrs Jacquelyn Neill

Employees 11

Total Value of Funds Managed £18 million

Number of Pension Fund Clients 5

Services Offered to Pension Funds Investment management - strong emphasis on U.K. and foreign equities

Clients Include Nuclear Power Co., Dun and Bradstreet (U.K.), Ash and Lacy

CIPFA SERVICES LTD, LOANS BUREAU (CHARTERED INSTITUTE OF PUBLIC FINANCE & ACCOUNTANCY)

232 Vauxhall Bridge Road, London SW1V 1AU
Telephone: 01-834 5269

Bureau Manager R.H.Turpin, IPFA

Other Pension Fund Experts Mrs. J.Clarke, Mrs.H.Gross, P.Shuttleworth (principal dealers for investment of pension monies)

Employees 21

Services Offered to Pension Funds The Loans Bureau is in contact with a number of pension funds on whose behalf it places funds in the local authority market. It also arranges with them development finance for local authority projects on a sale or lease back basis.

Other Information The Loans Bureau, a member of the Sterling Brokers Association has as members most of the local authorities and public corporations in the UK. It places with them funds ranging individually from as little as £20,000 to many millions-in periods from overnight to long term up to 10 or 20 years secured by bond or mortgage

(c) Other Financial Advisers

CITY FINANCIAL ADMINISTRATION LTD

Regis House, King William Street,
London EC4R 9AR
Telephone: 01-623 4951

Directors D. W. Bartlett, FCIS, D.W.James, FCA, P.J.Brickell

Employees 15

Number of Clients Approx 20

Parent Company M&G Group Holdings Ltd

Services Offered to Pension Funds Full range of services including valuations, investment management, exempt fund investment, administration

Other Office Luxembourg

CLIVE INVESTMENTS LTD AND CLIVE INVESTMENTS CAMBRIDGE LTD

1 Royal Exchange Avenue, London EC3V 3LU
Telephone: 01-283 1101

Directors J.J.Warr (Chairman), J.D.Nicholson, FFA (Managing), N.H.Chamberlen, J.R.L.Cuningham, D.C.Damant, A.C.Gibson, R.A.Kilborn,FCA

Consultant D.H.Grimes, BSc

Services Offered to Pension Funds Fund management of fixed interest portfolios (Clive Investments Ltd) and the management of equity portfolios by index matching (Clive Investments Cambridge Ltd)

Associated Company Clive Discount Company Ltd (member of the London Discount Market Association)

CRAIGMOUNT INVESTMENT MANAGEMENT LTD

40 Bucklersbury, London EC4N 8BD
Telephone: 01-248 4984

Director Acting for Pension Funds R.H.R.Latham, MBA

MARTIN CURRIE INVESTMENT MANAGEMENT LTD

29 Charlotte Square, Edinburgh EH2 4HA
Telephone: 031-225 3811

Directors Acting for Pension Funds J.A.R.Falconer, A.G.D.Johnston, W.M.C.Kennedy, D.L.Skinner, J.B.B.Stewart, A.D.R.Macphail, R. Young

Employees 25

Total Value of Funds Managed £12 million

Number of Pension Fund Clients 4

Services Offered to Pension Funds International Investment Management

Other Information Property investment advice not provided. International investment experience available. Money Management.

Parent Company Martin Currie & Co

Other Information The Group manages assets of approximately £300 million split betwen live investment trusts, charitable foundations, pension funds and a unit trust. Two directors act as investment advisers to 2 major U.K. pension funds

EDINBURGH FUND MANAGERS LTD.

4 Melville Crescent, Edinburgh EH3 7JB
Telephone: 031-226 4931

Go Abroad with F. & C. MANAGEMENT

We have been investing overseas for over a hundred years.
We meet the needs of pension funds and charities for overseas investment with two specialist funds

F. & C. Anglo-Nippon Exempt Fund
and
F. & C. North American Exempt Fund

For performance details and further information telephone or write to James Nelson or Anthony Baring

**F. & C. MANAGEMENT LIMITED
1/2 LAURENCE POUNTNEY HILL
LONDON EC4R 0BA**

Telephone: 01-623 4680
Telex: 886197

F&C GROUP

F. & C. Management has funds under management in excess of £500m.

Pension funds require efficient and impartial management

MARTIN CURRIE INVESTMENT MANAGEMENT

Offers— A wholly independent service entirely devoted to investment management for a limited number of clients

The personal attention of directors who are solely responsible for all investment decisions and are currently entrusted with funds of approximately £300m

A set fee structure with no hidden charges.

For further details contact
Michael Kennedy or David Skinner at
Martin Currie Investment Management Ltd.,
29 Charlotte Square, Edinburgh.
Telephone 031-225 3811

(c) Other Financial Advisers

EDINBURGH FUND MANAGERS LTD. Continued

Directors Acting for Pension Funds A.R.McInroy, CA, C.H.Ross, CA, G.A.Y.Maclennan, CA

Employees 30

Total Value of Funds Managed £160 million

Services Offered to Pension Funds Investment Management and Advice

Associated Company American Trust Co. Ltd.

Other Information EFM specializes in overseas investment and has three funds designed specifically to enable pension funds to invest in North America, Japan and the Pacific Basin without loss of their tax advantages. Oil is another area of specialization

ELECTRA GROUP SERVICES LTD

Electra House, Temple Place,
Victoria Embankment, London WC2R 3HP
Telephone: 01-836 7766

Director Acting for Pension Funds W.J.N.Wawn

Pension Fund Expert R.L.Hatt,APMI

Employees 45

Total Value of Funds Managed £400 million

Number of Pension Fund Clients 12

Services Offered to Pension Funds Investment management and any other requirements tailored to the needs or wishes of individual clients. An independent house

Associated Companies Electra Fund Managers Ltd, subsidiary of Electra Group Services Ltd, specialising in investment in small companies

Other Information Investment managers to Globe Investment Trust Ltd., Electra Investment Trust Ltd., and Temple Bar Investment Trust Ltd., with total assets of approximately £400 million. The Electra Group Services Ltd. is owned by the Investment Trusts. Investment management service applies to most of the major financial markets of the world

F & C MANAGEMENT LTD

1 Laurence Poutney Hill, London EC4R OBA
Telephone: 01-623 4680
Telex: 886197

Directors Acting for Pension Funds J.M.Davenport, O.N.Dawson, J.R.Mathias

Employees 56

Total Value of Funds In excess of £500 million including F.& C. Anglo-Nippon Exempt Fund and F.& C. North American Exempt Fund, which are designed for charities and pension funds who wish to invest in Japan and North America through a specialised trust.

Services Offered to Pension Funds The Investment Management Department manages funds in excess of £100 million for charities, pension funds and private individuals, and offers a comprehensive international investment service for equities and bonds.

FIDELITY INTERNATIONAL INVESTMENT MANAGEMENT

Buckingham House, 62-63 Queen Street,
London EC4
Telephone: 01-248 4891

Directors Acting for Pension Funds James E.Tonner, J.H.C.Leach

Pension Fund Experts 10

Employees 450 world wide

Total Value of Funds Managed $2 billion

Number of Pension Fund Clients 25

Services Offered to Pension Funds International investment management (Equities and Bonds)

Other Offices Boston, Mass USA, Tokyo, Bermuda

Associated Companies F.M.R.Corp. (parent), F.M.R. Investment Services, F.M.R.Japan, F.M.R.Jersey

JAMES FINLAY INVESTMENT MANAGEMENT LTD

Finlay House, 10-14 West Nile Street, Glasgow
Telephone: 041-204 1321

Directors Acting for Pension Funds J.D.B.Wood, J.A.L.Cumming

Employees 5

Total Value of Funds Managed or Advised Over £10 million

Number of Pension Fund Clients 4

Services Offered to Pension Funds Investment management services

Associated Companies The Company is part of James Finlay & Co.Ltd.

FRASER GREEN LTD

2 Friars Lane, Richmond, Surrey TW9 1NL
Telephone: 01-948 0164

Directors Acting for Pension Funds P.G.Cook, S.J.Green,MA,FIA, D.J.M.Lowe,BA

Number of Pension Fund Clients 30

Services Offered to Pension Funds Investment advice and investment management for funds not exceeding £35 million and investment advice and independent management consultancy for larger portfolios

Other Offices 24-28 Cheapside, London EC2V 6AB

Associated Companies Fraser Orr Ltd, Dublin

Other Information The company, which does not accept private clients, authorised unit trust or investment trust business, is a subsidiary of Messrs. Duncan C. Fraser & Co

GARTMORE PENSION FUND MANAGERS LTD

Cayzer House, 2 St. Mary Axe, London EC3A 8BP
Telephone: 01-283 3531

Directors Acting for Pension Funds W.Campbell Allan, CA, H.Jacobs, FCIS,FPMI, D.Sarchett, A.H.Mitchell, APMI, D.W.Watts,MA

Pension Fund Experts N.Cobby, G.M.Joblin, A.Young,MA,LLB

Employees 100

Total Value of Funds Managed £80 million

Total Value of Funds Advised £1 billion

IVORY & SIME

Pension Fund Investment Managers

•

IVORY & SIME LIMITED
ONE CHARLOTTE SQUARE
EDINBURGH EH2 4DZ
TELEPHONE 031-225 1357

•

ESTABLISHED 1895

(c) Other Financial Advisers

GARTMORE PENSION FUND MANAGERS LTD
Continued

Number of Pension Fund Clients 11

Services Offered to Pension Funds Investment management services (discretionary and non-discretionary), advice given on equities, fixed interest and property both in the U.K. and overseas and commodities. Investment administration and nominee services

Other Offices Glasgow, Isle of Man, Hong Kong, San Francisco

Associated Companies Gartmore Investment Ltd, British & Commonwealth Shipping, Gartmore Miller Hill Inc (San Francisco), Wardgate Commodity Fund Managers Ltd (Jersey)

JOHN GOVETT & CO LTD
Winchester House, 77 London Wall,
London EC2N 1DH
Telephone: 01-588 5620

Directors Acting for Pension Funds W.J.R.Govett (Chairman), M.R.Cornwall-Jones ACIS (Vice-Chairman and Director in charge of Pensions Department), D.A.H.Baer, M.J.Beaver

Pension Fund Managers R.G.Jenyns ACA, D.W.Makins

Total Value of Funds £50m (Managed), in excess of £500m (Advised)

Number of Pension Fund Clients 7

Services Offered to Pension Funds Full investment management services, secretarial and administrative services or consultancy to suit the needs of individual funds

Other information Global coverage

RICHARD GRENVILLE LTD
15 Wilson Street, London EC2M 2TQ
Telephone: 01-628 4892

Directors Acting for Pension Funds J.G.Sutton, J.S.Sandilands

Pension Fund Expert J.G.Sutton

Employees 5

Services Offered to Pension Funds Investment management and administration, employee benefit schemes

Other Offices Jersey, Channel Islands

Associated Companies R.Grenville Financial Management Ltd

Other Information Self-administered pension schemes for directors and senior executives. Tax planning for companies and their executives

G.T.MANAGEMENT LTD
Park House, 16 Finsbury Circus,
London EC2M 7DJ
Telephone: 01-628 8131

Directors Involved with Pension Funds (UK only) W.T.J.Griffin, R.C.Thornton, P.G.Glossop, J.A.Dick, D.Fitzwilliam-Lay

Other Pension Fund Experts M.D.H.Ness, T.G.Arthur, BSc, FIA, FIS (Consultant Actuary)

Employees 50

Total Value of Funds Managed £220 million

Number of Pension Fund Clients 3

Services Offered to Pension Funds Investment management and administration worldwide

Other Offices 2840 Bank of America Centre, 555 California Street, San Francisco, California, 94104, USA, 1008-1010 Hutchison House, 10 Harcourt Road, Hong Kong

HENDERSON PENSION FUND MANAGEMENT LTD.
11 Austin Friars, London EC2N 2ED
Telephone: 01-588 3622

Directors Acting for Pension Funds R.P.Cazalet, C.G.Clarke, C.Day

Other Pension Fund Expert Sally Marshall

Employees 70

Total Value of Pension Funds Managed £85 million

Total Value of Pension Funds Advised £45 million

Number of Pension Fund Clients 13 separate accounts

Services Offered to Pension Funds Independent investment management

Associated Company Henderson Baring Management Ltd., Hong Kong

Other Information HPFM Ltd. is a wholly-owned subsidiary of Henderson Administration, an independent investment management company offering a high degree of personal service on an international basis for pension funds, investment trusts, unit trusts and private clients

IDJ INVESTMENT SERVICES LTD
Suite 33, 140 Park Lane, London W1Y 3AA
Telephone: 01-499 0355

Directors John C.Duckworth, MA, FIEE, FinstP, FinstF, John D. Incledon, MBA (Harvard),ØØ William Le G.Jacob

Employees 9

Number of Pension Fund Clients Certain of the larger private sector-and public sector pension funds

Services Offered to Pension Funds Investment analysis and portfolio monitoring, primarily for the unquoted segment of the managed funds

Associated Company Trusteed Funds Inc, 1 Winthrop Square, Boston, Massachusetts 02110, USA

Areas of Specialisation Investment analysis and the development of investment opportunities. Unquoted companies, particularly those manufacturing and industrial distribution companies which pose complex investment analysis problems

INTEL PORTFOLIO MANAGEMENT LTD
15 Christopher Street, London EC2A 2HA
Telephone: 01-247 7243

Directors Acting for Pension Funds D.T.H.Davenport, P.D.Brown, P.M.Formby

Pension Fund Expert D.T.H.Davenport

Employees 15

Value of Pension Funds Managed £2 million

Pension Fund Clients 5

The M&G Pension Fund Investment Service

In addition to managing the assets of unit trusts and life assurance funds M&G have for many years provided an investment management service for the pension funds of companies and public corporations, as well as charitable foundations.

Our independent status, wide contacts with stockbrokers and the very substantial volume of investments under M&G management place us in an ideal position to provide an investment service of this type.

If you require further information or wish to make an appointment to discuss the investment management of your Company's pension fund, please write to:

David Morgan
M&G INVESTMENT MANAGEMENT LTD
Three Quays, Tower Hill
London EC3R 6BQ
Telephone: 01-626 4588

THE M&G GROUP

(c) Other Financial Advisers

INTEL PORTFOLIO MANAGEMENT LTD *Continued*

Services Offered to Pension Funds Investment management and administration

Parent Company Investment Intelligence Ltd

Associated Companies Intel Funds (Management) Ltd

Areas of Specialization Direct Property Investment (P.M.Formby)

IVORY & SIME LTD

1 Charlotte Square, Edinburgh EH2 4DZ
Telephone: 031-225 1357

Directors Acting for Pension Funds James T.Laurenson, MA,FCA, Walter G.Scott,BSc,PhD

Pension Fund Expert Giles Weaver, MSc,FCA

Employees 60

Total value of Funds Managed or Advised £600 million

Number of Pension Fund Clients 15

Services Offered to Pension Funds International investment management

Other Information Ivory & Sime has offered specialist investment services since 1898. All the firms' income arises from investment management fees. The success of Ivory & Sime is dependent on the well being of its clients. The package offered to pension clients is highly service oriented

LOCAL AUTHORITIES' MUTUAL INVESTMENT TRUST

Winchester House, 77 London Wall,
London EC2N 1DB
Telephone: 01-588 1815

Chairman F.D.Pickering, CBE, DL

Director Viscount Churchill

Consultant J.R.Green,IPFA

Assistant Investment Managers E.P.Colquhoun, G.M.Burton

Advisory Panel E.M.Dawson, W.T.J.Griffin,FCA, C.J.Kirman, sir Dennis Pilcher,CBE,FRICS

Secretary D.F.Hart

Employees 28 (including staff of associated bodies)

Funds Managed £183 million

Number of Pension Fund Clients 76

Services Offered to Pension Funds The Trust provides (a) an investment advisory and management service for individual local authbrities, and (b) a range of common investment funds (Equity, Fixed Interest and Property) for local authority superannuation fund monies

Other Information The Trust offers a wide range of specialisation including investment in fixed interest security markets, UK and overseas equity markets and agricultural, commercial and industrial property markets

LOCANA CORPORATION (LONDON) LTD

Chancery House, Chancery Lane,
London WC2A 1QX
Telephone: 01-831 6936

Directors Acting for Pension Funds T.S.K.Yeo, T.A.Barry

Employees 6

Number of Pension Fund Clients 1

Services Offered to Pension Funds Full investment management service. Advice on establishment of new schemes, drafting of Trust Deeds etc. Emphasis on smaller companies

THE LONDON & WESTMINSTER (STERLING BROKERS) LTD

Lonwest House, 57-63 Scrutton Street,
London EC2A 4RT
Telephone: 01-739 4399

Directors Involved with Pension Funds B.H.Fitch (Managing Director), P.J.S.Andersen (Dealing Director)

Other Pension Fund Experts P.R.Heard, S.F.Stosik

Employees 25 money brokers

Specialist Services Offered to Pension Funds Investment portfolio consultants and specialists in arranging investment of both long term and short term funds in the local authority, inter-bank and sterling certificates of deposit markets, gilt-edged securities and investment property. Licenced dealer in securities

Associated Companies The London and Westminster Property Co Ltd., Caledonian Municipal Investments

M & G INVESTMENT MANAGEMENT LTD

Three Quays, Tower Hill, London EC3R 6BQ
Telephone: 01-626 4588

Directors Acting for Pension Funds D.L.Morgan, L.E.Linaker, M.R.Block, D.N.Robertson, D.L.Tucker, J.A.Cornes, J.W.Boeckmann, J.A.T.Caulfield, P.D.A.Nix

Pension Fund Experts D.L.Morgan, D.L.Tucker, R.J.Laker

Employees 50

Total Value of Funds Managed £110 million

Number of Pension Fund Clients 14

Services Offered to Pension Funds Investment management

Associated Companies Parent Company:M&G Group Holdings Ltd

Other Information Full investment management service covering capital markets in the U.K. and all international markets

R.P.MARTIN & CO LTD

36-40 Coleman Street, London EC2R 5AN
Telephone: 01-600 8691

Directors Involved with Pension Funds P.D.Moore, M.D.Phelan

Other Pension Fund Expert P.D.Moore

Employees 160

Other Offices Edinburgh and overseas offices

Associated Companies Milan, Lugano, Nassau, Hong Kong, Singapore, New York, Toronto and Bahrain

PERSONAL ATTENTION WITH CONTINUITY

The board of Tower Pension Fund Management Limited consists of six investment specialists who have worked together as a successful team over a period of ten years. They have achieved above average investment performance in a wide range of investment areas including pension funds.

Funds and their trustees are given close personal attention by a specific director with the emphasis on continuity. We believe this precise identification is vital in pension fund management.

For further details of our services please write or telephone:
Jim Nichols, Tower Pension Fund Management Limited, City Gate House, 39/45 Finsbury Square, London EC2A 1PX. Telephone 01-628 2612/20.

TOWER PENSION FUND MANAGEMENT LIMITED

AVC Schemes with the Woolwich.

If you are considering an Additional Voluntary Pension Scheme, talk to the Woolwich before you decide. We have an impressive portfolio of client companies who appreciate the way we simplify the administration of schemes for the Pension Fund. Employees, too, appreciate the way that they can see exactly how their contributions are growing. If you would like to know more about us, please contact:—
Michael Tuke, Secretary, Woolwich Equitable Building Society, Equitable House, Woolwich, London SE18 6AB – Tel: 01-854 2400.

WOOLWICH
EQUITABLE BUILDING SOCIETY

(c) Other Financial Advisers

GEOFFREY MORLEY & PARTNERS LTD
27 Great James Street, London WC1N 3ES
Telephone: 01-405 4151

Directors Acting for Pension Funds C.G.Morley,MA (Chairman), Brian Peters, BL,CA, Norman Pilkington,BA

Other Pension Fund Expert A.J.Bond,BSc,FIA

Employees 8

Total Value of Funds Managed £250 million

Number of Pension Fund Clients 16

Services Offered to Pension Funds Investment management

Parent Company Minet Holdings Ltd

MURRAY JOHNSTONE LTD
163 Hope Street, Glasgow G2 2UH
Telephone: 041-221 5521

Directors Acting for Pension Funds J.R.Johnstone, CA, J.R.W.Stephens, D.H.Williams,MA

Total Value of Pension Funds Managed £250 million

Number of Pension Fund Clients 3

Services Offered to Pension Funds Comprehensive investment management for UK and overseas markets

Other Information Murray Johnstone Japan Exempt Fund and M.J.American Exempt Fund are unauthorised exempt unit trusts offering specialist geographic diversification

ROWAN INVESTMENT MANAGEMENT SERVICES
City Gate House, 39-45 Finsbury Square, London EC2A 1JA
Telephone: 01-606 1066

Directors Acting for Pension Funds The Hon.James Ogilvy (Chairman & Managing Director), R.C.Buist, J.C.R.D'Albiac, R.H.A.Southby

Pension Fund Experts I.A.Martin, B.Woolf

Employees 28

Total Value of Funds Managed or Advised £100 million

Number of Pension Fund Clients 11

Services Offered to Pension Funds Full range of investment management and investment administration

Parent Company Rowe & Pitman, members of Pitman Stock Exchange, London, with offices in San Francisco, Boston, Hong Kong, Tokyo and Johannesburg

Associated Companies Rowan Unit Trust Management Ltd., Rowan Managers (Channel Islands) Ltd.

ROWE RUDD & CO.LTD.
63 London Wall, London EC2M 5UQ
Telephone: 01-628 9666

Directors Acting for Pension Funds Tony Rudd, Gerald Kelly

Employees 30

Number of Pension Fund Clients 10

Other Offices Geneva, Jeddah

Other Information Provides a Risk Analysis Service

STEWART FUND MANAGERS LTD
45 Charlotte Square, Edinburgh EH2 4HW
Telephone: 031-226 3271

Directors Acting for Pension Funds J.W.A.Shaw Stewart, J.G.D.Ferguson, E.A.W.Tulloch

Employees 17

Total Value of Funds Managed Total Funds managed exceed £125 million

Number of Pension Fund Clients 3 gross funds

Services Offered to Pension Funds Independent investment management of equity and fixed interest securities, but not of property. Full administrative service

Associated Companies Stewart Unit Trust Managers Ltd

Other Information Stewart American Exempt Fund. Unauthorised Unit trust for equity investment in North America

TARGET TRUST MANAGERS LTD
Gerrard House, 31 Gresham Street, London EC2V 7DT
Telephone: 01-600 7533

Chairman A.P.W.Simon

General Manager I.G.Sampson

Director Acting for Pension Funds Richard I.E.Carswell

Investment Managers Dawnay Day & Co Ltd

Property Advisers Jones, Lang, Wootton

Total Value of Funds Managed £130 million

Services Offered to Pension Funds Investment management through a range of authorised unit trusts and Life Assurance Funds. Also advises on small self invested pension schemes

TAY & THAMES INVESTMENT SERVICES LTD
Belsize House, West Ferry, Dundee DD5 1NF
Telephone: 0382-78244

Managers A.K.Aitkenhead, W.D.Marr, B.C.Tait

Services Offered to Pension Funds Full investment management services

THROGMORTON MANAGEMENT LTD
7 Chandos Street, London W1M 9DE
Telephone: 01-637 5377

Directors R.C.B.Lane,FIA(Chairman), J.A.Mulligan, FIA(Managing Director), B.Benjamin,FIA, W.G.Nursaw,FCIS,ACII, M.G.Talbot-Rice,FCA, T.A.Warren,FIA

Staff 2

Number of Pension Fund Clients 8

Services Offered to Pension Funds Investment management, investment administration, fund administration, investment advisory service

Other Information Although Company itself is solely engaged in investment administration and management, and fund administration, it has links with other organisations which can provide advice on benefit structure and costing thereof

(c) Other Financial Advisers

TOUCHE, REMNANT & CO.

Winchester House, 77 London Wall, London EC2N 1BH
Telephone: 01-638 1737

Directors Acting for Pension Funds G.W.Hague, N.A.Crooks-Meredith, C.J.Kirman, A.Watson

Pension Fund Experts S.A.Fowler, M.B.Moule, G.Judd (Agricultural Consultant)

Employees 74

Total Value of Pension Funds Managed £200 million

Number of Pension Fund Clients 11

Services Offered to Pension Funds Investment Management together with a complete accounting service including reclaiming income tax

Other information Touche, Remnant is owned by Investment Trust Companies forming Touche, Remnant Group and is dedicated solely to the professional management of investment funds. It has specialists in leading capital markets of the world as well as in commercial and agricultural property

UNICO FINANCE LIMITED

32 Howard Street, Belfast BT1 6PF
Telephone: 0232 26264

Directors Acting for Pension Funds N.P.Dewbury, W.J.Hegarty, B.Sherlock

Pension Fund Experts W.J.Johnston,FCA

Associated Companies Unico Group Limited, Unico Finance (Ireland) Ltd, Unico (Isle of Man)Ltd, Unico Finance (Channel Islands) Ltd

Represented in Dublin, London, Belfast, Isle of Man, Channel Islands, Monte Carlo

ANTHONY WIELER & CO LTD

19 Widegate Street, London E1 7HP
Telephone: 01-247 8827

Directors and Experts Acting for Pension Funds P.J.Ridgwell, MA, J.F.Chown,MA, J.D.S.Taylor-Dickson

Employees 15

Total Value of Funds Managed £16 million

Number of Pension Fund Clients 3

Services Offered to Pension Funds Complete investment management and advisory service, discretionary and non-discretionary

Associated Company J.F.Chown & Co hold a 15% sharestake. Their business includes tax advice, and advice on all employee benefits including pension funds

Other Information Investment management service provided for all types of fund, corporate and private resident and external, in the UK, Channel Islands or Switzerland, inter alia

---

A Background to Pension Fund Investment

A guide to investment for Pension Funds containing 21 articles on how to choose your investment advisers, where to invest and how to invest

Available for £6.35 including postage and packing from:
A P Financial Registers Ltd
9 Courtleigh Gardens, London NW11 9JX
Telephone 01-458 1607

(d) Pooled Pension Funds

A pooled pension fund is a commingled fund of investments in which only tax-exempt investors, such as pension funds, may purchase units. These pooled pension funds are constituted as one of the following:

a Exempt Unit Trusts, which can be divided into —
1. Authorised Unit Trusts, which have been approved by the Department of Trade. These can advertise and normally invest predominantly in UK equities.
2. Unauthorised Unit Trusts, which have not been authorised by the Department of Trade and therefore may not advertise. There are no investment restrictions and they can invest in equities, fixed interest securities, real property or operate a mixed fund investing in any type of investment.

b Property Unit Trusts are a specialist type of unauthorised exempt unit trust investing in real property on a pooled basis.

c Managed Pension Funds, operated under a special form of unit-linked insured pension policy. Some of these funds are split into separate investment sections (e.g. equity, fixed interest and property) although most operate a mixed fund.

This section has been compiled with the help of Wyatt Harris Graham Ltd from information appearing in their *Survey of Pooled Pension Funds*. More detailed information about these funds can be found in this Survey, which is available from: Wyatt Harris Graham Ltd, 30 Queen Anne's Gate, London SW1H 9AW (Tel. 01-222 8033).

ABBOTSTONE AGRICULTURAL PROPERTY UNIT TRUST

88 Leadenhall Street, London EC3A 3DT
Telephone: 01-588 2830

Committee of Management Dr.J.R.G.Bradfield (Chairman), T.G.Abell, R.Caudwell, G.N.Mainwaring, FRICS, O.B.Harris, L.W.Robson, FCA

Director Responsible for Fund T.G.Abell

Trustees Baring Brothers & Co Ltd

Consultant Surveyors and Managing Agents Smiths Gore

Independent Valuers Cluttons

Fund Type Property Unit Trust

Fund Size (at 31.7.80) £18 million

Unit Holders 34

Properties Held 50

ALLIED HAMBRO EXEMPT SMALLER COMPANIES FUND

41 Bishopsgate, London EC2P 2AA
Telephone: 01-588 2851

Director Responsible for Fund T.A.Tacchi

Fund and Investment Managers Allied Hambro Ltd.

Fund Type Equity Fund Authorised Exempt Unit Trust

Fund Size (at 1.9.80) £4.1 million

Unit Holders 84

Securities Held 99

ALLIED HAMBRO FAR EAST EXEMPT FUND

41 Bishopsgate, London EC2P 2AA
Telephone: 01-588 2851

Director Responsible for Fund J.W.D.Olivier

Investment Managers Allied Hambro Ltd.

Trustees The Royal Bank of Scotland London Trustee Company

Fund Type Equity Fund Authorised Exempt Unit Trust

Fund Size (at 1.9.80) £3.2 million

Unit Holders 28

Securities Held 71

ALLIED HAMBRO INCOME EXEMPT FUND

41 Bishopsgate, London EC2P 2AA
Telephone: 01-588 2851

Unit Trust Manager Allied Hambro Ltd.

Director Responsible for Fund N.Roach

Trustees Midland Bank Trust Co. Ltd.

Fund Type Equity Fund, Authorized Exempt Unit Trust

ALLIED HAMBRO USA EXEMPT FUND

41 Bishopsgate, London EC2P 2AA
Telephone: 01-588 2851

Managing Director M.V.St. Giles

Director Responsible for Fund P.Armstrong

Fund and Investment Managers Allied Hambro Ltd.

Trustee Royal Bank of Scotland, London Trustee Co.

Fund Type Equity Fund, Authorised Exempt Unit Trust

Fund Size (at 1.9.80) £3.4 million

Unit Holders 50

Securities Held 72

(d) Pooled Pension Funds

AMERICAN PROPERTY TRUST
P&O Building, Leadenhall Street,
London EC3V 4DY
Telephone: 01-283 7727

Committee of Management P.R.Dashwood (Chairman), J.Edmead, J.W.Martin, D.E.Jackson, W.A.Lund, J.K.Lardner, A.J.M.Huntley

Financial Advisers County Bank Ltd

Trustees National Westminster Bank Ltd.

Investment Adviser Richard Ellis

Fund Type Property Unit Trust

Fund Size £12 million

Unit Holders 9

THE ARUNDEL EXEMPT FUND
33 Old Broad Street, London EC2N 1HT
Telephone: 01-283 8171

Fund Manager and Trustees Chemical Bank Trustee Co. Ltd.

Investment Manager Chemical Bank, International Investment Services

Fund Type Mixed Fund, Unauthorised Exempt Unit Trust

Fund Size (at 30.9.80) £520,000

Unit Holders 3

BANKERS TRUST EXEMPT FUND
9 Queen Victoria Street, London EC4P 4DB
Telephone: 01-236 5030

Fund and Investment Manager Bankers Trust Company Ltd

Director Responsible for Fund John D.Webb

Fund Type Mixed Fund, Unauthorised Exempt Unit Trust

Fund Size (at 30.6.80) £15.6 million

Unit Holders 16

BARBICAN EUROPEAN (EXEMPT) TRUST
91-99 New London Road, Chelmsford CM2 0PY
Telephone: 0245 51651

Unit Trust Manager Transatlantic and General Securities Co Ltd

Manager Responsible for Fund A.R.P.Bird (Phillips & Drew)

Trustees Lloyds Bank Ltd.

Fund Type Equity Fund, Authorised Exempt Unit Trust

Fund Size (at 27.08.80) £2,767,000

Unit Holders 77

Securities Held 32

BARCLAYS UNICORN EXEMPT TRUST
Unicorn House, 252 Romford Road,
London E7 9JB
Telephone: 01-534 5544

Fund Manager Barclays Unicorn Ltd.

Investment Manager Barclays Bank Trust Co.Ltd.

Trustees Royal Exchange Assurance

Fund Type Equity Fund, Authorised Exempt Unit Trust

Fund Size (at 25.4.80) £4,840,000

BRIDGE EXEMPT FUND
Regis House, King William Street,
London EC4R 9AR
Telephone: 01-623 4951

Fund Manager Bridge Fund Managers Ltd

Director Responsible for Fund P.J.Brickell

Investment Manager Vickers da Costa Ltd.

Trustees Lloyds Bank Ltd.

Fund Type Equity Fund, Authorised Exempt Unit Trust

Fund Size £800,000

Unit Holders 21

Securities Held 27

BRITANNIA EXEMPT TRUST
3 London Wall Buildings, London Wall,
London EC2M 5QL
Telephone: 01-588 2777

Fund and Investment Manager Britannia Trust Management Ltd

Trustees National Westminster Bank Ltd

Fund Type Equity Fund, Authorised Exempt Unit Trust

Fund Size (at 31.3.80) £471,000

THE CANADA LIFE MANAGED PENSION FUND
Canada Life House, High Street, Potters Bar,
Herts.EN6 5BA
Telephone: 51122

Fund Manager The Canada Life Assurance Company

Fund Type Mixed Fund. Managed Pension Fund - The Canada Life Assurance Company

Fund Size (at 15.4.80) £190,000

Unit Holders 3

CHARTERHOUSE EXEMPT FUND
23 St Swithin's Lane, London EC4N 8AD
Telephone: 01-248 3999

Fund Manager and Trustees Charterhouse Pensions Ltd

Company Secretary P.A.G.French

Investment Manager Charterhouse Japhet Ltd

Fund Type Mixed Fund, Unauthorised Exempt Unit Trust

Fund Size (at 31.3.79) £1.32 million

COLONIAL MUTUAL LIFE MANAGED FUND
24 Ludgate Hill, London EC4P 4BD
Telephone: 01-248 9861

Fund Manager Colonial Mutual Life (Pension Annuities) Ltd

Director Responsible for Fund E.K.V.Redfern

Fund Type Separate Equity, Fixed Interest and

(d) Pooled Pension Funds

COLONIAL MUTUAL LIFE MANAGED FUND *Continued*

Mixed Funds; Managed Pension Fund-Colonial Mutual Life Assurance Society Ltd

Fund Size (Mixed Fund) (at Oct.1980) £22 million

COMMERCIAL UNION MANAGED FUND

St. Helen's, 1 Undershaft, London EC3P 3DQ
Telephone: 01-283 7500

Fund Manager Commercial Union Assurance Co.Ltd.

Manager Responsible for Fund B.W.T.Dawson,FIA (Pensions Actuary)

Investment Manager S.R.Burley

Property Valuer St. Quintin

Fund Type Separate Property, Equity, Fixed Interest and Mixed Funds. Managed Pension Funds - Commercial Union Assurance Co.Ltd.

Fund Size (at 30.6.80) £73.1 million

Unit Holders 54

Securities/Properties held (at 31.12.79) 117 securities, 19 properties

CONFEDERATION LIFE GROUP PENSION POOLED FUNDS

Confederation Life House, 50 Chancery Lane, London WC2A 1HE
Telephone: 01-242 7126

Fund Manager Confederation Life Insurance Co

Director/Manager Responsible for Fund J.C.H.Tate, MA

Investment Managers J.Davies, R.E.Durrant, K.Honour

Property Valuer Jones Lang Wootton and others

Fund Type Separate Equity, Fixed Interest, Property and Mixed Funds. Managed Pension Fund

Fund Size (at 31.3.80) Mixed £4.24 million, Equity £6.98 million, Fixed Interest £6.01 million, Property £1.98 million

CO-OPERATIVE PENSION FUNDS FIXED INTEREST UNIT TRUST

St.Alban's House, Goldsmith Street, London EC2P 2DL
Telephone: 01-600 4555

Fund Manager Co-operative Pension Funds Unit Trust Managers Ltd

Investment Manager Co-operative City Investments Ltd

Investment Adviser S.G.Warburg & Co Ltd

Trustees Williams & Glyn's Bank Ltd

Fund Type Fixed Interest Fund, Unauthorised Exempt Unit Trust

Fund Size (at 29.8.80) £5.4 million

Unit Holders 95

Securities Held 12

CO-OPERATIVE PENSION FUNDS UNIT TRUST

St. Alban's House, Goldsmith Street, London EC2P 2DL
Telephone: 01-600 4555

Fund Manager Co-operative Pension Funds Unit Trust Managers Ltd

Director Responsible for Fund R.S.Malnick

Investment Manager Co-operative City Investments Ltd

Investment Adviser S.G.Warburg & Co Ltd

Trustees Williams & Glyn's Bank Ltd.

Fund Type Equity Fund, Authorised Exempt Unit Trust

Fund Size (at 29.8.80) £118.3 million

Unit Holders 138

Securities Held 161

COUNTY AMERICAN EXEMPT FUND

11 Old Broad Street, London EC2
Telephone: 01-638 6000

Committee of Management D.B.Chynoweth (Chairman), C.T.Fletcher, J.M.Marriott, P.W.Jenkins, C.J.Davies, G.E.Daniel, A.R.Porter

Investment Managers County Bank (J.Earl)

Trustees Royal Exchange Assurance

Fund Type Unauthorised exempt Unit Trust

Fund Size (at 1.9.80) £10.5 million

Unit Holders 7

Securities Held 66

COUNTY BANK SMALLER COMPANIES EXEMPT FUND

11 Old Broad Street, London EC2N 1BB
Telephone: 01-638 6000

Fund Manager County Bank Ltd.

Investment Managers County Bank (P.Allen)

Chairman of Investment Committee C.N.Villiers (County Bank Ltd.)

Trustees Royal Exchange Assurance

Fund Type Equity Fund, Unauthorised Exempt Unit Trust

Unit Holders 22

Securities/Properties Held 50

CROWN LIFE MANAGED PENSION FUNDS

Crown Life House, Woking, Surrey GU21 1XW
Telephone: 04862-5033

Fund Manager Crown Life Pensions Ltd.

Fund Type Separate Cash & Mixed Funds. Managed Pension Fund - Crown Life Insurance Company

Fund Size £19.8 million

Unit Holders 3,112

EAGLE STAR MANAGED PENSION FUNDS

Eagle Star House, 9 Aldgate High Street, London EC3N 1LD
Telephone: 01-377 8000

Registered Office 1 Threadneedle Street, London EC2R 8BE

Fund Manager Eagle Pension Funds Ltd

Fund Type Separate Cash, Equity, Fixed Interest,

593

(d) Pooled Pension Funds

EAGLE STAR MANAGED PENSION FUNDS *Continued*

Property and Mixed Funds; Managed Pension Fund-Eagle Star Insurance Group

Fund Size (at 12.3.80) Money Market £0.8 million, Stock Exchange £49.2 million, Fixed Interest £1.95 million,' Property £7.4 million, Overseas £1.6 million, Mixed £56.6 million. Total (at 10.9.80) £111.6 million

Unit Holders 67

EBOR PHOENIX ASSURANCE CO.LTD. MANAGED PENSION FUNDS

4-5 King William Street, London EC4P 4HR
Telephone: 01-626 9876

Fund Manager Ebor Phoenix Assurance Co.Ltd.

Pensions Manager J.Walker

Property Valuer Hillier Parker May & Rowden

Fund Type Separate Equity, Fixed Interest, Property, Money, Mixed and International Funds. Managed Pension Fund - Phoenix Assurance Co.Ltd.

Fund Size (at 8.4.80) Equity £3.0 million, Fixed Interest £5.5 million, Cash £1.1 million, Property £1.9 million, Mixed £3.4 million

Unit Holders 2

EDINBURGH EXEMPT AMERICAN FUND

4 Melville Crescent, Edinburgh EH3 7JB
Telephone: 031-226 4931

Fund and Investment Manager Edinburgh Fund Managers Ltd

Director Responsible for Fund C.H.Ross,CA

Trustees American Trust Co Ltd

Fund Type Equity Fund, Unauthorised Exempt Unit Trust

Fund Size (at 31.8.80) £15.3 million

Unit Holders 115

Securities Held 53

EDINBURGH EXEMPT JAPAN FUND

4 Melville Crescent, Edinburgh EH3 7JB
Telephone: 031-226 4931

Fund and Investment Manager Edinburgh Fund Managers Ltd

Director Responsible for Fund G.A.Y.MacLennan, CA

Trustee American Trust Co Ltd

Fund Type Equity Fund, Unauthorised Exempt Unit Trust

Fund Size (at 31.8.80) £10.2 million

Unit Holders 36

Securities Held 47

EDINBURGH EXEMPT PACIFIC FUND

4 Melville Crescent, Edinburgh EH3 7JB
Telephone: 031-226 4931

Director Responsible for Fund G.A.Y.MacLennan, CA

Fund and Investment Manager Edinburgh Fund Managers Ltd.

Trustees American Trust Co. Ltd.

Fund Type Equity Fund, Unauthorised Exempt Unit Trust

ELECTRA SMALL COMPANIES EXEMPT FUND

Electra House, Temple Place,
Victoria Embankment, London WC2R 3HP
Telephone: 01-836 7766

Investment Manager Electra Group Services Ltd

Fund Type Equity Fund, Unauthorised Exempt Unit Trust

ENGLISH INSURANCE MANAGED PENSION FUND

20-24 Addiscombe Road, Croydon CR9 5BS
Telephone: 01-686 3736

Fund Manager English Insurance (Pensions Management) Ltd.

Fund Type Separate Equity, Fixed Interest, Mixed Funds and property; Managed Pension Fund-The English Insurance Co Ltd

Fund Size (at 15.9.80) Equity £12.0 million, Fixed Interest £1.4 million, Property £1.5 million, Mixed £10.8 million (Total Segregated Funds £15.1 million)

EQUITY & LAW MANAGED FUND

Amersham Road, High Wycombe, Bucks HP17 0JP
Telephone: 0494 33377

Fund Manager Equity & Law (Managed Funds) Ltd

Manager Responsible for Fund J.Medlock, BSc (Econ), FIA

Investment Manager P.G.Smith, MA, FIA

Property Investment Manager R.A.Booth, FRICS

Assistant Investment Managers C.Pearson,MA,FIA, K.R.Gilham,BSc,FIA

Secretary R.E.Ellisdon, BSc(Econ), FIA

Fund Type Separate Equity, Fixed Interest, Property, Overseas, Mixed and Cash

Property Valuer Healey & Baker

Fund Size (at 13.8.80) Equity: £0.46M, Fixed Interest: £6.57M, Property: £14.51M, Overseas: £1.62M, Mixed: £75.27M, Cash: £0.06M

Unit Holders 36

Securities/Properties Held Equity: 36, Fixed Interest: 15, Property: 52, Overseas: 16, Mixed: 171

Unit Holders 22

Associated Funds Equity and Cash Funds

EQUITY CAPITAL UNIT TRUST ('EQUITY BANK')

Leith House, 47-57 Gresham Street,
London EC2V 7EH
Telephone: 01-606 8513

Fund Manager Equity Capital (Management) Ltd.

Secretary B.H.Dean

Trustees Equity capital Trustee Ltd.

Fund Type Equity Fund, Unauthorised Exempt Unit Trust

Fund Size (at 31.3.80) £15.3 million

(d) Pooled Pension Funds

EQUITY CAPITAL UNIT TRUST Continued

Unit Holders 150
Securities Held 9
Associated Fund Part of Equity Capital for Industry

F & C ANGLO-NIPPON EXEMPT FUND
1 Laurence Pountney Hill, London EC4R 0BA
Telephone: 01-623 4680
Fund and Investment Manager F & C Management Ltd.
Trustees General Investors and Trustees Ltd.
Fund Type Equity Fund, Unauthorised Exempt Fund
Fund Size (at 1.8.80) £1.7 million
Unit Holders 19
Securities Held 34

F & C NORTH AMERICAN EXEMPT FUND
1 Laurence Pountney Hill, London EC4R 0BA
Telephone: 01-623 4680
Fund and Investment Manager F & C Management Ltd.
Director Responsible for Fund A.H.Baring
Trustees General Investors and Trustees Ltd
Fund Type Equity Fund, Unauthorised Exempt Fund
Fund Size (at 1.8.80) £700,000
Unit Holders 11
Securities Held 19

THE FLEMING AMERICAN EXEMPT FUND
8 Crosby Square, London EC3A 6AN
Telephone: 01-638 5858
Fund Manager Robert Fleming Investment Management Ltd.
Director Responsible for Fund C.K.R.Nunneley, CA, APMI
Investment Manager N.W.A.Chapman
Trustees Robert Fleming Trustee Co. Ltd.
Fund Type Quoted U.S. and Canadian Equities and Convortibloc; Unauthorised Exempt Unit Trust
Fund Size (at 17.11.80) £11.8 million
Unit Holders 100
Securities Held 49

THE FLEMING JAPANESE EXEMPT FUND
8 Crosby Square, London EC3A 6AN
Telephone: 01-638 5858
Fund Manager Robert Fleming Investment Management Ltd.
Director Responsible for Fund C.K.R.Nunneley, CA, APMI
Investment Manager H.Shiozumi
Trustees Robert Fleming Trustee Co. Ltd.
Fund Type Quoted Japanese Equities and Convertible, Unauthorised Exempt Unit Trust
Fund Size (at 17.11.80) £63.4 million

Unit Holders 185
Securities Held 62

THE FLEMING PROPERTY UNIT TRUST
8 Crosby Square, London EC3A 6AN
Telephone: 01-638 5858
Fund Manager Robert Fleming & Co. Ltd.
Director Responsible for Fund D.C.F.Pearson, MA
Investment Managers J.Newman,BSc,FRICS, J.R.Sinclair,ARICS
Trustees Robert Fleming Trustee Co. Ltd.
Consultant Surveyor and Managing Agents Allsop & Co
Fund Type Property Unit Trust
Fund Size (at 27.11.80) £202 million
Unit Holders 454
Properties Held 122

FRASER EXEMPT UNIT TRUST
2 Friars Lane, Richmond, Surrey TW9 1NL
Telephone: 01-948 0164
Fund Manager Fraser Unit Trust Managers Ltd.
Investment Manager Fraser Green Ltd.
Trustees Barclays Bank Trust Co.Ltd.
Fund Type Equity Fund, Unauthorised Exempt Unit Trust
Fund Size (at 21.4.80) £115,000
Unit Holders 8

FRIENDS' PROVIDENT MANAGED PENSION FUNDS
Pixham End, Dorking, Surrey RH4 1QA
Telephone: 0306-5055
Fund Manager Friends' Provident Managed Pension Funds Ltd
Investment Managers Friends' Provident Life Office
Fund Type Separate Cash, Ordinary Share, Fixed Interest, Property and Mixed Funds
Fund Size (at 29.8.80) Cash: £0.17M, Ordinary Share: £11.33M, Fixed Interest:£14.50 Million, Property: £8.70 Million, Mixed: £28.78M

GARTMORE INTERNATIONAL EXEMPT FUND
2 St Mary Axe, London EC3A 8BP
Telephone: 01-283 3531
Fund & Investment Manager Gartmore Investments Ltd
Director Responsible for Fund W.Campbell Allan, CA
Trustees Coutts & Co
Fund Type Equity Fund, Authorised Exempt Unit Trust
Fund Size (at 30.9.78) £480,000
Unit Holders 30
Securities Held 23

GLOBE PENSIONS MANAGED FUND
PO Box 144, New Hall Place, Liverpool L69 3EN
Telephone: 051-227 4422

(d) Pooled Pension Funds

GLOBE PENSIONS MANAGED FUND *Continued*

Fund Manager Globe Insurance Company Ltd
Property Valuer Richard Ellis
Fund Type Mixed Fund. Managed Pension Fund - Royal Insurance Co.Ltd.
Fund Size (at 8.10.80) £32.7 million

G.T.PENSION EXEMPT FUND
Park House, 16 Finsbury Circus,
London EC2M 7DD
Telephone: 01-628 8131

Fund and Investment Manager G.T.Unit Managers Ltd
Director Responsible for Fund M.D.H.Ness
Trustees Lloyds Bank Ltd
Fund Type Equity Fund, Authorised Exempt Unit Trust
Fund Size (at 31.1.80) £334,000
Unit Holders 13
Securities Held 33

GUARDIAN ROYAL EXCHANGE MANAGED FUNDS
Royal Exchange, London EC3V 3LS
Telephone: 01-283 7101

Fund Manager G.R.E.Pensions Management Co Ltd
Investment Manager T.M.O'Connell
Fund Type Equity, Fixed Interest, Property, Deposit, International, Master and Mixed Funds. Managed Pension Fund - Guardian Royal Exchange Assurance Group
Fund Size (at 14.10.80) £46.03 million
Other Associated Funds GRE also manage pension funds on an individual basis

HANOVER PROPERTY UNIT TRUST
114 Old Broad Street, London EC2P 2HY
Telephone: 01-588 6464

Committee of Management J.A.Mulligan (Chairman), A.Conlong, R.D.Crook, J.B.Dennis, M.Lander, H.Morris, M.A.Vaughan-Lee
Property Advisers and Managing Agents Knight, Frank & Rutley
Financial Advisers Samuel Montagu & Co.Ltd.
Trustees Montagu Executor & Trustee Co.Ltd.
Property Valuer Knight, Frank & Rutley
Fund Type Property Unit Trust
Fund Size (at 20.3.80) £83.1 million
Unit Holders 170

HENDERSON EUROPEAN EXEMPT TRUST
11 Austin Friars, London EC2N 2ED
Telephone: 01-588 3622

Unit Trust Manager Henderson Unit Trust Management Ltd.
Director Responsible for Fund H.Priestley
Investment Managers Henderson Pension Fund Management Ltd.
Trustees Williams and Glyn's Bank Ltd.
Fund Type Equity, Authorised Exempt Unit Trust
Fund Size (at 30.9.80) £100,000
Unit Holders 2
Securities Held 6

HENDERSON HIGH INCOME EXEMPT TRUST
11 Austin Friars, London EC2N 2ED
Telephone: 01-588 3622

Fund Manager Henderson Unit Trust Management Ltd.
Director Responsible for Fund C.Clarke
Investment Managers Henderson Pension Fund Management Ltd.
Trustees Williams and Glyn's Bank Ltd.
Fund Type Equity, Authorised Exempt Unit Trust

HENDERSON JAPAN EXEMPT TRUST
11 Austin Friars, London EC2N 2ED
Telephone: 01-588 3622

Unit Trust Manager Henderson Unit Trust Management Ltd.
Manager Responsible for Fund James P.Williams
Investment Managers Henderson Baring Management Ltd. (Hong Kong)
Trustees Williams & Glyn's Bank Ltd
Fund Type Equity, Authorised, Exempt Trust
Fund Size (at 30.9.80) £6 million
Unit Holders 40
Securities Held 35

HENDERSON SMALLER COMPANIES EXEMPT TRUST
11 Austin Friars, London EC2N 2ED
Telephone: 01-588 3622

Unit Trust Manager Henderson Unit Trust Management Ltd
Director Responsible for Fund H.Priestley
Investment Managers Henderson Pension Fund Management Ltd.
Trustees Williams & Glyn's Bank Ltd
Fund Type Equity Fund, Authorised Exempt Unit Trust
Fund Size (at 30.9.80) £2 million
Unit Holders 20
Securities Held 40

HENDERSON NORTH AMERICAN EXEMPT TRUST
11 Austin Friars, London EC2N 2ED
Telephone: 01-588 3622

Unit Trust Manager Henderson Unit Trust Management Ltd.
Investment Manager Henderson Pension Fund Management Ltd.
Directors Responsible for Fund B.H.B.Wrey, R.I.Henderson
Trustees Williams & Glyn's Bank Ltd
Fund Size (at 30.9.80) £11.2 million

(d) Pooled Pension Funds

HENDERSON NORTH AMERICAN EXEMPT TRUST
Continued

Fund Type Equity Fund, Authorised Exempt Unit Trust
Unit Holders 160
Securities Held 40

HILL SAMUEL AGRICULTURAL UNIT TRUST
45 Beech Street, London EC2P 2LX
Telephone: 01-628 8011
Committee of Management D.S.Allison (Chairman), W.E.Broadfield, W.Hollinrake, Sir Emrys Jones, G.H.Ross Goobey
Investment Managers Hill Samuel Investment Management Ltd
Trustees Hill Samuel & Co Ltd
Consultant Surveyor Savills
Fund Type Property Unit Trust
Fund Size (at 8.9.80) £24.0 million
Unit Holders 133

HILL SAMUEL GENERAL EXEMPT TRUST
45 Beech Street, London EC2P 2LX
Telephone: 01-628 8011
Fund Managers Hill Samuel Unit Trust Managers
Investment Managers Hill Samuel Investment Management Ltd.
Trustees Midland Bank Trust Co Ltd
Fund Type Equity Fund, Authorised Exempt Unit Trust
Fund Size (at 17.9.79) £5.07 million

HILL SAMUEL PROPERTY UNIT TRUST
45 Beech Street, London EC2P 2LX
Telephone: 01-628 8011
Management Company Property Fund Management Ltd.
Directors D.S.Allison (Chairman), Miss A.M.Head, W.E.Broadfield, G.J.J.Dennis, A.A.Gaitskell, C.G.Morley, G.H.Ross Goobey
Investment Managers Hill Samuel Investment Management Ltd.
Managing Agents Edward Erdman & Co
Fund Type Property Unit Trust
Fund Size £79.5 million
Unit Holders 250

THE INDUSTRIAL AND COMMERCIAL PROPERTY UNIT TRUST
23 Great Winchester Street, London EC2P 2AX
Telephone: 01-588 4545
Fund Manager Morgan Grenfell Property Services Ltd.
Director Responsible for Fund N.E.Borrett
Trustees The Royal Bank of Scotland London Trustee Co.
Independent Valuers Hillier Parker May & Rowden, Cluttons
Fund Type Property Unit Trust

Fund Size (at 1.4.80) £31.3 million
Unit Holders 67
Properties Held 36

IRISH LIFE ASSURANCE CO.LTD. MANAGED PENSION FUNDS
Irish Life Centre, Lower Abbey Street, Dublin 1
Telephone: 720288
London Office 11 Finsbury Square, London EC2 (01-628 8253)
Fund and Investment Manager Irish Life Assurance Co.Ltd.
Fund Type Separate Equity, Fixed Interest, Managed Retirement, Pension Investment and Property Funds. Managed Pension Fund - Irish Life Assurance Co.Ltd.
Fund Size (at 1.4.80) Equity IR£2.9 million, Fixed Interest IR£5.0 million, Managed Retirement IR£1.0 million, Pension Investment IR£37.2 million, Property £24.0 million
Unit Holders Equity 7, Fixed Interest 8, Managed Retirement 32, Pension Investment 59, Property 96

KEY EXEMPT FUND
25 Milk Street, London EC2V 8JE
Telephone: 01-606 7070
Unit Trust Manager Key Fund Managers Ltd.
Investment Manager Keyser Ullmann Investment Managers Ltd
Director Responsible for Fund R.W.Seabrook
Trustees National Westminster Bank
Fund Type Equity Fund, Authorised Exempt Unit Trust
Fund Size (at 14.8.80) £5.5 million
Unit Holders 22
Securities Held 50

KEYSER ULLMANN PENSIONS MANAGED FUND
25 Milk Street, London EC2V 8JE
Telephone: 01-606 7070
Fund Manager Keyser Ullmann Pensions Management Ltd
Investment Managers Keyser Ullmann Investment Management Ltd.
Director Responsible for Fund P.H.Campbell
Trustees National Westminster Bank Ltd
Property Valuer Debeham Tewson & Chinnocks
Fund Type Separate Cash, Equity, Overseas, Smaller Company, Fixed Interest and Property Funds; Managed Pension Fund - Keyser Ullmann Pensions Management Ltd.
Fund Size (at 9.4.80) Equity £1.0 million, Fixed Interest £1.5 million, Overseas £0.5 million, Smaller Companies £0.5 million, Property £1.0 million

KING AND SHAXSON BOND FUND
52 Cornhill, London EC3V 3PD
Telephone: 01-623 5433
Fund Manager King & Shaxson Ltd

(d) Pooled Pension Funds

KING AND SHAXSON BOND FUND *Continued*

Directors Responsible for Fund J.C.Parrish, P.A.Johnson

Investment Manager King & Shaxson Fund Managers Ltd

Trustees The Bank of Scotland

Fund Type Restricted to Gilt Edged/Cash, Unauthorised Exempt Unit Trust

Securities Held Gilts and Cash only

Other Associated Funds King & Shaxson Gilt Edged Portfolio Management Service, King & Shaxson Gilt Fund (Jersey) Ltd. King & Shaxson Guernsey Gilt Fund, King & Shaxson Isle of Man Gilt Trust, King & Shaxson Government Securities Bond Target Gilt Fund, First International Securities Trust Ltd.

KLEINWORT, BENSON FARMLAND TRUST

20 Fenchurch Street, London EC3P 3DB
Telephone: 01-623 8000

Fund Manager Kleinwort Benson Farmland Trust (Managers) Ltd

Director Responsible for Fund A.C.Mortimer

Investment Managers Kleinwort, Benson Farmland Trust (Managers) Ltd.

Independent Valuers Strutt & Parker, Carter Jonas

Trustee Barclays Bank Trust Co.Ltd.

Fund Type Agricultural - unauthorised

Fund Size (at 30.9.80) £14.587 million

Unit Holders 24

KLEINWORT, BENSON PROPERTY FUND

20 Fenchurch Street, London EC3P 3DB
Telephone: 01-623 8000

Fund Managers Kleinwort Benson Unit Managers Ltd

Director Responsible for Fund A.C.Mortimer

Investment Managers Kleinwort Benson Investment Management Ltd.

Trustees Kleinwort, Benson (Trustees) Ltd.

Managing Agents & Surveyors Hillier Parker May & Rowden, Savills

Fund Type Property - unauthorised

Fund Size (at 30.9.80) £22.466 million

Unit Holders 50

Properties Held 8 Commercial and Industrial properties, 1 farm estate of approx 1,457 acres

KLEINWORT, BENSON EXEMPT PACIFIC FUND

20 Fenchurch Street, London EC3P 3DB
Telephone: 01-623 8000

Fund Managers Kleinwort, Benson Unit Managers Ltd.

Manager Responsible for Fund R.D.C.Prichard

Investment Managers Kleinwort, Benson Investment Management Ltd.

Trustees Barclays Bank Trust Co. Ltd.

Security Valuer Kleinwort, Benson Unit Managers Ltd.

Fund Type Equity - unauthorised

Fund Size (at 29.9.80) £5.136 million

Unit Holders 50

Securities Held 82

THE LAZARD INTERNATIONAL BOND EXEMPT FUND

21 Moorfields, London EC2P 2HT
Telephone: 01-588 2721

Fund Manager Lazard Securities Ltd.

Manager Responsible for Fund G.P.Dutton

Investment Manager S.Millman

Trustees Barclays Bank Trust Co. Ltd.

Fund Type Bond - unauthorised

Fund Size £2.5 million

Unit Holders 12

Securities/Properties Held 14

Other Associated Funds Lazard American Exempt Fund, Lazard Far Eastern Exempt Fund, Lazard Small Companies Exempt Fund, Lazard Property Unit Trust

THE LAZARD AMERICAN EXEMPT FUND

21 Moorfields, London EC2P 2HT
Telephone: 01-588 2721

Fund Manager Lazard Securities Ltd

Director Responsible for Fund Geoffrey P.Dutton

Investment Managers A.Puckridge & L.Higgitt

Trustees Barclays Bank Trust Co. Ltd.

Fund Type Equity Fund, Unauthorised Exempt Unit Trust

Fund Size (at 17.3.80) £32.2 million

Unit Holders 125

Securities Held 75

Other Associated Funds Lazard Far Eastern Exempt Fund, Lazard Small Companies Exempt Fund, Lazard International Bond Exempt Fund, Lazard Property Unit Trust

THE LAZARD FAR EASTERN EXEMPT FUND

21 Moorfields, London EC2P 2HT
Telephone: 01-588 2721

Fund Manager Lazard Securities Ltd

Director Responsible for Fund D.A.Roberts

Investment Managers A.Puckridge & T.Kimber

Trustees Chemical Bank Trustee Co Ltd

Fund Type Equity - Unauthorised

Fund Size (31.5.80) £4.7 million

Unit Holders 35

Securities Held 74

Other Associated Funds Lazard American Exempt Fund, Lazard Small Companies Exempt Fund, Lazard International Bond Exempt Fund, Lazard Property Unit Trust

LAZARD INTERNATIONAL BOND EXEMPT FUND

21 Moorfields, London EC2P 2HT
Telephone: 01-588 2721

(d) Pooled Pension Funds

LAZARD INTERNATIONAL BOND EXEMPT FUND
Continued

Fund and Investment Manager Lazard Securities Ltd.

Fund Type Equity Fund, Unauthorised Exempt Unit Trust

Fund Size (at 5.80) £2.4 million

Unit Holders 11

THE LAZARD PROPERTY UNIT TRUST

21 Moorfields, London EC2P 2HT
Telephone: 01-588 2721

Committee of Management E.W.Phillips (Chairman), P.C.Jones, J.D.Harris, D.A.Roberts, L.W.Smith

Fund Manager Lazard Brothers & Co Ltd

Property Department Manager P.M.Archer, ARICS

Trustees National Westminster Bank Ltd

Consultant Surveyors Pepper Angliss & Yarwood

Property Valuers Weatherall Green & Smith

Fund Size (at 9.80) £140 million

Properties Held 68

Unit Holders 225

Other Associated Funds Lazard American Exempt Fund, Lazard Far Eastern Exempt Fund, Lazard Small Companies Exempt Fund, Lazard International Bond Exempt Fund

LAZARD SMALL COMPANIES EXEMPT FUND

21 Moorfields, London EC2P 2HT
Telephone: 01-588 2721

Fund and Investment Manager Lazard Securities Ltd.

Manager Responsible for Fund G.P.Dutton

Investment Managers E.G.Bowden and M.Richardson

Trustees Barclays Bank Trust Co. Ltd.

Fund Type Equity Fund, Unauthorised Exempt Unit Trust

Fund Size (at 5.80) £5.0 million

Unit Holders 35

Securities/Properties Held 110

Other Associated Funds Lazard American Exempt Fund, Lazard Far Eastern Exempt Fund, Lazard International Bond Exempt Fund, Lazard Property Unit Trust

LEGAL & GENERAL MANAGED FUND

Temple Court, 11 Queen Victoria Street, London EC4N 4TP
Telephone: 01-248 9678

Fund Manager Legal & General Assurance (Pensions Management) Ltd.

Manager Keith Hall

Investment Managers Jim Robinson, Peter Sim, Ian Clarke, John Weld, John Hockin

Property Valuer Chestertons

Fund Type Separate U.K. equity, Fixed Interest, Property, Composite, Mixed and International funds. Managed Fund - Legal & General Assurance Society Ltd.

Fund Size (at 31.12.80) Equity £75 million, Fixed Interest £101 million, Property £725 million, Mixed £765 million, Composite £23 million, International £11 million Total £1,700 million

Unit Holders 589

N.B. October 1980 the size of the Property Fund was £715 million held by 525 Unit Holders

LEGAL & GENERAL PROPERTY FUND

Temple Court, 11 Queen Victoria Street, London EC4N 4TP
Telephone: 01-248 9678

Fund Manager Legal & General Property Fund Managers Ltd.

Directors R.I.M.Macaulay, J.F.Morton, R.H.Peet, P.W.Simon, K.G.Smith

Valuers Richard Ellis

Fund Type Property Unit Trust

Fund Size £2.5 million

Unit Holders 15

LIFE ASSOCIATION OF SCOTLAND MANAGED PENSION FUND

10 George Street, Edinburgh EH2 2YH
Telephone: 031-225 8494

Fund Manager LAS Pensions Management Ltd.

Secretary & Chief Executive J.Paterson

Investment Manager The Life Association of Scotland Ltd.

Fund Type Mixed Fund and Segregated Funds. Managed Pension Fund -The Life Association of Scotland Ltd.

Fund Size £3.0 million

Unit Holders 3

THE LOCAL AUTHORITIES' WIDER & NARROWER RANGE FUNDS

Winchester House, 77 London Wall, London EC2N 1DB
Telephone: 01-588 1815

Fund/Unit Trust Manager The Local Authorities' Mutual Investment Trust

Director Responsible for Fund Viscount Churchill

Assistant Investment Manager E.P.Colquhoun

Fund Type Two separate unauthorised exempt funds investing in equities and fixed interest securities respectively

Fund Size (at 31.8.80) Wider: £30.0 million, Narrower: £0.6 million

Unit Holders Wider: 89, Narrower:54

Securities Held Wider: 102, Narrower: 3

THE LOCAL AUTHORITIES' PROPERTY FUND

Winchester House, 77 London Wall, London EC2N 1DB
Telephone: 01-588 1815

Director Responsible for Fund Viscount Churchill

Investment Manager J.McAuslan,FRICS (Chief Surveyor)

(d) Pooled Pension Funds

THE LOCAL AUTHORITIES' PROPERTY FUND *Continued*

Fund Managers The Local Authorities Mutual Investment Trust

Property Valuer Weatherall, Green & Smith

Fund Type Property Fund, Unauthorised Exempt Unit Trust

Fund Size (at 31.8.80) £100 million

Unit Holders 74

Properties Held 80

THE LONDON AUSTRALIAN PENSION UNIT TRUST

117 Old Broad Street, London EC2N 1AL
Telephone: 01-588 1750

Management Committee K.E.Parry (Chairman), O.H.Edwards, R.P.Good, R.K.Ledson

Director Responsible for Fund D.P.F.Mount

Manager J.L.Compton

Investment Manager Drayton Montagu Portfolio Management Ltd.

Fund Type Equity Fund, Unauthorised Exempt Unit Trust

Fund Size (at 15.3.80) £2.0 million

Unit Holders 11

THE LONDON CONTINENTAL PENSION UNIT TRUST

117 Old Broad Street, London EC2N 1AL
Telephone: 01-588 1750

Management Committee J.Wickert (Chairman), R.P.J.Bleichroeder, A.Conlong, K.L.Watling

Director A.S.Reid

Manager P.D.I.Haig

Investment Manager Drayton Montagu Portfolio Management Ltd.

Fund Type Equity Fund, Unauthorised Exempt Unit Trust

Fund Size (at 15.3.80) £5.27 million

Unit Holders 28

THE LONDON FAR EAST PENSION UNIT TRUST

117 Old Broad Street, London EC2N 1AL
Telephone: 01-588 1750

Management Committee R.I.Cockerton (Chairman), N.A.D.Johnson, F.A.Mallett, G.J.Bowling

Director D.P.Mount

Manager N.A.D.Johnson

Investment Manager Drayton Montagu Portfolio Management Ltd

Fund Type Equity Fund, Unauthorised Exempt Unit Trust

Fund Size (at 15.3.80) £2.15 million

Unit Holders 22

THE LONDON FIXED INTEREST EXEMPT UNIT TRUST

117 Old Broad Street, London EC2N AL
Telephone: 01-588 1750

Management Committee R.W.C.Colvill (Chairman), M.A.Vaughan-Lee, N.D.Morrison

Manager N.D.Wightman

Investment Manager Drayton Montagu Portfolio Management Ltd.

Fund Type Fixed Interest Fund, Unauthorised exempt Unit Trust

Fund Size (at 15.3.80) £103,000

Unit Holders 1

LONDON LIFE MANAGED FUNDS

Turnall House, Sutton Park Road, Sutton, Surrey SM1 2AE
Telephone: 01-643 8977

Fund Manager London Life Managed Funds Ltd

Fund Type Separate Cash, Equity, Fixed Interest, Property and Mixed Funds. Managed Pension Fund - The London Life Association Ltd

Fund Size (at 30.9.80) Equity £5.7 million, Fixed Interest £5.7 million, Property £1.9 million, Mixed (includes amounts in other funds) £11.6 million

LONDON & MANCHESTER ASSURANCE CO LTD

P.O. Box 44, Winslade Park, Exeter EX5 1DS
Telephone: 0392 52155

Manager Responsible for Fund I.J.S.Henderson, MA, FIA

Investment Managers London and Manchester Assurance Co. Ltd.

Fund Type Secure Growth Fund-Deposit Administration

Fund Size (at 29.10.80) £10.2 million

Securities Held 62

THE LONDON NORTH AMERICA PENSION UNIT TRUST

117 Old Broad Street, London EC2N 1AL
Telephone: 01-588 1750

Management Committee M.Lander (Chairman), R.P.Good, M.A.Vaughan-Lee, K.L.Watling

Director Responsible for Fund M.A.Vaughan-Lee

Manager G.J.Bowling

Investment Manager Drayton Montagu Portfolio Management Ltd

Trustees Montagu Executor & Trustee Co.Ltd.

Fund Type Equity Fund, Unauthorised Exempt Unit Trust

Fund Size (at 15.5.80) £8.29 million

Unit Holders 39

M & G PENSION EXEMPT FUND

Three Quays, Tower Hill, London EC3R 6BQ
Telephone: 01-626 4588

Fund Manager M & G Investment Management Ltd.

Director Responsible for Fund D.H.L.Hopkinson

(d) Pooled Pension Funds

M & G PENSION EXEMPT FUND Continued

Investment Manager G.W.Robertson
Trustees Lloyds Bank Ltd.
Fund Type Equity Fund, Authorised Exempt Unit Trust
Fund Size (at 31.10.80) £22,656,000
Unit Holders 205
Securities Held 71
Associated Funds M & G Personal Pension Fund - £63.8 million, M & G Flexible Pension Plan Funds - 7 Funds, Total £2.7 million

MERCURY EXEMPT FUND
St Alban's House, Goldsmith Street, London EC2P 2DL
Telephone: 01-600 4555
Fund Manager Mercury Fund Managers Ltd
Investment Manager Warburg Investment Management Ltd
Director Responsible for Fund L.S.Licht
Trustees Williams & Glyn's Bank Ltd
Fund Type Authorised exempt
Fund Size (at 27.3.80) £8.09 million
Unit Holders 59
Securities Held 42

MIDLAND DRAYTON EQUITY EXEMPT TRUST
Courtwood House, Silver Street Head, Sheffield S1 3RD
Telephone: 0742 79842
Fund Manager Midland Bank Group Unit Trust Managers Ltd.
Managing Director H.I.Saul
Investment Manager Drayton Montagu Portfolio Management Ltd
Trustee Royal Exchange Assurance
Fund Type Equity Fund, Authorised Exempt Unit Trust
Fund Size (at 31.3.80) £431,000
Unit Holders 26
Securities Held 31

THE MINSTER EXEMPT FUND
Minster House, Arthur Street, London EC4R 9BH
Telephone: 01-623 1050
Fund and Investment Manager Minster Fund Managers Ltd.
Trustee National Westminster Bank Ltd.
Fund Type Equity Fund, Authorised Exempt Unit Trust
Fund Size (at 30.9.79) £1,031,000

M.J.AMERICAN EXEMPT FUND
163 Hope Street, Glasgow G2 2UH
Telephone: 041-221 5521
Fund Managers M.J. Unit Trust Management Ltd.
Investment Adviser Murray Johnstone Limited
Director Responsible for Fund J.Michael Watherston
Trustees Clydesdale Bank Ltd.
Fund Type Unauthorised Exempt Unit Trust
Fund Size (at 2.4.80) £1.85 million
Unit Holders 1
Securities/Properties Held 44

M.J.JAPAN EXEMPT FUND
163 Hope Street, Glasgow G2 2UH
Telephone: 041-221 5521
Fund Managers M.J.Unit Trust Management Ltd.
Investment Adviser Murray Johnstone Limited
Director Responsible for Fund Michael H.J.Parlett
Trustees Clydesdale Bank Ltd
Fund Type Equity Fund, Unauthorised Exempt Unit Trust
Fund Size (at 2.4.80) £1.9 million
Unit Holders 10
Securities/Properties Held 39

MORGAN GRENFELL SPECIAL EXEMPT FUND
23 Great Winchester Street, London EC2P 2AX
Telephone: 01-588 4545
Fund and Investment Manager Morgan Grenfell & Co Ltd
Manager Responsible for Fund D.T.A.Boyle
Trustees Coutts & Co
Fund Type Equity Fund, Unauthorised Exempt Unit Trust
Fund Size (at 31.10.79) £20.5 million
Unit Holders 65
Securities/Properties Held 110

NATIONAL EMPLOYERS' LIFE MANAGED PENSION FUND
Milton Court, Dorking, Surrey RH4 3LZ
Telephone: 0306-5911
Fund Manager N.E.L. Pensions Ltd.
Investment Manager The National Employers Life Group of Companies
Fund Type Nelex Money Fund, Mixed Fund, Growth Income Fund, Deposit Fund, International Fixed Interest Fund, Guaranteed Growth Assets. Managed Fund - National Employers Life Assurance Co.Ltd.
Fund Size (at 31.12.79) £62.6 million

NATIONAL MUTUAL LIFE MANAGED PENSION FUND
5 Bow Churchyard, London EC4M 9DH
Telephone: 01-236 1566
Fund Manager National Mutual Pensions Ltd.
Fund Type Mixed Fund. Managed Pension Fund - National Mutual Life Assurance Society
Fund Size (Sept. 1980) £6 million
Unit Holders 3

(d) Pooled Pension Funds

NEW COURT EXEMPT EQUITY FUND
New Court, St Swithin's Lane, London EC4P 4DU
Telephone: 01-626 4356
Fund and Investment Managers N.M.Rothschild Asset Management Ltd.
Director Responsible for Fund R.Alexander
Trustees National Westminster Bank
Fund Type Equity Fund. Authorised exempt unit trust
Fund Size (at 1.9.80) £1.2 million
Unit Holders 14

NEW COURT EXEMPT GILT TRUST
New Court, St Swithin's Lane, London EC4P 4DU
Telephone: 01-626 4356
Fund Manager N.M.Rothschild & Sons Ltd
Investment Manager N.M.Rothschild Asset Management Ltd.
Trustees National Westminster Bank
Director Responsible for Fund R.Alexander
Fund Type Gilt trust. Unauthorised exempt unit trust
Fund Size (at 1.9.80) £1.1 million
Unit Holders 20
Securities Held 3

NEW COURT PROPERTY FUND
New Court, St Swithin's Lane, London EC4P 4DU
Telephone: 01-626 4356
Fund Manager New Court Property Fund Managers Ltd
Surveyor N.M.Rothschild Asset Management Ltd.
Trustees National Westminster Bank Ltd
Valuers Hillier Parker May & Rowden, Cluttons
Fund Type Equity Fund, Unauthorised Exempt Unit Trust
Fund Size (at 10.80) £63 million
Unit Holders 150

NORWICH UNION MANAGED PENSION FUND
PO Box 4, Surrey Street, Norwich NR1 3NG
Telephone: 0603-22200
Fund Manager Norwich Union Insurance Group (Pensions Management) Ltd
Manager Responsible for Fund R.B.P.Ramsay FIA
Investment Managers E.M.Sandland,MA,FIA, D.F.Barker,FIA, P.F.Lovett
Fund Type Separate Fixed Interest, Equity and Property Funds (unauthorised); Managed Pension Fund - Norwich Union Life Insurance society
Fund Size (at 31.3.80) Equity £33.7 million, Fixed Interest £25.7 million, Property £30.8 million
Unit Holders 21
Securities/Properties Held Fixed Interest 57, Equity 95, Property 23

N.P.I. POOLED MANAGED FUND
48 Gracechurch Street, London EC3V 0BB
Telephone: 01-623 4200

Fund Manager N.P.I. Pension Management Ltd
Fund Type Mixed Fund; Managed Pension Fund-National Provident Institution
Fund Size (at 31.12.77) £3.882 million
Unit Holders 8

OCEANIC EXEMPT FUND
Founders Court, Lothbury, London EC2R 7HE
Telephone: 01-606 9833
Fund Manager Brown Shipley Fund Management Ltd
Investment Manager Brown Shipley & Co Ltd
Trustee Royal Bank of Scotland
Fund Type Equity Fund, Authorised Exempt Unit Trust
Fund Size (at 8.12.77) £380,000

PANEUROPEAN PROPERTY UNIT TRUST
114 Old Broad Street, London EC2P 2HY
Telephone: 01-588 6464
Management Committee J.W.Martin (Chairman), E.J.Baden, A.C.Brooking, R.W.C.Colvill, R.A.Coopman, R.K.Juddery, J.I.McGillivray, R.Smith
Consultant Surveyor and Managing Agents Jones Lang Wootton, Weatherall Green and Smith
Financial Advisers Samuel Montagu & Co Ltd
Independent Valuers Richard Ellis; Jones, Lang, Wootton
Fund Type Property Unit Trust
Fund Size (at 1.8.78) £17.0 million
Unit Holders 12

PENNINE PROPERTY UNIT TRUST
2-4 George Street, Cottingham, North Humberside HU15 5QU
Telephone: 0482-84627
Committee of Management H.C.Cottrell,FIA,FBIM, A.G.MacG.Fraser,FIA, J.Guthrie,MA,FPMI, K.C.Cook, OBE,FCA, M.Haddon-Grant,LLB, C.J.R.Bedford,LLB, M.R.Landau,FCA
Secretary S.A.Berry,FRICS
Managing Agents Matthews Goodman and Postlethwaite
Investment Consultant S.L.Houlston,FRICS
Consulting Actuaries Duncan C.Fraser & Co.
Trustees Guinness Mahon Executor & Trustee Co.Ltd.
Fund Type Property Unit Trust
Fund Size (at 30.11.80) £10.2 million
Unit Holders 70
Properties Held 19

PENSION FUNDS AND CHARITIES AGRICULTURAL PROPERTY UNIT TRUST (AG.PUT)
73 Brook Street, London W1Y 1YE
Telephone: 01-499 7191
Committee of Management C.J.Baker (Chairman), Sir Charles Graham, H.E.Hunter-Jones, A.J.Gibson-Watt, B.C.Johnston, Sir Nigel Strutt

(d) Pooled Pension Funds

PENSION FUNDS AND CHARITIES AGRICULTURAL
Continued

Trustees Hambros Bank Executor and Trustee Co Ltd

Chief Executive R.G.Nightingale,FCA

Surveyor J.H.Davey,MA,FRICS,FSVA

Secretary J.P.S.Ullman,FCA

Valuers Jones, Lang, Wootton

Land Agents Cluttons

Fund Size (at 29.8.80) £3.04 million

Unit Holders 26

Properties Held 6

THE PENSION FUND PROPERTY UNIT TRUST (PFPUT)

73 Brook Street, London W1Y 1YE
Telephone: 01-499 7191

Committee of Management C.J.Baker (Chairman), Sir Lawrence Boyle, D.H.Bretherton, J.E.Cullis, A.J.Gibson-Watt, A.E.C.Green, J.D. Hender, J.N.C.Jones, B.C.Johnston, J.H.Smith

Trustees Hambros Bank Executor and Trustee Co Ltd

Chief Executive R.G.Nightingale, FCA

Surveyors J.H.Davey,MA,FRICS,FSVA, D.G.Mathison,ARICS, W.J.Cox,ARICS

Secretary J.P.S.Ullman,FCA

Valuers Jones, Lang, Wootton

Land Agents Cluttons

Fund Type Property Unit Trust

Fund Size (at 18.9.80) £252 million

Unit Holders 600

Properties Held 124

PENSIONS AND CHARITIES PROPERTY FUND

44 Bloomsbury Square, London WC1A 2RA
Telephone: 01-242 7456

Committee of Management W.L.Grant (Chairman), R A Downard, D.S.Gibson, F.W.Holder, R.H.R.McGill, J.A.Langford, K.E.Parry

Secretary N.J.Ferguson, FCA

Property Manager Allsop & Co

Trustees Lloyds Bank Ltd.

Fund Type Property Unit Trust

Fund Size (at 1.10.80) £22 million

Unit Holders 47

Properties Held 27

PROPERTY GROWTH MANAGED PENSION FUND

Leon House, High Street, Croydon, Surrey CR9 1LU
Telephone: 01-680 0606

Fund Manager Property Growth Pensions & Annuities Ltd.

Investment Manager Property Growth Assurance (Subsidiary of Phoenix Assurance Group)

Fund Type Separate Gilt-Edged, Managed, Convertible and Property Funds. Managed Pension Fund - Property Growth Assurance

Fund Size (at 3.4.80) Gilt-Edged £497,000, Managed £1,440,000, Convertible £1,278,000, Property £1,422,000

THE PROPERTY UNIT TRUST FOR PUBLIC & GENERAL SUPERANNUATION SCHEMES (PUTPAGS)

73 Brook Street, London W1Y 1YE
Telephone: 01-499 7191

Committee of Management C.J.Baker (Chairman), J.W.Bamford, G.D.Borley, D.H.Bretherton, J.E.Cullis, A.J.Gibson-Watt, G.W.Hopkins, B.C.Johnston

Trustees Hambros Bank Executor and Trustee Co.Ltd.

Chief Executive R.G.Nightingale,FCA

Surveyors J.H.Davey,MA,FRICS,FSVA, D.G.Mathison,ARICS, W.J.Cox,ARICS

Secretary J.P.S.Ullman,FCA

Valuers Jones, Lang, Wootton

Land Agents Cluttons

Fund Type Property Unit Trust

Fund Size (at 30.9.80) £24.2 million

Unit Holders 47

Properties Held 37

PROVIDENCE CAPITOL MANAGED PENSION FUND

Circle House, 30 Uxbridge Road, London W12 8PG
Telephone: 01-749 9111

Fund Manager Providence Capitol Life Assurance Co. Ltd.

Investment Managers Baring Brothers & Co. Ltd.

Manager Responsible for Fund D.R.Braithwaite

Fund Type Equity and Fixed Interest Funds, Managed Pension Fund - Providence Capitol Life Assurance Co. Ltd.

Fund Size (at 28.10.80) Equity - £3.05 million, Fixed Interest - £4.22 million

Unit Holders 5

PROVIDENT MUTUAL MANAGED PENSION FUNDS LTD.

25-31 Moorgate, London EC2R 6BA
Telephone: 01-628 3232

Fund Manager Provident Mutual Managed Pension Funds Ltd

Managing Director and Actuary E.Brunet, BA

Property Valuer St Quintin

Fund Type Separate Cash, Equity, Fixed Interest, Property, Overseas Equity and diversified funds

Fund Size (at 1.9.80) Cash £7.4m, Equity £13.0m, Fixed Interest £14.2m, Property £7.8m, Overseas Equity £3.8m

Unit Holders 68

603

(d) Pooled Pension Funds

PROVIDENT MUTUAL MANAGED PENSION FUNDS LTD.
Continued

Securities/Properties Held Equity 38, Fixed Interest 11, Property 12, Overseas Equity 46

PRUDENTIAL GROUP INVESTMENT LINKED PENSION PLAN
142 Holborn Bars, London EC1N 2NH
Telephone: 01-405 9222

Fund Manager Prudential Pensions Ltd

Manager & Actuary T.J.L.Richards,MA,FIA

Investment Manager M.G.Newmarch,BSc

Property Manager P.G.Green,BSc,FRICS

Property Valuers Hillier Parker May and Rowden; Debenham Tewson and Chinnocks; Savills, Bidwells

Fund Type Separate Equity, Fixed Interest and Property Funds; Managed Pension Fund- The Prudential Assurance Co Ltd

Fund Size (at 31.3.80) Equity £167 million, Fixed Interest £165 million, Property £204 million. Total (at 17.9.80) £688 million

Unit Holders 213

ROYAL TRUST EXEMPT INTERNATIONAL FUND
Royal Trust House, 48-50 Cannon Street,
London EC4N 6LD
Telephone: 01-236 6044

Fund Manager The Royal Trust Co.of Canada Fund Management Ltd.

Investment Manager The Royal Trust Co of Canada

Managers Responsible for Fund A.J.Hall, A.J.Albert

Trustee Barclays Bank Trust Co Ltd

Fund Type International Equity Fund, Unauthorised Exempt Unit Trust

Fund Size £420,000

Unit Holders 10

Securities Held 44

Other Associated Funds Royal Trust Capital Fund, Royal Trust Income Fund

SAVE & PROSPER EXEMPT INCOME FUND
4 Great St Helens, London EC3P 3EP
Telephone: 01-588 1717

Fund Manager Save & Prosper Securities Ltd

Investment Manager Save & Prosper Group Ltd

Director Responsible for Fund P.J.Manser

Trustee Royal Bank of Scotland Ltd.

Fund Type Equity Fund, Authorised Exempt Fund

Fund Size £10.95 million

Unit Holders 391

Securities Held 68

SAVE & PROSPER EXEMPT INTERNATIONAL FUND
4 Great St Helens, London EC3P 3EP
Telephone: 01-588 1717

Fund Manager Save & Prosper Securities Ltd

Investment Manager Save & Prosper Group Ltd.

Director Responsible for Fund P.J.Manser

Trustee Royal Bank of Scotland Ltd.

Fund Type Equity Fund, Authorised Exempt Unit Trust

Fund Size (at 31.10.80) £3.85 million

Unit Holders 151

Securities Held 66

SAVE & PROSPER MANAGED PENSION FUND
4 Great St Helens, London EC3P 3EP
Telephone: 01-588 1717

Fund Manager Save & Prosper Pensions Ltd

Director Responsible for Fund P.J.Manser

Property Manager A.W.Laurie,BSc,ARICS

Property Valuer Cluttons

Fund Type Deposit, Cash, Equity, Fixed Interest, Property and Mixed Funds. Managed Pension Fund - Save & Prosper Pensions Ltd

Fund Size (at 31.12.80) Cash £176,000, Equity £8.5 million, Fixed Interest £3.5 million, Property £5.6 million, Mixed £8.0 million

Unit Holders Deposit 5 Equity 1,512, Fixed Interest 54, Property 1,311, mixed 7,525

Securities/Properties Held Deposit 2, Equity 90, Fixed Interest 5, Property 20

SCHLESINGER AMERICAN EXEMPT TRUST
Salisbury House, 31 Finsbury Circus,
London EC2M 5QL
Telephone: 01-588 2777

Fund and Investment Managers Britannia Group of Unit Trusts Ltd.

Directors Responsible for Fund Norman Riddell, Hugh Ward

Trustees Midland Bank Trust Co.Ltd.

Fund Type Equity Fund, Authorised Exempt Trust

Fund Size (at 31.12.80) £1,207,000

Unit Holders 52

Securities Held 69

SCHLESINGER EXEMPT HIGH YIELD TRUST
Salisbury House, 31 Finsbury Circus,
London EC2M 5QL
Telephone: 01-588 2777

Fund and Investment Manager Britannia Group of Unit Trusts Ltd.

Director Responsible for Fund Bryan Quinton,FCA

Trustee Midland Bank Trust Co.Ltd.

Fund Type Equity Fund, Authorised Exempt Unit Trust

Fund Size (at 31.12.80) £685,000

Unit Holders 30

Securities Held 73

(d) Pooled Pension Funds

SCHLESINGER EXEMPT MARKET LEADERS TRUST
Salisbury House, 31 Finsbury Circus, London EC2M 5QL
Telephone: 01-588 2777
Fund and Investment Managers Britannia Group of Unit Trusts Ltd.
Directors Responsible for Fund B.R.Reading, P.C.Baker, P.A.Jeffreys
Trustees Midland Bank Trust Co. Ltd.
Fund Type Equity Fund, Authorised Exempt unit Trust
Fund Size (at 31.12.80) £1,840,000
Unit Holders 18
Securities Held 155

SCHRODER PENSION AND CHARITY FUND
120 Cheapside, London EC2V 6DS
Telephone: 01-588 4000
Unit Trust Department 48 St Martin's Lane, London WC2N 4EJ
Telephone: 01-240 3434
Investment Manager J.Henry Schroder Wagg & Co Ltd
Manager Responsible for Fund P.Rowen
Trustees Lloyds Bank Ltd
Fund Type Equity Fund, Authorised Exempt Unit Trust
Fund Size (at 23.7.80) £5.1 million
Unit Holders 60
Securities Held 41

SCHRODER PROPERTY FUND FOR PENSION FUNDS AND CHARITIES
120 Cheapside, London EC2V 6DS
Telephone: 01-588 4000
Committee of Management Sir Ashley Ponsonby (Chairman), P.S.Edgson, R.Cockhill, A.W.John, D.L.Murison, B.M.Oliver, A.W.John, W.D.Scott, J.W.Shield, D.E.Taylor
Secretary J.Lambert
Surveyor to the Managers R.T.Coombes, FRICS
Trustees Lloyds Bank Ltd.
Property Managers Schroder Properties Ltd.
Consultant Surveyors Weatherall Green & Smith
Consultant Agricultural Surveyors Cluttons
Fund Type Property Unit Trust
Fund Size (30.9.80) £76.0 million
Unit Holders 240
Properties Held 71

SCHRODER RECOVERY FUND
120 Cheapside, London EC2V 6DS
Telephone: 01-588 4000
Unit Trust Dept; 48 St Martin's Lane, London WC2N 4EJ
Telephone: 01-240 3434
Investment Manager J.Henry Schroder Wagg & Co Ltd

Manager Responsible for Fund A.Sugden
Trustees Lloyds Bank Ltd.
Fund Type Equity Fund, Authorised Exempt Unit Trust
Fund Size £17 million
Unit Holders 104
Securities Held 55

SCHRODER SPECIAL EXEMPT FUND
120 Cheapside, London EC2V 6DS
Telephone: 01-588 4000
Unit Trust Dept. 48 St Martin's Lane, London WC2N 4EJ
Telephone: 01-240 3434
Investment Manager J.Henry Schroder Wagg & Co. Ltd.
Manager responsible for Fund A.Agrotis
Trustees Lloyds Bank Ltd.
Fund Type Equity Fund, Authorised Exempt Unit Trust
Fund Size £50 million
Unit Holders 150
Securities Held 181

SCOTTISH AMICABLE MANAGED FUND (S.C.A.M.P.I.)
150 St Vincent Place, Glasgow G2 5NQ
Telephone: 041-221 8844
Fund Manager Scottish Amicable Pensions Investments Ltd
Managers Responsible for Fund W.G.Knox, D.J.B.Sutherland, J.J.Guthrie
Fund Type Mixed Fund. Managed Pension Fund - Scottish Amicable Life Assurance Society
Fund Size (at 30.9.80) £170 million
Unit Holders 125

SCOTTISH EQUITABLE MANAGED FUND
28 St Andrew Square, Edinburgh EH2 1YF
Telephone: 031-556 9101
Fund Manager Scottish Equitable (Managed Funds) Ltd
Director Responsible for Fund David A.Berridge, BSc,FCA
Property Valuer Bernard Thorpe & Partners
Fund Type Equity, Fixed Interest, Property and Mixed Funds. Managed Pension Fund - Scottish Equitable Life Assurance Society
Fund Size (at 30.9.80) Equity £3.15 million, Fixed Interest £4.92 million, Property £2.59 million, Mixed £3.83 million
Unit Holders 10
Securities Held 38
Properties Held 5

SCOTTISH LIFE MANAGED FUND
19 St.Andrew Square, Edinburgh EH2 1YE
Telephone: 031-225 2211
Fund Manager The Scottish Life Pensions Annuity Co Ltd

(d) Pooled Pension Funds

SCOTTISH LIFE MANAGED FUND *Continued*

Investment Manager B.M.Rose,FIA

Fund Type Mixed Fund. Managed Pension Fund - The Scottish Life Assurance Co

Fund Size (at 30.9.80) £15.3 million

Unit Holders 20

SCOTTISH MUTUAL MANAGED FUND

109 St Vincent Street, Glasgow G2 5HN
Telephone: 041-248 6321

Fund Manager Scottish Mutual Pension Funds Investment Ltd

General Manager W.M.Henderson,FFA

Secretary W.McCorkindale,FFA

Investment Manager R.S.Clarkson,BSc,FFA

Fund Type Mixed Fund. Managed Pension Fund - The Scottish Mutual Assurance Society

Fund Size (at 30.9.80) £11.2 million. The total value of pooled and segregated funds was £19.4 million

Unit Holders 15

SCOTTISH PROVIDENT INSTITUTION MANAGED FUND

6 St. Andrew Square, Edinburgh EH2 2YA
Telephone: 031-556 9181

Fund Manager Scottish Provident Institution

Fund Type Managed Pension Fund (Starting 1.1.81)

SCOTTISH WIDOWS' EXEMPT UNIT TRUST

15 Dalkeith Road, Edinburgh EH16 5XA
Telephone: 031-655 6000

Fund and Investment Manager Scottish Widows' Fund and Life Assurance Society

Manager Responsible for Fund D.C.Ritchie,FFA (Investment Manager)

Trustees The Royal Bank of Scotland Ltd

Fund Type Mixed Fund, Unauthorised Exempt Unit Trust

Fund Size (at 31.8.80) £44 million

Unit Holders 58

SCOTTISH WIDOWS' MANAGED FUND

15 Dalkeith Road, Edinburgh EH16 5XA
Telephone: 031-655 6000

Fund Manager Pensions Management (SWF) Ltd

Manager Responsible for Fund D.C.Ritchie,FFA (Investment Manager)

Fund Type Mixed Fund, Managed Pension Fund- Scottish Widows' Fund & Life Assurance Society

Fund Size (at 30.9.80) £339 million

Unit Holders 181

THE SINGER & FRIEDLANDER PROPERTY EUROPEAN UNIT TRUST

20 Cannon Street, London EC4M 6XE
Telephone: 01-248 9646

Committee of Management J.W.Draper (Chairman), E.Butler, A.R.J.Dyas, J.A.Mulligan, R.B.Sutherland-Smith, M.J.Kerr, R.H.Crowther

Trustees Guardian Royal Exchange Assurance Ltd

Property Managers Singer Allsop Property Management Ltd.

Independent Property Valuers Jones, Lang, Wootton

Fund Type Property Unit Trust

Fund Size £9 million

Unit Holders 8

STANDARD LIFE MANAGED FUND

3 George Street, Edinburgh EH2 2XZ
Telephone: 031-225 2552

Fund Manager Standard Life Pension Funds Ltd

Investment Manager J.R.Gibson,FFA

Fund Type Equity Fund, Mixed Fund, Property Fund, Fixed Interest Fund and Segregated Funds. Managed Pension Fund -Standard Life Assurance Co

Fund Size (at 9.9.80) Mixed £132.4 million, Property £63.4 million, Equity £3.7 million, Fixed Interest £0.8 million. Total value of pooled and segregated funds managed by Standard Life Pension Fund Ltd was £269 million

Unit Holders Mixed 86, Property 106, Equity, 4, Fixed Interest 1

Securities Held Mixed 149, Property 74, Equity 59, Fixed Interest 7

STENHOUSE EXEMPT FUND

145 St Vincent Street, Glasgow G2 5NX
Telephone: 041-248 5070

Fund Manager Reed Stenhouse Pension Services Ltd.

General Manager Responsible for Fund Stuart Aird, BSc,FSA,AIA

Investment Manager Ivory & Sime Ltd.

Trustee Bank of Scotland

Fund Type Mixed Fund, Unauthorised Exempt Unit Trust

Fund Size (at 30.9.80) £50 million

Unit Holders 71

Securities Held 67

STENHOUSE EXEMPT GILT FUND

Two South Place, London EC2P 2DX
Telephone: 01-628 6011

Unit Trust Manager Reed Stenhouse Investment Services Ltd

Directors Responsible for Fund B.J.Willats,ACII, FPMI, S.W.Newton,ACA

Investment Managers Clive Investments Ltd

Trustees Williams & Glyn's Bank Ltd.

Fund Type Fixed Interest: Unauthorised Exempt Unit Trust

Fund Size (at 30.9.80) £4.4 million

Unit Holders 30

Securities Held 6

Relieves Pension Fund headaches

If your company's pension fund receives contributions of £50,000 a year or more, Sun Life can offer you a painless alternative to the chore of administration in addition to investment management and professional advisory services.

It's called the Sun Life Managed Pension Fund and it offers a choice of investment funds to meet varying needs and objectives.

Since establishment in 1973, funds under management have grown rapidly to more than £100 million. These funds are managed by a successful team of professional investment managers who combine with a group of experienced pensions advisers and administrators to provide a comprehensive range of services.

And it probably costs less in time and money than handling the operation yourself, or by commissioning services piecemeal from a variety of sources. (You can also select just a part of the service, for an even lower cost.)

For full details on the approach, track record and advantages of the Sun Life pension fund management service, please write to Sun Life Pensions Management Limited, Sun Life Court, St. James Barton, Bristol BS1 3TH, or telephone (0272) 426911.

SUN LIFE pensions management

(d) Pooled Pension Funds

STEWART AMERICAN EXEMPT FUND
45 Charlotte Square, Edinburgh EH2 4HW
Telephone: 031-226 3271

Committee J.W.A.Shaw Stewart (Chairman), P.A.Campbell Fraser,WS, E.A.W,Tulloch (Director Responsible for Fund)

Trustees The Royal Bank of Scotland Ltd

Manager & Registrar Stewart Unit Trust Managers Ltd

Investment Manager Stewart Fund Managers Ltd

Director Responsible for Fund E.A.W.Tulloch

Fund Type Equity Fund, Unauthorised Exempt Unit Trust

Fund Size (at 31.10.80) £1,115,000

Unit Holders 9

Securities Held 61

Other Associated Funds Stewart American Fund, Stewart British Capital Fund, Scottish American Investment Co. Ltd., Scottish European Investment Co. Ltd.

STOCKHOLDERS EXEMPT AMERICAN FUND
77 London Wall, London EC2N 1DH
Telephone: 01-588 5620

Committee of Management W.J.R.Govett, M.J.Beaver, M.R.Cornwall-Jones (Directors of John Govett & Co.)

Investment Manager John Govett & Co.Ltd.

Trustees The Stockholders Investment Trust Ltd.

Fund Type Equity Fund, Unauthorised Exempt Unit Trust.

Fund Size (at 20.5.79) £2.5 million

STOCKHOLDERS EXEMPT PACIFIC FUND
77 London Wall, London EC2N 1DH
Telephone: 01-588 5620

Committee of Management W.J.R.Govett, M.R.Corwall-Jones, A.S.Nicholson (Directors of John Govett & Co.

Investment Manager John Govett & Co.Ltd.

Trustees The Stockholders Investment Trust Ltd.

Fund Type Equity Fund, Unauthorised Exempt Unit Trust

Fund Size (at 23.5.79) £383,000

STRATTON SMALLER COMPANIES EXEMPT FUND
88 Leadenhall Street, London EC3A 3DT
Telephone: 01-588 2830

Fund Manager Stratton Trust Managers Ltd.

Investment Manager Baring Brothers & Co.Ltd.

Trustee Williams & Glyn's Bank Ltd.

Fund Type Equity Fund, Authorised Exempt Unit Trust

Fund Size (at 12.3.80) £3.1 million

SUN ALLIANCE MANAGED FUND
Sun Alliance House, North Street, Horsham, West Sussex RH12 1BT
Telephone: 0403 64141

Fund Manager Sun Alliance Fund Management Ltd.

Investment Manager Sun Alliance Insurance Group

Trustees Lloyds Bank Ltd

Fund Type Separate Equity and Fixed Interest Funds; Managed Pension Fund operating via authorised (Equity Fund) and unauthorised (Fixed Interest Fund) exempt unit trusts

Fund Size (at 8.10.80) Equity Trust - £15.9 million, Fixed Interest Trust - £9.1 million

Unit Holders 42

Securities Held Equity Trust - 65, Fixed Interest Trust - 6

SUN LIFE MANAGED PENSION FUND
107 Cheapside, London EC2V 6DU
Telephone: 01-606 7788

Fund Manager Sun Life Pensions Management Ltd

Director Responsible for Fund J.D.Webster,BSc,FIA

Investment Manager David Thomas,BSc,FIA

Property Valuer Richard Ellis

Fund Type Separate Mixed, Property and Stock Exchange Securities Fund: Managed Pension Fund - Sun Life Assurance Society Ltd.

Fund Size (at 28.9.80) £138.2 million

Unit Holders 128

TARGET EQUITY EXEMPT FUND
Garrard House, 31 Gresham Stret, London EC2V 7DT
Telephone: 01-600 7533

Fund Manager Target Trust Managers Ltd

Investment Manager Target Fund Managers Ltd

Director Responsible for Fund S. Bottomley

Trustees Williams & Glyn's Bank Ltd

Fund Type Equity Fund, Authorised Exempt Unit Trust

Fund Size (at June 1980) £1.9 million

Unit Holders 78

Securities Held 30

Other Associated Funds American Eagle, Commodity, Equity, Extra Income, Financial, Gilt Capital, Gilt Income, Growth, Income, Investment, Pacific, Preference Share, Professional, Special Situations, Energy, Income and Growth

TARGET NORTH AMERICAN EXEMPT FUND
Garrard House, 31 Gresham Stree, London EC2V 7DT
Telephone: 01-600 7533

Fund Manager Target Trust Managers Ltd.

Investment Managers Dawnay, Day & Co.Ltd.

Director Responsible for Fund I.E.Carswell

Trustees Midland Bank Trust Co.Ltd.

Fund Type Equity Fund, Authorised Exempt Unit Trust

(d) Pooled Pension Funds

TARGET PROPERTY FUND

Garrard House, 31 Gresham Stret,
London EC2V 7DT
Telephone: 01-600 7533

Fund Manager Target Trust Managers Ltd

Investment Manager Target Life Assurance Ltd (R.J.Neat)

Director Responsible for Fund Richard I.E.Carswell

Property Valuer Jones, Lang, Wootton

Fund Type Property Unit Trust

Fund Size (at 1.11.79) £4.5 million

Unit Holders 925

Properties Held 22

TARGET SMALLER COMPANIES EXEMPT FUND

Garrard House, 31 Gresham Street,
London EC2V 7DT
Telephone: 01-600 7533

Fund Manager Target Trust Managers Ltd

Investment Manager Dawnay, Day & Co Ltd

Director Responsible for Fund Richard I.E.Carswell

Trustees Midland Bank Trust Co Ltd

Fund Type Equity, Authorised Exempt Unit Trust

TYNDALL EXEMPT FUND

18 Canynge Road, Bristol BS99 7UA
Telephone: 0272 32241

Fund Manager Tyndall Managers Ltd

Investment Manager Tyndall Investment Services Ltd

Trustees Williams & Glyn's Bank Ltd

Fund Size (at 5.2.80) £5.5 million

TYNDALL MANAGED PENSION FUNDS

18 Canynge Road, Bristol BS99 7UA
Telephone: 0272 32241

Fund Manager Tyndall Pensions Ltd

Fund Type Separate Cash, Equity, Fixed Interest, Property and Mixed Funds. Managed Pension Fund - Tyndall Assurance Ltd

Fund Sizes (at 30.6.78) Equity £1.93 million, Fixed Interest £619,000, Property £582,000, Mixed £1.58 million (invested in other funds)

UNICORN EXEMPT TRUST

Unicorn House, 252 Romford Road,
London E7 9JB
Telephone: 01-534 5544

Fund Manager Barclays Unicorn Ltd

Investment Manager Barclays Bank Trust Co Ltd

Senior Investment Manager W.H.Hilling

Trustees Royal Exchange Assurance

Fund Type Equity Fund, Authorised Exempt Unit Trust

Fund Size (at 2.4.80) £4.5 million

Unit Holders 296

Securities Held 60

UNITED STATES PROPERTY TRUST

c/o Integrand, 107-111 Fleet Street,
London EC4A 2AB
Telephone: 01-353 1167

Investment Advisers Integrand (San Francisco)

Property & Management Agent Arthur Rubloff & Co. (Chicago)

Independent Joint Valuers Goddard & Smith, Coldwell Banker & Company

Trustees National Westminster Bank Ltd.

WELFARE LIFE GROUP MANAGED PENSION PLAN

PO Box 44, Winslade Park, Exeter EX5 1NS
Telephone: 0392 52155

Fund Manager London & Manchester Assurance Co.Ltd.

Investment Advisers Equity: Capel-Cure Myers; Property Advisers: de Groot Collis, Donaldson & Sons, Rowe & Pitman (Property Shares)

Property Valuer J.Trevor & Sons

Fund Type Separate Equity, Property and Mixed Funds. Managed Pension Fund - Welfare Insurance Co Ltd

Fund Size (at 3.10.79) Equity £1.5 million, Property £600,000, Mixed £2.3 million

Securities/Properties Held Equities 49; Property 11 shares & 8 properties; Mixed 165 & 8 properties

WESTGROVE EXEMPT PROPERTY UNIT TRUST

100 Park Street, London W1Y 3RJ
Telephone: 01-629 1248

Fund Manager Westgrove Fund Managers Ltd

Chairman A.Hagenbach

Director Responsible for Fund C.R.Smith

Promoters Westgrove Securities Ltd

Valuers Healey & Baker (Commercial); Bernard Thorpe & Partners (Residential)

Trustee National Westminster Bank Ltd

Fund Type Property Unit Trust

YORKSHIRE-GENERAL MANAGED FUND

2 Rougier Street, York YO1 1HR
Telephone: 0904-28982

Fund Manager Yorkshire-General (Pensions Management)

General Manager C.B.Heath,MC,FCII

Investment Managers General Accident Fire and Life Assurance Corporation Ltd.

Fund Type Separate Equity and Fixed Interest Funds. Managed Pension Fund - Yorkshire General Life Assurance Co Ltd (the Life company of General Accident)

Fund Size (at 15.9.79) £450,000

Unit Holders 2

The James Abbott Partnership

Retained Commercial
& Agricultural
Property Investment
Advisers
to Pension Funds,
Insurance Companies,
Local Trusts,
& Private Investors

The James Abbott Partnership
Chartered Surveyors
15/17 Alexandra Street,
Southend-on-Sea, Essex.
SS1 1JZ   Tel: (0702) 330073

Abbott

Property Advisers

Although almost all these firms have at times acted for Pension clients, this may have been only for individual purchases rather than being on a fully retained basis. Some Pension Funds retain up to six firms as property advisers whilst others use a range of firms purely on an ad hoc basis.

JAMES ABBOTT PARTNERSHIP

Commercial 15-17 Alexandra Street, Southend-on-Sea, Essex SS1 1JZ
Telephone: 0702-330073

Agricultural 69 Duke Street, Chelmsford, Essex CM1 1JP
Telephone: 0245-62464

Partners Acting for Pension Funds D.J.Skinner,BSc, ARICS, M.D.Moody,FRICS,ACIArb, P.J.Crafford, ARICS, A.L.Wilson,BSc,ARICS,ARVA (Commercial), D.S.R.Mills,MA,FRICS, N.M.Nott,ARICS (Agricultural)

Other Pension Fund Expert A.L.Wilson,BSc,ARICS, ARVA,ACIArb

Employees 206

Number of Pension Fund Clients 6

Services Offered Comprehensive commercial and agricultural property service.

Other Offices 15 Duke Street, Chelmsford, Essex, 67/69 Station Road, Clacton-on-Sea, Essex, 57/59 Crouch Street, Colchester CO3 3EU. A.E.Spear and Sons, Market Hill, Framlingham, Nr. Woodbridge, Suffolk, 8 Queen Street, Ipswich, Suffolk. Watson House, Broadway West, Leigh-on-Sea, Essex. 46 Broadway, Leigh-on-Sea, Essex. 128 High Street, Rayleigh, Essex, 22 South Street, Rochford SS4 1BQ. 42 Ipswich Street, Stowmarket 1P14 1AD. 154 The Broadway, Thorpe Bay, SS1 3ES. 93 High Street, Witham CM8 1AA. A.E.Spear and Sons, The Hill, Wickham Market, Nr. Woodbridge, Suffolk

ALLSOP & CO

21 Soho Square, London W1V 6AX
Telephone: 01-437 6977

Partners Acting for Pension Funds P.J.Crowson, G.J.Boyton, ARICS, J.R.Oxley, FRICS, S.P.Chambers, FRICS

Employees 100 (approx)

Number of Pension Fund Clients Numerous

Services Offered to Pension Funds Advice on the acquisition and sale of investment properties, valuations, portfolio management, property management, project management, office, shop and industrial letting throughout UK and Europe

Other Offices 6 Poultry, London EC2 8ET (01-248 1451), St. John's Wood, Knightsbridge

PHILIP ANDREWS & CO

97-99 Park Street, Mayfair, London W1Y 4NJ
Telephone: 01-492 1881

Partners Acting for Pension Funds Peter Maxwell-Brown,ARICS, J.S.Andrews,MSc,FRICS

Employees 20

Number of Pension Fund Clients Numerous

Services Offered to Pension Funds Comprehensive advice on the acquisition and sale of investment properties, portfolio valuations and management, building surveys and architects services.

Other Offices 7 Northumberland Buildings, Queen Square, Bath BA1 2JB (0255-313102)

BACCHUS GATHERCOLE & PARTNERS

Brookfield House, 62-64 Brook Street, London W1 2JB
Telephone: 01-493 2805

Philip Andrews & Co.

CHARTERED SURVEYORS
FOR
COMMERCIAL PROPERTY INVESTMENT
THROUGHOUT THE UNITED KINGDOM

For our Brochure Please Contact:

P. Maxwell-Brown, ARICS or John S. Andrews FRICS

**97/99 Park Street
London W1Y 4NJ
01-492 1881**
Telex No: 449728

And at BATH, Avon

Property Advisers

BACCHUS GATHERCOLE & PARTNERS Continued

Partner Acting for Pension Funds K.G.Gathercole

BAIRSTOW EVES
Provincial House, 218-226 Bishopsgate,
London EC2M 4QD
Telephone: 01-377 0137

Partners Acting for Pension Funds B.M.Northway, ARICS, C.J.Finch, FRICS, J.M.Mannering,ARICS, R.A.Richards, FRICS

Employees 350

Number of Pension Fund Clients 4

Services Offered to Pension Funds Acquisition and disposal of investments, surveys, rating, management, rent reviews, plant and machinery valuations and disposals

Other Offices 44 Offices and departments throughout London, Hertfordshire, Suffolk and Essex

BAKER HARRIS SAUNDERS
Blackwell House, Guildhall Yard,
London EC2V 5AB
Telephone: 01-606 5757

Partners R.Saunders, S.P.Harris, M.P.L.Baker, N.R.Clark, N.G.J.Baucher, R.A.J.Harraby

BARNETT BAKER & CO.
13/14 Hanover Street, London W1R OEH
Telephone: 01-493 6128

Partners Acting for Pension Funds N. Frankel-Pollen, BSc,FRICs, D.Barnett, FSVA

Employees 7

Number of Pension Fund Clients Various, including 4 English and 2 Overseas Private Funds for whom solely retained

Services Offered to Pension Funds Complete property investment consultancy; computerised management dept; reports; surveys; valuations; reviews etc.

BARRINGTON LAURANCE
71 South Audley Street, London W1Y 6HD
Telephone: 01-492 0141

Partners acting for Pension Funds David Lyall, FRICS, Alex Moss,FRICS, Edward Cooper,FRICS, Martin Smith,ARICS

Employees 45

Number of Pension Fund Clients No solely retaining fund

Services Offered Full range of property investment consultancy including valuation, management, sale and purchase

Other Information The partnership has an extensive investment practice and advises numerous Pension Funds and insurance companies on specific matters.

VICTOR BEHRENS, SANDHURST & CO
12 Harley Street, London W1N 2AE
Telephone: 01-636 2491

Partners Acting for Pension Funds Victor Behrens, FSVA, Richard Sharp, ARICS

Total Employees 8

Number of Pension Fund Clients Several small funds

Services Offered to Pension Funds Full Investment service

BELL-INGRAM
47-48 Piccadilly, London W1V 0DN
Telephone: 01-437 1274

Partners Acting for Pension Funds Douglas Chance, BSc, FRICS, Ronald M.Wilson, BSc, FRICS, William Howie, FRICS, Ian M.Darling,FRICS

Employees 100

Number of Pension Fund Clients 5

Services Offered Comprehensive advice on commercial industrial and agricultural investment

Other Offices Glasgow, Edinburgh, Perth, Aberdeen, Irvine, Kilmarnock

Other Information Large division dealing with agricultural investment and management

BIDWELLS
Trumpington Road, Cambridge CB2 2LD
Telephone: 0223-841841

Partners Acting for Pension Funds Sir Francis Pemberton,CBE,MA,FRICS, T.J.Lawson,FRICS, P.R.W.Pemberton,MA,FRICS, N.D.H.Sanders,ARICS, P.T.Day,ARICS, C.R.Buxton,FRICS

Employees Approx 150

Number of Pension Fund Clients 8

Services Offered to Pension Funds Acquisition, management, valuation and disposal of agricultural and commercial properties

BISCOE & STANTON
5-6 Staple Inn, Holborn, London WC1V 7QU
Telephone: 01-242 4321

Partner Acting on Behalf of Pension Funds D.L.Biscoe,MA,FRICS

Employees 16

Pension Fund Clients 2

Services offered to Pension Funds Comprehensive investment advice together with purchase, sale and management services including rent review negotiations.

Other Office 4 King Street, Wakefield, West Yorkshire, WF1 2SQ

BODY SON AND FLEURY
22 Lockyer Street, Plymouth, Devon PL1 2QY
Telephone: 0752 266291

Partners Acting for Pension Funds Plymouth Office: A.H.Kennedy, TD,FRICS. Bath Office:B.W.Metcalf, BSc,FRICS,MRTPI

Employees 34

Number of Pension Fund Clients 1

Services Offered to Pension Funds Valuations, negotiation acquisition/disposal, rent reviews etc.

Other Offices 16 Southernhay West, Exeter, Devon (0392-72043); 30 Milsom Street, Bath, Avon (0225-61656); 57 Tufton Street, London SW1 (01-222 5786)

WILLIAM H. BROWN

INVESTMENT SURVEYORS

to

AGRICULTURE AND COMMERCE

15 Albemarle Street, London W1
(Tel. 01-499-5281)

with 30 Branches throughout
Lincolnshire, Norfolk, Humberside,
Nottinghamshire, Cambridgeshire,
Yorkshire and Leicestershire

SMITH MELZACK

Property Investment Advisers to
PENSION FUNDS
INSURANCE COMPANIES
& FAMILY TRUSTS

17/18 OLD BOND STREET, LONDON W1X 3DA
TEL: 01-493 1613
109 OLD BROAD STREET, LONDON EC2N 1AP
TEL: 01-638 1856
AND WEMBLEY

Property Advisers

BRECKER, GROSSMITH & CO

63 Wigmore Street, London W1H 0BQ
Telephone: 01-486 3531

Partners Acting for Pension Funds S.M.Brecker, S.Grossmith

Total Employees 9

Number of Pension Fund Clients 1

Services Offered to Pension Funds Confidential advice on acquisition, property company leaseback situations and development undertaken

BROWETT TAYLOR & CO

1-2 Lincoln's Inn Fields, London WC2A 3BA
Telephone: 01-242 8275

Partners Acting for Pension Funds John Cameron, FRICS, T.Hitman,FRICS

Number of Pension Fund Clients Several

Services Offered to Pension Funds Advice on acquisition and sale of investment properties including portfolio management, rent reviews, lease renewals and redevelopment

ANTHONY BROWN STEWART

35 Sackville Street, London W1X 1DB
Telephone: 01-437 0035

Partners Acting for Pension Funds J.Bruce Brown, BSc,FRICS, David E.B.Walls,FRICS, Hugh R.Tyler, BSc,FRICS, Paul F. Purchase FRICS

Employees 25

Number of Pension Fund Clients 3

Services Offered to Pension Funds Portfolio management, property acquisition, valuation, disposal, rent reviews

Other Offices Rockhill Lane, Bierley, Bradford BD4 6QB (0274 68740)

WILLIAM H. BROWN & SON

15 Albemarle Street, London W1
Telephone: 01-499 5281

and at Northgate House, Sleaford, Lincs.
Telephone: 0529-303040

Partners Acting for Pension Funds M.W.L.Brown, FRICS, J.R.Smith, ARICS, I.J.Youdan, MA,ARICS, N.G.Reiss,ARICS

Employees 150

Number of Pension Fund Clients 8

Services Offered to Pension Funds Comprehensive advice on the purchase, sale and management of Agricultural, Commercial and Industrial Investment Properties

Other Offices Throughout the counties of Lincolnshire, Norfolk, Cambridgeshire, Leicestershire, Nottinghamshire, Yorkshire and Humberside (30 offices in all)

Pension Fund Clients Pilkington Bros Ltd (Glass) Pension Fund, Northern Food Pension Trustees Ltd and Blue Circle Group Associated Cement Pensions Trustees Ltd

BRUTON KNOWLES & CO

Albion Chambers, 55 Barton Street, Gloucester GL1 1PZ
Telephone: 0452 21267

Partner Acting for Pension Funds R.A.Brown,FRICS

Employees 70

Number of Pension Fund Clients None solely retained

Services Offered to Pension Funds Advice on purchase and sale of commercial and agricultural property investments including management and valuation

Other Offices Cheltenham and Cinderford

BUCKELL AND BALLARD

58 Cornmarket Street, Oxford OX1 3HU
Telephone: 0865 40801
and at 103 Park Street,London W1Y 4JH
Telephone: 01-499 9681 (Ernest Owens, Buckell & Ballard)
Telephone: 01-935 1351

Partner Acting for Pension Funds D.F.Ferrand, FRICS

Other Pension Fund Expert Duncan Cairns,ARICS (Swindon Office, 0793-44511)

Employees 150 (Approx.)

Number of Pension Fund Clients Several

Services Offered to Pension Funds Introduction and advice on investment property, management, sales and landlord/tenant negotiations

Other Offices Reading, Newbury, Charlbury Wallingford, Banbury, Bicester, Witney, Wantage, Kidlington, Chipping Norton, Pangbourne, Swindon, Headington

HENRY BUTCHER & CO. INCORPORATING LEOPOLD FARMER & SONS

Brownlow House, 50-51 High Holborn, London WC1V 6EG
Telephone: 01-405 8411

Partners Acting for Pension Funds John M.Phillips, FRICS,FSVA, R.B.Norden, FRICS,FSVA

Other Pension Fund Expert R.V.Chadwick

Employees 100

Number of Pension Fund Clients 3 Trust Funds

Services Offered to Pension Funds Valuation, acquisition, disposal, rent reviews and management of commercial and industrial property

Other Offices 79-83 Colmore Row, Birmingham B3 2AP (021-236 5736); 27 St. Paul's Street, Leeds LS1 2JG (0532-457356)

CAMPBELL GORDON

48 Queens Road, Reading, Berks RG1 4HU
Telephone: 0734-585727

Partner Acting for Pension Funds I.G.Campbell, BSc, FRICS

Employees 5

Number of Pension Fund Clients 1

Services Offered to Pension Funds Sale and purchase of investments for clients, development funding, surveys of property market and analysis of trends, including rental growth of industrial and office buildings throughout the South of England. Property management and landlord tenant negotiation

Keith Cardale Groves
Chartered Surveyors

Retained investment advisers to Friendly Societies, Pension Funds and institutions for over 30 years

West End Office
43 North Audley Street,
Grosvenor Square,
London W1Y 2AQ
Tel: 01·629 6604
Telex: 27839.

City Office
Blossoms Inn,
23 Lawrence Lane,
London EC2V 8DA
Tel: 01·606 4581

Also in Los Angeles USA.

Property Advisers

KEITH CARDALE GROVES
43 North Audley Street, Grosvenor Square, London W1Y 2AQ
Telephone: 01-629 6604

Partners Acting for Pension Funds M.H.Groves, FRICS, P. Dean, FRICS,FRVA, J.M.Phillips, FRICS

Employees 100

Number of Friendly Society and Pension Fund Clients 5 in house, plus others on a non-exclusive basis

Services Offered to Pension Funds Comprehensive advice on all aspects of investment, including professional work arising from property ownership

Other Offices 36 St. Andrew's Hill, London EC4V 5DJ (01-248 9771) and California

Clients Include The Independent Order of Odd Fellows (Manchester Unity) FS, Post Office Insurance Society, Police Mutual Assurance Society, Teachers Assurance Company, Scottish Life Assurance Co Ltd

CARTER JONAS
90 Jermyn Street, London SW1Y 6JD
Telephone: 01-930 2401

Partners Acting for Pension Funds M.W.Taylor, FRICS, W.T.S.Lee,FRICS (London), F.D.Newton, MA, FRICS(Huntingdon), J.M.Dyke,FRICS(Cambridge), D.A.Heasman,BSc,FRICS(York), G.P.Candy, BSc, FRICS (Kidlington)

Employees 120

Number of Pension Fund Clients and Like Institutions 3

Services Offered to Pension Funds Purchases, sales, valuations, management of commercial and agricultural investments

Other Offices Cambridge, Huntingdon, Ipswich, Kidlington, Marlborough, Oxford, Slaithwaite, York

CHAMBERLAIN & WILLOWS
Church House, Ironmonger Lane, London EC2V 8EU
Telephone: 01-606 9611

Partners Acting for Pension Funds R.G.Hemingway, FRICS, C.F.Wilson,FRICS

Number of Pension Fund Clients A number of Private and Public Funds

Services Offered to Pension Funds Full range of professional services

Other Offices 1 South Audley Street, Mayfair, London W1Y 6JS (01-493 7863); Hale House, Green Lanes, Palmers Green, London N13 5TG(01-882 4633)

CHANCELLORS & CO
32 Greyfriars Road, Reading, Berkshire RG1 1NN
Telephone: 0734 586833

And at 33 Bancroft, Hitchin, Herts.
Telephone: 0462-4455

Partner acting for Pension Funds C.R.Boddy,ARICS, ARVA

Other Pension Fund Expert J.E.Cushing

Employees 60

Number of Pension Fund Clients 2 regular and numerous occasional clients

Services Offered to Pension Funds Advice on purchase and disposal of prime and secondary investments, investigation into development financing projects, analysis of market trends in industrial and office buildings throughout the Home Counties, valuations, rent reviews, and management of investment portfolios, specialist departments in town planning, rating and project management

Other Offices Ascot, Bagshot, Chobham, Lightwater, Sunningdale, Virginia Water, Woking

CHESSHIRE, GIBSON & CO
63 Temple Row, Birmingham B2 5LY
Telephone: 021-632 4292

Partners Acting for Pension Funds John A.R.Evans, FRICS, Hugh W.M.Cave, FRICS, Derek J. Hannam, FRICS, Peter A.Bingham, FRICS

Employees 67

Number of Pension Fund Clients 3

Services Offered to Pension Funds Periodic valuations of property portfolios, advice and negotiations regarding rent reviews, termination of leases and purchase of properties for the Fund (and occasionally the sale thereof).

Other Office 16 Berkeley Street, London W1X 5AE (01-492 0954)

CHESTERTONS
75 Grosvenor Street, London W1X 0JB
Telephone: 01-499 0404
Telex: 8812560 (Grosvenor Street), 8812898 (City Office)

Partners Acting for Pension Funds R.A.Catling, W.N.Bolt, J.R. King-Smith (City Office)

Employees 391

Number of Pension Fund Clients 7

Services Offered to Pension Funds Advice on the acquisition and sale of investment properties, their valuation and portfolio management, building surveying services and property management

Other Offices City Office, 28 Queen Street, London EC4R 1BB Tel:01-606 3055, Kensington, Hyde Park, Little Venice, Chelsea

Clients Include Legal & General (Pensions Management) Ltd, Gallaher Pensions Ltd, Nuffield Foundation, Oxford University Chest, Lloyds Life Assurance Co Ltd, Rolls Royce Motors Pension Funds, Devonshire County Council Superannuation Fund

CHURSTON, HEARD & CO
Berkeley Square House, Berkeley Square, London W1X 6DE
Telephone: 01-409 2199

Partners Acting for Pension Funds W.Ferguson, FRICS, J.E.Rodbourne, S.A.J.Powell, FRICS, A.H.Low

Employees 50

Number of Pension Fund Clients 10

Services Offered to Pension Funds Advice on all aspects of property investment, acquisition, disposals, valuation, management and landlord and tenant negotiations

Cooke & Arkwright

INVESTMENT, INDUSTRIAL, COMMERCIAL, AGRICULTURAL

AND

DEVELOPMENT PROPERTY CONSULTANTS

10 Harcourt House, 19a Cavendish Square, London, W1M 0LB. Tel. 01-580 4949

Cooke & Arkwright
Chartered Surveyors
London Bangor Bridgend Cardiff Carmarthen
Haverfordwest Hereford Pembroke Swansea

The fast movers

YOUR U.K. LINK WITH THE HOUSTON REAL ESTATE MARKET

With over 2½ years experience in the Texas market place we hope we can satisfy your property requirements for investment, development or owner/tenant occupation.

For further information and a free copy of our 1981 Real Estate Report on the city of Houston please contact:

In the U.K.		In the United States.
our international partner	5 Upper George Street,	Jack Sutter or Mike Mahoney
Clive Faine FRICS, FRVA	Luton, Beds.	3100 Edloe, Suite 306,
62 Grosvenor Street,	LU1 2QY	Houston,
London W1X 9DA	Tel: (0582) 31261	Texas 77027
Tel: 01.493.4932	Telex: 826314	Tel: 0101-713-629.6090
	BUSAID-G	

Property Advisers

CLIFFORD BONNEY
Neville House, 26 Milton Road, Swindon, Wilts SN1 5JA
Telephone: 0793-31414

Partner acting for Pension Funds C.Clifford-Jones, ARICS

Number of Pension Fund Clients The firm is consistently in direct involvement with a number of leading and smaller Pension Funds

Services Offered to Pension Funds Comprehensive advice on all aspects of commercial property investment throughout the U.K.

CLUTTONS
5 Great College Street, Westminster London SW1P 3SD
Telephone: 01-222 7080

Partners Acting for Pension Funds P.W.Trumper, FRICS, Street, N.H.Clutton, W1 R.A.Crockett, FRICS, O.H.Scammell, FRICS, D.M.S.Hampton, FRICS, E.V.Desson, ARICS, R.W.Jonas,ARIvenor 3 Beer Cart Lane, Osborne 20 Victoria 11 Charlotte Square, Edinburgh

Employees 350 (approx)

Number of Pension Fund Clients Large Number

Services Offered to Pension Funds Complete service in all aspects of property ownership

Other Offices 5 Great College Street, London SW1, 48 Pelham Street, Kensington, London SW7, 24 Milsom Street, Bath, 17 New Dover Road, Canterbury, 23 Beaumont Street, Oxford, 10 New Street, Wells, Osborn House, Victoria Avenue, Harrogate and Edinburgh

COLLIER & MADGE
5 St. Bride Street, London EC4A 4DE
Telephone: 01-353 9161

Partner Acting for Pension Funds R.H.Palmer, FRICS,FSVA

Employees 17

Number of Pension Fund Clients Various, but 2 in particular

Services Offered to Pension Funds Full range of professional services including acquisition, sale, valuation and management

Clients include The Fitch Lovell Pension Scheme

CONNELLS COMMERCIAL
5 Upper George Street, Luton, Bedfordshire LU1 2QY
Telephone: 0582-31261

And at 62 Grosvenor Street, London W1X 9DA
Telephone: 01-493 4932

Partners Acting for Pension Funds J.D.Wetherman, FRICS, C.A.Faine, FRICS,FRVA, P.M.Brown, FRICS M.J.Mahony, J.F.Sutter in USA

Employees 200

Number of Pension Fund Clients Retained by three as sole adviser. Active on behalf of many others, including overseas investors

Services Offered to Pension Funds Acquisition, sale and portfolio management of office, shop, industrial and warehouse investments

Other Offices 28 offices throughout United Kingdom and as Connells International Real Estate at 3100, Edloe, Suite 306, Houston, Texas 77027 (713-629 6090)

CONRAD RITBLAT & CO
Milner House, 14 Manchester Square, London W1M 6AA
Telephone: 01-935 4499

Partners Acting for Pension Funds R.E.Bowden, BSc,ARICS,FRVA, D.R.Stein,BSc

Employees 138

Number of Pension Fund Clients Retained by 3 Pension Funds exclusively but also act on an ad hoc basis for a number of Pension Funds in respect of individual properties

Services Offered to Pension Funds A complete service in all aspects of property ownership, investment and management

Other Offices Plantation House, Fenchurch Street, London EC3 (01-623 9116); 78 St. Vincent Street, Glasgow G2 5TX (041-226 3971); Representative Office: Rotterdam Building, Aert Van Nes Straat, 3012-CA Rotterdam (010-130566)

Clients Include Dixons Photographic Pension Fund, Cannon Assurance Staff Pension Scheme

CONWAY RELF
44 St. James's Place, London SW1A 1PG
Telephone: 01-629 9100

Partners acting for Pension Funds A.I.Conway, R.R.Neale, M.J.A.Lepper, M.F.Sheardown, M.J.Brooks

Other Pension Fund Experts D.H.Relf,Consultant

Employees 26

Number of Pension Fund Clients 2

Services Offered to Pension Funds Property acquisition and management

Clients Include B.A.T Industries Ltd. and Associated Companies Staff Pension Funds, Montague Burton Pensions Trustee Ltd.

COOKE & ARKWRIGHT
10 Harcourt House, 19a Cavendish Square, London W1M 0LB
Telephone: 01-580 4949
Telex 299589

Partners Acting for Pension Funds R.W.S.Knight, FRICS, R.H.Knight,FRICS, L.J.A.Phipps,FRICS, I.R.Peill,ARICS, R.P.Head,ARICS

Other Pension Fund Experts T.R.W.Davies,FRICS (Agricultural Consultant), R.D.Thomas,ARICS

Employees 150

Number of Pension Fund Clients 3

Services Offered to Pension Funds Search, acquisitions, sale and portfolio management of office, shop, industrial, warehouse & agricultural investment properties

Other Offices Bangor (0248-2414), Bridgend (0656-55051), Cardiff (0222-398151), Carmarthen (05584-4984), Haverfordwest (0437-4349), Hereford (0432-67213), Pembroke (06463-2706), Swansea (0792-51615)

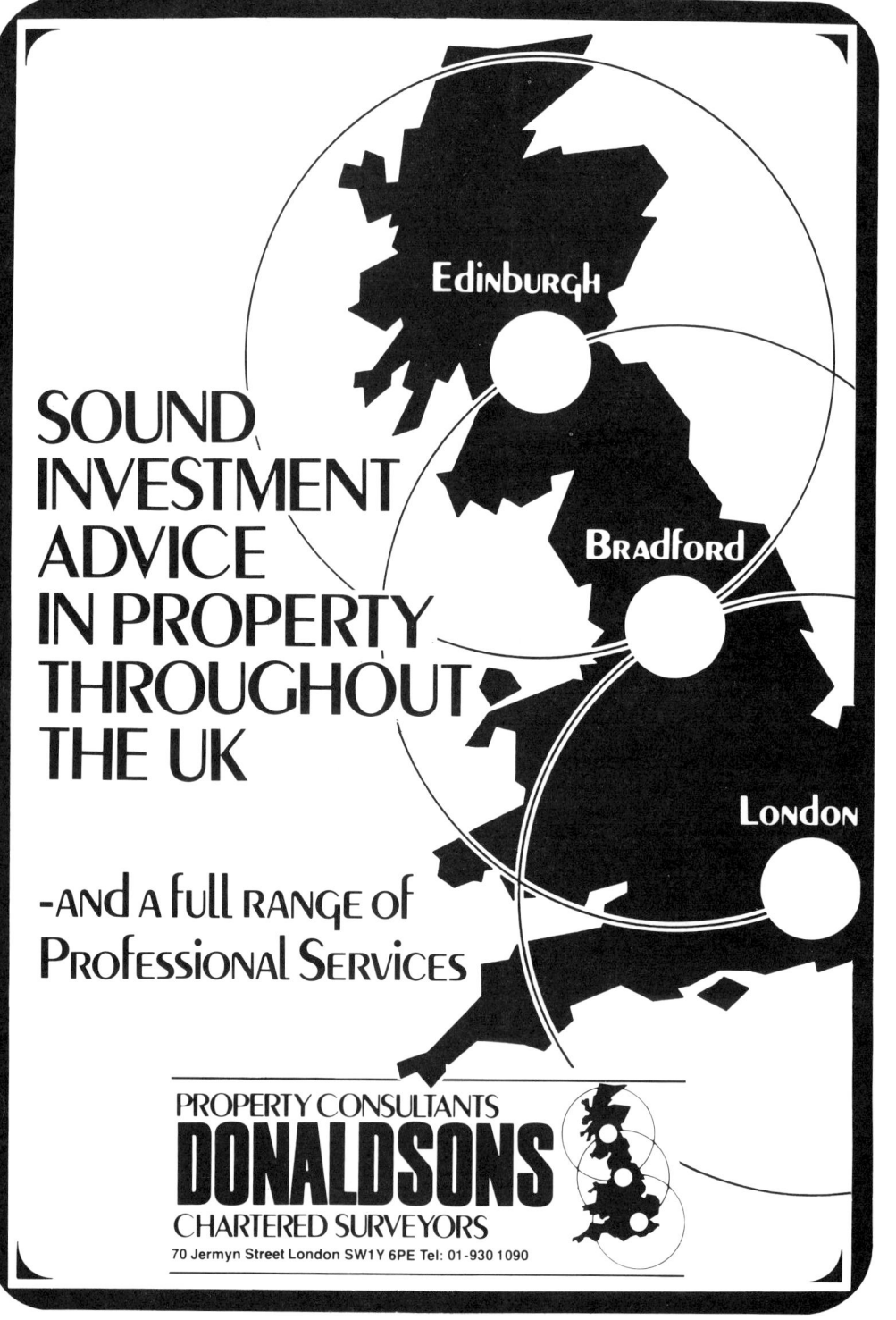

Property Advisers

COOPER KENDALL & CO
25 Duke Street, Manchester Square,
London W1M 5DB
Telephone: 01-935 1191

Partners Acting for Pension Funds Leslie B.Kendall, FRICS, Jeffrey S.Cooper,FRICS

Employees 6

Number of Pension Fund Clients 3

Services Offered to Pension Funds Acquisition and sale. Advice and valuation

CRUICKSHANKS COMMERCIAL
28 High Street, High Wycombe, Bucks. HP11 2AF
Telephone: 0494 23701

Partner acting for Pension Funds D.A.Martin, FRICS

Employees 50

Number of Pension Fund Clients One regular client and numerous occasional clients

Services Offered to Pension Funds Acquisition, disposal, management, project management, surveying, valuation, arbitration, planning etc

Other Offices Berkhamstead, Beaconsfield, Marlow, Tring, Thame, High Wycombe

CUTHBERT LAKE DREW PEARCE
9 Stone Buildings, Lincoln's Inn,
London WC2A 3TA
Telephone: 01-405 1953

Partner Acting for Pension Funds David Cadman

CYRIL LEONARD & CO
52 Brook Street, London W1Y 2EJ
Telephone: 01-408 2222

Partners Acting for Pension Funds C.Blausten,JP, FSVA, D.Blausten,MA,ARICS, J.N.Kennedy,BSc, ARICS, C.J.Glenn,ARICS,ARVA, A.D.Imrie,ARICS

Employees 30

Number of Pension Fund Clients Various

Services Offered to Pension Funds Comprehensive

DACRE, SON & HARTLEY
Royal Exchange House, Boar Lane, Leeds LS1 5NS
Telephone: 0532-444421

Partners acting for Pension Funds Kenneth E.Hanson,FRICS, J.Bruce Entwlsle,ARICS

Employees 150

Number of Pension Fund Clients 7

Services Offered to Pension Funds Acquisitions, development, management and sales

Other Offices The Estate Office, Station Road, Otley, 1-5 The Grove, Ilkley, 22-26 Devonshire Street, Keighley, 32 Sheep Street, Skipton, The Manor House, 97 High Street Knaresborough, 10 Queen Street, Ripon, 24 Albert Street, Harrogate, 93 Main Street, Bingley, 56 Albion Street, Leeds

HENRY DAVIS & CO
101 New Bond Street, London W1Y 9LG
Telephone: 01-499 2271

Partner Acting for Pension Funds H.W.Davis,FRICS

Number of Pension Fund Clients Various

Services Offered to Pension Funds Investment

advice, portfolio and property management, lease negotiations, letting, sales, project management etc

Other Office 23 St. Swithin's Lane, London EC4 (01-626 8944)

DEBENHAM TEWSON & CHINNOCKS
Bancroft House, Paternoster Square,
London EC4P 4ET
Telephone: 01-236 1520

Partners Acting for Pension Funds C.R.Vaughan, FRICS, R.N.Lay,FRICS, D.M.Butler,FRICS, H.J.K.Bagnall-Oakeley,MA,FRICs, J.A.C.Roberts, ARICS

Employees Approx 220 in the UK

Clients Include British Petroleum Pension Trust Ltd., Glaxo Trustees Ltd., Mobil Oil Trustee Co. Ltd., Grindlays Bank Pension Fund, Price & Pierce Group Pension Scheme, Wyndham Investments

Services Offered to Pension Funds Advice on investment and management of property portfolios

Other Offices 44/46 Brook Street, London W1Y 1YB (01-408 1161); 2 St.Andrew's Hill, London EC4V 5DX. Cardiff, Australia, Bahrain, Belgium, Germany, New York

DE GROOT COLLIS
9 Clifford Street, London W1X 2AL
Telephone: 01-734 1304

Partners Acting for Pension Funds Jack Collis, JP, FRICS, Harry K.Hemmings,FSVA, Norman J.Rose, BSc,FRICS,FIArb

Other Pension Fund Expert Clifford Krieger, FSVA

Employees 40

Number of Pension Fund Clients 2

Services Offered to Pension Funds Portfolio management, property management, valuation etc

Other Offices 309-310 High Holborn, London WC1V 7LX (01-831 7651); Basildon House, 7-11 Moorgate, London EC2R 6AD (01-606 1455); 93 Knightsbridge, London SW1X 7RB (01-235 4166)

Associated Offices Europe, Australia, USA, Middle East

DIAMOND & COMPANY
3 Cork Street, London W1X 1HA
Telephone: 01-439 6781

Partner Acting for Pension Funds P.A.Diamond

Employees 4

Number of Pension Fund Clients 3

Services Offered to Pension Funds Advice on the acquisition and sale of investment properties which include portfolio valuation, management, lease negotiation, building surveying services etc.

DONALDSON & SONS
70 Jermyn Street, London SW1Y 6PE
Telephone: 01-930 1090

Partners Acting for Pension Funds J.B.Murphy, FRICS, P.J.Stowers, FRICS,FSVA, J.P.D.Burmester, ARICS, R.Hofbauer, ARICS

Other Pension Fund Experts R.C.Miall,FRICS, J.M.Burnett,ARICS, B.Wright,FSCA

Employees 150

Reaching key conclusions...

on funding and investment propositions for institutional clients

DRIVERS JONAS

Chartered Surveyors

London · Norwich · Aberdeen
16 Suffolk Street, London SW1Y 4HQ
01-930 9731

Property Advisers

DONALDSON & SONS Continued

Number of Pension Fund Clients 10

Services Offered to Pension Funds A comprehensive range of professional and agency services

Other Offices Kensington, Bradford, Edinburgh

Associated Companies Donaldsons Property Management

Clients Include General Accident, Yorkshire Insurance Group, English Insurance Co. Ltd, Lothian Regional Council Pension Fund, Liverpool Victoria Friendly Society, and several public company and private superannuation schemes

DRIVER JONAS

16 Suffolk Street, London SW1Y 5HQ
Telephone: 01-930 9731

Partners Acting for Pension Funds C.W.Jonas, FRICS, D.E.H.Chapman,BSc,FRICS

Other Pension Fund Experts T.M.Savage,BSc, ARICS, C.H.Armon-Jones,ARICS, J.C.Michell, BSc, ARICS

Employees 100 approx

Number of Pension Fund Clients Several

Services Offered to Pension Funds Professional advice on all aspects relating to the acquisition and disposal of property investments and the financing of development schemes. Computer based modelling for fund simulation and performance monitoring

Other Offices Aberdeen, Norwich

DRON & WRIGHT

5 Burgon Street, London EC4V 5DB
Telephone: 01-248 5799

Partner Acting for Pension Funds Geoffrey E.T.Castle,FRICS

Other Pension Fund Experts S.P.Wainwright,BSc, ARICS, A.L.Bond,BSc

Employees 50

Number of Pension Fund Clients Several

Services Offered to Pension Funds Acquisition and disposal of property investments, professional advice on all aspects of property once acquired, including performance measurement and analysis, portfolio management, rent reviews and lease renewals.

Other Information Main client is Provident Life Association of London Ltd

DRUCE & CO

23 Manchester Square, London W1A 2DD
Telephone: 01-486 1252
Telex: 261038

Partners Acting for Pension Funds S.A.Parnes, FRICS, M.C.Green, BSc (Est Man),FRICS

Employees 80

Number of Pension Fund Clients 60(approx). In-house clients 3

Services Offered to Pension Funds Acquisition, disposal, project management, portfolio analysis, valuation, rent review, negotiation and management of investment properties

Other Offices 1 Heath Street, Hampstead, London NW3 6TP (01-435 9851), 21 Aylmer Parade, Highgate, London N2 0PH (01-340 2222). Druce House, 54-56 Baker Street, London W1 (01-486 9851), 3a Albert Court, Prince Consort Road, Knightsbridge, London SW7 2BE (01-581 3771)

Clients Include Crown House Pension Trustees Ltd. Cope Allman International Pension Fund

DUNCAN STUPPLES

21 High Street, High Wycombe Bucks. HP11 2BZ
Telephone: 0494-20451

Partner Acting for Pension Funds R.F.Stupples, FRICS,FSVA

Services Offered to Pension Funds Acquisition, disposal, management, valuation etc.

DUNLOP HEYWOOD & CO

90 Deansgate, Manchester M3 2QP
Telephone: 061-834 8384

Partners Acting for Pension Funds R.J.Weston,BSc, FRICS,K.Bailey,FRICS, J.C.Prince,FRICS, R.W.Dyson, ARICS, P.N.Jones,ARICS

Employees 75

Number of Pension Fund Clients 12

Services Offered to Pension Funds Full range of property investment advice, including buying and selling, insurance revaluations, rent reviews, portfolio valuation and management.

Other Offices 27 Old Bond Street, London W1X 3AA. Associated throughout Western Europe

EADON, LOCKWOOD & RIDDLE

6A Campo Lane, Sheffield S1 2EF
Telephone: 0742 71277

Partners Acting for Pension Funds T.M.Newton, BSc,FRICS, D.Everingham,FRICS,FBIM, A.R.F.Twelves,FRICS,DipTP

Employees Over 50

Number of Pension Fund Clients 15

Services Offered to Pension Funds Advice on purchase and sale of freehold and leasehold property. Capital and fire insurance valuations. Rent reviews and management of commercial and industrial properties. Portfolio management and valuations, Project management

Other Offices Residential Offices, 2 St James Street, Sheffield S1 1XJ, Broomhill, Sheffield; London Office at Albemarle Street, London W1

THE A.G.EBBAGE PARTNERSHIP

Exchange Street, Norwich NR2 1DJ
Telephone: 0603-29971

Partners Acting for Pension Funds A.G.Ebbage, FSVA, E.Webster,FRICS

Employees 29

Number of Pension Fund Clients Several, plus Insurance Companies and Family Trusts

Services Offered to Pension Funds Disposals and acquisitions, valuation, management, lease renewals and rent reviews

Other Offices 3 branches in Norfolk

Our homeground in the North West provides the ideal geographical location to offer our nationwide Property Investment Service.

Dunlop Heywood & Co.
Chartered Surveyors
90, Deansgate, Manchester, M3 2QP.
061-834 8384 Telex 667262

also Associated throughout Western Europe

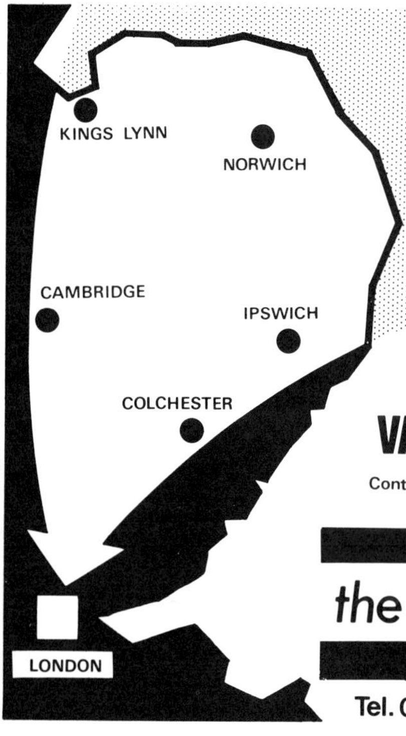

NORWICH
and the
SOUTH EAST

A personal, hardworking and professional approach to

DISPOSALS · AQUISITIONS
VALUATION · RENEWALS & REVIEWS

Contact: Alan G. Ebbage F.S.S. F.S.V.A or Ernest Webster F.R.I.C.S
at Headquarters, EXCHANGE STREET, NORWICH

the **AG Ebbage** partnership
Commercial & Industrial **AGE**ncy

Tel. 0603 – 29971   Telex 97372

Property Advisers

EDDISONS

10 Greek Street, Leeds LS1 5RZ
Telephone: 0532 30101
Telex: 55169

Partners Acting for Pension Funds B.G.F.Shearman, FRICS, J.H.Brearley,FRICS, J.A.Thorpe,FRICS, N.A.E.Robinson,FRICS, R.J.R.Allan, FRICS, J.R.Burkitt,BSc,ARICS, M.Brodrick,ARICS

Employees 140

Number of Pension Fund Clients Several

Services Offered to Pension Funds Full range of property investment services, including acquisition and disposal, insurance valuations, rent reviews, portfolio valuations and management (also specialist plant and machinery valuers)

Other Offices Bradford, Huddersfield, Halifax, Brighouse Guiseley and Horsforth

EDWARDS, BIGWOOD & BEWLAY

78 Colmore Row, Birmingham B3 2HG
Telephone: 021-236 8477

and at Parkside House, 51-53 Brick Street, London W.1
Telephone: 01-499 9452

Partners Acting for Pension Funds D.A.Good,MA, FRICS, R.A.Ford,FRICS

Employees 137 (including 10 associate Partners)

Number of Pension Fund Clients 8

Services Offered to Pension Funds Acquisition, sale, management, general market reports

Other Offices Banbury, Shipston-on-Stow, Stratford

Principal Pension Fund Clients Ash & Lacy Ltd Fund, Imperial Metal Industries Ltd Fund

EKINS, DILLEY & HANDLEY

Centenary House, Castle Moat Road, Huntingdon, Cambridgeshire PE18 6PQ
Telephone: 0480 56171

Partners Acting for Pension Funds H.Storey,FRICS, S.D.Cox,FRICS, P.C.Handley,FRICS, J.M.Johnson, FRICS

Employees 85

Services Offered to Pension Funds Valuation, advice on sale and purchase, management

Other Offices Cambridge, St.Ivos, Ely, St.Neots

ELLIOTT, SON & BOYTON

79 Wimpole Street, London W1M 7DD
Telephone: 01-487 4401
Telex: 299237

Partner Acting for Pension Funds Richard A. Martin, FRICS

Employees 55

Services Offered to Pension Funds Sale and purchase of investment property and financing of development schemes

Other Offices 30 Waterloo Road, Birmingham B2 5TJ (021-236 8811), MacIntosh House, 77 Fountain Street, Manchester M2 2EE (061-236 1418)

RICHARD ELLIS

64 Cornhill, London EC3V 3PS
Telephone: 01-283 3090

Partners Acting for Pension Funds A.J.M.Huntley, FRICS, D.A.Sizer,FRICS, M.D.G.Wheldon,BSc,FRICS, R.J.F.Wildman,ARICS, C.D.Budden, BSc,FRICS, R.G.C.Clarke,ARICS, E.T.D.Luker,ARICS, G.A.C.Wood,ARICS, R.Dade,BSc,ARICS, I.A.Reid, ARICS, A.J.B.Oakes,MA,ARICS, G.E.Webster,ARICS (Glasgow)

Other Pension Fund Experts A.E.Goodens,FRICS, J.A.D.Croft,BSc,FRICS

Number of Pension Fund Clients 23 with property assets exceeding £1,000 million

Services Offered to Pension Funds Full range of services offered

Other Offices 6/10 Bruton Street,London W1X 8DU (01-408 0929); 7/17 Jewry Street, London EC3N 2ND (01-480 5633); York House, York Street, Manchester M60 2DL (061-236 9335); 75 Hope Street, Glasgow G2 6AJ (041-204 1931); Avenue des Arts 39, Bte. 3, 1040 Brussels, Belgium (02-513 8187); 17 rue de la Baume, 75008 Paris, France (563 0808); Leidseplein 29, 1017 PS Amsterdam (020-262691); Edificio Iberia Mart, Pedro Teixeira 8, Madrid 20, Spain (455 3500). Also in USA (Chicago, Atlanta and San Francisco); South Africa as Richard Ellis, Dunlop Heywood (Johannesburg, Cape Town, Durban); Australia (Melbourne, Adelaide, Sydney, Perth, Brisbane); Singapore and Hong Kong

Pension Fund Clients Include Booker McConnell Ltd Pension Fund, Courage Group Pension Fund, Dickinson Robinson Group Ltd, Electricity Supply Nominees Ltd, South of Scotland and Northern Ireland Electricity Superannuation Schemes, Hampshire County Council Superannuation Fund, Imperial Tobacco Co Pension Trust, Kent County Council Superannuation Fund, Kimberly Clark Pension Trusts Ltd, Powell Duffryn Superannuation Trust Ltd, Rank Hovis McDougall Pension Fund, Rank Xerox Pension Scheme, Ready Mixed Concrete Pension Fund, Reed International Ltd Pension Schemes, Strathclyde Regional Council Superannuation Fund, Tate & Lyle Group Pension Scheme, United Biscuits (Pension Trustees) Ltd, United Shoe Machinery Co International Pension Property Trust Ltd.

EDWARD ERDMAN

6 Grosvenor Street, London W1X 0AD
Telephone: 01-629 8191
Telex 28169

Partners Acting for Pension Funds E.L.Erdman, FSVA (Consultant), E.T.Mowle,FSVA (Consultant), C.A.L.Kerr,FRICS (Joint Senior Partner), M.J.Fowler, FRICS (Partner in Charge of Investment Department), A.R.Trump, ,FRICS, P.Morrison-Wells, ARICS, C.A.Ross,BSc,ARICS,P.R.Dudman,ARICS

Employees Approximately 250

Number of Pension Fund Clients Public and private pension funds, a property unit trust and insurance companies

Services Offered to Pension Funds Full range of professional services

Other Offices 23 College Hill, Cannon Street, London EC4R 2RT (01-236 3611); 184 St. Vincent Street, Glasgow G2 5SG (041-221 8345); Edward Erdman et Cie, 12 Rue de Penthievre, 75008 Paris (265-23-41) Edward Erdman Europe B.V., Rokin 92-96, Amsterdam

In association with Arthur Rubloff & Co., Erdman

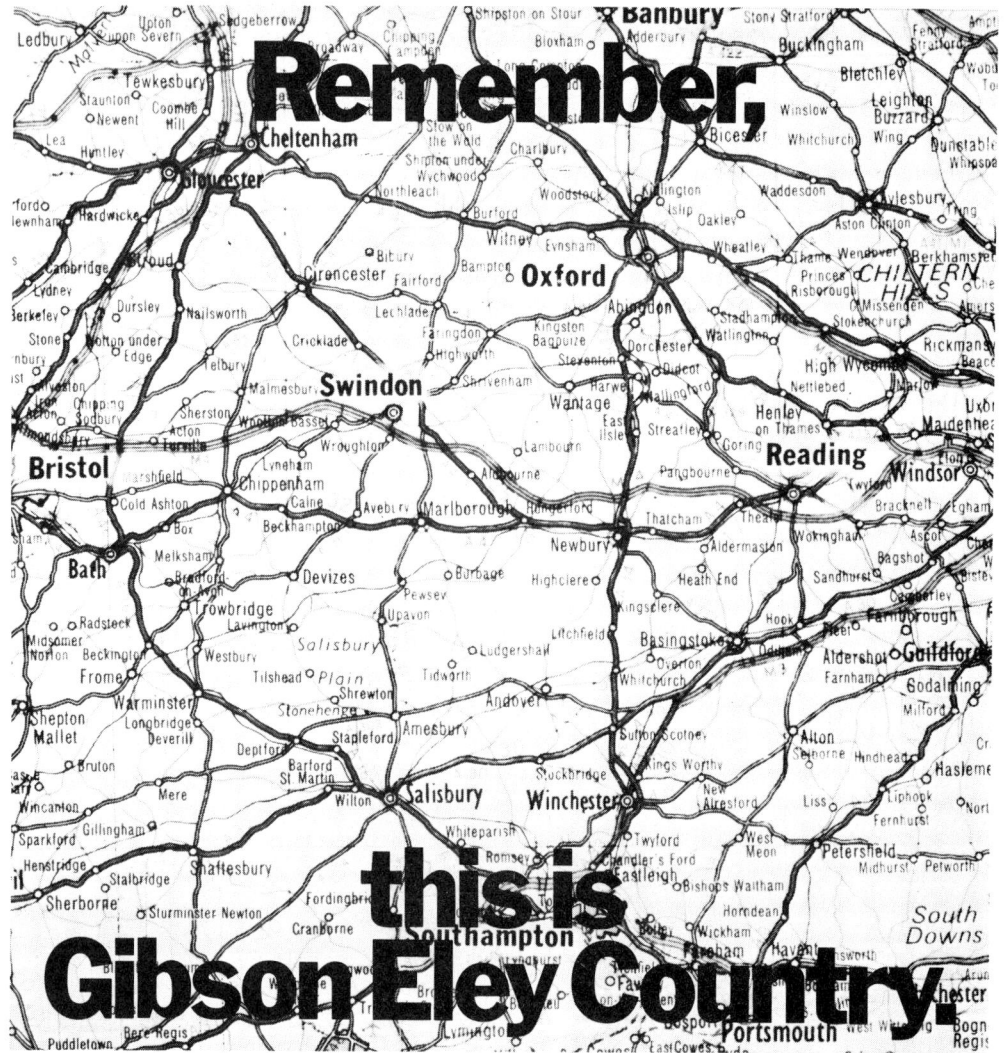

We offer the Property Investment Funds a comprehensive service including acquisitions, development appraisals, market reports, funding, letting, rent reviews, disposals, valuations and portfolio management.

Invest in our many years experience in a territory which we have made very much our own.

It's called Gibson Eley Country.

Gibson Eley

Consultant Surveyors to Commerce and Industry.
9 Castle Street, Reading RG1 7SB
Telephone: 0734 588311 Telex: 847386
And at Swindon, Wilts.

Property Advisers

EDWARD ERDMAN *Continued*

Rubloff International, Chicago, Atlanta, Cincinnati, Houston, Los Angeles, San Francisco, Washington D.C.

In association with August-Thouard S.A., Erdman Auguste-Thouard International, Paris, Bordeaux, Lille, Lyon, Marseille, Nice, Strasbourg, Toulouse

GERALD EVE & CO

18 Savile Row, London W1X 2BP
Telephone: 01-437 0488

Partners Acting for Pension Funds M.St.J.Hopper, FRICS, M.Beaman,FRICS, F.G.Hinks,ARICS

Employees About 160

Number of Pension Fund Clients 5

Services Offered to Pension Funds Advice on purchase, sale and development of freehold and leasehold property, periodic capital and fire insurance valuations, rent reviews and management

Other Offices Cardiff, Merseyside, Glasgow and Brussels

Clients Include The Plessey Pension Trust Ltd, The Plessey Executive Pension Trust Ltd, The Harmsworth Group Pension Fund, Albright & Wilson Pension Trustees Ltd., 600 Group Pensions Trustees Ltd.

FAREBROTHER

29 Fleet Street, London EC4Y 1AL
Telephone: 01-583 0303

Partners Acting for Pension Funds M.Bridges Webb,MA,FRICS, R.M.Timmins

Employees 25

Number of Pension Fund Clients Four retaining clients

Services offered to Pension Funds Comprehensive advice on the appraisal, valuation, purchase, management and disposal of investment properties and portfolios

FAWDRY & EVANS

28 Conduit Street, London W1R OHH
Telephone: 01-629 5002

Partners Acting for Pension Funds A.A.Jeffrey, FSVA, K.P.Buckler,FRICS A.A.Jeffrey,FSVA, K.P.Buckler,FRICS

Number of Pension Fund Clients Many

Services Offered to Pension Funds Valuation, acquisition, development, management and disposal of commercial and industrial property

Other Information Sole purchasing surveyors and management agents to Exchange Telegraph Pension Fund Trust

FENN WRIGHT

146 High Street, Colchester CO1 1PW
Telephone: 0206 46161

Partners Acting for Pension Funds R.W.Whybrow, FRICS, R.E.Weston,BSc, FRICS

Employees 50

Number of Pension Fund Clients Close connections with several funds, although not exclusively retained by any fund

Services Offered to Pension Funds The search, acquisition, valuation and management of all types of property investments, specialising particularly in Essex and East Anglia

Other Offices 1 Butter Market, Ipswich, IP1 1BA, 10 Market Place, Saxmundham IP17 1AG

FISHER AND CO

40 High Street, Market Harborough,
Leicestershire LE16 7NX
Telephone: 0858 62201

Partners Acting for Pension Funds M.C.C.Sandell, FRICS, J.Cowen FRICS

Total Employees 37

Number of Pension Fund Clients Two exclusively, but advising other Pension Funds

Services Offered to Pension Funds Buying, valuing, selling, and managing investments in agricultural land, including farm consultancy, management and farmbuilding design

Other Offices Dumbleton, near Evesham, Worcs (0386 881214)

FLETCHER KING

10-12 Cork Street, London W1X 1PD
Telephone: 01-734 7701

Partners Acting for Pension Funds D.J.R.Fletcher, FRICS, M.C.Sabey,FRICS, A.J.White,ARICS

Employees 25

Number of Pension Fund Clients 5

Services Offered to Pension Funds Acquisition, project and portfolio management, valuation and disposal

Pension Fund Clients Include British Enkalon Pension Trust, Chichester Diocesan Fund, Debenhams Pension Trust, J.Lyons Pension Trust

FOLKARD & HAYWARD

115 Baker Street, London W1M 2AY
Telephone: 01-935 7799

Partners acting for Pension Funds J.P.Stacey,TD, FRICS, N.H.P.Vereker,FRICS

Consultants and Associates Acting for Pension Funds A.R.Harrold,FSVA, A.J.M.Fear,ASVA, A.R.Hall, ARICS

Employees 80 (approx)

Number of Pension Fund Clients Several Pension Funds in the various aspects of business

Services Offered to Pension Funds The valuation, acquisition, development, letting, management and disposal of all types of property for Pension Funds

Other Information A quick efficient professional service is provided covering all aspects of property by an experienced partnership of Chartered Surveyors, who give their clients personal attention

FOX & SONS

44-52 Christchurch Road, Bournemouth,
Dorset BH1 1LN
Telephone: 0202 24242

**Professional Advisers
for
the acquisition,
management & disposal
of
Investment Property
and
Development Projects
throughout the
United Kingdom**

Established 1898

Goddard & Smith

**22 King Street St. James's, London SW1Y 6QZ
Telephone 01-930 7321 Telex: 8955411**

Property Advisers

FOX & SONS *Continued*

Partner Acting for Pension Funds D.J.King

Other Offices Over 60 throughout South and West

A.C.FROST & CO
3 High Street, Windsor, Berks SL4 1LE
Telephone: 07535 54555

Partner Acting for Pension Funds Richard H. Hodgson,AIBA

Other Pension Fund Expert A.F.Euren

Employees 9

Number of Pension Fund Clients Many major funds

Services Offered to Pension Funds Property investment and development, portfolio management

Other Offices 19 offices throughout Buckinghamshire, Berkshire, Oxfordshire, Surrey and in Channel Islands

FULLER PEISER
Thavies Inn House, 3-4 Holborn Circus,
London EC1N 2HL
Telephone: 01-353 6851

Partners Acting for Pension Funds J.E.G.Peiser, FRICS, R.G.Taylor, BSc,FRICS, J.W.Stephenson, FRICS

Other Pension Fund Experts S.Wong Chong,FRICS, A.P.Francis, ARICS

Employees 80

Number of Pension Fund Clients One, as sole advisers, and many others on a non-exclusive basis

Services offered to Pension Funds Valuation surveys, project management, rating, management, acquisition and disposal of property in UK and Western Europe

Other Offices London, West End, Sheffield, Edinburgh, Paris

Main Pension Fund Client City of Westminster Superannuation Fund

GARRETT, WHITE & POLAND
36 St. Andrew's Hill, London EC4V 5DJ
Telephone: 01-248 9771

Partners Acting for Pension Funds B.P.Bottling, FRICS, FIArb, J.W.Osbourn,ARICS

Services Offered to Pension Funds Purchase and sale, rating, valuation, rent reviews and general advice

GEERING & COLYER
133 South Road, Haywards Heath,
W.Sussex RH16 4LJ
Telephone: 0444 57311

Partner Acting for Pension Fund G.H.Sparks

Employees 100

Number of Pension Fund Clients 40 approx.

Services Offered to Pension Funds Management, valuation, survey, disposal and acquisition, lease renewal etc.

Other Offices 12 offices in Sussex and Kent, with branches concerned in Commercial Practice at Ashford, Tunbridge Wells, Maidstone, Canterbury

GENIS AND PARTNERS
285 Edgware Road, London W2
Telephone: 01-723 3675

Partner Acting for Pension Funds N.Genis

GIBSON ELEY & CO
Castle House, 9 Castle Street, Reading,
Berks RG1 7SB
Telephone: 0734-583945

Partner Acting for Pension Funds David V.Nassif, FSVA

Other Pension Fund Expert I.M.S.V.Eley,FRICS, FRVA

Employees 20

Number of Pension Fund Clients Many major Institutional Funds and Private Trusts

Services Offered to Pension Funds Property acquisition, disposal, development appraisal, project management, rent review negotiations, lettings valuations for all purposes, planning

Other Offices 33 Regent Circus, Swindon, (07935-41851) 16-18 Friar Street, Reading, Berks (0734-583945)

Other Information A full professional service to clients covering an area within a 50 mile radius of Reading, Berks.

GODDARD & SMITH
22 King Street, St. James's, London SW1Y 6QZ
Telephone: 01-930 7321
Telex: 8955411

Partners acting for Pension Funds B.M.K.Glass, FRICS,FRVA, A.E.Solomon,FRICS, J.L.S.Crossley, MA,FRICS, A.C.Smith,FCIA, L.M.Biddle,BSc,ARICS, R.A.Harper,FRICS

Other Pension Fund Experts C.E.Corlett, BSc, ARICS, F.T.Diprose, FSVA

Employees 150

Number of Pension Fund Clients Numerous

Services Offered to Pension Funds Property investment and development, funding, valuation and full management services

Other Offices 104-106 Westbourne Terrace, London W2 6QF

Associated Offices California and Florida, U.S.A.

GOLDENBERG AND COMPANY
39 Bruton Place, Berkeley Square,
London W1X 7AB
Telephone: 01-491 4101

Partner Acting for Pension Funds S.A.Goldenberg, ASVA,ARVA,MRSH

Specialist Services Offered to Pension Funds Sale, purchase, letting, survey, valuation, auction and management of all types of property and land

GOOCH & WAGSTAFF
73 Watling Street, London EC4M 9BL
Telephone: 01-248 2044

Partners Acting for Pension Funds P.T.C.Nevard, J.H.Cheshire and J.E.T.Kennerley

Services Offered to Pension Funds Comprehensive investment advisory and management services

PROPERTY INVESTMENT

Full and independent advice available to all investors in commercial and industrial property throughout the U.K.

Investment Property Consultants
Estate Agents
Surveyors
Valuers
And Florida, USA.

50 Mount Street, London W1Y 5HA
Telephone: 01-629 8501

Property investment at your finger tips.

We offer our clients positive property portfolio management including acquisitions, valuations and sales.

Grimley & Son
CHARTERED SURVEYORS

9 St. James's Square, Manchester M2 6DN
061-834 7187

2 St Philip's Place, Birmingham B3 2QQ
021-236 8236

10 King Street, Covent Garden, London WC2E 8HZ
01-836 9654

rue Guimard 7a 1040 Brussels
02-512 16 12

Property Advisers

GOOCH & WAGSTAFF Continued

Other Office 27 Bolton Street, London W1 (01-629 6542)

Associated Offices Amsterdam, Frankfurt, Denver, U.S.A.

GOODMAN MANN ASSOCIATES

31 St. James's Place, London SW1A 1NR
Telephone: 01-499 8231

Partners Acting for Pension Funds C.Biggs, J.B.Austin, P.C.Barber

Other Pension Fund Experts M.Dudley-Williams, R.Ingham

Total Number of Staff 20

Number of Pension Fund Clients 5 - all in-house

Services Offered to Pension Funds Full range

GRANT & PARTNERS

50 Mount Street, London W1Y 5RE
Telephone: 01-491 4120

Partners Acting for Pension Funds and Other Pension Fund Experts Keith Noble,FRICS, Stephen Rayleigh

Employees 35

Services Offered to Pension Funds Complete property acquisition, disposal, management and associated professional services

GRAVES, SON & PILCHER

32 St. James's Street, London SW1A 1HD
Telephone: 01-839 1728

Partners Acting for Pension Funds P.J.Bexson, FRICS, R.R.Orr,FRICS

Number of Pension Fund Clients 2

Pension Fund Clients National Farmers Union Mutual Insurance Society Limited, Staffordshire County Council

GRIMLEY & SON

2 St Philip's Place, Birmingham B3 2QQ
Telephone: 021-236 8236

Partners Acting for Pension Funds Oliver J N Ogborn,FRICS, W.Warrack,ARICS

Employees 95

Services Offered to Pension Funds A total service. Acquisitions, sales, management, portfolio management, development and redevelopment including project management

Other Offices 10 King Street, Covent Garden, London WC2E 8HZ (01-836 9654), 9 St. James's Square, Manchester M2 6DN (061-834 7187), Rue Guimard 7A-Bte 3, 1040 Bruxelles (02-512 1612)

Clients Include Serck Pension Scheme, Wilmot Breeden Employees Trust Ltd

GROSS FINE & KRIEGER CHALFEN

27 Princes Street, London W1R 8NQ
Telephone: 01-493 3993

Partners Acting for Pension Funds Anthony I.Fine, FRICS,W.S.Grossmith,FSVA, Montague D.Doffman, FRICS, Jason A.Salter,FRICS

Employees 50

Number of Pension Fund Clients Numerous

Services Offered to Pension Funds Comprehensive advice on sales, acquisitions, management, valuations and rent reviews

HAARER & GOSS

33 and 39 Princesshay, Exeter, Devon EX1 1NF
Telephone: 0392 51171

Partner Acting for Pension Funds W.S.Haarer, ARICS,ARVA

Employees 9

Number of Pension Fund Clients 6

Services Offered to Pension Funds Valuations and surveys, searches for investment, full appraisal of scheme potential, management services (full)

Associated Offices Newton Abbot, Torquay

HALL PAIN & FOSTER

21 London Road, Southampton, SO1 2AD
Telephone: 0703-28915
Telex: 47283

Partners Acting for Pension Funds J.S.W.Locke, FRICS, M.R.Horton,FRICS (Southampton), J.Robt.Bannell,FRICS (Portsmouth)

Employees Approx. 50

Number of Pension Fund Clients None exclusively, several regionally

Services Offered to Pension Funds Sale/purchase, survey and valuation, rent reviews and management

Other Offices Portsmouth, Fareham,Havant, Waterlooville, Parkgate

HALLAM BRACKETT & CO

8 Low Pavement, Nottingham NG1 7DR
Telephone: 0602 51414

Partners Acting for Pension Funds J.L.Crockford, FRICS, S.J.Marlow,FRICS

Employees 50 (approx)

Number of Pension Fund Clients Act for several Pension Funds

Services Offered to Pension Funds Purchase, valuation, management (including rent reviews) and disposals

HAMNETT RAFFETY

PO Box 1,30 High Street, High Wycomce, Bucks HP11 2AQ
Telephone: 0494 21234

Partners Acting for Pension Funds R.T.H.Heeley, FRICS, J.R.Holland,MA,BSc,FRICS

Other Pension Fund Expert N.R.O.Foreman,ARICS

Employees 90

Number of Pension Fund Clients 2

Services Offered to Pension Funds General advice, particularly tax advice on D.L.T. implications

Other offices London, Amersham, Aylesbury, Beaconsfield, Gerrards Cross, Princes Risborough, Marlow, Farnham Common

HAMPTON & SONS

6 Arlington Street, London SW1A 1RB
Telephone: 01-493 8222

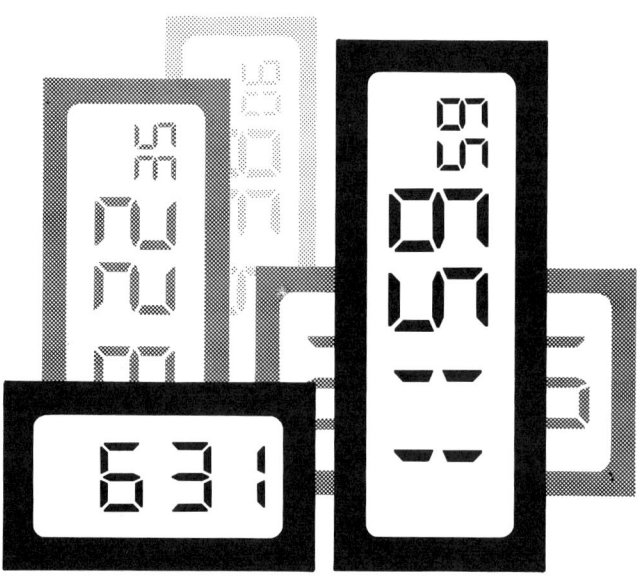

Time: the first investment to make in property

Spend a few hours with experts in the UK letting
and investment markets. The advice and help you gain in
site acquisition, development and
funding could prove it to be the most timely
investment you will make.

Hampton & Sons

6, Arlington Street, London SW1A 1RB. Telex: 25341.
01-493 8222

9, Dowgate Hill, City of London EC4R 2TD.
01-236 7831

Property Advisers

HAMPTON & SONS Continued

Partners Acting for Pension Funds G.R.Rohleder, FRICS, A.R.Early,FRICS, FSVA

Employees 175

Number of Pension Fund Clients 4

Services Offered to Pension Funds Property investment, portfolio management, investment advice, property purchasing and sales, valuation, etc.

Other Offices Skinners' Hall, 9 Dowgate Hill, EC4R 2TD, Wimbledon, Hampstead, Guildford, Cranleigh, Mayfield, Jersey

Associated Office Hampton & Sons SA, Paris

Principal Investment Client National Employers Group

HARTNELL/TAYLOR/COOK

20 The Mall, Clifton, Bristol BS8 4DR
Telephone: 0272-39061

Partners Acting for Pension Funds St.John Hartnell, Graham Calver,FRICS

Other Pension Fund Expert David Bingham, MA, ARICS

Employees 75

Number of Pension Fund Clients 2 funds for whom firm acts exclusively. Several funds for whom firm acts in the West

Services Offered to Pension Funds Comprehensive advice on acquisition, disposals, valuation and rent reviews, and of commercial property management

Other Offices 8 branches

HEALEY AND BAKER

29 St. George Street, Hanover Square,
London W1A 3BG
Telephone: 01-629 9292
Telex: 21800

Partners Acting for Pension Funds A.E.Orchard-Lisle,CBE,FRICS, P.S. Winfield, FRICS, P.D.Orchard-Lisle, MA,FRICS, R.E.Pryce,FRICS, D.J.Wheeler, FRICS, A.E.G.Gulliford,BSc (Est Man),ARICS

Employees Over 250

Number of Pension Fund Clients A wide range of clients of varied size

Services Offered to Pension Funds Advice on acquisition, letting, management, survey, valuation, development co-ordination, portfolio management, research

Other Offices 118 Old Broad Street, London, EC2N 1AR (01-628 4361); Amsterdam, Brussels, Glasgow, Jersey, New York and Paris

G.L.HEARN & PARTNERS

Delta House, 44-48 Borough High Street,
London SE1 1XP
Telephone: 01-407 5321

Partners Acting for Pension Funds E.J.Davies,BSc, FRICS, D.T.Jeffery,FRICS

Employees 120

Number of Pension Fund Clients 2

Services Offered to Pension Funds General advice, valuation, acquisition, disposals and management

Other Offices 104 West Campbell Street, Glasgow G2 4TY (041-248 4007); 7 St Andrews Hill, Norwich NR2 1AD (0603-618461); 6 Windsor Terrace, Southampton SO1 0FR (0703-21361); 45 Frederick Street, Sunderland SR1 1NF (0783-59046); 2-4 Bridge Street, Warrington WA1 2QW (0925-52171)

JOHN HEDDLE AND CO.

85A Duke Street, Grosvenor Square, London W.1
Telephone: 01-629 0066

Partner acting for Pension Funds John Heddle, FSVA,FRVA

Services Offered to Pension Funds A personal valuation, acquisition, development/project management service of all types of Commercial, Industrial, Real Estate through Great Britain and Europe

HEPPER WATSON & SONS

18/24 New Station Street, Leeds LS1 5DP
Telephone: 0532 442020

Partner Acting for Pension Funds J.H.Watson, FRICS

Employees 100

Services Offered to Pension Funds A full range of services

Other Offices 27 Cheapside, Bradford BD1 4HR; 31 High Petergate, York YO1 2HP; 9 Albert Street, Harrogate HG1 1JX; Market Place, Wetherby LS22 4LN; 6 Sheep Street, Skipton BD23 1JH; 32 The Grove, Ilkley LS29 9EE; Thorp Arch Trading Estate, Wetherby

HERRING SON & DAW

26-28 Sackville Street, London W1X 2QL
Telephone: 01-734 8155
Telex: 265162

Partners Acting for Pension Funds Nicholas A.S.Owen,MA,FRICS, Peter C.C.Sidebottom,MA, FRICS

Employees 90

Number of Pension Fund Clients 4

Services Offered to Pension Funds Property investment advice, all aspects of portfolio management including acquisition, valuation, letting, surveying and project management, rating and taxation advice

HILLIER PARKER MAY & ROWDEN

77 Grosvenor Street, London W1A 2BT
Telephone: 01-629 7666

Partners Acting for Pension Funds R.Cockhill, FRICS, M.J.Hallett,MA,FRICS, M.E.Dibgy,FRICS, I.D.Cave,FRICS, R.N.Mead,BSc,FRICS, FSVA, A.E.Bland,FRICS, R.A.Grant,ARICS, D.A.Gore,ARICS, J.Stubb,ARICS, R.A.Farnes,ARICS, C.R.L.Dunnett, ARICS

Employees 300

Number of Pension Fund Clients Numerous

Services Offered to Pension Funds All aspects of property portfolio management including acquisition, letting, management, project management, survey and valuation

Other Offices 39 King Street, London EC2V 8BA (01-606 3851); 5 South Charlotte Street, Edinburgh EH2 4AN (031-225 5988); In

633

The symbol for successful investment in the West

Auctioneers, Valuers, Surveyors & Estate Agents

The Mall, Clifton, Bristol
Telephone: 0272–39061

35 Bruton Street, Mayfair
London W1X 7DD
Telephone: 01–491 7323

We specialise

in the funding, purchase sale and valuation of commercial and industrial investments throughout the U.K.

CONWAY RELF

01 629 9100

CHARTERED SURVEYORS
44 ST JAMES'S PLACE LONDON SW1A 1PG

Property Advisers

HILLIER PARKER MAY & ROWDEN Continued

association with J.Bourdais,SA, 160-166 Boulevard Haussman, 75008 Paris, Telephone: 562 1189, Telex: 660978; in Association with M.I.van Engelen & Zoon, 132 Herengracht, Amsterdam Telephone: 020-254414, Royal Exchange Building, 56 Pitt Street, Sydney, NSW 2000 (27 8031); and at Melbourne, Brisbane, Adelaide, and Perth; Landauer Associates Inc., 200 Park Avenue, New York, (676148): Telephone: (212) 687 2323, Telex: 220417; and at Los Angeles, Santa Ana and West Palm Beach

Pension Fund Clients Courtaulds Limited Pensions Common Investment Fund, Greater London Council Superannuation Fund, Rowntrees Limited Pension Fund, Trustee Savings Bank Pension Scheme, Vauxhall and Associated Companies Pension Scheme, Massey-Ferguson Pension Fund, BPB Industries Ltd., Shell County of Avon Superannuation Fund, and several public company and Local Authority Superannuation schemes

NORMAN HIRSHFIELD, RYDE & BROWNE

42 Welbeck Street, London W1M 7HF
Telephone: 01-486 4601

Partners and Associates Acting for Institutional and Pension Funds N.E.Hirshfield, JP,FSVA, C.A.Gershinson,FRICS,FSVA, R.H.Rose,FRICS,FSVA, A.N.Hertz,FRICS, I.M.Hirshfield

Employees 40

Number of Institutional and Pension Fund Clients 4

Services Offered to Pension Funds Acquisition & sales, valuation & feasibility studies, survey & project management, rating & property management

HOWARTH & GREEN

13 Chapel Street, Preston, Lancs.PR1 8BG
Telephone: 0772-53848

Partners Acting for Pension Funds L.Howarth,JP, FRICS, J.Rogers,FRICS, N.K.Green,BSc,FRICS, D.R.Park,FRICS, P.E.Gilkes,ARICS

Employees 25

Other Offices 153 Towngate, Leyland; 12 New Street, Lancaster; 20 High Street, Garstang; 47 Fishergate, Preston

HOWELL, BROOKS & PARTNERS

41-42 Cloth Fair, London EC1A 7JQ
Telephone: 01-606 7976

Partner Acting for Pension Funds David H.Wiseman,FRICS

Employees 19

Number of Pension Fund Clients 4

Services Offered to Pension Funds Investment Advice and acquisitions, portfolio management, valuations

Other Offices Royal Exchange House, City Square, Leeds 1 (0532-35184)

PERCY HOWES & CO

3 Cathedral Close, Norwich NR1 4DL
Telephone: 0603-29992
Telex: 975461

Partners Acting for Pension Funds C.K.Howes,BSc, FRICS, T.Carr,BSc,ARICS

Employees 23

Number of Pension Fund Clients 5

Services Offered to Pension Funds Acquisition, management and disposal of property assets

HUMBERTS

6 Lincoln's Inn Fields, London WC2A 3DB
Telephone: 01-242 3121

Partners Acting for Pension Funds Bryan Keatley, FRICS (Agricultural Investment), Lawrie Freeman, FRICS (Commercial/Industrial Investment), Andrew Gladstone,ARICS (Agricultural Investment), Owain Venmore-Rowland,FRICS (Commercial Investment Partner), Alan Hay,ARICS (Commerical Investment Partner)

Employees 150

Number of Pension Fund Clients 4-6

Services Offered to Pension Funds Complete purchase and management of all investment portfolios

Other Offices 14 UK offices and Frankfurt (West Germany)

Other Information Pension fund clients include both nationalised industries and private institutional clients. A complete service is offered and number of funds acted for is restricted at any one time as a deliberate policy in order to avoid conflicts of interest. Available to be retained as Managers for any one fund

DAVID C. HUNTER

26 Great Tower Street, London EC3R 5AL
Telephone: 01-623 5577

Partners Acting for Pension Funds David C. Hunter, FRICS, R.K.H.Martin,FRICS

Employees 15

Number of Pension Fund Clients 2

Services Offered to Pension Funds Complete property services, including advice as to policy on investment acquisitions and management

Other Offices Greenwich, London SE10 and Coulsdon, Surrey, and Associate Practice: Granby Hunter (Commercial Estate Agents); 97 Uxbridge Road, London W12

JACKSON-STOPS & STAFF

14 Curzon Street, London W1
Telephone: 01-499 6291

Partners Acting for Pension Funds T.W.A.Jackson-Stops,FRICS, M.A.Jackson-Stops,ARICS,MA, Q.A.Jackson-Stops,ARICS, W.B.Robbins,FRICS, A.C.H.Froude,FRICS, R.Downer (Dublin)

Employees 120

Number of Pension Fund Clients A number

Services Offered to Pension Funds Advice on the purchase, sale and valuation of agricultural and commercial investments. Property management, and specialist forestry department

Other Offices Chichester, Chipping Campden, Cirencester, Fulham, Midhurst, Newmarket, Northampton, York, Yeovil

Associated Office Jackson-Stops and McCabe (Dublin)

Property Fund Management Services

Commercial and Agricultural
U.K. and Overseas
Investment Policy Advice
Selection and Acquisition
Active Management
Performance Analysis
Portfolio Valuation

from their Offices
at
20 Hanover Square London W1R 0AH Telephone: 01-629 8171
7 Birchin Lane London EC3V 9BY Telephone: 01-283 0041

Probably the most diversified property service in the world

Property Advisers

JOHN H. JAMES & COMPANY
Chells Manor, Stevenage, Herts SG1 7AA
Telephone: 0438 61341

Partners Acting for Pension Funds John H.James, FPCS, Gerald R.Dale,ARICS

Other Pension Fund Expert V.F.Lewis, ASVA

Employees 27

Number of Pension Fund Clients Sole UK advisers to several pension funds and overseas trusts

Services Offered to Pension Funds Advice with regard to all aspects of property and property taxation

Other Offices Hatfield, Harpenden, Brookmans Park, Baldock, Welwyn Garden City

DOUGLAS L. JANUARY & PARTNERS
7-8 Downing Street, Cambridge CB2 3DR
Telephone: 0223 63291

Partners Acting for Pension Funds D.W.January, J.D.Callin,ARICS, D.A.Dazeley,FRICS

Employees 50

Number of Pension Fund Clients 10

Services Offered to Pension Funds Acquisition of investments

Other Offices 2-3 Fish Hill, Royston SG8 9LE (0763-42921), 124 High Street, Newmarket CB8 8JP (0638-5731)

HENRY JOEL & CO
19 Garrick Street, London WC2E 9BB
Telephone: 01-836 0736

Partner Acting for Pension Funds D.Hayes,FSVA

Other Pension Fund Expert G.Berry,BA,ARICS

Employees 10

Number of Pension Fund Clients 4

services Offered to Pension Funds Highly confidential valuation & acquisition

JONES LANG WOOTTON
103 Mount Street, London W1Y 6AS
Telephone: 01-493 6040

Partners Acting for Pension Funds N.E.H.Taylor, W.J.Preston, L.F.Barr-Smlth, K.J.Douglass-Mann, J.A.S.Bassett, R.W.Hinde, M.T.Myers, M.E.Follett, R.S.Broadhurst, B.G.Payne, N.D.Holmes, C.A.J.Drury, and A.R.Wyatt

Employees UK 420, Worldwide 850

Number of Pension Fund Clients Several

Services Offered to Pension Funds Comprehensive

City Office 33 King Street, London EC2V 8EE (01-606 4060)

Other Offices 32 Offices in 12 countries

KEMSLEY WHITELEY & FERRIS
20-24 Ropemaker Street, London EC2Y 9AJ
Telephone: 01-628 2873

Partners Acting for Pension Funds R.H.Kemsley, MA,FRICS, P.L.Luff,ARICS

Other Pension Fund Experts 2

Employees 40 (approx)

Number of Pension Fund Clients Direct involvement with a number of Leading Pension Funds but no direct sole agency at present

Other Offices Ealing, Romford and Witham

Other Information General practice and building surveyors for several National Public Companies and a number of charities and property owning institutions

KING & CO
1 Snow Hill, London EC1A 2DL
Telephone: 01-236 3000

Partners Acting for Pension Funds M.J.G.King, E.P.Williams M.J.G.King,FRICS,MBA,E.P.williams, ARICS

Other Pension Fund Experts R.J.Hannington, J.P.Asquith J.P.Asquith,BSc,ARICS,R.Hennington

Employees 160

Number of Pension Fund Clients 6

Services Offered to Pension Funds Advice on all aspects of property investments

Other Offices Manchester, Leeds, Birmingham and Brussels

Major Clients Provident Mutual Managed Pension Fund, Westland Staff Pension Scheme, Customs Life Fund

KINNEY & GREEN
2a Eastcheap, London EC3M 1AA
Telephone: 01-283 1191

Partners Acting for Pension Funds L.W.Kinney, FRICS, R.J.Hurles,FRICS, R.Taylor,ARICS, S.P.Seymour-Taylor,ARICS

Other Pension Fund Expert M.R.Green,FRICS

Employees 7 (excluding partners)

Number of Pension Fund Clients The firm has a continuing direct involvement with a number of leading and smaller pension funds although no sole agencies

Services Offered to Pension Funds Comprehensive advice on all aspects of the commercial property investment and development market in the U.K. and the U.S.Ø

EDMUND KIRBY & SONS
State House, 22 Dale Street, Liverpool L2 4TU
Telephone: 051-236 4552

Partners Acting for Pension Funds J.S.Marsden, M.C.Donnor

Employees 80

Number of Pension Fund Clients 2

Services Offered to Pension Funds Comprehensive services of group practice

Other Offices London, Maidenhead and Wigan

Pension Fund Clients Merseyside County Council Superannuation Fund, Ocean/Nestor Pension Fund

KNIGHT FRANK & RUTLEY
20 Hanover Square, London W1R 0AH
Telephone: 01-629 8171
Telex: 265384

LALONDE
BROS & PARHAM

Property advice for institutional and pension fund investors. Nationwide.

PAI

MEMBERS OF PROPERTY
AGENTS INTERNATIONAL LTD.

64 Queens Road,
Bristol BS8 1RH.
Tel: 0272-290731

also at:
20 Southernhay West,
Exeter EX1 1PR.
Tel: 0392-34247

Lander Burfield
Chartered Surveyors

With many years of experience in property
we can advise you on all aspects of development
and investment.

75 Shoe Lane, London EC4A 3BQ.
Telephone: 01-353 7841. Telex: 23862

Property Advisers

KNIGHT FRANK & RUTLEY Continued

Partners Acting for Pension Funds Commercial: G.E.Richardson,FRICS, D.McIntosh-Whyte,ARICS, P.M.Steward,BSc,ARICS,R.G.Edgell,ARICS Agricultural: J.G.Haworth,MA,FRICS, J.E.M.Inge, FRICS, P.R.Caroe,ARICS

Employees Over 200

Number of Pension Fund Clients Substantial

Services Offered to Pension Funds Complete range of services

City Office 7 Birchin Lane, London EC3V 9BY (01-283 0041)

Other UK Offices Edinburgh, Hereford, Hungerford, Ascot, Boroughbridge, Shrewsbury

Associated Offices Amsterdam, Brussels, Paris, 7 offices in Nigeria and 2 offices in USA

LALONDE BROS & PARHAM

64 Queen's Road, Bristol BS8 1RH
Telephone: 0272 290731

Partners Acting for Pension Funds John Pool, FRICS, Alasdair Cochran,ARICS, John Laurence, FRICS (Exeter)

Other Pension Fund Experts Neill Pitcher,ARICS, Nicholas Chapman

Employees 115

Number of Pension Fund Clients Two main Pension Fund Clients

Services Offered to Pension Funds Principally the sale to, or acquisition of, properties for the Funds, throughout the U.K. and particularly in the South and West of England

Other Offices 20 Southernhay West, Exeter (0392-34247), 22 Waterloo Street, Weston-Super-Mare, (0934-28282), 3 East Quay, Bridgewater TA6 5AZ (0278 51117), 53 High Street, Taunton TA1 3PP (0823-75620)

LAMBERT SMITH & PARTNERS

3 Deanery Street, London W1Y 5LH
Telephone: 01-499 6621

Partners Acting for Pension Funds R.P.Dyke-Price, BSc,ARICS, R.J.S.Palmer

Employees 30

Services Offered to Pension Funds Full range of advice on property investment purchase concerning yields, investment alternatives, e.g shops as opposed to office or industrial, management, rent reviews and valuations

Other Information Advising Insurance Companies, Superannuation and Pension Funds on investment purchases. Annual investment turnover is in excess of £40 million

LAMBOURNE FOREMAN & PARTNERS

8 Harcourt House, 19a Cavendish Square,
London W1M 9AD
Telephone: 01-636 3276

Partner Acting for Pension Fund R.C.Lambourne

LANDER BURFIELD

75 Shoe Lane, Fleet Street, London EC4A 3BQ
Telephone: 01-353 7841

Partners Acting for Pension Funds T.L.J.Burfield, FRICS, T.F.Brown,FRICS

Services Offered to Pension Funds Full range of professional services

Other Offices 36-38 Lamb's Conduit Street, London WC1N 3LL (01-831 6311)

LANE FOX & PARTNERS

36 North Audley Street, London W1Y 2EL
Telephone: 01-499 4785

Partners Acting for Pension Funds M.J.Lane Fox, FRICS, E.J.Lane Fox,FRICS J.R.Fonnereau,FRICS, S.J.Chamberlayne,FRICS

Employees Approx 40

Number of Pension Fund Clients 2 in-house clients, several more occasional clients

Services Offered to Pension Funds Acquisitions & Disposals, Management including collection of rents. Rent reviews, renewals and relettings, improvements and redevelopments

Other Offices Middleton Cheney, Banbury, Oxon OX17 2ND, The Estate Office, Middle Aston, Oxford OX5 3PX

Clients Include Portals Group Trustees Ltd, The Fleming Property Unit Trust (Agricultural)

LANGLEY-TAYLOR

5 Verulam Buildings, Gray's Inn,
London WC1R 5LP
Telephone: 01-242 5038
10A Rutland Square, Edinburgh EH1 2OW (031-229-5302)

Partners acting for Pension Funds The Earl of Kinnoull,FRICS, N.J.Harper,MA,FRICS, P.N.Offord, ARICS, V.J.Aptaker,BSc (Econ),ARICS

Total Employees 16

Number of Pension Fund Clients 3 in-house clients and other investing Insurance Company clients, Collegiate Funds, Charities and Trusts

Services Offered to Pension Funds Complete range of urban commercial, retail and industrial expertise and agricultural services, providing a total property investment service to clients

MICHAEL LAURIE & PARTNERS

Fitzroy House, 18-20 Grafton Street,
London W1X 4DD
Telephone: 01-493 7050

Partners Acting for Pension Funds E.Bernerd, J.W.Lockhart,FRICS, Kenneth M.Posner,BSc,ARICS, R.A.H.Townley,BSc,ARICS, D.Warwick

Employees 60

Number of Pension Fund Clients 3

Services Offered to Pension Funds Comprehensive advice on the acquisition, disposal and management of shops, offices and industrial/warehouse property, agricultural land/forestry. The Partnership, as co-ordinating surveyors of the Country Land Agents Investment Group, provides a complete advisory and management service in respect of agricultural investments. In addition the partnership provides a full letting and professional service including investment advice and research

Specialising in commercial and agricultural
property investments and
developments for Pension Funds . . . . .

Lane Fox & Partners

36 NORTH AUDLEY STREET,
GROSVENOR SQUARE,
LONDON W1Y 1WG

TELEPHONE
01-499 4785

Commercial Investments throughout the British Isles

Mason, Owen & Partners

Commercial Property Consultants

**GLADSTONE HOUSE, UNION COURT, CASTLE STREET,
LIVERPOOL L2 4UQ.
TELEPHONE: 051-227 3651**

Also at: Dublin (0001-76035), Manchester (061-832 7262) & Hull (0482 562141)

Property Advisers

LAWSON & LAWSON
3 Regent Street, Cheltenham GL50 1HF
Telephone: 0242 21677/9

Partners acting for Pension Funds Ralph C.Lawson, FRICS, John Lawson,JP,BSc,(Est Man),FRICS, Timothy J.F.Smith,ARICS

Other Pension Fund Experts Jeffrey Getvoldsen, ASVA, Julian Warington-Smyth,ARICS

Employees 11

Number of Pension Fund Clients 4

Services Offered to Pension Funds Comprehensive range including acquisitions, disposals, lettings, valuations, project management, estate agency, management town planning, rating surveys, appraisals, rent review negotiations

Associated Office Thorncroft & Partners, 17 Berkeley Street, London W1X 5AE (01-493 1947)

LEAVERS
36 Bruton Street, London W1X 8AD
Telephone: 01-629 4261

Partners acting for Pension Funds A.Essex,FSVA, S.Long, K.Ezard,ARICS

Employees 60

Number of Pension Fund Clients 3

Services Offered to Pension Funds Comprehensive

Other Offices Edinburgh and an Associated Office in Dublin

Other Information Close working relationship with many major funds

D.E.& J.LEVY
130 Jermyn Street, London SW1Y 4UL
Telephone: 01-930 1070

Investment Manager Alan Marks,FSVA

Services Offered to Pension Funds Full range of services including acquisition, disposal, valuation and management of investments

CLIVE LEWIS & PARTNERS
16 Stratton Street, London W1X 5FD
Telephone: 01-499 1001
Telex: 27382

Partners Acting for Pension Funds Clive H.Lewis, FRICS, Leonard E.Baker,MA,FRICS, Christopher J.Hoddell,BSc,ARICS, Colin P.Brain

Employees 55

Number of Pension Fund Clients Three exclusively but several advised frequently

Services Offered to Pension Funds General property services including the acquisition of suitable investments, management of portfolios, rent reviews, sales and valuations. The letting of any available accommodation and professional and rating services

Clients Include The Civil Aviation Authority Superannuation Fund

LEWIS & TUCKER
16 Hanover Square, London W1
Telephone: 01-629 5101

Partners Acting for Pension Funds 3

Number of Pension Fund Clients Several

Services Offered to Pension Funds Full Investment advice including acquisition, valuation, survey

ANTHONY LIPTON & CO
38 Curzon Street, London W1
Telephone: 01-491 2700

Partners Acting for Pension Funds A.P.Bremer, FRICS, M.A.Stotesbury,FRICS

Employees 14

Number of Pension Fund Clients 1 (specifically retained, Lopex Pension Fund)

Services Offered to Pension Funds Acquisition of suitable investments and portfolio advice

Other Offices STGI Lipton S.A, 109 Boulevard Haussmann, 75008 Paris

LISNEY & SON
24 St. Stephen's Green, Dublin 2
Telephone: 601222

Partner Acting for Pension Funds J.C.Brett, FRICS

Employees 90

Number of Pension Fund Clients Several

Services Offered to Pension Funds Comprehensive

Other Offices 35 Grand Parade, Cork, Ireland (002-25079); 19-20 Donegall Square East, Belfast, Northern Ireland (0232-38955/38940)

LOCKS & CO
1A Delancey Street, London NW1 7NL
Telephone: 01-388 2512

Partner Acting for Pension Funds R.D.Locks,FSVA

Services Offered to Pension Funds Appraisal and acquisition of suitable properties

MANN AND CO
22 Commercial Way, Woking, Surrey GU21 1HB
Telephone: 04862 70071

Partners Acting for Pension Funds J.L.McGuffog, FRICS,FRVA,ACIArb, J.M.Agace,FRICS

Total Employees 38 (Surveyors Office only)

Number of Pension Fund Clients 2

Services Offered to Pension Funds Acquisition, portfolio management, rent reviews, project management, rating

Other Offices 8 Other regional surveyors offices dealing with general practice matters in Surrey, Berkshire, Hampshire

MASON, OWEN & PARTNERS
Gladstone House, Union Court, Castle Street, Liverpool L2 4UQ
Telephone: 051-227 3651

Partner Acting for Pension Funds M.Barry Owen

Employees 23

Number of Pension Fund Clients 3

Services Offered to Pension Funds Full range of services including acquisitions, disposals and valuations of investments

Other Offices 41 Upper Mount Street,Dublin 2 (767035)

Clients Include Johnsons (Pontefract) Ltd. and the Austin Pension Trust

Investing in advice is like any investment. The right choice pays dividends.

Property is no exception.

When questions regarding yield, reversionary prospects and value arise, informed independent professional advice is essential.

Advice based upon a practical experience in the commercial property market in the UK and Europe.

In shops, industrial, and offices.

Advice made invaluable by the up-to-date knowledge and research so vital to effective performance.

The right advice is the vital link in property investment.

Healey & Baker

Established 1820 in London

29 St. George Street, Hanover Square, London W1A 3BG   01-629 9292
City of London 118 Old Broad Street London EC2N 1AR
Amsterdam Brussels Glasgow Jersey New York Paris

Property Advisers

MASON PHILIPS

56 Grosvenor Street, London W1X 9DA
Telephone: 01-499 9793

Partners Ramsay Mason, George Philips, Patrick Hall

Services offered to Pension Funds Comprehensive advice on a person level to institutional investors. This includes a Property Investment Performance and Portfolio Analysis

MATTHEWS GOODMAN & POSTLETHWAITE

Malvern House, 72 Upper Thames Street,
London EC4R 3UA
Telephone: 01-248 3200

Partners Acting for Pension Funds J.F.Doubleday, FRICS, K.Bland-Botham,FRICS, T.R.Robinson,FRICS, B.C.Skinner,ARICS, M.J.Hill,MA,FRICS

Number of Pension Fund Clients 6

Services Offered to Pension Funds Advice on acquisition and sale of Commercial Property including valuation and management of property investment portfolios

Other Offices Martins Building, 4 Water Street, Liverpool (051-236 8732); 63 Avenue Marceau, 75116 Paris (720 2317)

Clients Include BICC Group Pension Trust, Black Horse Bond, Cornhill Insurance Co. Ltd., Lloyds Bank Staff Pension Fund, The National Mutual Life Association of Australasia, Pennine Property Unit Trust

MAURICE ANDREW

18 Charing Cross Road, London WC2H 0HR
Telephone: 01-379 6871

Partner acting for Pension Funds M.A.Minsky, Dip.Est.Man., ARICS, ASVA, AIAS

Services Offered to Pension Funds A complete property advice on the acquisition, disposal and management of investment properties, including valuations, lease renewals, rent reviews, surveys, planning and rating appeals, building and development services

MCDANIEL & DAW

Bailey House, Old Seacoal Lane,
London EC4M 7LR
Telephone: 01-236 4881

Partners Acting for Pension Funds E.J.C.McDaniel, FRICS,FSVA, J.E.Cullis,BSc,FRICS,FSVA,APMI, M.J.Norris,FRICS,FSVA

Other Pension Fund Experts D.A.Steward, M.Frenkel

Employees Approx. 25

Number of Pension Fund Clients Several

Services Offered to Pension Funds Portfolio, property management and policy advice, acquisition, disposal and letting of properties, project management, all types of property; U.K. and Overseas

Other Offices Birmingham and Sittingbourne, Kent

MELLERSH & HARDING

43 St. James's Place, London SW1A 1PA
Telephone: 01-493 6141

Partners Acting for Pension Funds K.J.Tilley,FRICS, C.F.H.Waters,ARICS

Employees Approx 35

Number of Pension Fund Clients 1 (The Solicitors Staff Pension Fund)

Services Offered to Pension Funds The disposal and acquisition of commercial property, valuation and management

Other Offices 248 Avenue Louise, 1050 Brussels

MOLYNEUX ROSE

Savory & Moore House, 143 New Bond Street,
London W1Y 9FD
Telephone: 01-499 9851
Telex: 8954280

Partner Acting for Pension Funds M.R.Little, ARICS, ARVA, ACIArb

Number of Pension Fund Clients 1

Services Offered to Pension Funds Comprehensive advice on acquisition, sale, valuation and management of Commercial and Industrial Investment Properties throughout the U.K.

Whilst the partnership has only one solely retaining Pension Fund, it advises several Trusts and Investment Companies upon the purchase of suitable investments

MONTAGU EVANS & SONS

11 Kingsway, London WC2B 6YE
Telephone: 01-838 6361

Partners acting for Pension Funds W.W.B.Rodger, M.B.Evans

Other Offices Edinburgh (031 225 2184)

MYDDELTON & MAJOR

18 Kings Park Road, Southampton SO1 2AT
Telephone: 0703 37255

Partner Acting for Pension Funds David J.Mallinson,ARICS

Employees 12

Number of Pension Fund Clients Act for various private Trust Funds, investors, Pension Funds and Assurance and Insurance Companies

Services Offered Advice on the purchase, active management, reviews and re-gearing of leases and sale of property investments throughout Southern England

Other Offices 49 High Street, Salisbury, Wiltshire

NEALE & ALLDRIDGE

Sabena House, 36 Piccadilly, London W1V 9PFA
Telephone: 01-734 5371

Partners Acting for Pension Funds L.J.McMulloch, FRICS, B.R.Ordish,FRICS, T.J.Corns,FRICS, R.K.England,FRICS,ARVA, M.S.H.Cook,RD,ARICS

Employees 60

Number of Pension Fund Clients 10

Services Offered to Pension Funds Acquisitions, sales, management and redevelopment including project management

Other Offices Cornwall House, 50 Newhall Street, Birmingham B3 3QE

STEWART NEWISS

31 Manor Row, Bradford, West Yorkshire BD1 4PX
Telephone: 0274 27316

INTERNATI🌐NAL
PAI
PROPERTY AGENTS INTERNATIONAL·INDUSTRIAL & COMMERCIAL PROPERTY SERVICE

EUROPEAN HEAD OFFICE: 19 ALBEMARLE
STREET, MAYFAIR, LONDON W1X 3HA
TEL. 01-499 5651 TELEX 299968

NORTH AMERICAN HEAD OFFICE: P.O. BOX 28241
ATLANTA, GA 30328, U.S.A. TEL. 010-1-404-255-6666

NATIONAL COVERAGE AND LOCAL KNOWLEDGE

The complete professional service for commercial and industrial property

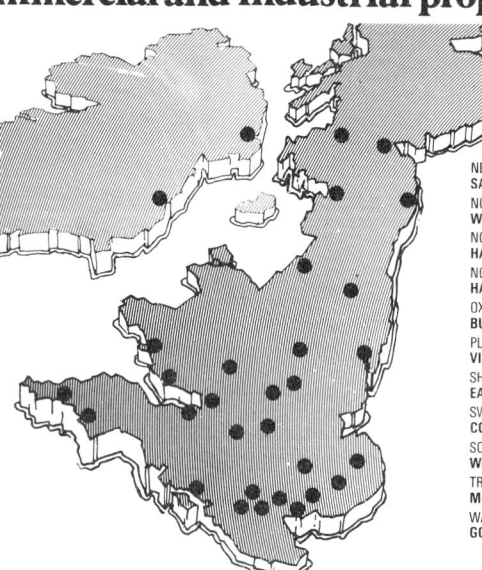

BELFAST 0232 33111
ALEXANDER REID & FRAZER
BIRMINGHAM 021-236 8236
GRIMLEY & SON
BLACKBURN 0254 52424
G. F. SINGLETON & CO.
BRISTOL 0272 290731
LALONDE BROS. & PARHAM
BURY ST. EDMUNDS 0284 63531
LACY, SCOTT & SONS
CAMBRIDGE 0223 68811
GRAY, COOK & PARTNERS
CARDIFF 0222 40244
STEPHENSON & ALEXANDER
CARLISLE 0228 24408
GIBBINGS & JOHNSTON
CHELMSFORD 0245 55561
TAYLOR & CO.
COLCHESTER 0206 46161
FENN WRIGHT
CRAWLEY 0293 516661
STILES HORTON LEDGER
DUBLIN 0001 765781
DANIEL MORRISEY & SONS LTD.
EDINBURGH 031-225 3271
BELL-INGRAM
FAREHAM 032 92 8311
HALL, PAIN & FOSTER
GLASGOW 041 221 9191
MILLAR, MACRE & STEWART
GLOUCESTER 0452 21267
BRUTON, KNOWLES & CO.

HULL 0482 26639
F. A. LARARD & SONS
LEEDS 0532 444421
DACRE, SON & HARTLEY
LEICESTER 0533 52111
JARROMS
LONDON 01 437 6977
ALLSOP & CO.
NEWCASTLE-UPON-TYNE 0632 612681
SANDERSON TOWNEND & GILBERT
NORTHAMPTON 0604 22817
WILSON & PARTNERS
NORWICH 0603 29691
HANBURY WILLIAMS
NOTTINGHAM 0602 51414
HALLAM BRACKETT & CO.
OXFORD 0865 40801
BUCKELL & BALLARD
PLYMOUTH 0752 23355
VINER CAREW & CO.
SHEFFIELD 0742 71277
EADON LOCKWOOD & RIDDLE
SWANSEA 0792 51615
COOKE & ARKWRIGHT
SOUTHEND-ON-SEA 0701 330717
WATSON, TEMPLE, TALBOT & WHITE
TRURO 0872 74211
MILLER & CO.
WATFORD 0923 39711
GORDON HUDSON & CO.

Property Advisers

STEWART NEWISS Continued

Partners Acting for Pension Funds Reginald Stewart Newiss,FRICS,FRVA, J.R.S.Newiss, ARICS

Other Pension Fund Expert A.W.A.Outhwaite, ARICS

Employees 49

Number of Pension Fund Clients 1

Services Offered to Pension Funds Acquisitions, project management, rent reviews, lease renewals, property management, general professional services

Other Offices Cardiff, Leeds, London and Preston

NEWTON PERKINS & FORBES

10 Northumberland Alley, Fenchurch Street, London EC3N 3EP
Telephone: 01-488 4421

Partner Acting for Pension Funds B.W.Davis

OSMOND, TRICKS & SON

7 & 8 Queen Square, Bristol BS1 4JG
Telephone: 0272 293171

Partners Acting for Pension Funds M.E.Davis,MSc, FRICS, D.A.Lowe,BSc,ARICS

Total Employees 30

Number of Pension Fund Clients Various

Services Offered to Pension Funds Advice on Acquisitions, and disposal, valuation, management and general professional services

Other Offices Clifton (Bristol), Wells, Blagdon

ERNEST OWERS & WILLIAMS

103 Park Street, London W1Y 4JH
Telephone: 01-629 8386

Partners Acting for Pension Funds Hunter J.Bodkin,FRICS, Laurence W.S.Ellison,FRICS, Lionel E.Trussell,FSVA

Employees 40

Number of Pension Fund Clients Numerous

Services Offered to Pension Funds All professional services

Other Offices Hampstead, West Hampstead and Golders Green

Clients Include The Trustees of the British Council Superannuation Scheme, The Ancient Order of Foresters Friendly Society and others

OXBORROWS

3 Princes Street, Ipswich IP1 1PQ
Telephone: 0473 212531

Partners Acting for Pension Funds Martin Spettigue,FRICS, Peter Elsom,FRICS

Other Pension Fund Expert I.May

Services Offered to Pension Funds Acquisition, sales and full management services

Other Offices 160 Hamilton Road, Felixstowe (70235); 12 Ipswich Street, Stowmarket (2665)

Clients Include Fisons Pension Trust Ltd

PARNIS BIRD AND PARTNERS

42 Hertford Street, London W1Y 7TF
Telephone: 01-491 2959

Partners acting for Pension Funds T.C.Bird,BSc, ARICS, V.L.Parnis, BSc,FRICS

Employees 8

Number of Pension Fund Clients Several

Services Offered to Pension Funds Valuation, purchase and sale, lettings, rent reviews, financing of development projects, industrial and commercial property management

Other Offices 8 Rue d'Artois, 75008 Paris

PEARSONS

1a Grafton Street, London W1X 3LB
Telephone: 01-499 2104

Partners Acting for Pension Funds R.F.Sayer,BSc, ARICS, C.W.Warner,BSc,FRICS, M.N.Godwin,FSVA, P.F.Woodford,FRICS

Employees 280

Number of Pension Fund Clients Various

Services Offered to Pension Funds Disposal, acquisition and all associated professional services

Other Offices Commercial: 27 London Street, Basingstoke, Hants (0256 62222) and 21 other offices in South and West England

PEPPER ANGLISS & YARWOOD

6 Carlos Place, London W1Y 6LL
Telephone: 01-499 6066

Partners Acting for Pension Funds J.D.Harris, FRICS, R.M.Harris, FRICS, E.H.J.Davies, BSc (Est Man),ARICS, H.J.Spence,FRICS

Services Offered to Pension Funds Shop, office, industrial letting, rent reviews, arbitrations, project management, sale and purchase advice and agency, valuation

Clients Include Lazard Property Unit Trust, Property Growth Assurance Co Ltd

CONRAD PHOENIX & CO.

24 Fitzroy Square, London W1P 5HJ
Telephone: 01-388 9241

Partner Acting for Pension Funds C.N.Phoenix

PHOENIX BEARD

15 Hanover Street, London W1R 9HG
Telephone: 01-493 4213

Partners Colin S.Beard,FRICS, Anthony R.Phoenix, FRICS

Other Offices St. James' House, 17 Horse Fair, Birmingham B1 1DB (021-622 5351)

CHARLES PRICE & CO

1 Berkeley Square, London W1X 5HG
Telephone: 01-493 2222

Partners Acting for Pension Funds C.I.Price, D.J.Price,BA, C.H.Barber,ARICS

Employees 15

Number of Pension Fund Clients 34

Some of our credentials

- 133 years property advisory service to many of the country's largest institutional investors.
- Managing hundreds of thousands of acres*
- The sale and purchase of millions of £'s worth of investment property.

There's no substitute for experience

*The schematic map shows the approximate locations of properties managed by Smiths Gore which total many hundreds of thousands of acres.

Investment Department:
Fielden House, 12 Little College Street, Westminster, London SW1P 3SH
Telephone 01-222-4054

Branches at Carlisle, Corbridge, Darlington, Dumfries, Edinburgh, Fochabers, Leyburn, Lichfield, Newmarket, Newport, Peterborough, Petworth, Winchester, York.   Smiths Gore (Overseas) Limited.

CHARLES PRICE & CO *Continued*

Services Offered to Pension Funds All professional services including project management and management of refurbishments and new developments together with investment, management and project management in the United States

Other Offices Cliffords Inn, Fetter Lane, London EC4; New York, USA

RATCLIFFES

55 South Audley Street, Grosvenor Square, London W1Y 5FA
Telephone: 01-629 4036

Partners Acting for Pension Funds Anthony H.Ratcliffe, Malcolm O.Brown

Number of Pension Fund Clients Several

Services Offered to Pension Funds Investment portfolio creation and active management. Individual property appraisal, acquisition or disposal. Valuations rent reviews and management

Clients Include A number of private investment companies, trusts and insurance companies

REEDS

48 Fishergate, Preston PR1 8DD
Telephone: 0772 57923

Partner Acting for Pension Funds D.E.Eaves

Other Offices Blackburn, Lancaster, Leyland, Chorley, Carnforth, Kirkham, Bamber Bridge, Tarleton

RICHMAN CONWAY & CO.

169 Piccadilly, London W1V 9DD
Telephone: 01-499 9646

Partners Acting for Pension Funds N.Harker,FRICS, ACIArb

Employees 13

Services Offered to Pension Funds Advice, at partner level, on every aspect of commercial property, including purchases, sales, valuation, letting, management, landlord & tenant Act and rent review negotiations, arbitrations, rating and development

W.H.ROBINSON & CO

79 Mosley Street, Manchester M2 3LP
Telephone: 061-228 6411

Partners and Associates Acting for Pension Funds H.Richards,FRICS, J.P.Wainwright,MA,FRICS, P.E.Higginbottom,ARICS

Employees 70

Number of Pension Fund Clients Solely retained by Several Pension Funds

Services Offered to Pension Funds Specialists in the management of Investment Portfolios, including the acquisition and sale of retail, offices, industrial and residential properties

N.M.ROTHSCHILD ASSET MANAGEMENT LTD

New Court, St. Swithin's Lane, London EC4P 4DU
Telephone: 01-626 4356

Senior Investment Surveyor D.J.M.Doubble,MA, FRICS

Services Offered The creation and management of directly held property portfolios for pension funds and other institutional investors

EDWARD RUSHTON SON & KENYON

10 Carlos Place, Grosvenor Square, London W1Y 6HA
Telephone: 01-493 6787

Partners acting for Pension Funds G.A.M.Tompkins, FRICS,FRVA, M.C.G.Davey,ARICS, P.R.Hicks

Other Pension Fund Experts M.C.G.Davey,ARICS, J.Rayner,ARICS

Employees 100

Number of Pension Fund Clients 6

Services Offered to Pension Funds Full range of services including property investment and development, project management, finance in relation to property, property maintenance, valuations and purchases and disposals

Other Offices 19 Marine House, Clanwilliam court, Dublin 2 (766823, Telex 5287); Kings Court, Exchange Street, Manchester M2 3AX (061-834 1814, Telex 667429); also at Sydney and Melbourne

RUSSELL, CASH & CO.

49 Welbeck Street, London W1M 7HE
Telephone: 01-935 5437

Partners Acting for Pension Funds P.L.Cash, A.D.Quill, ARICS

Employees 14

Services Offered to Pension Funds Full range of property investment consultancy, including valuation, management, sale and purchase, together with building works supervision and surveys

KENNETH RYDEN & PARTNERS

117-121 West George Street, Glasgow G2 1QS
Telephone: 041-221 8591

Partner Acting for Pension Funds M.J.D.Ryder

Other Office 71 Hanover Street,Edinburgh EH2 1EF (031-225 6533)

ST.QUINTIN

Vintry House, Queen Street Place, London EC4R 1ES
Telephone: 01-236 4040

Partners Acting for Pension Funds T.F.Wilson, FRICS, C.Wheeler,FRICS, D.W.R.Hobbs,ARICS

Pension Fund Clients A number

Services Offered to Pension Funds Comprehensive

Other Offices Leeds, Brussels

RICHARD SAUNDERS & PARTNERS

27-32 Old Jewry, London EC2R 8DQ
Telephone: 01-606 7461

Partners Acting for Pension Funds David J.Bell,MA, ARICS, Alan Tunstill,FRICS

Employees 15

Number of Pension Fund Clients Various

Services Offered to Pension Funds Acquisition, disposal, development, valuation and management

Agricultural investment prospers

Provided it is well managed

Our advice on your agricultural portfolio does not stop with its purchase

We also have nationwide expertise in its management

Investment partner:
Rodney Gillington, Ashwell office

200 years of experience
SMITH-WOOLLEY

Cheyneys Lodge, Ashwell
Baldock, Herts. SG7 5RP
Tel: Ashwell (046 274) 2481

48 Prince of Wales Road,
Norwich. NR1 1LL
Tel: Norwich (0603) 21015

5 Edward Street, Bath, BA2 4DT
Tel: Bath (0225) 64969

8 Oxford Street, Woodstock
Oxford OX7 1TR
Tel: Woodstock (0993) 811624

Collingham, Newark
Notts. NG23 7LG
Tel: Newark (0636) 892456

Property Advisers

SAVILLS
20 Grosvenor Hill, London W1X 0HQ
Telephone: 01-499 8644

Partners Acting for Pension Funds J.C.Wilson,DFC, FRICS, R.L.Dean, BSc,FRICS, E.W.T.Malcolm,BSc, FRICS, G.P.F.Inge,FRICS, P.R.Wilson,MA,FRICS, T.J.A.Simon,FRICS, J.F.Dean,ARICS

Employees 350

Number of Pension Fund Clients Numerous

Services Offered to Pension Funds Purchase, sale and management of commercial and agricultural investment properties

Other Offices Banbury, Brechin, Beccles, Cambridge, Chelmsford, Croydon, Hereford, Lincoln, Norwich, Salisbury, Wimbourne, York, Paris and Amsterdam

SHIPWAY DOBLE & EARLE
93-95 Hagley Road, Edgbaston, Birmingham B16 8LG
Telephone: 021-454 8111

Partners Acting for Pension Funds Roy V.Stroud, B.R.Davies,FRICS, FRVA, J.Bradbeer,ARICS

Employees 110

Number of Pension Fund Clients 6

Services Offered to Pension Funds Development and investment, advice in all forms of commercial and industrial property with particular emphasis on the Midland region

Other Offices East Midland Office, Haymarket House, Haymarket, Leicester LE1 3YR

Other Information Closely associated with a number of the large Scottish Funds in addition to advising a variety of local Pension Funds and trusts on an ad hoc basis

SINCLAIR GOLDSMITH
39-41 Queen Anne Street, London W1M 0AD
Telephone: 01-486 6060

Partners acting for Pension Funds Peter N. Goldsmith,FRICS, R.Neil Sinclair,FRICS,FSVA

Investment Manager Peter D. Morgan

Employees 20

Number of Pension Fund Clients Various but none exclusively

Services Offered to Pension Funds Full investment service

City Office 9-10 Fenchurch Street, London EC3M 3BE (01-623 6644)

DANIEL SMITH, BRIANT & GONE
32 St. James's Street, London SW1A 1HT
Telephone: 01-930 9385

Other Offices 157 Kennington Lane, London SE11 4HA (01-735 2292); Upper Thames Street, London EC4R 3TR (01-626 7501)

SMITH MELZACK & CO.
17 St. Helens Place, London EC3A 6ED
Telephone: 01-638 4591

Partner Acting for Pension Funds A.A.Michaelson

Other Office 17-18 Old Bond Street, London W1X 3DA (01-493 1613)

PETER F. SMITH & CO
4 South Parade, Leeds LS1 5QX
Telephone: 0532-450904

Partners Acting for Pension Funds Peter F. Smith, ARICS, Robert Austin,ARICS, B.R.Spragg,ARICS

Employees 9

Number of Pension Fund Clients 12

Services Offered to Pension Funds Valuation, management, appraisal and finance of development projects, rent reviews, acquisition and disposal of commercial and industrial property investments

SMITH-WOOLLEY
Cheyneys Lodge, Ashwell, Baldock, Hertfordshire SG7 5RP
Telephone: 046274-2481

Investment Partners R.J.F.Gillington, TD, FRICS C.J.K.Fordham, MA,FRICS

Employees 80

Number of Institutional Clients 2-3 Pension Funds, Oxford and Cambridge Colleges and Duchy of Cornwall

Services Offered to Pension Funds All matters relating to agricultural land including Reports and Valuations of Properties for investment, acquisitions, management, farm consultancy and management, farm building and house designs, sales

Other Offices Bath, Collingham (Notts), Norwich, Woodstock

SMITHS GORE
Fielden House, Little College Street, London SW1P 3SH
Telephone: 01-222 4054

Partners Acting for Pension Funds P.Dickinson, FRICS, G.N.Mainwairing,BA,FRICS

Other Pension Fund Expert J.H.Powell,MBE

Staff 17 Partners, 7 Associate Partners, plus full supporting staff - total 190

Number of Pension Fund Clients Numerous Major institutions, pension funds, charities and unit trusts

Services Offered to Pension Funds Advisers to pension funds on all matters relating to investments in agricultural land, including valuations, purchases, sales, management, farm consultancy and management, farm building design

Other Offices Carlisle, Corbridge, Darlington, Dumfries, Edinburgh, Fochabers, Leyburn, Lichfield, Newmarket, Newport, Peterborough, Petworth, Winchester, York

Associated Companies Smiths Gore (Overseas), British Virgin Islands

HENRY SPENCER & SONS
20 The Square, Retford, Nottingham DN22 6DJ
Telephone: 0777 706767
Telex: 56212

Partners Acting for Pension Funds Agricultural Property Investment-Richard Green,FRICS,FSVA, Commercial Property Investment-Stuart Carvell, FRICS, and David Margerison,ARICS

649

PROPERTY INVESTMENT

HENRY SPENCER & SONS have advised on all aspects of the investment of funds in the property world since 1840.

AGRICULTURAL INVESTMENT & MANAGEMENT
This has been our business since 1840, we ensure that the purchase and management of agricultural investments, from initial search to final completion, is conducted in a clear and efficient manner.
20 THE SQUARE, RETFORD, NOTTS.
DN22 2DJ. Tel: 0777 706767. Telex: 56212.

COMMERCIAL and INDUSTRIAL
We are able to advise on sales, purchases and valuations of all types of investments and act for several institutional purchasers in the north. We are also actively engaged in disposing of prime investment properties for clients throughout the country.
3 ST. JAMES ROW, SHEFFIELD S1 1WZ.
Tel: 0742 79102.

FINE ARTS
Investment in antiques and fine arts may sound strange but millions of ordinary people have been doing it for centuries. With such a proven background isn't it worth thinking about.
20 THE SQUARE, RETFORD, NOTTS.
DN22 2DJ. Tel: 0777 706767.

Henry Spencer & Sons
HSS 1840

Commercial and Industrial Property throughout THE MIDLANDS

West Midlands:
93/95 Hagley Road
Edgbaston
Birmingham B16 8LG
021-454 8111

East Midlands:
Haymarket House
Haymarket
Leicester
0533-24513

Property Advisers

HENRY SPENCER & SONS Continued

Other Pension Fund Expert Fine Arts-Bazil Kemp, FSVA

Employees 175

Number of Pension Fund Clients 6

Services Offered to Pension Funds Acquisition and management of agricultural and commercial property

Other Offices Bradford, Brigg, Chesterfield, Doncaster, Grimsby, Leeds, Retford, Scunthorpe, Sheffield, Rotherham, Leeds

STILES HORTON LEDGER

6 Pavilion Buildings, Brighton BN1 1EE
Telephone: 0273 21561

Partners Acting for Pension Funds R.D.Stiles,BSc, FRICS, R.H.Stapleton,FRICS, P.G.L.Ross,FRICS

Employees 90

Number of Pension Fund Clients 3

Services Offered to Pension Funds Advice on all property and related matters including management, rent reviews, sale and acquisition particularly in Sussex and the adjoining counties

Other Offices Crawley, Eastbourne, Worthing and Hove

STOREY SONS & PARKER

Higham House, New Bridge Street,
Newcastle upon Tyne NE1 8AU
Telephone: 0632-26291

Partners Acting for Pension Funds R.Scott,FRICS, N.Blezard,FRICS

Employees 150

Number of Pension Fund Clients 2

Services Offered to Pension Funds Complete property service, including valuation,acquisition, building surveys and management service

Other Offices Middlesborough, Stokesley, Morpeth

STRUTT & PARKER

13 Hill Street, London W1X 8DL
Telephone: 01-629 7282

Partners Acting for Pension Funds G.L.Lyotor, MA, DL,FRICS, A.C.Ball,FRICS (Agricultural), M.C.Harris, FRICS, D.R.P.Cripps,BSc,ARICS, J.G.Donald,BSc (Est.Man),ARICS (Commercial)

Other Pension Fund Experts M.F.Strutt,MC,TD,DL, FRICS J.A.Lauder,ARICS

Employees 376

Number of Pension Fund Clients 10

Services Offered to Pension Funds Full property investment and management service

Other Offices Canterbury, Chelmsford, Cheltenham, Cheshire, Edinburgh, Grantham, Harrogate, Ipswich, Lewes, Norwich, Salisbury

J.P. STURGE & SONS

24 Berkeley Square, Bristol BS8 1HU
Telephone: 0272-276691

Partners Acting for Pension Funds D.W.Marsh, FRICS, W.H.R.Durie,FRICS, P.S.Bitmead,ARICS

Employees 60

Number of Pension Fund Clients 3

Services Offered to Pension Funds Complete property service. Acquisitions, sales, full management, including rent reviews, valuations and project management

Other Office 2 Wood Street, Queen Square, Bath BA1 2JG; 37 Regent Circus, Swindon SN1 1QD

Clients Include Lovells Pension Trustees, Bristol Charities

STURGIS & SON

61 Park Lane, London W1Y 3TF
Telephone: 01-493 1401

Partners Acting for Pension Funds Martin Sturgis, BSc (Est Man), D.Potts,FRICS

Employees 65

Number of Pension Fund Clients 2

Services Offered to Pension Funds Valuations Valuations

Other Offices Kensington, East Sheen, Putney, Wimbledon, Barnes, Chiswick

SWEBY COWAN MCGLASHAN

12 John Princes Street, Cavendish Square,
London W1M 9HB
Telephone: 01-408 2131
Telex: 28427

Partner Acting for Pension Funds Robert A.Livock, ARICS

Other Pension Fund Expert Clive Eminson, BSc (Est.Man), ARICS

Employees 40

Number of Pension Fund Clients Private investment companies and trust funds on exclusive basis and several pension funds and insurance companies on a non-exclusive basis

Services Offered to Pension Funds Comprehensive advice regarding purchase and sale, portfolio performance and composition, funding, management, property development and refurbishment

Other Offices 503 High Road, Wembley HA0 2DL; Covent Garden; Craven Park

Clients include Howard Tenens, Kyle Stewart, Granchard, Metrostore

SYKES WATERHOUSE COMMERCIAL

7 Hanover Street, London W1R 0LA
Telephone: 01-629 9372

Partners Acting for Pension Funds David P.Phillips, FRICS, Aldon P.Ferguson,ARICS

Total Employees 100

Number of Pension Fund Clients 2

Services Offered to Pension Funds Complete property service, acquisitions, sales, full management including rent reviews and valuations

Other Offices 9 North John Street, Liverpool L2 5TS (051-236 9152) and Chester

EDWARD SYMMONS & PARTNERS

56-62 Wilton Road, London SW1V 1DH
Telephone: 01-834 8454

Property Advisers

EDWARD SYMMONS & PARTNERS Continued

Partner Acting for Pension Funds R.A.Sice,FRICS, FSVA

Other Pension Fund Expert P.A.George

Employees 45

Number of Pension Fund Clients Several trust funds and substantial private investors

Services Offered to Pension Funds Consultants on professional agency and tax matters relating to property. Experienced plant and machinery valuers and auctioneers

Other Offices 515-516 Royal Exchange, Manchester M2 7EN

TAYLOR & CO

17 Duke Street, Chelmsford, Essex CM1 1HP
Telephone: 0245-355561

Partners Acting for Pension Funds W.B.Andrade, FRICS, B.Rowley,FRICS

Total Employees 50

Number of Pension Fund Clients 3

Services Offered to Pension Funds Comprehensive investment advice on acquisition, sale and letting of commercial, industrial and agricultural investment properties. Valuations, rent review, landlord/tenant negotiations, building surveys and management services where required

Other Offices 158 High Street, Colchester, Essex (0206-78541); Market Place, Braintree, Essex (0376-21333); 15 High Street, Malden, Essex (0621-52551)

PETER TAYLOR & COMPANY

16 Bolton Street, London W1Y 8HX
Telephone: 01-499 5511

Partners Acting for Pension Funds Peter Taylor, FRICS, Stephen Rogers,BSc,FRICS, Peter Fielding, ARICS

Services Offered to Pension Funds Specialist service in the industrial and warehousing sector, including investment and development acquisition, valuation and management. Also general advice, valuation and acquisition of other types of commercial property

TEACHER MARKS & CO

46 Mount Street, London W1Y 5RD
Telephone: 01-499 5255

Partners Acting for Pension Funds R.B.Marks,FSVA, ACIArb, C.V.Teacher, FSVA,ACIArb

Employees 9

Number of Pension Fund Clients No solely retaining fund

Services Offered to Pension Funds Full range of property investment consultancy i.e. valuation, sale, purchase, portfolio management, lease renewals and rent reviews

Other Information The partnership has an extensive investment practice which advises a number of pension funds and insurance companies and has tended to specialise in arranging institutional finance for office development

TEMPLES

32 Grand James Street, London WC1N 3HB
Telephone: 01-404 3115

Partners Acting for Pension Funds W.F.H.Gibbon, FRICS, R.B.J.Gibbon,FRICS, A.J.Rogers,BSc,ARICS, D.L.Temple,DLC,FRICS, J.Marsh,ARICS

Employees 27

Number of Pension Fund Clients 6

Services Offered to Pension Funds Valuation, acquisition and management of properties for pension funds

Other Offices 59 London Street, Norwich NR2 1HL (0603 29941);45 Station Road, Sheringham NR26 8RG (0263 822488); 3 The Market Place, Holt NR25 6BE (026371 3143); 21 Church Plain, Gt. Yarmouth NR31 8QW (0493 58825)

Associated Office KOK Groep, Nederland BV, Rotterdam

THORNCROFT & PARTNERS

17 Berkeley Street, London W1X 5AE
Telephone: 01-493 1947

Partners Acting for Pension Funds John Lawson, JP,BSc (Est Man),FRICS, Ralph C.Lawson,FRICS

Employees 3

Number of Pension Fund Clients 3

Services Offered to Pension Funds Comprehensive range including acquisitions, disposals, valuations for all purposes, rent reviews, management, town planning, project management and appraisals

Other Offices 3 Regent Street, Cheltenham GL50 1HF (0242 24979)

Other Information A chartered surveyors practice which specialises in commercial and industrial premises and developments

BERNARD THORPE & PARTNERS

1 Buckingham Palace Road, London SW1W 0QD
Telephone: 01-834 6890

Partners Acting for Pension Funds P.Patchett, FRICS,FSVA, P.J.Chuck,FRICS, M.F.Stonehouse, ARICS

Other Pension Fund Experts Viscount Stuart of Findhorn,FRICS, J.K.Scrace,BSc, FRICS, N.J.Edwards,FRICS, Brian T.Read, ARICS

Employees 325

Number of Pension Fund Clients 4

Services Offered to Pension Funds Advice on all property and related matters

City Office Blossoms Inn, 23 Lawrence Lane, London EC2V 8DA (01-600 7281)

Other Offices Bournemouth, Brighton, Tunbridge Wells, Oxted, Bath, Monmouth, Abergavenny, Cheltenham, Stow-on-the-Wold, Hereford, Worcester, Birmingham Manchester, Leeds, Wetherby, York, Middlesbrough, Hexham, Newcastle upon Tyne, Glasgow, Edinburgh, Paris, Brussels, Antwerp

Clients Include Post Office Staff Superannuation Fund, Tyne and Wear Metropolitan County Council Superannuation Fund, Co-operative Insurance Society Ltd. Pension Fund, Lankro-Mahler Pension Fund (Diamond Shamrock (Europe) Ltd.)

Watts+Partners
Chartered Building Surveyors Construction Consultants

Independent advice on building and construction;
condition surveys;
the design and supervision of works;
advice on building defects

London
☎ 01-852 9151

Property Advisers

J. TREVOR AND SONS
58 Grosvenor Street, London W1X 0DD
Telephone: 01-629 8151

Partner Acting for Pension Funds J.Gorringe-Smith, FRICS

Employees 65

Services Offered to Pension Funds Full property service relating to acquisition, sale and letting, plus rent reviews, management, valuation etc.

Other Offices 85 London Wall, London EC2M 7AD (01-628 0735); Barnett House, Fountain Street, Manchester M2 2AN (061-228 6752); Bank House, Queen Street, Sheffield S1 2DW (0742-750945)

GEORGE TROLLOPE & SONS
13 Hobart Place, London SW1W 0HP
Telephone: 01-235 8099

Partners Acting for Pension Funds W.I.N.Kennett, FRICS, N.P.s.Jupp, BSc, ARICS, P.T.Richards,ARICS

Other Pension Fund Experts J.A.Crossley, ARICS, J.W.Owen,BSc,ARICS

Number of Pension Fund Clients 3

Services Offered to Pension Funds Full property investment, valuation and management service

Other Offices P&O Deck, P&O Building, Leadenhall Street, London EC3V 3PT 01-283 3641)

L. S. VAIL & SON
18 High Street, Fareham, Hampshire PO16 7AF
Telephone: 0329-285811
Telex: 86221

Partners Acting for Pension Funds J.R.Vail,FRICS, J.R.Lear,FRICS

Employees 80

Number of Pension Fund Clients Several small funds, primarily based in Southern England and other Pension Funds and Insurance companies on a non-exclusive basis

Services Offered to Pension Funds Comprehensive advice in connection with the acquisition, sale, letting, valuation and surveying of commercial and industrial investment property. Also portfolio management

Other Offices 4 High Street, Gosport, 175 High Street, Lee-on-the-Solent, 192 West Street, Fareham, 226 London Road, Waterlooville, 102 Bitterne Road, Southampton, 40a London Road, Southampton and 137 London Road, North End, Portsmouth

VIGERS
4 Frederick's Place, Old Jewry, London EC2R 8DA
Telephone: 01-606 7601

Partner Acting for Pension Funds J.C.Deas,ARICS

Other Pension Fund Expert R.G.Bunnett,ARICS

Employees 50

Number of Pension Fund Clients (i) London Transport Executive Pension Fund; (ii) London Borough of Hackney Superannuation Fund; (iii) Nottinghamshire County Council Superannuation Fund; (iv) Several other Pension Funds and Insurance Companies on a non exclusive basis

Services Offered to Pension Funds Comprehensive advice regarding purchase, sale, performance, improvement and management of property investment

Other Offices Vigers McEvoy, 8 Randolph Crescent, Edinburgh (031-225 7137), Burton Barnes & Vigers, 22 Cannon Street, Preston, Lancs. (0772-50858), Vigers Hong Kong, 18 Carnarvon Road, Kowloon, Hong Kong

WALKER SON & PACKMAN
Blossoms Inn, 3/6 Trump Street, London EC2V 8DD
Telephone: 01-606 8111

Partners Acting for Pension Funds G.F.Packman, FRICS, P.B.Giles,MA,FRICS, M.R.K.Holden,FRICS

Other Offices West End, Bristol, Exeter, Truro, East Grinstead, Edinburgh, Leeds, Cairo, New York

E. W. WALLAKER & CO
282 Kensington High Street, London W14 8NZ
Telephone: 01-602 2333

Partners Acting for Pension Funds E.W.Wallaker, FSVA, M.J.Doubleday,FRICS

Total Employees 60

Number of Pension Fund Clients 2

Services Offered to Pension Funds Complete service: acquisition and management, project management, sales and lettings. Valuations for all purposes

Other Offices Surbiton, Thames Ditton, Chessington and Lancing

Clients Include London Borough of Newham Superannuation Fund, NALGO Superannuation Fund and several others for whom firm is not solely retained

WATTS & PARTNERS
Queenscroft, 150 Eltham Hill, London SE9
Telephone: 01-859 3011

Partners Acting for Pension Funds T.Watts,FRICS, ACIArb, R.A.Porter,FRICS,ACIArb

Employees 60

Number of Pension Fund Clients 3

Services Offered to Pension Funds Independent advice on building and construction; conditions surveys; advice on building defects and the design and supervision of works of modernisation and alterations

Other Offices Lewisham and Bromley

WEATHERALL GREEN & SMITH
22 Chancery Lane, London WC2A 1LT
Telephone: 01-405 6944

And at 24 Austin Friars, London EC2N 2EN
01-638 9011

Partners And Associates Acting for Pension Funds G.Mason,FRICS, J.Green,FRICS, R.Lewsley,FRICS, T.Knight,FRICS, H.Chatwin,ARICS, D.Bianco,ARICS, D.Bond,ARICS

Other Pension Fund Experts Paris-P.Buttery,ARICS; Frankfurt-C.Bull-Diamond,ARICS

Employees 250

Number of Pension Fund Clients Numerous

Services Offered to Pension Funds Complete range

ADVISERS ON COMMERCIAL PROPERTIES
THROUGHOUT THE U.K. FOR
INVESTMENT ACQUISITION & SALE

WHITE DRUCE & BROWN

5 ST. HELENS PLACE, EC3A 6AU
TELEPHONE 01-638 5181 OR 5182

3 & 4 GT MARLBOROUGH STREET
OXFORD CIRCUS LONDON W1V 2HE
TELEPHONE 01-629 2102-4

Investment Advice – There's no substitute for experience

Sales, Acquisitions and Letting of Commercial & Industrial Property, Rent Reviews, Valuations, Rating, Building Design Services, Property Management.

JP Sturge & SONS
Chartered Surveyors

2 WOOD STREET,
QUEEN SQUARE,
BATH BA1 2JG.
TEL: (0225) 319300

24 BERKELEY SQUARE,
BRISTOL BS8 1HU
TEL: (0272) 276691
TELEX: 449157

37 REGENT CIRCUS,
SWINDON SN1 1QD
TEL: (0793) 33155

WEATHERALL GREEN & SMITH *Continued*

Other Offices Leeds, Wakefield, Paris, Frankfurt and Munich

WEBSTER & CO

21 West Nile Street, Glasgow G1 2PJ
Telephone: 041-204 0771

Partner Acting for Pension Funds G.H.Webster, BSc, FRICS

Total Employees 25

Other Offices 60 Union Street, Aberdeen AB1 1BB (0224 52687)

WHITE, DRUCE & BROWN

5 St Helen's Place, Bishopsgate,
London EC3A 6AU
Telephone: 01-638 5181

Partner Acting for Pension Funds Len Wallis,FRICS

Consultant E.A.G.Jennings,FRICS

Employees 13

Services Offered to Pension Funds Advice on acquisition and sale of investments

Other Offices 3-4 Gt. Marlborough Street, London W1V 2HE (01-629 2102)

Associated Offices 87/89 Mosley Street, Manchester M2 3LL

HAROLD WILLIAMS BENNETT AND PARTNERS

78 Buckingham Gate, Westminster,
London SW1E 6PE
Telephone: 01-222 4477

Partners Acting for Pension Funds R.A.Park,FRICS, N.M.H.Fallowfield, BSc,FRICS

Employees 60

Number of Pension Fund Clients 4

Services Offered to Pension Funds Advice on the purchase and sale of commercial property; valuation rent revision and lease renewal; full estate management

Other Offices Croydon, Caterham, Godstone, Redhill, Reigate, Merstham

Principal Pension Fund Clients British Gas Corporation, Central Fund of the Gas Manual Workers' Pension Scheme

P.J.WILLIAMS & CO

6 Stratton Street, London W1X 5FD
Telephone: 01-493 4164

Partner Acting for Pension Funds D.H.Duval

WILSON & PARTNERS

5 Spencer Parade, Northampton, NN1 5AA
Telephone: 0604 22817

Partners Acting for Pension Funds H.G.Smith, FRICS, J.M.Ainsworth,BSc,FRICS, A.C.Hewitt,BSc, MIHE, R.E.Tassell,FRICS

Employees 75

Number of Pension Fund Clients 6

Services Offered to Pension Funds Valuation for acquisition, rent revision and lease renewal, disposal, advice on performance improvement and management of property investment, building surveying

Other Offices St.Giles Street, Northampton NN1 1JW (0604-228 17); Dalkeith Place, Kettering NN16 0DT (0536-3441); Queens Square, Corby NN17 1PD (05366-3887); The Square, Raunds NN9 6HP (0933-623300); High Street, Rushden NN10 0PN (09334-2363); Westgate, Peterborough PE1 2SY (0733-42801); Sheep Street, Wellingborough NN8 1BS (0933-223291); 78 Saxon Gate West, Milton Keynes, Bucks.MK9 2DL (0908-604630)

JOHN D. WOOD

23 Berkeley Square, Mayfair, London W1X 6AL
Telephone: 01-629 9050
Telex: 21242

Partners Acting for Pension Funds V.A.E.Wood, FRICS, A.S.Browne, ARICS

Employees 130

Number of Pension Fund Clients Several

Services Offered to Pension Funds Complete purchase, valuation and management of property investment portfolio

City Office Warnford Court, Throgmorton Street, London EC2N 2AT (01-588 0557)

Other Offices Chelsea, Kensington, Regents Park, Edinburgh, Harpenden, Southampton, Winchester, Paris; also Martin & Pole, John D. Wood at Reading, Earley, Caversham, Pangbourne, Goring-on-Thames, Mortimer Common, Thatcham and Newbury

WRIGHT & PARTNERS

8 St. James's Place, London SW1A 1PD
Telephone: 01-493 4121

Partners Acting for Pension Funds R.C.M.Green, FRICS, D.T.H.Deagle, FRICS

Employees 40

Number of Pension Fund Clients 1 principal pension fund for whom firm advises exclusively on commercial property in the UK. Advice on valuation given to other smaller pension funds

Services Offered to Pension Funds Consultants in connection with the purchase and sale of shops, offices and industrial property investments and advice in connection with lease renewals, rent reviews and other associated matters relating to commercial and industrial property

Other Offices 13 Charlotte Square, Edinburgh, EH2 4DJ

Other Information Sole Consultants to the British Railways Pension Funds for commercial property throughout the UK

**FORESTRY INVESTMENT PLANNING,
WOODLAND ACQUISITIONS, AND PORTFOLIO
MANAGEMENT**

For the UK Pension Fund Manager — A sophisticated advisory and monitoring service — acting independently of woodland managers and contractors.

CONSULTANTS' LOCATIONS

1. London, Guildford, Odiham, Shaftesbury, Crediton, Tavistock, Truro, Uckfield, Maidstone and Diss
2. Reading, Westbury, Bruton, Llandovery, Carmarthen, Machynlleth and Bangor
3. Northampton, Lincoln, York, Northallerton and Hexham
4. Edinburgh, Perth, Aberdeen, Forres and Lochgilphead
5. Glasgow, Newton Stewart, Belfast and Penrith

Directors:

115 Mount Street, London W1Y 5HD
Tel: 01-493 6807   P. K. Marlow F.C.A.

FORESTRY INVESTMENT MANAGEMENT LIMITED

25 Archery Fields, Odiham, Hants RG25 1AE
Tel: (025 671) 2742   K. N. Rankin C.A.

F I M

Ridgemount, The Ridgeway, Guildford GU1 2DG
Tel: (0483) 72383   Dr. F. C. Hummel M.A. F.I.For

Park House, Shaftesbury, Dorset SP7 8BG
Tel: (0747) 4414   W. N. Seymour F.R.I.C.S.

FORESTRY

For real growth and a Vital Raw Material —
Invest in Forestry.
For a comprehensive forestry service
including the acquisition and management
of forestry land and stocked woodland
contact —

swoac

The Investment Director.
**SCOTTISH WOODLAND OWNERS ASSOCIATION
(COMMERCIAL) LTD.**
6 Chester Street, Edinburgh EH3 7RD.
Telephone: 031-225 1905.

SWOAC

Forestry and Agricultural Consultants

JOHN CLEGG & CO
Bury Estate Office, Church Street, Chesham, Bucks HP5 1JF
Telephone: 02405 4711

Partners J.A.Clegg,FRICS, C.M.Gee,ARICS, A.N.Crow,ARICS, D.W.G.Taylor,BSc(For)

Number of Pension Fund Clients Close connections with many funds but not exclusively retained by any Fund

Specialist Services Offered to Pension Funds Professional advice on all aspects of forestry including the search for, appraisal, valuation and acquisition of Forestry and Agricultural investments throughout the U.K. and in America

Other Offices 4 Rutland Square, Edinburgh EH1 2AS (031 229 8800)

ECONOMIC FORESTRY LIMITED
26 Old Bailey, London EC4M 7LL
Telephone: 01-236 8682

and at 27 Rutland Square, Edinburgh EH1 2BW
Telephone: 031-229 5435

Directors Involved with Pension Funds A.C.S.Jennings,MA,FIFor J.A.Fell,MA,BSc(For),MIFor

Forest Economist G.R.Watt, BSc, BLitt, C.Dip.AF

Employees 700

Number of Pension Fund Clients Numerous

Specialist Services Offered to Pension Funds Professional advice on all aspects of forestry and detailed economic and financial appraisals of forestry investment in the UK and overseas. A comprehensive forest management service is provided throughout Britain

Other Offices 49 including 15 main forest management offices

Other Information A leading forestry investment and management company providing services throughout the United Kingdom and currently managing over 200,000 acres of commercial woodlands and upland farms. In recent years EFG have been responsible for over one quarter of all private forestry planting in Britain. Consultancy services can be provided world-wide and EFG is currently retained by Funds investing in the South-Eastern United States

FORESTRY INVESTMENT MANAGEMENT LTD
115 Mount Street, London W1Y 5HD
Telephone: 01-493 6807

Directors Involved with Pension Funds P.K.Marlow, FCA, K.N.Rankin,CA

Associated Consultants 24

Number of Pension Fund Clients 3

Services Offered to Pension Funds Sophisticated forestry investment and tax planning. Woodlands acquisitions and portfolio management, an advisory and monitoring service acting independently of woodland managers and contractors

Associated Offices Throughout the UK

FOUNTAIN FORESTRY LTD.
1 Camomile Street, London EC3A 74J
Telephone: 01-623 7511

Director Acting for Pension Funds B.N.Howell, MA (Cantab) MI For

Consultant J.P.Trower

Employees 200

Number of Pension Fund Clients 14

Specialist Services Offered to Pension Funds Complete investment, acquisition and Forestry Management

Other Offices 15 throughout the U.K.

Associated Company Stewart Wrightson Holdings Ltd.

Other Information A long established professional Forestry Management Company backed by the resources of one of the largest International Insurance Broking Groups. The Company specialises in acquiring and managing Forestry Investments for a wide range of corporate and individual clients numbering several hundreds in the U.K. and North America

GAUDERY LTD
The Hall, Willisham, Ipswich, Suffolk
Telephone: 047 333 527

Director Acting for Pension Funds R.Jones

LAURENCE GOULD & COMPANY LTD
Birmingham Road, Saltisford, Warwick CV34 4TT
Telephone: 0926 496121

Directors Involved with Pension Funds J.L.Gould, C.Berry Savory, H.D.Thompson, J.P.Bedford

Employees 110

Number of Pension Fund Clients 4

Area of Specialisation Farm Management, Agricultural Consultancy, Appraisal & Management of Agricultural Investments

Other Offices Burgess Hill, Edinburgh, Hungerford, Newark, Newmarket

Associated Companies Laurence Gould Consultants Ltd, ULG Consultants Ltd, Halcrow-ULG Ltd

HALLSWORTH LTD
Hallsworth House, Station Road, Attleborough, Norfolk
Telephone: 0953 453999

Chairman and Chief Executive R.C.Bilborough

Area of Specialisation Agricultural land and farm management

INTERNATIONAL FOREST SCIENCE CONSULTANCY
21 Biggar Road, Silverburn, Penicuik EH26 9LQ, Midlothian, Scotland
Telephone: 0968-75112

- ✺ FORESTRY NOW HOLDS A PLACE IN MANY BALANCED INSTITUTIONAL PORTFOLIOS
- ✺ ITS TRACK RECORD OVER MANY YEARS IS IMPRESSIVE
- ✺ WORLD SHORTAGES OF TIMBER ARE FORECAST
- ✺ INVESTMENT IN A RENEWABLE RAW MATERIAL MAKES FINANCIAL SENSE

SOME OF THE REASONS WHY YOU SHOULD KNOW MORE ABOUT FORESTRY INVESTMENT IN THE U.K. AND NORTH AMERICA

Send for our booklet:
"**FORESTRY INVESTMENT FOR INSTITUTIONS**"

FOUNTAIN FORESTRY LIMITED
1, Camomile Street
London, EC3A 7HJ
Telephone: 01-623-7511

A member of the Stewart Wrightson Holdings Group

25 YEARS EXPERIENCE IN PROFESSIONAL FORESTRY MANAGEMENT

Forestry and Agricultural Consultants

INTERNATIONAL FOREST SCIENCE CONSULTANCY
Continued

Partners Involved with Pension Funds Dr.A.I.Fraser, A.D.K.Hardie

Employees 3

Number of Pension Fund Clients 1

Specialist Services Offered to Pension Funds Woodland valuation and acquisition. Professional forest management

TILHILL FORESTRY ADVISORY LTD

Greenhills, Tilford, Farnham, Surrey GU10 2DY
Telephone: 025-125 3265

Directors Involved with Pension Funds D.Brierton, BSc(For),FIFor, R.T.Gray,BSc(For),MIFor, A.F.Macpherson,MSc(For),MI For R.T.Collet,MA,FCA

Number of Employees 189

Number of Pension Fund Clients 4

Services Offered to Pension Funds Forestry investment and comprehensive forestry management services

Other Offices Old Sauchie, Sauchieburn, Stirling, Scotland and at Bury St. Edmunds, Crowborough, Frome, Church Stretton, Thirsk, Carlisle, Jedburgh, Gifford, Oban, Elgin, Dunoon, Muir of Ord

WESTERN FORESTRY

130 Holland Park Avenue, London W11
Telephone: 01-229 9629

Services offered to Pension Funds Forestry Management

FORESTRY
The investment in growth

World demand for timber is increasing; our import bill for wood products is now approaching £3000 million per annum. Conditions for commercial timber production in Britain are among the best in Europe. An investment in forestry is in a tangible asset producing a vital and versatile raw material and provides a unique vehicle for capital growth.

Tilhill's expert management and marketing services are available throughout the UK. Fund managers who wish to know more about the opportunities now being recognized by the institutions are invited to send off today for our booklet "Investing in Woodlands".

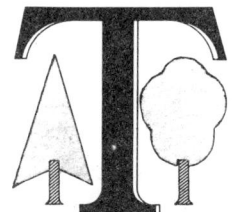

Tilhill Forestry Advisory Ltd., Greenhills, Tilford, Farnham, Surrey.

Tilhill, Greenhills, Tilford, Farnham, Surrey.

Please send me a copy of your booklet "Investing in Woodlands".

Name _____

Fund _____

Address _____

To advertise in

PENSION FUNDS
&THEIR ADVISERS

contact:

Telephone **Mrs Jill Platford**
01-353 3712 (5 lines)

J E P Advertising Associates Ltd
Space Brokers & Publishers
107-111 Fleet Street
London EC4

Actuaries

Actuarial advice may be obtained either through:

1. Actuaries in professional practice who operate as individuals or (more usually) in partnership in firms of Consulting Actuaries. Most firms are members of the Association of Consulting Actuaries.

2. Corporate bodies such as insurance companies, pension fund consultants or employee benefit consultants who make available actuarial advice given to them by actuaries in their employment.

The following are the main professional bodies and associations:

THE INSTITUTE OF ACTUARIES

Staple Inn Hall, High Holborn, London WC1V 7QJ
Telephone: 01-242 0106

President A.R.N.Ratcliff

Vice-Presidents F.B.Corby,MA, D.E.Fellows, M.H.Field, E.A.Johnston,CB,BA

Treasurer M.J.Burns

Hon Secretaries R.D.Corley,BSc F.B.Wales

Secretary-General N.J.Page, MC,FCIS,FCCA,FSS

Secretary C.D.A.Mackie,FCA,MBIM

Deputy Secretaries J.M.Henty,ACIS, G.W.Mills,FCA, J.Waugh,BSc

THE FACULTY OF ACTUARIES IN SCOTLAND

23 St. Andrew Square, Edinburgh EH2 1AQ
Telephone: 031-556 6791

President D.D.McKinnon, BSc, FFA, FIMA

Hon Secretaries A.J.Pfaff, FFA, J.R.Gray, BSc, FFA, FIMA

Secretary W.W.Mair,MA

THE ASSOCIATION OF CONSULTING ACTUARIES

Metropolis House, 39-45 Tottenham Court Road, London W1P 0JL
Telephone: 01-636 7777

Chairman P.R.Francis,MA,FIA,FSS

Secretary K.G.Whitehead,BA,FIA,ASA,FPMI

Other Office 66 Merrion Square South, Dublin 2

The following firms are members of the Association of Consulting Actuaries:

BACON & WOODROW

Empire House, St.Martin's-Le-Grand, London EC1A 4ED
Telephone: 01-606 9033,

Partners R.W.Abbott,CBE,FIA,ASA, M.T.L.Bizley,FIA, FIS, Miss P.E.Merriman, MA,FIA,ATII, R.M.Bangert, FIA, P.Basten,FIA, J.H.Prevett,OBE,FIA, S.Benjamin, MA,FIA,FIS, Miss B.S.Cairns,MA,FIA, C.Rich,FIA, ASA, C.D.Lever,MA,FIA, J.D.Sparks,BA,FIA, J.J.Simon,BSc,FIA, A.E.M.Fine, MA,FIA,ASA, R.N.Jarvis,MA,FIA, A.S.A.Siddick,FIA,ASA, N.S.Buckland,MA,FIA, M.J.Jones,MA,FIA, M.A.Pomery,MA,FIA, L.M.Eagles,BA,BSc(Econ),FIA, W.F.Ogston,FIA, Mrs.V.M.Miller,MA,FIA, A.S.Brown, BSc(Econ),FIA, G.R.Farren,MA,FIA, E.S.Thomas,MA, FIA, R.D.Moore,MA, FIA, A.R.Hewitt,MA,FIA, Miss J.Keith-Lucas,MA,FIA, D.P.Hager,MA,FIA, H.E.Clarke, FIA, D.I.Tomlinson,MA,FIA, R.J.Chapman,BA,FIA, R.B.Millard,MA,MSc,FIA, S.J.Ainsworth,MA,FIA, M.C.Thomas,BSc,FIA, Mrs.V.M.Miller,MA,FIA, R.B.Abramson,BSc,FIA, R.J.Jagelman,MA,FIA, M.J.Ward,MA,FIA, J.D.Clamp,BSc,FIA, P.R.C.Jowett, BSc,FIA, P.J.Morgan,MA,FIA, M.A.Posner,BSc(Econ), FIA,ASA

Dublin Partner J.V.Armstrong,MA,FIA

Consultant Partners F.W.Bacon,MA,FIA, A.Farncombe,FIA

Actuaries

BACON & WOODROW *Continued*

Other Pension Fund Experts Miss D.M.Bates,BA, Barrister at Law, Miss M.Roney, Solicitor, D.A.Joshua,LIB, J.Andrews,FBCS

Total Employees 283

Services Offered to Pension Funds Actuarial valuations, scheme design, investment performance service and advice, drafting documents and booklets, employee communications, administration service and negotiating with government departments

Other Offices 55 High Street, Epsom, Surrey KT19 8DH (26671); 11 Albion Street, Leeds, LS1 5ES (0532-441494) Baryta House, 29 Victoria Avenue, Southend-on-Sea, Essex SS2 6AZ (0702-49807), 58 Fitzwilliam Square, Dublin 2 (762031); Albert House, South Esplanade, St.Peter Port, Guernsey, C.I. (0481-28432)

Associated Firm Bacon, Woodrow & De Souza (Trinidad)

RODNEY BARNETT & CO.

35 Great Peter Street, Westminster, London SW1P 3LR
Telephone: 01-222 1961

Partners R.E.Hayward,FIA, J.H.Fullerton,BSc,FIA, H.A.R.Barnett,FIA,ASA, J.V.Evans,FIA

Other Pension Fund Experts R.P.A.Leandro,BSc, J.A.Edgeworth,BSc

Type of Work Undertaken Pension fund valuations and other calculations. Life Office and Friendly Society valuations, reversions, life interests, compensation claims for loss of financial support, mortality and sickness investigations. Computer programs for pension funds

Other Offices 72 Langdale Road, Hove, Sussex BN3 4HP (0273- 739820), 1 Park Lane, Budleigh, Salterton, Devon EX9 6QT (03954 5225)

Associated Company Whitehall Computing Ltd.

CLAY & PARTNERS

70 Brook Street, London W1Y 2HN
Telephone: 01-408 1600

Partners K.G.Whitehead,BA,FIA,ASA,FPMI, A.S.Fishman, BSc,FIA,ASA,MAAA,FPMI, I.S.Aitken, BSc,FIA,APMI, S.L.Gooch,BSc,FIA, B.Tatch,BSc,FIA, APMI, A.J.Wilson,BSc,ARCS,FIA, T.M.Ross,BSc,FFA, FCIA,ASA,APMI G.H.M.Goddard,BSc(Econ),FIA,ASA, APMI, Helen James,MA,FIA, D.Crowther,BSc,FIA, G.Mitchell,MA,FIA, J.R.P.Checkley,MA,FIA, L.Clark, BSc,FIA, Pauline Gover,BSc,FIA, J.G.Spain,BSc,FIA, ASA, R.C.W.Strattan,BSc,FIA M.Dyson,MA,FIA, ASIA, S.C.Stoye,MA,FIA, D.Tillson,MA,FIA

Professional Staff Philippa Aaronson,BSc, R.J.Abraham,BSc, G.H.Baker,MA,AIA, R.E.Barker, S.J.Bennett,BSc, G.Booth,BSc,FIA E.C.Bruce-Gardner,BSc, R.J.Burger, G.F. Chamberlin,MA,AIA, R.M.Chandler, D.M.Cogan, BSc,PhD,MRAeS,FIA, P.J.Cross,MA, J.Cullen,BA, Lynne Davis,MA,AIA, J.D.Fisher,BSc,AIA, P.F.Hawker,BSc, C.H.Hicks,MA, D.R.Judd,FCA, Rosemary Kennell,BA(Econ),AIA,FSS, H.R.Laird,BA, P.Lauper,BSc,ARCS, Rosemary Mounce,BSc,ARCS,AIA, R.E.O'Brien, J.N.Sharples, BA, J.E.Shepley,BSc,AIA, A.G.Skinner,AIB, D.G.C.Stevens,BA, M.A.J.Stone,BSc, O.H.Y.Tang, BSc, R.S.Thomson,BSc, G.J.Warren,BA, T.R.Webb, J.P.Woodhouse,BSc,FIA, S.F.Yeo, R.J.Young,BSc

Employees 85

Services Offered to Pension Funds A complete service offering action and advice on all aspects of occupational pensions

Associated Companies Claybrook Computing Ltd, Clay & Partners Pension Trustees Ltd

Other Information Fully familiar with North American pension practice and able to perform actuarial services under ERISA. Services offered include a wide range of non actuarial activities in connection with pension schemes both in the UK and overseas

A.R.H.COLLINS & CO

34 West George Street, Glasgow G2 1DA
Telephone: 041-331 2080

Partners D.F.Shearer,MA,FFA, T.F.Marshall,MA,FFA

Other Office 6 York Place, Edinburgh EH1 3ED (031-556 2031)

Associated Company Robertson, Hymans & Co

P.J.CONSTABLE

Barford Forge, Barford St. Martin, Wiltshire
Telephone: 072-274 2354

Partner P.J.Constable

AMIT DE & CO

44 Bedford Row, London WC1R 4LL
Telephone: 01-405 0402

Partners Amit De, D.H.Craighead

DUNCAN C. FRASER & CO

30 Exchange Street East, Liverpool L2 3QB
Telephone: 051-236 9771

Partners Geoffrey Heywood, Maxwell Lander, A.G.MacG.Fraser, K.Muir McKelvey, J.D.U.Harsant, K.F.Trott, B.S.Reddin, A.E.G.Round M.B.Reid, A.J.Low, M.J.Day, P.E.Felton, N.J.Braithwaite, M.J.Fairclough, D.W.Howard, J.S.Roffe, F.I.Bowles, J.V.Betts, J.R.Kehoe, D.G.Johnson, R.A.J.Waddingham, A.A.S.Bryans, Robert Chadwick, G.H.Redman, D.E.A.Sanders, C.J.Lloyd, G.Pollock, W.F.Ashburner

Employees Approximately 200

Type of Work undertaken All aspects of occupational pension schemes (including actuarial, benefit design, investment policy and advice and administration); audio-visual communications; computer packages; insurance companies; assessment of damages; life interests and reversions; friendly societies

Other Offices 24/28 Cheapside, London EC2V 6AB (01-248 6981); 10 Greenfield Crescent, Birmingham B15 3AU (021-455 7485); Iveagh Court, 6-8 Harcourt Road, Dublin 2 (720544/ 720764); Erskine House, 68-73 Queen Street, Edinburgh EH2 4NF (031-226 5504); Dennis House, Marsden Street, Manchester M2 1HF (061-832 5688) Holbeck House, 105 Albion Street, Leeds (0532-443753)

Associated Companies Duncan C.Fraser & Co Inc, 1133 15th Street, NW, Washington DC 20005 (202-785 4995); Heywood & Partners Ltd., 30 Exchange Street, East, Liverpool L2 3QB (051-237 9771); Duncan C. Fraser & Co (CI), PO Box 133, St. Julian's Court, St. Peter Port, Guernsey, CI (0481-25887); Duncan C. Fraser & Co (Far East), 1501 D International Plaza Building, Anson Road, Singapore 2 (Singapore 2204691); Duncan C.

Actuaries

DUNCAN C. FRASER & CO *Continued*

Fraser & Co Sdn Bhd, 13th Floor, Angkasa Raya, 123 Jalan Ampang, Kuala Lumpur (Kuala Lumpur 21189); Fraser Unit Trust Managers Ltd, 2 Friars Lane, Richmond, Surrey TW9 1NL (01-948 0164); Fraser Green Ltd., 66 Hill Street, Richmond, Surrey TW9 1TW (01-948 0164); Fraser Orr Ltd., Confederation House, Kildare Street, Dublin 2 (714933); Fraser Watson Actuaries Ltd., Suite 203, 1 Eva Road,Etobicoke, Ontario M9C 4Z5 (416-622 2225); Pension Communications Ltd., 12/13 Henrietta Street, London WC2 (01-836 0437/8); Pensioneer Trustees Ltd., 30 Exchange Street East, Liverpool L2 3QB (051-236 9771)

HYMANS, ROBERTSON & CO

35 New Bridge Street, London EC4V 6BJ
Telephone: 01-248 0102

ROBERTSON, HYMANS & CO

34 West George Street, Glasgow G2 1DA
Telephone: 041-331 1323

Partners (both of Hymans, Robertson & Co. and Robertson Hymans & Co.) N.D.Freethy, K.F.Sanjana, P.D.Esslemont, M.Arnold, D.Moakes, I.L.Seller, S.H.Bell, N.A.Shuker

Consultants J.C.S.Hymans, P.Geddes

Other Professional Staff R.Bowie, S.I.Lowry, J.A.McKay, S.M.Pollard, R.P.C.Tewkesbury

Total Employees 29

Services Offered to Pension Funds Everything regarding self-administered and insured pension schemes from inception to winding-up including actuarial, administration, documentation, computerisation, negotiations with government departments, trusteeship and investments

Subsidiary Company City of London Computer Services Ltd., 35 New Bridge Street, London EC4V 6ØJ (01-248 8204); Offers wide range of computer services including pensions administration

Associated Companies A.R.H.Collins & Co., 6 York Place, Edinburgh EH1 3EP (031-556 2031)

LANE, CLARK & PEACOCK

Regent House, 89 Kingsway, London WC2B 6RH
Telephone: 01-404 5881

Partners K.J.Burton, B.J.Clark, D.W.Peacock, T.A.Warren, C.R.C.Hawkes, R.J.N.Young, S.M.Wilcock, G.W.Orpwood Price, M.R.Slack, A.Bradley, R.R.Heard, V.Harding

Services Offered to Pension Funds All actuarial fields, including, in relation to pension schemes, their design and introduction and subsequent administration and financial management

PHARHAD SADEQUE

59 Cheam Road, East Ewell, Epsom, Surrey KT17 3EG
Telephone: 01-394 1960

Partner P.Sadeque

Employees 3

Number of Pension Fund Clients 125

Type of Work Undertaken Actuarial valuations, investment performance evaluation, all aspects of life and pensions consultancy, administration, pensioneer trusteeship

R. WATSON & SONS

2-4 King Street, St. James's, London SW1Y 6QN
Telephone: 01-839 3624

Partners J.P.Holbrook, D.F.Gilley, P.R.Francis, L.J.Martin, M.H.Winters, E.M.Lee, R.C.Cooper, G.E.Barrow, J.A.Jolliffe, M.J. de H. Bell, H.Gracey, J.C.M.Casale, J.M.Bibby, A.F.Wilson, D.H.Miles, R.R.Munro, J.R.D.Orrett, A.H.Godson, R.D.Masding, D.E.Reynolds, G. McD.Bell, P.A.Kelly, J.R.Wigley, J.M.Hill, I.D.A.Young, V.J.Chambers, R.P.Jessett, A.J.Wise, P.N.Thornton, L.M.Aitken, P.Lofthouse, R.G.Ashurst, P.A.Cockbain, M.J.Grundy, R.V.Williams

Services Offered to Pension Funds Professional advice on all aspects of pension fund actuarial work and consultancy

Other Offices Watson House, London Road, Reigate, Surrey RH2 9PQ (Reigate 41144), 21 Albany Street Edinburgh EH1 3QN (031-556 0689). 7 Fitzwilliam Square, Dublin 2, Ireland (Dublin 761923). 9 Barbados Avenue, New Kingston, Kingston 5, Jamaica, West Indies (926-1659)
Kimathi stret P-B 43013, Nairobi, Kenya (338406).

Among firms and individuals in practice as actuaries are:

T.G.ARTHUR & CO

17 Highfield Road, Edgbaston, Birmingham B15 3DU
Telephone: 021-454 6398

Partners T.G.Arthur, R.J.A.Unwin, D.G.Hargrave

Employees 5

Number of Pension Fund Clients 70 (approx)

Services Offered Include Financial analysis, cost and funding recommendations, strategic planning, portfolio investment, pension fund trusteeship, communication and pension scheme planning

Other Office Rooms 144/145 Temple Chambers, Temple Avenue, London EC4Y ODT (01-353 2476)

NEIL HAYTER,FIA

40 Central Way, Oxted, Surrey RH8 0LZ
Telephone: 988-5066

Services Offered A wide range of employee benefit consultancy services, though capacity for new work in this field is now limited; valuations of interests in will trusts and settlements

A. ROBERTS, MA, MBA, FIA

3 Bengarth Road, Southport, Merseyside PR9 7HB
Telephone: 0704 24224

Services Offered to Pension Funds Independent professional advice on all aspects of actuarial and consultancy work for all types of pension funds

C. D. SHARP, FIA, FPMI

Knapp House, Gillingham, Dorset SP8 4NQ
Telephone: 07476 2426

R. J. SHRUBB & CO

Royal Oak House, Prince Street, Bristol BS1 4QH
Telephone: 0272-213348

R. J. SHRUBB & CO *Continued*

Partner R.J.Shrubb BSc(Econ), FIA, APMI
Other Pension Fund Expert R.M.Curtis, BSc, FIA
Employees 5
Number of Pension Fund Clients 100
Type of Work Undertaken All types of actuarial work

SHUCKSMITH & CO
Roquebrune, 139 Blackborough Road, Reigate, Surrey RH2 7DA
Telephone: 64008

Principal T.S.Shucksmith, MA,FIA, Barrister-at-law
Services Offered to Pension Funds All aspects of insured and self-administered pension schemes

N.S.SLOAM
69 Erskine Hill, London NW11 6EY
Telephone: 01-455 5569

L.W.G.TUTT, MSC, FFA, FIS, FPMI
21 Sandilands, Croydon, Surrey CR0 5DF
Telephone: 01-654 2995

PENSION FUNDS AND THEIR ADVISERS 1981

TO PURCHASE EXTRA COPIES PRICE £21.00
(plus £1.50 postage and packing)

WRITE OR PHONE
A.P. FINANCIAL REGISTERS LTD
9 COURTLEIGH GARDENS
LONDON NW11 9JX
Telephone: 01-458 1607

ALSO AVAILABLE FROM ALL MAJOR BOOKSHOPS

Pension Fund Consultants

The following section covers those firms and companies offering a range of general pension consultancy services rather than the specific services, such as investment advice, offered by firms and companies in other sections of this book. It should, however, be noted that most firms of actuaries also act as Pension Fund Consultants and that several of the larger firms listed in this section employ actuaries.

This list includes the names of all the full members of the Society of Pension Consultants as well as certain other firms.

THE SOCIETY OF PENSION CONSULTANTS

Ludgate House, Ludgate Circus, London EC4A 2AB
Telephone: 01-353 1688/9

President D.C.Bandey, FPMI

Chairman Sir Donald Sargent, KBE, CB, FPMI

Honorary Treasurer G.Cave, FPMI

Secretary J.Mortimer

ADMINISTRATION, INDUSTRIAL & MANAGEMENT SERVICES LTD.

Mayfield, St.Leonards, Tring, Herts.
Telephone: 024020-203

Managing Director L.P.Cleminson,MA,FCA,FPMI

AEGIS INSURANCE SERVICES (LIFE & PENSIONS) LTD.

Aegis House, Castle Hill, Maidenhead, Berks SL6 4JL
Telephone: 0628-23484

Directors W.A.Warbey,ACII,ACIS,APMI, Mrs.M.R.A.Ellis,ACII

Other Pension Fund Experts M.R.Nathan, G.Naldrett

Total Employees 7 - Employee Benefits Division only

Number of Pension Fund Clients 60

Services Offered to Pension Funds Fully servicing broker offering a wide range of services

Other Offices London, Sheffield, Bristol, Edinburgh, Yeovil, Belfast

Associated Companies Aegis Insurance Services Limited; Aegis Insurance Services (Scotland) Limited; F.P.Clarke Limited; Aegis Insurance Services (Northern Ireland) Limited,

ALEXANDER & ALEXANDER INC.

Aldwych House, Aldwych, London WC2B 4HH
Telephone: 01-831 6516

J. C. ARMSTRONG & CO LTD.

10-12 Pilgrim Street,
Newcastle-upon-Tyne NE1 6QB
Telephone: 0632 611741

Director J.E.Clarke

ASSURANCE & COMMERCIAL SERVICES

12b West Street, Congleton, Cheshire CW12 1JR
Telephone: 02602-71226

Director R.C.Davey

BAIN DAWES & PARTNERS LTD

Bain Dawes House, 15 Minories,
London EC3N 1NJ
Telephone: 01-481 3232

Directors involved with Pension Funds G.Cave, FPMI, P.Harvey,APMI, J.L.Humphreys,APMI, D.J.Hughes,FPMI,

Other Pension Fund Specialists R.T.Adlard,APMI, J.M.Brown,APMI, J.R.Connolly,APMI, G.C.Cowley, R.M.Esden,APMI, D.V.Hatherley, J.W.Longhurst, APMI, J.E.T.Morris,APMI, K.Sowerby,APMI, K.D.Timmins, D.E.Warren,FPMI, Mrs.B.A.Wood, APMI

Actuary I.F.Shepherd,FIA

Total Number of Staff 100 plus

The Complete Pension Service

Throughout the United Kingdom

Bain Dawes and Partners
Limited

London
Bain Dawes House,
15 Minories,
London EC3N 1NJ.
Tel: 01-481 3232
Telex: 8813411

Bristol
Tower House,
Fairfax Street,
Bristol BS1 3BT.
Tel: 0272-293031
Telex: 449135

Leicester
General Buildings,
5 Granville Road,
Leicester LE1 7JD.
Tel: 0533 555253

Nottingham
69 Loughborough Road,
West Bridgford,
Nottingham NG2 7QX.
Tel: 0602 817590

Leeds
P.O. Box 35,
9 South Parade,
Leeds LS1 1JW.
Tel: 0532-443234
Telex: 557503

Edinburgh
80 George Street,
Edinburgh EH2 3BU.
Tel: 031-225 9441
Telex: 727588

Manchester
11 St. James's Square,
Manchester M2 6DN.
Tel: 061-834 2010
Telex: 666964

Plymouth
167 Armada Way, Plymouth,
Devon PL1 1HR.
Tel: 0752 28511
Telex: 45474

Birmingham
Alpha Tower,
Suffolk Street Queensway,
Birmingham B1 1EJ.
Tel: 021-632 4211
Telex: 336118

Haywards Heath
Bain Dawes House,
Harlands Road,
Haywards Heath,
West Sussex RH16 1GA.
Tel: 0444 58133 Telex: 87477

Newcastle-upon-Tyne
St. Nicholas Precinct,
35 Mosley Street,
Newcastle-upon-Tyne NE1 1XP.
Tel: 0632 23056
Telex: 53176

Sheffield
423/427 Glossop Road,
Sheffield S10 2PS.
Tel: 0742-663076

Pension Fund Consultants

BAIN DAWES & PARTNERS LTD Continued

Services Offered to Pension Funds Scheme design, actuarial advice, documentation, member communications, trustee courses and administration systems in addition to general consultancy services

Branch Offices Alpha Tower, Suffolk Street, Queensway, Birmingham B1 1EJ (021-632 4211)
Tower House, Fairfax Street, Bristol BS1 3BT (0272-276453)
80 George Street, Edinburgh EH2 3BU (031-225 9441)
P.O.Box 35, 9 South Parade, Leeds LS1 1JW (0532-443234)
General Buildings, 5 Granville Road, Leicester, LE1 7JD (0533-553253)
11 St. James's Square, Manchester M2 6DN (061-834 2010)
St. Nicholas Precinct, 35 Mosley Street, Newcastle-upon-Tyne, NE1 1XP (0632-23056)
69 Loughborough Road, West Bridgford, Nottingham NG1 5DT
167 Armada Way, Plymouth PL1 1HR (0752-28511)
423-427 Glossop Road, Sheffield S10 2PS (0742-663076)

Parent Company Inchcape Group

G.& J. E. BANKART LTD

Assurance House, Loughborough Road, West Bridgford, Nottingham NG2 7QR
Telephone: 0602 815222

Directors D.T.Weston,ACII,FCIB, D.J.Birch, FCIB, B.G.Dixon,ACII,FCIB, M.T.Weston,ACII,FCIB, J.R.Stewart,APMI, W.D.Robinson

Other Pension Fund Specialists 3

Employees 50

Number of Pension Fund Clients 350

Services Offered to Pension Funds All necessary

JOHN BANNERMAN (LIFE & PENSIONS LTD)

35 Wellington Street, London WC2 7BP
Telephone: 01-836 1023/5

Director J.L.Bannerman

BARCLAYS INSURANCE SERVICES CO LTD.

Churchill House, 33 Dingwall Road, Croydon CR9 2YA
Telephone: 01-686 0422

Superintendent-Pensions S.C.Barker,ACII,APMI

BARTLETT & CO (LIFE & PENSION) LTD

Broadway Hall, Horsforth, Leeds LS18 4RS
Telephone: 0532-585711

Directors A.L.Daffern,FCII,APMI, R.J.Rattray,FCII, D.M.Buckle,FCII

Actuary R.V.Whitefoord, BSc, FIA

Employees 20

Services Offered to Pension Funds Overall pensions consultancy service including self-administered schemes and pensioneer trustee service, investment advice to retiring members of pension schemes

Associated Company Bartlett Kemp Gee & Co Ltd,
20 Copthall Avenue, London EC2R 7JS. Director: L.J.Hollis,ACII

B.B.H. TRUSTEES LTD.

B.B.H. House, 22-26 Station Road, West Wickham, Kent BR4 0PS
Telephone: 01-776 1297

Directors D.L.Berry,ACII,FCIB, D.J.Birch,ACII,FCIB, J.Cutting,ACII,FCIB

Other Pension Fund Experts B.D.Sibthorpe, M.J.Smith

Employees 65

Pension Fund Clients 52

Services Offered to Pension Funds Professional and actuarial advice on insured and self-administered funds. Full administrative service including trusteeship available

Other Offices 62 Queen Anne St., London W1 (01-486 6131)

Associated Company Berry Birch & Hawksford (Insurance Brokers)Ltd.

ALFRED BLACKMORE (LIFE & PENSIONS) LTD

16 Eastcheap, London EC3M 1BQ
Telephone: 01-626 9251

Directors P.J.Dredge, J.W.Fowler, C.M.Scarff

Other Pension Fund Expert Mrs.K.Smith

Employees 3

Pension Fund Clients 50-60

Services Offered to Pension Funds Full advice on scheme design, inauguration, staff meetings etc.

P. & G. BLAND LTD

28 De Montford Street, Leicester LE1 7GQ
Telephone: 0533 546221

Directors P.A.Bland,FCII, G.L.Bland,ACII, R.B.King, FCII, P.K.Clark,ACII, D.I.Ball,FCII

Other Pension Fund Experts D.Ruffett, T.T.Steele, B.W.Bell

Employees 30

Pension Fund Clients 200

Services Offered to Pension Funds Complete pensions advisory, planning and implementation service

Associated Company P. & G. Bland (Wales) Ltd., 8 Park Grove, Cardiff CF1 3BN

BOLTON CORDER LTD.

52/7 Mark Lane, London EC3R 7ST
Telephone: 01-709 0722

Directors Sir Frederic Bolton,MC, K.B.Ohlson,MC, C.M.Dallas,JP, M.J.Sheehan, J.M.Chaumeton, D.J.Horne, A.J.McBain, G.W.Palmer, D.Walker

Other Pension Fund Experts J.C.Easden, D.Sherburn

Total Employees 10 (Employees Benefits Division)

Number of Pension Fund Clients Approx.70

Services Offered to Pension Funds General consultancy

Other Offices Sunderland, Poole, Newcastle-upon-Tyne, St. Albans, Bedford, York, Wakefield,

BOWRING EMPLOYEE BENEFIT SERVICES

A new name for an old outfit

WE OFFER...
an efficient, speedy computerised pensions administration system that copes with all your entrances and exits and produces your membership data on time – smoothly and efficiently, without interminable delays, prevarications and excuses – and with attractive benefit statements as a routine bonus.

WE OPERATE...
an effective system of pension fund investment performance measurement – one that tells you not only exactly how you have performed, avoiding spurious figures and artificial jargon but also how you might have performed if you'd adopted a different course of action.

Naturally we make available the full range of services considered essential to operate effectively in the complex pensions world of the 80's – such as actuarial, benefit design, communications, documentation and international.

Bowring Employee Benefit Services
A division of
Bowring & Layborn
142-152 Long Lane, London SE1 4DE. Tel: 01-623 1811

A Member of The Bowring Group

Pension Fund Consultants

BOLTON CORDER LTD. *Continued*

Malvern, Market Drayton, Hexham, Darlington, South Shields, Plymouth

Associated Companies F.Bolton & Co Ltd (Lloyd's Brokers), F.Bolton International Ltd., F.Bolton Marine Ltd.

C.T.BOWRING & LAYBORN LTD

PO Box 130, 142/152 Long Lane,
London SE1 4DE
Telephone: 01-623 1811

Directors P.C.Price,BA(Hons),FCII,FPMI,(Chief Executive), A.H.Carter,ACII,APMI, R.V.Craig, A.A.Child,FCII,FPMI, L.W.Hughes,FCII, R.C.Callinan,

BEBS (Bowring Employee Benefit Services) Division R.W.Syme,FCII,FPMI,(Managing Director), K.W.Doe,FPMI,(Deputy Managing Director), G.G.Bannerman,MA,FFA,AIA,ACII, D.L.Barrett,AIA, MA,APMI, H.R.Beaven,FPMI, C.McGarrigle,ACII, APMI, M.Owen,APMI

BIFS (Bowring Individual Financial Services) Division A.D.Casswell,ACII,(Managing Director), C.M.Auer,FCII(Deputy Managing Director)
The Directors of BEBS and BIFS are also Directors of the Company

Other Pension Fund Specialists P.Bradley,BSc, P.Gray,ACII, R.Endacott,ACII, Mrs.V.Green,FCII, APMI, J.L.King, Mrs.S.A.Paterson,BA, A.M.Pillans, APMI, P.J.Shore,BSc,FFA, J.B.Swain, I.Hopper,ACII, K.Upfold,ACII, M.T.Perry,FIA,APMI,

Employees 130

Pension Fund Clients BEBS and their Provincial Associates have more than 1,500 corporate pension clients

Services Offered to Pension Funds Consultancy on all principal types of employee benefit provision. Services in the pensions field include actuarial administration, benefit design, communications, documentation, fund performance measurement and international record keeping

Other Branch Offices C.T.Bowring & Layborn Ltd, 5 Hinton Road, Bournemouth BH1 2EE (0202-291888)

The following companies are not direct subsidiaries, branches or regional offices of Bowring & Layborn but sister companies within the Bowring Group and the Marsh & McLennan Companies USA. All these companies report, like C.T.Bowring & Layborn Ltd., to C.T.Bowring (UK) Ltd. and constitute the Bowring pensions network throughout the UK
James M. MacAlaster & Alison Ltd., Pensions Division, The Bowring Building, 151 West George Street, Glasgow G2 2NZ (041-204 2600)
Bowring Martin (Life & Pensions) Ltd., Bedford House, Bedford Street, Belfast BT2 7DX (0232-43681)
Bowring Tyson & Co. Ltd., 291 Sefton House, Exchange Buildings, Liverpool L2 3RP (051-236 9681)
Jowitt & Freeman (Pensions) Ltd., Bowring House, Rooms Lane, Morley, Leeds LS27 9PT (0532-539244)
Bowring Rose (Life & Pensions Brokers) Ltd., Havelock Chambers, Queens Terrace, Southampton SO9 4NS (0703-34333)
C.T.Bowring (Trustees) Ltd., P.O. Box 130, 142-152 Long Lane, London SE1 4DE (01-623 1811)

T.L.Dallas Associates, Forster House, Bradford BD1 4TF (0274-24243)
C.T.Bowring & Hughes Ltd., Life & Pensions Division, Bank House, Cherry Street, Birmingham B2 5HH (021-632 6100)
Bowring Scholfields (Life & Pensions) Ltd., 13 St. Ann Street, Manchester M60 8BA (061-834 2323)
C.T.Bowring (Western) Ltd., York House, Bond Street, Bristol BS99 7AE (0272-423571)
W.Smith & Co. (Insurance Brokers) Ltd., 44 Warwick Road, Carlisle CA1 1EU (0228-34201)
George Ewer Insurance Services Ltd., Scott's Corner, Ipswich Road, Colchester CO4 4HS (0206-73338 and 63528)
Ian Hood Ltd., 5 Tor Hill Road, Torquay, Devon TQ2 5RW (0803-211851)
Bowring Scholfields (Eastern) Ltd., Stephenson House, Brunel Centre, Bletchley, Milton Keynes MK2 2EB (0908-648001)
Preston Powell (Holdings) Ltd., Bulman House, Regent Centre, Gosforth, Newcastle-upon-Tyne NE3 3LG (0632-850141)

BRADSTOCK, BLUNT & BARNEY LTD.

5A Wardrobe Place, London EC4V 5ED
Telephone: 01-236 5233

Directors R.Luff,ACII, R.W.Barney,ACII, D.F.Bradstock, A.J.Butler,FIA, B.F.Howard,ACII, A.F.Phillpotts, G.Smith,BA,FIA

BRENTALL BEARD (LIFE & PENSIONS) LTD

31 St. John's Hill, Shrewsbury, Salop SY1 1JG
Telephone: 0743 52345

Director E.W.Bellinger

GRAHAM BROWN & COMPANY (LIFE & PENSIONS) LTD

Trevone House, Pannells Court, Guildford, Surrey
Telephone: 0483 65651

Director A.J.Adams

NORMAN BUTCHER & JONES (LIFE & PENSION BROKERS) LTD

120-122 Southwark Street, London SE1 0SW
Telephone: 01-928 7654

Directors K.H.H.Jones, M.J.C.Christopherson, C.J.McCombie, B.A.Stewart, C.L.Vander Gracht

Other Pension Fund Specialists P.A.Robinson, S.L.Ballantyne

Number of Pension Fund Clients 67

Services Offered to Pension Funds Pre-retirement counselling, full scheme design and administration. Advice to individual members. Specialised services to medium sized schemes

Other Offices Fountain House, Fenchurch Street, London EC3

Associated Companies Norman Butcher and Jones Group of Lloyds Brokers

BYAS MOSLEY (LIFE & PENSIONS) LTD

Bymos House, 9 Southwark Street,
London SE1 1RZ
Telephone: 01-407 6241

Directors G.H.Fletcher,CBE,FCA,(Chairman), K.C.L.Webb,(Joint Managing), P.O'M.Mears,(Joint Managing), W.Letchford, R.W.Keeble, G.M.Pitcher, D.C.Edgerton, N.K.L.Webb

CUBIE, WOOD & CO. LTD.

Norfolk House, Wellesley Road, Croydon, Surrey, CE9 3EB
Telephone: 01-686 2466

The advice of our actuaries is available to our clients on all aspects of Pension Funds including

- costing of proposed benefits
- regular investigations of solvency
- statutory requirements
- dissolution of funds
- merger of funds

The Cubie, Wood Investment Performance Monitoring Service provides trustees and companies with

- an individual analysis of fund performance
- comparison of performance with an objectively determined Standard Fund
- comparison of performance with over 400 similar funds

Enquiries in the first instance should be addressed to
Nigel S. Ball B.A., FIA, AASA., Managing Director.

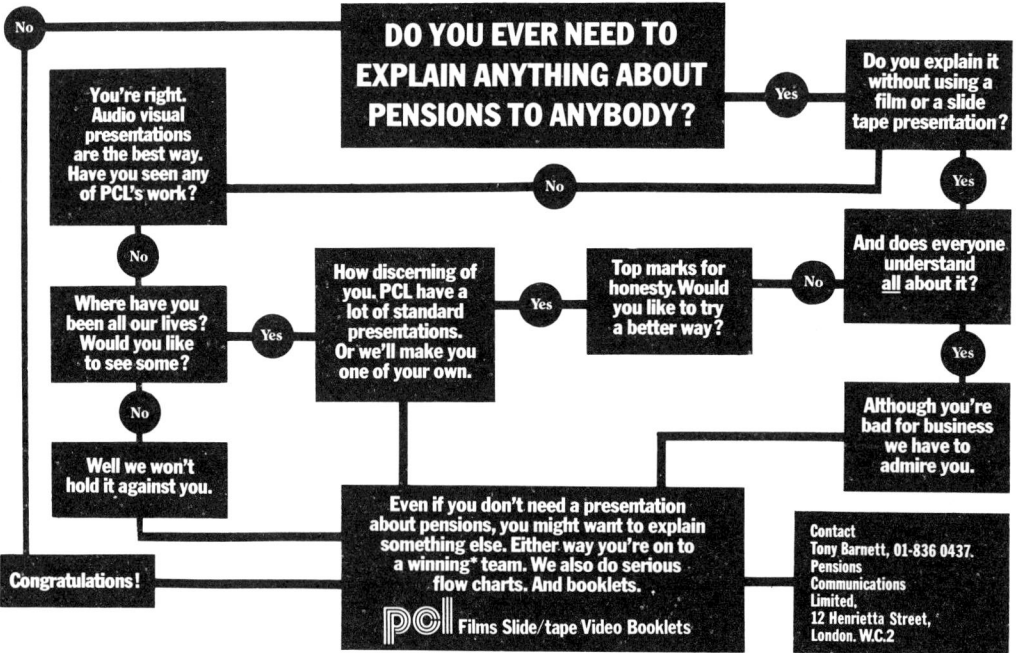

*Two firsts in UK Slide/Strip competition, Gold Camera award in Chicago in 1979 and 1980!

Pension Fund Consultants

CALLUND & COMPANY LTD

15/17 King Street, St. James's,
London SW1Y 6QU
Telephone: 01-839 3316

Directors D.F.Callund,FPMI, T.J.Geoghegan, FIA, ASA, M.Nightingale,ACIS, R.L.Arnold,MSc,FIA

Employees 16

Services Offered to Pension Funds Advice on all aspects of employee benefits with particular emphasis on international considerations

Other Information Consultancy services offered on a world-wide basis. Clients include major multinationals, financial institutions, state-owned industries and Governments, and local national companies abroad. Publishers of 'Employee Benefits in Europe'

HOWARD CHELLINGWORTH LTD

6 Wilford Lane, West Bridgford, Nottingham
Telephone: 0602 868781

Director (Life & Pensions) C.F.Henson,ACII,ACIB

Employees 26

Number of Clients 200 client employers with employees in the range of 1-5000

Services Offered to Pension Funds Design, implementation and administration of all forms of employee benefits schemes, including taxation and financial planning advice to employers and members

Associated Company Bain Dawes & Partners Ltd

CHESHAM HILL LTD

11-12 Pall Mall, London SW1
Telephone: 01-839 1963

Directors S.B.Best-Shaw, R.H.Godfrey-Faussett, M.P.R.Welch

Employees 10

Services Offered to Pension Funds All aspect of pensions

Other Offices 3 Lloyds Avenue, London EC3; St. James's Buildings, Manchester; 3DA; Charlotte House, 17 Charlotte Square, Edinburgh EH2 4DJ; 3 Temple Row West, Birmingham B2 5PA

Other Information Members of the Chesham Group

C.H.W. PENSION CONSULTANTS LTD

Chandler House, 5-7 Marshalsee Road,
London SE1 1EF
Telephone: 01-407 8000

Directors P.J.Jackson,APMI, R.J.Bramble, A.D.Tennant, J.P.R.Love, B.T.Tunnell, J.A.Burrows

Other Pension Fund Experts D.Judson,APMI, E.McGranaghan, K.Johnston, G.Jackson

Total Employees 5

Number of Pension Fund Clients 100 approx

Services Offered to Pension Funds All services

Other Offices Norwich, Dursley (Glos). Masham (N.Yorks)

F.P. CLARKE (INSURANCES) LTD

16 High Street, Yeovil, Somerset
Telephone: 0935-3191

Director R.Johnson

H.CLARKSON (LIFE & PENSIONS CONSULTANTS) LTD.

Clarkson House, Canterbury, Kent CT1 2UT
Telephone: 0227-51717
and Ibex House, Minories, London EC3M 1HJ (01-709 0744)

Directors D.C.Millwater,FPMI, B.M.Waters,FCII, P.L.Moriarty,FPMI, G.T.Read,FCII

Other Pension Fund Experts B.G.Harrison,(Actuary), C.A.R.Agnew, C.Bradshaw, C.M.Cripps, W.de la Hoyde, J.S.Hustwayte, C.B.McLean, T.V.Stanley, R.E.Woodrow

Employees 60 plus (including provincial offices)

Number of Pension Fund Clients Over 700

Services Offered to Pension Funds All aspects of employee benefits

Other Offices Clarkson, Head, Harris Ltd, Scala House, Holloway Circus, Birmingham B1 1EN; Clarkson Tiley & Hargreaves Ltd, Devere House, 62 Vicar Lane, Bradford BD1 5EA; H. Clarkson (Midland) Ltd, Clarkson House, 32 Friargate, Derby, DE1 1BZ; H. Clarkson (Dudley) Ltd, P.O. Box 27, Falcon House, The Minories, Dudley, West Midlands, DY2 8PF; H. Clarkson (Scotland) Ltd, 392 Ferry Road, Edinburgh, EH5 3QG; H. Clarkson (Scotland) Ltd, 7 Albyn Terrace, Aberdeen, AB1 1YP; Clarkson Holt Ltd, 56 Currier Lane, Ashton-under-Lyne, Lancs., OL6 6TB; Clarkson Bardwick & Co Ltd, 29-31 Kingstone Crescent, Portsmouth, Hants PO2 8AF; H. Clarkson Thomas & Co Ltd, 1 Nicholl Street, Swansea, SA1 5QA

Associated Companies Pension Fund Administration & Management Ltd

COCKMAN COPEMAN & PARTNERS LTD

178 Temple Chambers, Temple Avenue,
London EC4Y 0DU
Telephone: 01-353 1976

Director J.F.Briggs,FCA

CUBIE, WOOD & CO LTD

Norfolk House, Wellesley Road, Croydon CR9 3EB
Telephone: 01-686 2466

Directors B.C.Coote,BSc,FIA,FPMI, (Chairman), N.S.Ball,BA,FIA (Managing Director), B.J.Guttmann, FIA, A.A.Jenkinson, MBA,BSc (Econ),FIA, ASA, MBIM

Other Pension Fund Experts 22 actuaries

Total Employees 75

Number of Pension Fund Clients Over 750

Services Offered to Pension Funds The Company provides advice on all aspects of pensions including actuarial advice received from its actuaries. Pensioneer trusteeship

Associated Companies Member of the Hill Samuel Group, Noble Lowndes & Partners

CUTHBERT SERVICE (LIFE & PENSIONS) LTD

19 St. Vincent Place, Glasgow G1 2DG
Telephone: 041-204 1651

Directors N.P.Henley-Price (Managing), Sir Simon Dunning Bt. (Chairman), M.H.Garrett-Cox, J.N.Peyton-Jones and F.H.L.Horner

Employees 3

Number of Pension Fund Clients 29

Take four before retiring.

Our four pension funds have one ingredient in common. A powerful anodyne for concerned pension fund managers. And that is sustained, above-average growth.

Both in the short term and the long term our three sector funds and our managed fund regularly appear in the upper quartiles of comparative performance. Not always in the lead, but usually among the leaders.

There is no secret formula for our success. It is a combination of the skills of our investment team, and some highly developed analytical processes they operate. Systems of analysis tried and proven by a company with over £300 million of pensions investments.

If you would like to see a short presentation on our funds and the systems we adopt to improve investment performance, write to Colin Wilkinson, Agency Manager – Broker Division, Confederation Life, 50 Chancery Lane, London WC2A 1HE. Or telephone on 01-242 7126.

Confederation Life
A mutual company incorporated in Canada in 1871

Pension Fund Consultants

CUTHBERT SERVICE (LIFE & PENSIONS) LTD
Continued

Services Offered to Pension Funds All aspects of employee benefits

A.DALE-COOKE & CO. LTD.
Albert Buildings, 49 Queen Victoria Street, London EC4N 4SA
Telephone: 01-236 5177/8

Directors A.Dale-Cooke,APMI, M.R.Dale-Cook

T.L.DALLAS ASSOCIATES
Forster House, Bradford, West Yorkshire BD1 4TF
Telephone: 0274-24243

Associates I.M.Dallas,DFC,FCIB, W.N.Shaw,FCIB, APMI, C.M.Dallas,MA,ACII, E.N.Chary, M.Holmes, APMI, A.S.Wicks

Other Pension Fund Experts Miss M.Holmes,APMI, L.G.Lamb,ACII

Services Offered to Pension Funds Mostly insured schemes, Also permanent disablement, and hospital expenses consultants

Associated Companies Bowring Employee Benefit Services, Members of the Bowring Group

DEWEY WARREN (INSURANCE SERVICES) LTD.
Ruxley Towers, Claygate, Esher,Surrey KT10 0TR
Telephone: (78-65411)

Directors N.P.Burman, G.F.K.Morgan, P.K.Wigram

Other Pension Fund Expert M.Moffatt

Employees 40

Services Offered to Pension Funds All aspects of pensions consultancy

Other Offices 10 St. Mary-at-Hill, London EC3 8EE

J.N.DOBBIN (PENSION CONSULTANTS) LTD
18 York Road, Maidenhead, Berks SL6 1SG
Telephone: 0628 33131

Directors J.N.Dobbin,MC, G.R.Fisher, D.J.Dobbin, FCII, J.L.Child,APMI, R.Bernie

Employees 35

Number of Pension Fund Clients Over 200

Associated Companies J.N.Dobbin (Personal Financial Planning) Ltd

E.B.CONSULTANTS LTD
Rawplug House, 147 London Road, Kingston-upon-Thames, Surrey KT2 6NG
Telephone: 01-549 8011

Directors J.S.Wait,FPMI, R.J.Side,FPMI, P.B.Eastwood,FIA,FPMI, A.E.Lewis,ACII

Other Pension Fund Expert H.W.McLellan,FIA,FPMI

Employees 10

Services Offered to Pension Funds Actuarial advice and valuations; administration advice and complete facility, communications programmes; pensioner trustee and normal trustee service; benefit structure design

Associated Company E.B.C. Trustee Ltd.

E.B.S. (MANAGEMENT) LTD. (EMPLOYEE BENEFIT SERVICES)
38 Finsbury Square, London EC2A 1PX
Telephone: 01-588 1932

Directors Dryden Gilling-Smith,MA,FCII, Geoffrey Gilling-Smith

Actuary Richard Walker,MA,FIA

EDIS & CO
Bradford House, St. Stephen's Avenue, Bristol BS1 1YL
Telephone: 0272-22351

Partners K.J.Edis,APMI, P.Burfitt,ACIS

Specialist Services Offered to Pension Funds Consulting pensions managers giving advice on all matters relating to pension scheme management and administration,SFO and OPB approvals and pensioneer trustee services

ROBIN ELLISON (PENSION CONSULTANTS) LTD
13 Imperial Towers, Netherall Gardens, London NW3 5RT
Telephone: 01-435 9194
and at 31 Princess Street, Manchester M2 4EW
Tel: 061-236 9178

Director R. Ellison

ESTRIDGE AND ROPNER LIFE AND PENSIONS SERVICES LTD
Boundary House, 7/17 Jewry Street, London EC3N 2HP
Telephone: 01-488 4533

Directors Include C.R.I. Estridge, MA,FPMI, J.V. Powell, A. Hill

Employees 15

Pension Fund Clients 100 plus

Services Offered to Pension Funds Full range of services for private and insured funds

Other Offices Manchester and Newbury

Associated Company Henry Cooke, Estridge (Pensions) Ltd

FEDERATED PENSION SCHEMES
Rosehill, Park Road, Banstead, Surrey SM7 3BX
Telephone: Burgh H.57272

General Manager & Secretary G.W.Darroch

Deputy General Manager A.H.Wilcok, APMI

Total Employees 37

Number of Pension Fund Clients 422

Services Offered to Pension Funds Trusteeship and administration of pension funds for clients in the fields of health, social services and education, including charities. Advice on design of schemes and procedures for commencement. Approved Pensioneer Trustee for small self-administered schemes.

FENCHURCH LIFE AND PENSIONS CONSULTANTS LTD
136 Minories, London EC3N 1QN
Telephone: 01-505 3333

Directors D.H.Taylor (Managing), F.W.Bowden,FIA, FPMI, P.Kirby,ACII,FPMI, A.W.Kellerd,ACII, P.C.Thompson,APMI

Pension Fund Consultants

FENCHURCH LIFE AND PENSIONS CONSULTANTS LTD
Continued

Employees 45

Services Offered to Pension Funds Consultancy, actuarial and administration services

Other Offices Bristol, Hull, Leeds, Leicester, Manchester

Associated Company Fenchurch Trustees Ltd (The companies are members of the Guinness Peat Group)

A.R.O.FOSTER LTD

1 Redcotts Lane, Wimborne, Dorset BH21 1LW
Telephone: 0202 886165

Director A.R.Foster

FRIAR GATE INSURANCE SERVICES LTD.

100 Friar Gate, Derby DE1 1FH
Telephone: 0332-367021

Director E.J.Buque

NORMAN FRIZZELL LIFE & PENSIONS LTD.

Frizzell House, 14/22 Elder Street, London E1 6DF
Telephone: 01-247 6595

Directors A.J.Horton,ACII, FPMI,(Managing), E.K.Constable, R.B.A.James,ACII, W.D.T.Scott,ACII, APMI, M.W.Watt

Other Pension Fund Experts 6

Employees 50

Number of Pension Fund Clients About 200

Services Offered to Pension Funds Benefit design for insured, managed and self administered funds. Communication. Union negotiations. Documentation. Actuarial and administration services. Aspects of taxation. General Employee benefit consultation.

Other Offices Bath, Bournemouth, Birmingham, Glasgow, Leeds, Manchester

Parent Company The Frizzell Group Ltd.

Other Information Lloyd's Insurance Brokers

FURNESS-HOULDER (LIFE & PENSIONS) LTD

52 Victoria Road, Ruislip, Middlesex
Telephone: 71-37141

Directors R.Seymour,ACII,FCIB, P.A.Tobias,MA, ACIB,ACII, N.A.Danvers, C.V.Moore, G.F.Tong,ACII, G.J.Handley

Pension Fund Clients Several

Services Offered to Pension Funds Actuarial, benefit design, communications, scheme administration, individual financial planning, documentation

Other Offices 39 Pilgrim Street, Newcastle-upon-Tyne, NE1 6PX (0632-537749); 99 Bradford Road, Pudsey LS28 6AP (0532-579851); Cranham House, High Street, Amblecote, Stourbridge, DY8 4BZ (03843-2100)

GARDNER WATTS LTD

36 Regent Street, Cambridge CB2 1DB
Telephone: 0223-69545

Managing Director P.D.Watts
Pensions Manager W.J.Hose

GARRATT, SON & FLOWERDEW LTD.

7 Winckley Square, Preston, Lancashire PR1 3JD
Telephone: 0772 51841

Director J.T.Garratt

Other Pension Fund Expert G.W.Horrex,ACII

Services Offered to Pension Funds Full range for insured funds, non-actuarial services for self administered funds

Other Offices London and Blackpool

ANTONY GIBBS PENSION SERVICES LTD

Standard House, Bonhill Street, London EC2A 4RZ
Telephone: 01-588 4111

Directors G.Puttergill (Managing), S.Glanfield, R. Haines, C.Mearns, R.Winch, D.Wright, S.Wright

Employees 58

Number of Pension Fund Clients 400

Services Offered to Pension Funds Scheme design, documentation and revenue approval, actuarial, computerised administration, computerised investment performance analysis, trusteeship

Other Offices Manchester, Edinburgh

GILROY, BROOME & SCRINI LTD.

Orleans House, Edmund Street, Liverpool L3 9NG
Telephone: 051-227 5551

Directors K.A.Broome,ACIS,APMI, R.A.Gilroy,ACII, A.Woolfall,ACII

Other Pension Fund Expert J.A.Hughes

GISSING SELLON BRESLIN & CO LTD

Albert Buildings, 49 Queen Victoria Street, London EC4N 4SA
Telephone: 01-248 0071

Director C.D.Scott

GLANVILL ENTHOVEN (LIFE, PENSIONS & MORTGAGES) LTD

144 Leadenhall Street, London EC3P 3BJ
Telephone: 01-283 4622

Directors C.M.L.Paine,FPMI,(Managing), D.M.Hunt

Other Pension Fund Experts N.J.Otty,APMI, P.C.Lunt, APMI, J.Hazzard, T.Krishna

Services Offered to Pension Funds Scheme design, investment advice, costings, installation, documentation (including explanatory literature), revenue negotiation, insurance fund valuations and all employee benefits

Other Offices Glanvill Enthoven (Coventry) Ltd, Park House, Station Square, Coventry, Warwickshire (0203 28466). Glanvill Enthoven (Croydon) Ltd, Grosvenor House, 125 High Street, Croydon CR9 1AL (01-686 4981). Glanvill Enthoven (Midlands) Life & Pensions Brokers Ltd, Bristol & West House, 2 St. Phillips Place, Birmingham B3 2OG (021-236 9091). Glanvill Enthoven (Northern) Ltd, Boulton House, 17-21 Chorlton Street, Manchester M1 3NY (061-236 8192). Also Bradford, Newcastle, Edinburgh, Southampton, East Anglia, Gloucester and Glasgow

Pension Fund Consultants

PHILIP GLENNON ASSOCIATES (PENSION SCHEME PLANNING) LTD
Bank Chambers, 4 Fir Road, Bramhall Green, Stockport, Cheshire
Telephone: 061-440 9819

Director P.M.Glennon

GODWINS LTD
Fleet House, Victoria Road, Farnborough, Hants GU14 7NS
Telephone: 0252 44484

Directors R.N.Singer (Chairman), D.J.D.McLeish (Managing), J.Crawshay-Williams, J.H.Devine, J.S.Elliot, T.F.M.Mitchell, J.A.Porter, D.N.B.Richards, V.J.Simone, C.F.Williams, P.S.Wilson

Employees 300

Services Offered to Pension Funds Actuarial, benefit design, communications, individual financial planning, international compensation, scheme administration, retirement counselling, investment monitoring and insurance analysis, documentation, corporate trustees

Other Offices Godwins (Central) Ltd, Godwins (Central Services) Ltd, Godwins (Overseas) Ltd, Fleet House, Victoria Road, Farnborough, Hants GU14 7NS (0252 44484); Godwins (South West) Ltd, Leslie & Godwin House, Hampton Street, Plymouth PL4 8EN (0752 262411); Town Quay Chambers, Arwenack Street, Falmouth TR11 2FZ (0326 313504); 14 Lessingham Avenue, Wyke Regis, Weymouth (03057 71812); Corporation House, King's Terrace, Southsea, Hants PO5 3AR (0705 25448); Godwins (Midlands & West) Ltd, Alpha Tower, Suffolk Street, Queensway, Birmingham B1 1TS (021-643 8671); 37/39 Corn Street, Bristol BS1 1HT (0272-294001/2); 94-96 Friar Lane, Nottingham NG1 6EB (0602-49866); 166-167 St.Helen's Road, Swansea SA1 5LA Godwins (North) Ltd., 226 West George Street, Glasgow G2 2PH (041-204 1071); Blackfriars House, Parsonage, Manchester M3 2JA (061-831 7971); 10 Golden Square, Aberdeen (0224-24274); 103-105 Station Parade, Harrogate, N.Yorks. HG1 1HD (0423-55281)

Ultimate Holding Company Frank B. Hall & Co Inc

GORRILL, MAULE-OATWAY & CO LTD
60 Wilbury Road, Hove, Sussex BN3 3PA
Telephone: 0273 779341/2

Director E.C.Gorrill

GOUDIE PENSION CONSULTANTS
Brent House, Friern Park, North Finchley, London N12 9BP
Telephone: 01-446 2144

Pension Fund Experts B.J.Hollingsworth,ACII, H.J.Hollingsworth,FCIB

Services Offered to Pension Funds General advisory services on employee benefits. Specialise in pension arrangements/schemes for small/medium size companies and arrangements for executives and directors

Associated Companies H.J.Hollingsworth & Co Ltd; H. Goudie (Insurance) Ltd

GRIFFITHS & ARMOUR
101 Derby House, Exchange Flags, Liverpool L2 3QJ
Telephone: 051-236 5656

Partners K.E.O.Griffiths,ACII, B.O.H.Griffiths,TD,MA, ACII, R.M.H.Griffiths,MA,FCII, D.G.Pownall,ACII, G.A.Kilgour,FCII

Pensions Manager F.Griffiths,ACII,APMI

Services Offered to Pension Funds Advice on pension for home and overseas directors and staff and on pension opportunities for partners

Other Offices 23 College Hill, London EC4R 2TP (01-248 3412)

Associated Company Griffiths & Armour (Trustees) Ltd

DAVID HAGUE CONSULTANTS
147 Fleet Street, London EC4A 2BU
Telephone: 01-583 0202

Directors D.K.Hague, J.A.Tudhope

FRANK B. HALL CONSULTING CO.
Creechurch House, 37-45 Creechurch Lane, London EC3A 5DJ
Telephone: 01-283 6235

Director D.M.Grimsell,FPMI

Other Pension Fund Experts 3

Total Employees 6 in U.K., 300 in U.S.A.

Number of Pension Fund Clients 100

Services Offered to Pension Funds General and international (including consultancy, administration and trusteeship)

Other Offices Throughout the USA and in major territories elsewhere in the world

Associated Companies Godwins Ltd

PETER HARDY (LIFE & PENSIONS CONSULTANTS) LTD.
12 High Street, Stevenage, Herts.
Telephone: 0438-4135

Director P.H.Stallard,ACII,FCIB

Other Pension Fund Expert R.A.Maunder

Employees 4

Pension Fund Clients 80-100

Services Offered to Pension Funds Full range of services for employees/director benefit schemes

Other Offices 3 Aysgarth Road, Redbourne, St. Albans, Herts.

HAREWOOD RIDGEWAY PROFESSIONAL SERVICES LTD
7 Melville Crescent, Edinburgh
Telephone: 031-225 2041

Directors P.J.Froggatt,BSc,FIA,ASA,FPMI, D.J.Townley,FFA, J.A.Wild,APMI

Number of Pension Fund Clients 100

Services Offered to Pension Funds Actuarial, trustee (including pensioneer trustee) legal investment, accounting and reporting

Other Offices 61 Preston New Road, Blackburn, Lancs; Grapes House, 79 High Street, Esher, Surrey

Associated Companies PM & M Life & Pensions Services Ltd, Lonburn Heritable Ltd, Braithwaite Wild & Associates Ltd, Townley-Wild Associates Ltd.

HARRAP BROTHERS

Crescent House, Regent Road, Leicester LE1 6YJ
Telephone: 0533-555500

Partners J.A.Harrap, H.G.Lawson

Associate Partners J.J.Harrap, C.H.Lawson

Associated Company Harrap Flint Ltd., Crescent House, 40 Regent Road, Leicester LE1 6YJ

HARRIS, MARRIAN & CO LTD

Ulster Bank House, Shaftesbury Square, Belfast BT2 7BY
Telephone: 0232 42131

Directors P.M.Thomas, J.A.Greenfield, J.W.S.Bailey, V.C.Haslett, J.McGarry, A.D.Rose

Other Pension Fund Specialist Harry Wakelin,APMI

Employees 120 (10 of whom deal with Employee Benefits)

Associated Companies Part of the Willis Faber Ltd Group

R.K.HARRISON (LIFE & PENSIONS) LTD

32 Bromham Road, Bedford MK40 2QD
Telephone: 0234-45353

Director M.S.Dowding

Subsidiary R.K.Harrison (Jersey) Ltd, 18 Hill Street, St. Helier, Channel Isles (22471)

HARTLEY COOPER LIFE & PENSIONS BROKERS LTD

Cliffords Inn, Fetter Lane, London EC4A 1BU
Telephone: 01-405 5881

Directors P.A.de Pinna (Chairman), M.J.Hunt (Managing Director) J.M.Niblett, J.H.Miller

Employees 15

Services Offered to Pension Funds Full administration, benefit design executive benefits, international benefits

Parent Company Hartley Cooper Holdings Ltd

Associated Company Hartley Cooper Trustees Ltd

Other Offices Enfield, Colchester, Ayr, Aberdeen and Associates in Germany and Holland

DOUGLAS HAYDEN & CO LTD

Granville House, 132 Sloane Street, London SW1X 9BE
Telephone: 01-730 0168

Directors D.W.Hayden, J.Gower, E.M.Hayden, G.H.Martin

Life & Pensions Manager J.F.Rayner

HAYMAN JACKSON INSURANCE BROKERS LTD.

24 High Street, Petersfield, Hants GU32 3AD
Telephone: 0730-5351/535

Directors G.J.Hayman, FCII,FFIB, P.J.Hayman

Employees 7

Other Offices Welland House, 16-18 High Street, Haslemere, Surrey (51345/6)

Other Information Emphasis on the small to medium-sized company

C.E.HEATH, URQUHART (LIFE AND PENSIONS) LTD

177 King's Road, Reading, Berkshire RG1 4EY
Telephone: 0734 585036

Registered Office Cuthbert Heath House, 151-154 Minories, London EC3N 1NR (01-488 2488)

Directors D.N.Newton,FCII (Chairman & Managing) K.L.Boyce,FCII, S.C.J.Loades, D.W.Nichols,FCII, APMI, R.L.Walker,APMI

Employees 50

Number of Pension Fund Clients 650

Services Offered Full range of advice including benefits structure, communications, documentation and investment advice and compensation planning

Parent Company C.E.Heath & Co Ltd

Associated Companies C.E.Heath Loades & Co Ltd, 177 King's Road, Reading RG1 4EY (0734 585036) Managing Director D.W.Nichols; C.E.Heath & Co (East Anglia) Ltd, Norwich, Managing Director M.J.Harrison,; C.E.Heath & Co (Home) Ltd, Southend, Managing Director J.A.Dawson; C.E.Heath & Co (Lancashire) Ltd, Bolton & Manchester, Managing Director F.J.Morris; C.E.Heath & Co (London) Ltd, London, Managing Director B.A.Bateson: C.E.Heath & Co (Midlands) Ltd, Birmingham, Managing Director J.A.Dawson; C.E.Heath & Co (Scotland) Ltd, Aberdeen and Dundee, Managing Director W.M.McDonald; C.E.Heath & Co (Southern) Ltd London, Managing Directors R.M.Harrison, B.M.Routledge; C.E.Heath & Co (Teeside) Ltd, Middlesborough, Managing Director F.J.Morris

WALTER HERRIOT (LIFE & PENSIONS) LTD

Herriot House, 9 The Street, Ashtead, Surrey KT21 2AD
Telephone: 76441

Director H.G.Hunt

Services Offered to Pension Funds Full Broker's service

Other Offices Walter Herriot & Co., 1759 London Road, Leigh-on-Sea, Essex SS9 2SW

Associated Company Cheltenham Insurance Brokers Ltd., Herriot House, North Place, Cheltenham, Glos GL50 4DS

HOGG ROBINSON (BENEFIT CONSULTANTS) LTD

Lloyds Chambers, 9-13 Crutched Friars, London EC3N 2JS
Telephone: 01-709 0575

Directors K.G.Weir,FFA,FPMI (Managing Director), C.S.Stewart,FPMI (Assistant Managing Director), D.G.Jay,APMI, R.M.Westwood,MA,FFA,APMI, G.Marshall,APMI, G.A.Pearson,APMI, K.S.Robertson, FPMI

Employees 160

Number of Pension Fund Clients Pension Pooled Funds - 750-850

Services Offered to Pension Funds Pension consultancy, actuarial services, pension administration, investment performance analysis, international benefits, individual financial planning

Other Offices Commercial Union House, Martineau Square, Birmingham B2 4US (021-236 8686); Netherton House, 23-29 Marsh Street, Bristol BS1 4BW (0272-28991); 11 Windsor Place, Cardiff,

Pension Fund Consultants

HOGG ROBINSON (BENEFIT CONSULTANTS) LTD
Continued

CF1 3BY (0222-374616); McIver House, 51 Cadogan Street, Glasgow G2 7HE (041-204 1261); Phoenix House, 16 New Walk, Leicester LE1 6TZ (0533-50131); Scottish Life House,Bridge Street, Manchester M3 3BZ (061-832 9502); 1 Collingwood House, Street, Newcastle upon Tyne, NE1 1JW (0632-242871); Wessex House, 25-31 London Street, Reading Berks RG1 4PJ (0734-595111); Beethoven House, Leopold Street, Sheffield S1 2GZ (0742-77858); 31 St. John's Hill, Shrewsbury, SY1 1JG (0743-53955)

Associated Companies Hogg Robinson (Pensions Management) Ltd., Hogg Robinson (Financial Planning) Ltd.

HOLMWOODS & CRAWFURD (LIFE & PENSION BROKERS) LTD.
52/56 Minories, London EC3N 1AQ
Telephone: 01-488 1450

Directors R.N.Amos, A.G.Robson, M.T.Cornwell, APMI,(Managing), A.C.D.Inglby-Mackenzie

Other Pension Fund Experts D.J.Higgins,APMI, K.E.D.Titchmarsh, J.Wilkinson

Employees 14

Services Offered to Pension Funds Planning, installation and administration of pension and other employee benefit schemes, personal pensions, life assurance, mortgages, school fees

Other Office Harlands House, Haywards Heath, West Sussex RH16 1IA (04444-58144)

Associated Companies A member of the Brown Shipley Group

HOUSLEY HEATH & CO. (LIFE & PENSIONS) LTD.
PO Box 19, Bartholomew Court, Waltham Cross, Hertfordshire
Telephone: 97-31961

Director H.A.French

GRAHAM HOW (LIFE & PENSIONS) BROKERS
Windsor House, The Green, Esher, Surrey KT10 9SA
Telephone: 0372-62061

A Division of Graham How & Co (Insurance Brokers) Ltd.

Directors R.G.How, S.V.How, R.H.Burrage,ACCA, ACII, D.A.R.May,ACII, B.P.Martin, D.A.Kitchin, Lord Wall, P.A.Howell-Jones

Other Pension Fund Expert J.P.Lawson

Employees 26

Number of Pension Fund Clients 20

Services Offered to Pension Funds Scheme design, documentation, OPB and IR negotiations, actuarial (via Clay & Partners), administration, investment selection, comparison and monitoring, communications, insurance

Associated Companies Ritchie Baird & Partners Ltd., Glasgow; O'Brien Associates Ltd., Dublin

ALEXANDER HOWDEN INSURANCE BROKERS LTD, LIFE & PENSIONS DIVISION
Export House, Cawsey Way, Woking, Surrey GU21 1YU
Telephone: 04862-5081

Directors J.D.Walkden,FPMI (Managing), J.B.Hills, ACII,APMI,(Deputy Managing), A.Brown,FPMI, J.D.Clarke,APMI, N.K.Ward,APMI, D.Fairhurst,ACII, APMI

Other Pension Fund Experts R.M.Benjamin,BA,FIA, P.Hunter,ACII,APMI, G.E.Presley,APMI, W.J.Vaughan,ACII, APMI, Miss E.A.Law,APMI, I.J.Walker,BSc,APMI

Total Employees 60

Services Offered to Pension Funds Full pension consultancy and administration, actuarial services, international benefits

Other Offices Birmingham, Liverpool, Manchester, Glasgow, Cardiff, Chelmsford, Southampton

Parent Company Alexander Howden Group Ltd., 22 Billiter Street, London EC3M 2SA (01-488 0808)

HOWSON DEVITT (LIFE & PENSIONS BROKERS) LTD
Saracens Head House, 92 Fenchurch Street, London EC3M 4EA
Telephone: 01-488 3191

Pensions Manager N.J.Wills

HURST & MARSH LTD
121 Cannon Street, London EC4N 5BD
Telephone: 01-283 0141

Director B.P.Marsh

HUTCHISON & CRAFT LTD
6 Rose Street, Glasgow G3 6RA
Telephone: 041-332-9898

Directors C.M.Watson,ACII,FCIB,(Managing), D.L.Wood,JP,FCII,ACIS,ACIB

Employees 60

Number of Pension Fund Clients 20

Services Offered to Pension Funds Benefit design, documentation, revenue approval, administration, advice to members and trustees

679

HUTCHISON & CRAFT LTD Continued

Other Offices Aberdeen and Coatbridge

Associated Company Hutchison & Craft (London) Ltd.

IRISH PENSION TRUST LTD
Hill Samuel House, Adelaide Road, Dublin 2
Telephone: 762345

Director P.Brew

DAVID JAMESON (I.P.S.) LTD. INVESTMENT AND PENSION SERVICES
106 High Street, Epping, Essex CM16 4AF
Telephone: 78-77711

Directors D.R.Jameson, R.D.Jameson, T.J.Green, R.J.Shrubb

Employees 12

Number of Pension Fund Clients 40

Services Offered to Pension Funds Complete specialist service for self-administered funds

Associated Companies David Jameson & Co (Life & Pensions), David Jameson (Insurance Brokers) Ltd

JEWELL, PEARCE, DAVY & CO LTD
1155 London Road, Leigh-on-Sea, Essex
Telephone: 0702 79397

Director D.W.Davy

JOWITT & FREEMAN (PENSIONS) LTD
Minerva House, East Parade, Leeds LS1 5PT
Telephone: 0532-36053

Director K.Hill

Associated Companies Members of the Bowring Group

C.R.KING & PARTNERS LTD
316-318 Wellingborough Road,
Northampton NN1 4EP
Telephone: 0604-20151

Director K.R.Smith

F.S.LAMB & CO LTD
49 Queen Victoria Street, London EC4 4SA
Telephone: 01-248 5261

Directors F.S.Lamb, A.S.Lane, C.W.Swan, G.C.McLeish, C.J.Lamb

R.D.LANCASTER & ASSOCIATES LTD
243 Caledonian Road, London N1
Telephone: 01-278 4882

Executive Chairman R.D.Lancaster,AIA,APMI

Employees 3

Number of Pension Fund Clients 15

Services Offered to Pension Fund Clients Pension consultancy, actuarial services, trusteeship, administration etc.

Other Information Company advises on other forms of employee benefits

MICHAEL LEWIS ASSOCIATES LTD
3 Castle Street, Cardiff CF1 2BS
Telephone: 0222 396512

Directors M.G.Lewis,MA(Oxon), CA (Ontario),APMI, R.W.Harris,ACII,FCIS,APMI, D.E.Lewis

Other Pension Fund Specialist G.S.Joinson,ACII, APMI

Employees 8

Number of Pension Fund Clients 125

Services Offered to Pension Funds Full pension fund consultancy for companies and individuals

EDWARD LUMLEY (LIFE & PENSIONS) LTD
Lumley House, 43-51 St Mary Axe,
London EC3A 8AL
Telephone: 01-283 5266

Director R.G.Whitford

LYLE, GIBSON & CO LTD
12 Princes Square, Glasgow G1 3JU
Telephone: 041-204 2161

Directors H.A.Walkinshaw,OBE,VRD (Chairman), R.M.Gibson,VRD,MA,FCIB (Managing), T.S.Shearer, FCIS, C.L.Kennedy,FCII,ACIB, P.A.Usher,FCII,ACIB, APMI

MACALASTER & ALISON LTD
The Bowring Building, 151 West George Street, Glasgow G2 2NZ
Telephone: 041-204 2600

Directors A.G.O.Walker (Chairman), A.W.Murray (Dep. Chairman), B.A.Groom (Managing-Pension Division), M.A.Adam, A.W.Laird, D.C.Martin, J.L.Paul

Employees 120

Number of Pension Fund Clients 125

Services Offered to Pension Funds Complete range of pension consultancy services is available

Other Office Aberdeen

Associated Companies All companies of the Bowring Group, including, in Scotland, Bowring Robertson Mitchell and Bowring, Smith & Raphael

Parent Company Bowring Group

MATHEWS, SMITH (FINANCIAL CONSULTANTS) LTD.
24 Week Street, Maidstone, Kent
Telephone: 0622-52182

Director D.Mathews

IAN MCCALL EMPLOYEE BENEFITS LTD
16-17 Devonshire Square, London EC2M 4SN
Telephone: 01-377 8585

Directors F.J.Richardson,FCII,FCIB,APMI, A.J.Sales

Other Pension Fund Experts 2

Employees 54

Number of Pension Fund Clients 40

Associated Company Ian McCall International Ltd.

WILLIAM M.MERCER BENEFITS LTD.
4 Southampton Place, London WC1A 2DA
Telephone: 01-405 4343

Pension Fund Consultants

WILLIAM M.MERCER BENEFITS LTD. Continued

Principal Consultants in London D.E.Boden, MAAA (Managing Director for Europe), T.A.Rowley,FIA, ASA,FPMI (UK Manager), G.Clare,FPMI,ACII, E.M.Smyth,BSc,FIA,ASA, D.R.Barford,BSc,ARCS,FIA, M.Post,FIA,FPMI,ASA, D.C.Evans,PhD,FIA, C.Beaumont,BSc

Employees 2,400 worldwide, 55 in London

Services Offered to Pension Funds Primarily for international companies and include all aspects of design, communication, financing and the management of all forms of employee benefit-both in the United Kingdom and throughout the world

Other Offices European offices in Belgium, France, Netherlands, Germany, Spain, Switzerland. Offices throughout Far East and Australasia. Offices in all major cities of United States and Canada, with further facilities in South America

Parent Company Marsh & McLennan Companies Inc.

Other Information Mercer is the world's largest employee benefit consultancy with offices in over 20 countries with associated offices (normally wholly or partly owned by parent company) in another 50 countries

METROPOLITAN PENSIONS ASSOCIATION (HOLDINGS) LTD
Burwood House, 16 Caxton Street,
London SW1H 0QU
Telephone: 01-222-9121

Directors F.Grant (Chairman), P.Coster (Managing), D.C.Bandey, C.E.Dixon,FCA, A.R.Escolme,FIA, R.A.Leach, R.V.Pratt, J.C.Sampson, R.Simmons,LLB, R.Shepherd,FIA, H.A.Stevenson

Other Pension Fund Experts Numerous

Employees 350

Services Offered to Pension Funds Full range of services (except pensioneer trusteeship)

Parent Company Mercury Securities Ltd

Other U.K. Offices Administration Centre, Metropolitan House, Northgate, Chichester PO19 1BE, Sussex (0243 785151); Edgbaston House, 3 Duchess Place, Birmingham B16 8HH (021-454 5866); 43 Melville Street, Edinburgh EH3 /JF (031-225 4012); Wellington House, 126 Wellington Street, Glasgow G2 2XQ (041-332 8621); Permanent House, The Headrow, Leeds LS1 8DS (0532 36671); Permanent House, Horsefair Street, Leicester LE1 5BP (0533 25431); Barlow House, Minshull Street, Manchester M1 3DZ (061-236 7288)

International Offices Brussels, Dublin, Frankfurt, Hong Kong, Johannesburg, Melbourne and Sydney

Associated Companies Grant Simmons Ltd. - Executive Compensation Consulting; Metropolitan Computer Services Ltd. - Computerised Administration Consultancy

MIDLAND BANK INSURANCE SERVICES LTD
Suffolk House, 5 Laurence Pountney Hill,
London EC4R 0EU
Telephone: 01-606 9911

Directors Include R.Mainwaring, R.Low

MINET CONSULTANCY SERVICES LTD
Minet House, 100 Leman Street, London E1 8HG
Telephone: 01-481 0707

Directors N.McGregor-Wood,MA,Barrister,FPMI, P.R.Wilson,FPMI, R.L.Robertson,FPMI, D.McCulloch, APMI, C.T.Fagan, R.S.Reid

Other Pension Fund Specialists T.G.Arthur,FIA (Consultant Actuary), M.J.Clarke (Service Director), R.Jones, G.Jenkala, M.Winch, K.Thomas

Total Number of Staff 34

Services Offered to Pension Funds Consultancy, investment, communications, administration, legal/ tax, trusteeship, financial planning, personal taxation, actuarial, documentation, retirement counselling, international benefits schemes

Other Offices 41 in UK and overseas

Associated Companies Minet Holdings Ltd, Minet Ransome Bentley Ltd, Geoffrey Morley & Partners Ltd, Minet Trustees Ltd

CHRISTIAN MORGAN PENSION CONSULTANTS LTD
26-28 Great Portland Street, London W1N 5AD
Telephone: 01-631 1787

Directors K.A.Morgan,ACII,FCIB,(Chairman), D.W.Thomas,FIA,(Managing), P.G.Fiddimore,ACII, APMI,MBIM, A.Christian,ACII,FCIB,MBIM, D.J.Green,FLIA, R.A.Conway,FCCA

Subsidiary Company Christian Morgan Trustees Ltd.

R.W.MOUNTJOY
20 Irwins Drive, Horsham, West Sussex RH12 1NH
Telephone: 0403 3037

Services Offered to Pension Funds An independent service covering administration, booklets, documentation, trusteeship, audio-visual presentations

M P W (TRUSTEES) LTD
New Dominion House, Henley-on-Thames RG9 2EG
Telephone: 04912-78234

Directors B.H.Lee,(Chairman), A.G.Nicholson, (Managing Director)

Services Offered to Pension Funds Scheme design (documentation - trust deed and rules, employee announcements, revenue and OPB approval), Actuarial valuations, Trusteeship - pensioneer trustee service investment advice, aid in selecting investment manager, performance analysis

Other Offices Trafalgar House, Waterloo Place, London SW1Y 4AU

Associated Companies MPW Life & Pensions Consultants Ltd.; MPW (General Insurance Brokers) Ltd.

NOBLE LOWNDES & PARTNERS LTD
PO Box 144, Norfolk House, Wellesley Road, Croydon CR9 3EB
Telephone: 01-686 2466

Directors B.C.Coote,ARCS,BSc,FIA,MBIM,FPMI, K.Daniels,ACII,FPMI, S.C.Gee,FCII,FPMI, J.S.Irvine, MBIM,FPMI, I.McIntyre,AIB,FPMI, J.L.McKirdy, M.Pilch,BA,FCII,FPMI, R.Shenton FInstM

Other Pension Fund Experts B.J.Carroll,FCII,FPMI, P.H.Cooke,FPMI, A.R.Duff,FCII,FPMI, A.A.Jenkinson,

Pension Fund Consultants

NOBLE LOWNDES & PARTNERS LTD Continued

MBA,BSc(Econ),FIA,ASA,FPMI,MBIM, D.R.Jones, FPMI, M.A.Kirk,ACII,FPMI, A.G.McHoul,ACII,FPMI, J.C.Malpass,BA,ACII,FPMI, G.B.FPMI, N.Watts,FPMI

Employees 747

Number of Pension Fund Clients Over 2,000

Services Offered Actuarial services, trusteeship, documentation, administration, investment advice, employee communications and advice, international benefit planning

Parent Company Hill Samuel Group

Associated Companies Include Hill Samuel Investment Management Ltd, Hill Samuel & Co Ltd. (Banking), Lowndes Lambert Group Ltd (Insurance Broking), Hill Samuel Life Assurance Ltd (Insurance)

Subsidiaries Include English Pension Trustees Ltd, Lowndes Associated Pensions Ltd, Scottish Pension Trustees Ltd, Ulster Pension Trustees Ltd, Noble Lowndes Personal Financial Services Ltd, Noble Lowndes Pensions Ltd, Lowndes Management Incentives Ltd, Noble Lowndes International Ltd & Cubie Wood & Co Ltd

Overseas Subsidiaries Include Noble Lowndes Australia Ltd (Sydney, Melbourne), Andre de Larrard, Noble Lowndes et Cie (Paris), Noble Lowndes Deutschland GmbH (Frankfurt), Lowndes Lambert Consulting Services GmbH (Frankfurt), Irish Pension Trust Ltd (Dublin, Cork), Noble Lowndes International (Hong Kong, Kuala Lumpur, Singapore), Noble Lowndes (N.Z.) Ltd (Auckland, Wellington); Noble Lowndes Inc. (New York)

Other Offices Claremont House, North Claremont Street, Glasgow G3 7LG (041-332 6582), Tower House, Merrion Way, Leeds LS2 8PA (0532-457401); Colmore Centre, 115 Colmore Row, Birmingham B3 3AW (021-233 2371), Regent House, 27a Regent Street, Clifton, Bristol BS8 4HF (0272 32271), St. Martins House, 31-35 Clarendon Road, Watford WDl 1JA (92-48911), Warwickgate House, Warwick Road, Old Trafford, Manchester M16 0QQ (061-872 4661), Norfolk House, Wellesley Road, Croydon CR9 3EB (01-686 2466)

NORFOLK & SUFFOLK INSURANCE SERVICES LIMITED

117 London Road North, Lowestoft, Suffolk NR32 1LZ
Telephone: 0502-63165

Directors P.J.Hardiman, D.I.Needham

Other Pension Fund Expert P.Sherington

Employees 5

Number of Pension Fund Clients 21

Services Offered to Pension Funds Insured funds only

Associated Companies Norfolk & Suffolk Finance Ltd, Norfolk & Suffolk Credit Ltd, Norfolk & Suffolk Securities Ltd.; Norfolk & Suffolk Insurance Services Ltd.

NOTCUTT LIFE & PENSIONS LTD.

Mackenzie House, 221 Beckenham Road, Beckenham, Kent BR2 4UB
Telephone: 01-778 7878

Directors I.L.Mackeson-Sandbach, P.A.C.Edwardes, N.R.O'Keefe, M.C.F.Sears

Other Pension Fund Experts 3

Employees 11

Number of Pension Fund Clients 60

Services Offered to Pension Funds Scheme design, administration, trusteeship, documentation, membership records, payment of pensions

Associated Company Walker Frampton (Life & Pensions Consultants) Ltd.

PARKDALE PENSIONS MANAGEMENT

32 Park Square, Leeds LS1 2PF
Telephone: 0532-449251

Director N.J.Bailey

MARTIN PATERSON ASSOCIATES LTD

10 Buckingham Place, London SW1E 6HT
Telephone: 01-828 7243

Directors M.Paterson,MA,FPMI, T.H.Beech,MA,FIA, FPMI, B.R.Moir,ACII,FPMI, R.K.Sloan,FFA,FPMI, R.W.A.Fowler,FIA, R.P.Delany,FIA,FPMI, D.L.Woodward,FIA, R.B.Colbran,FIA,FPMI

Number of Pension Fund Clients About 175 all on a fee basis

Services Offered to Pension Funds Independent advice on the design, financing and management of pension and benefit plans in UK and overseas

Other Offices 9 Albyn Place, Edinburgh EH2 4NG (031-225 3324), 50 Northumberland Road, Dublin 4 (682988)

Associated Companies Copeman Paterson Ltd (Management Consultants)

P M & M LIFE & PENSIONS SERVICES LTD.

61 Preston New Road, Blackburn, Lancashire
Telephone: 0254-662811

Managing Director J.A.Wild,APMI

POINTON YORK (PENSIONS & EMPLOYEE BENEFITS) LTD

The Crescent, King Street, Leicester LE1 6RX
Telephone: 0533-547545

Directors G.N.Pointon, W.W.Huggins, S.R.Hornbuckle, D.A.Godfrey, G.G.Marr, B.W.Lee

Other Pension Fund Specialist N.W.L.Sclater

Employees 45

Number of Pension Fund Clients Over 400

Services Offered to Pension Funds Pensioneer trustees, investment management, self administration management, inland revenue approval, documentation and design. Actuarial services, licensed dealers in securities, licensed deposit taking institution

Other Offices 19 Walker Street, Edinburgh EH3 7HX; 59 Bounds Green Road, Wood Green, London N22 4HB; 25 Bedford Row, London WC1

Associated Companies Pointon York Sclater Ltd., Pointon York Hopkin Ltd., P.A. Trustees Ltd., P.A. Trustees (Scotland) Ltd.

Other Information Licensed dealers in securities

Pension Fund Consultants

PRESTON POWELL (HOLDINGS) LTD
Bulman House, Regent Centre, Gosforth, Newcastle-upon-Tyne
Telephone: 0632-850141

Director W.D.Stewart

PROFESSIONAL ASSURANCE SERVICES LTD
5 College Street, Nottingham NG1 5AQ
Telephone: 0602-48686

Directors D.W.Allwright,ACII,APMI, G.Selby,ACII, APMI

Pensions Manager K.J.Douglass, BA, APMI

Employees 9

Number of Pension Fund Clients 120

RAMSAY INSURANCE CONSULTANTS LTD
94 Mount Pleasant, Tunbridge Wells, Kent
Telephone: 0892 34255

Directors J.W.Walder,ACII,APMI, R.Ramsey,MA, APMI

Employees 10

Number of Pension Fund Clients Over 30

REA BROTHERS (LIFE LOANS & PENSIONS) LTD
Trade Indemnity House,
12-34 Great Eastern Street, London EC2A 3AX
Telephone: 01-729 2525

Director B.A.Jones

REED STENHOUSE BENEFIT CONSULTANTS LTD.
P.O. Box 214, Two South Place, London EC2P 2DX
Telephone: 01-628 6011

Directors B.J.Willats,ACII,FPMI,(Managing), W.T.Green,LL.B.,ACIS,FCII,ATII,FPMI, T.N.Allen, FPMI,MInstM, B.R.Gibson,ACII, J.W.Gilchrist,CA, C.B.C.Hill,ACII,FPMI, R.A.Durward,ACII,FPMI

Other Pension Fund Experts S.B.Aird,BSc,FSA,AIA, J.F.Baird,FPMI, J.Bannon,FIA, E.P.Ferebee,ACII, APMI, T.F.Gilmore,FFA,APMI, G.A.Hunt,APMI, T.J.Hunt,ACII,APMI, A.Jackson,BSc,FIA, A.A.Johnstone,APMI, J.Schreiber,AB,FSA

Employees 190

Number of Pension Fund Clients 1,750 (approx)

Services Offered to Pension Funds Design of employee benefit schemes, benefits consultancy, documentation full computerised administration, communication with members, actuarial services, trusteeship, retirement and executive counselling

Other Offices Davis House,69-77 High Street, Croydon CR9 2XD (01-686 7421); Rawdon House, Green Lane, Yeadon, Leeds LS19 7EA (0532 506116); Argyll House, Marketgait, Dundee DD1 1QT (0382-24692); 78-80 George Street, Edinburgh EH2 3P0 (031-226 2515); 145 St. Vincent Street, Glasgow G2 5NX (041-248 5070); Brazennose House, Brazennose Street, Manchester M60 8AU (061-832 4312); Midland House, 132 Hagley Road, Edgbaston, Birmingham B16 9PE (021-455 7181);230 High Street, Potters Bar, Herts. EN6 5BU (0707 51222); Norman Insurance House, King's Road, Reading RG1 4LW (0734 61100) 6011)

Associated Companies Reed Stenhouse Investment Services, Reed Stenhouse Pension Services, Reed Stenhouse Trustee Services

R.G.REIS PENSION FUND TRUSTEES LTD.
10 Jesus Lane, Cambridge CB5 8BA
Telephone: 0223-311471

Directors R.W.Westgate,ACII, A.J.Roe, D.G.Gibbs, ACII, P.G.Neighbour,ACMB

Pensions Manager P.R.W.Garside

Employees 40

Services Offered to Pension Funds Pensioneer trustee, corporate trustee, investment management, self-administration management, inland revenue approval, documentation and design

Other Offices 15 Angel Hill, Bury St. Edmunds, Suffolk IP33 1XG (0284-68568/9)

Associated Company Westgate Investments, 73 Cheapside, London EC2V 6ES - Westgate Investments are licensed dealers in securities

JOHN REYNOLDS & COMPANY (LIFE & PENSIONS) LTD
Byrom House, 21 Quay Street, Manchester M3 3JA
Telephone: 061-832 9022

Directors M.G.Shaw,FCIB, J.Neil Shaw,FCIB, N.Ross,APMI

Employees 6

Associated Companies John Reynolds & Company (Insurance) Ltd, John Reynolds & Company (Credit Insurance) Ltd

RICHARDS, LONGSTAFF LTD.
Dominion House, 37-45 Tooley Street, London SE1 2QF
Telephone: 01-407 4466

Group Pensions Director P.J.Lonsdale,BSc,APMI

Employees 60

Number of Clients Approx.200 are administered with annual investment income of £8 million

Services Offered to Pension Funds Computerised administration, trusteeship and plan design, communications, employee benefits, personal financial planning, total compensation, self administered fund management

Other Offices 6 King Street, Bristol BS1 4EQ, 24 George Street, Glasgow G2 1EV

Associated Companies Laing & Cruickshank Financial Services Ltd., Richards, Longstaff (Pension & Trustee) Ltd., Simdo-Kyle Financial Services Ltd.

CHRISTOPHER J. ROWLANDSON LIFE & PENSIONS
The Stones, Jack's Lane, Torquay
Telephone: 0803 38529

Principal Christopher J.Rowlandson,FLIA

Other Pension Fund Experts 4 Associates, including an independent consulting actuary and a pensioneer trustee

Employees 4

683

Pension Fund Consultants

CHRISTOPHER J. ROWLANDSON LIFE & PENSIONS
Continued

Services Offered to Pension Funds Scheme design, revenue approval, pensioneer trustee, fund trusteeship, fund administration, presentation services, specimen documents, investment performance analysis, help for scheme members, actuarial valuations

Other Offices Sutton, Plymouth, Teignmouth

HENRY RUSSELL (LIFE & PENSIONS) LTD
Wellington House, Wellington Circus, Nottingham NG1 5AL
Telephone: 0602 55024-8

Director B.Tomlinson

SEDGWICK EMPLOYEE BENEFITS CONSULTANTS LTD.
52 Leadenhall Street, London EC3A 2AL
Telephone: 01-377 3456

Directors S.W.Britton,APMI (Deputy Chairman), C.R.Labrow,APMI, G.Lipschitz,FFA,AIA,APMI, C.W.F.Low,FFA,AIA,FPMI, D.S.Macbeth,APMI, B.E.Mitchell,MA,FPMI,ACII, D.G.Squires,ACII,APMI, R.C.Steven,TD (Chairman), J.R.Tapscott, M.R.Tong, BSc,FIA,APMI, R.Walker,FCII,APMI

Assistant Directors W.B.Barden, P.F.Bull,APMI, D.L.Chambers,APMI,ACII, D.J.Griswood,APMI, C.R.Lakie,APMI,ACII, J.L.Russell, R.P.Springford, T.M.D.Williams,APMI

Employees 130

Other Offices Tricorn House, 51-53 Hagley Road, Edgbaston, Birmingham B16 8TP; Crusader House, St. Stephen Street, Bristol BS1 1EL; St. Andrew House, 141 West Nile Street, Glasgow G1 2RS; 158 Market Square, Aberdeen AB1 2PP; 32/34 St Andrew Square, Edinburgh EH2 2QR; West Riding House, 67 Albion Street, Leeds LS1 5AA,; Lowgate House, Lowgate, Hull HU1 1EL; 3 Collingwood Street, Newcastle-upon-Tyne NE1 1LX; 2 Deans Court, Crown Square, Manchester M3 3JJ; 49 Friar Street, Reading RG1 1BP

Services Offered to Pension Funds Associated companies throughout the world, benefit design, financing of pension schemes and investment decisions, pensions administration and secretarial services, communications, retirement benefit service, making available actuarial advice

W.J.SHORE (PENSIONS MANAGEMENT) LTD
Bush House, Prince Street, Bristol BS1 4HU
Telephone: 0272 290061

Directors W.J.Shore (Chairman), J.W.Humphries (Sec), R.J.Gibbons,APMI (Managing), F.A.A. James

Other Pension Fund Experts Mrs. S.J.L.Neville (Pensions Manager), H.J.Phillips (Fund Manager), R.J.Shrubb (Actuary)

Employees 5

Number of Pension Fund Clients 35

Services Offered to Pension Funds Complete fund service

Parent Company W.J.Shore & Co. Ltd.

Associated Companies Yeovil Ins. Brokers Ltd; Roberts, Morris Bray (Insurance Brokers) Ltd.

SMALLWOOD, WALLIS & CO LTD
135a New Street, Birmingham B2 4QJ
Telephone: 021-643 1658

Director C.W.E.Astill

SMITHSON MASON & CO
Yorkshire Insurance Buildings, 4 South Parade, Leeds LS1 5RG
Telephone: 0532 450756

Partners R.E.Mason, H.C.Mason, D.C.Mason, J.M.Mason

SPECIFIC CONSULTANCY RESOURCES LTD
142 Vauxhall Street, London SE11
Telephone: 01-735 1234

Directors L.P.Cleminson,MA,FCA,FPMI, (Chairman), J.C.B.Deverell,FCIS (Managing), C.M.Oxley

Other Pension Fund Experts Actuary and Legal Associates

Employees 4

Number of Pension Fund Clients 25

Services Offered to Pension Funds Advisory, trusteeship, investment advice, setting up schemes, SFO and OPB dealings. personal financial advice to members of schemes and self employed

Associated Companies Cleminson Pension Trustees Ltd

PETER E. SPENCER & PARTNERS(PENSIONS) LTD
30 Bell Street, Romsey, Hampshire SO5 8GW
Telephone: 0794 515745

Directors Peter E.Spencer,APMI, Ian M.Taylor,ACII, Sally Spencer

Other Pension Fund Expert P.I.Mulle, FCII, ACIS, APMI

Employees 15

Number of Pension Fund Clients 200

Services Offered to Pension Funds Complete pension consultancy service

Associated Companies Peter E. Spencer & Partners Ltd., Peter E. Spencer Trustees Ltd.

STEWART STEVENSON & CO
124 St Vincent Street, Glasgow G2 5ET
Telephone: 041-221 0019

STEWART WRIGHTSON ASSURANCE CONSULTANTS LTD
Kingston Bridge House, Church Grove, Kingston-upon-Thames, Surrey KT1 4AG
Telephone: 01-977 8888

Directors D.T.Hall,ACII,FPMI,(Managing), J.C.King, FCII,FPMI, G.J.Gilbert,ACII,FPMI, C.R.Berry,FCII, APMI, R.H.Griffiths,FPMI, W.L.Reed,FCII, G.E.N.Tinley,MBIM,APMI, S.C.Dunford,FPMI

Other Pension Fund Experts 27 (24 other staff involved in pension matters at above address)

Employees 110

Number of Pension Fund Clients 405

Services Offered to Pension Funds Comprehensive consultancy including actuarial, documentation, investment and trusteeship facilities using

Pension Fund Consultants

STEWART WRIGHTSON ASSURANCE CONSULTANTS LTD *Continued*

computer based systems when appropriate which also generates benefits statements

Other Offices 46 Queen's Road, Aberdeen AB1 6YE (0224-321115); Calthorpe House, Hagley Road, Five Ways, Edgbaston, Birmingham B16 8QE (021-252 4431); Howard House, Queens Avenue, Bristol BS8 1SD (0272 22091); Northfield Road, Netherton, Dudley, Worcs. DY2 9JB (0384-52631); 285 Queen Street, Broughty Ferry, Dundee DD5 2ND (0382-730211); 31 Drumsheugh Gardens, Edinburgh EH3 7RN (031-225 5333); 48 St. Vincent Street, Glasgow G2 5TP (041-221 9655); 16 Blenheim Terrace, Woodhouse Lane, Leeds LS2 9HW (0532-448266) (Director M.E.Ingle); 60 Charles Street, Leicester LE1 1FB (0533-29881) (Director M.B.Skyrme), Richmond House, 1 Rumford Place, Chapel Street, Liverpool L3 9QN (051-236 4762), Medway House, London Road, Maidstone, Kent ME16 0ED (0622-55601); Barlow House, 4 Minshull Street, Manchester M1 3DJ (061-228 6220); Westlegate House, Westlegate, Norwich NR1 3LP (0603-29666); NEM House, Bridlesmith Gate, Nottingham NG1 2GQ (0602-50736); Royal Thames House, Portsmouth Road, Thames Ditton, Surrey KT7 0YF (01-398 4131)

Associated Companies Part of the Stewart Wrightson Group of Companies within the Matthews Wrightson Holdings Group of Companies

Other Information In addition to acting as consultant for various major British and International Companies, the Company acts as Manager to a number of Pension Funds and, in particular, is appointed to manage trust funds set up under the auspices of the Brewers' Society, the Army, the Royal Navy etc. The Company also provides trustee services through its subsidiary Stewart Wrightson Trustees Ltd. and personal financial planning services

SUMNER & MCMILLEN (LIFE & PENSIONS) LTD

29 College Gardens, Belfast BT9 9BT
Telephone: 0232 661931

Directors R.Kerr,FCII,APMI, W.H.E.Robinson, E.T.McMillan,FCII

Actuary J.G.Tinsley,FIA

SUPERANNUATION ADVISORY SERVICES LTD

22-26 St. George's Court, New Oxford Street, London WC1A 1EN
Telephone: 01-405 3400

Director H.Mendoza,ACII

TENNANT, BUDD LIFE & PENSIONS BROKERS (SOUTHERN) LTD

Tennant House, 43 High Street, Fareham, Hampshire PO16 7BX
Telephone: 0329-288621

Directors T.A.Robinson,ACII, A.H.Davies,ABIBA, (Managing), L.W.F.Davis,ABIBA, B.K.Walker,ACII, ABIBA, C.D.Le Voi,FCII,ABIBA

Employees 30

Services Offered to Pension Funds Advice and administration for corporate and private clients

Other Offices Saracen's Head House, 92 Fenchurch Street, London EC3M 4EE; Hildenbrook House, The Slade, Tonbridge, Kent TN9 1HY

TILLINGHAST, NELSON & WARREN LTD.

48 Red Lion Street, London WC1R 4PF
Telephone: 01-405 7994

Directors J.C.H.Anderson,BA,ASA,MAAA, R.P.Burrows,BSc,FIA, W.A.Ferguson,B.Comm,FSA, MAAA, J.Goford,MA,FIA,MAAA, R.A.C.Lawrey,MA, FIA, W.J.MacGinnitie,FCAS,FSA,MAAA, J.P.Ryan, MA,FIA,ASIA,ACAS,MAAA, I.C.Smart,BA,FIA,MAAA

Employees 13

Services Offered to Pension Funds Advice of a predominantly actuarial nature, including all aspects of consultancy, administration and communications for employee benefit plans

Other Offices Boston, Columbus, Dallas, Denver, Fort Worth, Hartford, Jacksonville, Kansas City, Los Angeles, New Orleans, New York, St. Louis, San Antonio, Toronto, Bermuda

Associated Company Tillinghast, Nelson & Warren Inc. (Actuaries/Consultants), Atlanta

TOWERS, PERRIN, FORSTER & CROSBY, INC

110 Jermyn Street, London SW1Y 6HB
Telephone: 01-839 5666

Actuaries P.G.Grant,FSA,AIA, A.C.Dawrant,FIA, D.F.Spargo,FIA, M.P.Clarke,FIA, H.Turrall-Clarke,FIA, I.B.Walker,FFA,AIA S.R.Baker,FIA

Other Pension Fund Experts R.V.Bevan, J.S.Carney, J.Carrick,AIA, D.R.Lincoln, P.Massey, A.C.Miller, L.N.Moss,AIA, A.J.Reese,AIA, V. van Dijk, R.Walkling,AIA

Employees Worldwide 1,300, UK 60

Number of Pension Fund Clients Worldwide 2,000, UK 300

Services Offered to Pension Funds Actuarial services; plan design, funding and implementation: international employee benefit policy and cost controls; communications including audio-visual material, booklets, employee statements and funding reports; documentation and filing with government bodies; taxation and social security; computerised and non-computerised administrative systems; advice on administration

Other Offices USA: Atlanta, Boston, Chicago, Cleveland, Dallas, Los Angeles, Minneapolis, New York, Philadelphia, Pittsburgh, San Francisco, Seattle, St Louis, Tampa, Washington DC; Canada: Calgary Toronto, Montreal, Vancouver; South America: Caracas, Sao Paulo; Europe: Brussels, Frankfurt, Paris

TOWNLEY WILD ASSOCIATES LTD.

Century House, St. Peters Square, Manchester
Telephone: 061-236 2257

and at 61 Preston New Road, Blackburn, Lancs BB2 6BL (0254-662811)

Directors T.E.Caro,FCA, J.A.Wild,APMI, D.J.Townley,FFA

Other Pension Fund Expert A.Hodgkiss

Employees 6

Services Offered to Pension Funds Actuarial, documentation, trustee, pensioneer trustee, scheme design

685

Pension Fund Consultants

TOWNLEY WILD ASSOCIATES LTD. *Continued*

Associated Companies P.M.&M. Life & Pensions Services Ltd., Harewood Ridgeway Professional Services Ltd.

TOWRY LAW (PENSION SERVICES)LTD

Towry Law House, 57 High Street, Windsor, Berks SL4 1LX
Telephone: 07535 68244

Directors Hon C.T.H.Law, K. Paget Brown, Lord Ellenborough, C.E.Scott-Hopkins, R.R.Cockroft, C.P.Kerr-Moller, T.Goodfellow, S.J.Jackson, (Managing), P.P.Rylatt, B.F.Macken

Other Pension Fund Experts Mrs.K.Kadri, M.K.H.Palmer, A.Y.Anaafi, R.B.Palmer, G.R.Ashley, C.J.McCaffery, M.C.Ainscough, C.W.Mullins, A.M.Jenkins

Employees 27

Number of Pension Fund Clients 1,025

Services Offered to Pension Funds Reports on benefits design and investment management, incorporating the necessary actuarial aspects, communication to employees by staff meetings and design, printing and issue of explanatory booklets, full corporate trusteeship services and full administration service, monitoring investment performance and broking group death in service benefits, full services for small self-administered pension schemes including pensioneer trusteeship

Other Offices Leeds, Edinburgh, London

Associated Companies Towry Law (Pension Consultants) Ltd.; Towry Law Trustee Co. Ltd.

Other Information Member of the Towry Law Group of Companies which employs over 200 people

G.P.TURNER (LIFE & PENSIONS BROKERS) LTD

30-34 New Bridge Street, London EC4V 6BJ
Telephone: 01-236 4451

Director C.S.Kay

ULSTER PENSION TRUSTEES

33-37 Wellington Place, Belfast BT1 6GD, Northern Ireland
Telephone: 0232 27891

Director A.Baird

VAIRON (INSURANCE BROKERS) LTD

18 City Road, London EC1Y 2AY
Telephone: 01-638 9331

Directors B.J.N.Vaizey, A De Lord, D.T.Abraham, APMI, I.C.Cleverley

Other Pension Fund Expert B.E.Critchell,ACII

Employees 10

Number of Pension Fund Clients 45

Services Offered to Pension Funds Pension consultancy, administration and individual financial planning

Associated Companies A member of the Vairon Group of companies

WADMANS INSURANCE LTD.

132 Lewisham Way, New Cross, London SE14 6PE
Telephone: 01-692 3864

Directors C.C.Wadman,FCIB,FAIB, W.E.Wadman, FCIB,APMI,FAIB, G.H.Rose,AAIB, G.W.J.Wadman, AAIB, L.J.Goman,FAIB,APMI, T.W.Keen,FCA

Employees 25-30

Number of Pension Fund Clients 100-200

Services Offered to Pension Funds Negotiating, arranging and servicing pension funds

Other Information Clients are broadly based in manufacturing, distributive and servicing trades

C.D.WAIN (LIFE & PENSIONS) LTD

St Nicholas Chambers, Talbot Lane, Leicester LE1 4LQ
Telephone: 0533 58139

WALKER FRAMPTON LTD

125 Shenley Road, Boreham Wood, Herts WD6 1AG
Telephone: 01-953 2092

Other Offices 19 London Road, Bromley, Kent BR1 1DO (01-460 8581); Vincent House, Grove Lane, Epping, Essex CM16 4LH (78 76121); 14 Commercial Street, Newport, Gwent NPT 1HG (0633 213431)

WALROND, SCARMAN & CO

Crown House, 151 High Street, Loughton, Essex LG0 4L9
Telephone: 01-508 5533

Director L.E.Gill

J.D.WARD AND CO LTD

55 Lincoln's Inn Fields, London W2A 3LX
Telephone: 01-242 2263

Directors J.D.Ward, M.R.Woodward, R.J.Surridge, J.R.Newnham, R.A.Howells, A.P.Wibroe

Employees 14

Number of Pension Fund Clients 200

Services Offered to Pension Funds All except portfolio management and documentation

WEST YORKSHIRE INSURANCE BROKERS LTD.

8 New North Parade, Huddersfield, Yorkshire HD1 5JW
Telephone: 0484 36601

Director D.H.Ball

Other Pension Fund Expert P.Stowe

Employees 20

Number of Pension Fund Clients Many

WHITEHOUSE MOORMAN & PARTNERS LTD

Malvern House, New Road, Solihull, West Midlands B91 3EE
Telephone: 021-704 2531

Directors I.M.Whitehouse,ACII,FCIB, P.G.Moorman, ACII,FCIB, B.J.Lancaster,ACII,FCIB,APMI, E.Hutchings,ACII, L.Hanby,FCA

Other Pension Fund Specialist D.J.Kew

Employees 18

WHITEHOUSE MOORMAN & PARTNERS LTD
Continued

Number of Pension Fund Clients 70

Services Offered to Pension Funds Full actuarial and investment service

WHITLOW COOMBE & CO

46 Birkenhead Road, Hoylake, Wirral, Merseyside L47 3DT
Telephone: 051-632 3371

Director J.Laing

WIGHAM POLAND PENSION CONSULTANTS LTD

Bevington House, 24-26 Minories, London EC3N 1BY
Telephone: 01-481 0505

Directors L.D.Grouse,BSc(Econ),ATII,FPMI, (Chairman & Managing), P.G.Barker, I.R.Eggleden, APMI, S.Johnson,MA,FIA,FPMI, C.Johnstone,ACII, C.D.Sewell

Employees 35

Number of Pension Fund Clients 400

Services Offered A complete consultancy, administration and trustee service including CEBA (computerised employees benefits administration)

Other Office 78 Queen Street, Glasgow (041-248 3382)

Associated Companies Wigham Poland Trustees Ltd,Wigham Poland Assurance Consultants Ltd

Other Information A member of the Wigham Poland Group at Lloyds

WILLIAMS & GLYN'S INSURANCE CONSULTANTS LTD

PO Box 448, 20 Birchin Lane, London EC3P 3DP
Telephone: 01-623 4356

Director J.E.Martin,APMI

WILLIS FABER ADVISORY SERVICES LTD

Ten Trinity Square, London EC3P 3AX
Telephone: 01-481 8111

Directors J.S.Cohen,FPMI,(Managing), S.A.Phillips, FPMI, D.G.Shannon,FPMI, J.H.Rogers,FIA,ASA,FPMI, S.W.Batt, R.F.W.Byles,FIA,ASA,FPMI, B.K.Hanson, APMI, J.C.Harrison, N.W.Loveday, R.M.F Ramsey, FPMI, R.A.Soward,FIA,APMI, B.Young,FPMI

Assistant Director A.K.LeCras, FCII, APMI

Manager (Manchester) J.R.White, APMI

Employees 80

Services Offered to Pension Funds Full range of services for national and international companies including consultancy, actuarial, documentation, administration, communication and investment performance evaluation

Other Offices Friars Street, Ipswich, Suffolk IP1 1TA (0473-217911); Phoenix House, 43-47 Cross Street, Manchester M2 4JF (061-832 7705)

Associated Companies Willis Faber Champness Ltd, 4 Imperial Square, Cheltenham, Glos. GL50 1QB (0242-43331); Willis Faber (Midlands) Ltd, Rutland House, Edmund Street, Birmingham B3 2JJ (021-233 1313); Willis Faber (Northern) Ltd, Pegasus House, 463a Glossop Road, Sheffield S10 2QD (0742-668161); Willis Faber (North East) Ltd, 2 Collingwood Street, Newcastle-upon-Tyne NE1 1JF (0632-611391); Willis Faber (North West) Ltd, 655 Sefton House, Exchange Buildings, Liverpool L2 3SE (051-236 2914); Willis Faber (Scotland) Ltd, 95 Bothwell Street, Glasgow G2 7HP (041-221 4301); Willis Faber (South West) Ltd., Nelson House, Rupert Street, Bristol BS1 2QQ (0272-292876/9); Willis Faber (Wales) Ltd., 29 Newport Road, Cardiff CF2 1TL (0222-20245)

Other information A member company of Employee Benefit Consultants A.G.(Euroben) Zurich with partners in Belgium, France, Germany, Holland, Spain and U.S.A. Other associates and partners in 130 offices throughout the world

HAROLD WILSON CONSULTANTS LTD.

Wilson House, 1 Waverley Street, Nottingham NG7 4HG
Telephone: 0602-782241

Director M.R.Lucas

Employees 6

Number of Pension Fund Clients 450

Services Offered to Pension Funds Administration, actuarial design, membership publicity, pension trusteeship

Other Offices London , Bristol

WOOD & STEVEN LTD.

24 Bennetts Hill, Birmingham B2 5RD
Telephone: 021-643 9531

Life & Pensions Manager K.D.Timmins,ACII

F.E.WRIGHT & CO. (LIFE & PENSIONS) LTD.

Dominion House, Tooley Street, London Bridge, London SE1
Telephone: 01-407 4477

Director L.R.Keeling

WYATT HARRIS GRAHAM LTD.

30-32 Queen Anne's Gate, London SW1H 9AW
Telephone: 01-222 8033

Directors M.D.Evans,FPMI, M.T.Ballisat, FPMI, R.F.A.Boyce, D.J.Bright, FPMI, R.G.A.Craven,APMI, C.N.Hedderwick,FIA, P.J.Hunt, MIPM, M Inst AM, M.C.Lutyens, R.Machin,FIA,FCIA,ASA,FPMI, C.H.Petre, C.R.Simms,FCA(USA), R.A.Sperl,JD(USA), R.White, Barrister H.Wolanski,FIA

Other Pension Fund Experts M.Brandman,AIA, Grad.IMA, J.Brown, C.P.Clegg,AIA, D.Compton, J.G.Haslam,FIA,ASA,FPMI, J.W.Hough,AIA, S.D.Jacobson,AIA, H.Jago, G.P.D.Jones,FIA, N.Mitten, C.B.Ramamurthy, R.C.Ross, T.S.Tinner, FIA, A.F.M.Watson,FFA

Employees 70 approx (U.K. only)

Services Offered to Pension Funds Complete range of employee benefit and compensation consulting services provided for U.K. and multinational companies on an independent and professional basis, all services provided solely on a fee-for-service basis

Other Offices Wyatt Harris Graham is the international consulting division of the Wyatt Company, one of the leading firms of Actuaries and Consultants in North America, with offices in - Europe: London, Manchester, Lucerne, Stockholm; U.S.A.: Boston, Chicago, Cleveland, Dallas, Detroit, Fort Worth, Honolulu, Houston, Los Angeles,

WYATT HARRIS GRAHAM LTD. *Continued*

Memphis, Miami, Minneapolis-St.Paul, New York, Orlando, Philadelphia, Phoenix, San Diego, San Francisco, Stamford, Washington; Canada: Calgary, Halifax, Montreal, Ottawa, Toronto, Vancouver; Far East: Hong Kong, Kuala Lumpur, Manila

Other Information No outside shareholders

WYCHERLEY PENSION SERVICES

Wycherley House, 38 Gully Hill Road,
Church Crookham, Hampshire
Telephone: 02514-6111

Director J.L.Lennon

Employees 6

Services Offered to Pension Funds Full range of services

Other Office Godalming

Associated Company Wycherley Financial Services

HAROLD YATES, BURGESS & CO. (MANCHESTER) LTD.

74 King Street, Manchester M2 7AX
Telephone: 061-834 3517

Insurance Companies

This section lists the major insurance companies who are active in the Pension Business. This is not however a fully comprehensive list since certain other companies offer individual insured pensions policies, mainly for the self-employed. The majority of the companies listed are members of The Life Offices' Association or the Associated Scottish Life Offices. Their addresses are:

The Life Offices' Association, Aldermary House, Queen Street, London EC4N 1TP. Telephone: 01-236 5117.

Associated Scottish Life Offices, 23 St.Andrew Square, Edinburgh EH2 1AQ. Telephone: 031-556 7171.

ABBEY LIFE ASSURANCE COMPANY LTD.

Head Office: Abbey Life House, PO Box 33, 80 Holdenhurst Road, Bournemouth BH8 8AL Telephone: 0902 292373

Registered Office 1-3 St. Paul's Churchyard, London EC4M 8AR. Telephone 01-248 9111

Executive Directors R.F.Richardson,BA,FSA (Managing Director), M.L.Hepher,FIA (Deputy Managing Director), T.J.R.Gordon,BA,FIA, P.D.King, P.W.Dyson

Pension Fund Managers P.W.Dyson,MA (Director, Abbey Life Investment Services), T.J.R.Gordon,BA, FIA,ASA (Director, Abbey Life Investment Division), R.E.Milton,FRICS (Assistant Director, Property Investment), M.McIvor,MA,FIA (Assistant Director, Stock Exchange Investment), T.E.Bowen, P.Challen (Investment Managers)

Chief Actuary N.H.Carpenter,FIA

Employees 1,407

Gross Funds (at 31.12.78) £566.4 million

Premium Income £170 million

Number of Clients Company Pensions, 24,000 schemes (31,000 members)

Other Offices About 65 throughout UK

Other Information Choice of Unit Linked Pension Funds: managed property, equity and security. Investment can also be on a guaranteed basis. Current Plans: Director and Executive retirement plan, personal retirement plan

Independent Valuers Richard Ellis, Cluttons

ALBANY LIFE ASSURANCE COMPANY LTD

Station House, 3 Darkes Lane, Potters Bar, Herts EN6 1AJ
Telephone: 42311

Managing Director R.Sepel,BA,LLB

Finance Director & Actuary M.R.Granville,BSc,FIA, ASA

Director of Administration & Secretary R.H.Wiseman

Pensions Manager A.J.Ford

Employees 200

Total Pensions Staff 7

Gross Long Term Funds (at 31.12.79) £41.4 million

Annual Premium Income £4.2 million

Annual Investment Income £2.2 million

Investment Managers Warburg Investment Management Ltd.

Property Managers Knight Frank & Rutley, Weatherall Green & Smith

Property Valuers Weatherall Green & Smith

Other Offices London Executive Office; 31 Old Burlington Street, London W1X 1LB (01-437 5962) and 20 offices throughout U.K.

AUSTRALIAN MUTUAL PROVIDENT SOCIETY

AMP House, Dingwall Road, Croydon, Surrey CR9 2AP
Telephone: 01-686 5611

Chief Manager (UK) I.F.Stanwell

AUSTRALIAN MUTUAL PROVIDENT SOCIETY
Continued

Manager Administration Division B.A.B.Eagle

Manager Policy Service H.Rich, FIA

Investment Manager A.Scriminger

Head Pension Department A.J.Baldwin, FCII, APMI

Pensions Administration Manager M.J.Carley, FCII

Employees 200 (approx)

Total Pension Staff 10

Gross Long Term Funds £79.6 million

Annual Premium Income £8.2 million

Annual Investment Income £7.9 million

Number of Pension Fund Clients 200 (approx)

Property Advisers McDaniel & Daw

Other Offices 10 offices in UK. Also principal office in Sydney, Australia and offices throughout Australia and New Zealand

BRITANNIC ASSURANCE COMPANY LTD
Moor Green, Moseley, Birmingham B13 8QF
Telephone: 021-449 4444

General Managers J.A.Jefferson, B.H.Shaw, FIA, FCA

Actuary M.A.H.Willett, FIA

Investment Manager F.P.Weavers, FCA

Property Manager J.W.Dalman, FCII

Employees 4,360

Gross Long Term Funds (at 31.12.79) £434.4 million

Premium Income £75 million

Investment Income £48.4 million

Other Offices 270 throughout UK

CANADA LIFE ASSURANCE COMPANY
Canada Life House, High Street, Potters Bar, Herts EN6 5BA.
Telephone: 51122

Vice-President and General Manager F.L.Strevens, FLMI

Assistant General Manager, Chief Underwriter and Chief Medical Officer Dr. M.A.Reynolds, MB

Actuary and Assistant General Manager D.A.Loney, MA, FIA

Assistant General Manager, Secretary V.P.Knowles, FIA

Assistant General Manager, Investments I.C. Gunn, MA

Investment Manager, Securities S.McClean, BA

Investment Manager, Properties D.J.Houghton, FRICS

Agency Manager J.F.Cowan

Manager, Pensions Administration C.S. Bennett

Marketing Manager R.D.Mills, ACII

Assistant Actuary S.C.Tsu, BSc, ARCS, FIA

Employees 630

Pensions Staff 17

Gross Long Term Funds (at 31st December 1979) £1,510 million

Annual Premium Income £207 million

Annual Investment Income £128 million

Pension Fund Clients 602

Other Offices 26

CLERICAL, MEDICAL & GENERAL LIFE ASSURANCE SOCIETY
15 St. James's Square, London SW1Y 4LQ
Telephone: 01-930 5474

General Manager L.G.Hall, FIA

Actuary & Deputy General Manager R.D.Corley, FIA

Secretary & Assistant General Manager A.G.O'Leary, FIA

Assistant General Managers N.Jones, D.Moat, R.P.Walther, FIA

Assistant General Manager (Investments) R.P.Walther, FIA

Senior Investment Manager W.John Bishop, FIA

Property Investment Manager B.High, FRICS, FCII,

Investment Manager P.Wakefield, FCIS, ACII

Pensions Development Manager D.M.Claisse, FPMI

Deputy Secretary P.J. Henson, FPMI

Deputy Actuary E.W.Hodson, FIA

Employees 1,122

Total Pensions Staff 252

Gross Long Term Funds (at 31.12.79) £700 million

Annual Premium Income £105 million

Annual Investment Income £46 million

Number of Pension Fund Clients 624

Other Offices Bristol Head Office and 44 Branch Offices

Pension Fund Management Company

Senior Management P.A. Wakefield, FCIS, ACII (Investment Manager), J.P. Williams, AIA (Fund Manager), P.J.W. Henderson, ACA (Deputy Fund Manager)

Funds Managed 20

Total Assets of Funds Managed £85 million

Annual Premium Income £6 million

Annual Investment Income £6 million

Number of Pension Fund Clients 18

Other Information The Society entered this field in 1974 and has been steadily increasing the number of funds managed.

Each fund has a separate investment portfolio which is managed on an individual basis.

COLONIAL MUTUAL LIFE ASSURANCE SOCIETY LTD
24 Ludgate Hill, London EC4P 4BD
Telephone: 01-248 9861

General Manager & Actuary Richard J.Durden, FIA

Assistant General Managers Alec L.Merrifield, JP (Marketing) Keneth Redfern, MA, FIA (Investments), Robert I.Edmondson, FCII, APMI (Operations)

Chief Sales Manager Charles Towers

Insurance Companies

COLONIAL MUTUAL LIFE ASSURANCE SOCIETY LTD
Continued

Pensions Manager Alan Daunt, BSc, FCII
Investment Managers Andrew B.McCreadie, LLB, A.J.Dye
Specialised Staff Over 100
Employees 1,200
Gross Long Term Funds £249 million
Annual Premium Income £44 million
Annual Investment Income £23 million
Pension Fund Clients 3,500
Services Offered to Pension Funds Full administration
Area Sales Offices 30 administered through 5 regional offices throughout the UK
Associated Companies Colonial Mutual Life (Pension Annuities) Ltd. This Managed Fund subsidiary commenced unit business in 1976 and had assets in October 1980 of £22 million

COMMERCIAL UNION ASSURANCE COMPANY LTD

St. Helen's, 1 Undershaft, London EC3P 3DQ
Telephone: 01-283 7500

Chief General Manager J.F.G.Emms, FIA
Deputy Chief General Manager C.R.Harris, FCIS
Executive Directors J.Linbourn, ACIS, A.Macfadyne, A.G.Mackenzie, CBE, MC, Dr.H.C.O'Connor, R.I.Sloan, FCII, W.K.Evans, E.D.Rainbow
UK General Manager V.C.Bryan
Deputy General Manager and Actuary J.H.Webb, MA, FIA
Assistant General Manager G.H.Wagstaff
UK Life Manager J.G.T.Carter, MA, FIA
Life Operations Manager D.Dobson
Investment Manager M.A.Evans
Property Manager J.R.Parry
Pensions Actuary B.W.T.Dawson, FIA
Employees 8,020
Total Pensions Staff 300
Gross Long Term Funds (at 31.12.79) £2,330.0 million
Annual Premium Income £290.5 million
Annual Investment Income £212.1 million
Number of Pension Fund Clients 16,800
Property Advisers/Valuers Commercial Union Properties Ltd
Other Offices About 200 in the UK
Pension Fund Management Company Commercial Union Pensions Management Ltd.
Funds Managed Mixed Fund, Equity, Property and Fixed Interest Funds
Pensions Actuary B.W.T.Dawson, FIA
Fund Manager S.R.Burley
Total Assets of Funds Managed (at 31.12.79) £75.9 million

Annual Premium Income £6.4 million
Annual Investment Income £5.7 million
Number of Pension Fund Clients 54

CONFEDERATION LIFE INSURANCE COMPANY

50 Chancery Lane, London WC2A 1HE
Telephone: 01-242 7126

Vice President and General Manager for the UK P.Wortman, B.Comm.
Director of Marketing K.M.Hilton
Secretary L.A.Howard, FCII
Investment Manager J.C.H.Tate
Actuary G.L.Willman, MA, FIA
Manager, Segregated Fund Investments J.Davies
Manager, Insurance Investments R.E.Durrant
Property Manager K.J.Honour
Manager, Pensions Marketing P.A.W.Cotterill, BSc
Manager, Pensions Administration M.Delaporte
Agency Manager, Broker Division C.R.Wilkinson, FCII, APMI
Employees 2,795
Total Pensions Staff 1,101
Gross Long Term Funds £1,137.9 million
Annual Premium Income £451.4 million
Annual Investment Income £68.7 million
Number of Pension Fund Clients Over 3,000 including individual arrangements
Property Advisers (UK) Jones, Lang, Wootton
Other Offices 28 offices in UK and offices in Canada, USA and the Carribean

CO-OPERATIVE INSURANCE SOCIETY LTD

Miller Street, Manchester M60 0AL
Telephone: 061-832 8686

Chief General Manager A.Duval, FIA
Deputy Chief General Manager and Secretary A.Cochrane, FIA
General Manager and Actuary (Life) A.D.Sneddon, FFA
Assistant General Managers A.H.Liddle, ACIS, P.D.Johnson, MA, FIA
Property Manager H.Bradbury
Property Consultants Bernard Thorpe & Partners
Employees 10,899
Gross Long Term Funds (at 31.12.79) £897.2 million
Annual Premium Income (at 31.12.79) £167.0 million
Annual Investment Income (at 31.12.79) £80.9 million

CROWN LIFE GROUP OF COMPANIES

Crown Life House, Woking, Surrey GU21 1XW
Telephone: 04862 5033

Managing Director & Actuary A.J.Duggin, FIA
Director of Pensions & Group Insurance D.W.Johnstone, ACII

In the long term, what <u>really</u> counts?

It is success in *consistently* meeting long term commitments – this marks the most effectively managed pension fund.

In adopting a long term approach, Eagle Pension Funds (EPF) offers fund trustees:

* **Expertise** – A full range of employee benefit services.

* **Pooled Funds** – Up to seven funds to choose from.

* **Flexibility** – We can respond to your needs and, for a large pension fund, can create a segregated fund.

For full details of our services ask your pensions consultant. Alternatively, contact any Eagle Star branch or Eagle Pension Funds Limited, Eagle Star House, 9 Aldgate High Street, London, EC3N 1LD. Telephone: 01-377 8000.

The Golden Eagle is found in mountainous regions throughout the northern hemisphere. It is probably the world's best known large eagle.

Eagle Pension Funds Limited

EPF — A member of the Eagle Star Group.

EQUITY & LAW LIFE ASSURANCE SOCIETY LTD.
Continued

Funds Managed Equity, fixed interest, property, overseas, mixed and cash
Manager J.Medlock,BSc(Econ),FIA
Investment Manager P.G.Smith,MA,FIA
Property Investment Manager R.A.Booth,FRICS
Secretary R.E.Ellisdon,BSc(Econ),FIA
Total Assets of Funds Managed £97 million
Annual Premium Income £8.8 million
Annual Investment Income £7.0 million
Number of Pension Fund Clients 36
Other Information Full range of pensions contracts for individuals and groups

FRIENDS' PROVIDENT LIFE OFFICE
Pixham End, Dorking, Surrey RH4 1QA
Telephone: 0306-5055

London Office 7 Birchin Lane, London EC3P 3BA
Telephone: 01-626 4511
Chief General Manager W.L.Stubbs,FIIC
Deputy Chief General Manager F.G.Cotton,FIA, FCIA,ASA
Chief Assistant General Manager and Actuary D.R.King,FIA
Assistant General Managers M.S.Hardie,CA (Investments), M.F.Doerr,FIA,MBIM (Operations)
Group Investment Manager A.Pendleton, FIA
Investment Manager R.V.Sankey,FCIS,ASIA
Property Manager W.H.Evans
Assistant General Manager (Pensions) P.Silvester, FIA,FPMI
Employees 1,206
Pensions Staff 210
Gross Long Term Funds (at 31.12.79) £750.2 million
Annual Premium Income £108.7 million
Annual Investment Income £78.5 million
Other Offices 21 throughout U.K.
Subsidiary Friends' Provident Managed Pension Funds Ltd. This company invests and manages contributions on behalf of pension scheme trustees, normally with annual contributions of £50,000 or more

FS ASSURANCE LTD
190 West George Street, Glasgow G2 2PA
Telephone: 041-332 6462

General Manager A.J.Pfaff,FFA
Actuary and Secretary A.Scobbie,FFA
Pensions Manager A.J.Small,FFA
Regional Pension Consultants T.Harrison, P.F.S.Buzalek, D.Gautrey
Employees 189
Gross Long Term Funds £28.2 million
Annual Premium Income £2.88 million
Annual Investment Income £3.05 million
Other Offices 9 throughout UK

GRESHAM LIFE ASSURANCE SOCIETY LTD
PO Box 1, 2-6 Prince of Wales Road, Bournemouth BH4 9HD
Telephone: 0202 767655

Chief Executive J.S.Leighton, BA, FIA
Actuary S.H.Alfert, FIA
General Manager Sales and Marketing C.S.Lewis, A Inst M, FBIM
Assistant Manager Pensions T.D.Elliott, AIA
Assistant Actuary Pensions D.Lewis, BSc, FIA
Investment and Property Advisers N.M.Rothschild Asset Management Ltd
Employees 299
Pension Staff 31
Gross Long Term Funds £88.1 million
Annual Premium Income £13.5 million
Annual Investment Income £9.6 million
Number of Pension Fund Clients 880
Advisers D.Doubble (N.M.Rothschild Asset Management Ltd.)
Valuer Weatherall Green and Smith
Other Offices Branches throughout the United Kingdom

GUARDIAN ROYAL EXCHANGE ASSURANCE LTD
Royal Exchange, London EC3V 3LS
Telephone: 01-283 7101

Pensions Department 68 King William Street, London EC4N 7BU
Telephone: 01-283 7101
Managing Director P.R.Dugdale,MA
General Managers J.D.Brennan,FCA, E.P.Greenfield, FFA,AIA, G.M.Paterson,CA, N.E.Shepherd,MA, G.L.Williams
Actuary D.V.Hackett,FIA,ASA
Assistant General Manager (Investments) D.W.Allen
Investment Executives J.W.King, Miss C.M.Burton
Property Manager M.F.Collins
Assistant General Managers (Life) S.A.Hopkins,ACII, G.C.Nunn,Bsc,FIA
Pensions Actuary G.T.C.Barnes,MA,FIA
Employees 9,913
Gross Long Term Funds (at 31.12.79) £1,420 million
Annual Premiums £106.8 million
Annual Investment Income £119.4 million
Subsidiaries Include G.R.E.Pensions Management Co Ltd, G.R.E. Investment Services Ltd
Offices The Group has offices throughout the UK
Pensions Management Subsidiary G.R.E.Pensions Management Co Ltd
Fund Type Equity, fixed interest, property, deposit, international, master and mixed
Fund Size (at 9.10.79) £30.8 million

Insurance Companies

GUARDIAN ROYAL EXCHANGE ASSURANCE LTD
Continued

Annual Premium Income £2.3 million
Annual Investment Income £1.5 million
Services Offered to Pension Funds Providing both investment facilities and administration services for pension funds, the Trustees of which wish to have a direct interest in a portfolio of Stock Exchange securities
Fund Type Asset management of pension funds on an individual basis having regard to the nature of the liabilities

HAMBRO LIFE ASSURANCE LTD
7 Old Park Lane, London W1Y 3LJ
Telephone: 01-499 0031
Administrative Office Hambro Life House, Station Road, Swindon SN1 1EL
Telephone: 0793-28291
Chairman J.M.Clay
Joint Managing Directors M.A.Weinberg, B.Com, LL.M., M.S.Lipworth,B.Com, LL.B.
Administrative Director J.G.Joffe, B.Com, LL.B.
Marketing Director M.S.Wilson
Executive Directors J.Carr, C.Davies, A.A.Khan, A.P.Leitch, M.F.Murray, D.F.A.Pell, S.Myers, G.Westall,BSc,FIA, A.R.Young
Investment Panel G.H.Fletcher, P.D.Hill-Wood, M.S.Lipworth, C.G.Morley, M.A.Weinberg
Property Panel J.E.Cullis,BSc,FRICS,FSVA, J.N.C.James,FRICS, C.G.Morley,MA,AIB
Hambro Life Property Director M.S.Lipworth, B.Com, LL.B.
Independent Valuers to the Property Funds Jones Lang Wootton
Actuary Alan Ford,FIA,FSA
Life Manager A.R.Young
Pensions Manager John Carr
Pensions Administrator D.Wicks
Employees 1,378
Total Pensions Staff 109
Gross Long Term Funds (at 31.12.79) £813.4 million
Annual Premium Income £133.2 million
Annual Investment Income £67.9 million
Other Offices Throughout UK
Pension Funds Managed Managed, property, fixed interest, deposit, gilt-edged, equity
Total Assets of Funds Managed £274.5 million
Annual Premium Income (at 31.12.79) £86.3 million

HILL SAMUEL LIFE ASSURANCE LTD.
NLA Tower, 12-16 Addiscombe Road, Croydon CR9 2DR
Telephone: 01-686 4355
Managing Director and Actuary J.A.Geddes, FIA
Deputy Managing Director S.W.Pressman, FIA
Financial Director F.Vickers, FCA, MIMC
Marketing Director A.W.P.Ross, BA
Special Duties Director B.Johnson, ACIS
Investment Director A.A.Gaitskell, MA
General Manager Pensions Dept R.F.Sibthorpe, FCII
Actuary Geoffrey Dunsford
Employees 405
Gross Long Term Funds £270.8 million
Annual Premium Income £16.6 million
Annual Investment Income £29.9 million
Property Valuers Weatherall Green & Smith
Other Offices 24 throughout the U.K.

IMPERIAL LIFE ASSURANCE COMPANY OF CANADA
Imperial Life House, London Road, Guildford, Surrey
Telephone: 0483 71255
Investment Department 28-29 St. James's Square, London SW1 (01-930 7585)
General Manager for GB J.A.Kempton
Resident Actuary W.N.Anderton

LEGAL & GENERAL ASSURANCE SOCIETY LTD
A Member of Legal & General Group Ltd.
Temple Court, 11 Queen Victoria Street, London EC4N 4TP
Telephone: 01-248 9678
Pensions Administration Centre Kingswood House, Kingswood, Nr Tadworth, Surrey (25 53456)
Chief Executive R.H.Peet,CBE,FIA
Chief General Manager E.Wynn Owen
General Managers T.J.Palmer, P.W.Simon (Investment Manager)
Chief Actuary C.S.S.Lyon,FIA
Pensions Group Manager W.A.Sibly
Pensions Actuary B.K.Worbey, FIA
Other Pension Managers Robert Hardy (Research); Hu Mann (Administration), Keith Hall (Sales and Managed Funds)
Employees 5,408
Pensions Group Employees 700 directly (plus resources of the Investment Management and other Legal & General Group Companies)
Gross Long Term Funds (at 31.12.79) £3,350 million (plus investment reserve £519 million)
Annual Pensions Premium Income £482 million
Annual Interest Income £320 million
Number of Pension Fund Clients 9,000
Other Pension Offices Birmingham, Leeds, Manchester, Glasgow, Newcastle and Bristol
Other Information Legal & General is placed league-leaders on insured plus managed fund business
Pension Management Subsidiary Legal & General Assurance (Pension Management) Ltd
Manager Keith Hall

Insurance Companies

LEGAL & GENERAL ASSURANCE SOCIETY LTD
Continued

Assistant Managers (Managed Funds) L.H.Stenning, J.B. Weir

Investment Managers Jim Robinson (Mixed Fund), Peter Sim (Property Fund), Ian Clarke (Ordinary Shares Fund), John Weld (Fixed Interest Fund, Composite Fund), John Hockin (International Fund)

Employees 40 (plus resources of L&G Investment Division: and of L&G Pensions Division)

Number of Clients 500

Capital Value of Funds (at November 1980) £1,710 million

Annual Premium Income £140 million

Annual Investment Income £89 million

Property Valuers Weatherall, Green & Smith, Chestertons

Other Information Fund clients include more than 30 out of Top 100 UK Companies. The Managed Fund offers services (administrative, actuarial, pension payments etc) beyond investment, sub-contracted to the L&G Pensions Group

LIFE ASSOCIATION OF SCOTLAND LTD
10 George Street, Edinburgh EH2 2YH
Telephone: 031-225 8494

General Manager & Actuary J.M.Souness, FFA, MA

Assistant General Manager M.A.Forrest, MA, CA

Actuary J.Paterson, BSc, FFA

Investment Manager K.McLean, ACII

Pensions Manager R.M.Paul, FFA

Sales Manager (Pensions) N.Randall

Employees 308

Pensions Staff 50

Gross Long Term Funds (at 31.12.79) £120 million

Annual Premium Income £24.7 million

Annual Investment Income £12.2 million

Pension Fund Clients 700

Other Offices Branches throughout UK and Ireland

Pension Fund Management Co.

Funds Managed Mixed Fund plus Segregated Funds

Senior Management J.Paterson, (Secretary and Chief Executive), R.M.Paul, (Actuary), K.McLean, (Investment Manager)

Total Assets of Funds Managed £3 million

Annual Premium Income £0.5 million

Pension Fund Clients 3

LLOYD'S LIFE ASSURANCE LTD
20 Clifton Street, London EC2A 4HX
Telephone: 01-247 7699

Pensions Department Telephone: 01-628 4781

Managing Director & Actuary J.T.Woolhouse,MA, FIA

Director/Company Secretary D.J.Collett, FCA

Marketing Director M.J.Gordon

Investment Director M.J.Kershaw, BA

Pensions Supervisor C.C.A.Coote, MA, FIA

Other Pensions Management Miss S.M.Tate, BSc

Employees 130

Pensions Staff 14

Gross Long Term Funds (at 30.9.79) £60.0 million

Total Pension Assets Managed £3.5 million

Annual Premiums Income £7.4 million

Annual Investment Income £5.2 million

Number of Pension Fund Clients 860

Property Advisers Chestertons

Property Valuers Knight Frank & Rutley

THE LONDON LIFE ASSOCIATION LTD.
Head Office, 81 King William Street,
London EC4N 7BD
Telephone: 01-626 0511

Pensions Department Turnall House, Sutton Park Road, Sutton, Surrey SM1 2AE
Telephone: 01-643 8977

General Manager and Director A.K.Tudor,FIA

Actuary and Deputy General Manager A.C.Black, Bsc,AKC,FIA

Assistant General Manager and Secretary A.L.Lodde

Pensions Manager W.B.McBride,MA,FFA,FPMI

Investment Manager E.J.Richardson,ACIS

Property Surveyor D.A.Brightwell,FRICS

Employees 570

Gross Funds (at 31.12.78) £290.8 million

Annual Premium Income £28.5 million

Annual Investment Income £26.8 million

Other Offices 20 throughout U.K. and Northern Ireland

Pension Fund Management Co. London Life Managed Funds Ltd.

Funds Managed Equity, fixed interest, property, cash and pooled

Total Assets of Funds Managed (at 29.8.80) £97.8 million

LONDON AND MANCHESTER ASSURANCE CO LTD
P.O. Box 44, Winslade Park, Clyst St. Mary,
Exeter EX5 1DS
Telephone: 0392-52155

Chairman H.L.K.Browne,FCA

Chief Executive D.A.L.Jubb,FIA

Group Actuary P.T.Hodge,FIA

General Manager (Investment) I.J.S.Henderson, MA, FIA

Assistant General Manager (Investment) A.J.Frost, BSc, FIA

LONDON AND MANCHESTER ASSURANCE CO LTD
Continued

Pensions Department Management D.J.Newman, APMI (Assistant General Manager, Marketing), N.R.J.Hardy,FIA,APMI (Pensions Actuary), R.E.H.Orchard,ACII (Life & Pensions Manager), J.J.Mackenzie,ACII,APMI (Manager, Pensions Department), A.R.Webster,APMI (Pensions Marketing Manager)

Pensions Consultants L.C.Chamberlain (Senior), D.J.Cooper,ACII, D.F.Guyers, W.B.Moodie,APMI, C.D.Sandrawich, BSc,FCII, S.W.M.Youngson

Employees 2,045

Pensions Staff 56

Gross Long Term Funds £339.6 million

Annual Premium Income £47.5 million

Annual Investment Income £37.5 million

Number of Pension Fund Clients 443

Property Valuers J.Trevor & Sons

Other Offices 7 Regional offices

MANUFACTURERS LIFE INSURANCE COMPANY (UK) LTD
ManuLife House, St. George's Way, Stevenage, Herts SG1 1HP
Telephone: 0438 56101

General Manager J.E.Clark

Actuary A.H.Fraser

Internal Financial Vice-President J.B.Mounsey

Pensions Officer P.Ashdown

Pensions Administration Manager E.Jones

Employees 625

Pensions Staff 12

Gross Long Term Funds £1,896 million

Annual Premium Income £158 million

Annual Investment Income £202 million

Pension Fund Clients 12,000

Other Offices 22 branches in the U.K.

MARINE AND GENERAL MUTUAL LIFE ASSURANCE SOCIETY (MGM ASSURANCE)
MGM House, Heene Road, Worthing, West Sussex BN11 2DY
Telephone: 0903 204631

General Manager P.A.Slattery, FPMI Barrister

Deputy General Manager and Actuary J.L.Robertson,FIA,APMI

Investment Manager A.M.Lamb,MA,FIA

Property Manager W.H.E.Flint

Pensions Administration Manager and Secretary C.W.Ford,FCIS,APMI

Pensions Sales Manager M.M.Powell,BSc,ACII, APMI

Property Advisers Richard Ellis

Employees 281

Pensions Staff 15

Gross Long Term Funds £76.4 million

Annual Premium Income £13.4 million

Annual Investment Income £7.9 million

Other Offices 15 Branches, 5 Sub-Offices

Subsidiary Company MGM Assurance (Trustees) Ltd.

MERCHANT INVESTORS ASSURANCE CO LTD
Leon House, 233 High Street, Croydon CR9 1LP
Telephone: 01-686 9171

Managing Director E.R.Fairman,BSc(Econ)

Assistant Managing Director B.A.Foreman,ACII

Actuary B.Brindley

Pensions Manager K.J.V.Wrench

Employees 170

Pension Staff 13

Number of Pension Fund Clients 4,000 policy holders (Insured pensions: funds not open to direct investment)

Gross Funds £45.4 million

Annual Premium Income £3.4 million

Annual Investment Income £2.5 million

Other Offices Birmingham, Bristol, Cardiff, Croydon, London, Manchester, Edinburgh

Associated Companies Members of Nationale-Nederlanden Group

Other Information Merchant Investors runs five pension funds, with specialist outside investment managers: John Govett & Co.Ltd. for equities, Gerrard & National (Fund Management) Ltd. for gilts and money, and Richard Ellis for property. Merchant Investors' investment panel advises a managed fund

NATIONAL EMPLOYERS' LIFE GROUP OF COMPANIES
Milton Court, Dorking, Surrey RH4 3LZ
Telephone: 0306 5911

Chairman L.C.T.Cottrell, FCIS, ACII

Chief Executive J.A.Green, BSc, FIA

General Manager G.N.Dingsdale, LLB

Actuary M.R.Field, FIA

Assistant General Manager and Chief Accountant W.E.Washer, FCA

Manager, NELPHI G.Webster, ACII

Investment Manager M.S.Ruscoe

Chief Pensions Manager B.T.Jones,ACII,APMI

Assistant Actuary(Pensions) R.E.Bednarek,MSc,FIA

Pensions Manager (Group) C.W.Hart,APMI

Employees 598

Pensions Staff 83

Long Term Gross Fund (1979) £143.5 million

Annual Premium Income £41.1 million

Annual Investments Income £14.7 million

Other Offices 8 Regional offices, plus branches throughout the U.K.

Pension Fund Management Co NEL Pensions Ltd

Insurance Companies

NATIONAL EMPLOYERS' LIFE GROUP OF COMPANIES
Continued

Senior Management L.C.T.Cottrell,FCIS,ACII (Chairman), J.A.Green,BSc,FIA, G.N.Dingsdale,LLB, M.R.Field,FIA, B.T.Jones,ACII,FPMI

Funds Managed Nelex Money Fund, Growth Income Fund, Mixed Fund, Deposit Fund, Guaranteed Growth Assets International fixed interest fund

Value of Funds Managed £62.6 million

Annual Premium Income £18.4 million

Annual Investment Income £6.8 million

Number of Pension Fund Clients 7,200 Group schemes and individual Pensions arrangements

THE NATIONAL FARMERS UNION MUTUAL INSURANCE SOCIETY LTD.
15 Church Street, Stratford-Upon-Avon, Warwickshire
Telephone: 0789-4211

Chief General Manager C.A.Thomas, ACII

General Managers N.H.Keegan,ACIS, C.T.Bilby,FCA, J.Bridgewater,FCII, E.D.Browning,ACII, R.H.Catton, ACII, J.Morgan,FCII, D.A.Tuckey,BA,MIPM

Investment Manager N.E.Newton, MSc, FIA

Assistant Investment Manager Mrs.K.M.Lloyd,BSc

Actuary and Life Manager, Pensions Dept. P.R.Pedlingham, FIA

Deputy Actuary, Pensions Dept. K.M.R.Price, MA, FIA

Employees 2,000 (approx)

Pensions Staff 10 (full time) plus 'shared' and part-time staff

Gross Long Term Funds (at 31.12.79) £173.8 million

Annual Premium Income £17.4 million

Annual Investment Income £18.6 million

Pension Fund Clients 1,000 (approx)

Property Adviser Sir Dennis Pilcher, CBE, FRICS

Other Offices Throughout U.K.

NATIONAL MUTUAL LIFE ASSURANCE SOCIETY
5 Bow Churchyard, London EC4M 9DH
Telephone: 01-236 1566

Chairman D.A.Pease

Managing Director D.McD.Sumner

Secretary and Operations Manager W.P.Jackson, FIA

Actuary G.K.Hazell,MA,FIA

Investment Manager M.A.L.Young

Property Manager P.J.Hadden

Sales Director A.R.C.Jenks

Deputy Actuary (Pensions) D.J.Booth, BSc, FIA

Employees 378

Pensions Staff 32

Gross Long Term Funds (at 31.12.79) £123.3 million

Annual Premium Income £20.7 million

Annual Investment Income £13.0 million

Pension Fund Clients 750

Other Offices 17 throughout UK

Pension Fund Management Co National Mutual Pensions Ltd.

Total Value of Funds Managed £6 million

Annual Premium Income £1 million

Pension Fund Clients 3

NATIONAL PROVIDENT INSTITUTION
48 Gracechurch Street, London EC3P 3HH
Telephone: 01-623 4200

Pensions Department National Provident House, Tunbridge Wells, Kent TW1 2UE
Telephone: 0892-26181

General Manager and Actuary G.V.Bayley,CBE,FIA, FIMA

Deputy General Manager M.T.Maurice,FIA

Assistant General Manager and Actuary C.A.Gates, FIA

Investment Managers W.A.R.Goodsall, C.J.Holmes

Property Manager J.S.Harris

Manager, Group Pensions M.R.Nash,AIA,APMI

Property Advisers St Quintin

Employees 900

Total Pensions Staff 110

Gross Long Term Funds £384.6 million

Annual Premium Income £73.9 million

Annual Investment Income £42.2 million

Number of Pension Fund Clients 296 Group Funds, 4,429 Individual Pension Funds

Other Offices Throughout UK

Subsidiary NPI Pensions Management Ltd

Total Value of Pension Funds Managed (at 30.9.80) £7.6 million

Annual Premium Income £1.5 million

Annual Investment Income £0.6 million

Pension Fund Clients 8

NORWICH UNION LIFE INSURANCE SOCIETY
PO Box 4, Surrey Street, Norwich NR1 3NG
Telephone: 0603 22000

Chief General Manager P.W.Sharman,MA,FIA

General Manager J.Campbell

General Manager and Actuary V.W.Hughff,FIA

General Manager and Secretary H.H.Scurfield,FIA

Deputy Actuary R.Elven,MA,FIA,FPMI

Chief Estates Manager J.A.Darby,FRICS

Chief Investment Manager G.Mills,FFA

Pensions Manager R.B.P.Ramsay, FIA, APMI

Employees 8,313

Gross Long Term Funds (1978) £2,032.5 million

Annual Premium Income £262.5 million

Annual Investment Income £161.2 million

Insurance Companies

NORWICH UNION LIFE INSURANCE SOCIETY
Continued

Other Offices Over 100 throughout UK and in 12 other countries

Principal Subsidiaries Include A.P.Bank Ltd., Maritime Insurance Co.Ltd., Norwich Union Insurance Group (Managed Funds) Ltd., Norwich Union Fire Insurance Society Ltd.

Pensions Management Subsidiary Norwich Union Insurance Group (Pensions Management) Ltd. Directors: G.N.Holmes (Chairman), J.A.Darby, V.W.Hughff (General Manager), G.Mills

NRG LONDON REINSURANCE COMPANY LTD.
Fountain House, 130 Fenchurch Street,
London EC3P 3BD
Telephone: 01-626-3851

Managing Director K.M.Dublon

General Manager A.V.Spain, ACII

Manager and Secretary K.W.Haddon, FCA

Manager and Underwriter T.M.Warrilow

Actuary R.W.Michaelson, MA, FIA

Employees 50

Gross Long Term Fund £5 million

Associated Companies Member of Nationale Nederlanden Group, Subsidiary of Nederlandse Reassurantie Groep N.V. Amsterdam

PEARL ASSURANCE COMPANY LTD.
252 High Holborn, London WC1V 7EB
Telephone: 01-405 8441

Chief General Manager R.E.Holland BSc,FIA

General Managers R.Younger, N.N.Proddow,MA, FIA,ACII

Actuary J.R.C.Elmslie,MBE,FIA

Controller of Investments S.A.Maitland,MA

Investment Managers R.V.Huxley,K.G.Thwaites, J.V.Wood,B.P.Pain

Property Manager S.Bennett

Controller Pensions E.E.Voller,FCII,APMI

Employees 9,204

Long Term Funds £1,211 million

Annual Premium Income £180 million

Annual Investment Income £120 million

City Pensions Office 16 Mark Lane, London EC3R 7AP (01-623 1691)

Other Offices About 450 throughout U.K.

Subsidiaries Include Pearl Assurance (Unit Funds) Ltd, Pearl Trust Managers Ltd, Pearl Assurance (Unit Linked Pensions) Ltd

PHOENIX ASSURANCE CO LTD
4-5 King William Street, London EC4P 4HR
Telephone: 01-626 9876

Pensions Dept. Phoenix House, Redcliff Hill, Bristol BS1 6SQ
Telephone: 0272-294941

Chief General Manager R.K.Bishop,FCII,FCIS

Deputy CGM's A.R.Matanle,FCII K.Wilkinson,FCII

General Manager and Actuary M.H.Field, FIA, FCIA

General Manager (Investment) B.D.Oram

Deputy General Manager (Investment) D.P.Tandy

Property Manager S.B.Smee

Manager J.Walker,FIA

Assistant Pensions Managers E.D.Cross, R.G.Brown,BSc,FIA, A.Howes,ACII

Total Employees 3,495

Pensions Staff 115

Gross Long Term Funds (at 31.12.79) £546.7 million

Annual Premium Income £97.8 million

Annual Investment Income £52.3 million

Number of Pension Fund Clients 373

Subsidiaries Include Property Growth Assurance Company Ltd

Other Offices 90 throughout UK

Pension Fund Management Co Ebor Phoenix Assurance Co. Ltd.

Funds Managed Equity, fixed interest, property, money mixed international

Pensions Manager J.Walker

Total Value of Pension Funds Managed £13.4 million

Annual Premium Income £1.5 million

Annual Investment Income £1.0 million

Pension Fund Clients 2

PROPERTY GROWTH ASSURANCE COMPANY LTD.
Leon House, High Street, Croydon CR9 1LU
Telephone: 01-680 0606

Managing Director D.D.Stringer

Actuary S.A.Barnett,BSc,FIA

Investment Director D.Tandy,BSc,FIA

Life & Marketing Manager M.J.Austen

Pensions Manager E.Morris

Property Valuers Weatherall Green & Smith

Employees 285

Total Pensions Staff 25

Gross Long Term Funds £112 million

Annual Premium Income £4.5 million

Annual Investment Income £8 million

Parent Company Phoenix Assurance Co.Ltd.

Subsidiary Property Growth Pensions & Annuities Ltd.

Total Funds Managed £10 million

Annual Premium Income £3 million

Number of Pension Fund Clients 17,000

Funds Open to Investors Include Convertible pension fund, property pension fund, managed pension fund, building society linked pension fund and gilt pension fund.

Other Offices London, Manchester, Leeds, Birmingham, Leicester, Bristol, Southampton

PROVIDENCE CAPITOL LIFE ASSURANCE COMPANY LTD, PROVIDENCE CAPITOL ASSURANCE (PENSIONS) LTD

Providence House, 30 Uxbridge Road, London W12 8PG
Telephone: 01-749 9111

Chief Executive A.R.Peirce,FCA

Managing Director Peter Oliver

Director & Actuary M.J.Taylor,FIA

Director of Administration B.K.Pudney,FCII

Investment Managers Baring Brothers & Co Ltd

Group Pensions Manager P.J.Gates,ACII,APMI

Individual & International Pensions Manager D.R.Braithwaite,ACII

Employees 130

Pension Fund Employees 24

Gross Long Term Funds (at 31.8.79) £66.0 million

Annual Premium Income £2.4 million (including £0.6 million Managed Fund)

Annual Investment Income £8.2 million

Number of Pension Fund Clients Group 111, Individual 376, Sponsored Pension Plan 200

Property Advisers Elliott, Son & Boyton

Property Valuers St Quintin

Other Offices (Brokers Division) Birmingham, Manchester

Associated Company Providence Capitol Assurance Pensions Ltd.

Managed Fund Pension Investment Fund (Deposit Administration Contract)

Other Information Managed Fund introduced 1st April 1977

PROVIDENT LIFE ASSOCIATION OF LONDON LTD

266 Bishopsgate, London EC2M 4QP
Telephone: 01-247 3200

Managing Director D.H.Radley,FIA

General Manager & Actuary B.E.Radley,FIA

General Manager & Investment Manager R.A.F.Ostime,FIA

Assistant General Managers J.D.Fox,FCA (Secretary), E.E.Holland(Agency)

Deputy Investment Manager J.Shaddick,BA

Life Manager R.K.Muddle, FCII

Deputy Actuary (Pensions) D.M.Lampert,FIA

Assistant Actuary (Pensions) G.V.A.Budd, FIA

Employees 640

Gross Long Term Funds £95.6 million

Annual Premium Income £14.4 million

Annual Investment Income £7.6 million

Number of Pension Fund Clients 100 (approx) Group Pension Schemes plus 2,000 (approx) Individual Pension arrangements

Services Offered to Pension Funds Controlled funding and individual arrangements using insurance contracts. Full Inland Revenue negotiations and all documentation

Other Offices Birmingham, Brighton, Bristol, Cheltenham, Harrow, Leeds, Maidenhead, Manchester, Plymouth, Romford, Southampton, Tunbridge Wells

PROVIDENT MUTUAL LIFE ASSURANCE ASSOCIATION

25-31 Moorgate, London EC2R 6BA
Telephone: 01-628 3232

Pensions Department Wedgwood Way, Stevenage, Hertfordshire SG1 4PU
Telephone: 0438 -4343

General Manager B.Richardson,FCA

Secretary G.W.Stirling

Investment Manager C.E.Hughes,BA,FIA

Property Manager N.A.Hill

Actuary P.Norton,FIA

Joint Actuary E.Brunet,BA,FIA

Deputy Actuary J.D.Neville,MA,FIA

Pensions Manager G.A.Brown,ACII

Employees 779

Gross Assets (1976) £197.7 million

Annual Premiums £43.6 million

Investment Income £18.1 million

Subsidiary Provident Mutual Managed Pension Funds Ltd. Total Funds £51 million, Annual Premiums £2.9 million

PRUDENTIAL ASSURANCE COMPANY LTD

142 Holborn Bars, London EC1N 2NH
Telephone: 01-405 9222

Chief General Manager D.S.Craigen,BA

General Managers F.B.Corby,MA,FIA (Chief Actuary), F.G.Wood,FIA,ACII, D.C.Bourdon,FIA

Chief Investment Managers R.E.Artus,MA B.Medhurst, MA, FIA

Group Pensions Manager D.E.Fellows, FIA, FPMI

Development Manager J.A.Clark,FPMI

Manager,Development Division J.E.K.Spickett, FPMI

Deputy Group Pension Managers R.H.Rawlinson, FIA,FPMI, J.V.Swales, ACIS

Employees 21,282

Pensions Staff 565 (approx)

Gross Long Term Funds (at 31.12.79) £4,944.6 million

Annual Premium Income £773.9 million

Annual Investment Income £481.3 million

Number of Pension Fund Clients 4,300

Other Offices Bristol, Birmingham, Leeds, Manchester

Pension Fund Management Co. Prudential Pensions Ltd

Funds Managed Unitised equity, fixed interest and property funds. Contributions apportioned between funds either by PPL or by the client

Directors D.A.Reid (Chairman), R.E.Artus,MA, Lord Carr of Hadley, H.G.Clarke,BSc,FIA, F.B.Corby,MA,

Insurance Companies

PRUDENTIAL ASSURANCE COMPANY LTD Continued

FIA, M.G.Newmarch, BSc, D.E.Fellows,FIA, T.J.L.Richards,MA,FIA

Manager and Actuary T.J.L.Richards,MA,FIA

Investment Manager M.G.Newmarch,BSc

Property Manager P.G.Green,BSc,FRICS

Property Valuers Hillier Parker May and Rowden, Savills, Debenham Tewson and Chinnocks, Bidwells

Total Value of Pension Funds Managed (at 17.9.80) £687.6 million

Annual Premium Income £100 million (approx)

Annual Investment Income £37 million (approx)

Number of Pension Fund Clients 213

Services Provided Investments and administration (including funding reviews and documentation)

ROYAL INSURANCE COMPANY LTD.

P.O.Box 144, New Hall Place, Liverpool L69 3EN
Telephone: 051-227 4422

General Manager and Chief Actuary A.C.Baker,FIA, FFA,FCII

Deputy General Manager and Actuary H.B.Johnson,MA.FIA

Chief Investment Manager D.Malcolm, MA, FCII

Investment Manager D.I.W.Reynolds, MA, MSc, FIA, FSS

Property Manager J.V.Strong, ARICS

Pensions Manager K.R.Percy,BSc,FIA

Employees 9,412

Long Term Insurance Funds (at 31.12.79) £1,014.9 million

Annual Premium Income £139.3 million

Annual Investment Income £100.4 million

Other Offices 15 Life Branches, over 60 other Branches throughout UK

ROYAL LONDON MUTUAL INSURANCE SOCIETY LTD

Royal London House, Finsbury Square, London EC2A 1DP
Telephone: 01-606 3044

Chairman & Deputy Chief General Manager B.G.Skinner

Chief General Manager W.H.Forsey

General Manager P.A.Taylor,BSc,FIA

Actuary M.J.Pickard,FIA

Investment Manager C.Brill

Property Manager R.K.Pollard

Employees 3,544

Gross Long Term Funds £616.6 million

Annual Premium Income £44.2 million

Annual Investment Income £46.4 million

THE ROYAL NATIONAL PENSION FUND FOR NURSES

Burdett House, 15 Buckingham Street, London WC2N 6ED
Telephone: 01-839 6785

Manager C.M.O'Brien

Deputy Managers V.G.West, R.F.Milsom

Employees 60

Gross Long Term Funds £71.5 million

Annual Premium Income £5.2 million

Annual Investment Income £8 million

Property Advisers/Valuers Gooch & Wagstaff

SAVE & PROSPER GROUP LTD

4 Great St Helens, London EC3P 3EP
Telephone: 01-554 8899

Chairman & Joint Managing Director D.H.Maitland, FCA

Joint Managing Director C.J.Messer

Group Actuary R.J.Squires,FIA,ASA

Executive Directors S.E.Baker, A.H.Doggart (Sales), R.J.Hebblethwaite,FCA, P.J.Manser,FCA (Investment), W.G.N.Miller

Pensions Department Managers D.R.Butcher,MA, K.F.McCulloch

Gross Long Term Funds (at 31.12.79) £281.1 million

Annual Premium Income £50 million

Branch Offices Birmingham, Brentford, Bristol, Croydon, Edinburgh, Glasgow, Ilford, Leeds, Manchester, Newcastle-upon-Tyne, Nottingham, Plymouth, Southampton and Aberdeen

Parent Company Save & Prosper Group Ltd. (Founded in 1934 it now manages over £1,000 million for some 650,000 investors).

Subsidiaries Save & Prosper Insurance Ltd, Save & Prosper Pensions Ltd

SCHRODER LIFE GROUP

Enterprise House, Isambard Brunel Road, Portsmouth PO1 2AW
Telephone: 0705 27733

Managing Director R.W.Taylor

Deputy Managing Director I.A.P.Michaelson-Yeates

Actuary John W.P.Earle

Joint Actuary M.J.Taylor

Controller, Management Services C.W.Bond

Controller, Life Operations P.W.Cashen

Manager, Agency Division E.F.T.Desbois

Financial Controller N.R.Dunseath

Chief Accountant C.J.Dyke

Manager, Brokerage Division A.Fouche

Pensions Manager T.Sponton

Investment Management J.Henry Schroder Wagg & Co. Ltd.

Property Management Schroder Properties Ltd.

Employees 221

Property Valuers Weatherall Green & Smith

SCHRODER LIFE GROUP *Continued*

Annual Premium Income £4.364 million
Annual Investment Income £5.325 million
Pension Fund Clients (at 31.10.79) 2,821

SCOTTISH AMICABLE LIFE ASSURANCE SOCIETY
150 St Vincent Street, Glasgow G2 5NQ
Telephone: 041-221 8844

Pensions Department Craigforth, Stirling FK9 4UE
Telephone: 0786-314

General Manager and Actuary William D.Proudfoot
Investment Management J.D.Campbell, W.G.Knox, MA,FFA, M.A.Hogg,FFA,MA,ARICS, J.J.Guthrie,CA, D.J.B.Sutherland,BSc,FFA, C.J.Bartram
Pension Fund Managers K.J.Hurry,FIA,FPMI, R.M.Nicholson,FFA,APMI, A.N.D.Shaw,FFA
Pensions Marketing Manager M.R.Heane
Employees 1,117
Pensions Employees 126
Gross Long Term Funds (at 31.12.79) £664 million
Annual Premium Income £93.2 million
Annual Investment Income £55.9 million
Number of Pension Fund Clients 1,000 (approx)
Other Offices Branch offices throughout country
Pension Subsidiary Scottish Amicable Pensions Investments Ltd
Managed Funds SCAMPI - Mixed Managed Pension Fund
Total Value of Pension Funds Managed (at 31.8.80) £161.5 million
Annual Premium Income £37.6 million
Investment Income £7 million
Number of Pension Fund Clients 125

SCOTTISH EQUITABLE LIFE ASSURANCE SOCIETY
28 St. Andrew Square, Edinburgh EH2 1YF
Telephone: 031-556 9101

General Manager & Actuary A.M.Robertson,MA, BSc,FFA
Investment Manager and Deputy General Manager I.J.S.Henderson,MA,FIA
Marketing Manager R.B.Howarth
Secretary W.W.Park,ACII
Pensions Manager D.A.Berridge,BSc,FFA
Deputy Pensions Manager J.G.Elliott
Employees 542
Net Assets (at 31.12.78) £329.8 million
Annual Premium Income £59.8 million
Investment Income £29.5 million
Other Offices 24 throughout U.K.
Other Information The Pensions Department offers three main contracts: S.E.Funding, a highly flexible deposit administration scheme- Exsel, an A.P. costed scheme for directors and small companies, Exselfund, a contract for small self-administered schemes

SCOTTISH LIFE ASSURANCE COMPANY
PO Box 54, 19 St. Andrew Square,
Edinburgh EH2 1YE
Telephone: 031-225 2211

General Manager W.M.Morrison,FFA
Deputy General Manager G.M.Murray,FFA
Assistant General Manager A.P.Limb, FIA
Pensions Manager T.Young,FFA
Assistant Pensions Managers D.Morrice,FFA, D.M.Graham,FFA
Actuary R.P.Bews,FIA
Investment Manager B.M.Rose,BSc,FIA
Property Manager R.C.Pugh
Regional Pensions Managers D.J.C.Patterson,FPMI, J.C.W.Hood,FPMI
Area Pensions Manager B.S.Jones, FPMI
Total Staff 550 (approx)
Pensions Staff 160 (approx)
Gross Long Term Funds (1979) £285 million
Annual Premium Income £52 million
Annual Investment Income £27 million
Pension Fund Clients 2,000 (approx)
Other Offices 22 Life and 5 Pension branches in the U.K.
Pension Fund Management Co Scottish Life Pensions Annuity Co.
Funds Managed Mixed Fund - Managed Pension Fund
Senior Management T.Young, Pensions Manager, B.M.Rose, Investment Manager
Total Value of Pension Funds Managed (at 31.7.80) £14.6 million
Annual Premium Income £2.7 million
Annual Investment Income £0.8 million
Pension Fund Clients 20

THE SCOTTISH MUTUAL ASSURANCE SOCIETY
109 St.Vincent Street, Glasgow G2 5HN
Telephone: 041-248 6321

General Manager and Actuary R.E.Macdonald,MA, FFA
Deputy General Manager D.D.McKinnon,BSc,FFA
Secretary W.McCorkindale,FFA
Agency Manager Owen Connarty
Investment Secretary R.S.Clarkson,BSc,FFA
Property Secretary R.D.Scott,ASVA
Pensions Manager W.M.Henderson,FFA
Pensions Secretary A.F.Pearson,FFA
Joint Pensions Secretary W.G.C.Sharp,FFA
Assistant Pensions Secretaries D.M.Livingston,Bsc, FFA, H.W.Brown,BSc,FFA
London Actuary R.J.Amy,BSc,FFA
Regional Pensions Representatives K.Martin,

How does your pension fund grow?

The Scottish Mutual offers pension trustees the chance to have a stake in the Stock Market through their own pension funds. The well proven investment skills of the Society are at your service in our Managed Fund. Your pensions consultant will be able to give you full details of the Scottish Mutual Managed Fund. Ask him or contact our pensions department

The Scottish Mutual Assurance Society
HEAD OFFICE 109 ST. VINCENT STREET, GLASGOW G2 5HN 041-248 6321

Insurance Companies

THE SCOTTISH MUTUAL ASSURANCE SOCIETY
Continued

Regional Pensions Representatives K.Martin, N.Davies,ACII, H.Thomson,ACII, I.D.Vernon,BA, P.Rudge,ACII, M.McPherson,BSc

Total Employees 437

Pensions Employees 51

Gross Long Term Funds (at 31.12.78) £194.1 million

Annual Premium Income £27.0 million

Annual Investment Income £17.3 million

Number of Pension Fund Clients 2,040

Other Offices 21 throughout U.K.

Pensions Subsidiary Scottish Mutual Pension Funds Investment Ltd.

Funds Managed Mixed Fund, Managed Pension Fund

Total Funds Managed (at 29.6.79) ££9,300,000

Annual Premium Income (at 31.12.78) £800,000

Investment Income £325,000

THE SCOTTISH PROVIDENT INSTITUTION

6 St. Andrew Square, Edinburgh EH2 2YA
Telephone: 031-556 9181

General Manager and Actuary J.M.Macharg,FFA

Deputy General Manager and Actuary J.M.MacLaren, BSc, FFA

Assistant General Manager and Secretary W.A.B.Scott, MA, FFA

Assistant General Manager (Marketing) P.W.Bullough, TD

Assistant General Manager (Investment) G.M.Dobbie, BSc, FFA

Investment Manager K.W.B.Inglis, FFA

Investment Secretary T.K.Brown, FCII

Joint Investment Secretary J.E.Paterson, BSc, FFA

Assistant Investment Secretary J.F.Lawrie, MA

Assistant General Manager and Pensions Manager H.W.Gillon, FFA, FPMI

Deputy Pensions Manager W.Davidson, BSc, FFA, APMI

Senior Assistant Actuary J.H.R.Thom, BSc, FFA

Assistant Actuaries J.S.Colls,BA,FFA, N.M.Bryson, MSc,D.Phil,FFA, J.Graham,FFA

Joint Pensions Secretaries C.A.D.Smith,BL,ACII, APMI, D.J.Moore,MA

London Pensions Manager W.J.Donaldson,FCII, APMI

Employees 650

Pension Employees 120

Gross Long Term Funds (at 31.12.79) £441 million

Annual Premium Income £58 million

Number of Pension Fund Clients 1,000 plus individual arrangements

Annual Investment Income £44 million

Other Offices 25 offices throughout U.K. and Republic of Ireland

Pension Fund Management Co Scottish Provident Managed Pension Funds Ltd.

SCOTTISH WIDOWS' FUND & LIFE ASSURANCE SOCIETY

15 Dalkeith Road, Edinburgh EH16 5XA
Telephone: 031-655 6000

General Manager and Actuary C.M.Cavaye,FFA

Deputy General Manager and Secretary J.Elder,FFA

Assistant General Managers D.Whitehead,FIA, E.S.Robertson,FFA, A.Neill,FFA,FIA

Investment Manager D.C.Ritchie, FFA

Investment Secretary D.A.K.Park, FFA

Property Investment Secretary J.H.McDonald

Joint Investment Secretary M.E.Pearson, FFA

Pensions Manager J.A.Cairns, FFA

Actuaries and Assistant Pensions Managers A.P.Scott,FFA, A.E.Miller,FFA, N.E.Gould,FIA, J.N.Darvell,FFA, L.J.G.Purdie,FFA, Miss L.S.Reid, R.J.Hyder,FIA

Employees 1,640

Pensions Employees 430

Gross Long Term Funds (at 31.12.79) £1,286 million

Annual Premium Income (1979) £170 million (approximately 65% pensions)

Annual Investment Income (1979) £130 million

Pension Fund Clients Over 2,000

Branches 19 branches throughout the U.K.

Regional Pensions Centres Edinburgh, London, Birmingham, Bristol, Leeds, Manchester

Pension Fund Management Co Pension Management (SWF) Ltd

Funds Managed (at 30.8.80) £324 million

Annual Premium Income (1979) £44 million

Annual Investment Income (1979) £27 million

Number of Pension Fund Clients 170

Other Information Full technical and administrative services are available as well as investment

STANDARD LIFE ASSURANCE CO

3 George Street, Edinburgh EH3 2XZ
Telephone: 031-225 7971

Pensions Department 23 Annandale Street, Edinburgh EH7 4BP
Telephone: 031-556 9200

General Manager and Actuary G.D.Gwilt,MA,FFA, FBCS

Deputy General Manager and Secretary G.C.Philip, FFA

Assistant General Managers G.P.Glover (Life), A.S.Bell,FFA,FPMI (Finance), A.U.Lyburn,MA,FFA, FPMI (Pensions), A.D.Shedden,BSc,FFA,FSA (Actuary)

Investment Manager D.M.Simpson, BA, FFA

Property Investment Manager P.J.Henwood, FRICS

Deputy Investment Manager J.R.Gibson, FFA

1 2 3 good reasons for choosing the Sun Alliance Additional Pension Plan

1 No cost to Employer

2 Life assurance without medical evidence for suitable Plans

3 Simple units of premium

Our audio-visual presentation and new brochure with full details is now available. Contact Group Pensions Marketing at Horsham (0403) 64141 extension 6211 or your usual Sun Alliance Office.

The Additional Pension Plan — the new AVC Scheme from Sun Alliance

SUN ALLIANCE
INSURANCE GROUP

Insurance Companies

STANDARD LIFE ASSURANCE CO *Continued*

Deputy Property Investment Manager J.S.Black, BSc, Est.Man.,ARICS

Joint Pensions Manager R.G.Lauener,FFA

Pensions Managers A.N.Calder,MA,FFA, (Admin.), A.S.McLeigh,MA,LLB (Legal), A.M.Skinner,MA,FFA, FPMI (Sales)

Pensions Actuary C.F.Stuart,FFA

Employees 1,978 (in U.K.)

Total Pensions Staff 530 (in U.K.)

Gross Long Term Funds (at 15.11.79) £1,487.7 million

Annual Premium Income £227.4 million

Annual Investment Income £144.8 million

Pension Fund Clients Over 2,000

Other Offices 68 Offices throughout U.K. and Republic of Ireland

Pension Fund Management Co Standard Life Pension Funds Ltd

Manager and Actuary A.U.Lyburn,MA,FFA,FPMI

Secretary G.Dickson,MBE

Property Investment Manager J.S.Black,BSc(Est Man),ARICS

Investment Manager J.R.Gibson,FFA

Pensions Manager D.D.Fotheringham,FFA

Total Value of Pension Funds Managed £269 million (pooled and segregated funds)

Annual Premium Income £25 million

Annual Investment Income £23 million

Number of Pension Fund Clients 131

Other Information Four pooled funds operated; Mixed, property, equity and fixed interest. In addition segregated funds are operated

SUN ALLIANCE & LONDON ASSURANCE CO.

Sun Alliance House, North Street, Horsham, West Sussex RH12 1BT
Telephone: 0403-64141

Chief General Manager G.Bowler,FCIS

General Manager & Chief Actuary A.E.Tinckler,FIA

Deputy Chief General Manager K.G.Addison,FCIS, FCII

Assistant General Manager and Actuary S.P.L.Kennedy, BA, FIA

Chief Investment Manager G.E.Browne, BSc(Econ), FCII

Investment Manager I.M.Trotter, ACIS

Manager Pensions Department J.J.Woods, BA, FIA, APMI

Employees 9,577

Pensions Staff 180

Gross Long Term Funds £714.7 million

Annual Premium Income £136.5 million

Annual Investment Income £63.6 million

Number of Pension Fund Clients Over 5,000

Pension Fund Management Co Sun Alliance Fund Management Ltd.

Directors G.Bowler,FCIS (Chairman), J.H.Bishop,FIA, S.P.L.Kennedy,BA,FIA, F.B.Nicholls,FCIS, W.G.Niven,FCA S.L.Smaller,MA,FIA, A.E.Tinckler,FIA

Funds Managed Sun Alliance (Exempt) Equity Trust, Sun Alliance (Exempt) Fixed Interest Trust

Total Assets of Funds Managed £18.8 million

Pension Fund Clients 35

SUN LIFE ASSURANCE SOCIETY LTD.

Head Office, 107 Cheapside, London EC2V 6DU
Telephone: 01-606 7788

Administration Headquarters and Pensions Department Sun Life Court, St. James Barton, Bristol BS1 3TH
Telephone: 0272-426911

Managing Director R.F.C.Zamboni,FCA

Assistant Managing Director and Chief Actuary P.D.Bairstow,BSc,FIA

General Managers J.D.Webster,BSc,FIA (Investment), F.A.J.Berry,ACII,APMI (Marketing and Sales), M.Carlisle,FCIS,ACII (Administration)

Pensions Actuary M.J.Turner,BSc,FIA,APMI

Employees About 2,300 including Branch and Sales staff, many of whom specialise in pension fund matters

Gross Long Term Funds (at 31.12.79) £1,040 million

Annual Premium Income £185 million

Annual Investment Income £104 million

Number of Pension Fund Clients Over 3,000 group pension schemes and a substantial number of individual arrangements

Services Offered to Pension Funds Full range of administrative services; actuarial advice on the level of funding and benefits, documentation, statements of benefits, payment of pensions. Employee benefit communication including retirement counselling, pensioneer trustee and other services for small self-administered schemes

Other Offices Nationwide branch and area office network

Subsidiaries Sun Life Unit Assurance Ltd., Suntrust Ltd.

Pension Management Subsidiary Sun Life Pensions Management Ltd

Funds Managed Separate mixed, property, stock exchange securities and Prospect funds

General Manager J.D.Webster,BSc,FIA

Actuary M.J.Turner,BSc,FIA,FPMI

Investment Manager D.G.Thomas,BSc,FIA

Secretary L.A.Hunt,FCIS,ACII

Assistant Actuary P.G.M.Channack,FIA,APMI

Total Assets of Funds Managed (at 28.9.80) £138.2 million (Group Pension Contracts)

Annual Premium Income £25.5 million

Annual Investment Income £8.8 million

Number of Pension Fund Clients 128 (Group Pension Contracts)

SWISS LIFE INSURANCE AND PENSION COMPANY
9 Cheapside, London EC2V 6AL
Telephone: 01-236 3841

UK Manager J.W.Manaton,AIA,FPMI

TRIDENT LIFE
London Road, Gloucester GL1 3LE
Telephone: 0452-36541

Gross Long Term Funds £100 million

TYNDALL ASSURANCE LTD
18 Canynge Road, Bristol BS99 7UA
Telephone: 0272 32241

Managing Director B.R.Pepperall

General Manager A.F.Mayne

Chief Actuary A.C.Johnson,FFA

Life Manager J.D.Waight

Ordinary Life Fund £49 million

Annual Premium Income £5 million

UK PROVIDENT
Dolphin House, New Street, Salisbury SP1 2QQ
Telephone: 0722 6242

Investment Department 3-13 Arthur Street, London EC4P 4DS
Telephone: 01-626 6543

Managing Director S.G.Brooksbank

General Manager and Actuary A.SPedding,FIA

Deputy General Manager Investments J.J.Gunning

Property Manager S.V.Finn

Pensions Actuary I.D.Hammond,FIA

Employees 530

Gross Long Term Funds £264.8 million

Annual Premium Income £31.1 million

Annual Investment Income £20.5 million

Other Offices 29 branches and offices throughout UK

YORKSHIRE-GENERAL LIFE ASSURANCE COMPANY LTD
2 Rougier Street, York YO1 1HR
Telephone: 0904 28982

General Manager and Actuary N.S.Graham, MA, FIA, FCII

Assistant General Manager J.D.K.Philp, ACII

Pensions Manager R.Bridgeman, FCII, APMI

Investment Secretary A.D.Begg,MA

Other Pension Fund Experts J.H.R.Tonks,BSc,FIA, E.Sheffield,BSc,FFA, E.A.Knight,ACII,APMI, R.C.Amor,ACII,APMI

Employees 520

Gross Long Term Funds (at 31.12.79) £402.7 million

Annual Premium Income £52.2 million

Annual Investment Income £43.6 million

Number of Pension Fund Clients over 28,000

Services Offered to Pension Funds Fully insured pension and life assurance schemes by, with or non-profits policies, or on a managed fund basis

Parent Company General Accident Fire & Life Assurance Corporation Ltd.

Pension Fund Management Co Yorkshire-General Pensions Management) Ltd

Funds Managed Equity, Fixed Interest

Total Value of Pension Funds Managed (at 15.10.80) £1.9 million

Annual Premium Income £83,000

Annual Investment Income £41,000

Pension Fund Clients (at 15.10.80) 4

ZURICH LIFE ASSURANCE COMPANY LTD
Zurich House, Stanhope Road, Portsmouth PO1 1DU
Telephone: 0705 22200

General Manager F.R.Hall,ACII

Actuary C.Redman, BSc, FFA

Investment Manager R.Farr

Assistant Actuary G.J.Allan, BSc, FIA

Sales & Marketing Manager B.Hopper

Employees 85

Gross Long Term Funds £30 million

Annual Premium Income £11 million

Annual Investment Income £0.8 million

Miscellaneous

(a) Associations and Professional Bodies

This section lists a variety of advisory services and sources of information:
(a) Associations and Professional Bodies
(b) Public Organisations
(c) Publications and Sources of Information
(d) Employee Communications
(e) Computer and Administration Services Bureaux
(f) Investment Research

ASSOCIATION OF CONSULTING ACTUARIES

Metropolis House, 39 Tottenham Court Road, London W.1
Telephone: 01-636 7777
See also under Actuaries

ASSOCIATION OF PENSIONEER TRUSTEES

The Crescent, King Street, Leicester LE1 6RX
Telephone: 0533-547545

Chairman G.N.Pointon

Secretary W.T.Green

Treasurer B.Tatch

Other Committee Members N.D.Freethy, F.Low, M.Lander, D.W.Thomas, J.Quarrell

Aims To promote high standards of conduct within the profession, to negotiate with the SFO on all rulings affecting small self administered funds and to provide outside bodies and the public generally with a better understanding of the pensioneer trustee's function

FACULTY OF ACTUARIES

23 St Andrew Square, Edinburgh EH2 1AQ
Telephone: 031-556 6791
See also under Actuaries

INSTITUTE OF ACTUARIES

Staple Inn Hall, High Holborn, London WC1V 7QJ
Telephone: 01-242 0106
See also under Actuaries

THE NATIONAL ASSOCIATION OF PENSIONS FUNDS

Sunley House, Bedford Park, Croydon CR0 0XF
Telephone: 01-681 2017

Director General H.James

President G.H.Ross Goobey,FIA,FSS

Vice President G.J.J.Dennis

Chairman M.Pilch,BA,FCII,FPMI

Vice-Chairmen M.H.Oldfield,FPMI, T.Heyes,BSc (Econ)

Treasurer F.R.Langham,FIA,ASA,FPMI

Secretary C.I.Luckhoo,MA

Deputy Secretary B.Lofthouse

THE PENSIONS MANAGEMENT INSTITUTE

Carolyn House, Dingwall Road, Croydon CR0 9XF
Telephone: 01-681 3580

President R.E.Brimblecombe, FIA, FPMI

Vice Presidents D.G.Hosegood,FPMI, K.M.MacKelvey,FIA,ASA,FPMI

Honorary Treasurer E.A.Drake,FIA,FPMI

Secretary Mrs.J.E.March,BSc

(a) Associations and Professional Bodies

THE PENSIONS MANAGEMENT INSTITUTE *Continued*

The Institute exists to promote a high standard of professional conduct amongst those working in the pensions field and is the only professional organisation providing examination and tuition facilities leading to a nationally recognised qualification which is uniquely appropriate to a career in pension scheme management

PENSIONS RESEARCH ACCOUNTANTS GROUP (PRAG)

c/o National Water Council, St. Peter's House, Hartshead, Sheffield S1 1EU
Telephone: 0742 737331

Chairman J.M.Young,FCA,FPMI

Honorary Secretary J.C.Richards,IPFA,APMI

Honorary Treasurer A.S.Herbert, FCIS, FPMI

Other Information The Group consists of the accountants or managers of some of the leading UK occupational pension schemes, together with practitioners in the actuarial and auditing professions who are interested in the financial administration and reporting of pension schemes. It exists to sponsor research in fields directly of concern to the members and act as a forum for discussion of current developments.

THE SOCIETY OF PENSION CONSULTANTS

Ludgate House, Ludgate Circus, London EC4
Telephone: 01-353 1688
See also under Pension Fund Consultants

(b) Public Organisations

DEPARTMENT OF EMPLOYMENT
8 St. James's Square, London SW1
Telephone: 01-214 8695

Under Secretary G.A.Brand

Area of Interest Questions of pay policy and pensions

DEPARTMENT OF THE ENVIRONMENT
Tolworth Tower, Surbiton, Surrey KT6 7EA
Telephone: 01-399 5191

Superannuation Department John E. Blachford, FPMI

Area of Interest Local Authority superannuation schemes

DEPARTMENT OF HEALTH AND SOCIAL SECURITY
Alexander Fleming House, Elephant and Castle, London SE1 6BY
Telephone: 01-407 5522

Insurance Division K State House, High Holborn, London WC1R 4SX
Telephone: 01-242 9020

Areas of Interest Occupational pension schemes and the Occupational Pensions Board, contracting-out (ext 6072)

Solicitors Division Sol A1

Areas of Interest Occupational pensions and graduated pensions (ext 6563)

Benefits Division Newcastle Central Office, telephone 0632 857111

Areas of Interest Contracted out employment and national insurance retirement

GOVERNMENT ACTUARY'S DEPARTMENT
22 Kingsway, London WC2B 6LE
Telephone: 01-242 6828

Government Actuary E.A.Johnston,CB,FIA,FPMI

Two Main Services (a) Consultancy services: on superannuation to Government departments; to OPB; acting as actuary to certain public sector superannuation schemes (Directing Actuary R.C.Gilder,FIA,APMI)

Areas of Interest Public service superannuation (Principal Actuary J.R.Watts,FIA). Overseas and nationalised industries superannuation and OPB (Principal Actuary R.T.Foster,FIA)

(b) Advice to Government departments on social security (Directing Actuary C.M.Stewart, FIA)
Areas of Interest: Surveys of occupational pension schemes; relation with State scheme (Principal Actuary J.L.Field,FIA)

OCCUPATIONAL PENSIONS BOARD
Secretariat Almack House, 26-28 King Street, London SW1Y 6RB
Telephone: 01-214 8739

Executive Office Executive Office, Apex Tower, High Street, New Malden, Surrey KT3 4DN

Chairman Lord Brimelow,GCMG,OBE

Secretary Miss M.E.Grainger,OBE

The Board is an independent Statutory body. It administers the arrangements under the Social Security Act 1973 and the Social Security Pensions Act 1975 as they affect occupational pension schemes and advises the Secretary of State for Social Services on questions relating to occupational pension schemes

SUPERANNUATION FUNDS OFFICE (INLAND REVENUE)
Apex Tower, High Street, New Malden, Surrey KT3 4DN
Telephone: 01-942 8949

Controller H.B.Thompson

Are your other messages getting through?

New benefit packages
Redundancy arrangements
Executive resources schemes
Financial results
Job evaluation schemes
Special pension plans

Our skill lies in communicating a full range of difficult and complicated subjects clearly. **Not just pensions.**

ringley communications
51 London Road, Reigate, Surrey RH2 9QH.
Telephone Reigate 49409.

(c) Publications and Sources of Information

Statistics relating to pensions and superannuation schemes appear in 'Financial Statistics' published monthly by the Central Statistical Office as well as quarterly in 'M5 Business Monitor - Insurance Companies and Private Pension Fund Investment'. Both can be obtained from Government bookshops (HMSO) or from the Business Statistics Office, Cardiff Road, Newport, Gwent NPT 1XD

BENEFITS INTERNATIONAL

30 Queen Anne's Gate, London SW1H 9AW
Telephone: 01-222 8033

Editor Irena St.John-Brooks

Contributions Editors Jan Hottings, William B.Jadden, R.M.Leblond

Published by Pension Publications Ltd

COMPANY PENSIONS INFORMATION CENTRE

7 Old Park Lane, London W1Y 3LJ
Telephone: 01-493 4757

Chairman The Rt Hon The Lord Byers PC,OBE

Director of Information M.Brown

Corporate Body Occupational Pensions Information Ltd

Function A nonprofit-making body which gives general information about company pensions but not individual advice. The centre has published six booklets on company pensions. Copies are available from the centre

INTERNATIONAL BENEFITS INFORMATION SERVICE (IBIS)

222 West Adams Street, Suite 629, Chicago, Ill.60606,USA
Telephone: 312-236 2615

Published by Charles D.Spencer & Associates Inc

Editors John K.Dyer,FSA, Vincent Simone, Bruce F.Spencer

PENSIONS

150-152 Caledonian Road, London N1 9RD
Telephone: 01-278 6854

Managing Editor James Wootten

Published by Wootten Publications Ltd.

Editor Mihir Bose

Advertisement Manager Tom Orsler

Other Information Monthly journal of employee benefits and retirement planning.

PENSIONS TODAY

Rectory Road, Great Waldingfield, Sudbury, Suffolk CO10 0TL
Telephone: 0787-78607

Publisher Monitor Press

PENSIONS WORLD

60 Thames Street, Sunbury on Thames, Middx.TW16 6AF
Telephone: 76-82627

Managing Editor Trevor R.Warren

Editorial Board M.Pilch,BA,FCII,FPMI, M.H.Oldfield, FPMI, T.Heyes,BSc, G.J.J.Dennis,BSc, F.R.Langham, FIA,FPMI,FSS,ASA D.Blair,FCIS,FPMI, Mrs.M.S.Rewcastle,APMI

Published by CARL Communications Ltd. It also carries the Information Bulletin of the National Association of Pension Funds and is distributed to all its members

PLANNED SAVINGS

150-152 Caledonian Road, London N1 9RD
Telephone: 01-278 6854

Managing Editor J.Wootten

Editor M.Hockings

Advertisement Director G.Reid

Other Information Monthly journal covering all aspects of savings and investment

(d) Employee Communications

Most of the larger firms of Pension Fund Consultants advise their clients on employee communications and in certain cases will prepare the necessary brochures, presentation etc.

In addition the following companies offer Employee Communication Services.

A & A BENEFACTS (UK) LTD

Aldwych House, Aldwych, London WC2B 4HH
Telephone: 01-242 0651

Managing Director R.M.Kirkland

Sales Manager C.Horton

Employees 20

Number of Pension Fund Clients 80

Specialist Services Offered to Pension Funds Communication to members; employee benefit statements, handbooks, etc.

Other Offices Baltimore Baltimore

Associated Company Benefacts Inc. U.S.A.

AXON COMMUNICATIONS

c/o Noble Lowndes & Partners Ltd., Norfolk House, Wellesley Road, Croydon, Surrey CR9 3EB
Telephone: 01-686 2466

Manager Byron West

Number of Pension Fund Clients 350

Services Offered to Pension Funds Basic analysis of client's employee communications approach. From agreed brief, the design and production of all forms of pension communication services including script/copywriting, design, storyboards, photography, artwork, and overall co-ordination of production of audio-visual and printed material. Apart from specially prepared material, library programmes and information can be provided for a number of topics

Associated Companies Noble Lowndes & Partners (Parent Company)

Other Information Apart from pensions material a wide range of other employee communications are produced by Axon.

PENSIONS COMMUNICATIONS LTD

12-13 Henrietta Street, London WC2E 8LH
Telephone: 01-836 0437

Directors A.Mackenzie,MA (Chairman), A.H.S.Barnett,MA (Joint Managing Director), M.J.Fairclough,BSc (Joint Managing Director), D.Bosdet,CA, M.J.Day,BSc, G.Heywood,MBE, Beryl Stevens (Creative Director)

Company Founded Jointly by The British Petroleum Co Ltd and Duncan C. Fraser & Co

Employees 10

Pension Fund Clients 700

Associated Companies A-V Communications Ltd and Beryl Stevens Associates

Services Offered to Pension Funds A comprehensive range of standard audio-visual programmes and leaflets available on various aspects of pensions. Also the production of new material undertaken including slide/tape programmes, film, videotape, booklets, leaflets, trustee reports, etc. Pension training seminars run at regular intervals

Other Office 30 Exchange Street East, Liverpool L2 QB (051-227 4685)

Other Information (1) PCL produced for the DHSS the official audio-visual programme on the new State Pension Scheme which was introduced in April 1978 and over 100 copies have been made. (2) PCL have won several major international film prizes.

RINGLEY EMPLOYEE BENEFIT COMMUNICATIONS LTD (RINGLEY COMMUNICATIONS)

Ringley House, 51 London Road, Reigate, Surrey RH2 9QH
Telephone: 74-49409

Directors Acting for Pension Funds P.R.Francis,MA, FIA, D.F.Gilley,FIA,ASA,FPMI, G.E.Barrow,MBE,FIA, ASA, MI, M.J. de H.Bell,FIA,FPMI

Employees 6

Specialist Services Offered to Pension Funds Preparation of printed and audio-visual material explaining benefit packages, special pension plans, redundancy arrangements, executive resources schemes and financial results to employees. Trustee training material written and audio-visual can be supplied and seminars can be arranged. Equipment hire and projection services are also available.

Other Office 2-4 King Street, St. James's, London SW1Y 6QN

Associated Firm R.Watson & Sons

S.B.MODULES LTD

159 Great Portland Street, London W1N 5FD
Telephone: 01-323 1144

Director Acting for Pension Funds M.L.Broun

Other Pension Fund Expert S.Bayliss

Specialist Services Offered to Pension Funds Design, preparation and production of employee communications in the form of audio-visual and printed materials. Projection and presentation services available

TRISKEL COMMUNICATIONS

55 High Street, Epsom, Surrey KT19 8DH
Telephone: 78-26671

Directors Acting for Pension Funds R.W.Abbott, CBE, M.T.L.Bizley, R.M.Bangert, J.D.Sparks,BA, M.J.Jones,MA, R.D.Moore,MA

Communications Manager W.A.Eakins

Employees 6

Specialist Services Offered to Pension Funds Integrated approach to pension communications, from research to design, production and presentation. Booklets, benefit statements, announcements, reports, audio-visual presentations and overhead slides

Associated Company Bacon & Woodrow

Other Information In-house graphic, photographic and scriptwriting facilities. Presentation theatre and projection services available

(e) Computer and Administration Services Bureaux

BARIC COMPUTING SERVICES LTD
West Avenue, Kidsgrove, Stoke on Trent
Telephone: 0782 29681

Employees 800

Number of Pension Fund Clients 20 plus

Specialist Services Offered to Pension Funds Computer Services for i) Fund administration ii) Pension payments

Other Offices Glasgow, Leeds, Manchester, Birmingham, Bristol, Exeter

Parent Companies ICL and Barclays Bank

London Office Forest Road, Feltham, Middlesex (01-890 1414)

CLAYBROOK COMPUTING LTD
70 Brook Street, London W1Y 2HN
Telephone: 01-408 1600

Directors/Partners Acting for Pension Funds R.E.Barker (Managing), A.S.Fishman,BSc,FIA,FPMI, K.G.Whitehead,BA,FIA,FPMI, A.J.Wilson,BSc,FIA

Other Pension Fund Experts D.Tillson,MA,FIA, A.G.Skinner,AIB, R.J.Burger

Employees 16

Specialist Services Offered to Pension Funds Comprehensive on-line systems covering Pension Scheme Administration (PENSHARE), Personnel information and pensions payroll

Other Information A wholly owned specialist subsidiary of Clay & Partners (Consulting Actuaries)

DATASTREAM INTERNATIONAL LTD
Atlas House, 1 King Street, London EC2V 8BX
Telephone: 01-600 6411

Directors A.L.Helman (Managing Director), B.R.J.Bateman, H.A.F.Kearns, R.Willis, L.A.Pinner

Employees 220

Number of Pension Fund Clients 100 plus

Specialist Services Offered to Pension Funds Investment research services covering all major equity and fixed interest securities markets in depth, together with an extensive international economic/money market database. Administrative facilities include comprehensive portfolio valuation services and an on-line investment accounting system, backed by a range of printed reports. These can be linked to provide a fully integrated service for fund managers

Other Offices Rotterdam, Frankfurt, Geneva

Other Information More than 300 clients subscribe to dataSTREAM's terminal-based services including major pension funds from public and private sectors, plus stockbrokers, clearing and merchant banks, insurance and industrial companies, Government agencies and academic institutions. Approximately 300 more use our printed services only

EXTEL COMPUTING LTD
Lowndes House, 1-9 City Road, London EC1Y 1AA
Telephone: 01-638 5544

Directors G.F.Laurence (Chairman), B.G.Botten, M.P.Dineen, J.F.McDonald, D.E.Samuel, P.Camber, M.W.Warburg (Managing)

Other Pension Fund Expert J.C.Keaney

Employees 115

Specialist Services Offered to Pension Funds A computerised Pension Fund Investment Accounting Service which covers all aspects of accounting and administration for pension fund investments, available in printed form or on-line. It maintains investment, income and general ledgers as well as providing income forecasting facilities, portfolio valuations and a variety of management report

Associated Companies Extel Statistical Services Ltd and other members of the Extel Group

Other Information The company's first major service was FOCUS, a joint venture with Reuters established in 1967. It provides daily price, dividend and other information on more than 30,000 international securities in computer-readable form. FOCUS is widely used by banks, stockbrokers, insurance companies and financial institutions, and is marketed internationally. The Investment Accounting Service is used by insurance companies, banks, investment trusts and other financial institutions as well as major pension funds

GMS COMPUTING LTD
Smithfield House, Blonk Street, Sheffield S1 2BU
Telephone: 0742 730191

Pension Expert K.C.Smith

Employees 85

Specialist Services Offered to Pension Funds The PENSAD range of computer systems for Pensions Administration and associated tasks providing comprehensive record updating, maintenance, calculation, reporting and output facilities. PENSAD systems may be implemented on the Client's own equipment or, alternatively, a complete Bureau service is available

HEYWOOD & PARTNERS LTD
30 Exchange Street East, Liverpool L2 3QB
Telephone: 051-236 0881

Directors Acting for Pension Funds G.Heywood, J.D.U.Harsant, P.E.Felton, N.J.Braithwaite, F.I.Bowles, I.G.Hodgson

Other Pension Fund Experts R.Chadwick, W.F.Ashburner, M.B.Reid, E.P.Moynihan

Employees 60

Number of Pension Fund Clients 100

Specialist Services Offered to Pension Funds Heywood & Partners have developed PASSMAN, a sophisticated computer system for pension administration, and they provide pensions/ computer expertise to help implement the system effectively. Heywood & Partners also have a major role in the CLASS system; a computerised pension system designed specifically for Local Authorities. As well as their package service, Heywood &

(e) Computer and Administration Services Bureaux

HEYWOOD & PARTNERS LTD *Continued*

Partners also provide a bureau service for pensions administration and payroll

Other Offices 24-28 Cheapside, London EC2V 6AB (01-248 6981)

Associated Company Duncan C. Fraser & Co

PENSION SCHEME REGISTRARS AND PENSION DATA SERVICES

Bradford House, St. Stephen's Avenue, Bristol BS1 1YL
Telephone: 0272 22351

Directors Involved with Pension Funds K.J.Edis, APMI, D.G.Cross

Specialist Services Offered to Pension Funds Pension Scheme Registrar-independent specialists providing comprehensive pensions administration services. Provides smaller companies with all the facilities of a large company's pensions department. Pension Data Services-two services-SYSTEM 80 an advanced interactive pensions administration package which comes complete with hardware and software ready to work. Based on Texas Instruments 990/10 computer, SYSTEM 80 includes a complete maintenance, updating, calculations, benefit statements, pensioner payroll and valuations statistics. Also, a conventional bureau service offering all the above facilities.

Parent Company United Pension Services Ltd

PENSIONS AND INSURANCE COMPUTER SERVICES

5 St. John's Lane, London EC1M 4BH
Telephone: 01-250 1500

General Manager K.Kelly, AIA

Other Pension Fund Expert D.Higgins, FCII

Employees 31

Number of Pension Fund Clients 50

Specialist services Offered to Pension Funds Computer-based systems for administration and valuation of pension funds

Associated Companies Unilever Ltd, Unilever Computer Services Ltd

Other Information A complete computing service which includes Pensions Administration - record keeping, benefit statements, membership and special reports, Contracting Out - statutory calculations, DHSS returns, integration with other systems, Specialist Services - pension payments, investment, valuation

PETERBOROUGH DATA PROCESSING SERVICES LTD

Borough House, Newark Road, Peterborough PE1 5YJ
Telephone: 0733 41010

General Manager, Marketing A.D.Bews

Marketing Administrator Ms.P.A.Murrell

Employees 120

Services Offered to Pension Funds The UNIPENSIONS system - a comprehensive and fully maintained computerised pension administration system designed to meet all requirements of the Social Security Pensions Act 1975

Other Offices Unit 8, 14-18 Low Pavement, Nottingham NG1 7DL

Associated Companies Peterborough Data markets an on-line version of the UNIPENSION system for IBM mainframe computers, in association with the pension consultants C.E.Heath Ltd. who provide consultancy and training

Other Information Peterborough Data Processing Services Limited is the U.K.'s leading supplier of application software packages for manpower resource management. In addition to UNIPENSION, the company markets the UNIPAY payroll administration system and the UNIPERSONNEL personnel information system

SPECIALIST SOFTWARE LTD

44 London Wall, London EC2M 5TB
Telephone: 01-920 0522

Directors Acting for Pension Funds E.B.Caplin, O.D.London

Specialist Services Offered to Pension Funds Computer systems using mini-computers and bureaux for pension funds, investment managers and advisers for transaction processing, accounting and research covering U.K. and Overseas securities

SYSTEMSOLVE (COMPUTER SERVICES) LTD.

Brenntag House, 45c High Street, Hampton Wick, Kingston-on-Thames KT1 4DG, Surrey
Telephone: 01-943 2371

Sales Director P.S.Wemyss

Other Pension Fund Experts Several consultants within the Company

Employees 150

Number of Pension Fund Clients 6

Specialist Services Offered to Pension Funds Computer systems for all aspects of the pension fund administration

Other Offices Sunbury and Manchester

Associated Companies BOC/Datasolve

Major Clients Ferranti, Merchant Navy Officers Pension Fund, RAC

UNITED PENSION SERVICES LTD.

Bradford House, St Stephen's Avenue, Bristol BS1 1YL
Telephone: 0272 22351

Directors Acting for Pension Funds K.J.Edis,APMI, P.Burfitt,ACIS

Services Offered to Pension Funds Wide range of management services including management consultancy, complete computer systems, pension administration and bureau service. Also suppliers of System 80 business machine.

Associated Companies Pension System Registrars, Pension Data Systems, UPS Rentals Ltd., United Pension Funds Trust Ltd.

Other Information Clients cover a broad spectrum of British industry and commerce and range from major public companies with 40,000 or more employees to small companies employing 10 or 20.Included are large multiple retailers, battery manufacturers, house builders, consulting engineers, housing associations, whisky distillers, component manufacturers, professional practices and insurance companies.

(e) Computer and Administration Services Bureaux

WOOD, MACKENZIE & CO (COMPUTER SERVICES)

Erskine House, 68-73 Queen Street,
Edinburgh EH2 4NS
Telephone: 031-225 8525

Partners/Senior Executives Involved in Computer Services D.M.Eadie, B.A.Smith, J.G.L.Hogg, P.P.Harkin, G.M.Bagot, J.M.Gillies, J.C.Williams

Specialist Services Offered to Pension Funds "Fund Management Services" provides an integrated computer-based management information system for pension fund investments. There are specific services to cover pension fund performance measurement, valuations and reports, investment accounting and property valuations and reports. The services do not operate on a normal bureau basis, as they all include clerical support and consultancy

Other Information Brochures to describe 'Fund Management Services' are available on request. See also entry under Stockbrokers

---

PENSION FUNDS AND THEIR ADVISERS 1981

TO PURCHASE EXTRA COPIES PRICE £21.00
Plus £1.50 for Postage and Packing

WRITE OR PHONE
A.P. FINANCIAL REGISTERS LTD
9 COURTLEIGH GARDENS
LONDON NW11 9JX
Telephone: 01- 458 1607

ALSO AVAILABLE
FROM ALL
MAJOR BOOKSHOPS

(f) Investment Research

Many of the banks, stockbrokers and other financial advisers listed earlier maintain their own investment research departments, some of which prepare either specific reports for individual clients or more general economic or company analysis reports. In addition the following firms supply investment research services.

EXTEL STATISTICAL SERVICES LTD
37-45 Paul Street, London EC2A 4PB
Telephone: 01-253 3400

Directors M.P.Dineen (Chairman), G.T.A.Rason (Managing), R.A.Bohee, G.F.Quick, T.J.A.Tummon (Sales & Marketing)

Secretary P.C.Harris

Employees 200

Specialist Services Offered to Pension Funds Extel Card Services: British Quoted Company Service. Analyst's Service. British Unquoted Companies Service, Australian Service, European Service, North American Service, International Bonds Service, Extel's Taxation Services, Extel's Issuing Services, Registrar's Service, Extel Shareholding Service, Companies House Searches; EXSTAT, a computer readable data base of company information

Other Offices Manchester

Associated Companies Extel Computing Ltd and other members of the EXTEL Group

INVESTMENT RESEARCH
28 Panton Street, Cambridge CB2 1DH
Telephone: 0223 56251

Partners A.G.Ellinger, T.H.Stewart, D.C.Damant, J.R.L.Cuningham

Services Offered Fund management and investment advice. Advice on commodities and currencies, index matching analysis

Associated Company Clive Investment Cambridge Ltd

ISIS
c/o Laurie, Milbank & Co., Portland House, 72-73 Basinghall Street, London EC2V 5DD
Telephone: 01-606 6622

Partner Involved K.E.Ayers,FIA,FSS,APMI

LONDON BUSINESS SCHOOL FINANCIAL SERVICES
Sussex Place, Regent's Park, London NW1 4SA
Telephone: 01-262 5050

Staff Acting for Pension Funds P.Marsh, E.Dimson, P.Zinkin, I.Cooper, S.Hodges, Prof.R.Brealey

Other Pension Fund Experts J.Franks, J.Broyles, B.Brown

Pension Fund Clients 50

Services Offered to Pension Funds Risk measurement service, portfolio analysis service, transactions analysis service, asset allocation management service. Specialist seminars and courses in the application of modern portfolio theory.

ROWE RUDD & COMPANY
63 London Wall, London EC2
Telephone: 01-628 9666

Partners Acting for Pension Funds R.A.W.Rudd, G.P.Kelly

Other Pension Fund Expert J.J.MacQueen

Employees 80

Pension Fund Clients 10

Services Offered to Pension Funds International portfolio diversification, portfolio risk analysis

Other Offices Geneva, Jersey, Edinburgh.

Associated Company Rowe Rudd Overseas Services

(g) Trustees

THE LAW DEBENTURE CORP.LTD.
Estates House, 66 Gresham Street, London EC2V 7AX
Telephone: 01-606 5451

Services Offered to Pension Funds Leading independent trust corporation acting as trustee for pension funds

Index of Advisers

A & A Benefacts (UK) Ltd *714*
Abbey Life Assurance Co Ltd *689*
Abbott, James, Partnership *611*
Abbotstone Agricultural Property Unit Trust *591*
Administration, Industrial & Management Services Ltd *667*
Aegis Insurance Services (Life & Pensions) Ltd *667*
Albany Life Assurance Co Ltd *689*
Alexander & Alexander Inc *667*
Alliance Capital Management International Inc *579*
Allied Hambro Exempt Funds *591*
Allsop and Co *611*
American Property Trust *592*
Andrews, Philip, & Co *611*
Ansbacher Investment Management Ltd *555*
Arbuthnot Investment Management Services Ltd *555*
Armstrong, J. C., & Co Ltd *667*
Arthur, T. G., & Co *665*
Arundel Exempt Fund *592*
Association of Consulting Actuaries *663*
Association of Pensioner Trustees *709*
Assurance & Commercial Services *667*
Australian Mutual Provident Society *689*
Axon Communications Unit *714*

Bacchus Gathercole & Partners *611*
Bacon & Woodrow *663*
Baillie, Gifford & Co *579*
Bain Dawes & Partners Ltd *667*
Bairstow Eves *613*
Baker Harris Saunders *613*
Bank of America *555*
Bank of Scotland, Investment Services *557*
Bankart, G. & J. E., Ltd *667*
Bankers Trust Exempt Fund *592*
Bankers Trust Company *557*
Bannerman, John (Life & Pensions) Ltd *669*
Barbican European (Exempt) Trust *592*
Barclays Bank Trust Co Ltd *557*
Barclays Insurance Services Co Ltd *669*
Barclays Unicorn Exempt Trust *592*
Baric Computing Services Ltd *715*
Baring Brothers & Co Ltd *557*
Barnett Baker & Co *613*
Barnett, Rodney, & Co *664*
Barrington Laurance *613*
Bartlett & Co (Life & Pensions) Ltd *669*
B.B.H. Trustees Ltd *669*
Beardsley Bishop Escombe *567*
Behrens, Victor, Sandhurst & Co *613*
Bell-Ingram *613*
Bell, Lawrie, MacGregor & Co *567*

Index of Advisers

Benefits International 713
Bidwells 613
Biscoe & Stanton 613
Blackmore, Alfred (Life & Pensions) Ltd 669
Bland, P. & G., Ltd 669
Blythe Eastman Dillon 579
Body Son & Fleury 613
Bolton Corder Ltd 669
Bowring, C. T., & Layborn Ltd 671
Bradstock Blunt & Barney Ltd 671
Brecker, Grossmith & Co 613
Brentall Beard (Life & Pensions) Ltd 671
Brewin Dolphin & Co 567
Bridge Exempt Fund 592
Britannia Exempt Trust 592
Britannia Institutional Fund Management Ltd 579
Britannic Assurance Co Ltd 690
Brombard Financial Services Ltd 579
Browett Taylor & Co 615
Brown, Graham, & Co (Life & Pensions) Ltd 671
Brown, Shipley & Co Ltd 557
Brown, Anthony, Stewart 615
Brown, William H., & Son 615
Bruton Knowles & Co 615
Buckell & Ballard 615
Buckmaster & Moore 567
Butcher, Henry, & Co 615
Butcher, Norman, & Jones (Life & Pension Brokers) Ltd 671
Byas Mosley (Life & Pensions) Ltd 671

Callund & Co Ltd 673
Cambridge Communications Ltd 739
Campbell Gordon 615
Canada Life Managed Pension Fund 592
Canada Life Assurance Company 690
Capel, James & Co 567
Capel-Cure Myers Ltd 567
Capital Partners International 581
Cardale, Keith, Groves & Co 617
Carr, Sebag & Co 567
Carrington, John, & Co Ltd 581
Carter Jonas 617
Cazenove & Co 569
Chamberlain & Willows 617
Chambers & Remington 569
Charlton, Seal, Dimmock & Co 569
Chancellors & Co 617
Charterhouse Exempt Fund 592
Charterhouse Japhet Investment Management Ltd 557
Chellingworth, Howard, Ltd 673
Chemical Bank Trustee Co Ltd 559

Chesham Hill Ltd 673
Chesshire, Gibson & Co 617
Chestertons 617
Churston, Heard & Co 617
C. H. W. Pension Consultants Ltd 673
CIPFA Services Ltd 581
City Financial Administration Ltd 581
Clarke, F. P. (Insurances) Ltd 673
Clarkson, H. (Life & Pensions Consultants) Ltd 673
Clay & Partners 664
Claybrook Computing Ltd 715
Clegg, John, & Co 659
Clerical, Medical & General Life Assurance Society 690
Clifford Bonney 619
Clive Investments Ltd 581
Cluttons 619
Cockman, Copeman & Partners Ltd 673
Collier & Madge 619
Collins, A. R. H., & Co 664
Colonial Mutual Life Assurance Society Ltd 690
Colonial Mutual Life Managed Fund 592
Commercial Union Assurance Co Ltd 691
Commercial Union Managed Fund 593
Company Pensions Information Centre 713
Confederation Life Group Pension Pooled Funds 592
Confederation Life Insurance Co 691
Coni, Gilbert & Sankey 569
Connells Commercial 619
Conrad Ritblat & Co 619
Constable, P. J. 664
Continental Illinois Ltd 559
Conway Relf 619
Cooke & Arkwright 619
Cooke, Henry, Lumsden & Co 569
Cooper Kendall & Co 621
Co-operative Insurance Society Ltd 691
Co-operative Pension Funds Fixed Interest Unit Trust 593
Co-operative Pension Funds Unit Trust 593
County Bank Exempt Funds 593
County Bank Ltd 559
Craigmount Investment Management Ltd 581
Crown Life Group of Companies 691
Crown Life Managed Pension Funds 593
Cruickshanks Commercial 621
Crusader Insurance Co Ltd 693
Cubie, Wood & Co Ltd 673
Martin Currie Investment Management Ltd 581
Cuthbert Lake Drew Pearce 621
Cuthbert Service (Life & Pensions) Ltd 673
Cyril Leonard & Co 621

Index of Advisers

Dacre, Son & Hartley *621*
Dale-Cooke, A., & Co Ltd *675*
Dallas, T. L., Associates *675*
DataSTREAM International Ltd *715*
Davis, Henry, & Co *621*
De, Amit & Co *664*
de Groot Collis *621*
de Zoete & Bevan *569*
Debenham Tewson & Chinnocks *621*
Department of Employment *711*
Department of the Environment *711*
Department of Health & Social Security *711*
Dewey Warren (Insurance Services) Ltd *675*
Diamond & Company *621*
Dobbin, J. N. (Pension Consultants) Ltd *675*
Donaldson & Sons *621*
Drayton Montagu Portfolio Management Ltd *559*
Drivers Jonas *623*
Dron & Wright *623*
Druce & Co *623*
Duff Stoop & Co *569*
Duncan Stupples *623*
Dunkley Marshall *569*
Dunlop Heywood & Co *623*

Eadon, Lockwood & Riddle *623*
Eagle Star Insurance Co Ltd *693*
Eagle Star Managed Pension Funds *593*
Earnshaw, Haes & Sons *569*
Easton, Watson & Smith *569*
The A. G. Ebbage Partnership *623*
E. B. Consultants Ltd *675*
Ebor Phoenix Assurance Co Ltd Managed Pension Fund *594*
E.B.S. (Management) Ltd *675*
Ecclesiastical Insurance Office Ltd *694*
Economic Forestry Ltd *659*
Eddisons *625*
Edis & Co *675*
Edinburgh Exempt Pacific Fund *594*
Edinburgh Exempt American Fund *594*
Edinburgh Exempt Japan Fund *594*
Edinburgh Fund Managers Ltd *581*
Edwards, Bigwood & Bewlay *625*
Ekins, Dilley & Handley *625*
Electra Group Services Ltd *583*
Electra Small Companies Exempt Fund *594*
Elliott, Gilbert, & Co *570*
Elliott, Son & Boyton *625*
Ellis, Richard *625*
Ellison, Robin (Pension Consultants) Ltd *675*
English Insurance Co Ltd *694*

English Insurance Managed Pension Fund *594*
Equitable Life Assurance Society *694*
Equity & Law Life Assurance Society Ltd *694*
Equity & Law Managed Fund *594*
Equity Capital Unit Trust *594*
Edward Erdman *625*
Estridge & Ropner Life & Pensions Services Ltd *675*
Eve, Gerald & Co *627*
Extel Computing Ltd *715*
Extel Statistical Services Ltd *718*

F & C Management Ltd *583*
F & C Anglo-Nippon Exempt Fund *595*
F & C North American Exempt Fund *595*
The Faculty of Actuaries in Scotland *663*
Farebrother *627*
Fawdry & Evans *627*
Federated Pension Schemes *675*
Fenchurch Life & Pension Consultants Ltd *675*
Fenn Wright *627*
Fidelity International Investment Management *583*
Fielding, Newson-Smith & Co *570*
James Finlay Investment Management Ltd *583*
Finn, J. M., & Co *570*
Fisher and Co *627*
Fleming Exempt Funds *595*
Fleming, Robert, Investment Management Ltd *559*
Fleming Property Unit Trust *595*
Fletcher King *627*
Folkard & Hayward *627*
Forestry Investment Management Ltd *659*
Foster, A. R. O., Ltd *676*
Foster & Braithwaite *570*
Fountain Forestry Ltd *659*
Fox & Sons *627*
Fraser, Duncan C., & Co *664*
Fraser Exempt Unit Trust *595*
Fraser Green Ltd *583*
Friar Gate Insurance Services Ltd *676*
Friends' Provident Life Office *695*
Friends' Provident Managed Pension Funds *595*
Frizzell, Norman Life & Pensions Ltd *676*
Frost, A. C., & Co *629*
FS Assurance Ltd *695*
Fuller Peiser *629*
Furness-Houlder (Life & Pensions) Ltd *676*

Index of Advisers

Galloway & Pearson *570*
Gardner Watts Ltd *676*
Garratt, Son & Flowerdew Ltd *676*
Garrett, White & Poland *629*
Gartmore Pension Fund Managers Ltd *583*
Gartmore International Exempt Fund *595*
Gaudery Ltd *659*
Geering & Colyer *629*
Genis & Partners *629*
Gibbs, Antony, Investment Management Ltd *561*
Gibbs, Antony Pension Services Ltd *676*
Gibson Eley & Co *629*
Gilroy, Broome & Scrini Ltd *676*
Gissing Sellon Breslin & Co Ltd *676*
Glanvill Enthoven (Life, Pensions & Mortgages) Ltd *676*
Glennon, Philip, Associates (Pension Scheme Planning) Ltd *677*
Globe Pensions Managed Fund *595*
GMS Computing Ltd *715*
Goddard & Smith *629*
Godwins Ltd *677*
Goldenberg & Co *629*
Gooch & Wagstaff *629*
Goodman Mann Associates *631*
Gordon, Panmure & Co *570*
Gorrill, Maule-Oatway & Co Ltd *677*
Goudie Pension Consultants *677*
Gould, Laurence & Co Ltd *659*
Government Actuaries Department *711*
Govett, John, & Co Ltd *585*
Grant & Partners *631*
Graves, Son & Pilcher *631*
Greenwell, W., & Co *570*
Greig, R. C., & Co *570*
Grenfell & Colegrave *570*
Grenville, Richard, Ltd *585*
Gresham Life Assurance Society Ltd *695*
Grieveson, Grant & Co *570*
Griffiths & Armour *677*
Grimley & Son *631*
de Groot Collis *621*
Gross Fine & Krieger Chalfen *631*
G. T. Management Ltd *585*
G. T. Pension Exempt Fund *596*
Guardian Royal Exchange Assurance Ltd *695*
Guardian Royal Exchange Managed Funds *596*
Guinness Mahon & Co Ltd *561*

Haarer & Goss *631*
Hague, David, Consultants *677*
Hall, Frank, B. Consulting Co *677*
Hall, Pain & Foster *631*
Hallam Brackett & Co *631*
Halliday, Simpson & Co *570*
Hallsworth Ltd *659*
Hambros Bank Ltd *561*
Hambro Life Assurance Ltd *696*
Hamnett Raffety *631*
Hampton & Sons *631*
Hanover Property Unit Trust *596*
Hanson & Co *571*
Peter Hardy (Life & Pensions Consultants) Ltd *677*
Harewood Ridgeway Professional Services Ltd *677*
Harrap Brothers *678*
Harris, Allday, Lea & Brooks *571*
Harris, Marrian & Co Ltd *678*
Harrison, R. K. (Life & Pensions) Ltd *678*
Hartnell/Taylor/Cook *633*
Hartley Cooper Life & Pensions Brokers Ltd *678*
Hayden, Douglas, & Co Ltd *678*
Hayman Jackson Insurance Brokers Ltd *678*
Hayter, Neil *665*
Healey & Baker *633*
Hearn, G. L., & Partners *633*
Heath, C. E., Urquhart (Life & Pensions) Ltd *678*
Hedderwick, Stirling, Grumbar & Co *571*
John Heddle & Co *633*
Henderson Crosthwaite & Co *571*
Henderson Exempt Trusts *596*
Henderson Pension Fund Management Ltd *585*
Hepper, Watson & Sons *633*
Herring Son & Daw *633*
Heseltine Moss & Co *571*
Herriot, Walter (Life & Pensions) Ltd *678*
Heywood & Partners Ltd *715*
Hill Samuel Agricultural Unit Trust *597*
Hill Samuel General Exempt Trust *597*
Hill Samuel Investment Management Ltd *561*
Hill Samuel Life Assurance Ltd *696*
Hill Samuel Property Unit Trust *597*
Hillier Parker May & Rowden *633*
Hirschfield, Norman, Ryde & Brown *635*
Hoare Govett Ltd *571*
Hogg Robinson (Benefit Consultants) Ltd *678*
Holmwoods & Crawfurd (Life & Pension Brokers) Ltd *679*
Housley Heath & Co (Life & Pensions) Ltd *679*
How, Graham (Life & Pensions) Brokers *679*
Howarth & Green *635*
Howden, Alexander, Insurance Brokers Ltd *679*

Index of Advisers

Howell, Brooks & Partners 635
Howes, Percy, & Co 635
Howson Devitt (Life & Pensions) Brokers Ltd 679
Humberts 635
Hunter, David C. 635
Hurst & Marsh Ltd 679
Hutchison & Craft Ltd 679
Hymans, Robertson & Co 665

IDJ Investment Services Ltd 585
Illingworth & Henriques 571
Imperial Life Assurance Co of Canada 696
Industrial & Commercial Finance Corporation Ltd 563
Industrial & Commercial Property Unit Trust 597
Institute of Actuaries 663
Intel Portfolio Management Ltd 585
International Benefits Information Service (IBIS) 713
International Forest Science Consultancy 659
Investment Research 718
Irish Life Assurance Co Ltd Managed Pension Funds 597
Irish Pension Trust Ltd 680
ISIS 718
Ivory & Sime Ltd 587

Jackson-Stops & Staff 635
James, John H., & Co 637
Jameson, David (IPS) Ltd 680
January, Douglas L., & Partners 637
Jewell, Pearce, Davy & Co Ltd 680
Joel, Henry, & Co 637
Jones Lang Wootton 637
Jowitt & Freeman (Pensions) Ltd 680

Keith, Bayley, Rogers & Co 571
Kemp-Gee & Co 571
Kemsley Whiteley & Ferris 637
Key Exempt Fund 597
Keyser Ullmann Pensions Managed Fund 597
Keyser Ullmann Pensions Management Ltd 563
King & Co 637
King, C. R., & Partners Ltd 680
King & Shaxson Bond Fund 597
Kinney & Green 637
Edmund Kirby & Sons 637
Kitcat & Aitken 573
Kleinwort, Benson Exempt Pacific Fund 597
Kleinwort, Benson Farmland Trust 597
Kleinwort, Benson Investment Management Ltd 563

Kleinwort, Benson Property Trust 597
Knight Frank & Rutley 637

Laing & Cruickshank 573
Lalonde Bros & Parham 639
Lamb, F. S., & Co Ltd 630
Lambert Smith & Partners 639
Lambourne Foreman & Partners 639
Lancaster R. D., & Associates Ltd 680
Lander Burfield 639
Lane, Clark & Peacock 665
Lane Fox & Partners 639
Langley-Taylor 639
Laurence, Prust & Co 573
Laurie, Milbank & Co 573
Laurie, Michael, & Partners 639
Law Debenture Corp. Ltd 718
Lawson & Lawson 641
Lazard Exempt Funds 598, 599
Lazard Property Unit Trust 599
Lazard Securities Ltd 563
Leavers 641
Legal & General Assurance Society Ltd 696
Legal & General Managed Fund 599
Legal & General Property Fund 599
Le Mare, Martin & Co 573
Levy, D. E. & J. 641
Lewis, Clive & Partners 641
Lewis, Michael, Associates Ltd 680
Lewis & Tucker 641
Life Association of Scotland Ltd 697
Life Association of Scotland Managed Fund 599
Lipton, Anthony, & Co 641
Lisney & Son 641
Lloyds Bank Ltd Investment Dept 563
Lloyd's Life Assurance Ltd 597
Local Authorities' Mutual Investment Trust (LAMIT) 587, 599
Local Authorities' Property Fund 599
Locana Corporation (London) Ltd 587
Locks & Co 641
London & Manchester Assurance Co Ltd 697
London & Manchester Assurance Co Managed Fund 600
London & Westminster (Sterling Brokers) Ltd 587
London Australian Pension Unit Trust 600
London Business School 718
London Continental Pension Unit Trust 600
London Far East Pension Unit Trust 600
London Fixed Interest Exempt Unit Trust 600
London Life Association Ltd 697
London Life Managed Funds 600

Index of Advisers

London North America Pension Unit Trust *600*
Lumley, Edward (Life & Pensions) Ltd *680*
Lyddon & Co *573*
Lyle, Gibson & Co Ltd *680*

M&G Investment Management Ltd *587*
M&G Pension Exempt Fund *600*
MacAlaster & Alison Ltd *680*
Mann & Co *641*
Manufacturers Life Insurance Co (UK) Ltd *698*
Marine & General Mutual Life Assurance Society *698*
Martin, R. P., & Co Ltd *587*
Mason, Owen & Partners *641*
Mason Philips *643*
Matthews, Goodman & Poslethwaite *643*
Matthews, Smith (Financial Consultants) Ltd *680*
Maurice Andrew *643*
McAnally, Montgomery & Co *573*
McCall, Ian, Employee Benefits Ltd *680*
McDaniel & Daw *643*
Mellersh & Harding *643*
Mercer, William M., Benefits Ltd *680*
Merchant Investors Assurance Co Ltd *698*
Mercury Exempt Fund *601*
Messel, L., & Co *573*
Metropolitan Pensions Association (Holdings) Ltd *681*
W. N. Middleton & Co *575*
Midland Bank Insurance Services Ltd *681*
Midland Bank Trust Co Ltd *563*
Midland Drayton Equity Exempt Trust *601*
Minet Consultancy Services Ltd *681*
Minster Exempt Fund *601*
M.J. Japan Exempt Fund *601*
M.J. American Exempt Fund *601*
Molyneux Rose *643*
Montagu Evans & Sons *643*
Montagu, Loebl, Stanley & Co *575*
Morgan, Christian, Pension Consultants Ltd *681*
Morgan Grenfell & Co Ltd *564*
Morgen Grenfell Special Exempt Fund *601*
Morgan Guaranty Trust Co of New York *564*
Morley, Geoffrey, & Partners Ltd *589*
Mountjoy, R. W. *681*
MPW (Trustees) Ltd *681*
Mullens & Co *575*
Murray Johnstone Ltd *589*
Myddelton & Major *643*

National Association of Pension Funds *709*

National Employers' Life Group of Companies *698*
National Employers' Life Managed Pension Fund *601*
National Farmers' Union Mutual Insurance Society Ltd *699*
National Girobank *564*
National Mutual Life Managed Pension Fund *601*
National Mutual Life Assurance Society *699*
National Provident Institution *699*
National Westminster Bank Ltd *564*
Neale & Alldridge *643*
New Court Exempt Equity Fund *602*
New Court Exempt Gilt Trust *602*
New Court Property Fund *602*
Newiss, Stewart *643*
Newton Perkins & Forbes *645*
Nicholson, J. W., & Sons *575*
Nivison, R., & Co *575*
Noble Lowndes & Partners Ltd *681*
Norfolk & Suffolk Insurance Services Ltd *681*
Northcote & Co *575*
Norwich Union Life Insurance Society *699*
Norwich Union Managed Pension Fund *602*
Notcutt Life & Pensions Ltd *682*
NPI Pooled Managed Fund *602*
NRG London Reinsurance Co Ltd *700*

Occupational Pensions Board *711*
Oceanic Exempt Fund *602*
Osmond, Tricks & Son *645*
Owers, Ernest, & Williams *645*
Oxborrows *645*

Paneuropean Property Unit Trust *602*
Panmure Gordon & Co *570*
Parkdale Pensions Management *682*
Parnis Bird & Partners *645*
Parsons & Co *575*
Paterson, Martin, Associates Ltd *682*
Pearl Assurance Co Ltd *700*
Pearsons *645*
Pember & Boyle *575*
Penney, Castello, Carlebach & Co *575*
Pennine Property Unit Trust *602*
Pension Fund & Charities Agricultural Property Unit Trust *602*
Pension Fund Property Unit Trust (PFPUT) *603*
Pension Management (SWF) Ltd *704*
Pensions *713*
Pension Scheme Registrars *716*
Pensions & Charities Property Fund *603*
Pensions Communications Ltd *714*

Index of Advisers

Pensions & Insurance Computer Services *716*
Pensions Research Accounts Group *710*
Pensions Management Institute *709*
Pensions Today *713*
Pensions World *713*
Peterborough Data Processing Services Ltd *716*
Pepper Angliss & Yarwood *645*
Phillips & Drew *575*
Phoenix Assurance Co Ltd *700*
Phoenix, Beard *645*
Phoenix, Conrad & Co *645*
Pidgeon de Smitt *575*
Planned Savings *713*
PM & M Life & Pensions Services Ltd *682*
Pointon York (Pensions & Employee Benefits) Ltd *682*
Preston Powell (Holdings) Ltd *683*
Price, Charles, & Co *645*
Professional Assurance Services Ltd *683*
Property Growth Assurance Company Ltd *700*
Property Growth Managed Pension Fund *603*
Property Unit Trust for Public and General Superannuation Schemes (PUTPAGS) *603*
Providence Capitol Life Assurance Co Ltd *701*
Providence Capitol Managed Pension Fund *603*
Provident Life Association of London Ltd *701*
Provident Mutual Life Assurance Association *701*
Provident Mutual Managed Pension Funds Ltd *603*
Prudential Assurance Co Ltd *701*
Prudential Group Investment-Linked Pension Plan *604*

Quilter, Hilton, Goodison & Co *576*

Ramsay Insurance Consultants Ltd *683*
Raphael, Zorn *576*
Ratcliffes *647*
Rea Brothers (Life Loans & Pensions) Ltd *683*
Reed Stenhouse Benefit Consultants Ltd *683*
Reeds *647*
Reis, R. G., Pension Fund Trustees Ltd *683*
Rensburg & Co *576*
Reynolds, John, & Co (Life & Pensions) Ltd *683*
Richards, Longstaff Ltd *683*
Richman Conway & Co *647*

Ringley Communications *714*
Roberts, A. *665*
Robertson, Hymans & Co *665*
Robinson, W. H., & Co *647*
Rothschild, N. M., Asset Management Ltd *564, 647*
Rowan Investment Management Services *589*
Rowe & Pitman *576*
Rowe Rudd & Co Ltd *589, 713*
Rowlandson, Christopher J., Life & Pensions *683*
Royal Bank of Scotland Ltd *555*
Royal Insurance Co Ltd *702*
Royal London Mutual Insurance Society Ltd *702*
Royal National Pension Fund For Nurses *702*
Royal Trust Co of Canada *565*
Royal Trust Exempt International Fund *604*
Rushton, Edward, Son & Kenyon *647*
Russell, Cash & Co *647*
Russell, Henry (Life & Pensions) Ltd *684*
Ryden, Kenneth, & Partners *647*

St Quintin *647*
Sadaque, Pharad *665*
Saunders, Richard, & Partners *647*
Save & Prosper Exempt Income Fund *604*
Save & Prosper Exempt International Fund *604*
Save & Prosper Managed Pension Fund *604*
Save & Prosper Group Ltd *702*
Savills *649*
Savory, E. B., Milln & Co *576*
SB Modules Ltd *714*
Schlesinger American Exempt Trust *604*
Schlesinger Exempt High Yield Trust *604*
Schlesinger Exempt Market Leaders Trust *605*
Schroder Life Group *702*
Schroder Pension & Charity Fund *605*
Schroder Property Fund for Pension Funds & Charities *605*
Schroder Recovery Fund *605*
Schroder Special Exempt Fund *605*
Schroder, J. Henry, Wagg & Co Ltd *565*
Schweder, Paul E., Miller & Co *576*
Scott, Goff, Hancock & Co *576*
Scottish Amicable Life Assurance Society *703*
Scottish Amicable Managed Fund (SCAMPI) *605*
Scottish Equitable Life Assurance Society *703*
Scottish Equitable Managed Fund *605*
Scottish Life Assurance Co *703*
Scottish Life Managed Fund *605*
Scottish Mutual Assurance Society *703*
Scottish Mutual Managed Fund *606*

Index of Advisers

Scottish Provident Institution (The)   705
Scottish Provident Institution Managed Fund   606
Scottish Widows' Exempt Unit Trust   606
Scottish Widows' Fund & Life Assurance Society   705
Scottish Widows' Managed Fund   606
Scrimgeour, Kemp-Gee & Co   576
Sedgwick Employee Benefits Consultants Ltd   684
Seymour Pierce & Co   576
Sharp, C. D.   665
Sharp, Albert E., & Co   576
Sheppards & Chase   576
Shipway Doble & Earle   649
Shrubb, R. J., & Co   665
Shore, W. J. (Pensions Management) Ltd   684
Shucksmith & Co   666
Simon & Coates   576
Sinclair Goldsmith   649
Singer & Friedlander Ltd   565
Singer & Friedlander European Property Unit Trust   606
Sloam, N. S.   666
Smallwood, Wallis & Co Ltd   684
Smith, Daniel, Briant & Gone   649
Smith, Peter F., & Co   649
Smith Keen Cutler   576
Smith Melzack & Co   649
Smith-Woolley   649
Smiths Gore   649
Smithson Mason & Company   684
Society of Pension Consultants   667
Specialist Software Ltd   716
Specific Consultancy Resources Ltd   684
Spiers & Jeffrey   577
Spencer, Peter E., & Partners (Pensions) Ltd   684
Spencer, Henry, & Sons   649
Stancliffe, Todd & Hodgson   577
Standard Life Assurance Company   705
Standard Life Managed Fund   606
Stanley, Charles, & Co   577
Stenhouse Exempt Fund   606
Stenhouse Exempt Gilt Fund   606
Sternberg, Thomas Clarke & Co   577
Stewart American Exempt Fund   608
Stewart Fund Managers Ltd   589
Stewart Stevenson & Co   684
Stewart Wrightson Assurance Consultants Ltd   684
Stiles Horton Ledger   651
Stirling, Hendry & Co   577
Stock, Beech & Co   577
Stockholders Exempt American Fund   608
Stockholders Exempt Pacific Fund   608

Storey, Sons & Parker   651
Stratton Smaller Companies Exempt Fund   608
Strauss, Turnbull & Co   577
Strutt & Parker   651
Sturge, J. P., & Sons   651
Sturgis & Son   651
Sumner & Mcmillen (Life & Pensions) Ltd   685
Sun Alliance & London Assurance Co   707
Sun Alliance Managed Fund   608
Sun Life Assurance Society Ltd   707
Sun Life Managed Pension Fund   608
Superannuation Advisory Services Ltd   685
Superannuation Funds Office (Inland Revenue)   711
Sweby Cowan McGlashan   651
Swiss Life Insurance & Pension Co   708
Sykes Waterhouse Commercial   651
Symmons, Edward, & Partners   651
Systemsolve (Computer Services) Ltd   716

Target Trust Managers Ltd   589
Target Equity Exempt Fund   608
Target North American Exempt Fund   608
Target Property Fund   609
Target Smaller Companies Exempt Fund   609
Tay & Thames Investment Services Ltd   589
Taylor & Co   653
Peter Taylor & Company   653
Teacher Marks & Co   653
Temples   653
Tennant, Budd Life & Pensions Brokers (Southern) Ltd   685
Thorncroft & Partners   653
Thorpe, Bernard, & Partners   653
Throgmorton Management Ltd   589
Tilhill Forestry Advisory Ltd   661
Tillinghast, Nelson & Warren Ltd   685
Tilney & Co   577
Touche, Remnant & Co   590
Towers, Perrin, Forster & Crosby Inc   685
Townley Wild Associates Ltd   685
Towry Law (Pension Services) Ltd   686
Trevor, J., & Sons   655
Trident Life   708
Triskel Communications   714
Trollope, George, & Sons   655
Turner, G. P. (Life & Pensions Brokers) Ltd   686
Tutt, L. W. G.   666
Tyndall Assurance Ltd   708
Tyndall Exempt Fund   609
Tyndall Managed Pension Funds   609

Ulster Bank Ltd   565

Index of Advisers

Ulster Pension Trustees *686*
Unico Finance Ltd *590*
Unicorn Exempt Trust *609*
UK Provident *708*
United Pension Services Ltd *716*
United States Property Trust *609*

Vail, L. S. , & Sons *655*
Vairon (Insurance Brokers) Ltd *685*
Vickers Da Costa Ltd *577*
Vigers *655*
Vivian, Gray & Co *577*

Wadmans Insurance Ltd *686*
Wain, C. D. (Life & Pensions) Ltd *686*
Walker Frampton Ltd *686*
Walker Son & Packman *655*
Wallaker, E. W., & Co *655*
Walrond, Scarman & Company *686*
Warburg Investment Management Ltd *566*
Ward, J. D., & Co Ltd *686*
Watson, R., & Sons *665*
Watts & Partners *655*
Weatherall Green & Smith *655*
Webster & Co *657*
Welfare Life Group Managed Pension Plan *609*
Western Forestry *661*
Westgrove Exempt Property Unit Trust *609*
West Yorkshire Insurance Brokers Ltd *686*
White Druce & Brown *657*
Whitehouse Moorman & Partners Ltd *686*

Whitlow Coombe & Company *687*
Wigham Poland Pension Consultants Ltd *687*
Wieler, Anthony, & Co *550*
Williams & Glyn's Bank Ltd *566*
Williams & Glyn's Insurance Consultants Ltd *687*
Williams, Harold, Bennett & Partners *657*
Williams de Broe Hill Chaplin & Co *577*
Williams, P. J., & Co *657*
Willis Faber Advisory Services Ltd *687*
Wilson & Partners *657*
Wilson, Harold, Consultants Ltd *687*
Wise, Speke & Co *578*
Wood, John D. *657*
Wood, Mackenzie & Co *578*
Wood, Mackenzie & Co (Computer Services) *716*
Wood & Steven Ltd *687*
Wright, F. E., & Co (Life & Pensions) Ltd *687*
Wright & Partners *657*
Wyatt Harris Graham Ltd *687*
Wycherley Pension Services *688*

Yates, Harold, Burgess & Co (Manchester) Ltd *688*
Yorkshire-General Managed Fund *609*
Yorkshire-General Life Assurance Co Ltd *708*

Zurich Life Assurance Co Ltd *708*

To advertise in

PENSION FUNDS
&THEIR ADVISERS

contact:

Telephone **Mrs Jill Platford**
01-353 3712 (5 lines)

J E P Advertising Associates Ltd
Space Brokers & Publishers
107-111 Fleet Street
London EC4